# ALGEBRA
## Structure and Method

### Book 1

**Mary P. Dolciani**
**Richard G. Brown**
**William L. Cole**

**EDITORIAL ADVISER**
Robert H. Sorgenfrey

**TEACHER CONSULTANTS**
Gail H. Clark
Allen C. Demmin
James F. Dudley
Donald Field
Lois A. Martin
Sister Patricia Supple, CSJ

**HOUGHTON MIFFLIN COMPANY · BOSTON**

*Atlanta     Dallas     Geneva, Ill.     Hopewell, N.J.     Palo Alto     Toronto*

## THE AUTHORS

**Mary P. Dolciani,** Professor of Mathematical Sciences, Hunter College of the City University of New York.

**Richard G. Brown,** Mathematics Teacher, The Phillips Exeter Academy, Exeter, New Hampshire.

**William L. Cole,** Associate Professor of Mathematics Education, Michigan State University.

## EDITORIAL ADVISER

**Robert H. Sorgenfrey,** Professor of Mathematics, University of California, Los Angeles.

## TEACHER CONSULTANTS

**Gail H. Clark,** Mathematics Teacher, Johnson High School, Gainesville, Georgia.

**Allen C. Demmin,** Mathematics Coordinator, Middleton High School, Middleton, Wisconsin.

**James F. Dudley,** Mathematics Teacher, Rio Grande High School, Albuquerque, New Mexico.

**Donald Field,** Mathematics Teacher, Niles West High School, Skokie, Illinois.

**Lois A. Martin,** Mathematics Teacher, Downingtown High School, Downingtown, Pennsylvania.

**Sister Patricia Supple, CSJ,** Mathematics Teacher, Daniel Murphy Catholic High School, Los Angeles, California.

ISBN: 0-395-35249-5

IJ-D-94321

# Contents

# 3 Solving Equations and Problems

# 4 Polynomials

# 5 Factoring Polynomials

# 6 Fractions

# 7 Applying Fractions

# 8 Linear Equations and Systems

# 9 Introduction to Functions

# 10 Inequalities

# 11 Rational and Irrational Numbers

## 12 Quadratic Functions

## Looking Ahead

## Using a Computer with This Course

There are two types of optional computer material in this text: Computer Key-In features and Computer Exercises. The Computer Key-In features can be used by students without previous programming experience. These features teach some programming in BASIC and usually include a program that students can run to explore an algebra topic covered in the chapter. Some writing of programs may be required in some of these features.

The optional Computer Exercises are designed for students who have some familiarity with programming in BASIC. Students are usually asked to write one or more programs related to the lesson just presented.

An appendix that summarizes BASIC programming may be found beginning on page 653. This appendix can be used as a summary by students who are learning BASIC or as a review by students who are familiar with BASIC.

# Reading Your Algebra Textbook

An algebra textbook requires a different type of reading than a novel or a short story. Every paragraph of a mathematical text must be read with great care and concentration. You should not only read the words, but you should think about their meaning. You should read slowly through the explanations in this book. Algebra builds upon itself; the method of multiplying binomials you will study on page 196 will be useful to you on page 531. Read with a pencil in your hand; do calculations, draw sketches, take notes.

## Vocabulary

You will be exposed to many new words in algebra. Some, such as *axiom* and *polynomial*, are mathematical in nature, while others, such as *line* and *side*, are used in everyday speech but have different meanings when used in algebra. Important words whose meanings you will learn are printed in heavy type. (See page 10.) Also, they are listed at the beginning of each Self-Test. If you cannot recall the meaning of a word, you can look it up in the Glossary or the Index at the back of the book. The Glossary will give you a definition, and the Index will give you page references for more information.

## Symbols

Algebra, and mathematics in general, has its own symbolic language. You must be able to read these symbols in order to understand algebra. For example, $x \in \{-1, 0, 1, 2\}$ means "$x$ is a member of the set whose members are $-1$, $0$, $1$, and $2$." A list of symbols appears on page xii. If you cannot recall what a symbol means, check this list.

## Diagrams

Throughout this book you will find many diagrams. These contain information that will help you to understand the concepts under discussion. Study these diagrams carefully when you read the text that accompanies them.

## Displayed Material

Throughout the book important information is displayed in red boxes. This information includes axioms, properties, definitions, methods, and summaries. Be certain to read and understand the material in these boxes. You will also find these boxes useful when reviewing for tests and exams. Be sure to study the worked-out examples, such as the ones on page 218, as they will help you in doing many of the exercises and problems.

## Reading Aids

Throughout this book you will find sections called Reading Algebra. These sections deal with such topics as problem-solving strategies and inequalities. Be sure to read these sections, as they will help you to better understand the subjects with which they deal.

## SYMBOLS

| | | Page | | | Page |
|---|---|---|---|---|---|
| · | × (times) | 1 | $(a, b)$ | ordered pair whose first component is $a$ and second component is $b$ | 335 |
| = | equals, is equal to | 2 | $f(x)$ | $f$ of $x$, the value of $f$ at $x$ | 405 |
| ≠ | is not equal to | 2 | ≥ | is greater than or equal to | 449 |
| ( ) | parentheses—a grouping symbol | 2 | ≤ | is less than or equal to | 449 |
| [ ] | brackets—a grouping symbol | 5 | ∩ | the intersection of | 465 |
| $\pi$ | pi, a number approximately equal to $\frac{22}{7}$ | 8 | ∪ | the union of | 465 |
| ∴ | therefore | 10 | ≈ | is approximately equal to | 506 |
| ∈ | is a member of, belongs to | 10 | $\sqrt{\phantom{x}}$ | principal square root | 510 |
| $\stackrel{?}{=}$ | is this statement true? | 25 | $\overleftrightarrow{AB}$ | line $AB$ | 576 |
| − | negative | 30 | $\overline{AB}$ | segment $AB$ | 576 |
| + | positive | 30 | $AB$ | the length of $\overline{AB}$ | 576 |
| $-a$ | opposite or additive inverse of $a$ | 34 | $\overrightarrow{AB}$ | ray $AB$ | 576 |
| $|a|$ | absolute value of $a$ | 35 | ∠ | angle | 576 |
| < | is less than | 37 | ° | degree(s) | 577 |
| > | is greater than | 37 | △ | triangle | 581 |
| $\frac{1}{b}$ | reciprocal or multiplicative inverse of $b$ | 76 | ∼ | is similar to | 584 |
| ∅ | empty set, null set | 112 | $\cos A$ | cosine of $A$ | 587 |
| $a:b$ | ratio of $a$ to $b$ | 277 | $\sin A$ | sine of $A$ | 587 |
| | | | $\tan A$ | tangent of $A$ | 587 |
| | | | $P(A)$ | probability of event $A$ | 599 |

## Metric Units of Measure

**Length:**
- mm  millimeter
- cm  centimeter
- m  meter
- km  kilometer

**Area:**
- mm² square millimeter
- cm² square centimeter
- m² square meter
- km² square kilometer
- ha  hectare

**Volume:**
- cm³ cubic centimeter
- mL  milliliter
- L  liter

**Time:**
- s  second
- min  minute
- h  hour

**Speed:**
- m/s  meters per second
- km/h  kilometers per hour

**Mass:**
- mg  milligram
- g  gram
- kg  kilogram

**Temperature:**  °C  degrees Celsius

# *Reading Algebra / Symbols*

Close attention is needed to read mathematics because mathematical materials usually involve special symbols as well as words. And, often, those symbols can be read in several ways. Here are some examples.

**7 + 3**

"seven plus three"
"the sum of seven and three"
"add seven and three"
"seven increased by three"
"three more than seven"

**8 — 1**

"eight minus one"
"the difference of eight and one"
"subtract one from eight"
"eight decreased by one"
"one less than eight"

**11 × 4**

"eleven times four"
"the product of eleven and four"
"multiply eleven by four"

**10 ÷ 2**

"ten divided by two"
"the quotient of ten and two"
"divide ten by two"

$\frac{1}{2} \times 5$

"one half times five"
"one half of five"
"the product of one half and five"

$\frac{5}{2}$

"five halves"
"five divided by two"
"the quotient of five and two"

## *Exercises*

Read each of the following expressions in at least three ways.

**1.** 4 × 8      **2.** 15 — 0      **3.** 2 + 9      **4.** $\frac{7}{4}$

Translate the given words into mathematical symbols and then write the common numeral for the number described.

**Example**   Four increased by six      **Solution**   4 + 6; 10

5. Twelve decreased by five
6. Eleven more than six
7. The product of fifteen and three
8. Five less than thirty
9. Two thirds of six
10. Twice seven
11. The difference of fifty and thirty
12. The product of zero and nine

The symbols on the facing page are commonly used in mathematics. In studying this book, you will learn how to read and use them.

# 1 Introduction to Algebra

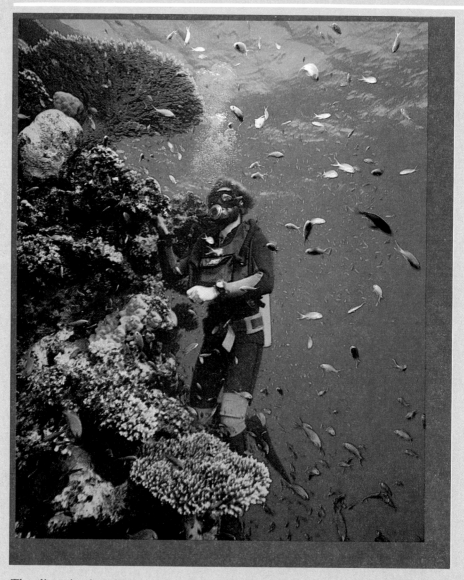

The diver in the photograph is swimming by a coral reef in the Red Sea. Depths below water level can be thought of as values of a variable, as discussed on the facing page.

# Variables and Equations

## 1-1 Variables

**Objective**   To simplify and to evaluate numerical expressions and variable expressions.

A scientist needed to gather data for an underwater experiment. Diving in sea water, the scientist measured the pressure of the water at different depths, as illustrated in the photograph at the left. These water pressures were then arranged in a table similar to the one below, which shows pressures at depths of 10, 20, 30, and 40 meters.

| Depth in meters | Water pressure in atmospheres |
|:---:|:---:|
| 10 | $0.104 \times 10$ |
| 20 | $0.104 \times 20$ |
| 30 | $0.104 \times 30$ |
| 40 | $0.104 \times 40$ |

Each of the expressions for water pressure fits the pattern

$$0.104 \times n$$

where the letter $n$ stands for 10, 20, 30, or 40. We call $n$ a *variable*.

A **variable** is a symbol used to represent one or more numbers. The numbers are called the **values of the variable.**

An expression, such as $0.104 \times n$, that contains a variable is called a **variable expression.** Expressions, such as $0.104 \times 2$, that name a particular number are called **numerical expressions** or **numerals.**

When you write a product that contains a variable, you usually omit the multiplication symbol.

$0.104 \times n$ is usually written $0.104n$.

$y \times z$ is usually written $yz$.

In numerical expressions for products like $0.104 \times 20$, you must use a multiplication symbol to avoid confusion. The raised dot $\cdot$ is also used as a multiplication sign.

$0.104 \times 20$ can be written $0.104 \cdot 20$.

The number named by a numerical expression is called the **value of the expression.** Since the expressions $3 + 5$ and 8 name the same number, they have the same value. To show that these expressions have the same value, you use the *equals sign,* $=$. You write

$$3 + 5 = 8$$

and say "three plus five equals (or is equal to or is) eight." Of course, 8 is the *simplest,* or most common, name for the number eight.

The symbol $\neq$ means is not equal to. You write

$$3 + 5 \neq 7$$

to show that the expressions $3 + 5$ and 7 do not have the same value.

Replacing a numerical expression by the simplest name of its value is called **simplifying the expression.** In simplifying a numerical expression, you use the following principle.

### Substitution Principle

Changing the numeral by which a number is named in an expression does not change the value of the expression.

*Example 1* Simplify. **a.** $(56 \div 7) + 9$ **b.** $36 \div (9 - 3)$

*Solution* The parentheses ( ) show how the numerals in the expression are to be grouped. The numerals within parentheses are simplified first.

**a.** $(56 \div 7) + 9 = 8 + 9 = 17$
**b.** $36 \div (9 - 3) = 36 \div 6 = 6$

Note that to read the symbols "$(56 \div 7) + 9$," you may say "the sum of the *quantity* fifty-six divided by seven, plus nine."

Replacing each variable in a variable expression by a given value and simplifying the result is called **evaluating the expression** or **finding the value of the expression.**

*Example 2* Evaluate $(5x) - (3 + y)$ if $x = 12$ and $y = 9$.

*Solution* Replace $x$ with 12 and $y$ with 9, and insert the necessary multiplication symbol. Then simplify the result.

$$(5x) - (3 + y) = (5 \times 12) - (3 + 9)$$
$$= 60 - 12$$
$$= 48$$

## Oral Exercises

**State whether or not each statement is true. Give a reason for your answer.**

*Example 1*  $5 \times 4 = 10 + 10$    *Solution*  True, because the value of both $5 \times 4$ and $10 + 10$ is 20.

*Example 2*  $2 \times 7 = 2 + 7$    *Solution*  False, because $2 \times 7 = 14$, whereas $2 + 7 = 9$.

**1.** $9 \times 7 = 7 \times 9$

**2.** $4 \times 0 = 0 \times 6$

**3.** $8 \div 1 \neq 1 \div 8$

**4.** $48 \times \frac{1}{2} \neq 48 \times 0.5$

**5.** $3 \times (4 \times 9) = (3 \times 4) \times 9$

**6.** $(14 - 3) - 1 = 14 - (3 - 1)$

**7.** $\frac{(8 - 2)}{2} = 8 - 1$

**8.** $0.12 \times 5 = 1.2 \times 0.5$

**Simplify each expression.**

**9.** $9 + (5 \times 4)$

**10.** $(9 + 5) \times 4$

**11.** $17 - (3 \times 3)$

**12.** $(17 - 3) \times 3$

**13.** $\frac{(32 - 7)}{5}$

**14.** $\frac{(13 + 11)}{(6 - 2)}$

**Evaluate each expression if $a = 1$, $b = 2$, and $c = 3$.**

**15.** $4b$

**16.** $6a$

**17.** $c - 3$

**18.** $9 - c$

**19.** $\frac{2}{b}$

**20.** $(5c) - 4$

**21.** $b + (ac)$

**22.** $(bc) + a$

**23.** $3(a + 1)$

**24.** $2(b - 2)$

**25.** $\frac{a + b}{c}$

**26.** $\frac{a}{c - b}$

## Written Exercises

**Simplify each expression.**

A  **1.** $(8 - 3) + 3$

**2.** $9 + (18 - 2)$

**3.** $5 \times (11 + 1)$

**4.** $(13 - 6) \times 7$

**5.** $(6 + 12) \div 3$

**6.** $6 + (12 \div 3)$

**7.** $29 - (0 \times 9)$

**8.** $5 - (16 \div 4)$

**9.** $(8 \times 17) + (2 \times 17)$

**10.** $(12 \times 11) - (2 \times 11)$

**11.** $(26 + 4) \div (30 \div 2)$

**12.** $(40 \div 10) \div (1 \times 4)$

**Evaluate each expression if $x = 2$, $y = 1$, $z = 9$, $a = 7$, $b = 0$, and $c = 3$.**

**13.** $xy$

**14.** $ab$

**15.** $z - (xc)$

**16.** $y + (xa)$

**17.** $(2c) + (2x)$

**18.** $(3a) - (5y)$

Evaluate each expression if $x = 2$, $y = 1$, $z = 9$, $a = 7$, $b = 0$, and $c = 3$.

**19.** $(bc) + 6y$        **20.** $(xz) + (ca)$        **21.** $(5y) \cdot (x + z)$

**22.** $(4c) \cdot (z + b)$        **23.** $\dfrac{(z - x)}{(a + b)}$        **24.** $\dfrac{(c + z)}{(a - y)}$

Simplify the expression on each side of the __?__. Then make a true statement by replacing the __?__ with the symbol $=$ or $\neq$.

**B**     **25.** $(8 + 3) \times (8 - 3)$ __?__ $(8 \times 8) - (3 \times 3)$

        **26.** $(5 + 2) \times (5 + 2)$ __?__ $(5 \times 5) + (2 \times 2)$

        **27.** $(7 - 1) \times (7 - 1)$ __?__ $(7 \times 7) - (1 \times 1)$

        **28.** $(6 + 4) \times (6 - 4)$ __?__ $(6 \times 6) - (4 \times 4)$

Evaluate each expression shown in color for the given values of the variables.

**29.** $lw$   (Area of a rectangle)
     if $l = 25$ and $w = 12$

**30.** $(2l) + (2w)$   (Perimeter of a rectangle)
     if $l = 50$ and $w = 40$

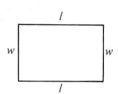

**31.** $(a + b) + c$   (Perimeter of a triangle)
     if $a = 29$, $b = 21$, and $c = 15$

**32.** $\dfrac{1}{2} \cdot (ab)$   (Area of a right triangle)
     if $a = 17$ and $b = 36$

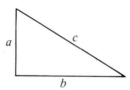

**33.** $(1.8 \times C) + 32$   (Temperature in degrees Fahrenheit given degrees Celsius)
     if $C = 15$

**34.** $\left(\dfrac{1}{2} \times g\right) \times (t \times t)$   (Distance in meters traveled by an object falling for $t$ seconds)
     if $g = 9.8$ and $t = 16$

**35.** $P \times (rt)$   (Simple interest on a loan of $P$ dollars)
     if $P = 5000$ (dollars), $r = 0.125$ (12.5% per year), and $t = 2$ (years)

**36.** $\dfrac{W \times c}{1000}$   (Cost of electricity to operate an electric light for one hour)
     if $W = 75$ (watts) and $c = 9.5$ (cents) per kilowatt hour

Make a true statement by replacing each variable with a numeral. If possible, find more than one replacement.

**37.** $n \times 1 = 1$        **38.** $x + 5 = 5$

**39.** $2\dfrac{1}{2} - y = 1 \times 2$        **40.** $\dfrac{3}{4} + m = 0.75 - m$

**C**   **41.** $a \times a = 2a$        **42.** $(b \times b) + 3 = 4b$

# 1-2 Grouping Symbols

**Objective** To simplify expressions with and without grouping symbols.

Parentheses have been used to show you how to group the numerals in an expression. Different groupings may produce expressions for different numbers.

$$(600 \div 10) + 2 \text{ means } 60 + 2, \text{ or } 62.$$
$$600 \div (10 + 2) \text{ means } 600 \div 12, \text{ or } 50.$$

A **grouping symbol** is a device, such as a pair of parentheses, used to enclose an expression. Brackets [ ] are also used.

Multiplication symbols are often omitted from expressions with grouping symbols. For example,

$$9 \times (5 - 3) = 9(5 - 3) = 9(2).$$

Note that 9(2) stands for $9 \times 2$. Other ways to write this product using parentheses are (9)2 and (9)(2).

In a fraction such as $\dfrac{11 + 3}{12 - 5}$ the bar is a grouping symbol as well as a division sign.

$$\frac{11 + 3}{12 - 5} = \frac{14}{7} = 14 \div 7 = 2$$

Throughout your work in algebra you will use these symbols:

## Grouping Symbols

| Parentheses | Brackets | Fraction Bar |
|:---:|:---:|:---:|
| $9(5 - 3)$ | $9[5 - 3]$ | $\dfrac{11 + 3}{12 - 5}$ |

**Example 1** Read each expression and then give its value.

      **a.** $9(5 - 3)$      **b.** $9(5) - 3$

**Solution**

**a.** Solution 1  "Nine times the quantity five minus three."

    Solution 2  "The product of nine and the difference of five and three."

    Solution 3  "Multiply nine by the difference of five and three."

$$9(5 - 3) = 9(2) = 18$$

**b.** Solution 1  "Nine times five minus three."

    Solution 2  "Multiply nine by five. Subtract three from the product."

$$9(5) - 3 = 45 - 3 = 42$$

**Caution!**   When you read expressions that contain parentheses, be sure that your words show that the symbols inside any pair of parentheses name one quantity.

If an expression contains more than one grouping symbol, first simplify the numeral in the innermost grouping symbol. Then work toward the outermost grouping symbol until the simplest expression is found.

**Example 2**   Simplify $18 - [52 \div (7 + 6)]$.

**Solution**   $18 - [52 \div (7 + 6)] = 18 - [52 \div 13]$
$$= 18 - 4$$
$$= 14$$

When there are no grouping symbols, you take the following steps to simplify an expression.

Step 1   Do all multiplications and divisions in order from left to right.

Step 2   Do all additions and subtractions in order from left to right.

$$29 + \underline{15 \times 4}$$
$$\underline{29 + \quad 60}$$
$$89$$

$$19 - 7 + \underline{12 \times 2} \div 8$$
$$19 - 7 + \underline{\quad 24 \quad \div 8}$$
$$\underline{19 - 7} + \quad\quad 3$$
$$\underline{12 \quad + \quad\quad 3}$$
$$15$$

**Example 3**   Evaluate $\dfrac{4a + 5b}{3a - b}$ if $a = 3$ and $b = 8$.

**Solution**   Replace $a$ with 3 and $b$ with 8, and insert the necessary multiplication symbols. Then simplify the result.

$$\frac{4a + 5b}{3a - b} = \frac{4(3) + 5(8)}{3(3) - 8}$$
$$= \frac{12 + 40}{9 - 8}$$
$$= \frac{52}{1} = 52$$

Note that in Example 3 each of the variable expressions $4a$, $5b$, and $3a$ is considered to be grouped even though no grouping symbol is used; that is, $4a = (4 \times a)$, $5b = (5 \times b)$, and $3a = (3 \times a)$. Note also that

$$yz \div 10n \quad \text{means} \quad (y \times z) \div (10 \times n)$$

## Oral Exercises

In Exercises 1–10, the given expression involves one or more operations to be performed. Describe the operation(s) for each expression.

**Example**   $3(x + 1) + 5$

**Solution 1**   "Multiply three by the sum of $x$ and one, and then add five to the product."

**Solution 2**   "Add $x$ and one, multiply the sum by three, and then add five to the product."

**1.** $7y$

**2.** $z - 2$

**3.** $4 + 9x$

**4.** $8z - 5$

**5.** $6(z + 4)$

**6.** $4(2x - 1)$

**7.** $\dfrac{z - y}{x}$

**8.** $\dfrac{z}{x + y}$

**9.** $\dfrac{13 - x}{y} - 2$

**10.** $\dfrac{9 + 6x}{z + 8}$

**11–20.** In Exercises 1–10, evaluate each expression if $x = 1$, $y = 3$, and $z = 7$.

## Written Exercises

Evaluate each expression if $x = 1$, $y = 0$, $z = 8$, $a = 2$, $b = 3$, and $c = 5$.

**A**   **1.** $ay + z$

**2.** $cx + y$

**3.** $b - 2x$

**4.** $xb - a$

**5.** $8z + 5x$

**6.** $7c - ab$

**7.** $z(c - x) + a$

**8.** $(z - a)x + y$

**9.** $(3b - 2a)(c + y)$

**10.** $(c - 4x)(2a + z)$

**11.** $\dfrac{ac - z}{x + b}$

**12.** $\dfrac{bz - 2x}{31 - 4c}$

**13.** $a(c + x) - \dfrac{zb}{a}$

**14.** $y(ac - x) + \dfrac{z}{b}$

Simplify each expression.

**15.** $\dfrac{7 \times 2 + 2 \times 5 \times 5}{12 - 3 - 1}$

**16.** $\dfrac{48 \div 6 + 2}{9 - 7}$

**17.** $(26 - 5 + 9 \div 3) \div (18 \div 9)$

**18.** $16(13 - 8) - 40 \div (10 - 5)$

Evaluate each expression in color for the given values of the variables.

**19.** $2(a + b)$   (Perimeter of a parallelogram)
   if $a = 6.5$ and $b = 24.3$

**Ex. 19**

**Evaluate each expression in color for the given values of the variables.**

**20.** $2a + b + c$  (Perimeter of an isosceles trapezoid)
if $a = 34$, $b = 58$, and $c = 25$

**21.** $\frac{1}{2}h(b + c)$  (Area of a trapezoid)
if $h = 15$, $b = 23$, and $c = 19$

**Exs. 20 and 21**

**22.** $(\pi r)r$  (Area of a circle)
if $r = 28$. Use $\frac{22}{7}$ as an approximate value for $\pi$.

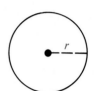

**Ex. 22**

**B  23.** $2(r + h) + \pi r$  (Perimeter of a Norman window)
if $r = 2.00$ and $h = 3.00$. Use 3.14 as an approximate value for $\pi$.

**Ex. 23**

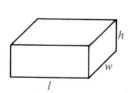

**Ex. 24**

**24.** $2(lw + wh + lh)$  (Surface area of a rectangular solid)
if $l = 14$, $w = 12$ and $h = 10$

**Simplify the expression on each side of the __?__. Then make a true statement by replacing the __?__ with the symbol = or ≠.**

**25.** $\frac{24 \times 8}{12 + 4}$ __?__ $\frac{12 \times 4}{6 + 2}$

**26.** $\frac{23 + 19}{7 \times 2}$ __?__ $(54 \div 9) - 3$

**27.** $2[3(12 - 7)]$ __?__ $(5 \times 5) + 5$

**28.** $3[36 \div (3 + 6)]$ __?__ $30 - [(36 \div 3) + 6]$

**29.** $\frac{(16 \times 6) \div 24}{4 - (12 \div 4)} + 1$ __?__ $23 - \frac{34 + 4}{8 - 6}$

**30.** $1 + \frac{31 - 4}{7 + 2}$ __?__ $\frac{8 \times 12 - 16}{108 \div 3 + 4} + 2$

**C  31.** $[(3 \times 2 + 5)2]2 - 4$ __?__ $3 \times 2 \times 2 \times 2 + 5 \times 2 \times 2 - 4$

**32.** $[(7 \times 3 - 4)3]3 + 6$ __?__ $7 \times 3 \times 3 - 4 \times 3 \times 3 + 6$

**33.** $1 \times 1 + 2 \times 2 + 3 \times 3 + 4 \times 4$ __?__ $\frac{4(4 + 1)(2 \times 4 + 1)}{6}$

**34.** $(4 \times 1 + 1) + (4 \times 2 + 1) + (4 \times 3 + 1) + (4 \times 4 + 1)$ __?__ $2[4(4 + 1)] + 4$

**35.** $\frac{[9 - (4 \times 2)] + (3 \times 8)}{[(28 \div 4) + 3] - 5}$ __?__ $[3 + (3 \times 3) - (33 \div 3)] \times \frac{14 - 4}{7 - 2}$

**36.** $(2)(2)(2) + (3)(3)(3) + (4)(4)(4) + (5)(5)(5)$ __?__ $(2 + 1)(2 + 1)(2 + 3)(2 + 3) - 1$

People communicate with computers by using *programs*. Programs tell the computer what to do. However, it is not always necessary for a person to be able to write a program in order to use a computer. Programs can be written in such a way that an operator can use them by answering a series of questions that are written into the program. Nevertheless, the best way to learn what a computer can and cannot do is to learn a little about programming. We shall use the programming language BASIC.

To program arithmetic calculations in BASIC, you use the following symbols:

+ for addition          * for multiplication

− for subtraction       / for division

Parentheses are used when grouping symbols are needed.

BASIC follows the order of operations described on page 6.

A BASIC program is made up of numbered *statements*. These statements are usually numbered 10, 20, 30, . . . , instead of 1, 2, 3, . . . , so that additional statements may be inserted later, if they are found to be necessary.

Here is a two-line program:

```
10   PRINT 21 * 34 + 35/7
20   END
```

The last statement tells the computer that the program is finished. Line 10 tells the computer to compute $21 \times 34 + 35 \div 7$ and print the answer. Type in the program, and then type the *command* RUN. The computer will respond by typing 719.

### Exercises

Change the expression in line 10 above to each of the following and RUN the changed program.

**1.** 20 * (48 + 72)/8

**2.** 20 * 48 + 72/8

**3.** 30 * 42 − 16 * 5

**4.** 30 * (42 − 16) * 5

Translate each expression into BASIC. Substitute the BASIC statement in line 10 above and RUN the program.

**5.** $\dfrac{21 + 33}{6}$

**6.** $36(42 − 17)$

**7.** $(24 + 10)(24 − 10)$

**8.** $\dfrac{144 − 24}{100 − 40}$

*Note:* The program given above can be used to do Exercises 15–18 on page 7.

# 1-3 Equations

**Objective**  To find solution sets of equations.

Here are three equations:

$$10 - 4 = 6 \qquad 5x - 1 = 9 \qquad c + 3 = 3 + c$$

the two sides     the two sides     the two sides

An **equation** is formed by placing an equals sign between two numerical or variable expressions, called the **sides** of the equation.

Sentences containing variables (like the equations $5x - 1 = 9$ and $c + 3 = 3 + c$) are called **open sentences**. The given set of numbers that a variable may represent is called the **domain** of the variable. When you replace each variable in an open sentence by one of the numbers in its domain, you obtain either a true statement or a false statement.

You may use *braces* $\{\ \}$ to show a set of numbers. A short way to write "the set whose members are 1, 2, and 3" is $\{1, 2, 3\}$.

**Example 1**  The domain of $x$ is $\{1, 2, 3\}$. Find any values in the domain of $x$ for which $5x - 1 = 9$ becomes a true statement.

**Solution**  Replace $x$ in turn by 1, 2, and 3.

$$5x - 1 = 9$$
$$5(1) - 1 = 9 \quad \text{False}$$
$$5(2) - 1 = 9 \quad \text{True}$$
$$5(3) - 1 = 9 \quad \text{False}$$

$\therefore$ (read "therefore") the required value of $x$ is 2.  **Answer**

Any value of a variable that converts an open sentence into a true statement is called a **solution** or **root** of the sentence, and is said to **satisfy** the sentence.

The set of *all* solutions of an open sentence is called the **solution set** of the sentence. Finding the solution set is called **solving** the sentence.

You may use braces to show a solution set. Thus, for Example 1, you may say either

"The solution is 2"   or   "The solution set is $\{2\}$."

**Example 2**  Solve the equation $y(4 - y) = 3$ if $y \in \{0, 1, 2, 3, 4\}$ (read "$y$ is a member of (or belongs to) the set whose members are 0, 1, 2, 3, and 4").

**Solution**    Replace $y$ in turn by 0, 1, 2, 3, and 4.

$$y(4 - y) = 3$$
$$0(4 - 0) = 3 \quad \text{False}$$
$$1(4 - 1) = 3 \quad \text{True}$$

$$2(4 - 2) = 3 \quad \text{False}$$
$$3(4 - 3) = 3 \quad \text{True}$$
$$4(4 - 4) = 3 \quad \text{False}$$

$\therefore$ the solution set is $\{1, 3\}$. ***Answer***

You can see that the solution set of the equation $c + 3 = 3 + c$ is the set of *all* numbers, because the sentence is true no matter what number is substituted for $c$. If you are asked to solve this equation *over the domain* $\{0, 1, 2, 3\}$, you state that the solution set is the domain itself, $\{0, 1, 2, 3\}$.

## Oral Exercises

Solve each equation if $x \in \{0, 1, 2, 3, 4, 5, 6\}$. If there is no solution over the given domain, state, "No solution."

**1.** $x + 2 = 6$      **2.** $x - 1 = 4$      **3.** $2x = 6$      **4.** $x \div 3 = 1$

**5.** $x - 3 = 3$      **6.** $x + 1 = 5$      **7.** $x + 2 = 2 + x$      **8.** $x + 4 = x$

**9.** $3x = x + 2x$      **10.** $3x = x + 2$      **11.** $x + x = 0$      **12.** $(5 - x)x = 0$

## Written Exercises

Solve each equation if $x \in \{0, 1, 2, 3, 4, 5, 6, 7\}$.

**A**    **1.** $x + 5 = 9$      **2.** $6 + x = 11$      **3.** $x - 2 = 3$      **4.** $x - 5 = 1$

     **5.** $7 - x = 2$      **6.** $6 - x = 3$      **7.** $2x = 12$      **8.** $5x = 10$

     **9.** $8x = 16$      **10.** $2x = 14$      **11.** $3x = 0$      **12.** $0 = 4x$

     **13.** $x \div 3 = 1$      **14.** $x \div 3 = 2$      **15.** $\frac{1}{2}x = 2$      **16.** $\frac{1}{3}x = 1$

     **17.** $x \cdot x = 1$      **18.** $9x = 9$      **19.** $x - x = 0$      **20.** $x \cdot x = 25$

Solve each equation over the domain $\{0, 1, 2, 3, 4, 5, 6, 7, 8, 9\}$.

**B**    **21.** $2a + 9 = 17$      **22.** $3b - 4 = 11$      **23.** $10 = 8c - 6$

     **24.** $13 = 6d - 5$      **25.** $9 + 9r = 81$      **26.** $5 + 5s = 50$

     **27.** $2t = t + 7$      **28.** $3w = w \cdot 3$      **29.** $2z = z \cdot z$

     **30.** $y(8 - y) = 0$      **31.** $(6 - v)(1 + v)v = 0$      **32.** $27k = (3k)(3k)(3k)$

Write two different equations for which the solution set over the domain $\{0, 1, 2, 3, 4\}$ is the given set.

**C**    **33.** $\{3\}$      **34.** $\{0\}$      **35.** $\{0, 1, 2, 3, 4\}$      **36.** $\{0, 3\}$

# Self-Test 1

**Vocabulary**    variable (p. 1)                             equation (p. 10)

value of a variable (p. 1)           side of an equation (p. 10)

variable expression (p. 1)         open sentence (p. 10)

numerical expression (p. 1)        domain of a variable (p. 10)

value of a numerical expression     solution (p. 10)

    (p. 2)                                 root (p. 10)

simplify an expression (p. 2)       satisfy an open sentence (p. 10)

substitution principle (p. 2)        solution set (p. 10)

evaluate an expression (p. 2)       solve an open sentence (p. 10)

grouping symbol (p. 5)

**Evaluate each expression if $x = 5$, $y = 4$, and $z = 12$.**

**1.** $(3x - 1) + (2y + z)$            **2.** $x + \left(\dfrac{z}{y}\right)$                     Obj. 1-1, p. 1

**3.** $xy - 2(z - x)$                  **4.** $\dfrac{2(x + 3)}{7y - z}$                 Obj. 1-2, p. 5

**Solve each equation if $x \in \{0, 1, 2, 3, 4\}$.**

**5.** $x + 1 = 4$                     **6.** $10 - 2x = 4$                   Obj. 1-3, p. 10

Check your answers with those at the back of the book.

## Calculator Key-In

Does your calculator follow the steps for simplifying an expression stated on page 6? Experiment with your calculator by entering the following example exactly as it appears here:

$$8 + 3 \times 4 =$$

If your calculator displays the answer 20, it followed the order of operations you learned for simplifying expressions: multiplication before addition. Your calculator has an algebraic operating system. The answer 20 is correct.

If your calculator displays the answer 44, it performed the addition and the multiplication in the order in which you pressed the keys. One way to get the correct answer on your calculator is to multiply 3 and 4 first and then add 8, just as you would if you were using pencil and paper.

Use a calculator to simplify each expression.

**1.** $21 - 2.8 \times 7.5$                **2.** $0.8 + 1.2 \div 0.4$

**3.** $0.75 \div 0.25 \times 0.5 - 1.4$      **4.** $0.45 \times 369 + 0.55 \times 369$

**5.** $364 \div 13 \times 15{,}873 - 5291 \times 7 \times 3$

# Applications and Problem Solving

## 1-4 Words into Symbols: Expressions

**Objective**   To represent numerical relationships stated in words by mathematical expressions.

To solve problems using algebra, you must often translate word phrases about numbers into numerical or variable expressions.

Suppose you think of two numbers, one nine more than the other. If $x$ stands for the smaller number, then the greater number is represented by

$$x + 9.$$

**Example 1**   Represent each word phrase by a variable expression.

        **a.** Nine less than a number $x$

        **b.** Nine times a number $x$

        **c.** One ninth of a number $x$

        **d.** Nine divided by a number $x$

**Solution**   **a.** $x - 9$   **b.** $9x$   **c.** $\frac{1}{9}x$   **d.** $\frac{9}{x}$

**Example 2**   Jan is $y$ years old. Use $y$ to write an expression for each of the following numbers.

        **a.** Jan's age two years ago

        **b.** Jan's age five years from now

        **c.** Jan's father's age, if he is three times as old as Jan

        **d.** Jan's cousin's age, if he is half as old as Jan

        **e.** Kit's age, if the sum of Jan's and Kit's ages is 28

**Solution**   **a.** $y - 2$   **b.** $y + 5$   **c.** $3y$   **d.** $\frac{1}{2}y$   **e.** $28 - y$

Formulas are often used in algebra. **Formulas** are equations that state rules about measurements. Here are four formulas:

| | |
|---|---|
| $A = lw$ | Area of rectangle = length of rectangle × width of rectangle |
| $P = 2l + 2w$ | Perimeter of rectangle = (2 × length) + (2 × width) |
| $D = rt$ | Distance traveled = rate × time traveled |
| $C = np$ | Cost = number of items × price per item |

***Example 3*** Using the given variable, write an expression for the measure required to complete each statement.

    **a.** A rectangle has length 10 units and width *d* units. The area is __?__ square units.

    **b.** A rectangle has length 16 cm (centimeters) and width *w* cm. The perimeter is __?__ cm.

    **c.** You travel $(t + \frac{1}{2})$ hours at 80 km/h (kilometers per hour). The distance you travel is __?__ km.

    **d.** You buy 5 pencils at *x* cents each and 3 pads at *y* cents each. The total cost is __?__ cents.

***Solution***    **a.** Area = length × width = $10d$

    **b.** Perimeter = (2 × length) + (2 × width) = 2 × 16 + 2w = $32 + 2w$

    **c.** Distance = rate × time = $80(t + \frac{1}{2})$

    **d.** Cost of pencils = $5x$; cost of pads = $3y$; total cost = $5x + 3y$

## Oral Exercises

**Represent each word phrase by a variable expression. Use *n* for the variable.**

***Example***    Seven less than double the number    ***Solution***    $2n - 7$

  **1.** Eight times the number      **2.** The product of three and the number

  **3.** Five greater than the number      **4.** One fourth of the number

  **5.** The number decreased by four      **6.** The number divided by five

  **7.** Nine less than half the number      **8.** Nine more than twice the number

**Complete each statement with a variable expression.**

  **9.** A rectangle has width 6 units and length $(x + 2)$ units. Its area is __?__ square units.

**10.** You travel for $(t - 2)$ hours at 75 km/h. You travel __?__ km.

**11.** You buy $(m + 5)$ rolls at 40 cents each. The cost is __?__ cents.

**12.** Cheryl earns $(p + 3)$ dollars per hour. In 8 hours, she earns __?__ dollars.

**13.** Hal is *y* years old. Four years ago he was __?__ years old.

**14.** The Eiffel Tower was erected *n* years ago. Three years from now it will have been standing __?__ years.

**15.** The Science Museum was *d* years old 15 years ago. It is now __?__ years old.

**16.** Nine years from now Jo will be *g* years old. She is now __?__ years old.

# Written Exercises

**Match the word phrase in Column I with the corresponding variable expression in Column II. (You will not use all the variable expressions.)**

<table>
<tr><td colspan="2" align="center">COLUMN I</td><td align="center">COLUMN II</td></tr>
</table>

**A**

1. Four less than half a number
2. Seven decreased by three times a number
3. Twice the sum of a number and three
4. The product of five and two more than a number
5. The difference of three times a number and one
6. Six times the difference of a number and five

**a.** $2(x + 3)$
**b.** $3x + 1$
**c.** $3x - 7$
**d.** $\frac{1}{2}x - 4$
**e.** $3x - 1$
**f.** $5x + 2$
**g.** $\frac{1}{2}(x - 4)$
**h.** $2x + 3$
**i.** $5(x + 2)$
**j.** $6(x - 5)$
**k.** $7 - 3x$
**l.** $6x - 5$

**Represent the required numbers in terms of the given variables.**

7. What number is two more than twice the number $a$?
8. What number is one less than half the number $b$?
9. What number is six less than one third of the number $y$?
10. What number is three more than eight times the number $z$?
11. The sum of two numbers is thirty. One number is $x$. What is the other number?
12. The sum of two numbers is eighteen. One number is $w$. What is the other number?

**Using the given variable, write an expression for the measure required to complete each statement.**

13. Fred is $t$ cm tall. Joe is 6 cm shorter than Fred. Joe is __?__ cm tall.
14. Wilma weighs $m$ kg (kilograms). Fran is 3 kg heavier than Wilma. Fran weighs __?__ kg.
15. In $x$ years there are __?__ months.
16. In $y$ weeks there are __?__ days.
17. The length of a rectangular lot is 15 m (meters) less than twice its width, $w$ m. The length is __?__ m. The perimeter is __?__ m.

**Using the given variable, write an expression for the measure required to complete each statement.**

18. The width of a rectangular field is 3 km more than half the length, $l$ km. The width is __?__ km. The perimeter is __?__ km.

19. Dick, who is $a$ years old, is 4 years younger than Tom. Tom is __?__ years old.

20. Mae is 3 years older than Ray. If Mae is $b$ years old, then Ray is __?__ years old.

**B** 21. Oranges sell for $s$ cents per pound at Lou's Convenience Store. They cost 5 cents per pound less at the Big L supermarket. Ten pounds of oranges cost __?__ cents at Lou's and __?__ cents at the Big L.

22. Vera drove at the rate of $r$ km/h. Her friend's average speed was 3 km/h faster. In two hours, Vera traveled __?__ km and her friend traveled __?__ km.

23. For lunch, a student bought a glass of milk costing $y$ cents and a sandwich costing eight times as much. The student spent __?__ for lunch.

24. One day a service station sold $x$ L (liters) of gasoline for cash. Six times as much gasoline was bought that day with credit cards. The service station sold a total of __?__ L of gasoline on that day.

25. The difference between two numbers is five. The greater number is $n$. The smaller number is __?__ .

26. The difference between two numbers is eight. The smaller number is $m$. The larger number is __?__ .

27. A store sold $r$ cameras during the first week of December. Weekly sales increased by 120 cameras during each of the next two weeks of the month. During the third week of December the store sold __?__ cameras.

28. On the third weekly examination, the class average was 78. If the average had increased at the rate of $p$ points per week, the class average on the first examination was __?__ .

29. Mel is $t$ years old. Joe, who is twice as old as Mel was 6 years ago, is __?__ years old.

30. Rhonda is $k$ years old. Mary, who is half as old as Rhonda will be 5 years from now, is __?__ years old.

31. Each of the congruent sides of an isosceles triangle is $s$ cm long. The third side is 6 cm shorter. The perimeter of the triangle is __?__ cm.

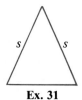

**Ex. 31**

32. One number is two more than a certain number $n$. Another number is five less than $n$. The sum of the three numbers is __?__ .

**C** **33.** An apple has 29 more calories than a peach and 13 fewer calories than a banana. If an apple has $c$ calories, then there are __?__ calories in a fruit cup made with one apple, two peaches, and one banana.

**34.** A pound of peanuts contains about 10 fewer grams of carbohydrates than a pound of walnuts and 26 fewer grams of carbohydrates than a pound of almonds. If a pound of peanuts contains $w$ grams of carbohydrates, then a mix of one pound of peanuts, one pound of walnuts, and one pound of almonds contains __?__ grams of carbohydrates.

## Computer Key-In

BASIC uses variables to hold numerical values. One way to give a value to a variable is to use an INPUT statement. The INPUT statement causes the computer to print a question mark and wait for you to type in a value.

Given below is a program that will find the area and the perimeter of a rectangle. The expressions in quotation marks will be printed exactly as they appear in the program. The semicolon at the end of line 40 will cause the question mark from line 50 to be printed right after the quoted expression. The semicolon at the end of line 60 has the same effect on the question mark from line 70.

```
10   PRINT "TO FIND THE AREA AND THE PERIMETER OF A"
20   PRINT "           RECTANGLE:"
30   PRINT                              ←⌐ Leaves a blank line
40   PRINT "WHAT IS THE LENGTH";
50   INPUT L
60   PRINT "WHAT IS THE WIDTH";
70   INPUT W
80   PRINT "THE AREA IS: ";L*W
90   PRINT "THE PERIMETER IS: ";2*L+2*W
100  END
```

Notice that the computer has been given the area and perimeter formulas in the program. That is, we have solved the problems. The computer simply does the computation.

RUN this program with several sets of values for L and W.

### Exercises

**1.** Write a program to find the area and perimeter of a square. RUN the program for several sets of values.

**2.** Write a program to find the area and perimeter of an isosceles trapezoid. RUN the program for several sets of values.

# 1-5 Words into Symbols: Equations

**Objective**  To translate word sentences describing the equality of numbers into equations.

Applications of algebra frequently require you to translate word sentences about numbers into equations.

**Example 1**  Write an equation for each word sentence.

  **a.** The difference of the number $t$ and nine is fifty-four.
  **b.** Five is eight more than twice the number $w$.
  **c.** One half of the number $a$ is ten less than three times $a$.

**Solution**  **a.** $t - 9 = 54$
  **b.** $5 = 2w + 8$
  **c.** $\frac{1}{2}a = 3a - 10$

The next examples show how you can choose a variable to represent a number and then write an equation to relate the facts in a given situation.

**Example 2**  A gardener needs 78 m of fence to enclose a rectangular garden. The length of the garden is 9 m more than the width.

  **a.** Choose a variable to represent the width in meters and use it to write an expression for the length.

  **b.** Write an equation that represents the given facts.

**Solution**  **a.** Let $w$ = width in meters.
  Then $w + 9$ = length in meters.

  **b.** Draw a sketch to help you see the relationship given. Since the perimeter is 78 m, you have:

$$2(w + 9) + 2w = 78$$

*Example 3*  Fran rode her bicycle from her home to school and back in 23 min (minutes). The return trip took two minutes less than the trip to school.

   **a.** Choose a variable to represent the number of minutes Fran rode from her home to school and use it to write an expression for the number of minutes for the return trip.

   **b.** Write an equation that represents the given facts.

*Solution 1*  **a.** Let $x$ = the number of minutes Fran rode to school; then $x - 2$ = the number of minutes to return.

   **b.** Since the round-trip took 23 min you have:

$$x + (x - 2) = 23$$

*Solution 2*  **a.** Let $x$ = the number of minutes Fran rode to school; then $23 - x$ = the number of minutes to return.

   **b.** Since the return trip took 2 min less than the trip to school,

$$23 - x = x - 2.$$

   Notice that the equations obtained in Solutions 1 and 2 of Example 3 are not the same. However, as soon as your familiarity with algebra increases, you will see that these equations have the same solution set.

## Oral Exercises

**State an equation for each sentence.**

1. Twelve more than the number $p$ is 37.
2. Eight is 5 less than twice the number $r$.
3. Forty decreased by the number $m$ is 24.5.
4. The number $a$ increased by $\frac{2}{3}$ is $8\frac{1}{3}$.
5. The sum of one third of the number $s$ and 12 is 23.
6. The product of 58 and the number $n$ is 1.
7. The quotient of the number $b$ and 4 is 8.
8. Three fourths of the number $h$ is 192.
9. The product of 12 and the quantity 1 less than the number $d$ is 84.
10. Multiply the sum of twice the number $x$ and 3 by 7, and the product is 126.

**State an equation for each sentence.**

**11.** Divide the difference of 15 and the number $y$ by 4, and the quotient is 32.

**12.** The product of the number that is one more than $c$ and the number that is one less than $c$ is 35.

**State an equation that represents the given sentence.**

**Example**    Rick has $n$ dimes worth a total of $9.80.

**Solution**   Express $n$ and $9.80 in the same unit, cents. $10n = 980$

**13.** In $m$ slices of cheese, each containing 115 calories, there are 920 calories.

**14.** After a deposit of $a$ dollars in an account containing $74, the new balance is $132.

**15.** The customer received $34.80 in change from a fifty-dollar bill given in payment for an item costing $x$ dollars.

**16.** A total of $b$ twenty-four cent stamps costs $4.32.

**17.** A baseball priced at $2.50 costs $\frac{2}{15}$ as much as a bat costing $k$ dollars.

**18.** The winner received 486 votes, or $\frac{2}{3}$ of the total number, $v$, of votes cast.

**19.** The area of a rectangular field that is 8 m wide and $y$ m long is 108 m² (square meters).

**20.** After selling $z$ cans of tomatoes from a 180-can shipment, the store had 38 cans left.

## Written Exercises

**Use the given facts to state an equation that represents the sentence shown in color.**

**Example**    Yolanda is $b$ years old. Sara is 2 years younger. The sum of their ages is 34.

**Solution**   $b + (b - 2) = 34$

**A**    **1.** In April, the O'Briens spent $150 more for food than for housing. Their food bill was $p$ dollars. For both food and housing they spent $675 in April.

2. On a trip, the Romeros traveled 640 km farther by airplane than by automobile. They traveled $q$ km by automobile. On the trip, they traveled 900 km.

3. A house cost 5.5 times as much as the lot it stands on. The lot cost $c$ dollars. The house and lot cost $105,000.

4. Jill is half as old as her brother, who is $k$ years old. The sum of their ages is 32.

5. Team A scored one point less than twice team B's score. Team B scored $x$ points. Team A scored 47 points.

6. Team X scored five points less than three times team Y's score. Team Y scored $a$ points. Team X scored 67 points.

7. Fred is 3 years older than Max, who is $t$ years old. The sum of their ages is 29.

8. The length of a rectangle is 9 cm more than its width. Its width is $s$ cm. The area of the rectangle is 630 cm² (square centimeters).

9. A bag of potatoes weighing 74 kg weighs half a kilogram more than twice as much as a bag of onions weighing $z$ kg.

10. The length of a corridor that is $w$ meters wide is 2 m more than 5 times its width.

**In Exercises 11–17,**
**a. Choose a variable to represent the number described by the words in parentheses.**
**b. Write an equation that represents the given information.**

*Example*  The perimeter of an equilateral triangle is 54 cm. (Length of a side)

*Solution*  **a.** Recall that an equilateral triangle has three sides of equal length. Let $s$ = the length of each side in centimeters.

   **b.** $3s = 54$

11. The perimeter of a square is 68 m. (Length of a side)

12. A dozen eggs cost $1.49. (Cost of one egg)

13. Ten years ago Roger was 7 years old. (Roger's age now)

14. Eight years from now Sue will be 23 years old. (Sue's age now)

15. A car dealer has sold all but 14 of the cars in a consignment of 285 subcompacts. (Number of cars sold)

16. A student solved all but the last 3 problems in an assignment of 20. (Number of problems solved)

17. One eighth of a pizza sold for 95¢. (Cost of the whole pizza)

**In Exercises 18–34,**

**a. Choose a variable to represent the number described by the words in parentheses.**

**b. Write an equation that represents the given information.**

**18.** A seventeen-year-old building is one fourth as old as a nearby bridge. (Age of the bridge)

**19.** A train traveled 462 km at the rate of 132 km/h. (Number of hours traveled)

**20.** A rectangular floor is tiled with 928 square tiles. The floor is 32 tiles long. (Number of tiles in the width)

**21.** In the floor plan of a house, dimensions are shown $\frac{1}{100}$ of actual size. The length of the family room in the plan is 8.5 cm. (Actual length of the room)

**22.** A season ticket good for fifteen admissions to a theme park sells for $33.75. (Cost of one admission with this ticket)

**23.** An astronaut spent 42.8 days in space. This was 3.2 days longer than her previous record. (Number of days in her previous record)

**24.** The last check written on an account was for $79.43. The next bank statement showed an overdraft of $5.32 on the account. (Amount in the account before the last check was written)

**B 25.** Each marble in a bag of 24 marbles is either red or blue. There are 3 more blue marbles than twice the number of red ones. (Number of red marbles)

**26.** The sum of three numbers is 120. The second of the numbers is eight less than the first, and the third is four more than the first. (First number)

**27.** In an isosceles triangle whose perimeter is 54 cm, the base is 9 cm longer than each of the two congruent sides. (Length of each of the congruent sides)

**28.** A purse contains $3.50 in nickels and dimes. There are 16 more nickels than dimes in the purse. (Number of dimes)

**29.** Ten years from now, Sofia will be three times as old as she was eight years ago. (Sofia's age now)

**30.** The hourly rate for a typist is seventy-five cents more than the hourly rate for a file clerk. In five hours, the typist earns as much as the file clerk does in six hours. (Hourly rate for the file clerk)

**31.** If a stone were 5 kg heavier, its mass would be 1 kg more than twice what it is. (Mass of the stone)

**32.** Jill is three times as old as her brother, Jack. Two years ago, the sum of their ages was 12. (Jack's age now)

**C 33.** The length of one side of a triangular lot is 6 m less than three times the length of the second side. The third side is 8 m longer than the first side. The perimeter of the lot is 80 m. (Length of the second side)

**34.** Phyl is 2 years older than Maria and Maria is 4 years older than Les. The sum of their ages is 37. (Maria's age)

## Biographical Note / *Albert Einstein*

Albert Einstein was born in Ulm, Germany, in 1879. He attended school in Munich and did his college work in Switzerland where his family had moved. As he was not a very distinguished student (excelling only in mathematics and science), Einstein was unable to secure a teaching position upon graduation in 1901 and ended up working as a minor official in the Swiss patent office. The job, however, did leave him time to pursue his scientific studies.

In 1905 Einstein published five papers, three of which were to have a profound effect on science. One paper helped to establish the quantum, or particle, theory of light and for this Einstein was awarded the 1921 Nobel Prize in physics. A second paper contained equations that described molecular motion and that could be used to work out the size of molecules.

It was Einstein's paper on the special theory of relativity that made him famous. This theory, later generalized in 1915, supplanted Isaac Newton's theories of the universe when dealing with objects whose speeds approach that of light. The theory was essentially proved in 1919 by two teams of British astronomers who observed the bending of light during the solar eclipse of that year, an occurrence predicted by Einstein's theory.

After the publication of his papers, Einstein became a professor at the University of Zurich. In 1913 he went to the University of Berlin where he remained until 1933, when he took a position with the Institute for Advanced Study in Princeton, New Jersey. At the time of his death in 1955, Einstein, like Newton, left science vastly different from the way it was before he began his work.

# 1-6 Solving Problems

**Objective**  To identify five steps in solving word problems.

An important type of problem in algebra is the *word problem*. A word problem describes a situation in which certain numbers are related to each other. If you can state the relationship in an equation, then you can solve the problem by solving the equation.

Here are two simple examples to show you a general plan for solving word problems. This five-step problem solving plan is summarized in the chart on page 26.

**Example 1**  On a street 75 m long, a fire hydrant is placed so that it is 1 m farther from one end of the street than from the other end. How far is the hydrant from each end of the street?

**Solution**

*Step 1*  Read the problem carefully a few times. What numbers are asked for? What information is given? Drawing a sketch may help.

The problem asks for the number of meters from the hydrant to each end of the street.

*Step 2*  Choose a variable. Use it with the given facts to represent the numbers in the problem.

Let $d$ = distance in meters from the hydrant to the closer end of the street.
Then, $1 + d$ = distance in meters from the hydrant to the farther end.

*Step 3*  Write an equation based on the given facts.

The sketch helps you to see that

$$(1 + d) + d = 75.$$

*Step 4* Solve the equation.

The diagram below shows why
$$d + d = 74.$$

From arithmetic, you know that
$37 + 37 = 74$.

$$\therefore d = 37$$
$$1 + d = 38$$

*Step 5* Check your results with the statement of the problem. Give the answer.

Does the sum of the distances from the hydrant to the ends of the street equal the total length of the street?

$$37 + 38 \overset{?}{=} 75$$
$$75 = 75 \quad \checkmark$$

$\therefore$ the hydrant is 38 m from one end and 37 m from the other end of the street. ***Answer***

***Example 2*** A food scientist measured the vitamin C in an orange and a banana. She found that the orange contained 66 mg (milligrams) of the vitamin. That was 18 mg less than seven times the number of milligrams of vitamin C in the banana. How much vitamin C was in the banana?

### Solution

*Step 1* The problem asks for the number of milligrams of vitamin C in the banana. There are 66 mg in the orange. This is 18 less than 7 times the number in the banana.

*Step 2* Let $n$ = number of milligrams of vitamin C in the banana. Then $7n - 18$ = the number of milligrams of vitamin C in the orange.

(*Solution continued on next page.*)

*Step 3* The number of milligrams of vitamin C in the orange is 66.

$$7n - 18 \qquad = 66$$

*Step 4* The diagram suggests why

$$7n = 84.$$

From arithmetic, you know that

$$7 \cdot 12 = 84.$$
$$\therefore n = 12$$

*Step 5* Checking the result of Step 4 is left to you.

$\therefore$ the banana contained 12 mg of vitamin C. *Answer*

The five steps used to solve the problems in Examples 1 and 2 form a plan that often helps in solving word problems.

## Plan For Solving a Word Problem

*Step 1* Read the problem carefully a few times. Decide what numbers are asked for and what information is given. Making a sketch may be helpful.

*Step 2* Choose a variable and use it with the given facts to represent the number(s) described in the problem.

*Step 3* Reread the problem. Then write an open sentence that represents relationships among the numbers in the problem.

*Step 4* Solve the open sentence and find the required numbers.

*Step 5* Check your results with the words of the problem. Give the answer.

In Examples 1 and 2, we solved the equation obtained in Step 3 of this plan by inspection. Often, you cannot solve the equation that easily. Therefore, developing other methods to solve equations is an important goal of the study of algebra.

## Problems

**Use the five-step plan to solve each problem. Write out each step.**

A **1.** The area of a rectangle 12 units long is 103.2 square units. What is the width of the rectangle?

**2.** Ann is skimming across the water on a sailboard at an average rate of 20 km/h. How long will it take her to travel 8 km?

3. An airplane's altimeter reads 982.5 m. What is the plane's altitude if this reading is 2.8 m less than the true reading?

4. The first one-mile speed record was made by Henry Ford in 1904 when he drove the mile in 39.40 s (seconds). This time was 33.62 s slower than the record achieved in 1970. What was the record time in 1970?

5. a. If a number is increased by 8, the result is 32. What is the number?
   b. If four times another number is increased by 8, the result is 32. Find the number.

6. a. If a number is decreased by 14, the result is 39. What is the number?
   b. If half of another number is decreased by 14, the result is 39. Find the number.

7. On a grand jury of 22 people, there were 4 more women than men. How many men were on the jury?

8. In a county election 7836 people cast valid votes for one or the other of two candidates for sheriff. The loser lost the election by 178 votes. How many votes did the winner receive?

9. There were twice as many brown eggs as white eggs in a shipment of nine dozen eggs. How many white eggs were in the shipment?

10. Water is a compound made up of 8 parts "by mass" of oxygen and 1 part "by mass" of hydrogen. How many grams of hydrogen are there in 765 g (grams) of water?

B 11. A hockey team played 86 games and finished only 2 games in a tie. It lost one sixth as many games as it won. How many games did it win?

12. Algonquin City levies a tax of 5 cents per dollar on all restaurant meals. Including tax and tip, the cost of a meal was $8.77. The tip was $1.00. What was the cost of the meal before the tax and tip?

13. A soccer field has a perimeter of 348 m. The width is 37 m less than the length. What are the dimensions of the field?

14. One of the longer sides of An Wong's rectangular lot borders on a straight river. He needs 500 m of fence to fence the three sides not on the river. If the length of the lot is 65 m more than the width, what are the dimensions of the lot?

C 15. At the beginning of a seven-week speed reading course, Ted read at the rate of 250 words per minute (wpm). At the end of the course, his reading speed was 1020 wpm. What was the average weekly increase in his reading speed over the course?

# Self Test 2

***Vocabulary***   formula (p. 13)

1. A variable expression for nine times the difference of the number *n* and one is __?__ .

   Obj. 1-4, p. 13

2. One person traveled for *t* hours at 60 km/h. Another person traveled three hours longer at the same speed. The second person traveled __?__ km.

**Write an equation that represents the given information.**

3. Half of the number *a* is 7 less than *a*.

   Obj. 1-5, p. 18

4. A 100-meter length of coaxial cable is cut so that one piece is *c* m long and the other is 10 m more than twice as long as the first piece.

5. Use the five-step plan to solve this problem.

   Obj. 1-6, p. 24

   Carmen worked 7 hours on a computer program. She spent 2 hours longer testing the program than writing it. How long did she spend writing the program?

   Check your answers with those at the back of the book.

## Historical Note / *Why We Call It "Algebra"*

The word "algebra" comes from the title of a ninth-century mathematical treatise by the mathematician and astronomer Muhammed ibn-Musa al-Khwarizmi. The book, entitled *hisab al-jabr w'al muqabalah,* which means "the science of reduction and comparison," deals with the solving of equations. While the entire work may not have been original, it was the first time that algebra was systematically discussed as a distinct branch of mathematics. Al-Khwarizmi's book made its way into Europe and was translated into Latin in the twelfth century as *Ludus algebrae et almucgrabalaeque.* The title was eventually shortened to "algebra," which is what this branch of mathematics is called today.

# Reading Algebra / Problem-Solving

Accurate reading is a vital part of problem solving. When you read a problem, go very slowly and carefully to be sure that you fully understand every word, fact, and idea. Look up any words that you do not know in a dictionary (or in the glossary at the back of this book if they are mathematical terms). Reread the problem several times and give special attention to any parts that give you difficulty.

When you have read the information carefully, try to answer any questions asked. You can then check your answers with those printed at the back of the book or with your teacher. If your answer is wrong, try rereading the problem. Try to discover your error, because good problem solvers learn from their mistakes as well as their successes.

A good way to find your error is to explain to a classmate or other friend how you reached your answer. Explaining to someone else—or even explaining aloud to yourself—often helps you to clarify your own thinking.

Now try these exercises and remember: *good problem solvers are careful readers*.

## Exercises

One day a cafeteria served twice as much milk as apple juice, and three times as much milk as fruit juice. A total of 660 cartons of the three drinks, at an average cost of 45 cents each, was served. This is 100 more than 80% of the usual number of cartons served.

**1.** If $x$ represents the number of cartons of fruit juice sold, write an expression to represent the number of cartons of apple juice.

**2.** Which of the given information is necessary to determine the number of cartons of milk sold?

**3.** Write an equation to determine the number of cartons usually sold.

**4.** Rob found the number of cartons of milk served by using the equation $x + 2x + 3x = 660$, where $x$ represents the number of cartons of milk served. Was this method correct? Explain.

**5.** If $x$ represents the number of cartons of apple juice served, what does $\frac{2}{3}(660 - x)$ represent?

**6.** Which is greater, the number of cartons of apple juice served, or the number of cartons of fruit juice served?

**7.** Based on the given information, is it possible to determine the total cost of the cartons served?

**8.** If 180 cartons of apple juice were served, how many cartons of fruit juice were served?

**9.** Write an equation to determine the number of cartons of milk served.

**10.** Given the equation $x = 0.45\left(\frac{660 - 100}{0.8}\right)$, what does $x$ represent?

# Numbers on a Line

## 1-7 Number Lines

**Objective**   To graph real numbers on a number line.

When you count or measure, you use real numbers. These numbers can be pictured as points on a line, called a *number line*. To construct a number line:

1. Choose a starting point on a line and label it "0" (zero). This point is called the **origin.** The origin separates the line into two sides, the **positive side** and the **negative side.** If the line is horizontal, the side to the right of the origin is taken to be the positive side.

2. Mark off equal units of distance on both sides of the origin. On the positive side, pair the endpoint of successive units with the **positive integers**

$$1, 2, 3, 4, 5, \ldots$$

The three dots are read "and so on" and indicate that the list continues without end. On the negative side, pair the endpoints with the **negative integers**

$$^-1, {}^-2, {}^-3, {}^-4, {}^-5, \ldots$$

You read $^-1$ as "negative one." You usually read 1 as "one." You may also read 1 as "positive one," and you may write it as $^+1$.

The positive integers, the negative integers, and zero make up the set of **integers.** The positive integers and zero are often called **whole numbers.**

$$\{\text{the integers}\} = \{\ldots {}^-3, {}^-2, {}^-1, 0, 1, 2, 3, \ldots\}$$
$$\{\text{the whole numbers}\} = \{0, 1, 2, 3, \ldots\}$$

In general, a **positive number** is a number paired with a point on the positive side of a number line. A **negative number** is a number paired with a point on the negative side of a number line. For example:

*A* is 1.5 units from 0 on the *positive* side.
The *positive* number 1.5 is paired with *A*.

*B* is 1.5 units from 0 on the *negative* side.
The *negative* number $^-1.5$ is paired with *B*.

On a number line, the point paired with a number is called the **graph** of the number. The number paired with a point is called the **coordinate** of the point. On the number line on the previous page, point $C$ is the graph of $2\frac{1}{3}$, and $2\frac{1}{3}$ is the coordinate of $C$. Any number that is either a positive number, a negative number, or zero is called a **real number.** When you graph real numbers, you take the following for granted:

1. Each real number is paired with exactly one point on a number line.

2. Each point on a number line is paired with exactly one real number.

Thus, the graphs of *all* the real numbers make up the entire number line:

The arrowheads indicate that the number line and the graphs go on indefinitely in both directions.

Because positive and negative numbers suggest opposite directions, they are sometimes called *directed numbers.* You use them for measurements that have *direction* as well as size. For example:

A wage *increase* of $15: 15      A wage *decrease* of $15: ⁻15

A *gain* of 10 yards: 10      A *loss* of 10 yards: ⁻10

71 km *north:* 71      71 km *south:* ⁻71

A temperature *rise* of 8.25°C      A temperature *drop* of 8.25°C: ⁻8.25
(degrees Celsius): 8.25

## Oral Exercises

**Exercises 1–16 refer to the number line below.**

**Name the point that is the graph of the given number.**

**Example 1** ⁻7      **Solution** Point $C$

**1.** 8            **2.** 0            **3.** ⁻1            **4.** ⁻6            **5.** 4            **6.** ⁻4

**State the coordinate of the given point.**

**7.** $G$            **8.** $R$            **9.** $T$            **10.** $H$            **11.** $B$            **12.** $J$

**Example 2** The point halfway between $P$ and $Q$      **Solution** 5.5

**13.** The point halfway between $L$ and $M$      **14.** The point halfway between $D$ and $E$

**15.** The point one third of the way from $E$ to $K$

**16.** The point one fourth of the way from $I$ to $A$

## Written Exercises

**Write a positive number for each measurement. Then write the opposite of that number and describe the measurement indicated by that opposite.**

A
1. Five floors up
2. Two steps to the right
3. 190 m above sea level
4. Nine degrees above freezing (0°C)
5. A profit of $18
6. Four wins
7. 15 km east
8. Latitude 41° north
9. Receipts of $85
10. A bank deposit of $25
11. One second after liftoff
12. 3 points above par
13. A credit of $50
14. A counterclockwise angle of 20°

**Name the coordinates of the points shown in color.**

15.

16.

17.

18.

19.

20.

21.

22.

**List the letters for the points whose coordinates are given.**

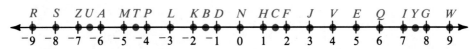

23. ⁻8, 2
24. ⁻5, 4
25. 0, ⁻9
26. ⁻6, 8
27. 6, ⁻6, ⁻6$\frac{1}{2}$
28. 1, ⁻1, ⁻1$\frac{1}{2}$
29. ⁻5, ⁻4, ⁻4$\frac{1}{2}$
30. ⁻8, ⁻7, 7$\frac{1}{2}$

**Graph the given numbers on a number line. Draw a separate line for each exercise.**

31. ⁻2, ⁻1, 1, 2
32. 3, 6, ⁻3, ⁻6
33. ⁻4, 0, $\frac{1}{2}$, 1
34. ⁻2, ⁻1.5, ⁻1, 0

B
35. ⁻3, ⁻1$\frac{2}{3}$, $\frac{-1}{3}$, 0
36. ⁻1, ⁻0.5, 0, 1.5
37. ⁻1$\frac{1}{4}$, $\frac{-1}{4}$, $\frac{3}{4}$, 2$\frac{1}{4}$
38. $\frac{-2}{3}$, $\frac{2}{3}$, $\frac{5}{3}$, $\frac{10}{3}$

**On a horizontal number line, point P has coordinate ⁻5 and point Q has coordinate 3. Write the coordinate of each point described.**

**39.** 4 units to the right of Q

**40.** 4 units to the left of P

**41.** 7 units to the left of Q

**42.** 7 units to the right of P

**43.** Halfway between P and Q

**44.** One fourth of the way from P to Q

**C** **45.** On a number line, point M has coordinate 2 and point T has coordinate 5. What is the coordinate of the point between M and T that is half as far from M as it is from T?

**46.** On a number line, point C has coordinate ⁻2 and point D has coordinate 4. What is the coordinate of the point between C and D that is twice as far from C as it is from D?

## *Career Note* / *Astronomer*

Present-day astronomers do very little observation with telescopes. Instead, they use mathematics and physics to explore the nature of the universe. Theories are represented as mathematical equations, and astronomers spend time analyzing these theories with computers, using data collected by observatories.

Observatories gather much of this data with spectroscopes and radio telescopes. Spectroscopes analyze light from stars and assist scientists in determining a star's composition. Radio telescopes gather x rays and radio waves that tell astronomers even more about these stellar bodies.

Astronomers work primarily as researchers and teachers. Most have a Ph.D. in astronomy and are highly trained in mathematics and physics. They are most often employed by universities or by government space programs.

# 1-8 Opposites and Absolute Values

**Objective**   To use opposites and absolute values.

The diagram below shows pairings of points on a number line. The paired points are at the same distance from the origin but on opposite sides of the origin. The origin is paired with itself.

The coordinates of the paired points can also be paired:

   0 with 0      ⁻1 with 1      ⁻5 with 5      ⁻7.5 with 7.5

Each number in a pair such as 5 and ⁻5 is called the **opposite** of the other number. The symbol for the opposite of a number $a$ is

   $-a$   (note the lowered position of the minus sign)

For example:

$$-5 = {}^{-}5, \quad \text{read "The opposite of five equals negative five."}$$
$$-({}^{-}1) = 1, \quad \text{read "The opposite of negative one equals one."}$$
$$-0 = 0, \quad \text{read "The opposite of zero equals zero."}$$

Notice that the numerals $-5$ (lowered minus sign) and $^{-}5$ (raised minus sign) name the same number. Thus, $-5$ can mean "negative five" as well as "the opposite of five." Therefore:

> *To simplify notation, lowered minus signs will be used in the numerals for negative numbers through-out the rest of this book.*

Be sure you understand the meaning of the expression $-a$, the opposite of $a$. If the value of $a$ is $-3$, then $-a$ is the positive number 3. In general:

1. If $a$ is a positive number, then $-a$ is a negative number; if $a$ is a negative number, then $-a$ is a positive number; if $a$ is 0, then $-a$ is 0.
2. The opposite of $-a$ is $a$; that is $-(-a) = a$.

**Example 1**   Simplify.

   **a.** $-(8 + 3)$      **b.** $-(-1.6)$      **c.** $-0$      **d.** $-(-t)$

*Solution*      **a.** $-11$      **b.** 1.6      **c.** 0      **d.** $t$

**Example 2**   Evaluate $-n + 14$, if $n = -8$.

*Solution*      $-(-8) + 14 = 8 + 14 = 22$

In any pair of nonzero opposites, such as $-5$ and $5$, one number is negative and the other is positive. The positive number of any pair of opposite nonzero real numbers is called the **absolute value** of each number in the pair.

The absolute value of a number $a$ is denoted by $|a|$. For example,

$$|-5| = 5 \quad \text{and} \quad |5| = 5.$$

Notice that the absolute value of a real number $a$ is $a$ if $a$ is nonnegative and $-a$ (the opposite of $a$) if $a$ is negative. (See Exercise 45, page 36.)

The absolute value of a number may also be thought of as the distance of the graph of the number from the origin on a number line. The graphs of both $-5$ and $5$ are $5$ units from the origin.

The absolute value of $0$ is defined to be $0$ itself:

$$|0| = 0.$$

*Example 3*  $8|-3| + |-15| = (8 \times 3) + 15 = 24 + 15 = 39$

*Example 4*  Give the solution of $|x| = 3$ over the set of real numbers.

*Solution*     $|x| = 3; \; x = 3 \text{ or } x = -3$

## Oral Exercises

**Name the opposite and the absolute value of each number.**

| | | | | |
|---|---|---|---|---|
| **1.** 6 | **2.** 5 | **3.** $-1$ | **4.** $-9$ | **5.** 194 |
| **6.** $-78$ | **7.** 0 | **8.** 0.3 | **9.** 2.8 | **10.** $-1\frac{1}{4}$ |

**Simplify.**

**11.** $-(-7)$          **12.** $-\left(-\frac{1}{2}\right)$          **13.** $|12|$

**14.** $-(7 + 3)$        **15.** $-(7 - 3)$          **16.** $-[-(-3)]$
**17.** $-[-(-0)]$        **18.** $|-14|$            **19.** $|-2.7|$
**20.** $-|-4|$           **21.** $-|0|$             **22.** $9 - |-9|$

**Complete.**

**23.** If $n$ is a negative number, then $-n$ is a __?__ number.
**24.** If $n$ is a positive number, then $-n$ is a __?__ number.
**25.** The one and only number whose absolute value is zero is __?__ .
**26.** A real number that is its own opposite is __?__ .

## Written Exercises

**Simplify.**

**A**  1. $-(8 + 5)$    2. $-(9 - 3)$    3. $-(12 - 12)$    4. $-(0 + 0)$

5. $[-(-9)] + 10$    6. $[-(-7)] + 1$    7. $6 + [-(-2)]$    8. $5 - [-(-1)]$

9. $8 + |-3|$    10. $|-11| + 4$    11. $|-8| + |6|$

12. $|2| + |-9|$    13. $\left|-\frac{3}{2}\right| + |0|$    14. $|-1| - |0|$

15. $|-0.4| + |-3.6|$    16. $|-2.8| + |2.8|$    17. $\left|\frac{1}{2}\right| + \left|-\frac{1}{2}\right|$

18. $\left|-\frac{3}{4}\right| - \left|\frac{1}{4}\right|$    19. $|6| - |6|$    20. $|6| - |-6|$

**Give the solution set of each equation over the set of real numbers. If there is no solution, explain why there is none.**

21. $|n| = 0$    22. $|p| = 2$    23. $|t| = \frac{1}{2}$    24. $|z| = 0.3$

**B**  25. $|a| = -2$    26. $|b| = -9$    27. $|-q| = 1$    28. $|-x| = 5$

29. $|q| + 1 = 6$    30. $12 + |w| = 20$    31. $|m| - 3 = 2$

32. $|p| - 20 = |-2|$    33. $10 - |s| = |-8|$    34. $7 - |t| = 4$

**Evaluate each expression if $a = 1.5$, $b = -2$, and $c = -1.7$.**

35. $|a| + |b| - (-c)$    36. $a + |-b| + (-c)$

37. $4a - |b| - |c|$    38. $2|b| - |a| + |c|$

39. $(a + 8.5) - [(-b) + |c|]$    40. $(10 \cdot 5 - a) - [|c| + (-b)]$

41. $|c| + [-(-|a| + |b|)]$    42. $|a - 1.5| + [-(-|(-b) + (-c)|)]$

43. $|a - |b| + |-c| - (b + a)|$    44. $\left|\frac{3b}{-a} - c\right| - \left|-c + \left|\frac{6}{ab}\right| - bc\right|$

**C**  45. Explain why the following statement is true.

If $a$ is a real number, then

$|a| = a$    if $a$ is zero or a positive number;

$|a| = -a$   if $a$ is a negative number.

46. Two of the following statements are true and one is false. Which one is false? Why is it false?
   **a.** The absolute value of every real number is a positive number.
   **b.** There is at least one real number whose absolute value is zero.
   **c.** The absolute value of a real number is never a negative number.

# 1-9 Comparing Real Numbers

**Objective**   To show the order of real numbers.

You know that 3 is less than 7 and that 7 is greater than 3. **Inequality symbols** are used to show the *order* of pairs of real numbers.

$$<\quad \text{means}\quad \text{is less than:}\quad 3 < 7$$
$$>\quad \text{means}\quad \text{is greater than:}\quad 7 > 3$$

To avoid confusing the symbols $>$ and $<$, notice that the name of the greater number is placed at the greater (or open) end of the inequality symbol. The statements $3 < 7$ and $7 > 3$ give the same information.

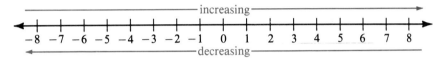

On a horizontal number line, such as the one above, the numbers increase from left to right and decrease from right to left. By studying the number line, you can see that the following statements are true.

$$-5 < -2 \qquad -5 < 0 \qquad -5 < 3$$
$$-2 > -5 \qquad 0 > -5 \qquad 3 > -5$$

**Example**   Graph the numbers 4, $-1$, 2.5, 0, $|-6|$, $-3$ on a number line, and then name them in order from least to greatest.

**Solution**

From least to greatest, the numbers are

$$-3,\ -1,\ 0,\ 2.5,\ 4,\ |-6|.$$

---

## Oral Exercises

**Translate the following statements into words.**

1. $3 < 8$      2. $0 < 1$      3. $0 > -1$      4. $-2 > -3$

5. $-5 > -9$      6. $\frac{1}{2} < \frac{3}{4}$      7. $-\frac{1}{2} > -\frac{3}{4}$      8. $1.25 < 1.40$

9. $-0.5 > -2.5$      10. $0 > -100$      11. $3 > -30$      12. $|3| < |-30|$

13. $|-8| > |3|$      14. $-\frac{2}{3} < -\frac{1}{2}$      15. $-2.4 > -7.1$      16. $|2| < |-12|$

In Exercises 17-24, tell whether or not the given statement is true. Give a reason for your answer.

**Example** $7 \times |-3| > 7 + |-3|$     **Solution**    True, because
$$7 \times |-3| = 7 \times 3 = 21,$$
$$7 + |-3| = 7 + 3 = 10, \text{ and}$$
$$21 > 10.$$

**17.** $-2 < 0 + \frac{1}{2}$             **18.** $\frac{2}{3} \times \frac{1}{3} > \frac{2}{3} + \frac{1}{3}$

**19.** $5 \times 6 < 6 \times 5$          **20.** $7 + (1 + 29) < (7 + 1) + 29$

**21.** $\frac{7+1}{2} > -\left(\frac{17-1}{4}\right)$      **22.** $-1 < \frac{4+10}{8+6}$

**23.** $-[4(3 - 1)] < -[3(4 - 1)]$      **24.** $5(0 + 8) > (5 \times 0) + (5 \times 8)$

## Written Exercises

**Translate each statement into symbols.**

**A**   **1.** Six is greater than negative nine.

    **2.** Negative eleven is less than negative one.

    **3.** Negative eight is greater than negative twenty.

    **4.** Ten is greater than seven.

    **5.** Six is less than six and five tenths.

    **6.** Zero is greater than negative three tenths.

    **7.** Negative thirteen is less than zero.

    **8.** One eighth is less than one seventh.

    **9.** The absolute value of negative five is greater than two.

    **10.** Four is less than the absolute value of negative ten.

    **11.** The opposite of negative two is greater than the opposite of negative one.

    **12.** The opposite of eight is less than the opposite of four.

**Replace each ? with one of the symbols < or > to make a true statement.**

**13.** $-4 \underline{\ ?\ } 0$     **14.** $0 \underline{\ ?\ } -5$     **15.** $6 \underline{\ ?\ } 5 + 4$     **16.** $8 - 7 \underline{\ ?\ } -1$

**17.** $|0| \underline{\ ?\ } -1$     **18.** $0 \times 0 \underline{\ ?\ } 1$     **19.** $-3.1 \underline{\ ?\ } -3.2$     **20.** $-\frac{2}{5} \underline{\ ?\ } -\frac{1}{5}$

**21.** $|-7| \underline{\ ?\ } -(-9)$     **22.** $-(-2) \underline{\ ?\ } |-3|$     **23.** $|-8| \underline{\ ?\ } |-10|$

**24.** $|-15| \underline{\ ?\ } |-6|$     **25.** $-(8 + 2) \underline{\ ?\ } |-20|$     **26.** $|-40| \underline{\ ?\ } -(9 + 11)$

**27.** $21.5 - 15.9 \underline{\ ?\ } \frac{18.1 + 16.1}{6}$     **28.** $3(36 \div (5 + 4)) \underline{\ ?\ } 64 - 8 \times 8$

**Write the given numbers in order from least to greatest.**

B **29.** $0, -5, 8, -7$      **30.** $-5, -8, 0, -9$      **31.** $-1, 5, -3, 2$

**32.** $-8, 7, -7, -1$    **33.** $-\frac{1}{2}, -\frac{1}{4}, -\frac{1}{3}, -\frac{1}{6}$    **34.** $-\frac{2}{3}, -\frac{3}{4}, -\frac{1}{7}, -\frac{1}{10}$

**35.** $-1.5, 1.4, -0.7, 0.3$    **36.** $2.7, -3.6, -2, 3.5$    **37.** $3.14, -3.141, 3.1416$

**38.** $-1.7, -1.732, 1.7$    **39.** $-4\frac{1}{3}, -4\frac{1}{6}, -4\frac{1}{2}$    **40.** $-5\frac{1}{3}, -5\frac{1}{7}, -5\frac{1}{2}$

**41.** $|-3|, -(-2), |-6|, -(-1)$      **42.** $-(-4), |-7|, |-1|, -(-3)$

**43.** Flo is taller than Cal but shorter than Sal. Sal is taller than Flo but shorter than Nell. List the names of these four people in order from shortest to tallest.

**44.** Jack and Nick are both older than Mel, while Pete is older than Jack but younger than Nick. List the names of these four people in order from oldest to youngest.

**In Exercises 45–54, let $x$ be any positive number and $y$ any negative number. Classify each sentence as true or false. If the sentence is false, give a reason.**

C **45.** $x < y$     **46.** $y < 0$     **47.** $x > y$     **48.** $0 > x$

**49.** $-y < 0$     **50.** $-x < -y$     **51.** $-x < 0$     **52.** $-y > 0$

**53.** On a number line, the graphs of $x$ and $y$ are on opposite sides of the origin.

**54.** On a number line, the graph of $y$ is on the opposite side of the origin from the graph of 1.

**55.** Why is the following statement false?
Every real number is greater than its opposite.

## Challenge

1, 3, 6, 10, 15, . . . are called triangular numbers because they can be represented by dots arranged to form triangles.

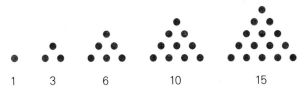

1     3     6     10     15     and so on

**1.** Find the next five triangular numbers.

**2.** If $n$ represents the number of the triangular number in the list ($n = 1$ for 1, $n = 2$ for 3, and so on), verify for the first ten triangular numbers that the $n$th triangular number $= \dfrac{n(n + 1)}{2}$.

# Self-Test 3

**1.** Graph the given numbers on the same number line: $^-3, \, ^-1, \, 0, \, 4$        **Obj. 1-7, p. 30**

**Simplify.**

**2.** $-(-12) + 4$                      **3.** $|-3| + 2$                          **Obj. 1-8, p. 34**

**4.** Translate the given statement into words: $-2 < 1$                          **Obj. 1-9, p. 37**

**5.** Write the given numbers in order from least to greatest: $6, \, 0, \, -5, \, -1$

Check your answers with those at the back of the book.

# Chapter Summary

1. A numerical expression represents a particular number. To simplify a numerical expression, replace the expression by the simplest name of the number that the expression represents.

2. A variable expression is evaluated by replacing each variable with its given value and simplifying the resulting numerical expression.

3. Grouping symbols are used to show the order in which operations are to be performed to simplify an expression. If no grouping symbols appear, the steps listed on page 6 are followed.

4. Replacing each variable in an open sentence by each of its values in the domain, in turn, is a way to find solutions of the open sentence.

5. A word problem can often be solved by using the plan outlined on page 26 to write an open sentence based on the given facts and then solving the open sentence.

6. The positive numbers, the negative numbers, and zero make up the real numbers and can be paired with the points on a number line, thereby showing their order.

7. The opposite of a number $a$ is denoted by $-a$. The positive number of any pair of opposite nonzero real numbers is called the absolute value of each number in the pair. The absolute value of a number $a$ is denoted by $|a|$.

# Chapter Review

**Give the letter of the correct answer.**

1. Simplify $36 \div (9 \times 4)$.      **1-1**
   **a.** 16      **b.** 0      **c.** 81      **d.** 1

2. Evaluate $(x + y) - 3z$ if $x = 7$, $y = 8$, and $z = 0$.
   **a.** 12      **b.** 0      **c.** 15      **d.** 5

3. Simplify $\dfrac{24 - 6 \times 2}{8 + 16 \div 4}$.      **1-2**

   **a.** 1      **b.** 3      **c.** 2      **d.** 6

4. Find the solution set of the equation $\frac{1}{3}w = 0$ if $w \in \{0, 1, 2, 3, 4, 5, 6\}$.      **1-3**

   **a.** $\{0, 1, 2, 3, 4, 5, 6\}$      **b.** $\{0\}$
   **c.** $\{3\}$      **d.** $\{0, 3, 6\}$

5. Write a variable expression for the word phrase "the difference of      **1-4**
   seven times the number $n$ and three."
   **a.** $7(n - 3)$      **b.** $3 + 7n$      **c.** $7n - 3$      **d.** $7(3 - n)$

6. Write an equation for the word sentence "The product of nine and four
   less than the number $n$ is twenty-seven."
   **a.** $9n - 4 = 27$      **b.** $9(n - 4) = 27$
   **c.** $9(4 - n) = 27$      **d.** $9 + 4 - n = 27$

7. Use the given facts to choose the equation that represents the sentence      **1-5**
   shown in color. The length of a rectangle is 3 cm longer than its width.
   Its width is $x$ cm. Its perimeter is 54 cm.
   **a.** $3x = 54$      **b.** $2x + 2(x + 3) = 54$
   **c.** $2x + 3 = 54$      **d.** $x + 3 = 54$

8. Choose the equation you would write in Step 3 of the five-step plan to      **1-6**
   solve the following problem. Lesley and Michael jogged a total of thirteen miles. If Michael jogged three less miles than Lesley, now many
   miles did Lesley jog?
   **a.** $x - 3 = 13$      **b.** $2x - 3 = 13$      **c.** $3 - x = 13$      **d.** $3 - 2x = 13$

9. If a surplus of 45 items is represented by $^+45$, choose the opposite of      **1-7**
   that number and describe the measurement indicated by that opposite.

   **a.** 45; a gain of 45 items.      **b.** $\frac{1}{45}$; each item is $\frac{1}{45}$ of the total.

   **c.** $|45|$; there are 45 items.      **d.** $-45$; a shortage of 45 items.

10. Simplify $|^+7| - |-7|$.      **1-8**
    **a.** 14      **b.** 49      **c.** 0      **d.** 1

11. Give the solution set of $|m| + 3 = 2$ over the set of real numbers.
    **a.** no solution      **b.** $\{-5\}$      **c.** $\{-1, 1\}$      **d.** $\{-2, 2\}$

12. Which of the following is a true statement?      **1-9**

    **a.** $-5(0) > |-5| + 0$   **b.** $6 < -(-6)$   **c.** $-\frac{3}{4} > -\frac{5}{4}$   **d.** $6 - |-4| > 9$

# Chapter Test

**Simplify.**

**1.** $(42 + 9) \times 3$            **2.** $4 + 5(6 - 2)$          1-1

**3.** Evaluate $a \div bc$ if $a = 315$, $b = 35$, and $c = 3$.      1-2

**Simplify.**

**4.** $38 + 38 \div (15 + 4)$        **5.** $25 + 15 \cdot 5 \div 25$

**6.** Evaluate $2\pi r$ (circumference of a circle) if $r = 49$. Use $\frac{22}{7}$ as an approximate value for $\pi$.

**Solve.** $x \in \{0, 1, 2, 3, 4, 5, 6\}$

**7.** $56 = 14 + 7x$      **8.** $x \cdot x = 0$      **9.** $\frac{1}{2}x = \frac{x}{2}$    1-3

**10.** Inga is 3 times as old as Adriano. If Adriano is $n$ years old, represent Inga's age 5 years ago.      1-4

**11.** Use the given facts to state an equation that represents the sentence shown in color. Marta spent one hour less than twice as long researching a paper than she spent writing it. It took her $x$ hours to write the paper. She spent five hours total working on the paper.      1-5

**12.** Use the five-step plan to solve the following problem. Diane plans to plant a rectangular garden next to a barn so that she only has to fence the other three sides. She has 63 m of fencing and wants to use it all. She also wants the length of the garden to be 6 m more than the width. Find the dimensions of the garden.      1-6

**On a horizontal number line, point $P$ has coordinate $-1$ and point $Q$ has coordinate $-4$. Write the coordinate of each point described.**

**13.** $\frac{1}{2}$ unit to the left of $P$      **14.** 8 units to the right of $Q$      1-7

**Simplify.**

**15.** $5 - |-1.6|$      **16.** $6 - \left(-2\frac{3}{4}\right)$      **17.** $-|(4 + 1.5)|$      1-8

**Give the solution set of each equation over the set of real numbers. If there is no solution, explain why.**

**18.** $|t| = 6.75$      **19.** $|x| = -\frac{1}{2}$

**20.** Translate $-8 < -(-7)$ into words.      1-9

**Replace each __?__ with < or > to make a true statement.**

**21.** $-(-5)$ __?__ $-4$      **22.** $-|-10|$ __?__ $|8|$

# Maintaining Skills

**Perform the indicated operations.**

**Example 1**
$$\begin{array}{r} \overset{1\,2\quad 1}{729.35} \\ 84. \\ +\ 68.29 \\ \hline 881.64 \end{array}$$

**Example 2**
$$\begin{array}{r} 625.3 \\ \times\ 32.1 \\ \hline 6253 \\ 12506 \\ 18759 \\ \hline 20072.13 \end{array}$$

**1.**
$$\begin{array}{r} 0.0056 \\ 2.3 \\ 18.232 \\ +\ 9.41 \\ \hline \end{array}$$

**2.**
$$\begin{array}{r} 42.31 \\ 8.79 \\ +\ 13.26 \\ \hline \end{array}$$

**3.**
$$\begin{array}{r} 22.6 \\ 153.3 \\ +\ 201.8 \\ \hline \end{array}$$

**4.**
$$\begin{array}{r} 27 \\ 6.25 \\ 108.1 \\ +\ 35.72 \\ \hline \end{array}$$

**5.**
$$\begin{array}{r} 318 \\ \times\ 5.2 \\ \hline \end{array}$$

**6.**
$$\begin{array}{r} 208.2 \\ \times\ 10.3 \\ \hline \end{array}$$

**7.**
$$\begin{array}{r} 7.51 \\ \times\ 2.2 \\ \hline \end{array}$$

**8.**
$$\begin{array}{r} 0.876 \\ \times\ 0.09 \\ \hline \end{array}$$

**9.**
$$\begin{array}{r} 824.2 \\ \times\ 1.2 \\ \hline \end{array}$$

**10.**
$$\begin{array}{r} 0.222 \\ \times\ 11.1 \\ \hline \end{array}$$

**11.**
$$\begin{array}{r} 35.83 \\ +\ 9.96 \\ \hline \end{array}$$

**12.**
$$\begin{array}{r} 20.05 \\ +\ 8.87 \\ \hline \end{array}$$

**Rewrite the fractions with their least common denominator.**

**Example 3** $\frac{7}{8}$ and $\frac{2}{3}$

**Solution** The least common denominator is 24.
$$\frac{7}{8} = \frac{7}{8} \times \frac{3}{3} = \frac{21}{24} \qquad \frac{2}{3} = \frac{2}{3} \times \frac{8}{8} = \frac{16}{24}$$

**13.** $\frac{5}{8}$ and $\frac{3}{4}$

**14.** $\frac{2}{3}$ and $\frac{3}{5}$

**15.** $\frac{2}{7}$ and $\frac{2}{3}$

**16.** $\frac{5}{12}$ and $\frac{3}{2}$

**Perform the indicated operations.**

**Example 4** $\frac{3}{7} + \frac{2}{3}$

**Solution** $\frac{3}{7} + \frac{2}{3} = \frac{3}{7} \times \frac{3}{3} + \frac{2}{3} \times \frac{7}{7} = \frac{9}{21} + \frac{14}{21} = \frac{23}{21}$

**Example 5** $\frac{2}{5} \times \frac{7}{8}$

**Solution** $\frac{2}{5} \times \frac{7}{8} = \frac{\overset{1}{\cancel{2}} \times 7}{5 \times \underset{4}{\cancel{8}}} = \frac{7}{20}$

**17.** $\frac{3}{5} + \frac{4}{9}$

**18.** $\frac{2}{7} + \frac{1}{4}$

**19.** $\frac{3}{8} + \frac{5}{9}$

**20.** $\frac{7}{10} + \frac{2}{5}$

**21.** $\frac{5}{13} \times \frac{3}{4}$

**22.** $\frac{5}{9} \times \frac{3}{5}$

**23.** $\frac{10}{11} \times \frac{11}{12}$

**24.** $\frac{5}{6} \times \frac{15}{16}$

**25.** $\frac{2}{3} + \frac{3}{7}$

**26.** $\frac{9}{10} \times \frac{5}{3}$

**27.** $\frac{7}{8} \times \frac{14}{16}$

**28.** $\frac{9}{13} + \frac{2}{5}$

# 2 Working with Real Numbers

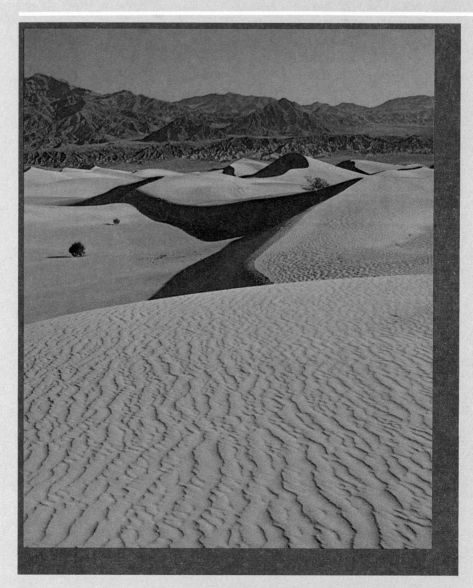

The lowest point in Death Valley, California, is 86 m below sea level. Altitudes below sea level can be thought of as negative numbers, while those above sea level can be thought of as positive numbers.

# Addition and Subtraction

## 2-1 Basic Assumptions

***Objective***   To use number properties to simplify expressions.

The rules used in adding and multiplying real numbers are based on several properties that you can take for granted. For example, the following statements are accepted as facts.

1. Every pair of real numbers has a unique (one and only one) sum that is also a real number.

2. Every pair of real numbers has a unique product that is also a real number.

3. When you add two real numbers, you get the same sum no matter what order you use in adding them.

$$8 + 5 = 5 + 8 \qquad 3.2 + 0.4 = 0.4 + 3.2$$

4. When you multiply two real numbers, you get the same product no matter what order you use in multiplying them.

$$2 \times 9 = 9 \times 2 \qquad \frac{1}{7} \times \frac{2}{5} = \frac{2}{5} \times \frac{1}{7}$$

Statements that are assumed to be true are called **axioms,** or **postulates.** Statements (1) and (2) above may be stated more formally as follows.

---

### Axioms of Closure

For all real numbers $a$ and $b$:

$$a + b \text{ is a unique real number.}$$

$$ab \text{ is a unique real number.}$$

---

Statements (3) and (4) above may be stated as follows.

---

### Commutative Axioms

For all real numbers $a$ and $b$:

$$a + b = b + a$$

$$ab = ba$$

---

In the sum $a + b$, $a$ and $b$ are called **terms.** In the product $ab$, $a$ and $b$ are called **factors.**

You find a sum or a product by working with two numbers at a time. To find the sum of several numbers, such as

$$79 + 65 + 35,$$

you usually do the additions in order from left to right:

$$(79 + 65) + 35 = 144 + 35 = 179$$

This example would be easier to compute if the terms were grouped as follows:

$$79 + (65 + 35) = 79 + 100 = 179$$

Note that the sum is 179 no matter which way the terms are grouped. When you add three or more real numbers, you get the same sum no matter how you group, or *associate*, the numbers.

Similarly, products of three or more real numbers do not depend on the way you group the factors. For example, you can verify that

$$\left(7 \times \frac{1}{2}\right) \times 20 = 7 \times \left(\frac{1}{2} \times 20\right).$$

---

### Associative Axioms

For all real numbers $a$, $b$, and $c$:

$$(a + b) + c = a + (b + c)$$

$$(ab)c = a(bc)$$

---

The commutative and associative axioms permit you to add or multiply numbers *in any order* and *in any groups of two.* Thoughtful use of these axioms can sometimes help you simplify expressions.

**Example 1** Simplify $7 \times 25 \times 31 \times 4$.

**Solution**
$$\begin{aligned}
7 \times 25 \times 31 \times 4 &= (7 \times 31)(25 \times 4) \\
&= 217 \times 100 \\
&= 21{,}700
\end{aligned}$$

**Example 2** Simplify $5 + 8a + 4$.

**Solution**
$$\begin{aligned}
5 + 8a + 4 &= 8a + 5 + 4 \\
&= 8a + 9
\end{aligned}$$

You use the sign $=$ to show that two expressions name the same number (page 2). In your work, you will usually use the following **properties of equality** without mention.

For all real numbers $a$, $b$, and $c$:

| | |
|---|---|
| Reflexive Property | $a = a$ |
| Symmetric Property | If $a = b$, then $b = a$. |
| Transitive Property | If $a = b$ and $b = c$, then $a = c$. |

*Throughout the rest of this book, the domain of all variables is the set of real numbers unless otherwise specified.*

## Oral Exercises

**Name the axiom or property illustrated.**

**Example** $7 + x = x + 7$     **Solution**   Commutative axiom for addition

1. $9 \times (-6) = (-6) \times 9$

2. $(83 + 99) + 1 = 83 + (99 + 1)$

3. $\frac{1}{3} + 4 = 4 + \frac{1}{3}$

4. $7(6 \times 0) = (7 \times 6)0$

5. $n + 3.5 = 3.5 + n$

6. If $28 = 2y$, then $2y = 28$.

7. $\frac{1}{3}(12p) = \left(\frac{1}{3} \cdot 12\right)p$

8. If $4 + s = 15$, then $15 = 4 + s$.

9. $(5 + b) + (-3) = (b + 5) + (-3)$

10. There is only one real number that is the sum of 0.8 and 7.2.

11. Every real number is equal to itself.

12. If $z + 2 = 7$ and $7 = 5 + 2$, then $z + 2 = 5 + 2$.

13. $r + 33 + 27 + s = r + (33 + 27) + s$

14. $3 \times (5x)y = (3 \times 5)xy$

**Name the axiom that justifies each step. A check ($\checkmark$) shows that the step is justified by the substitution principle (page 2).**

15. $57 + (32 + 13) = 57 + (13 + 32)$     (1) $\underline{\ ?\ }$
$\qquad\qquad\quad = (57 + 13) + 32$     (2) $\underline{\ ?\ }$
$\qquad\qquad\quad = 70 + 32$     (3) $\checkmark$
$\qquad\qquad\quad = 102$     (4) $\checkmark$

Name the axiom that justifies each step. A check (√) shows that the step is justified by the substitution principle (page 2).

16. $25 \times (83 \times 8) = 25 \times (8 \times 83)$    (1) __?__

$= (25 \times 8) \times 83$    (2) __?__

$= 200 \times 83$    (3) √

$= (100 \times 2) \times 83$    (4) √

$= 100 \times (2 \times 83)$    (5) __?__

$= 100 \times 166$    (6) √

$= 16{,}600$    (7) √

## Written Exercises

In each of Exercises 1–22, simplify the expression.

**A**

1. $439 + 42 + 61 + 8$

2. $833 + 26 + 67 + 24$

3. $2 \times 27 \times 5 \times 3$

4. $50 \times 7 \times 7 \times 20$

5. $25 \times 53 \times 2 \times 2$

6. $8 \times 17 \times 9 \times 25$

7. $6\frac{1}{2} + 4\frac{1}{3} + 1\frac{1}{2} + \frac{2}{3}$

8. $89\frac{7}{8} + \frac{3}{5} + \frac{1}{8} + 2\frac{2}{5}$

9. $0.1 + 1.8 + 5.9 + 0.2$

10. $4.75 + 2.95 + 1.05 + 10.25$

**Example**    $a + 3 + b + 9 = a + b + 3 + 9 = a + b + 12$

11. $7 + 2p + 3$

12. $18 + 4s + 7$

13. $6(5x)$

14. $4(9y)$

15. $(8t)(12)$

16. $(3c)7$

**B**

17. $m + 8 + f + 3 + g$

18. $5 + k + t + 7 + n$

19. $(2m)(11k)(5h)$

20. $(3p)(10q)(9r)$

21. $(75c)(7d)(10e)(2)$

22. $(250)(25b)(25c)(4)(8)$

23. Find the values of $(7 - 4) - 2$ and $7 - (4 - 2)$. Is subtraction of real numbers associative?

24. Find the values of $(48 \div 8) \div 2$ and $48 \div (8 \div 2)$. Is division of real numbers associative?

**C**

25. Is division of real numbers commutative? Why or why not?

In each of Exercises 26–28, an operation * is defined over the set of positive integers.
a. Find 3 * 4.
b. State whether or not * is a commutative operation.
c. State whether or not * is an associative operation.

26. $a * b = a + b + 2$

27. $a * b = ab + 1$

28. $a * b = a + 2b$

# 2-2 Addition on a Number Line

**Objective** To use a number line to add real numbers.

You already know how to add two positive numbers. You can use a horizontal number line to help you find the sum of *any* two real numbers.

To find the sum of $-2$ and $-5$, draw a number line and follow these directions. Starting at the origin, move your pencil along your number line 2 units to the left. Then, from that position, move your pencil 5 units to the left. Moves to the left represent negative numbers. Together, the two moves amount to a move of 7 units to the left from the origin. The arrows in the diagram below show the moves.

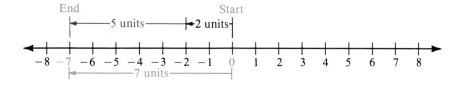

Thus, $-2 + (-5) = -7$.

Note the use of parentheses in "$-2 + (-5)$" to separate the plus sign that means "add" from the minus sign that is part of the numeral for negative five.

To find the sum $-2 + 5$, first move 2 units to the left from the origin. Then, from that position, move 5 units to the right. Moves to the right represent positive numbers. The two moves amount to a move of 3 units to the right, as shown below.

Thus, $-2 + 5 = 3$.

The next diagram shows how to find the sum $2 + (-5)$.

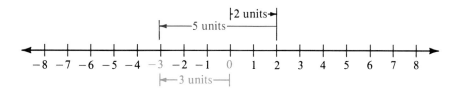

Thus, $2 + (-5) = -3$

Can you visualize $-3 + 0$ on a number line? Interpret "add 0" to mean "move no units." Then you can see that

$$-3 + 0 = -3 \quad \text{and} \quad 0 + (-3) = -3.$$

These equations illustrate the special property of zero for addition of real numbers: When 0 is added to any given number, the sum is *identical* to the given number. We call 0 the **identity element for addition.**

## Identity Axiom for Addition

There is a unique real number 0 such that for every real number $a$,

$$a + 0 = a \quad \text{and} \quad 0 + a = a.$$

Think of adding a pair of opposites, such as $4$ and $-4$, on a number line. As shown below,

$$4 + (-4) = 0 \quad \text{and} \quad -4 + 4 = 0.$$

The following axiom is a formal way of saying that the sum of a number and its opposite is always zero.

## Axiom of Opposites

For every real number $a$, there is a unique real number $-a$ such that

$$a + (-a) = 0 \quad \text{and} \quad -a + a = 0.$$

A number and its opposite are called **additive inverses** of each other because their sum is zero, the identity element for addition. Thus, the numeral $-4$ can be read "negative four," "the opposite of four," or "the additive inverse of four."

# Oral Exercises

**Give an addition statement illustrated by each diagram.**

**1.**

**2.**

**3.**

**4.**

**Simplify each expression. If necessary, think of moves along a number line.**

| | | | |
|---|---|---|---|
| **5.** $-8 + 0$ | **6.** $0 + (-5)$ | **7.** $-6 + 6$ | **8.** $1 + (-1)$ |
| **9.** $-4 + (-8)$ | **10.** $-9 + (-1)$ | **11.** $5 + (-1)$ | **12.** $-4 + 9$ |
| **13.** $-8 + 7$ | **14.** $6 + (-4)$ | **15.** $16 + (-19)$ | **16.** $-1 + (-99)$ |
| **17.** $102 + (-2)$ | **18.** $-100 + 1$ | **19.** $-10 + 0$ | **20.** $-67 + 67$ |

## Written Exercises

**Simplify each expression. If necessary, draw a number line such as the one below to help you.**

**A**

| | |
|---|---|
| **1.** $(-3 + 7) + 6$ | **2.** $(-5 + 8) + 2$ |
| **3.** $(-9 + 11) + (-2)$ | **4.** $(-6 + 9) + (-3)$ |
| **5.** $[14 + (-20)] + 5$ | **6.** $[5 + (-15)] + 7$ |
| **7.** $[-9 + (-8)] + 9$ | **8.** $[-4 + (-12)] + 4$ |
| **9.** $35 + [7 + (-14)]$ | **10.** $32 + [8 + (-16)]$ |
| **11.** $-26 + [-2 + (-8)]$ | **12.** $-7 + [-11 + (-19)]$ |
| **13.** $[28 + (-8)] + [1 + (-1)]$ | **14.** $(-3 + 3) + [16 + (-6)]$ |
| **15.** $[0 + (-8)] + [-7 + (-23)]$ | **16.** $(-9 + 9) + [8 + (-12)]$ |
| **17.** $-2 + (-3) + (-8)$ | **18.** $(-5) + (-7) + (-9)$ |
| **19.** $-4 + (-10) + 9 + (-6)$ | **20.** $-12 + 16 + (-2) + (-17)$ |
| **21.** $-6.4 + (-2.3) + 8.7$ | **22.** $5.9 + (-3.2) + (-7.8)$ |
| **23.** $-\frac{3}{2} + 5 + \left(-\frac{7}{2}\right)$ | **24.** $-\frac{13}{3} + (-2) + \left(-\frac{2}{3}\right)$ |

**In Exercises 25–36, solve each equation. Use a number line as needed.**

*Example*    $-2 + n = 8$

*Solution*    The equation states that $-2$ plus a number is 8. To go from $-2$ to 8 on the number line below, you move 10 units to the right.

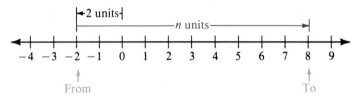

∴ the solution is 10.   *Answer*

B  **25.** $-5 + x = 1$         **26.** $-3 + y = 14$         **27.** $0 = 15 + a$

  **28.** $w + 0 = -7$        **29.** $-18 + p = -9$       **30.** $-1 + s = -8$

  **31.** $-30 = 8 + t$       **32.** $13 = -5 + b$        **33.** $c + (-2.5) = -3$

  **34.** $m + (-1.75) = -2$  **35.** $-83 + d = -83$      **36.** $0 = -25 + k$

**In Exercises 37–40, write equations leading to the given equation. Justify each step.**

*Example*    $(a + b) + [-a + (-b)] = 0$

*Solution*    $(a + b) + [-a + (-b)] = [a + (-a)] + [b + (-b)]$     Commutative and associative axioms of addition
                                $= 0 + 0$                          Axiom of opposites
                                $= 0$                              Identity axiom for addition

C  **37.** $b + [a + (-b)] = a$                  **38.** $-m + (k + m) = k$

  **39.** $-m + [-h + (m + h)] = 0$            **40.** $[a + (-b)] + [b + (-a)] = 0$

---

## Challenge

In order to conduct an experiment, a scientist needed exactly two liters of a solution. After searching the storeroom, the scientist could find only five-liter containers and eight-liter containers. How could the scientist measure exactly two liters of the solution?

---

## 2-3 Rules for Addition

**Objective**  To add real numbers.

The expression $-(2 + 5)$ represents the opposite of the sum of 2 and 5. Since $2 + 5 = 7$,

$$-(2 + 5) = -7.$$

The expression $-2 + (-5)$ represents the sum of the opposite of 2 and the opposite of 5. Using a number line, you know (page 49) that

$$-2 + (-5) = -7.$$

Since $-(2 + 5) = -7$ and $-2 + (-5) = -7$, it follows that

$$-(2 + 5) = -2 + (-5).$$

With a number line you can also show:

$$-[-4 + (-1)] = 4 + 1$$
$$-[8 + (-6)] = -8 + 6$$
$$-(-9 + 7) = 9 + (-7)$$

These equations suggest the following property.

---

### Property of the Opposite of a Sum

The opposite of a sum of real numbers is equal to the sum of the opposites of the numbers. That is, for all real numbers $a$ and $b$,

$$-(a + b) = -a + (-b).$$

---

Using the property of the opposite of a sum along with axioms you have learned and the familiar addition facts for positive numbers, you can compute sums of any real numbers without thinking of a number line.

**Example 1**  Simplify $-8 + (-3)$.

**Solution**    $-8 + (-3) = -(8 + 3)$
$$= -11$$

**Example 2**  Simplify $14 + (-5)$.

**Solution**    $14 + (-5) = (9 + 5) + (-5)$
$$= 9 + [5 + (-5)]$$
$$= 9 + 0$$
$$= 9$$

After computing many sums by using either a number line or the methods of Examples 1 and 2, you would probably discover the following rules.

---

### Rules for Addition of Positive and Negative Numbers

**1.** If $a$ and $b$ are both positive, then $a + b = |a| + |b|$.
   *Example.*   $3 + 7 = 10$

**2.** If $a$ and $b$ are both negative, then $a + b = -(|a| + |b|)$.
   *Example.*   $-6 + (-2) = -(6 + 2) = -8$

**3.** If $a$ is positive and $b$ is negative and $a$ has the greater absolute value, then $a + b = |a| - |b|$.
   *Example.*   $8 + (-5) = 8 - 5 = 3$

**4.** If $a$ is positive and $b$ is negative and $b$ has the greater absolute value, then $a + b = -(|b| - |a|)$.
   *Example.*   $4 + (-9) = -(9 - 4) = -5$

**5.** If $a$ and $b$ are opposites, then $a + b = 0$.
   *Example.*   $2 + (-2) = 0$

---

The following examples show how to add more than two real numbers.

**Example 3** Simplify $7 + (-9) + 15 + (-12)$.

**Solution 1** Add the numbers in order from left to right.

$$7 + (-9) = -2; \quad -2 + 15 = 13; \quad 13 + (-12) = 1 \quad \textbf{Answer}$$

**Solution 2** Add positive numbers.    Add negative numbers.    Add the sums.

| Add positive numbers. | Add negative numbers. | Add the sums. |
|:---:|:---:|:---:|
| 7 | $-9$ | 22 |
| 15 | $-12$ | $-21$ |
| 22 | $-21$ | 1  *Answer* |

**Example 4** Add.   $-291$
             $379$
             $185$
             $-462$

**Solution**

| Step 1 | Step 2 | Step 3 |
|:---:|:---:|:---:|
| 379 | $-291$ | $-753$ |
| 185 | $-462$ | 564 |
| 564 | $-753$ | $-189$  *Answer* |

## Oral Exercises

**Add.**

| | | | | | |
|---|---|---|---|---|---|
| **1.** 8 <br> 8 | **2.** −4 <br> −3 | **3.** −9 <br> 6 | **4.** 11 <br> −7 | **5.** −14 <br> −29 | **6.** −1 <br> 10 |
| **7.** −16 <br> 7 | **8.** −5 <br> −12 | **9.** −17 <br> 47 | **10.** 35 <br> −75 | **11.** −98 <br> 36 | **12.** 75 <br> −28 |

**Simplify.**

**13.** $-9 + (-12)$

**14.** $-18 + 8$

**15.** $14 + (-15)$

**16.** $14 + (-6)$

**17.** $2 + (-17)$

**18.** $-5 + 22$

**19.** $4 + (-1) + (-3)$

**20.** $-2 + (-8) + 8$

**21.** $-3 + (-6) + 9$

## Written Exercises

**Add.**

**A**

| | | | | | |
|---|---|---|---|---|---|
| **1.** 8 <br> 7 <br> −1 <br> 5 | **2.** −5 <br> −6 <br> 9 <br> 1 | **3.** 53 <br> −43 <br> 57 <br> −18 | **4.** −45 <br> 21 <br> 58 <br> −72 | **5.** 184 <br> −27 <br> −37 <br> −13 | **6.** −173 <br> 412 <br> −58 <br> −93 |

**Simplify.**

**7.** $-17 + 4 + (-12) + 39$

**8.** $-16 + (-9) + 8 + 25$

**9.** $109 + (-56) + (-91) + 26$

**10.** $-308 + (-87) + 272 + 64$

**11.** $-[31 + (-9)] + [-(-3 + 7)]$

**12.** $[-7 + (-1)] + [-(-7 + 1)]$

**13.** $3.7 + 4.2 + (-2.3) + 0 + 6.4 + 12.8$

**14.** $-7.2 + 11.4 + (-8.1) + (-9.7) + 0.6$

**15.** $27 + 43 + (-14) + 11 + (-57) + 5 + (-36) + (-14)$

**16.** $46 + (-33) + 18 + 0 + (-93) + (-2) + (-34)$

**17.** $-\frac{1}{3} + \left(-1\frac{2}{3}\right) + 2$

**18.** $3 + \left(-\frac{5}{2}\right) + \left(-\frac{7}{2}\right)$

**19.** $-1\frac{3}{4} + 2\frac{1}{4}$

**20.** $-3\frac{2}{5} + \left(-1\frac{4}{5}\right)$

**21.** $-\frac{7}{8} + \left(-\frac{11}{8}\right)$

**22.** $\frac{16}{3} + \left(-\frac{10}{3}\right)$

**Evaluate each expression if $x = -4$, $y = |-7|$, and $z = -5$.**

**B**

**23.** $x + y + (-1)$

**24.** $-21 + x + z$

**25.** $-15 + (-x) + y$

**26.** $-z + (-8) + y$

**27.** $1 + (-y) + z$

**28.** $-y + (-11) + x$

**Replace each __?__ with a number to make a true statement.**

**29.** __?__ $+ (-7) = 3$    **30.** $-13 +$ __?__ $= 6$    **31.** $4 +$ __?__ $= -11$

**32.** __?__ $+ (-6) = 3$    **33.** $0.6 +$ __?__ $= -1$    **34.** __?__ $+ 0.25 = -0.75$

**In Exercises 35–38, write equations leading to the given equation. Justify each step.**

**C** **35.** $-6 + [-a + (a + 6)] = 0$    **36.** $-(-x + y) + y = x$

**37.** $r + s + [-(r + s + t)] = -t$    **38.** $a + [-(a + b)] = -b$

## Problems

a. **Name a positive or a negative number to represent each measurement given in the problem.**
b. **Compute the sum of the numbers.**
c. **Answer each question.**

*Example*    A football team made the following yardage on five plays: lost 3, gained 15, gained 8, lost 9, and lost 4. What was the net yardage on the five plays?

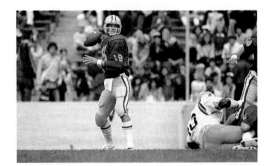

*Solution*    **a.** $-3$, $15$, $8$, $-9$, $-4$
   **b.** $-3 + 15 + 8 + (-9) + (-4) = 7$
   **c.** The team had a net gain of 7 yards.

**A** **1.** Marie Corot has $784 in her checking account. She deposits $96 and then writes two checks, one for $18, the other for $44. What is the new balance in the account?

**2.** A jet plane flying at an altitude of 28,600 ft descended 1200 ft and then rose 3500 ft. What was its new altitude?

**3.** An elevator started at the eighteenth floor. It then went down seven floors and up nine floors. At what floor was the elevator then located?

**4.** A diving bell descended to a level 230 m below the surface of the ocean. Later it ascended 95 m and then dove 120 m. What was the new depth of the bell?

5. The Drama Society had $498 in its treasury. The society presented a play, for which they paid a royalty of $125. Scenery and costumes cost $184, and programs and other expenses, $179. The sale of tickets amounted to $590. What was in the treasury after the play?

6. The stock of Ballard Foods Corporation opened on Monday at $32 per share. It lost $5 that day, dropped another $3 on Tuesday, but rallied to gain $4 on Wednesday and $2 on Thursday. On Friday it was unchanged. What was its closing price for the week?

7. During a four-day period at the Center Hotel, the numbers of guests checking in and out were as follows: 32 in and 27 out, 28 in and 31 out, 12 in and 18 out, and 15 in and 23 out. How did the number of guests in the hotel at the end of the fourth day compare with the number at the start of the four-day period?

8. During their first year after opening a restaurant, the Cataldos had a loss of $14,250. In their second year of operation, they broke even. During their third and fourth years, they had gains of $18,180 and $29,470, respectively. What was the restaurant's net gain or loss over the four-year period?

9. A boy walked 5 blocks west and 3 blocks north. Then he walked 8 blocks east and 12 blocks south. After his walk, where was he relative to his starting point?

10. During a freak storm, the temperature fell 8°C, rose 5°C, fell 4°C, and then rose 6°C. If the temperature was 32°C at the outset of the storm, what was it after the storm was over?

**B** 11. The Qattâra Depression in Egypt is 133 m below sea level. A helicopter flying at an altitude of 41 m above the Qattâra Depression climbed 28 m and then dropped 37 m. At what altitude relative to sea level was it then flying?

12. The rim of a canyon is 156 ft below sea level. If a stranded hiker 71 ft below the rim fired a warning flare that rose 29 ft, to what altitude relative to sea level would the flare rise?

13. Departing from Eastville at 1:00 P.M., Jennifer flew to Center City. The flight took 1.5 hours, but the time in Center City is 2 hours earlier than it is in Eastville. What time was it in Center City when Jennifer landed?

14. A passenger on a train traveling east at 135 km/h walks toward the back of the train at a rate of 7 km/h. What is the passenger's rate of travel with respect to the ground?

C  15. Jim Martin charged $175 worth of clothing and $287 worth of camera equipment to his charge account. He then made two payments of $50 each to the account. The next bill showed that he owed a balance of $495.25, including $11.50 in interest charges. How much had Jim owed on the account before making his purchases?

16. The volume of water in a tank during a five-day period changed as follows: up 375 L, down 240 L, down 164 L, up 93 L, and down 157 L. What was the volume of water in the tank at the beginning of the five-day period if the final volume was 54 L?

## Computer Key-In

Suppose that you want to write a program to find the sum of a list of non-negative numbers and that the list may vary in length from application to application. One way of doing this is shown by the program below.

You have used INPUT statements to give values to variables. Another way to give a value to a variable is to use a LET statement. For example,

LET A = 6

assigns the value 6 on the right side of the equals sign to the variable $A$ on the left.

The following program allows you to INPUT as many nonnegative numbers as you wish. When you want to end the INPUT, you type $-1$.

```
10    PRINT "TO FIND THE SUM OF SEVERAL"
20    PRINT "    NUMBERS (> = 0)"
30    PRINT "(TO END, TYPE -1):"
40    LET S=0
50    PRINT "NUMBER";
60    INPUT N
70    IF N<0 THEN 100
80    LET S=S+N
90    GOTO 50
100   PRINT "SUM = ";S
110   END
```

Line 80 is not an equation. It adds each new value of $N$ to $S$. It means, "Take the value of $S$, add the value of $N$ to it, and then put the new value into $S$."

Lines 50–90 form one kind of loop; that is, lines 50–90 will be repeated until line 70 ends the INPUT when $-1$ is entered. Line 90 sends the program back to line 50 to get a new value of $N$. Line 100 prints the final value of $S$. (If possible, save this program for later use.)

### Exercises

Find the sum of each list.
1. 2, 4, 6, 8, 10, 12, 14, 16, 18, 20
2. 1, 4, 9, 16, 25, 36, 49, 64, 81, 100
3. 2.25, 3.42, 5.15, 1.98, 4.82
4. 12.95, 27.59, 21.76, 38.25, 47.34

## 2-4 Subtracting Real Numbers

**Objective**  To subtract real numbers and to simplify expressions involving differences.

The first column below lists a few examples of subtraction of 2. The second column lists related examples of addition of $-2$.

| Subtracting 2 | Adding $-2$ |
|---|---|
| $3 - 2 = 1$ | $3 + (-2) = 1$ |
| $4 - 2 = 2$ | $4 + (-2) = 2$ |
| $5 - 2 = 3$ | $5 + (-2) = 3$ |
| $6 - 2 = 4$ | $6 + (-2) = 4$ |

Comparing the entries in the two columns shows that subtracting 2 gives the same result as adding the opposite of 2. This suggests the following **definition of subtraction.**

For all real numbers $a$ and $b$, the **difference** $a - b$ is defined by:

$$a - b = a + (-b)$$

*To subtract b, add the opposite of b.*

**Example**  Simplify.
  **a.** $12 - (-3)$
  **b.** $-7 - 1$
  **c.** $-4 - (-10)$
  **d.** $y - (y + 6)$

**Solution**  **a.** $12 - (-3) = 12 + 3 = 15$
  **b.** $-7 - 1 = -7 + (-1) = -8$
  **c.** $-4 - (-10) = -4 + 10 = 6$
  **d.** $y - (y + 6) = y + [-(y + 6)] = y + (-y) + (-6) = -6$

Note that in part (d) the property of the opposite of a sum is used. The opposite of $(y + 6)$ is $-y + (-6)$.

Using the definition of subtraction, you may replace any difference with a sum. For example,

$12 - 8 - 7 + 4$   means   $12 + (-8) + (-7) + 4$.

As shown at the right, you may simplify this expression by grouping from left to right.

$$12 - 8 - 7 + 4$$
$$4$$
$$-3$$
$$1$$

The preceding method is convenient if you are doing the work mentally or with a hand calculator. For written work, you may want to group positive terms and negative terms:

$$12 - 8 - 7 + 4 = (12 + 4) - (8 + 7) = 16 - 15 = 1$$

Certain sums are usually replaced by differences. For example,

$$9 + (-2x) \text{ is usually written } 9 - 2x.$$

Here are some important questions and answers about subtraction of real numbers:

1. Is subtraction commutative? No; for example,

$$8 - 3 = 5 \quad \text{but} \quad 3 - 8 = -5.$$

2. Is subtraction associative? No; for example,

$$(6 - 4) - 2 = 0 \quad \text{but} \quad 6 - (4 - 2) = 4.$$

3. What is the opposite of the difference $a - b$?

$$-(a - b) = -a + b.$$

To see why, write $a - b$ as a sum and use the property of the opposite of a sum.

$$-(a - b) = -[a + (-b)]$$
$$= -a + [-(-b)] = -a + b.$$

Thus, $-(a - 1) = -a + 1$ and
$$-(-2 - b) = 2 + b.$$

## Oral Exercises

**Simplify.**

**1.** $46 - 5$      **2.** $19 - 12$      **3.** $8 - 13$      **4.** $7 - 27$

**5.** $0 - 8$      **6.** $0 - (-4)$      **7.** $-16 - 0$      **8.** $-9 - 3$

**9.** $2 - (-1)$      **10.** $7 - (-3)$      **11.** $-7 - (-14)$      **12.** $-6 - (-4)$

**13.** $x - (x + 1)$      **14.** $y - (y + 5)$      **15.** $-(a - 3)$      **16.** $-(c - 6)$

**17.** $-(4 - t)$      **18.** $-(-1 - m)$      **19.** $5 - (r + 5)$      **20.** $2 - (k - 2)$

## Written Exercises

**Simplify.**

**A**      **1.** $52 - 312$      **2.** $154 - 281$      **3.** $39 - (-32)$      **4.** $47 - (-49)$

     **5.** $-19 - (-3)$      **6.** $-25 - (-9)$      **7.** $-2.8 - 4.4$      **8.** $-5.1 - 6.7$

     **9.** $157 - (-27)$      **10.** $-206 - (-59)$      **11.** $1.91 - (-1.03)$      **12.** $2.95 - (-2.55)$

13. $-18$ decreased by 7

14. $-6$ decreased by $-32$

15. 24 less than $-1$

16. 16 less than $-2$

17. $132 - (72 - 61)$

18. $275 - (80 - 65)$

19. $324 - (65 - 78)$

20. $193 - (30 - 75)$

21. $(22 - 33) - (55 - 66)$

22. $(63 - 70) - (92 - 80)$

23. $(3 - 8) - (-15 + 19)$

24. $(42 - 33) - (-7 + 12)$

25. $1066 - 1492 + 1776$

26. $1910 - 1939 - 2010$

27. $12 - (-9) - [5 - (-4)]$

28. $-15 - 6 - [-7 - (-10)]$

29. $4 - 5 + 8 - 17 + 31$

30. $18 - 14 + 15 + 7 - 26$

31. $-6 - 19 + 4 - 8 + 20$

32. $-11 - 43 + 1 - 9 + 30$

33. $-x - (-3 - x)$

34. $-t - (-t - 5)$

35. The difference of 81 and $-6$, decreased by $-29$.

36. $-54$ decreased by the difference of $-37$ and 15.

37. $-46$ decreased by the difference of $-23$ and $-61$.

38. The difference of $-59$ and 12, decreased by 72.

**B** 39. $7 + y - (7 - y) - y$

40. $s - (-3) - [s + (-3)] - 3$

41. $h + 8 - (-9 + h)$

42. $-(10 - k) - (k - 12)$

43. $(\pi + 2)$ subtracted from $\pi - 17$

44. $(7 - 2\pi)$ subtracted from $11 - 2\pi$

**Evaluate each expression if $a = -3$, $b = 7$, and $c = -1$.**

45. $c - |a - b|$

46. $b - |c - a|$

47. $|c - a| - b$

48. $|b - c| - a$

49. $a - |c| - (|a| - b)$

50. $|c| - b - (|a| - c)$

51. $(a - |c|) - |a| - b$

52. $(|c| - b) - |a| - c$

**In Exercises 53 and 54, name the definition, axiom, or property that justifies each step marked with __?__ .**

**C** 53. **a.** $b + (a - b) = b + [a + (-b)]$    (1) __?__

$= b + [(-b) + a]$    (2) __?__

$= [b + (-b)] + a$    (3) __?__

$= 0 + a$    (4) __?__

$= a$    (5) __?__

**b.** Use the result of part (a) to complete the following sentence:

$a - b$ is the number to add to $b$ to obtain __?__ .

54. **a.** $-(a - b) = -a + b$    (1) See page 60.

$= b + (-a)$    (2) __?__

$= b - a$    (3) __?__

**b.** Use the result of part (a) to complete the following sentence:

The opposite of $a - b$ is __?__ .

## Problems

**Express the answer to each question as the difference between two real numbers. Compute the difference. Answer the question and interpret the sign of the answer.**

*Example*   The floor of the Puerto Rico Trench in the Atlantic Ocean is about 9460 m below sea level. If a minisub is 1338 m below sea level, how far is the sea floor from the minisub?

*Solution*   $-9460 - (-1338) =$
$\quad -9460 + 1338 = -8122$
The sea floor is 8122 m *below* the minisub.

**A**  1. An astronaut entered her space capsule $1\frac{1}{2}$ hours before liftoff. How long had she been in the capsule $2\frac{1}{2}$ hours after liftoff?

2. Find the difference in altitude between Death Valley, California, 86 m below sea level, and Mount Rainier, Washington, 4392 m above sea level.

3. If Pythagoras, the Greek mathematician, was born in 582 B.C. and died on his birthday in 497 B.C., how old would he have been when he died?

4. The Roman poet Virgil was born in 70 B.C. How old was he on his birthday in 42 B.C.?

5. What is the difference of the melting and boiling points of krypton if it boils at 153.4° below 0°C and melts at 157.2° below 0°C?

6. Including the wind-chill factor, the temperature in Iroquois Heights was 8°C below zero at midnight and seventeen below at dawn. What was the change in temperature?

7. Sally Ryder took the bus from a stop 52 blocks east of Central Square to a stop 39 blocks west of Central Square. How many blocks did she ride?

8. Bill Duff drove a golf ball from a point 176 yd (yards) north of the ninth hole to a point 53 yd south of the hole. How far did the ball travel?

**B**  **9.** The highest recorded weather temperature on Earth is 58.0°C. The difference of that record and the lowest recorded weather temperature is 146.3°C. What is the record low?

**10.** The difference in altitude between the highest and lowest points in Louisiana is 164.592 m. If Driskill Mountain, the highest point, is 163.068 m above sea level, what is the altitude of New Orleans, the lowest point?

# Self-Test 1

***Vocabulary***    axiom (p. 45)
postulate (p. 45)
axioms of closure (p. 45)
terms (p. 46)
factors (p. 46)
associative axioms (p. 46)
reflexive property (p. 47)
symmetric property (p. 47)

transitive property (p. 47)
identity element for addition
  (p. 50)
additive inverses (p. 50)
opposite of a sum (p. 53)
subtraction (p. 59)
difference (p. 59)

**Simplify.**

**1.** $25 \times 97 \times 4$            **2.** $4 + 3x + 16$            **Obj. 2-1, p. 45**

**Simplify. If necessary, think of moves along a number line.**

**3.** $8 + (-8)$      **4.** $-5 + 0$      **5.** $-4 + (-2)$      **Obj. 2-2, p. 49**

**6.** $-15 + (-12)$      **7.** $-17 + 9 + (-6) + 5$      **Obj. 2-3, p. 53**

**8.** $24 - 35$      **9.** $-8 - (-10)$      **Obj. 2-4, p. 59**

Check your answers with those at the back of the book.

# *Challenge*

Recall (page 39) that the triangular numbers are

$$1, 3, 6, 10, 15, \text{ and so on.}$$

The square numbers are

$$1, 4, 9, 16, 25, \text{ and so on.}$$

**1.** Verify that each square number from 4 to 100 is the sum of two consecutive triangular numbers.

**2.** Illustrate Exercise 1 by dividing the square array of dots shown at the right into two triangular arrays.

# Multiplication

## 2-5 The Distributive Axiom

**Objective**   To use the distributive axiom to simplify expressions.

The board of a sailboard weighed 40 lb (pounds). The mast with sail and boom weighed 25 lb. Therefore, the total weight in pounds of a shipment of 4 sailboards was:

$$4(40 + 25) = 4 \times 65$$
$$= 260$$

The total weight was also the sum of the weights of the boards and the masts:

$$(4 \times 40) + (4 \times 25) = 160 + 100$$
$$= 260$$

Either way you compute it, the total weight is the same.

$$4(40 + 25) = (4 \times 40) + (4 \times 25)$$

Note that 4 is *distributed* as a multiplier of each term of $40 + 25$. This example illustrates another axiom that we use in working with real numbers: multiplication is *distributive with respect to addition.*

---

### Distributive Axiom of Multiplication with Respect to Addition

For all real numbers $a$, $b$, and $c$,

$$a(b + c) = ab + ac \quad \text{and} \quad (b + c)a = ba + ca.$$

By applying the symmetric property of equality, you can also state the distributive axiom in the following form.

---

For all real numbers $a$, $b$, and $c$,

$$ab + ac = a(b + c) \quad \text{and} \quad ba + ca = (b + c)a.$$

For example, the diagram below illustrates that

$$(3 \times 4) + (3 \times 2) = 3(4 + 2).$$

Area:
3 × 4

Area:
3 × 2

Area:
3 (4 + 2)

The following examples show some uses of the distributive axiom.

**Example 1  a.** $72\left(\dfrac{1}{6} + \dfrac{1}{4}\right) = 72 \times \dfrac{1}{6} + 72 \times \dfrac{1}{4} = 12 + 18 = 30$

**b.** $8(9.5) = 8(9 + 0.5) = (8 \times 9) + (8 \times 0.5) = 72 + 4 = 76$

**c.** $83 \times 7 = (80 \times 7) + (3 \times 7) = 560 + 21 = 581$

**d.** $75 \times 13 + 25 \times 13 = (75 + 25)13 = (100)13 = 1300$

**Example 2**  Show that $9x + 5x = 14x$ for every real number $x$.

**Solution**    $9x + 5x = (9 + 5)x$        Distributive axiom
$\qquad\qquad\quad = 14x$        Substitution principle

Because properties of real numbers and equality guarantee that for all values of the variable

$$9x + 5x \quad \text{and} \quad 14x$$

represent the same number, the two expressions are said to be **equivalent.** The expression $9x + 5x$ has two terms. The expression $14x$ has one term. Replacing an expression containing a variable by an equivalent expression with as few terms as possible is called **simplifying the expression.**

**Example 3**  Simplify $7r + 1 + (-2)r + 31$.

**Solution**    $7r + 1 + (-2)r + 31 = [7r + (-2)r] + (1 + 31)$
$\qquad\qquad\qquad\qquad\qquad\quad = [7 + (-2)]r + 32$
$\qquad\qquad\qquad\qquad\qquad\quad = 5r + 32$

Is multiplication distributive with respect to subtraction? Yes, it is! (See Exercise 44, page 71.)

For all real numbers $a$, $b$, and $c$,

$$a(b - c) = ab - ac \quad \text{and} \quad (b - c)a = ba - ca.$$

**Example 4** Simplify $8(n - 1) - 3n$.

**Solution**
$$8(n - 1) - 3n = 8n - 8 \cdot 1 - 3n$$
$$= 8n - 8 - 3n$$
$$= 8n - 3n - 8$$
$$= (8 - 3)n - 8$$
$$= 5n - 8$$

## Oral Exercises

**Use the distributive axiom to simplify each expression.**

**1.** $2(50 + 3)$      **2.** $3(40 + 1)$      **3.** $4(20 - 1)$

**4.** $5(60 - 2)$      **5.** $4(15)$      **6.** $6 \times 2\frac{1}{3}$

**7.** $10\left(5\frac{1}{2}\right)$      **8.** $8(2.25)$      **9.** $(35 + 56)\frac{1}{7}$

**10.** $\frac{1}{4}(24 + 52)$      **11.** $\left(\frac{1}{3} \times 20\right) - \left(\frac{1}{3} \times 2\right)$      **12.** $\left(37 \times \frac{1}{8}\right) + \left(3 \times \frac{1}{8}\right)$

**Simplify.**

**13.** $2x + 15x$      **14.** $12y + 8y$      **15.** $a + 5a$

**16.** $3b + b$      **17.** $(-2)x + (-6)x$      **18.** $(-3)y + (-8)y$

**19.** $6s + (-2)s$      **20.** $7t + (-9)t$      **21.** $5m - 3m$

**22.** $11k - 15k$      **23.** $2c - 4c$      **24.** $3(1 + z) + 7$

## Written Exercises

**Simplify.**

**A**  **1.** $60\left(\frac{1}{5} + \frac{1}{4}\right)$      **2.** $14\left(1\frac{1}{7}\right)$      **3.** $\frac{1}{6}(17) + \frac{1}{6}(13)$

**4.** $(0.75)(21) + (0.25)(21)$      **5.** $(14 \times 83) - (4 \times 83)$      **6.** $(62 \times 27) + (38 \times 27)$

**7.** $13a + 4a$      **8.** $21c + 19c$      **9.** $7n + 18n$

**10.** $99p + 5p$      **11.** $16t + (-7)t$      **12.** $28m + (-14)m$

**13.** $83q - 150q$      **14.** $68v - 59v$      **15.** $4x + 5x + 12$

**16.** $8 + 12y + 9y$      **17.** $9(r + 3) + 7$      **18.** $8(g + 9) + 18$

**19.** $25 + 3(2w - 6)$          **20.** $38 + 4(5d - 3)$

**21.** $8a + 7 + 5a + 6$          **22.** $21 + 11c + 19c + 4$

**23.** $(-3)x + 2 + 14x + 29$

**24.** $(-9)y + 6 + 17y - 12$

**25.** $-9 + 9p + 9 + (-1)p$

**26.** $14k + 7 + (-7)k - 7$

**27.** $10n + (-4)n + (-2)n$

**28.** $(-5)s + (-2)s + 21s$

**29.** $4h - 2 - 3h - 8$

**30.** $17b - 9 - 11b + 16$

**B** **31.** $5e + 7f + (-1)e + 13f$

**32.** $7k + (-3)m + 6k + 9m$

**33.** $10x + 15y + 8 - 2x - 4y + 1$

**34.** $9r + 4s - 6r - 1 - 3s + 5$

*Example*     $2(x + y - z) + 5(4x + 3y)$

*Solution*     $2(x + y - z) + 5(4x + 3y) = 2x + 2y - 2z + 20x + 15y$
$$= (2x + 20x) + (2y + 15y) - 2z$$
$$= 22x + 17y - 2z$$

**35.** $9(a + b) + 4(3a + 2b)$

**36.** $8(k + m) + 15(2k + 5m)$

**37.** $6(r + 5) + 9(r - 2) - 4r$

**38.** $4(s + 7) + 5(s - 3) - 2s$

**39.** $7(c + 2d + 8) + 3(9c - 2)$

**40.** $4(5x + 3y + 6) + 14(2y - 1)$

**In Exercises 41–44, represent each word phrase by a variable expression. Then simplify it.**

**41.** Seven times the sum of $c$ and $d$, increased by twice the sum of $3c$ and $2d$

**42.** Twice the sum of eleven and $x$, increased by three times the difference of $x$ and 7

**43.** Eight more than the sum of negative five and $15y$, increased by one half of the difference of $12y$ and eight

**44.** Six more than three times the sum of $a$ and $b$, increased by five less than the product of negative three and $b$

**45.** On Friday a store sold $x$ cameras at $69.95 each. The next day the store sold 3 more than were sold on Friday at the same price. What were the store's receipts from this two-day sale?

**46.** On Monday, Yolanda worked for $H$ hours at $4.85 per hour. The next day she worked 2 hours less at the same rate of pay. How much did she earn for those days?

**Simplify.**

**C** **47.** $8[5x + 7(3 + 4x)] - 16x - 8$

**48.** $-24 + 3[4y + 2(5y - 8)] - 9y$

**49.** $12(3n + 2p) + 11[n + 3(2n - p - 3)]$

**50.** $9[7(3a + 2b - 4) + 12(a - 2)] + 3(5a - 8b)$

# 2-6 Rules for Multiplication

**Objective**  To multiply real numbers.

When you multiply any given real number by 1, the product is identical to the given number. For example,

$$3 \times 1 = 3 \quad \text{and} \quad 1 \times 3 = 3.$$

The **identity element for multiplication** is 1.

---

### Identity Axiom for Multiplication

There is a unique real number 1 such that for every real number $a$,

$$a \cdot 1 = a \quad \text{and} \quad 1 \cdot a = a.$$

---

The equations

$$3 \times 0 = 0 \quad \text{and} \quad 0 \times 3 = 0$$

illustrate the *multiplicative property of zero:* When one of the factors of a product is zero, the product itself is zero.

---

### Multiplicative Property of Zero

For every real number $a$,

$$a \cdot 0 = 0 \quad \text{and} \quad 0 \cdot a = 0.$$

---

Would you guess that $3 \times (-1) = -3$? You can verify this product by noticing that

$$3 \times (-1) = (-1) + (-1) + (-1) = -3.$$

Multiplying *any* real number by $-1$ produces the opposite of the number (Exercise 43, page 71).

---

### Multiplicative Property of $-1$

For every real number $a$,

$$a(-1) = -a \quad \text{and} \quad (-1)a = -a.$$

---

A special case of the multiplicative property of $-1$ occurs when the value of $a$ is $-1$:

$$(-1)(-1) = 1.$$

Using the multiplicative property of $-1$ with the familiar multiplication facts for positive numbers and axioms that you have learned, you can compute the product of *any* two real numbers. Here are some examples:

1. $3(5) = 15$
2. $(-3)(5) = (-1)3(5) = (-1)15 = -15$
3. $3(-5) = 3(-1)(5) = 3(5)(-1) = 15(-1) = -15$
4. $(-3)(-5) = (-1)3(-1)5 = (-1)(-1)3(5) = 1(15) = 15$

Similarly, the following property can be shown.

## Property of Opposites in Products

For all real numbers $a$ and $b$:

$$(-a)(b) = -ab \qquad a(-b) = -ab \qquad (-a)(-b) = ab$$

Practice in computing products will lead you to discover the following rules for multiplication of positive and negative numbers.

## Rules for Multiplication of Positive and Negative Numbers

1. The product of a positive number and a negative number is a negative number.

2. The product of two positive numbers or of two negative numbers is a positive number.

3. The absolute value of the product of two real numbers is the product of the absolute values of the numbers:

$$|ab| = |a| \times |b|.$$

By pairing the negative numbers in a product of more than two factors, you will find that

the product of an *even* number of negative numbers is *positive;*

the product of an *odd* number of negative numbers is *negative.*

**Example 1** State whether the expression names a positive number, a negative number, or zero. Then simplify the expression.

a. $-9(-2)(-5)$  b. $16(74)(0)$  c. $8(-7)(-2)$

**Solution** a. Negative; $-90$  b. Zero; 0  c. Positive; 112

**Example 2** Simplify. a. $(-3x)(-12y)$  b. $4p + (-5p)$  c. $-2(a - 3b) + 5a$

**Solution** a. $(-3x)(-12y) = (-3)x(-12)y = (-3)(-12)xy = 36xy$
b. $4p + (-5p) = 4p + (-5)p = [4 + (-5)]p = (-1)p = -p$
c. $-2(a - 3b) + 5a = (-2)a - (-2)(3b) + 5a$
$= (-2 + 5)a - (-6)b$
$= 3a - (-6b)$
$= 3a + 6b$

# Oral Exercises

**Simplify.**

1. $(-7)(-1)$
2. $10(-8)$
3. $(-3)(-9)$
4. $(-8)(-5)$
5. $(-1)(4)(-4)$
6. $2(-6)(-1)$
7. $(-1)(-3)(-5)$
8. $(-2)(-4)(-6)$
9. $17(0)(-21)$
10. $-10(-8)(0)$
11. $(-6)(-10g)$
12. $(-7)(12p)$
13. $(-3p)(-4q)$
14. $(5x)(-7y)$
15. $(-9v)(12w)$
16. $6m + (-3m)$
17. $8t + (-14t)$
18. $-7b + 2b$
19. $-2h + 15h$
20. $7c + (-7c)$
21. $-5xy + 4xy$
22. $-2ab - 3ab$
23. $-w + 6w$
24. $-14n - n$
25. $5t + (-4t)$
26. $8u + (-8u)$
27. $-9xy + 8xy$
28. $-4mn + (-6mn)$
29. $-a + 12a$
30. $(-39k) + (-k)$

# Written Exercises

**Simplify.**

A  1. $(-28)(-3)$
2. $23(-5)$
3. $(-4)(10)(-12)$
4. $(-6)(-9)(20)$
5. $(-3)(-7)(-4)$
6. $(-2)(-8)(-4)$
7. $(-17)(-18)(0)$
8. $54(-47)(0)$
9. $5(-3)(-10)(-2)$
10. $(-4)(25)(-2)(-3)$
11. $(-6)(-1)(-7)(-10)$
12. $(-9)(-5)(-1)(-3)$

**13.** $-2(-1 - 8)$

**14.** $(-16 + 8)(-1)$

**15.** $(8 \times 1) + 8(-11)$

**16.** $(-7 \times 18) + (-7 \times 12)$

**17.** $(-9 \times 12) - (-9 \times 2)$

**18.** $-34 \times (-1) - [-34 \times (-11)]$

**19.** $8(-a + 5d)$

**20.** $-9(2m - k)$

**21.** $-2(-r - 5s)$

**22.** $-4(3v - 9w)$

**23.** $-x + 8 + 5x - 4$

**24.** $5 - b - 7 - 8b$

**25.** $14u - 3p - 8u - 8p$

**26.** $-y - 6z + 3y + 4z - y$

**B**  **27.** $3.4t + 1.6s - (-1.9t) - 3.6s$

**28.** $-0.8c + 4.1h - (-3.2c) - 0.1h$

**29.** $-m + \frac{2}{3}m - \frac{1}{2}n + \frac{5}{2}n$

**30.** $-5a - \left(-\frac{1}{2}b\right) + 3\frac{1}{2}a - \frac{1}{2}b$

**31.** $2(x + 5y) + (-3)(7x - y)$

**32.** $8(t - u) + 5(2u - 3t)$

**33.** $-2(2q + w) - 7(w - q)$

**34.** $-3(7c + d) - 2(10d - c)$

**35.** $-4(-e + 3f) - 3[e + (-5f)]$

**36.** $-6[v + (-9w)] + (-5)(3v - w)$

**37.** $2[-7(r + 2s) - r] - 3(s + 2r)$

**38.** $4[2(-5x + y) - y] - 10(y - 4x)$

**39.** $-15 + (-3)[2(g - 7) - 2(1 - g)]$

**40.** $-50 + (-2)[3(1 - f) - 3(-2 + f)]$

**41.** Sally owned 500 shares of Acme Tube. On Monday each share of the stock gained $p$ points. On Tuesday each share lost one more than twice as many points as it had gained the day before. By how much had the total value of Sally's shares of Acme Tube changed between the opening of trading on Monday morning and the closing on Tuesday afternoon?

**42.** A discount store bought a gross (12 dozen) of pocket radios, each to sell at $15 above cost. Suppose that $x$ of the radios were sold at that price. Each of the rest was sold at $4 below cost. If the discount store paid $11 for each radio, what was the store's gross income from the sale?

**C**  **43.** To show that $a(-1)$ is the opposite of $a$ for every real number $a$, you can show that the sum of $a(-1)$ and $a$ is zero as follows. Name the axiom or property that justifies each step.

$$
\begin{aligned}
a(-1) + a &= a(-1) + a(1) &\quad (1) \ \underline{\ ?\ } \\
&= a[(-1) + 1] &\quad (2) \ \underline{\ ?\ } \\
&= a(0) &\quad (3) \ \underline{\ ?\ } \\
&= 0 &\quad (4) \ \underline{\ ?\ }
\end{aligned}
$$

**44.** Name the axiom, property, or definition that justifies each step.

$$
\begin{aligned}
a(b - c) &= a[b + (-c)] &\quad (1) \ \underline{\ ?\ } \\
&= a(b) + a(-c) &\quad (2) \ \underline{\ ?\ } \\
&= ab + (-ac) &\quad (3) \ \underline{\ ?\ } \\
&= ab - ac &\quad (4) \ \underline{\ ?\ }
\end{aligned}
$$

# 2-7 Solving Problems; Consecutive Integers

**Objective**  To write equations to represent relationships among integers.

When you count by ones from any number in the set of integers

$$\ldots, -4, -3, -2, -1, 0, 1, 2, 3, 4, \ldots$$

you obtain **consecutive integers.** For example, $-3, -2, -1, 0, 1,$ and 2 are six consecutive integers. Those integers are listed in **natural order,** that is, in order from least to greatest.

**Example 1**  An integer is represented by $m$.
  **a.** Write the next three integers in natural order after $m$.
  **b.** Write in decreasing order the three integers that immediately precede $m$.
  **c.** Write an equation that states that the sum of seven consecutive integers is 63.

**Solution**
  **a.** $m + 1, m + 2, m + 3$
  **b.** $m - 1, m - 2, m - 3$
  **c.** $(m - 3) + (m - 2) + (m - 1) + m +$
  $\qquad (m + 1) + (m + 2) + (m + 3) = 63$

Ten is called an *even* integer because $10 = 2 \times 5$. The integers that are the products of 2 and any integer are the **even integers.** In natural order, they are:

$$\ldots, -4, -2, 0, 2, 4, 6, 8, \ldots$$

An **odd integer** is an integer that is not even. In natural order, the odd integers are:

$$\ldots, -5, -3, -1, 1, 3, 5, \ldots$$

If you count by *twos* from any even integer, you obtain **consecutive even integers.** For example:

  Three consecutive even integers:   8; $8 + 2$, or 10; $10 + 2$, or 12

If you count by *twos* from any odd integer, you obtain **consecutive odd integers.** For example:

  Three consecutive odd integers:   9; $9 + 2$, or 11; $11 + 2$, or 13

Thus, in natural order,

$$m, m + 2, m + 4$$

are consecutive even integers if $m$ is even, and consecutive odd integers if $m$ is odd.

***Example 2*** Write an equation to represent the data.

There are four consecutive odd integers. The third in natural order is the sum of the fourth and twice the second.

***Solution*** Let $m$ = the first of the four consecutive odd integers; then the four integers are:

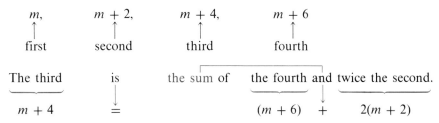

$\therefore$ the equation is $m + 4 = (m + 6) + 2(m + 2)$.  ***Answer***

## Oral Exercises

**1.** If $k = 3$, what are $k + 1$, $k + 2$, and $k + 3$?

**2.** If $r = 1$, what are $r - 1$, $r - 2$, and $r - 3$?

**3.** The least of four consecutive integers is $-1$. What are the other three integers?

**4.** The greatest of four consecutive integers is 20. What are the other three integers?

**5.** If $x = 15$, represent 14 and 16 in terms of $x$.

**6.** If $p = 20$, represent 18 and 22 in terms of $p$.

**7.** If $d = 7$, represent 3, 5, and 9 in terms of $d$.

**8.** If $e = 12$, represent 8, 10, 14, and 16 in terms of $e$.

**9.** Let $t$ represent an odd integer. Is $t + 1$ odd or even? $t + 2$? $t - 1$?

**10.** If $n$ is an integer, is $2n$ odd or even? What are the next two even integers greater than $2n$? the next smaller even integer?

**11.** If $n$ is an integer, is $2n + 1$ odd or even? What are the next two odd integers greater than $2n + 1$? the next smaller odd integer?

**12.** If $m$ and $n$ are even, is $m + n$ odd, or is it even? What about $m - n$ and $mn$?

**13.** If $m$ and $n$ are odd, is $m + n$ odd, or is it even? What about $m - n$ and $mn$?

**14.** If $m$ is odd, but $n$ is even, is $m + n$ odd, or is it even? What about $m - n$ and $mn$?

# Written Exercises

**Write an equation to represent the stated relationship among integers.**

**Example**    The product of two consecutive integers is 8 more than twice their sum.

**Solution**    Let $x =$ the first of the integers. Then
$x + 1 =$ the second integer.

Their product is 8 more than twice their sum.

$$x(x + 1) = 2[x + (x + 1)] + 8$$

$\therefore$ the equation is $x(x + 1) = 2[x + (x + 1)] + 8$.   ***Answer***

**A**   **1.** The sum of two consecutive integers is 87.

     **2.** The sum of three consecutive integers is 69.

     **3.** The sum of four consecutive integers is $-106$.

     **4.** The sum of four consecutive integers is $-42$.

     **5.** The sum of three consecutive odd integers is 81.

     **6.** The sum of three consecutive odd integers is 147.

     **7.** The product of two consecutive even integers is 168.

     **8.** The sum of four consecutive even integers is $-100$.

     **9.** The greater of two consecutive even integers is six less than twice the smaller.

   **10.** The smaller of two consecutive even integers is five more than one half of the greater.

   **11.** The four Smith children were born at two-year intervals. The sum of their ages is 36.

   **12.** A rectangle has a perimeter of 62 cm. The lengths in centimeters of its adjacent sides are consecutive integers.

**B**  **13.** There are four consecutive integers. Their sum is 100 decreased by twice the difference between the greatest and twice the least.

   **14.** There are four consecutive integers. Three times the greatest is 6 more than the sum of the other three.

   **15.** There are three consecutive integers listed in natural order. The sum of the second and the third is half the first decreased by 6.

   **16.** There are three consecutive integers listed in natural order. The sum of the first and half the third is 13 less than the second.

17. Find four consecutive integers such that the sum of the two largest subtracted from twice the sum of the two smallest is 15.

18. Dick is younger than Tom, but older than Harry. Their ages in years are consecutive odd integers. Dick's mother is three times as old as Dick, and 13 years older than twice as old as Tom.

19. Kate is taller than Ginger, but shorter than Rose. Their heights in centimeters are consecutive integers. If Kate were half as tall as she is, she would be just as tall as her sister who is 80 cm shorter than Rose.

**For Exercises 20 and 21, use this definition:**

*The product of any real number and an integer is called a **multiple** of the real number.*

C 20. The ages in years of three children are consecutive multiples of 3. Four years ago the sum of their ages was 42.

21. Jim weighs more than Joe but less than Jack. Their weights in kilograms are consecutive multiples of 7. If they each weighed 5 kg less, the sum of their weights would be 195 kg.

# Self-Test 2

**Vocabulary**  distributive axiom (p. 64)  consecutive integers (p. 72)
equivalent expressions (p. 65)  natural order (p. 72)
simplify a variable expression  even integer (p. 72)
  (p. 65)  odd integer (p. 72)
identity element for  consecutive even integers (p. 72)
  multiplication (p. 68)  consecutive odd integers (p. 72)

**Simplify.**

1. $-5y + 11y + 7$    2. $4(x - 3) + 1$    Obj. 2-5, p. 64
3. $7(4 + z) - 6$    4. $18 + 8t - 3t$
5. $9(-5)(-2)(-3)$    6. $(-a)(-1) + (-3)7$    Obj. 2-6, p. 68
7. $-6(3a - 5b)$    8. $(7 \times -13) + (7 \times 3)$
9. If $n = 54$, then in terms of $n$,    Obj. 2-7, p. 72
$53 = \underline{\quad?\quad}$ and $55 = \underline{\quad?\quad}$.

10. Write an equation to represent the relationship among the integers described as follows:

The sum of the least and the greatest of three consecutive integers is $-44$.

Check your answers with those at the back of the book.

# Division

## 2-8 The Reciprocal of a Real Number

**Objective**  To use reciprocals.

Two numbers whose product is 1 are called **reciprocals,** or **multiplicative inverses,** of each other. For example:

1. 3 and $\frac{1}{3}$ are reciprocals because $3 \times \frac{1}{3} = 1$.

2. $-1.25$ and $-0.8$ are reciprocals because $(-1.25)(-0.8) = 1$.

3. $\frac{2}{3}$ and $\frac{3}{2}$ are reciprocals because $\frac{2}{3} \cdot \frac{3}{2} = 1$.

4. 1 is its own reciprocal because $1 \times 1 = 1$.

5. $-1$ is its own reciprocal because $(-1)(-1) = 1$.

6. 0 has no reciprocal because the product of 0 and *any* real number is 0, *not* 1.

   The symbol for the reciprocal or multiplicative inverse of a nonzero real number $a$ is $\frac{1}{a}$.

   Every real number except 0 has a reciprocal. This fact is stated as an axiom.

---

### Axiom of Reciprocals

For every nonzero real number $a$, there is a unique real number $\frac{1}{a}$ such that

$$a \cdot \frac{1}{a} = 1 \quad \text{and} \quad \frac{1}{a} \cdot a = 1.$$

---

You know that $-3$ and $-\frac{1}{3}$ are reciprocals because $(-3)\left(-\frac{1}{3}\right) = 1$.

You can show in general that $(-a)\left(-\frac{1}{a}\right) = 1$ for $a \neq 0$ as follows:

$$(-a)\left(-\frac{1}{a}\right) = (-1 \cdot a)\left(-1 \cdot \frac{1}{a}\right) = [(-1)(-1)]\left(a \cdot \frac{1}{a}\right) = 1 \times 1 = 1.$$

Therefore, for every nonzero real number $a$,

$$\frac{1}{-a} = -\frac{1}{a}, \text{ read "The reciprocal of } -a \text{ is } -\frac{1}{a}."$$

**Example 1** Simplify each expression.

    **a.** $(7 \times 6)\left(\frac{1}{7} \times \frac{1}{6}\right)$

    **b.** $(ab)\left(\frac{1}{a} \cdot \frac{1}{b}\right)$, $a \neq 0$, $b \neq 0$

**Solution**   **a.** $(7 \times 6)\left(\frac{1}{7} \times \frac{1}{6}\right) = \left(7 \times \frac{1}{7}\right)\left(6 \times \frac{1}{6}\right) = 1 \times 1 = 1$

          **b.** $(ab)\left(\frac{1}{a} \cdot \frac{1}{b}\right) = \left(a \cdot \frac{1}{a}\right)\left(b \cdot \frac{1}{b}\right) = 1 \times 1 = 1$

Example 1(b) shows that the product of $ab$ and $\frac{1}{a} \cdot \frac{1}{b}$ is 1. Therefore, $\frac{1}{a} \cdot \frac{1}{b}$ is the reciprocal of $ab$. This fact can be stated as follows:

### Property of the Reciprocal of a Product

The reciprocal of a product of nonzero real numbers is the product of the reciprocals of the numbers. That is, for all nonzero real numbers $a$ and $b$,

$$\frac{1}{ab} = \frac{1}{a} \cdot \frac{1}{b}.$$

**Example 2** Simplify:   **a.** $\frac{1}{4} \cdot \frac{1}{-7}$    **b.** $(xy)\frac{1}{x}$, $x \neq 0$

**Solution**   **a.** $\frac{1}{4} \cdot \frac{1}{-7} = \frac{1}{4(-7)} = \frac{1}{-28} = -\frac{1}{28}$

          **b.** $(xy)\frac{1}{x} = (yx)\frac{1}{x} = y\left(x \cdot \frac{1}{x}\right) = y \cdot 1 = y$

## Oral Exercises

**State the reciprocal of each number in simplest form.**

  **1.** 8                **2.** 1               **3.** $-1$            **4.** $\frac{1}{11}$

  **5.** $-2$          **6.** $\frac{3}{5}$             **7.** 0.25          **8.** $-\frac{1}{7}$

  **9.** $-\frac{11}{6}$        **10.** $d$, $d \neq 0$     **11.** $\frac{a}{4}$, $a \neq 0$     **12.** $-\frac{1}{s}$, $s \neq 0$

**Simplify.**

  **13.** $\frac{1}{10} \cdot \frac{1}{5}$      **14.** $\frac{1}{-2} \cdot \frac{1}{-12}$      **15.** $\frac{1}{6} \cdot \frac{1}{-4}$      **16.** $\frac{1}{-x} \cdot \frac{1}{y}$, $x \neq 0$, $y \neq 0$

## Written Exercises

**Simplify each expression.**

**Example 1** $-72ab\left(-\frac{1}{9}\right) = (-1 \cdot 72)ab\left(-1 \cdot \frac{1}{9}\right)$

$= [(-1)(-1)]\left(72 \cdot \frac{1}{9}\right)ab$

$= 1 \cdot \left(8 \cdot 9 \cdot \frac{1}{9}\right)ab = 1 \cdot (8 \cdot 1)ab = 8ab$

**A**  **1.** $\frac{1}{4}(-20)$

**2.** $-\frac{1}{12}(48)$

**3.** $-1000\left(\frac{1}{100}\right)$

**4.** $-70\left(-\frac{1}{7}\right)$

**5.** $108\left(-\frac{1}{9}\right)\left(-\frac{1}{12}\right)$

**6.** $-63\left(-\frac{1}{3}\right)\left(-\frac{1}{21}\right)$

**7.** $\frac{1}{-3}(36)\left(\frac{1}{4}\right)$

**8.** $-150\left(\frac{1}{2}\right)\left(\frac{1}{-3}\right)$

**9.** $4rs\left(-\frac{1}{4}\right)$

**10.** $33sp\left(-\frac{1}{11}\right)$

**11.** $\frac{1}{x}(5xy),\ x \neq 0$

**12.** $(7tk)\left(\frac{1}{t}\right),\ t \neq 0$

**Example 2** $\frac{1}{3}(42m - 3v) = \frac{1}{3}(42m) - \frac{1}{3}(3v)$

$= \left(\frac{1}{3} \times 42\right)m - \left(\frac{1}{3} \times 3\right)v = 14m - v$

**13.** $\frac{1}{2}(-16a + 20)$

**14.** $\frac{1}{3}(18b - 39)$

**15.** $-\frac{1}{5}(-45c + 10d)$

**16.** $-\frac{1}{8}(56g - 72h)$

**17.** $(-42m - 91k)\left(-\frac{1}{7}\right)$

**18.** $(-39n - 52p)\left(-\frac{1}{13}\right)$

**B**  **19.** $\frac{1}{2}(8u + 10v) - \frac{1}{3}(15u - 3v)$

**20.** $\frac{1}{5}(-5a + 20b) - \frac{1}{2}(2b - 6a)$

**21.** $6\left(\frac{1}{3}x - \frac{1}{2}y\right) + 42\left(-\frac{1}{3}y - \frac{1}{7}x\right)$

**22.** $-8\left(-\frac{1}{8}p + q\right) + \frac{1}{9}(63p - 9q)$

**23.** $-\frac{1}{8}(48m - 16) - \frac{1}{4}(84m + 8)$

**24.** $-5\left(4 - \frac{1}{2}n\right) + \frac{1}{16}(-32n + 8)$

**25.** $\left(-\frac{1}{12}\right)(6r + 4s) + 7\left(\frac{1}{21}s - \frac{1}{14}r\right)$

**26.** $\left(-\frac{1}{20}\right)(5z - 4w) - 6\left(-\frac{1}{30}w - \frac{1}{24}z\right)$

**27.** $-3\left[\frac{1}{4}(12t + 1) - \frac{1}{4}\right] + 10t$

**28.** $3s + \left(-\frac{1}{2}\right)\left[6 + 24\left(-\frac{1}{3} + \frac{1}{4}s\right)\right]$

**Use the definition of reciprocals to find the value of $x$ that satisfies the equation.**

**C**  **29.** $-\frac{1}{4}x = 1$

**30.** $-0.5x = 1$

**31.** $x \cdot \frac{1}{\pi} = 1$

**32.** $\frac{1}{x} = 5$

**33.** $\frac{1}{\frac{1}{x}} = 2$

**34.** $\frac{1}{\frac{1}{x}} = -3$

The program given on page 58 can be modified to find the average of the numbers being added. This can be done by introducing a variable "counter" as follows:

```
45   LET C = 0
85   LET C = C + 1
105  PRINT "AVERAGE = ";S/C
```

If you were able to save the earlier program, you need only type the three lines above, and then type the command LIST to get a clean copy of the revised program. If you were not able to save the earlier program, retype it, adding the three new lines.

### Exercises

Find the average for each list of numbers.

**1.** 2, 4, 6, 8, 10, 12, 14, 16, 18, 20

**2.** 1, 4, 9, 16, 25, 36, 49, 64, 81, 100

**3.** 2.25, 3.42, 5.15, 1.98, 4.82

**4.** 12.95, 27.59, 21.76, 38.25, 47.34

Use the reciprocal key on a calculator to find the reciprocal of each number.

**1.** 0.0625     **2.** $-32$     **3.** 3125     **4.** 0.000064

**5.** For each number in Exercises 1–4, press the reciprocal key twice. Your results illustrate the property: The reciprocal of the reciprocal of a number is __?__ .

**6. a.** Copy and complete the table.

| $a$ | $b$ | $\dfrac{1}{ab}$ | $\dfrac{1}{a} \cdot \dfrac{1}{b}$ |
|---|---|---|---|
| 4 | 16 | ? | ? |
| $-32$ | $-0.5$ | ? | ? |
| 0.234 | 0.654 | ? | ? |
| 555 | 222 | ? | ? |

**b.** What property does your completed table illustrate?

# 2-9 Dividing Real Numbers

**Objective**   To divide real numbers and to simplify expressions involving quotients.

The first column below lists a few examples of division by 2. The second column lists related examples of multiplication by $\frac{1}{2}$.

<table>
<tr><td align="center">Dividing by 2</td><td align="center">Multiplying by $\frac{1}{2}$</td></tr>
<tr><td align="center">$2 \div 2 = 1$</td><td align="center">$2 \times \frac{1}{2} = 1$</td></tr>
<tr><td align="center">$4 \div 2 = 2$</td><td align="center">$4 \times \frac{1}{2} = 2$</td></tr>
<tr><td align="center">$6 \div 2 = 3$</td><td align="center">$6 \times \frac{1}{2} = 3$</td></tr>
<tr><td align="center">$8 \div 2 = 4$</td><td align="center">$8 \times \frac{1}{2} = 4$</td></tr>
</table>

Comparing the entries in the two columns shows that dividing by 2 gives the same result as multiplying by the reciprocal of 2. This suggests the following **definition of division.**

---

For every real number $a$ and every *nonzero* real number $b$, the **quotient** $a \div b$ is defined by:

$$a \div b = a \cdot \frac{1}{b}$$

*To divide by* b, *multiply by the reciprocal of* b.

---

A quotient is often represented as a fraction:

$$a \div b = \frac{a}{b}$$

You  can use the definition of division to replace any quotient by a product.

$$\frac{21}{7} = 21 \times \frac{1}{7} = 3 \qquad\qquad \frac{21}{-7} = 21\left(-\frac{1}{7}\right) = -3$$

$$\frac{-21}{7} = -21 \times \frac{1}{7} = -3 \qquad\qquad \frac{-21}{-7} = (-21)\left(-\frac{1}{7}\right) = 3$$

---

The quotient of two positive numbers or two negative numbers is positive.

The quotient of a positive number and a negative number is negative.

---

Here are some important questions and answers about division of real numbers:

1. Why can you never divide by zero? Dividing by 0 would mean multiplying by the reciprocal of 0. But 0 has no reciprocal (page 76). Therefore, *division by zero has no meaning in the set of real numbers.*

2. You cannot divide zero by zero, but can you divide zero by any other number? Look at these examples:

$$\frac{0}{5} = 0 \times \frac{1}{5} = 0 \qquad 0 \div (-2) = 0 \times \left(-\frac{1}{2}\right) = 0$$

*When zero is divided by any nonzero number, the quotient is zero.*

3. Is division commutative? No; for example,

$$8 \div 2 = 4 \quad \text{but} \quad 2 \div 8 = 0.25.$$

4. Is division associative? No; for example,

$$(12 \div 3) \div 2 = 4 \div 2 = 2 \quad \text{but} \quad 12 \div (3 \div 2) = 12 \div 1.5 = 8.$$

5. Is division distributive with respect to addition and with respect to subtraction? Yes, it is! (See Exercises 30 and 31, page 83.)

---

For all real numbers $a$, $b$, and $c$ such that $c \neq 0$,

$$\frac{a + b}{c} = \frac{a}{c} + \frac{b}{c} \quad \text{and} \quad \frac{a - b}{c} = \frac{a}{c} - \frac{b}{c}.$$

---

## Oral Exercises

**Read each quotient as a product. Then simplify.**

**Example 1** $8 \div \left(-\frac{1}{6}\right)$     **Solution** $8 \times (-6)$; $-48$

**Example 2** $\frac{54r}{-9}$     **Solution** $54r\left(-\frac{1}{9}\right)$; $-6r$

1. $\frac{-12}{3}$     2. $\frac{0}{8}$     3. $-25 \div 5$     4. $18 \div (-18)$

5. $\frac{0}{-9}$     6. $\frac{-6}{-6}$     7. $\frac{-2}{2}$     8. $\frac{49}{-7}$

9. $\frac{38}{-2}$     10. $\frac{-56}{-8}$     11. $\frac{4}{-64}$     12. $\frac{-8}{72}$

13. $x \div 1$     14. $x \div (-1)$     15. $8a \div (-2)$     16. $(-18b) \div 3$

17. $(-60a) \div (-10)$     18. $(-84b) \div (-7)$     19. $\frac{a}{a}$, $a \neq 0$     20. $\frac{-a}{a}$, $a \neq 0$

**Simplify.**

***Example 3*** $\frac{t}{15} \cdot 15$       ***Solution*** $\frac{t}{15} \cdot 15 = t \cdot \frac{1}{15} \cdot 15 = t \cdot 1 = t$

**21.** $6 \cdot \dfrac{x}{6}$       **22.** $\left(-\dfrac{s}{5}\right)(-5)$       **23.** $2\left(\dfrac{y}{-2}\right)$       **24.** $-3 \cdot \dfrac{n}{3}$

---

# Written Exercises

**Simplify.**

**A**  **1.** $-512 \div 64$       **2.** $408 \div (-34)$       **3.** $33 \div \left(-\dfrac{1}{3}\right)$       **4.** $0 \div (-47)$

**5.** $\dfrac{-49}{-\frac{1}{7}}$       **6.** $\dfrac{9}{-\frac{1}{4}}$       **7.** $\dfrac{-10}{\frac{1}{8}}$       **8.** $\dfrac{0}{-\frac{1}{5}}$

**9.** $\dfrac{156a}{-13}$       **10.** $\dfrac{384b}{-8}$       **11.** $\dfrac{-852x}{6x}, \; x \neq 0$       **12.** $\dfrac{-216y}{-24y}, \; y \neq 0$

**13.** $\dfrac{-w}{18}(-18)$       **14.** $-8 \cdot \dfrac{v}{8}$       **15.** $\dfrac{5c}{4} \cdot 4$       **16.** $\dfrac{-7d}{3}(-3)$

**Find the average of the numbers given in Exercises 17–20. (The *average* is the sum of the numbers divided by the number of numbers.)**

***Example 1***  $19, \, -3, \, -18, \, -2$

***Solution***   $\dfrac{19 + (-3) + (-18) + (-2)}{4} = \dfrac{19 - 23}{4} = \dfrac{-4}{4} = -1$

**17.** $-17, 4, -11, 2$       **18.** $8, -21, -7, 12$

**19.** $21, -17, -22, 13, 0$       **20.** $21, -17, -22, 13$

**Evaluate each expression if $a = -3$, $b = -1$, $c = 2$, and $d = 6$.**

***Example 2***  $\dfrac{abd}{a + c} = \dfrac{(-3)(-1)(6)}{-3 + 2}$

$$= \dfrac{3(6)}{-1} = \dfrac{18}{-1} = -18$$

**B**  **21.** $\dfrac{5c + b}{3 - d}$       **22.** $\dfrac{cbd}{(1 - b)a}$       **23.** $\dfrac{bca}{(1 - c)d}$

**24.** $\dfrac{d + 7a}{a + c}$       **25.** $\dfrac{a - 2d}{3c + b}$       **26.** $\dfrac{4a - d}{abc}$

**27.** $\dfrac{a - 3b}{bcd}$       **28.** $\dfrac{(c + a)(c - a)}{b + d}$       **29.** $\dfrac{(d + 5c)(d - 5c)}{a + b}$

**In Exercises 30 and 31 assume that $a$, $b$, and $c$ are any real numbers and $c \neq 0$.**

C  **30.** Name the axiom, property, or definition that justifies each numbered step.

$$\frac{a + b}{c} = (a + b) \cdot \frac{1}{c} \qquad (1) \ \underline{\ ?\ }$$

$$= \left(a \cdot \frac{1}{c}\right) + \left(b \cdot \frac{1}{c}\right) \qquad (2) \ \underline{\ ?\ }$$

$$= \frac{a}{c} + \frac{b}{c} \qquad (3) \ \underline{\ ?\ }$$

**31.** Using the fact that multiplication is distributive with respect to subtraction, show that $\frac{a - b}{c} = \frac{a}{c} - \frac{b}{c}$. (*Hint:* See Exercise 30.)

## *Application* / Understanding Product Prices

You may have noticed the Universal Product Code (UPC) on items in your supermarket. This code is a series of bands of alternating light and dark spaces of varying widths that represent the numbers printed underneath. Many supermarkets have installed electronic check-out counters that contain an optical reader that scans the UPC on items and transmits the information to a central computer. The computer "looks up" the price of the item and subtracts the item from the store's inventory listing of products. The name of the product and its price are then printed on the sales slip for the customer. Thus, the customer benefits by having a record of the transaction and the store benefits by having up-to-date inventory records.

Code number of the manufacturer   Code number of the product

Consumers must make many choices while shopping. Quality, price, and convenience are all important considerations. Sometimes it is difficult to compare prices of products in different-sized packages. Unit pricing can help you make the comparison. The unit price of an item is its price per unit of measure. In many supermarkets, unit prices are posted on the shelves with the products. The product with the lowest unit price is the best buy provided the quality is comparable and the quantity is convenient.

*Example*  Find the unit price of this beverage: $.35 for 250 mL

*Solution*  1 L = 1000 mL  or  250 mL = $\frac{1}{4}$ L

$.35 × 4 = $1.40 per liter

# Self-Test 3

***Vocabulary***    reciprocals (p. 76)                reciprocal of a product (p. 77)
                        multiplicative inverse           division (p. 80)
                        (p. 76)                            quotient (p. 80)

**State the reciprocal of each number.**

**1.** $-\dfrac{1}{6}$                       **2.** $2x,\ x \neq 0$                **Obj. 2-8, p. 76**

**Simplify.**

**3.** $\dfrac{1}{7} \cdot 7n$                  **4.** $-\dfrac{1}{4}(24c - 32)$

**5.** $\dfrac{48}{-3}$                    **6.** $-54 \div 9$             **Obj. 2-9, p. 80**

**7.** $-28 \div (-14)$           **8.** $-3y \div \dfrac{1}{3}$

Check your answers with those at the back of the book.

# Chapter Summary

1. A number line can be used to find the sum of two real numbers.

2. Opposites and absolute values are used in the rules for adding real numbers (page 54) and multiplying real numbers (page 69).

3. Real-number axioms are statements about numbers that are accepted as true and are the basis for computation in arithmetic and in algebra. The statements in the chart on the next page are true for all real values of each variable except as noted.

4. Useful properties about addition or multiplication:

    Property of the opposite of a sum:       $-(a + b) = -a + (-b)$
    Multiplicative property of zero:         $a \cdot 0 = 0 \cdot a = 0$
    Multiplicative property of $-1$:         $a(-1) = (-1)a = -a$
    Property of opposites in products:   $(-a)(b) = -ab;\ a(-b) = -ab;\ (-a)(-b) = ab$
    Property of the reciprocal of
    a product:                       $\dfrac{1}{ab} = \dfrac{1}{a} \cdot \dfrac{1}{b};\ a \neq 0,\ b \neq 0$

5. Subtraction and division are defined as follows:

$$a - b = a + (-b) \qquad a \div b = \frac{a}{b} = a \cdot \frac{1}{b} \quad (b \neq 0)$$

| Axioms of Real Numbers | | |
|---|---|---|

| Equality: | Reflexive property | $a = a$ |
|---|---|---|
| | Symmetric property | If $a = b$, then $b = a$. |
| | Transitive property | If $a = b$ and $b = c$, then $a = c$. |

| | Addition | Multiplication |
|---|---|---|
| Axioms of closure | $a + b$ is a unique real number. | $ab$ is a unique real number. |
| Commutative axioms | $a + b = b + a$ | $ab = ba$ |
| Associative axioms | $(a + b) + c = a + (b + c)$ | $(ab)c = a(bc)$ |
| Identity axioms | $a + 0 = 0 + a = a$ | $a \cdot 1 = 1 \cdot a = a$ |
| Axiom of opposites | $a + (-a) = (-a) + a = 0$ | |
| Axiom of reciprocals | | $a \cdot \dfrac{1}{a} = \dfrac{1}{a} \cdot a = 1;\ a \neq 0$ |
| Distributive axiom | $a(b + c) = ab + ac$ and $(b + c)a = ba + ca$ | |

# Chapter Review

**Give the letter of the correct answer.**

2-1
**1.** Simplify $74\frac{3}{8} + 1\frac{3}{5} + 7\frac{5}{8} + \frac{2}{5}$.

   **a.** 83       **b.** 82       **c.** $82\frac{13}{40}$       **d.** 84

**2.** Simplify $(16p)(5q)$.
   **a.** $21pq$       **b.** $80pq$       **c.** $21p + q$       **d.** $80(p + q)$

2-2
**3.** Simplify $-5 + (-1.7) + 1.3$.
   **a.** $-0.9$       **b.** $-8$       **c.** $-5.4$       **d.** 8

**4.** Solve the equation $-16 + x = -1$.
   **a.** 15       **b.** $-15$       **c.** 17       **d.** $-17$

2-3
**5.** Simplify $-4 + (-4) + [-(-6 + 2)]$.
   **a.** 4       **b.** $-4$       **c.** 0       **d.** $-12$

6. Evaluate $9 + a + (-b)$ if $a = -7$ and $b = |6|$.
   **a.** $-4$　　　　**b.** $4$　　　　**c.** $8$　　　　**d.** $10$

7. While Roberto waited for the bus he noticed that 14 people left a certain office building and 6 people entered. Then 5 more people entered and 7 people left. As the bus left, he saw 6 people leave the building and 4 more people enter. What was the net increase or decrease in the number of people in the office building while Roberto watched?
   **a.** an increase of 12 people　　　**b.** a decrease of 16 people
   **c.** an increase of 4 people　　　**d.** a decrease of 12 people

8. Simplify "17 decreased by $-19$."　　　　　　　　　　　　　　2-4
   **a.** $-36$　　　　**b.** $-2$　　　　**c.** $36$　　　　**d.** $2$

9. Simplify $t + 9 - (t - 7)$.
   **a.** $2$　　　　**b.** $16$　　　　**c.** $2t + 16$　　　　**d.** $2t + 2$

10. Simplify $720 \left( \frac{1}{8} + \frac{1}{9} \right)$.　　　　　　　　　　　　　　2-5

    **a.** $10$　　　　**b.** $20$　　　　**c.** $\dfrac{1440}{17}$　　　　**d.** $170$

11. Simplify $3 + 7(r - 4)$.
    **a.** $10r - 40$　　**b.** $10r - 28$　　**c.** $7r - 25$　　**d.** $7r - 31$

12. Simplify $(-12 \times 6) - (-12 \times 8)$.　　　　　　　　　　　　2-6
    **a.** $24$　　　　**b.** $-24$　　　　**c.** $-102$　　　　**d.** $-168$

13. Simplify $8 - p - 9 - p$.
    **a.** $-17$　　**b.** $-1$　　**c.** $-2p - 17$　　**d.** $-2p - 1$

14. Simplify $-6(9p - 7)$.
    **a.** $-12p$　　**b.** $-54p + 42$　　**c.** $-63p + 42$　　**d.** $-54p - 42$

15. Choose the equation that represents the following. The greater of two　2-7
    consecutive odd integers is nine less than twice the smaller.
    **a.** $x + 1 = 2x - 9$　　　　**b.** $x + 1 = 2(x - 9)$
    **c.** $x + 2 = 9 - 2x$　　　　**d.** $x + 2 = 2x - 9$

16. Simplify $(-63st)\left(-\frac{1}{9}\right)$.　　　　　　　　　　　　2-8

    **a.** $7s + t$　　**b.** $-7st$　　**c.** $7st$　　**d.** $7s - t$

17. Simplify $12\left(\frac{1}{4}x + \frac{1}{3}\right) - \frac{1}{2}(12x - 6)$.
    **a.** $-3x + 7$　　**b.** $3x + 7$　　**c.** $4$　　**d.** $-5x + 3$

18. Simplify $\dfrac{-64x}{-64x}$, $x \neq 0$.　　　　　　　　　　　　2-9

    **a.** $1x$　　　　**b.** $1$　　　　**c.** $-1$　　　　**d.** $0$

19. Simplify $-18y \div \dfrac{1}{3}$.

    **a.** $-6y$　　　　**b.** $6y$　　　　**c.** $54y$　　　　**d.** $-54y$

20. Evaluate $\dfrac{a + 15b}{c}$ if $a = -6$, $b = 9$, and $c = -3$.
    **a.** $-43$　　　　**b.** $137$　　　　**c.** $-13$　　　　**d.** $-47$

# Chapter Test

**Simplify.**

2-1

**1.** $16 + p + q + 5$      **2.** $2 \times 187 \times 5$      

**3.** $-5 + [-9 + (-9)]$      **4.** $(-7 + 13) + (-9)$      2-2

**5.** Solve the equation $-16 = 9 + b$.

**Simplify.**

**6.** $-\dfrac{8}{3} + \dfrac{7}{3} + 1$      **7.** $-7.6 + 5.9 - 4$      2-3

**8.** Meredith left home in the morning with $32.66 in her purse. The subway fare to the city was $1.45. She bought a magazine for $1.75 and a skirt on sale for $23. Lunch cost $3.84. Her subway fare home was also $1.45. As she left the station a friend caught up to her and repaid a $2 loan. How much money did Meredith have at the end of the day?

**Simplify.**

**9.** $(63 - 72) - (13 + 19)$      **10.** $x - (-8) - [x + (-8)]$      2-4

**11.** Camilla got up $1\dfrac{3}{4}$ hours before her first class. How long had she been up $1\dfrac{1}{2}$ hours after her first class started?

**Simplify.**

**12.** $23(0.25) - 7(0.25)$      **13.** $5(b - 1) + (-23)b + 5$      2-5

**14.** $2a(3.69) + 2a(1.31)$      **15.** $12x + 7 - (8x + 17)$

**16.** $-16(-3)$      **17.** $(-11 + 11)19$      2-6

**18.** $(-16 + 27)(-1)$      **19.** $(-5)(13)(-7)(-10)$

**20.** Write an equation to represent the following.      2-7
There are three consecutive integers listed in natural order. The sum of the first and third is seven more than the first.

**21.** State the reciprocal of $-1$.      2-8

**Simplify.**

**22.** $-51\left(\dfrac{1}{7}\right)\left(-\dfrac{1}{13}\right)$      **23.** $-\dfrac{1}{7}(-56m + 49n)$

**24.** $\dfrac{-96}{\frac{1}{6}}$      **25.** $-\dfrac{w}{7}(-343)$      2-9

**26.** Find the average of the numbers $-9, 8, 23, -26$.

# Cumulative Review (Chapters 1 and 2)

**Simplify.**

1. $(52 \div 4) - (33 \div 3)$

2. $\dfrac{12 + 72}{6 + 8}$

3. $|-12| - |-6|$

4. $-|20| \div |-4|$

5. $47 + [12 + (-2)]$

6. $3[27 \div (12 \div 4)]$

7. $2 + 10 \times 15 \div 5$

8. $2\dfrac{5}{9} + 7\dfrac{1}{8} + 8\dfrac{4}{9}$

9. $-89 - (-74)$

10. $-54 + 28 + (-41) + 66$

11. $3(x + 2y) + 5(2x + y)$

12. $(-9)(-5)(4) - 9(5)$

13. $-4(a + 2b) - 3(-a + b)$

14. $\dfrac{1}{12}(-552xy) \div (-23)$

15. $35 \div 7(4a - 3b) - \dfrac{5}{2}(8a - 6b)$

**Evaluate each expression if $a = -2$, $b = 2$, and $c = 3$.**

16. $a - |b| + |-c|$

17. $-a + (-4) - b$

18. $\dfrac{(a - b)(-c + b)}{b - c}$

**Write the numbers in order from least to greatest.**

19. $5,\ -3,\ 0,\ -\dfrac{1}{2},\ 7,\ -2$

20. $-5,\ |5|,\ -\dfrac{1}{3},\ -\dfrac{2}{3},\ |-3|$

21. Graph the numbers $-4$, $4$, $3$, $2$, $-\dfrac{1}{2}$, and $0$ on a number line.

**Solve. If the equation has no solution, state that fact.**

22. $|x| + 1 = 4$

23. $|-x| = 10$

24. $|y| = -3$

25. $c + 12 = 0$

26. $b + 9 = 1$

27. $a + 25 = 25$

**Represent each word phrase or sentence by a variable expression.**

28. twelve less than the product of fourteen and $z$

29. five less than the sum of negative two and $b$, increased by twice the product of twelve and $b$

30. The opposite of negative seven is five more than the opposite of $x$.

31. The sum of two consecutive odd integers is two less than twice the greater integer.

**Solve.**

32. One morning in January the temperature in Winnipeg, Manitoba, was $-13.3°C$. By noon the temperature had risen $1.7°C$. That night the temperature dropped $4.4°C$. What was the temperature then?

# Maintaining Skills

**Perform the indicated operations.**

*Example 1*   $\overset{8\ \ 11\ \ 2\ \ 18}{9\cancel{1}7.\cancel{3}\cancel{8}}$
$\phantom{xxxx}-\ \ 55.19$
$\phantom{xxxx}\overline{\phantom{xx}862.19}$

*Example 2*   $2.6\overline{)7.150}$ with quotient $2.75$
$\phantom{xxx}\underline{5\ 2}$
$\phantom{xxx}1\ 95$
$\phantom{xxx}\underline{1\ 82}$
$\phantom{xxxx}130$
$\phantom{xxxx}\underline{130}$
$\phantom{xxxxx}0$

| | | | |
|---|---|---|---|
| **1.** $\ \ 49.92$ $\ -38.6$ | **2.** $\ \ 575.25$ $\ -\ \ \ 9.009$ | **3.** $\ \ 337.14$ $\ -\ 45.32$ | **4.** $\ \ 700.07$ $\ -\ \ \ 38$ |
| **5.** $\ \ 3.4276$ $\ -0.828$ | **6.** $\ \ 16.8$ $\ -\ \ 9.25$ | **7.** $\ \ 5.52$ $\ -4.763$ | **8.** $\ \ 877.3$ $\ -\ 94.3$ |

**9.** $0.02\overline{)1.10}$
**10.** $0.8\overline{)0.036}$
**11.** $5.1\overline{)3376.2}$
**12.** $1.9\overline{)860.7}$
**13.** $3.4\overline{)0.0085}$
**14.** $0.05\overline{)2.367}$
**15.** $0.25\overline{)48}$
**16.** $0.34\overline{)1156}$

**Express each fraction in simplest form.**

*Example 3*   $\dfrac{16}{24}$
*Solution*   $\dfrac{16}{24}=\dfrac{2\times 8}{3\times 8}=\dfrac{2}{3}$

**17.** $\dfrac{14}{49}$
**18.** $\dfrac{21}{24}$
**19.** $\dfrac{39}{52}$
**20.** $\dfrac{27}{54}$
**21.** $\dfrac{27}{33}$

**Perform the indicated operations. Express the answers in simplest form.**

*Example 4*   $\dfrac{5}{6}-\dfrac{2}{13}$
*Solution*   The least common denominator is 78.

$$\dfrac{5}{6}-\dfrac{2}{13}=\dfrac{5}{6}\times\dfrac{13}{13}-\dfrac{2}{13}\times\dfrac{6}{6}$$
$$=\dfrac{65}{78}-\dfrac{12}{78}=\dfrac{65-12}{78}=\dfrac{53}{78}$$

*Example 5*   $\dfrac{7}{18}\div\dfrac{14}{15}$
*Solution*   $\dfrac{7}{18}\div\dfrac{14}{15}=\dfrac{7}{18}\times\dfrac{15}{14}=\dfrac{\overset{1}{\cancel{7}}\times\overset{5}{\cancel{15}}}{\underset{6}{\cancel{18}}\times\underset{2}{\cancel{14}}}=\dfrac{5}{12}$

**22.** $\dfrac{2}{3}-\dfrac{1}{6}$
**23.** $\dfrac{5}{7}-\dfrac{2}{3}$
**24.** $\dfrac{3}{4}-\dfrac{15}{21}$
**25.** $\dfrac{3}{4}-\dfrac{5}{12}$

**26.** $\dfrac{5}{6}-\dfrac{2}{13}$
**27.** $\dfrac{3}{7}-\dfrac{11}{28}$
**28.** $\dfrac{15}{16}-\dfrac{7}{8}$
**29.** $\dfrac{7}{12}-\dfrac{1}{3}$

**30.** $\dfrac{5}{6}\div\dfrac{5}{2}$
**31.** $\dfrac{12}{21}\div\dfrac{8}{14}$
**32.** $\dfrac{21}{25}\div\dfrac{9}{20}$
**33.** $\dfrac{10}{7}\div\dfrac{7}{10}$

**34.** $\dfrac{24}{25}\div\dfrac{5}{6}$
**35.** $\dfrac{24}{25}\div\dfrac{6}{5}$
**36.** $\dfrac{7}{8}\div\dfrac{14}{12}$
**37.** $\dfrac{24}{35}\div\dfrac{36}{25}$

# Mixed Review

## Skills and Problem Solving

**Simplify.**

1. $\dfrac{105xy}{-7x}$, $x \neq 0$

2. $-2(3 + 5c) + 4(-2 + 3c)$

3. $\left|\dfrac{3}{4}\right| + \left|-\dfrac{3}{4}\right|$

4. $-412 - (-38)$

5. $125 + 17 + (-25)$

6. $-7.2 - (-5.4) + (-0.3)$

7. Graph the numbers $-4$, $5$, $3$, $-2$, $0$, $2$ on a number line.

8. The average summer high temperature in Mason City is $31.4°C$. The average winter low temperature is $-3.2°C$. What is the difference between the two extremes?

9. Evaluate the expression $\dfrac{-|b - a|}{-c}$ if $a = 4$, $b = 3$, and $c = -2$.

10. Solve the equation $2x - 7 = 9$ if $x \in \{0, 1, 2, 3, 4, 5, 6, 7, 8, 9, 10\}$.

11. Eight more than a number is 3. Find the number.

12. Replace __?__ with $<$, $=$, or $>$ to make a true statement.

$$[76 \div (-4)] + 15 \underline{\ ?\ } 76 \div (-4 + 15)$$

13. Write an equation for the following word sentence.

    The sum of twice $x$ and seven is five greater than the difference between $x$ and three.

14. Evaluate the expression $\dfrac{a(-b + 3c) + b(-b + 3c)}{2c - 1}$ if $a = -3$, $b = 3$, and $c = 7$.

15. Eight less than the absolute value of a negative number is four. Find the number.

16. On a number line, point $X$ has coordinate $-4$ and point $Y$ has coordinate 6. Write the coordinate of the point halfway between $X$ and $Y$.

17. A submarine was at a depth of 195 m. It rose 65 m and then dove 25 m. If its original position is given as $-195$, write a positive or negative number to represent its final position relative to the surface of the water.

18. Write an equation to represent the relationship between two consecutive odd integers if their product is one less than 6 times their sum.

19. Write the numbers in order from least to greatest:

$$-7, \ 0, \ -\dfrac{1}{2}, \ \dfrac{1}{5}, \ \dfrac{1}{2}, \ -6, \ 0.3$$

20. The Forbes' checking account was overdrawn by $72.50. They deposited $323.00 in the account. What was their balance then?

# Preparing for College Entrance Exams

## Strategy for Success

If a problem that requires determining whether an algebraic expression has certain properties becomes too time-consuming, try appropriate substitution for the variables. For example, when appropriate, first try positive replacements for the variables and then negative replacements. You may be able to determine the answer without manipulating the variables.

**Decide which is the best of the choices given and write the corresponding letter on your answer sheet.**

1. Write an expression that corresponds to the following word sentence. Twice the sum of two consecutive even integers is twelve less than one third of their product.

   **(A)** $2[n + (n + 1)] = \frac{1}{3}[n(n + 1) - 12]$     **(B)** $2[n + (n + 1) = \frac{1}{3}[n(n + 1)] - 12$

   **(C)** $2[n + (n + 2)] = \frac{1}{3}[n(n + 2) - 12]$     **(D)** $2[n + (n + 2)] = \frac{1}{3}[n(n + 2)] - 12$

2. Brad is four years older than twice his sister Miriam's age. Which equation represents the relationship between Brad's age, $b$, and Miriam's age, $m$?

   **(A)** $m = 2b - 4$     **(B)** $b = 2m + 4$     **(C)** $b = 2m - 4$     **(D)** $m = 2b + 4$

3. Simplify the expression $73(19 + 31) - 48(24 + 26)$.

   **(A)** 1250     **(B)** 6050     **(C)** 1200     **(D)** 1750

4. On a number line, point $A$ has coordinate $-4$ and point $B$ has coordinate 8. What is the coordinate of the point one fourth of the way from $A$ to $B$?

   **(A)** 2     **(B)** $-2$     **(C)** $-1$     **(D)** 5     **(E)** 6

5. $*$ is an operation defined for all real numbers $a$ and $b$ by $a * b = ab + a + b$. Which of the following properties does $*$ have?

   I. Closure             II. Commutativity           III. Associativity

   **(A)** I only    **(B)** II only    **(C)** III only    **(D)** I and II only    **(E)** I, II, and III

6. Suppose $x$ is a nonzero real number. Which of the following is (are) always true?

   I. $\frac{1}{|x|} > 0$          II. $|x| > x$          III. $|x| > -x$

   **(A)** I only    **(B)** II only    **(C)** III only    **(D)** II and III only    **(E)** I and III only

7. $a$, $b$, $c$, and $d$ are positive real numbers. Which of the following guarantees that $\frac{a - b}{c - d} < 0$?

   **(A)** $a > b$ and $c > d$      **(B)** $a < b$ and $c < d$      **(C)** $a > b$ and $c < d$
   **(D)** $|a - b| > 0$ and $|c - d| > 0$      **(E)** $|a - b| > 0$ and $|c - d| < 0$

# 3 Solving Equations and Problems

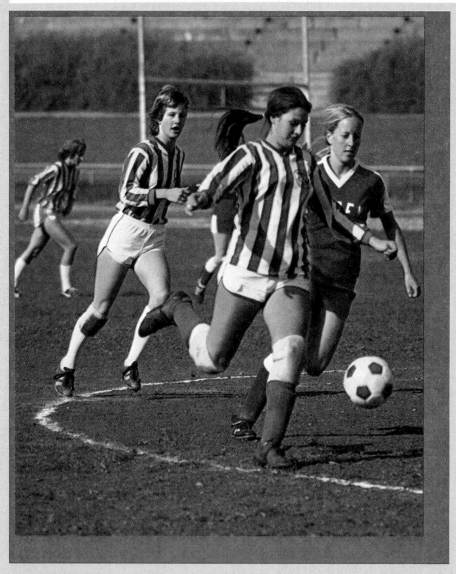

When two soccer teams that are tied score the same number of goals, the score remains tied. This illustrates the Addition Property of Equality given on the facing page.

# Transforming Equations

## 3-1 Transforming Equations: Addition and Subtraction

**Objective**   To solve equations using addition or subtraction.

Two soccer teams are tied: 4 to 4. If each team scores 2 goals in the next period, then the score is still tied:

$$4 + 2 = 4 + 2$$

Two service stations both charge 29.9¢ for a liter of gasoline. If each reduces the price by 3 cents a liter, they are still both charging the same price:

$$29.9 - 3 = 29.9 - 3$$

These examples illustrate the **addition and subtraction properties of equality:** *If the same number is added to equal numbers, the sums are equal. If the same number is subtracted from equal numbers, the differences are equal.*

---

### Addition Property of Equality

If $a$, $b$, and $c$ are any real numbers, and $a = b$, then

$$a + c = b + c \quad \text{and} \quad c + a = c + b.$$

---

Of course, because $a - c = a + (-c)$ and $b - c = b + (-c)$, the subtraction property of equality is just a special case of the addition property. For, if $a = b$, then the addition property of equality guarantees that

$$a + (-c) = b + (-c), \quad \text{or}$$
$$a - c = b - c.$$

---

### Subtraction Property of Equality

If $a$, $b$, and $c$ are any real numbers and $a = b$, then

$$a - c = b - c.$$

---

You can use these properties of equality to solve some equations. For example, study what occurs in the following steps when working with the equation $x - 5 = 7$.

$$(1) \qquad x - 5 = 7$$
$$(2) \; x - 5 + 5 = 7 + 5$$
$$(3) \qquad \quad x = 12$$

When you add 5 to each side of equation (1), as shown in equation (2), and simplify the result you obtain equation (3).

On the other hand, when you subtract 5 from (or add $-5$ to) each side of equation (3), as shown in equation (2′), you obtain equation (1), as shown below.

$$(3) \qquad \quad x = 12$$
$$(2') \; x - 5 = 12 - 5$$
$$(1) \; x - 5 = 7$$

The addition and subtraction properties of equality guarantee that any root, or solution, of equation (1) is also a root of equation (3), and any root of (3) is also a root of (1). Therefore the two equations have the same solution, namely 12.

Equations having the same solution set over a given domain are called **equivalent equations** over that domain. To solve an equation, you usually try to change, or *transform,* it into a simple equivalent equation whose solution or solutions can be seen at a glance. This transformation into a simple equivalent equation can be done by substitution, addition, or subtraction.

---

### Ways to Transform an Equation into an Equivalent Equation

**Transformation by Substitution:** Substitute for any expression in a given equation an equivalent expression.

**Transformation by Addition:** Add the same real number to each side of a given equation.

**Transformation by Subtraction:** Subtract the same real number from each side of a given equation.

---

**Example 1**  Solve $v + 8 = 3$.

**Solution**

$$v + 8 = 3$$
$$v + 8 - 8 = 3 - 8$$
$$v = -5$$

To obtain $v$ alone as the left side, subtract 8 from each side (or add $-8$ to each side).

Because errors may occur in transforming equations, you should check your work by showing that each root of the transformed equation satisfies the *original equation*.

*Check:* $v + 8 = 3 \longleftarrow$ original equation
$$-5 + 8 \stackrel{?}{=} 3$$
$$3 = 3 \ \checkmark$$

∴ the solution is $-5$.  ***Answer***

***Example 2*** Solve $-2 = -15 + p$.

***Solution***
$$\begin{array}{ll} -2 = -15 + p & \left\{\begin{array}{l} \text{To obtain } p \text{ alone as the} \\ \text{right side, add 15 to each} \\ \text{side.} \end{array}\right. \\ -2 + 15 = -15 + p + 15 \\ 13 = p \end{array}$$

*Check:* $\begin{aligned} -2 &= -15 + p \\ -2 &\stackrel{?}{=} -15 + 13 \\ -2 &= -2 \ \checkmark \end{aligned}$

∴ the solution is $13$.  ***Answer***

## Oral Exercises

**State the number to add to or to subtract from each side of the given equation to produce an equivalent equation with the variable alone as one side. Then state this equivalent equation.**

***Example 1*** $t - 3 = -1$  ***Solution*** Add 3; $t = 2$

***Example 2*** $z + 5 = 4$  ***Solution*** Subtract 5; $z = -1$

1. $x + 6 = 7$  2. $y + 2 = 5$  3. $v - 1 = 8$
4. $w - 11 = 4$  5. $a + 9 = 1$  6. $b + 7 = 6$
7. $5 + m = 0$  8. $-1 + n = 0$  9. $-2 + p = 2$
10. $-1 + r = -1$  11. $-8 + t = -8$  12. $-5 = u + 9$
13. $-6 = k - 10$  14. $-8 = -2 + t$  15. $1 = 3 + s$
16. $z - \dfrac{1}{4} = \dfrac{1}{4}$  17. $\dfrac{4}{5} = \dfrac{1}{5} + d$  18. $h + 1.7 = -2.1$

**State the addition property of equality when:**

19. $a$ and $b$ are replaced with $-x$ and $-y$, respectively
20. $c$ is replaced with $5d$

## Written Exercises

**Solve.**

**A**

| | | |
|---|---|---|
| **1.** $a - 11 = 15$ | **2.** $b - 8 = 17$ | **3.** $y + 7 = 29$ |
| **4.** $x + 18 = 31$ | **5.** $-76 + m = 92$ | **6.** $-49 + n = 63$ |
| **7.** $c - 30 = -19$ | **8.** $d - 24 = -15$ | **9.** $p + 18 = -32$ |
| **10.** $s + 90 = -55$ | **11.** $24 + t = 0$ | **12.** $0 = z - 14$ |
| **13.** $v - 37 = -54$ | **14.** $w - 94 = -110$ | **15.** $-7 + k = -17$ |
| **16.** $-18 + h = -38$ | **17.** $45 = x + 16$ | **18.** $39 = y + 12$ |
| **19.** $-19 + a = -23$ | **20.** $-32 + b = -82$ | **21.** $c + 9 = |-5|$ |
| **22.** $l - 8 = |25|$ | **23.** $f + 7 = |2 - 9|$ | **24.** $g - 6 = |8 - 14|$ |

**Example 1** $-x + 9 = 1$

**Solution**

$$-x + 9 - 9 = 1 - 9$$
$$-x = -8$$
$$x = 8 \quad \text{(Definition of opposite of a number)}$$

$\therefore$ the solution is 8.  **Answer**

**B**

| | | |
|---|---|---|
| **25.** $-x + 9 = 7$ | **26.** $-y + 3 = 21$ | **27.** $31 - k = 37$ |
| **28.** $-7 - h = 8$ | **29.** $5 = -11 - s$ | **30.** $12 = -t + 4$ |
| **31.** $(m + 3) + 6 = 5$ | **32.** $(r + 4) + 2 = 1$ | **33.** $2 = 11 + (x + 2)$ |
| **34.** $3 = 16 + (y + 1)$ | **35.** $-2 + (1 + p) = 5$ | **36.** $-3 + (1 + n) = 9$ |
| **37.** $(a - 3) + 19 = 125$ | **38.** $(b - 6) + 14 = 100$ | **39.** $4 - (1 + x) = 5$ |
| **40.** $2 - (3 + y) = 6$ | **41.** $-2 - (4 - w) = 1$ | **42.** $7 - (1 - q) = 11$ |

**Example 2** $|x| + 4 = 13$

**Solution**

$$|x| + 4 - 4 = 13 - 4$$
$$|x| = 9$$
$$x = 9 \text{ or } x = -9 \quad \text{(Definition of absolute value)}$$

$\therefore$ the solutions are 9 and $-9$.  **Answer**

**C**

| | |
|---|---|
| **43.** $|y| - 2 = 8$ | **44.** $|z| + 10 = 28$ |
| **45.** $-7 + |s| = 0$ | **46.** $6 + |t| = 14$ |
| **47.** $|x| + (-2) = 4$ | **48.** $|y| + (-1) = 1$ |
| **49.** $-5 + |r| = 0$ | **50.** $6 + |w| = 2$ |
| **51.** $-(|a| - 9) = 1$ | **52.** $-(|x| + 2) = -6$ |
| **53.** $4 - (2 - |n|) = 2$ | **54.** $7 - (3 - |m|) = 8$ |
| **55.** $9 - (|s| + 7) = 4$ | **56.** $-3 + (15 - |a|) = 12$ |

# Problems

**Write an equation based on the facts of each problem. Then, solve the equation and answer the question posed in the problem.**

**Example**   Nat has a temperature of 35.5°C. This is 1.5°C below normal body temperature. What is normal body temperature?

**Solution**

*Step 1*   The problem asks for the number of degrees in normal body temperature.

*Step 2*   Let $n$ = normal temperature in degrees Celsius. Then $n - 1.5$ = Nat's temperature

*Step 3*   $n - 1.5 = 35.5$

*Step 4*   $n - 1.5 + 1.5 = 35.5 + 1.5$
$$n = 37$$

*Step 5*   The check is left to you.

∴ normal body temperature is 37°C.   ***Answer***

**A**   **1.** Nine more than a number is 58. What is the number?

**2.** Eighteen less than a number is 46. What is the number?

**3.** A number decreased by 8 is $-31$. What is the number?

**4.** A number increased by 13 is $-11$. What is the number?

**5.** A basketball player scored 56 points in a game. This was 12 points more than he had scored in an earlier game. What was his score in the earlier game?

**6.** A gymnast outscored her competitor by 9 points. If her score was 56.5 points, what was her competitor's score?

**7.** Three members of the School Committee missed the last meeting. Twelve members were present at the meeting. How many members does the committee have?

**8.** Marita ran the 400-meter dash in 56.8 s. This was 1.3 s faster than her previous time. What was her previous time?

**9.** If the temperature of the water in a beaker rises six degrees Celsius above what it is now, the water will be at the boiling point (100°C). What is the temperature of the water now?

10. The temperature at dawn was $-2.5°C$. How many degrees did it rise to reach a temperature of $8°C$ at noon?

11. If the latitude of New York is about $41°N$ and the latitude of Rio de Janeiro is about $23°S$, what is the difference in latitude between the two cities?

12. The Busy Bee Diner charges 65 cents for a glass of juice. A customer paid $2.25 for a sandwich and a glass of juice. How much was the sandwich?

B 13. A discount store chain hired 130 new employees during a year in which 27 employees retired and 59 left for other reasons. If there were 498 employees in the chain at the end of the year, how many were there at the beginning?

14. During one day on the stock market, an investor lost $2500 on one stock, but gained $1700 on another. At the end of trading that day, the investor's holdings were worth $52,400. What were they worth when the market opened that day?

15. Rona paid $3.23 for 2 tubes of toothpaste. She paid the regular price of $1.79 for one tube, but bought the other one for less, because she used a "cents-off" coupon. What was the coupon worth?

16. During a sale, Art bought a tire pump for $4.69. A week later, he returned to the store to buy another pump. However, because the sale was over, he had to pay the regular price for the second one. If the two pumps cost Art $10.64, by how much had the store reduced the price for the sale?

## Calculator Key-In

Use the division key on a calculator to find a decimal equal to each expression.

***Example 1*** $\dfrac{-36}{8}$    ***Solution***    $\dfrac{-36}{8} = -36 \div 8 = -4.5$

1. $\dfrac{3}{4}$    2. $\dfrac{-5}{8}$    3. $\dfrac{7}{-16}$    4. $\dfrac{-3}{-20}$    5. $\dfrac{1}{40}$

6. $\dfrac{-11}{4}$    7. $\dfrac{12}{-50}$    8. $\dfrac{-7}{-8}$    9. $\dfrac{31}{32}$    10. $\dfrac{43}{-64}$

**11–20.** Use the reciprocal key on a calculator to find a decimal equal to each expression in Exercises 1–10. Are your answers the same as before?

***Example 2*** $\dfrac{-36}{8}$    ***Solution***    $\dfrac{-36}{8} = -36 \times \dfrac{1}{8} = -4.5$

# 3-2 Transforming Equations: Multiplication and Division

**Objective**  To solve equations using multiplication or division.

Suppose that a pound of peas costs the same as a pound of string beans. Then, you would expect to pay the same price for *two* pounds of peas as for *two* pounds of string beans, and the same price for *one-half* pound of peas as for *one-half* pound of string beans.

The ideas involved in this example are the **multiplication and division properties of equality.** *If equal numbers are multiplied by the same number, the products are equal. If equal numbers are divided by the same nonzero number, the quotients are equal.*

---

### Multiplication Property of Equality

If $a$, $b$, and $c$ are any real numbers and $a = b$, then
$$ca = cb \quad \text{and} \quad ac = bc.$$

### Division Property of Equality

If $a$ and $b$ are any real numbers, $c$ is any nonzero real number, and $a = b$, then
$$\frac{a}{c} = \frac{b}{c}.$$

---

These properties provide two more ways to transform an equation into an equivalent equation.

---

**Transformation by Multiplication:** Multiply each side of a given equation by the same *nonzero* real number.

**Transformation by Division:** Divide each side of a given equation by the same *nonzero* real number.

---

**Example 1**  Solve $6x = 222$.

**Solution**

$$6x = 222$$
$$\frac{6x}{6} = \frac{222}{6}$$
$$x = 37$$

*Check:*  $6x = 222$
$$6(37) \stackrel{?}{=} 222$$
$$222 = 222 \ \checkmark$$

To obtain $x$ alone as the left side, divide each side by 6 $\left(\text{or multiply by } \frac{1}{6}, \text{ the reciprocal of } 6\right)$.

$\therefore$ the solution is 37   *Answer*

---

***Example 2*** Solve $-\frac{1}{3}t = 8$.

***Solution***

$$-\frac{1}{3}t = 8$$

$$-3\left(-\frac{1}{3}t\right) = -3(8)$$

$$t = -24$$

⎰ To obtain $t$ alone as the left side,
⎱ multiply each side by $-3$, the
  reciprocal of $-\frac{1}{3}$.

*Check:* $-\frac{1}{3}t = 8$

$$-\frac{1}{3}(-24) \overset{?}{=} 8$$

$$8 = 8 \ \sqrt{}$$

$\therefore$ the solution is $-24$. ***Answer***

You know that zero cannot be a divisor (page 81). Do you know why zero is not allowed as a multiplier in transforming an equation? Look at the following equations.

$$\begin{aligned}
&(1) & 5z &= 45 \\
&(2) & 0 \cdot 5z &= 0 \cdot 45 \\
&(3) & (0 \cdot 5)z &= 0 \cdot 45 \\
&(4) & 0 \cdot z &= 0
\end{aligned}$$

Equation (1) has just one root, namely 9. Equation (4) is satisfied by *any* real number. Equations (1) and (4) are *not* equivalent (see page 94). *In transforming an equation, never multiply by zero.*

## Oral Exercises

**State the number by which to multiply or divide each side of the given equation to produce an equivalent equation with the variable alone as one side. Then, state this equivalent equation.**

**1.** $36x = 72$

**2.** $10y = -10$

**3.** $3c = -21$

**4.** $-8a = 32$

**5.** $\frac{1}{2}b = 4$

**6.** $\frac{1}{3}t = 7$

**7.** $-\frac{1}{10}r = 5$

**8.** $-\frac{1}{9}s = 9$

**9.** $0 = -4k$

**10.** $-7 = -7p$

**11.** $c \div 4 = -1$

**12.** $\frac{d}{2} = -6$

**13.** $-11f = -88$

**14.** $-27p = -81$

**15.** $4 = -\frac{u}{3}$

**16.** $-1 = \frac{n}{13}$

**17.** $-0.1x = -3$

**18.** $0.01y = -8$

## Written Exercises

**Solve.**

A **1.** $17m = 527$     **2.** $50n = 650$     **3.** $-1024 = 32a$     **4.** $-351 = 9b$

**5.** $\frac{1}{8}x = -32$     **6.** $\frac{1}{9}y = -27$     **7.** $-\frac{1}{13}p = -13$     **8.** $-\frac{1}{12}q = -24$

**9.** $-48 = -\frac{1}{8}r$     **10.** $-\frac{1}{6}s = 60$     **11.** $14v = -252$     **12.** $-32x = 768$

**13.** $600 = -25w$     **14.** $-675 = 27e$     **15.** $-35 = \frac{d}{7}$     **16.** $-28 = \frac{c}{4}$

**17.** $99 = -\frac{h}{3}$     **18.** $65 = -\frac{t}{5}$     **19.** $-\frac{1}{91}m = 0$     **20.** $-\frac{n}{10} = -64$

**21.** $-13f = -858$     **22.** $-74g = -962$     **23.** $2k = -\frac{4}{7}$     **24.** $3p = -\frac{9}{16}$

B **25.** $\frac{1}{3}x = 2\frac{1}{3}$     **26.** $\frac{1}{2}q = 3\frac{1}{2}$     **27.** $-1 = 2.5x$     **28.** $0 = -1.5y$

**29.** $\frac{1}{5}a = 6\frac{4}{5}$     **30.** $\frac{1}{2}b = 14\frac{1}{2}$     **31.** $-\frac{1}{3}y = 3\frac{2}{3}$     **32.** $-\frac{1}{2}z = 11\frac{1}{2}$

C **33.** $-2|x| = -30$     **34.** $\frac{|v|}{7} = 42$     **35.** $9 - \frac{|a|}{2} = 1$     **36.** $10 - 3|b| = 1$

## Problems

**Write an equation based on the facts of each problem. Then solve the equation and answer the question posed in the problem.**

A **1.** Negative eight times a number is 376. What is the number?

**2.** Twelve times a number is $-564$. What is the number?

**3.** One third of a number is $-912$. What is the number?

**4.** The opposite of one fourth of a number is 1132. What is the number?

**5.** Daniel Erik paid $147 for six theater tickets. How much did each ticket cost?

**6.** Denise Thomas paid $184.80 for a railroad pass allowing her 42 trips between Greenville and Central City. How much is that for each trip?

**7.** The perimeter of a square lot is 156 m. How long is each side of the lot?

**8.** A park in the shape of an equilateral triangle (a triangle with all sides equal) has a perimeter of 495 m. How long is each side of the park?

**9.** Twelve-year-old Lola is one fourth as old as her Uncle Hector. How old is Hector?

10. A restaurant charges $1.75 for one eighth of a quiche. How much does the restaurant receive for the whole quiche?

11. A 75-watt bulb consumes 0.075 kW · h (kilowatt hours) of energy when it burns for one hour. How long was the bulb left burning during a period when it consumed 3.3 kW · h of energy?

12. How many apples, averaging 0.2 kg each, are in a 50-kg shipment of apples?

B  13. A police helicopter clocked an automobile for 10 seconds over a stretch of highway one fifth of a mile long. At what rate was the automobile traveling in miles per **a.** second? **b.** hour?

14. How many hard-cover copies of a book selling for $16.50 each must a dealer sell to take in as much money as for 30 paperback copies of the book selling at $4.95 each?

15. For selling a home, an agent receives $6 for every one hundred dollars in the selling price. What was the selling price of a home for which the agent received $4725?

16. An employer claimed that each worker received $24 in "fringe benefits" for every $100 in wages. At this rate, what wages were earned by a worker whose fringe benefits were calculated to be $4140?

## *Career Note* / *Medical Laboratory Technician*

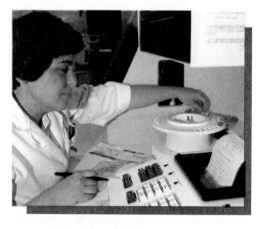

An eye for detail, the ability to work under pressure, and the ability to get accurate results are necessary qualities for a medical laboratory technician. Under the direction of physicians, medical laboratory technicians perform tests that are important in the diagnosis and treatment of many illnesses. They often use precision instruments in their work.

A medical technician needs two or more years of training after high school. Medical technicians take courses in biology, chemistry, and mathematics. Sometimes the training is specialized and involves some clinical experience. For those technicians who wish to teach or do research, many universities offer graduate programs in medical technology.

# 3-3 Using Several Transformations

**Objective** To use several transformations to solve an equation.

The equations

$$(16 + 4) - 4 = 16 \quad \text{and} \quad (16 - 4) + 4 = 16$$

are true statements. In fact:

---

For all real numbers $a$ and $b$,

$$(a + b) - b = a \quad \text{and} \quad (a - b) + b = a.$$

---

To "undo" addition of a number, you subtract that number. To "undo" subtraction of a number, you add that number. We call addition and subtraction **inverse operations.**

Similarly, multiplication and division are inverse operations.

---

For all real numbers $a$ and all nonzero real numbers $b$,

$$(ab) \div b = a \quad \text{and} \quad (a \div b)b = a.$$

---

To "undo" multiplication by a nonzero number, you divide by that number. To "undo" division by a nonzero number, you multiply by that number.

In transforming equations, you often use inverse operations.

**Example 1** Solve $4y + 43 = 19$.

**Solution**

$$4y + 43 = 19$$
$$4y + 43 - 43 = 19 - 43$$

To undo the addition of 43 to $4y$, subtract 43 from each side.

$$4y = -24$$
$$\frac{4y}{4} = \frac{-24}{4}$$

To undo the multiplication of $y$ by 4, divide each side by 4.

$$y = -6$$

*Check:* $4y + 43 = 19$
$$4(-6) + 43 \overset{?}{=} 19$$
$$-24 + 43 \overset{?}{=} 19$$
$$19 = 19 \quad \sqrt{}$$

$\therefore$ the solution is $-6$. *Answer*

The following steps are usually helpful when you solve an equation in which all the variables are on the same side.

1. Simplify each side of the equation.

2. If there are still indicated additions or subtractions, use the inverse operations to undo them.

3. If there are indicated multiplications or divisions involving the variable, use the inverse operations to undo them.

**Example 2** Solve $7(y - 1) - 2y = 13$.

**Solution**
$$7(y - 1) - 2y = 13$$
$$7y - 7 - 2y = 13$$ $\quad$ {Use the distributive property and simplify the left side.
$$5y - 7 = 13$$
$$5y - 7 + 7 = 13 + 7$$ $\quad$ {Add 7 to each side.
$$5y = 20$$
$$\frac{5y}{5} = \frac{20}{5}$$ $\quad$ {Divide each side by 5.
$$y = 4$$

**Condensed Solution**
$$7(y - 1) - 2y = 13$$
$$7y - 7 - 2y = 13$$
$$5y - 7 = 13$$
$$5y = 20$$
$$y = 4$$

*Check:* $\quad 7(y - 1) - 2y = 13$
$$7(4 - 1) - 2(4) \stackrel{?}{=} 13$$
$$7(3) - 8 \stackrel{?}{=} 13$$
$$13 = 13 \quad \checkmark$$

$\therefore$ the solution is 4. **Answer**

## Oral Exercises

**Describe how you would solve each equation.**

**Example 1** $\frac{1}{5}z + 2 = -1$

**Solution** First subtract 2 from each side; then multiply each side by 5.

**Example 2** $14 = \frac{2}{3}m$

**Solution 1** Multiply each side by $\frac{3}{2}$.

**Solution 2** Multiply each side by 3; then divide each side by 2.

**1.** $6x + 1 = 7$

**2.** $3y - 4 = 14$

**3.** $\frac{1}{4}a - 2 = -3$

**4.** $-\frac{1}{2}b + 9 = 5$

**5.** $-8 + \frac{t}{3} = 7$

**6.** $4 = -1 - \frac{x}{3}$

**7.** $\frac{3}{4}n = -12$

**8.** $-\frac{5}{9}z = 30$

**9.** $n + 7n = 16$

**10.** $-11r + 13r = -38$

**11.** $\frac{7}{8}s + 2 = 16$

**12.** $1 - \frac{4}{5}n = -19$

**13.** $5 = c + 8c - 4$

**14.** $10p - p + 2 = -7$

**15.** $-5(z + 9) = 40$

**16.** $\frac{y - 2}{3} = 7$

**17.** $\frac{3}{7}w + 2 = 17$

**18.** $1 - \frac{2}{9}v = 4$

## Written Exercises

Solve.

**A**

**1.** $3y + 7 = 16$

**2.** $2x - 9 = 13$

**3.** $-15 + 4g = -39$

**4.** $16 + 5p = -74$

**5.** $\frac{r}{2} - 6 = 6$

**6.** $\frac{s}{3} + 9 = 12$

**7.** $\frac{n}{5} + 25 = -10$

**8.** $-\frac{d}{4} + 3 = -2$

**9.** $11 = 7 - 2k$

**10.** $14 = -1 - 5h$

**11.** $-7v + 4v = 21$

**12.** $4w - w = -48$

**13.** $9t + 7t = -64$

**14.** $4m - 7m = -54$

**15.** $13a + 7a = 0$

**16.** $8z - 11z = 0$

**17.** $\frac{3}{7}c + 45 = 0$

**18.** $\frac{4}{5}f + 60 = 0$

**19.** $15g - 13g + 14 = 0$

**20.** $3e - e + 2 = 0$

**21.** $u - 4u + 4 = 7$

**22.** $x - 9 - 4x = -6$

**23.** $0 = y - 16 - 2y$

**24.** $0 = a + 25 + 4a$

**25.** $z + 2z + 3z = 36$

**26.** $3w - 2w + w = 24$

**27.** $7(m - 1) = -63$

**28.** $8(q + 7) = -72$

**29.** $-\frac{3}{2}(s - 2) = 21$

**30.** $-\frac{6}{5}(r + 3) = 66$

**B**

**31.** $3(a - 5) + 19 = -2$

**32.** $2(b + 8) - 9 = 5$

**33.** $4(k + 7) - 15 = -3$

**34.** $7(h - 2) + 17 = 3$

**35.** $4c + 3(c - 2) = -34$

**36.** $d + 4(d + 6) = -1$

**37.** $1 - \frac{3}{4}(v + 2) = -5$

**38.** $9 - \frac{4}{5}(u - 3) = 1$

**39.** $-9 - 3(2q - 1) = -18$

**40.** $-10 + 4(3p + 10) = 18$

**41.** $4(s + 8) - 3s = -2$

**42.** $3(t - 5) - t = -7$

**43.** $(x - 13) - (x - 5) + 2x = 0$

**44.** $(5 - y) + (6 - y) - (5 - y) = 0$

**45.** $b - (1 - 2b) + (b - 3) = -4$

**46.** $(c + 3) - 2c - (1 - 3c) = 2$

**C**

**47.** $5m - 3[7 - (1 - 2m)] = 0$

**48.** $\frac{1}{5}[4(k + 2) - (3 - k)] = 4$

**49.** $5(g - 7) + 2[g - 3(g - 5)] = 0$

**50.** $7n + 2[3(1 - n) - 2(1 + n)] = 14$

**51.** $3|z| - (2|z| - 2) = 9$

**52.** $9(|x| - 3) - 5|x| - 3 = 2$

The optional Computer Exercises that appear throughout this book require familiarity with the fundamental concepts and terminology of programming in BASIC. The appendix on page 653 summarizes these fundamentals.

## Computer Exercises

1. Write a BASIC program to solve an equation of the form $Ax + B = C$, where the values of $A$, $B$, and $C$ are entered with INPUT statements. Use the program to solve the following equations.

   **a.** $7x + 8 = 64$      **b.** $3y - 2 = 4$      **c.** $\frac{2}{5}n + 11 = 7$

   **d.** $\frac{2}{3}j - 8 = 14$      **e.** $\frac{w}{6} - 5 = 0$      **f.** $\frac{z}{2} + 4 = 13$

2. Use the program from Exercise 1 to solve $0x + 9 = 12$. What happens? What is the correct solution? Modify the program in Exercise 1 so that an appropriate response will appear if the value of $A$ is 0.

3. Modify the program from Exercise 1 to solve an equation of the form $A|x| + B = C$. Use this program to solve the following equations.

   **a.** $|x| + 8 = 10$      **b.** $|v| + 10 = 8$      **c.** $6|m| + 2 = 5$

   **d.** $\frac{|s|}{2} - 4 = 11$      **e.** $\frac{4}{3}|c| = 24$      **f.** $\frac{2}{3}|y| + 4 = 16$

# Self-Test 1

*Vocabulary*    equivalent equations (p. 94)
transformation by substitution (p. 94)
transformation by addition (p. 94)
transformation by subtraction (p. 94)
transformation by multiplication (p. 99)
transformation by division (p. 99)
inverse operations (p. 103)

**Solve.**

1. $x + 17 = 59$      2. $-14 + y = -1$      **Obj. 3-1, p. 93**

3. $7r = -119$      4. $18 = -\frac{1}{5}t$      **Obj. 3-2, p. 99**

**Write an equation to represent the relationship in Exercise 5. Then solve the equation and answer the question.**

5. In a school cafeteria one week, 1125 containers of milk were sold. Three times as many containers of milk as containers of juice were sold. How many containers of juice were sold?

**Solve.**

6. $5z - 2 = 33$      7. $m - 4m + 10 = 1$      **Obj. 3-3, p. 103**

Check your answers with those at the back of the book.

Everyday calculations are done either by hand or by calculator. Generally, computers are used only for more elaborate or tedious computations, or when a great deal of data must be processed.

However, it is informative sometimes to use a computer program to demonstrate the steps of a process. The program given below illustrates the use of inverse operations to solve simple equations. The program also introduces a *string variable*, which is used to represent a symbol. The first time S\$ (note the dollar sign) is used, its value is to be one of $+$, $-$, $*$, or $/$. The second time S\$ is used its value is to be Y or any other single letter. In line 190, Y stands for "yes" and N for "no."

```
10   PRINT "TO SOLVE AN EQUATION OF THE FORM"
20   PRINT "        X (SIGN) A = B:"
30   PRINT "INPUT SIGN,A,B";
40   INPUT S$,A,B
50   IF S$="+" THEN 110
60   IF S$="-" THEN 130
70   IF S$="*" THEN 150
80   IF S$="/" THEN 170
90   PRINT "WHAT DID YOU INTEND?"
100  GOTO 30
110  PRINT "X = ";B-A    ⟵⎡– is the inverse of +
120  GOTO 180
130  PRINT "X = ";B+A    ⟵⎡+ is the inverse of –
140  GOTO 180
150  PRINT "X = ";B/A    ⟵⎡/ is the inverse of *
160  GOTO 180
170  PRINT "X = ";B*A    ⟵⎡* is the inverse of /
180  PRINT
190  PRINT "ANOTHER (Y/N)";
200  INPUT S$
210  IF S$="Y" THEN 30
220  END
```

### Exercises

RUN the program to solve these equations.

**1.** $x + 4 = 20$ **2.** $x - 4 = 20$ **3.** $x \times 4 = 20$ **4.** $x \div 4 = 20$

RUN the program twice to solve these two-step equations.

**5.** $3x - 8 = 22$ **6.** $(x \div 5) + 6 = 30$

**7.** Write a program to solve $Ax + Bx + C + D = 0$.

*Note:* The program given above can be used to do Exercises 1–18 on page 96 and Exercises 1–20 on page 101.

# Solving Problems

## 3-4 Using Equations to Solve Problems

**Objective**  To use the five-step plan to solve word problems.

The skill you have gained in solving equations can often help you to solve a word problem. Use the five-step plan on page 26 to guide yourself to the solution.

### Example 1

Towne Florists, Inc. paid $3250 down toward the purchase of a delivery van. The balance of the cash price together with interest was paid over the next 60 months. The interest amounted to one half of the balance. If the total deferred payment price was $19,150, what was the cash price of the van?

### Solution

Step 1  The problem asks for the cash price.

$$\text{Cash price} = \underbrace{\text{Down payment}}_{\$3250} + \text{Balance}$$

$$\underbrace{\text{Total deferred payment price}}_{\$19,150} = \text{Cash price} + \text{Interest}$$

Interest = One half of Balance

Step 2  Let $b$ = the balance in dollars. Then:

Cash price $= 3250 + b$

Interest $\quad = \frac{1}{2}b$

$$\underbrace{\text{Total deferred payment price}}_{} = 3250 + b + \frac{1}{2}b$$

Step 3  $\qquad 19,150 \qquad\qquad = 3250 + b + \frac{1}{2}b$

Step 4  $\qquad\qquad 19,150 = 3250 + \frac{3}{2}b$

$$15,900 = \frac{3}{2}b$$

$$b = 10,600 \text{ (balance)}$$

$$3250 + b = 13,850 \text{ (cash price)}$$

$$\frac{1}{2}b = 5300 \text{ (interest)}$$

**Step 5** Does the cash price plus interest equal the total deferred payment price?

$$13{,}850 + 5300 \overset{?}{=} 19{,}150$$
$$19{,}150 = 19{,}150 \quad \checkmark$$

∴ the cash price was $13,850. *Answer*

Notice that in Example 1 you did not use the fact that the balance was paid over 60 months. Sometimes word problems contain unnecessary information. When this occurs, you have to select the facts that are necessary in order to find the solution.

To solve the problem in the next example, you must recall your work with consecutive integers. You may wish to reread Section 2-7, pages 72–75, at this time.

**Example 2** The width and the length, in meters, of a rectangle are consecutive even integers. The perimeter is 292 m. What are the dimensions of the rectangle?

### Solution

**Step 1** The problem asks for the numbers of meters in the width and the length of a rectangle whose perimeter ($p$) is 292 m. The width and length are consecutive even integers.

**Step 2** Let $w$ = the width in meters.
Then $w + 2$ = the length in meters.

**Step 3** $2l + 2w = p$
∴ $2(w + 2) + 2w = 292$

**Step 4** $\quad 2w + 4 + 2w = 292$
$$4w + 4 = 292$$
$$4w = 288$$
$$w = 72$$
$$w + 2 = 74$$

**Step 5** Does the sum of two times the width and two times the length equal the perimeter of 292 m?

$$2(72) + 2(74) \overset{?}{=} 292$$
$$144 + 148 \overset{?}{=} 292$$
$$292 = 292 \quad \checkmark$$

∴ the dimensions are 72 m and 74 m. *Answer*

# Problems

**Use the five-step plan on page 26 to solve each problem.**

A  1. The sum of 85 and twice a number is 237. Find the number.

2. The sum of three times a number and 28 is 484. Find the number.

3. Five times a number, decreased by 87, is $-12$. Find the number.

4. Six times a number, increased by 13, is $-161$. Find the number.

5. If you add 15 to the product of 4 and a number, you get 363. Find the number.

6. If you subtract 27 from the product of 8 and a number, you get 1789. Find the number.

7. The perimeter of a rectangle is 326 and its length is 94. Find its width.

8. The perimeter of a rectangle is 908 and its width is 220. Find its length.

9. Together, a boat and outboard motor cost $1500. The boat cost five times as much as the motor. What was the cost of each?

10. Bill's Burger Barn sold 584 hamburgers today. Three times as many hamburgers were sold with cheese as were sold without cheese. How many cheeseburgers were sold?

11. When Joe Darrico retired from his parcel delivery service, his daughter Rose took over the business. By now, Rose has been running the service three years longer than her father did. If the business has been in operation for 27 years, how long did Joe run it?

12. An oil tank contains 250 barrels of oil more than another tank. Together they contain 2750 barrels of oil. How much oil does each tank contain?

13. Eighteen-year-old Manolo is 4 years older than twice as old as his sister, Julia. How old is Julia?

14. A sports jacket costing $129 is priced $11 more than twice the cost of a coordinated pair of slacks. How much are the slacks?

15. Find three consecutive integers whose sum is 81.

16. Find four consecutive integers whose sum is 50.

17. Find four consecutive odd integers whose sum is $-112$.

18. Find three consecutive odd integers whose sum is $-129$.

19. The lengths in meters of the sides of a triangle are consecutive even integers. The perimeter is 210 m. How long are the sides?

20. The lengths in centimeters of the sides of a triangle are consecutive odd integers. The perimeter is 171 cm. How long are the sides?

B  21. Two numbers differ by 3. Four times the lesser diminished by three times the greater is 7. Find the numbers.

22. A magazine reported that in a survey of 100 teenagers, the number preferring broiled steak for dinner was 8 more than the number preferring beef stew. But the number preferring macaroni and cheese was 2 more than 4 times the number preferring beef stew. How many teenagers in the survey preferred beef stew?

23. Of the 10 highest waterfalls of the world, one is in Africa and another is in New Zealand. There are just as many in Europe as in South America, but there are twice as many in North America as in South America. How many are in Europe?

24. In triangle *ABC*, side *AB* is 2 cm shorter than side *AC*, while side *BC* is 1 cm longer than *AC*. If the perimeter is 62 cm, find the lengths of the 3 sides.

25. Five centimeters are cut off one side of a square piece of paper and 8 cm are added to an adjacent side. The resulting rectangular piece of paper has perimeter 98 cm. What was the area of the original square?

26. Tom has $5 more than Dick and Dick has $11 more than Harry. Together they have $45. How much does each have?

27. Carol has twice as much money as Nina, and Nina has $6 less than Lynn. Together they have $54. How much does each have?

28. Ray is 15 years older than Sam and Sam is 12 years younger than Bert. Their ages total 42 years. How old is each?

29. Sally is 17 years younger than Tilly and Tilly is 10 years older than Angie. Their ages total 60 years. How old is each?

30. The total cost of a sandwich, a glass of milk, and an apple is $2.35. What was the price of each, if the sandwich cost twice as much as the milk and the apple cost 90 cents less than the sandwich?

31. In one day, Machine *A* caps twice as many bottles as Machine *B*. Machine *C* caps 500 more bottles than Machine *A*. If the total number of bottles capped in a day is 40,000, how many bottles does each machine cap?

C 32. With the major options package and destination charge, a sports car cost $24,416. The base price of the car was ten times the price of the major options package and fifty times the destination charge. What was the base price of the car?

33. On the first of three tests, Juan scored 72 points. On the next test, he got a higher score. On the third test, his score was 1 more than on the second. His average on the three tests was 83. What were his grades on the second and third tests?

34. The perimeter of a rectangular lot is 260 m. The length exceeds the width by 20 m. Find the dimensions of the lot.

# 3-5 Equations Having the Variable in Both Sides

**Objective**   To solve equations having the variable in both sides.

The variable appears in both sides of the equation

$$7z = z - 54.$$

Are you allowed to transform the equation by subtracting $z$ from both sides? The answer is yes. Because variables represent numbers, you may transform an equation by adding a variable expression to each side or by subtracting a variable expression from each side.

**Example 1**   Solve $7z = z - 54$.

**Solution**
$$
\begin{aligned}
7z &= z - 54 \\
7z - z &= z - 54 - z \\
6z &= -54 \\
\frac{6z}{6} &= \frac{-54}{6} \\
z &= -9
\end{aligned}
$$

**Condensed Solution**

$$
\begin{aligned}
7z &= z - 54 \\
6z &= -54 \\
z &= -9
\end{aligned}
$$

*Check:*

$$
\begin{aligned}
7z &= z - 54 \\
7(-9) &\overset{?}{=} -9 - 54 \\
-63 &= -63 \quad \checkmark
\end{aligned}
$$

$\therefore$ the solution is $-9$.   **Answer**

It is possible that an equation may have *no* roots, or that it may be satisfied by *every* real number. Example 2 illustrates a situation in which an equation has no roots. Example 3 illustrates a situation in which an equation is satisfied by every real number.

**Example 2**   Solve $3(1 - r) + 5r = 2(r + 1)$.

**Solution**
$$
\begin{aligned}
3(1 - r) + 5r &= 2(r + 1) \\
3 - 3r + 5r &= 2r + 2 \\
3 + 2r &= 2r + 2 \\
3 + 2r - 2r &= 2r + 2 - 2r \\
3 &= 2
\end{aligned}
$$

Since the given equation is equivalent to the false statement, "$3 = 2$," it has no root.   **Answer**

It is customary to call the set with no members the **empty set,** or the **null set.** It is denoted by the symbol $\emptyset$. Thus, you may say that the solution set of the equation in Example 2 is $\emptyset$.

**Example 3** Solve $\frac{1}{3}(12x - 21) + 16 = 1 + 4(x + 2)$.

**Solution**     $\frac{1}{3}(12x - 21) + 16 = 1 + 4(x + 2)$

$$4x - 7 + 16 = 1 + 4x + 8$$
$$4x + 9 = 9 + 4x$$

The given equation is equivalent to $4x + 9 = 9 + 4x$, which is satisfied by every real number.

∴ the solution is the set of real numbers.  **Answer**

An equation that is true for every value of the variable(s) is called an **identity**. Thus, the equation in Example 3,

$$\frac{1}{3}(12x - 21) + 16 = 1 + 4(x + 2),$$

is an identity.

## Oral Exercises

**Solve. If the equation is an identity or if it has no root, state that fact.**

**1.** $4x = 3x + 5$

**2.** $2y + 9 = 3y$

**3.** $8r + 1 = 9r$

**4.** $2p - 1 = 3p$

**5.** $a + 4 = 1 + a$

**6.** $2b = 6 + 2b$

**7.** $3k = 2k + k$

**8.** $4c = c$

**9.** $3s = s - 2$

**10.** $4t + 1 = 4t + 3$

**11.** $2(v - 1) = 2v - 2$

**12.** $3(w + 1) = 2w$

## Written Exercises

**Solve each equation. If the equation is an identity or if it has no root, state that fact.**

A  **1.** $9n = 7n + 16$

**2.** $16m = 45 + 11m$

**3.** $y = 57 - 2y$

**4.** $2k = 90 - 8k$

**5.** $12v - 84 = 5v$

**6.** $4x + 49 = -3x$

**7.** $39q + 78 = 33q$

**8.** $61w - 56 = 54w$

**9.** $98 - 4b = -11b$

**10.** $126 - 13t = -19t$

**11.** $-7a = -12a - 65$

**12.** $-8y - 27 = -17y$

**13.** $9h + 4 = 6h - 2$

**14.** $5r - 9 = 2r + 12$

**15.** $2p - 7 = 7 + 2p$

**16.** $3 - d = 7d + 27$

**17.** $59 + x = 2 - 2x$

**18.** $5c + 1 = -1 + 5c$

**19.** $2(y - 8) = 3y$

**20.** $3(f + 7) = 2f$

**21.** $4w - 1 = 7(w + 2)$

**22.** $8v + 77 = 5(5 - v)$

**23.** $\frac{1}{3}(12 - 9n) = 4 - 3n$

**24.** $m - 6 = \frac{1}{2}(8 - 18m)$

**Solve each equation. If the equation is an identity or if it has no root, state that fact.**

**B**  **25.** $5(2 + n) = 3(n + 6)$

**26.** $3(30 + s) = 4(s + 19)$

**27.** $5u + 5(1 - u) = u + 8$

**28.** $2(g - 2) - 4 = 2(g - 3)$

**29.** $3(m + 5) - 6 = 3(m + 3)$

**30.** $3(2 + v) - 4v = v + 16$

**31.** $3(5t + 2) - t = 2(t - 3)$

**32.** $4(3y - 1) + 13 = 5y + 2$

**33.** $6r - 2(2 - r) = 4(2r - 1)$

**34.** $5x + 2(1 - x) = 2(2x - 1)$

**35.** $3 + 4(p + 2) = 2p + 3(p + 4)$

**36.** $4(a + 2) = 14 - 2(3 - 2a)$

**C**  **37.** $3x + 2[1 - 3(x + 2)] = 2x$

**38.** $2[5(w + 3) - (w + 1)] = 3(1 + w)$

**39.** $5(2m + 3) - (1 - 2m) = 2[3(3 + 2m) - (3 - m)]$

**40.** $3(r + 1) - [2(3 - 2r) - 3(3 - r)] = 2(r + 5) - 4$

## *Problems*

Solve.

**A**  **1.** Find a number that is 96 greater than its opposite.

**2.** Find a number that is 38 less than its opposite.

**3.** Find a number whose product with 9 is the same as its sum with 56.

**4.** Find a number that is 68 greater than three times its opposite.

**5.** Three times a number, decreased by 8, is the same as twice the number, increased by 15. Find the number.

**6.** Four times a number, increased by 25, is 13 less than six times the number. Find the number.

**7.** The sum of two numbers is 15. Three times one of the numbers is 11 less than five times the other. Find the numbers.

**8.** The difference of two integers is 9. Five times the smaller is 7 more than three times the larger. Find the integers.

**9.** The greater of two consecutive integers is 15 more than twice the lesser. Find the integers.

**10.** The greater of two consecutive even integers is 20 more than twice the lesser. Find the integers.

**11.** Dina has 6 steel balls of equal mass. If she puts 5 of them in one pan of a beam balance and one ball along with a mass of 100 g in the other pan, the pans balance each other. What is the mass of each steel ball?

**12.** Jon is three times as old as Cal, while Ron is 12 years older than Cal. If Jon and Ron are twins, how old is each of the three people?

**B** **13.** The lengths of the sides of a triangle are consecutive even integers. Find the length of the longest side if it is 14 units shorter than the perimeter.

**14.** The lengths of the sides of a triangle are consecutive odd integers. Find the length of the shortest side if the perimeter is 19 units shorter than four times the length of that side.

**15.** Jean Ackyroyd's starting salary is $18,000, with semi-annual raises of $750. Sue Bathgate's starting salary is $16,200, with semi-annual raises of $900. After how many years will the two women be earning the same salary?

**16.** An 800-liter tank is half full of water and is being filled with water pumped at the rate of 45 liters per minute from a full 940-liter tank. How long will it take before the two tanks contain the same amount of water?

**17.** Mary has $6 more than Frank. Together Mary and Frank have $90 more than Joe, who has half as much money as Frank. How much does Frank have?

**18.** A sofa costs $160 more to manufacture than a matching lounge chair. Three lounge chairs cost as much to manufacture as two sofas. How much does it cost to manufacture a lounge chair?

**C** **19.** Find four consecutive multiples of 4 such that twice the sum of the least and greatest exceeds three times the least by 32.

**20.** Find four consecutive multiples of 5 such that three times the sum of the two least exceeds twice the sum of the two greatest by 55.

## Computer Exercises
*For students with some programming experience*

Write a BASIC program to solve an equation of the form $AX + B = CX + D$, where the values of $A$, $B$, $C$, and $D$ are entered with INPUT statements. Be sure that the program works correctly for identities and for equations that have no solution. Use the program to solve the following equations.

**1.** $3x + 4 = 5x + 10$

**2.** $\frac{r}{2} + 1 = -2r + 11$

**3.** $4m - 7 = 3 + 4m$

**4.** $\frac{k}{2} + 5 = 5 + \frac{1}{2}k$

**5.** $3y - 7 = \frac{2}{3}y$

**6.** $a - 10 = -2a + 2$

# Self-Test 2

**Vocabulary**    empty set (p. 112)             identity (p. 113)
                      null set (p. 112)

1. In a 2-hour TV movie program, 9 times as many minutes were devoted to the movie as to commercials. How long did it take to show the movie?

**Obj. 3-4, p. 108**

**Solve.**

2. $3t - 7 = t + 11$            3. $2(1 - x) = 3(x + 9)$      **Obj. 3-5, p. 112**

4. In a baseball game, the Hawks had 3 more hits than the Eagles. If 3 times the number of hits by the Eagles was 8 greater than twice the number of hits by the Hawks, how many hits did each team make?

Check your answers with those at the back of the book.

## Historical Note / *Variables*

Until the sixteenth century, there was no symbolic convention for representing unknowns in equations. Unknown quantities were represented by words such as "heap," "root," or "thing." Occasionally the unknown quantity acted as the narrator of the problem, as was the case in Problem 36 of the Rhind mathematical papyrus: "I go three times, and my third and my fifth are then added to me. . . ." The Chinese used the position of rods on a computing board to represent unknown quantities. In India the names of various colors were used. Eventually, abbreviations and drawings of squares and cubes were used to symbolize unknowns.

    In the late sixteenth century, a lawyer and member of the Bretagne parliament, François Vieta (Viète), who enjoyed studying algebra during his leisure hours, wrote his most famous work, *In artem*. Vieta introduced vowels to represent unknowns and the use of consonants to represent constants. The later widespread adoption of algebraic symbols is largely due to the printing of Vieta's book. An English mathematician, Thomas Harriot, later adopted lower case letters to stand for variables. In 1637, René Descartes, a French mathematician, began using the final letters of the alphabet to represent the unknowns and the first letters of the alphabet to represent constant coefficients, thus giving his work a modern appearance. Compare, for example, the modern form of the equation

$$y^2 = cy - \frac{cx}{b}y + ay - ac$$

with the form that Descartes used:

$$yy \infty cy - \frac{cx}{b}y + ay - ac$$

# Computer Key-In

The program given below will compute the wages of employees when their hourly rates and the numbers of hours they worked are given.

Lines 70–130 form a FOR-NEXT loop. This kind of loop can be used when we know how many times we want to have a sequence of steps repeated. The steps between line 70 and line 130 will be repeated T times.

Line 80 will print only one question mark, but 3 values (for N, R, H) separated by commas must be INPUT.

In line 100, the symbol $<=$ means "less than or equal to." Line 110 will compute "overtime" pay—at time and a half for any time over 40 hours.

In line 120, the comma will cause the items to be spaced out across the line. In this case, the "first column" is blank.

```
10   PRINT "HOW MANY EMPLOYEES";
20   INPUT T
30   PRINT "FOR EACH EMPLOYEE:"
40   PRINT "INPUT EMPLOYEE ID NO.,";
50   PRINT " PAY/HOUR,"
60   PRINT "     NO. OF HOURS:"
70   FOR I=1 TO T
80   INPUT N,R,H
90   LET W=R*H
100  IF H <= 40 THEN 120
110  LET W=W+.5*R*(H-40)
120  PRINT " ","WAGES  = ";W
130  NEXT I
140  END
```

(If possible, save this program for use in the next computer section.)

## Exercises

**1.** Write out in words what happens in line 110.

**2.** RUN the program for three employees:

| ID NO. | WAGES PER HOUR | HOURS |
|---|---|---|
| 1234 | 11.50 | 37 |
| 3412 | 10 | 40 |
| 4321 | 12 | 42 |

**3.** RUN the program for these employees.

| ID NO. | WAGES PER HOUR | HOURS |
|---|---|---|
| 7890 | 9.75 | 38.5 |
| 9870 | 11.25 | 41.75 |
| 7809 | 10.85 | 40.25 |

# Extending Your Problem Solving Skills

## 3-6 Using Charts in Solving Problems

**Objective**  To arrange the facts of a problem in a chart.

Using a chart to organize the facts of a problem can be a helpful strategy in solving the problem. Charts are especially useful in solving problems about ages.

**Example**  Lisa is one third as old as her father. Next year their ages in years will total 50. How old is each now?

**Solution**

Step 1  The problem asks for the ages of Lisa and her father.

Step 2  Let $x$ = Lisa's age in years now.
Then $3x$ = father's age in years now.
Make a chart of the given facts.

|  | Age now | Age next year |
|--------|--------|--------|
| Lisa | $x$ | $x + 1$ |
| Father | $3x$ | $3x + 1$ |

Step 3  The only fact not recorded in the chart is that next year their ages will total 50. Use this fact to write an equation.

$$(x + 1) + (3x + 1) = 50$$

Step 4
$$(x + 1) + (3x + 1) = 50$$
$$4x + 2 = 50$$
$$4x = 48$$
$$x = 12$$
$$3x = 36$$

Step 5  Will the sum of Lisa's age next year and her father's age next year total 50?

$$(12 + 1) + (36 + 1) \stackrel{?}{=} 50$$
$$13 + 37 \stackrel{?}{=} 50$$
$$50 = 50 \quad \surd$$

∴ Lisa is 12 years old now and her father is 36 years old now.  **Answer**

# Oral Exercises

**Use the given information to complete each chart.**

**1.** Dana is 2 years younger than Gary.

|  | Age now | Age next year |
|---|---|---|
| Gary | $x$ | ? |
| Dana | ? | ? |

**2.** Mark is half as old as Sue.

|  | Age now | Age 3 years ago |
|---|---|---|
| Sue | $x$ | ? |
| Mark | ? | ? |

**3.** Tim was twice as old as Tom last year.

|  | Age last year | Age now |
|---|---|---|
| Tom | $y$ | ? |
| Tim | ? | ? |

**4.** A mat is 4 cm longer than it is wide. A second mat is 1 cm wider and 2 cm longer than the first.

|  | Length | Width |
|---|---|---|
| First mat | ? | $z$ |
| Second mat | ? | ? |

**5.** In a game played with white, blue, and red chips, one player had twice as many blue chips as white ones and 3 more red ones than blue ones. Each chip has the point value shown in the chart.

|  | Number | Point value of each chip | Total value of all chips of this kind |
|---|---|---|---|
| White | $w$ | 1 | $w$ |
| Blue | ? | 2 | ? |
| Red | ? | 5 | ? |

**6.** The ages in years of three sisters are consecutive odd integers.

|  | Age now | Age last year | Age 10 years from now |
|---|---|---|---|
| The youngest sister | ? | ? | ? |
| The middle sister | $m$ | ? | ? |
| The oldest sister | ? | ? | ? |

## Problems

**A**

1. Toby is 3 years older than Sarah. Last year their ages totaled 37. How old is each now?

2. Luisa is 5 years younger than José. Next year their ages will total 53. How old is each now?

3. Bob is 24 years younger than his father. In 2 years he will be half as old as his father. How old is each now?

4. Karl is seven times as old as Jane, but in six years he will be only three times as old. Find the age of each now.

5. Tom is 8 and his mother is 31. How long will it be before she is twice as old as he?

6. Bill Phipps is six times as old as his five-year-old niece. How long will it be before he is twice as old as she?

7. The length of a rectangle is 15 cm more than the width. A second rectangle whose perimeter is 72 cm is 5 cm wider but 2 cm shorter than the first rectangle. What are the dimensions of each rectangle?

8. The base of an isosceles triangle is 12 cm longer than each of its equal legs. A second isosceles triangle whose perimeter is 85 cm has a base that is 15 cm shorter than the base of the first triangle. Each of the equal legs of the second triangle is 8 cm longer than each leg of the first. How long are the three sides of each triangle?

9. Zelda Carter weighs 55 lb less than her husband. Their combined weight is 215 lb more than that of their daughter, who weighs half as much as her father. How much does Zelda Carter weigh?

10. Fran Massey earns three times as much as an actuary than she does as a writer. Her total income is $40,000 more than that of her brother, who earns only half as much as Fran does as an actuary. What is Fran's salary as an actuary?

**B**

11. Jack's age next year will be twice Jill's age last year. Their present ages total 45. How old is each now?

12. Al is $\frac{3}{4}$ as old as Ann. Six years ago Al was $\frac{1}{2}$ as old as Ann. How old is each now?

13. Susan is six years older than Ralph and Ralph is twice as old as Neil. Next year Susan's age will total the ages of Ralph and Neil. How old is each now?

14. Ruby is 6 years younger than Carlo, and the average of their ages is twice Ruby's age 5 years ago. How old are they?

15. George Washington was born eleven years before Thomas Jefferson. In 1770 Washington's age was three years more than seven times the age of Jefferson in 1748. How old was each man in 1750?

**16.** In one match Marcia scored three times as many points as Dina. In the next match, Marcia scored 7 fewer points than she did in the first match, while Dina earned 9 more than she did in the first match. If they tied in the second match, what were their scores in the first match?

**17.** Suppose that 9 servings of juice cost the same as 5 fruit cups. Suppose, also, that one fruit cup costs 50 cents more than one bowl of soup, while one bowl of soup costs 50 cents more than one serving of juice. What would be the cost of each item: serving of juice, fruit cup, bowl of soup?

**18.** The upper falls of Angel Falls, the highest waterfall on Earth, are 750 m higher than Niagara Falls. If each of the falls were 7 m lower, the upper Angel Falls would be sixteen times as high as Niagara Falls. How high is the upper Angel Falls? Niagara Falls?

**19.** One serving $\left(\frac{1}{2} \text{ cup}\right)$ of cooked green peas contains 45 more calories than 1 serving of cooked carrots and 50 more calories than 1 serving of cooked green beans. If 1 serving of cooked carrots and 3 servings of cooked green beans contain the same number of calories as 1 serving of cooked green peas, how many calories are there in 1 serving of cooked green peas?

**C**   **20.** Ann is 6 years older than Mary. She is also twice as old as Mary was when Ann was as old as Mary is now. How old is each now?

**21.** Two years ago, Paul was 7 times as old as Matt was. Two years from now, Paul will be 5 times as old as Matt will be. Find the present age of each.

**22.** For six consecutive years, a man's age was a multiple of his granddaughter's age. How old was each during the sixth year?

# *Challenge*

Ross Clevons received a license plate for his new car. He noted that all five digits were different and that if the plate was upside down his registration number would be increased by 7920. What was the number on the license plate?

# 3-7 Cost and Value Problems

**Objective**  To solve some problems involving cost and value.

The word problems in this section all involve cost, wages, and value, usually in terms of money. Organizing the given facts in a chart will help you to solve such word problems.

The following formulas will be useful in setting up your charts.

$$\text{Number} \times \text{price} = \text{cost}$$
$$\text{Hours worked} \times \text{wage per hour} = \text{income}$$
$$\text{Number of items} \times \text{value per item} = \text{total value}$$

**Example**  Roger paid 50 cents each for several programs for the football game. He sold all but 15 of them for $1 each, making a profit of $22.50. How many programs did he buy?

**Solution**

*Step 1*  The problem asks for the number of programs Roger bought.

*Step 2*  Let $x$ = number of programs Roger bought.
Then $x - 15$ = number of programs Roger sold.
Make a chart.

|        | Number | Unit Price | Cost = Number × Unit Price |
|--------|--------|------------|----------------------------|
| Bought | $x$    | 50         | $50x$                      |
| Sold   | $x - 15$ | 100      | $100(x - 15)$              |

*Step 3*  The only fact not recorded in the chart is the $22.50 profit. Use this fact to write an equation. (Since the prices are in cents, write the profit as 2250 cents.)

$$\text{Profit} = \text{Selling Cost} - \text{Buying Cost}$$
$$2250 = 100(x - 15) - 50x$$

*Step 4*  $2250 = 100x - 1500 - 50x$
$2250 = 50x - 1500$
$3750 = 50x$
$75 = x; \ x - 15 = 60$

*Step 5*  *Check:*  75 programs at 50 cents each cost Roger 3750 cents.
60 programs at 100 cents each brought in 6000 cents.
$\text{Profit} = 6000 - 3750 \overset{?}{=} 2250$
$2250 = 2250$  √

∴ Roger bought 75 programs.  *Answer*

# Problems

**Copy and complete each chart and then solve each problem.**

**A**  **1.** Lex spent $8.40 for several pencils costing 20 cents each and some notebooks costing $1.20 each. He bought 7 more pencils than notebooks. How many notebooks did he buy?

|  | Number | × Price = | Cost |
|---|---|---|---|
| Pencils | ? | ? | ? |
| Notebooks | $x$ | ? | ? |

**2.** Fritz makes $4 an hour working after school and $5 an hour working on Saturdays. Last week he made $52.50 working a total of 12 hours. How many hours did he work on Saturday?

|  | Hours worked | × Wage per hour = | Income |
|---|---|---|---|
| Saturdays | $s$ | ? | ? |
| Weekdays | ? | ? | ? |

**3.** Della has some nickels, dimes, and quarters worth $6.10. She has twice as many dimes as quarters and 50 coins in all. How many of each kind of coin has she?

|  | Number | × Value of coin = | Total value |
|---|---|---|---|
| Nickels | ? | ? | ? |
| Dimes | ? | ? | ? |
| Quarters | $q$ | ? | ? |

**4.** Ruth purchases some one-cent stamps, some fifteen-cent stamps, and some twenty-cent stamps for $5. There are three times as many one-cent stamps as twenty-cent stamps, and 8 fewer twenty-cent stamps than fifteen-cent stamps. How many stamps in all does she buy?

|  | Number | × Value of stamp = | Total value |
|---|---|---|---|
| One-cent | ? | ? | ? |
| Fifteen-cent | ? | ? | ? |
| Twenty-cent | $t$ | ? | ? |

5. Each of the 24 members of the Boosters' Club bought either a pennant or a cap at the football game. The pennants were $1.25 each and the caps were $1.50 each. If the total bill was $34, how many people bought pennants?

6. Adult tickets for the senior class play were $4 each and student tickets were $2. A total of 1250 tickets worth $3400 were sold. How many student tickets were sold?

7. A plumber makes $4.50 per hour more than an apprentice. During an 8 hour day, their earnings total $284. How much does each make per hour?

8. Sixty-five members of the Medical Society attended the annual dinner of the society. An equal number of nonmembers also attended. Tickets for nonmembers cost $10 more than for members. If ticket sales totaled $4095, how much did each ticket cost?

**B** 9. I have 40 coins, all dimes, nickels, and quarters, worth $4.05. I have 7 more nickels than dimes. How many quarters do I have?

10. Lizzie bought several apples at 20 cents each, ate two of them, and sold the rest for 30 cents each. She made a profit of $2.20. How many did she buy?

11. Mercedes had a total of 37 nickels, dimes, and quarters. She had 3 fewer dimes than nickels and 4 more quarters than nickels. How much money did she have?

12. Gunnar bought 47 stamps. He bought 5 more ten-cent stamps than fifteen-cent stamps and 6 fewer twenty-cent stamps than fifteen-cent stamps. How much did he pay for the stamps?

13. Roger claims: "I have $20 in quarters, half-dollars, and one-dollar bills. I have twice as many quarters as half-dollars, and half as many one-dollar bills as half-dollars." Explain why Roger must be wrong.

14. Can 46 pennies and nickels have a total value of a dollar? Justify your answer.

15. In a collection of coins worth $9.13, there are twice as many dimes as quarters, four more nickels than dimes, and twice as many pennies as nickels. How many of each kind of coin are in the collection?

**C** 16. Nadia has seven more nickels than Dean has dimes. If Dean gives Nadia four of his dimes, then Dean will have the same value of money as Nadia. How much money do they have together? (Assume that Nadia has only nickels and Dean has only dimes.)

17. Ned has some nickels, Dick has some dimes, and Quincy has some quarters. Dick has five more dimes than Quincy has quarters. If Ned gives Dick a nickel, Dick gives Quincy a dime, and Quincy gives Ned a quarter, they will all have the same value of money. How many coins did each have originally?

Jane has a total of 25 coins, some of which are nickels and the rest, dimes.

**1.** Using a FOR . . . NEXT loop, write a BASIC program to display in chart form every possible combination of nickels and dimes. Have the program give the value of the coins in each case.

**2.** Modify the program in Exercise 1 so that Jane has a total of $k$ coins, where the value of $k$ is entered with an INPUT statement.

## Biographical Note / *Maria Mitchell*

Maria Mitchell (1818–1889) was the first woman in the United States to be recognized for her work in astronomy. She was born on Nantucket, an island located off the southern coast of Massachusetts. As a child, Mitchell helped her father with astronomical calculations that he needed to rate the chronometers of whaling ships.

In 1836 Mitchell became the librarian of the Nantucket Atheneum. While there, she continued her studies in mathematics and astronomy and taught herself German.

In 1831 the king of Denmark had offered a gold medal to anyone who could discover a previously unknown comet. On October 1, 1847, while conducting telescopic observations, Mitchell discovered a new comet that was later named for her. She was awarded the medal and so gained worldwide recognition. The following year she became the first woman elected to the American Academy of Arts and Sciences. She was later elected to the American Association for the Advancement of Science.

In 1865 she became the first professor of astronomy and the director of the observatory at Vassar College. While at Vassar, she continued to study sunspots and solar eclipses and observed changes on the surfaces of the planets and their moons. In 1869 she was elected to the American Philosophical Society for her scientific achievements, the first woman accorded this honor. Mitchell was also a founder of the American Association for the Advancement of Women, serving as its president. In this office she worked for the recognition of the scientific abilities of women.

# 3-8 Proving Statements

**Objective** To prove statements in algebra.

Many number properties and rules have been stated earlier in this book. Some of these are axioms, that is, statements *assumed* to be true. Others are theorems. A **theorem** is a statement that is *shown* to be true by using axioms, definitions, and other proved theorems in a logical development.

Logical reasoning using definitions, given facts, and axioms to show a theorem is true is called a **proof.** The following example shows how a theorem is proved in algebra.

**Example 1** Prove: For all real numbers $a$ and $b$, $(a + b) - b = a$.

**Proof**

| STATEMENTS | REASONS |
|---|---|
| 1. $(a + b) - b = (a + b) + (-b)$ | 1. Definition of subtraction |
| 2. $(a + b) + (-b) = a + [b + (-b)]$ | 2. Associative axiom for addition |
| 3. $b + (-b) = 0$ | 3. Axiom of opposites |
| 4. $a + [b + (-b)] = a + 0$ | 4. Substitution principle |
| 5. $a + 0 = a$ | 5. Identity axiom for addition |
| 6. $(a + b) - b = a$ | 6. Transitive property of equality |

Generally, a shortened form of proof is given, in which only the *key reasons* are stated. (The substitution principle and axioms of equality are usually not stated.)

The proof shown in the example above may be shortened to the four steps shown below.

| STATEMENTS | REASONS |
|---|---|
| 1. $(a + b) - b = (a + b) + (-b)$ | 1. Definition of subtraction |
| 2. $\quad\quad = a + [b + (-b)]$ | 2. Associative axiom for addition |
| 3. $\quad\quad = a + 0$ | 3. Axiom of opposites |
| 4. $\quad\quad = a$ | 4. Identity axiom for addition |

**Example 2** Prove the property of the reciprocal of a product, given on page 77: For all real numbers $a$ and $b$ such that $a \neq 0$ and $b \neq 0$, $\dfrac{1}{ab} = \dfrac{1}{a} \cdot \dfrac{1}{b}$.

**Proof** Since $\dfrac{1}{ab}$ is the reciprocal of $ab$, we can prove that

$\dfrac{1}{ab} = \dfrac{1}{a} \cdot \dfrac{1}{b}$ by showing that the product of $ab$ and $\dfrac{1}{a} \cdot \dfrac{1}{b}$ is 1:

| STATEMENTS | REASONS |
|---|---|
| 1. $(ab)\left(\dfrac{1}{a}\cdot\dfrac{1}{b}\right)=\left(a\cdot\dfrac{1}{a}\right)\left(b\cdot\dfrac{1}{b}\right)$ | 1. Commutative and associative axioms for multiplication |
| 2. $\qquad\qquad =1\cdot 1$ | 2. Axiom of reciprocals for multiplication |
| 3. $\qquad\qquad =1$ | 3. Identity axiom for multiplication |

Once a theorem has been proved, it can be used as a reason in other proofs.

You may refer to the Chapter Summary on pages 84–85 for listings of axioms and theorems that you can use as reasons in your proofs in the following exercises.

## Oral Exercises

**State the missing reasons.**

**1.** Prove the *addition property of equality:*
If $a = b$, then $a + c = b + c$. Also, $c + a = c + b$.

Proof:

| | |
|---|---|
| 1. $a + c = a + c$ | 1. ___?___ |
| 2. $a = b$ | 2. Given |
| 3. $a + c = b + c$ | 3. ___?___ |
| 4. $a + c = c + a$; | 4. ___?___ |
| $\quad b + c = c + b$ | |
| 5. $c + a = c + b$ | 5. ___?___ |

**2.** Prove: If $a = b$, then $-a = -b$.

Proof:

| | |
|---|---|
| 1. $a = b$ | 1. Given |
| 2. $-a$ and $-b$ are unique real numbers. | 2. ___?___ |
| 3. $a + (-b) = b + (-b)$ | 3. Addition property of equality |
| 4. $b + (-b) = 0$ | 4. ___?___ |
| 5. $a + (-b) = 0$ | 5. ___?___ |
| 6. $-a + [a + (-b)] = -a + 0$ | 6. ___?___ |
| 7. $(-a + a) + (-b) = -a + 0$ | 7. ___?___ |
| 8. $\qquad 0 + (-b) = -a + 0$ | 8. ___?___ |
| 9. $\qquad\qquad -b = -a$ | 9. ___?___ |
| 10. $\qquad\qquad -a = -b$ | 10. ___?___ |

## Written Exercises

**Write the missing reasons in Exercises 1–6. Assume that each variable represents any real number, except as noted.**

**A**  **1. a.** Prove: If $b \neq 0$, then $\frac{1}{b}(ba) = a$.

Proof: 1. $\frac{1}{b}(ba) = \left(\frac{1}{b} \cdot b\right)a$    1.  $?$

     2.      $= 1 \cdot a$      2.  $?$

     3.      $= a$      3.  $?$

**b.** From step 3 prove that $(ab)\frac{1}{b} = a$.

Proof: 3. $\frac{1}{b}(ba) = a$     (above)

     4. $(ba)\frac{1}{b} = a$     4.  $?$

     5. $(ab)\frac{1}{b} = a$     5.  $?$

$\therefore$ if $b \neq 0$, $\frac{1}{b}(ba) = a$ and $(ab)\frac{1}{b} = a$.

**2.** Prove the *multiplication property of equality:*

If $a = b$, then $ca = cb$ and $ac = bc$.

Proof: 1. $ca = ca$     1.  $?$

     2. $a = b$     2. Given

     3. $ca = cb$     3.  $?$

     4. $ca = ac$;     4.  $?$

       $cb = bc$

     5. $ac = bc$     5.  $?$

**3.** Prove: If $a + c = b + c$, then $a = b$.

Proof: 1.         $a + c = b + c$     1. Given

     2. $(a + c) + (-c) = (b + c) + (-c)$     2.  $?$

     3.     $(a + c) - c = (b + c) - c$     3.  $?$

     4.              $a = b$     4.  $?$

**4.** Prove: If $ac = bc$ and $c \neq 0$, then $a = b$.

Proof: 1.      $ac = bc$     1. Given

     2. $(ac) \cdot \frac{1}{c} = (bc) \cdot \frac{1}{c}$     2.  $?$

     3.     $a = b$     3.  $?$

**B**  **5.** Prove: $-(-a - b) = a + b$

Proof: 1. $-(-a - b) = -[-a + (-b)]$     1.  $?$

     2.            $= -(-a) + [-(-b)]$     2.  $?$

     3.            $= a + b$     3.  $?$

**6.** Prove: $-(a - b) = b - a$.

Proof: 1. $-(a - b) = -[a + (-b)]$     1. ___?___
     2.              $= -a + [-(-b)]$    2. ___?___
     3.              $= -a + b$         3. ___?___
     4.              $= b + (-a)$       4. ___?___
     5.              $= b - a$         5. ___?___

**Write proofs, including statements and reasons, for Exercises 7–12.**

**7.** Prove: If $a$ is any nonzero real number, then $\dfrac{a}{a} = 1$.

**8.** Prove: If $a \neq 0$ and $b \neq 0$, then $\dfrac{1}{\frac{a}{b}} = \dfrac{b}{a}$. $\left(\text{Hint: Show that } \dfrac{a}{b} \cdot \dfrac{b}{a} = 1.\right)$

**9.** Prove: If $a = b$ and $c \neq 0$, then $\dfrac{a}{c} = \dfrac{b}{c}$.

**10.** Prove: If $c \neq 0$ and $\dfrac{a}{c} = \dfrac{b}{c}$, then $a = b$.

**C**   **11.** Prove: If $a \neq 0$ and $b \neq 0$, then $\dfrac{a + b}{ab} = \dfrac{1}{a} + \dfrac{1}{b}$.

**12.** Prove: $a + b + [(-a) + (-b)] = 0$

# Application / Consumer Credit

A car is one of the most important and expensive purchases a person may make. Many people do not have the money to pay for a car with cash. Instead, they pay a percentage of the cash price as a down payment and borrow the rest. The car buyer must pay the lender the amount of money borrowed (principal) plus interest. Often the buyer chooses to pay the lender over a period of two, three, or four years. The lender calculates the amount the buyer will owe in interest and then adds it to the principal. By dividing this total by the number of months, the amount of each monthly payment can be calculated.

    Suppose you want to purchase a car. You see an advertisement in the newspaper such as the following:

ONLY $3600         USED CAR

           :
           :

just $630 down and small monthly payments of $95 each month for 36 months.

How do you determine the total amount you must pay for the car and the amount of interest you are being charged?

***Example 1*** For the car on the previous page, find the total amount of the down payment and the monthly payments. Calculate the amount of interest.

***Solution*** The total amount is the sum of the down payment ($630) and the monthly payments (36 × $95 = $3420). Thus, the total amount is $4050. Subtracting the $3600 cash price from $4050 gives the amount of interest, $450.

Many stores, such as department stores, allow customers to purchase items on credit, that is, to "charge" them. If an item is not paid for within a specified period (often a month), the customer must pay a *finance charge* (interest) in addition to the purchase price. There are several common methods for calculating finance charges. One of the simpler methods is to take a fixed percent of the total amount that a customer owes at the end of a monthly billing period. This amount is called the *unpaid balance.*

***Example 2*** The previous balance of a customer's charge account is $56.32. If a payment of $10 is made, what will be the finance charge owed if the interest rate is $1\frac{1}{2}$% per month?

***Solution*** The balance after the payment is $46.32. At $1\frac{1}{2}$% interest, there is a finance charge of 0.015 × 46.32 = $.69.

## Exercises

1. The previous balance of a charge account is $185. If a payment of $25 is made, what will be the finance charge if the interest rate is $1\frac{1}{2}$% per month?

2. If a payment of $45 is made on a charge account with a balance of $125, what will be the finance charge owed if the interest rate is 1.65%?

3. A charge account has charges totaling $60.40. If a payment of $15 is made, what finance charge will be added if the rate of interest is $1\frac{1}{2}$%?

4. If a payment of $30 is made on the account in Exercise 3, what is the finance charge?

Find the total amount paid on each of the cars below. Then find the amount of interest the buyer would be paying.

5. _____
ONLY $3000          USED CAR

⋮

just $600 down and $117.50 per month over the next two years.

6. _____
ONLY $5346          USED CAR

⋮

just $540 down and $150 per month for the next 36 months.

# Self-Test 3

**Vocabulary**      theorem (p. 126)                     proof (p. 126)

1. Kay is 5 years younger than Sid. Make a chart showing their ages now, 2 years ago, and 3 years from now.

Obj. 3-6, p. 118

2. At the beginning of the year, Marcia had 3 times as much money in her savings account as Dora. During the year Dora saved $1400 more, while Marcia increased her savings by $860. At the end of the year, Marcia had twice as much money in her account as Dora. Not including interest earned during the year, how much was in each account at the end of the year?

3. Will has 4 times as many dimes as quarters and twice as many nickels as dimes. In all he has $25.20. How many dimes has he?

Obj. 3-7, p. 122

4. Write the missing reasons.

Obj. 3-8, p. 126

$$
\begin{array}{lll}
1. & -a + (a + b) = (-a + a) + b & 1. \underline{\ ?\ } \\
2. & \phantom{-a + (a + b)} = 0 + b & 2. \underline{\ ?\ } \\
3. & \phantom{-a + (a + b)} = b & 3. \underline{\ ?\ }
\end{array}
$$

Check your answers with those at the back of the book.

# Chapter Summary

1. The addition, subtraction, multiplication, and division properties of equality guarantee that:
   a. Adding the same real number to, or subtracting the same real number from, equal numbers gives equal results.
   b. Multiplying or dividing equal numbers by the same nonzero number gives equal results.

2. Transforming an equation by substitution, or by addition or subtraction, or by multiplication or division (not by zero) produces an equivalent equation. These transformations are used in solving equations.

3. Inverse operations are used in solving equations.

4. Equations can be used to solve word problems. Organizing the facts of a word problem in a chart is often helpful. Charts can be used to solve problems about ages, costs, and values.

5. The structure of algebra is built up of axioms and definitions and of theorems proved by using the axioms and definitions in a logical development.

# Chapter Review

**Give the letter of the correct answer.**

1. Solve $15 = 17 + x$.

   **a.** $-2$      **b.** $-32$      **c.** $32$      **d.** $2$      3-1

2. Solve $f - 17 = |6 - 25|$.

   **a.** $14$      **b.** $2$      **c.** $48$      **d.** $36$

3. Solve $\frac{1}{7}x = 3$.

   **a.** $2\frac{6}{7}$      **b.** $\frac{3}{7}$      **c.** $21$      **d.** $3\frac{1}{7}$      3-2

4. Solve $-1 = 3k$.

   **a.** $4$      **b.** $2$      **c.** $-3$      **d.** $-\frac{1}{3}$

5. Solve $\frac{x}{3} - 3 = -3$.

   **a.** $0$      **b.** $-18$      **c.** $18$      **d.** $2$      3-3

6. Solve $b - 3b = 24$.

   **a.** $-8$      **b.** $-12$      **c.** $12$      **d.** $-6$

7. During an 8-hour day, a veterinarian spent twice as much time tending animals at her clinic as she did making house calls. If she spent one hour of the day eating lunch, how many hours did she spend making house calls?      3-4

   **a.** $3\frac{1}{2}$ hours      **b.** $2\frac{2}{3}$ hours      **c.** 2 hours      **d.** $2\frac{1}{3}$ hours

8. Solve the equation $2m = 1 - m$.      3-5

   **a.** $\frac{1}{3}$      **b.** $2$      **c.** $1$      **d.** $3$

9. Solve the equation $3w - 13 = \frac{1}{4}(52 - 12w)$.

   **a.** $4\frac{1}{3}$      **b.** $-1$      **c.** no solution      **d.** identity

10. Courtney is four years older than Naomi. Fourteen years ago she was twice as old as Naomi. How old is Courtney now?      3-6
    **a.** 18 years old      **b.** 16 years old      **c.** 22 years old      **d.** 20 years old

11. Chase worked a total of 10 hours last week. He was paid $4.50 an hour to do yardwork and $5.50 an hour to work at a local supermarket. If he earned a total of $51, how many hours did he spend doing yardwork?      3-7
    **a.** 6 hours      **b.** 4 hours      **c.** 9.6 hours      **d.** 5 hours

12. Which of the following axioms should be given as the reason for the statement $a(bc) = a(cb)$?      3-8
    **a.** Distributive axiom      **b.** Associative axiom for multiplication
    **c.** Axiom of opposites      **d.** Commutative axiom for multiplication

# Chapter Test

**Solve.**

**1.** $a - 65 = -17$  | **2.** $-73 = 13 - h$ | 3-1
**3.** $c + 51 = |-38|$ | **4.** $87 - k = -64$

**Solve.**

**5.** $9 = \dfrac{c}{-18}$ | **6.** $-19v = -114$ | 3-2

**7.** $-144 = 16e$ | **8.** $-\dfrac{1}{11}x = -99$

**Solve.**

**9.** $13z - 65z = 0$ | **10.** $110 = -7 + 9t$ | 3-3

**11.** $\dfrac{3}{5}x + 90 = 0$ | **12.** $-\dfrac{7}{8}(w - 16) = 70$

**13.** Erica's teacher gave 4.5 points for each question answered correctly on a test. Erica received 15 points for correctly answering a bonus question. If she received a score of 87 points on the test, how many questions, not including the bonus question, did Erica answer correctly? 3-4

**Solve each equation. If the equation is an identity or if it has no root, state that fact.**

**14.** $7(a - 6) = -3 + 6a$ | **15.** $6(m - 1) = 6(m + 3)$ | 3-5

**16.** Twice a number increased by 51 is the same as the opposite of the number. Find the number.

**17.** Marlowe is half as old as Jean. Eight years from now he will be $\dfrac{3}{4}$ as old as Jean. How old is each now? 3-6

**18.** After delivering her newspapers, Vanessa noticed that she had 5 fewer quarters than dimes. Her dimes and quarters totaled $1.55. How many quarters did she have? 3-7

**19.** Write the missing reasons. 3-8

| 1. | $0 = 0 + 0$ | 1. __?__ |
| 2. | $a \cdot 0 = a(0 + 0)$ | 2. __?__ |
| 3. | $a \cdot 0 = a \cdot 0 + a \cdot 0$ | 3. __?__ |
| 4. | But $a \cdot 0 = a \cdot 0 + 0$ | 4. Identity axiom for addition |
| 5. | $\therefore a \cdot 0 + a \cdot 0 = a \cdot 0 + 0$ | 5. __?__ |
| 6. | $a \cdot 0 = 0$ | 6. __?__ |
| 7. | $0 \cdot a = 0$ | 7. __?__ |

*Solving Equations and Problems*    **133**

# Cumulative Review (Chapters 1–3)

**Simplify.**

**1.** $34 - 3(22 \div 2)$

**2.** $\dfrac{56 \div 7}{16}$

**3.** $48 \div (9 + 3)$

**4.** $|-21| - |-14|$

**5.** $51 - [25 \div 5]$

**6.** $48 \div 3 + 7(3)$

**7.** $-55 - (-42 + 7)$

**8.** $-22 + 31 + (-44) + 50$

**9.** $5\frac{3}{5} - 2\frac{3}{4} + 14\frac{2}{5}$

**10.** $-3.8 + 2.9 - 11.7$

**11.** $9 + x - (5 - x) - 6$

**12.** $4(x + 3y) - 3(x - 4y)$

**13.** $-5(42)\left(-\frac{2}{5}\right)\left(-\frac{1}{3}\right)$

**14.** $-5(-a - b) + 5(a + b)$

**15.** $\dfrac{144xy}{6x},\ x \neq 0$

**Evaluate each expression if $p = -3$, $q = 1$, $r = 0$, and $s = \dfrac{1}{2}$.**

**16.** $r - |p - q|$

**17.** $-\dfrac{p - q}{s}$

**18.** $-3(p + q)$

**19.** $\dfrac{-p + 2r - q}{r - 2s}$

**State the coordinate of the given point.**

**20.** $G$      **21.** $B$      **22.** $L$      **23.** $C$      **24.** $E$      **25.** $H$

**Solve. If the equation is an identity or has no solution, state that fact.**

**26.** $|x| = 5$

**27.** $|y| + 5 = 3$

**28.** $x + 7 = 12$

**29.** $z + 1 = -3$

**30.** $t + 4 = |-11|$

**31.** $(x - 3) + 17 = 30$

**32.** $-\dfrac{a}{3} = 14$

**33.** $9 = \dfrac{1}{2}q$

**34.** $2a + 5 = -1$

**35.** $\dfrac{1}{2}y - 3 = 9$

**36.** $16 = \dfrac{3}{4}k + 1$

**37.** $5(z - 3) = 40$

**38.** $5y - 2 = 7y + 8$

**39.** $9(2 - b) = b$

**40.** $6(3 - 4t) = -12\left(2t - \dfrac{3}{2}\right)$

**Solve.**

**41.** Grace is 3 years younger than $\frac{1}{4}$ of her father's age. The total of their ages is 42. How old is Grace's father?

**42.** Find three consecutive integers whose sum is 72.

**43.** Myron has 60 quarters and dimes. He has four times as many dimes as quarters. How much money does he have?

**44.** Leslie has 20 quarters and dimes. If she had as many dimes as she has quarters and as many quarters as she has dimes, she would have 30 cents less. How many of each coin does she have?

# Maintaining Skills

**Express each fraction as a mixed number.**

**Example 1** $\frac{35}{13}$     **Solution** $13\overline{)35}$  $\frac{35}{13} = 2\frac{9}{13}$
$\phantom{13\overline{)}}\frac{26}{\phantom{0}9}$

1. $\frac{25}{12}$

2. $\frac{45}{6}$

3. $\frac{78}{15}$

4. $\frac{86}{20}$

5. $\frac{91}{12}$

6. $\frac{83}{7}$

7. $\frac{111}{12}$

8. $\frac{115}{13}$

**Express each mixed number as a fraction.**

**Example 2** $5\frac{2}{5}$     **Solution** $5\frac{2}{5} = 5 + \frac{2}{5} = \frac{25}{5} + \frac{2}{5} = \frac{27}{5}$

9. $4\frac{1}{6}$

10. $8\frac{3}{5}$

11. $2\frac{7}{9}$

12. $12\frac{3}{4}$

13. $3\frac{8}{13}$

14. $17\frac{1}{3}$

15. $9\frac{11}{12}$

16. $10\frac{7}{8}$

**Perform the indicated operations. Express the answers in simplest form.**

**Example 3** $8\frac{2}{3} + 7\frac{5}{6}$     **Solution** $8\frac{2}{3} + 7\frac{5}{6} = \frac{26}{3} + \frac{47}{6}$
$$= \frac{52}{6} + \frac{47}{6} = \frac{99}{6} = \frac{33}{2}, \text{ or } 16\frac{1}{2}$$

**Example 4** $3\frac{1}{3} \div 7\frac{1}{2}$     **Solution** $3\frac{1}{3} \div 7\frac{1}{2} = \frac{10}{3} \div \frac{15}{2}$
$$= \frac{\overset{2}{\cancel{10}}}{3} \times \frac{2}{\underset{3}{\cancel{15}}} = \frac{4}{9}$$

17. $8\frac{7}{15} + 9\frac{11}{15}$

18. $5\frac{7}{9} - 6\frac{4}{9}$

19. $7\frac{1}{3} \times \left(-\frac{1}{7}\right)$

20. $4\frac{2}{5} \div 2\frac{1}{5}$

21. $10\frac{1}{5} \div 3\frac{2}{5}$

22. $20\frac{5}{13} + 8\frac{4}{5}$

23. $6\frac{5}{8} - 3\frac{2}{5}$

24. $6\frac{3}{5} \div 2\frac{3}{4}$

25. $12\frac{9}{10} - 8\frac{3}{5}$

26. $-9\frac{1}{2} + \left(-13\frac{2}{5}\right)$

27. $11\frac{4}{7} + 10\frac{1}{5}$

28. $8\frac{5}{6} \div 6\frac{5}{8}$

29. $4\frac{10}{11} - 7\frac{1}{2}$

30. $12\frac{3}{20} \times 1\frac{5}{9}$

31. $9\frac{5}{9} - 8\frac{1}{4}$

32. $3\frac{9}{10} \times 7\frac{1}{13}$

33. $-5\frac{2}{3} \div 3\frac{1}{2}$

34. $5\frac{5}{9} \times 4\frac{1}{2}$

35. $17\frac{3}{4} + 8\frac{1}{3}$

36. $10\frac{5}{6} \times 3\frac{4}{5}$

# 4 Polynomials

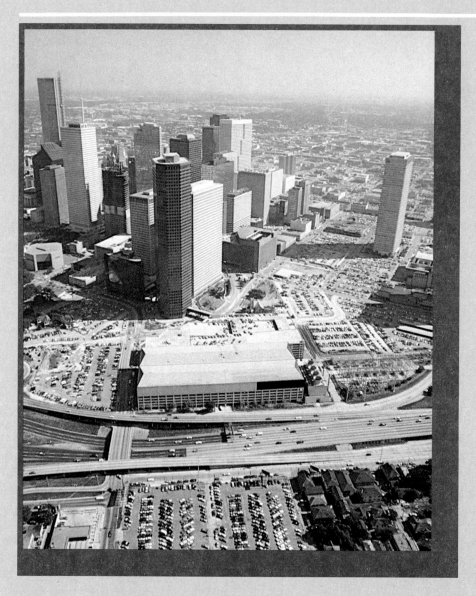

City planners use equations that contain exponents to project population growth in rapidly growing cities like Houston, Texas.

# Addition and Subtraction

## 4-1 Exponents

**Objective**   To write and simplify exponential expressions.

The number 9 can be written as

$$3 \times 3 \quad \text{or} \quad 3^2$$

(read "three to the second power" or "three squared"), and is called a *power* of 3. The numbers 27 and 81 are also powers of 3, since 27 can be written as

$$3 \times 3 \times 3 \quad \text{or} \quad 3^3$$

(read "three to the third power" or "three cubed"), and 81 can be written as

$$3 \times 3 \times 3 \times 3 \quad \text{or} \quad 3^4$$

(read "three to the fourth power").

In general, if $b$ is any real number and $n$ is any positive integer, the **$n$th power of $b$** is written $b^n$ and is defined as follows:

$$b^n = \underbrace{b \cdot b \cdot b \cdot \, \cdots \, \cdot b}_{n \text{ factors}}$$

In $b^n$, $b$ is called the **base** and the small raised symbol $^n$ is called the **exponent.**

$$\text{Exponent} \longrightarrow b^n = \text{the } n\text{th power of } b \longleftarrow \text{Base}$$

The exponent indicates the number of times the base occurs as a factor.

**Example 1**   Express each of the following using exponents.

      **a.** $5 \times 5 \times 5 \times 5 \times 5 \times 5 \times 5$

      **b.** $8 \times 8 \times 8 \times 8 \times 8 \times 8 \times 8 \times 8 \times 8$

      **c.** $11 \times 11 \times 11 \times 11 \times 11 \times 11 \times 11 \times 11 \times 11 \times 11$

**Solution**   **a.** $5^7$   **b.** $8^9$   **c.** $11^{10}$

Powers of $b$ can be written in **factored form** or in **exponential form** as shown below:

|  | Factored form | Exponential form |  |
|---|---|---|---|
| First power of $b$: | $b$ | $b^1$ | (read "$b$ to the first power." The exponent 1 is usually not written.) |
| Second power of $b$: | $b \cdot b$ | $b^2$ | (read "$b$ to the second power" or "$b$ squared," or "the square of $b$") |
| Third power of $b$: | $b \cdot b \cdot b$ | $b^3$ | (read "$b$ to the third power" or "$b$ cubed," or "the cube of $b$") |
| Fourth power of $b$: | $b \cdot b \cdot b \cdot b$ | $b^4$ | (read "$b$ to the fourth power" or "$b$ to the fourth") |

**Example 2**  Evaluate $x^3$ if $x = -2$.

**Solution**  Replace $x$ with $-2$, and simplify the result.

$$x^3 = (-2)^3 = (-2)(-2)(-2) = -8$$

The following examples show that you must use care when an expression contains both parentheses and exponents.

| | |
|---|---|
| $2x^3$ means $2(x \cdot x \cdot x)$. | 3 is the exponent of the base $x$. |
| $(2x)^3$ means $(2x)(2x)(2x)$. | 3 is the exponent of the base $2x$. |
| $-3^4$ means $-(3 \cdot 3 \cdot 3 \cdot 3)$, or $-81$. | 4 is the exponent of the base 3. |
| $(-3)^4$ means $(-3)(-3)(-3)(-3)$, or $81$. | 4 is the exponent of the base $(-3)$. |
| $(1 + 6)^2$ means $(1 + 6)(1 + 6)$, or $49$. | 2 is the exponent of the base $(1 + 6)$. |
| $1 + 6^2$ means $1 + 6 \cdot 6$, or $37$. | 2 is the exponent of the base 6. |

The following steps are used to simplify numerical expressions that contain powers.

---

### Summary of Order of Operations

1. First simplify expressions within grouping symbols.

2. Then simplify powers.

3. Then simplify products and quotients in order from left to right.

4. Then simplify sums and differences in order from left to right.

---

**Example 3** Evaluate $\dfrac{(x+1)^3}{9} + 5(x-8)^2 - 1$ if $x = 2$.

**Solution**   Replace $x$ with $2$ and simplify the result.

$$\dfrac{(x+1)^3}{9} + 5(x-8)^2 - 1 = \dfrac{(2+1)^3}{9} + 5(2-8)^2 - 1$$
$$= \dfrac{3^3}{9} + 5(-6)^2 - 1$$
$$= \dfrac{27}{9} + 5(36) - 1$$
$$= 3 + 180 - 1$$
$$= 182$$

## Oral Exercises

**Simplify.**

**1.** $5^2$      **2.** $5^3$      **3.** $4 \cdot 5^2$      **4.** $(4 \cdot 5)^2$

**5.** $(1 + 5)^2$      **6.** $1 + 5^2$      **7.** $(-2)^4$      **8.** $-2^4$

**9.** An even power of a negative number is a __?__ number.

**10.** An odd power of a negative number is a __?__ number.

**Write each expression in exponential form.**

**11.** $y \cdot y \cdot y \cdot y$      **12.** $x \cdot x \cdot x \cdot x \cdot x$      **13.** $a \cdot a \cdot b$      **14.** $a \cdot b \cdot a$

**15.** $3 \cdot y \cdot 2 \cdot y$      **16.** $y \cdot 3 \cdot 2 \cdot y$      **17.** $-p \cdot p$      **18.** $(-p)(-p)$

**19.** $z \cdot z \cdot z \cdot a \cdot a$      **20.** $(-3)(-5) \cdot x \cdot x$      **21.** $c \cdot 4 \cdot c \cdot 3 \cdot d$      **22.** $a \cdot y \cdot y \cdot a \cdot y \cdot c$

**Evaluate if $a = 2$ and $b = 3$.**

**23.** $ab^2$      **24.** $(ab)^2$      **25.** $(a+b)^2$      **26.** $a + b^2$

**27.** $a - b^3$      **28.** $(a-b)^3$      **29.** $a^4 - b^4$      **30.** $(a-b)^4$

**31.** $a^2 - b^2$      **32.** $(a-b)^2$      **33.** $a^3 + b^3$      **34.** $(a+b)^3$

**35.** Study the figures below. Explain why the second and third powers of $b$ are called "$b$ squared" and "$b$ cubed."

 Area = __?__       Volume = __?__

## Written Exercises

**Write each expression in exponential form.**

A  1. $a \cdot a \cdot a \cdot a \cdot a$  2. $x \cdot x \cdot x \cdot x \cdot x \cdot x$  3. $5 \cdot y \cdot y \cdot y$  4. $4 \cdot y \cdot y \cdot 4$

   5. $-8 \cdot x \cdot x$  6. $x(-8)x$  7. $(-7)(x)(x)$  8. $x(-7)x$

   9. $x$ plus the square of $y$  10. The cube of $-4y$

   11. The quantity $(x + y)$ squared  12. $-4$ times the cube of $y$

   13. One half the sixth power of $t$  14. The sixth power of one half of $t$

   15. The square of one third of $r$  16. One third the square of $r$

**Simplify.**

17. a. $-5^2$  18. a. $-2^4$  19. a. $-5 \cdot 2^3$  20. a. $-6^2 \cdot 2$
    b. $(-5)^2$      b. $(-2)^4$      b. $-(5 \cdot 2)^3$      b. $(-6 \cdot 2)^2$

21. a. $8 + 2^3$  22. a. $5 - 2^4$  23. a. $6 - 4^2$  24. a. $3 \cdot 5 - 4^2$
    b. $(8 + 2)^3$      b. $(5 - 2)^4$      b. $(6 - 4)^2$      b. $(3 \cdot 5 - 4)^2$

B  25. $6^3 \div [5^2 - 3^2 - (-2)^2]$   26. $(6^2 - 3 \times 2^2 + 1) \div [0 + (-5)^2]$

   27. $6(3^2 - 2^2) \div 3 + 4 \div (-4)$   28. $7(3^2 - 1) + 2^4 \times 3 \div (-3)2^2$

   29. $8 \times (-1)^3 - 7(-1)^2 + 2(-1) + 4$   30. $15(-2)^4 - 6(-2)^3 + 5(-2)^2 + 1$

**Evaluate if $x = 4$ and $y = -2$.**

31. a. $2x + y^2$  32. a. $8 + xy^2$  33. a. $2x - y^3$  34. a. $\dfrac{-3x}{y^2}$

    b. $(2x + y)^2$      b. $(8 + xy)^2$      b. $(2x - y)^3$      b. $\left(\dfrac{-3x}{y}\right)^2$

35. $\dfrac{(x + 2y)^2}{x - 2y}$   36. $\dfrac{x^3 + y^3}{x + y}$   37. $\left(\dfrac{8 - xy}{x}\right)^4$   38. $\left(\dfrac{4y}{4 - xy}\right)^2$

**Evaluate each expression for the given value of $x$.**

C  39. $(x^2 + 4x - 5)(2x^2 - 7x + 1)$, $x = -5$

   40. $(3x^2 + 8x - 1)(x^2 + x - 6)$, $x = -2$

   41. $2(x - 1)^3 - 11(x - 1)^2 + 12(x - 1) + 9$, $x = 3$

   42. $4(x + 1)^3 - 2(x + 1)^2 - 8(x + 1) + 6$, $x = \dfrac{1}{2}$

## Computer Exercises

*For students with some programming experience*

1. Write a BASIC program that uses a FOR . . . NEXT loop to print out the value of $n^n$ for $n = 1, 2, 3, 4, 5$.

2. The symbol 4! is read "4 factorial," and its value is $1 \cdot 2 \cdot 3 \cdot 4 = 24$. Similarly, $6! = 1 \cdot 2 \cdot 3 \cdot 4 \cdot 5 \cdot 6 = 720$. Write a BASIC program that uses a FOR ... NEXT loop to print out the value of $n!$ for $n = 1, 2, 3, 4, 5$.

3. Study the data in Exercises 1 and 2. For a given value of $n$, which appears to be larger, $n!$ or $n^n$? Can you explain why?

## Computer Key-In

In computing wages in the program on page 117, you INPUT the employee ID numbers and pay per hour as well as the numbers of hours worked. Most likely, the first two items would be read from files. This situation can be represented by using READ and DATA statements in the program as explained below. In this case, the number of employees also becomes part of the stored data. (See line 5 below.)

Compare this program with the one given on page 117. Notice that lines 30, 70, and 90–140 have not been changed.

```
5   LET T=3
10   PRINT "THIS PROGRAM HAS DATA FOR"
20   PRINT T;" EMPLOYEES."
30   PRINT "FOR EACH EMPLOYEE:"
40   DATA 1234,11.5          DATA statements may be placed
50   DATA 3412,10            anywhere in the program. You
60   DATA 4321,12            may prefer to put them
70   FOR I=1 TO T            at the end.
72   READ N,R
74   PRINT "HOURS FOR ";N;
80   INPUT H
90   LET W=R*H
100   IF H <= 40 THEN 120
110   LET W=W+.5*R*(H-40)
120   PRINT " ","WAGES = ";W
130   NEXT I
140   END
```

Line 72 READs the DATA in lines 40–60 in order, two at a time, into the variables $N$ and $R$. Then, when the number of hours is INPUT, the computation proceeds as before.

### Exercises

1. RUN the program given above, using the numbers of hours given on page 117 as INPUT.

2. Revise this program by changing $T$ to 4 and adding a line of DATA as line 65. RUN the program again.

# *Reading Algebra* / *Independent Study*

When you read an algebra textbook, it is helpful to know what you hope to achieve before you begin a lesson. The title of the lesson and the objective for the lesson, which appears directly below the title, will give you a good idea of what you should know when you have finished reading. You may find it useful to skim the lesson first. Notice any words or phrases that stand out; they are meant to attract your attention. **Heavy type** indicates new words or phrases that you must understand in order to understand the lesson. It is usually very helpful to learn the definitions of these words or phrases before you begin a slow and careful reading of the lesson. When you do start to read the lesson, pay particular attention to the important information set off in boxes or in italic type. If you come across any words whose meaning you do not understand, look them up in the glossary at the back of the book or in a dictionary. You may also find additional information by checking references from the index. Be sure to work through all the examples that are included in the lesson discussions. Try doing these examples on your own before reading the solutions that are given following the examples. If you do not understand a concept, and rereading does not seem to help, make a note of the concept so that you can discuss it with your teacher.

When you have finished reading a lesson and feel that you understand what you have read, try some of the Oral and Written Exercises. They will help you determine whether you have achieved the goal set forth in the objective. Doing the Self-Tests and checking your answers with those at the back of the book will help you to see whether you have understood a group of lessons. The Chapter Reviews, Chapter Tests, Cumulative Reviews, and Mixed Reviews will also give you a good idea of your progress.

## *Exercises*

Skim through Sections 4-2 and 4-3 and answer the following questions.

1. What should you be able to do when you have finished reading the text of these sections?

2. What new words or phrases are introduced?

3. What is a monomial? a polynomial? Find the definitions of these words in your book.

4. State the Rule of Exponents for Multiplication.

5. Look at Example 1 on page 143. Then simplify
$8x^2 + 3x - 7 + 2x - 5x^2 + 3$.

6. Suppose that you had forgotten the definition of the term variable. Where could you look it up? On what page of your textbook is this word first used?

7. Section 4-2 covers adding and subtracting polynomials. Where could you find information about addition and subtraction in general?

# 4-2 Adding and Subtracting Polynomials

**Objective**  To add and subtract polynomials.

Each of the expressions below is a *monomial*.

$$7 \qquad h \qquad \tfrac{1}{2}c \qquad -8x^2y$$

A **monomial** is an expression that is either a numeral, a variable, or a product of a numeral and one or more variables. A numeral, such as 7, is also called a **constant monomial,** or a **constant.**

A sum of monomials is called a **polynomial.** A polynomial such as $x^2 + (-3x) + (-2)$ is usually written as $x^2 - 3x - 2$. Some polynomials have special names:

|  |  |
|---|---|
| **Binomials** (two terms): $\quad 4x + 9$ | $6b^2 - 7a$ |
| **Trinomials** (three terms): $x^2 - 3x - 2$ | $5b^2 + 3ab - a^2$ |

A monomial is considered to be a polynomial of one term.

In the monomial $-8x^2y$, the number $-8$ is called the **coefficient,** or **numerical coefficient.** Two monomials that are exactly alike or that differ only in their numerical coefficients are called **similar,** or **like.** The following monomials are all similar:

$$-8x^2y, \quad 5yx^2, \quad x^2y, \quad \text{and} \quad \tfrac{1}{2}x^2y.$$

The following monomials are not similar: $-2xy^2$ and $-2x^2y$.

A polynomial is **simplified,** or **in simplest form,** when no two of its terms are similar. You may use the distributive property to add similar terms.

**Example 1**  Simplify $-4x^3 + 5x^2 + 3x^2 + 4x^3 - 7$.

**Solution**
$$\begin{aligned}
\underline{-4x^3} + \underline{\underline{5x^2}} + \underline{\underline{3x^2}} + \underline{4x^3} - 7 &= (-4 + 4)x^3 + (5 + 3)x^2 - 7 \\
&= 0x^3 + 8x^2 - 7 \\
&= 8x^2 - 7
\end{aligned}$$

The **degree of a monomial in a variable** is the number of times that variable occurs as a factor in the monomial. For example,

$$-3xy^2z^3 \text{ is of degree } \begin{cases} 1 \text{ in } x, \\ 2 \text{ in } y, \\ 3 \text{ in } z. \end{cases}$$

The **degree of a monomial** is the total number of times its variables occur as factors. Thus, the degree of $-3xy^2z^3$ is $1 + 2 + 3$, or 6. The degree of any nonzero constant monomial is 0.

The **degree of a polynomial** is the greatest of the degrees of its terms *after it has been simplified.* Since the polynomial

$$-4x^3 + 5x^2 + 3x^2 + 4x^3 - 7,$$

in Example 1, can be simplified to $8x^2 - 7$, the degree of the polynomial is 2, *not* 3.

To add two polynomials, you write the sum and simplify by adding similar terms.

**Example 2** Add $5x^2y + 3x^2 - 8$ and $4x^2y + 2x^2 - 3xy^2 + 9$.

**Solution 1** $(5x^2y + 3x^2 - 8) + (4x^2y + 2x^2 - 3xy^2 + 9) =$
$(5 + 4)x^2y + (3 + 2)x^2 - 3xy^2 + (-8 + 9) = 9x^2y + 5x^2 - 3xy^2 + 1$

**Solution 2** You can also arrange similar terms vertically and add:

$$
\begin{array}{l}
5x^2y + 3x^2 \qquad\quad - 8 \\
4x^2y + 2x^2 - 3xy^2 + 9 \\
\hline
9x^2y + 5x^2 - 3xy^2 + 1
\end{array}
$$

Subtracting polynomials is very much like subtracting real numbers. To subtract a number you add the opposite of that number. To subtract a polynomial, you add the opposite of *each* term of the polynomial that you are subtracting and then simplify.

**Example 3** Subtract $-5a^2 + 2ab + 3b^2 - 4$ from $7a^2 + 6ab - b^2 - 9$

**Solution 1** $(7a^2 + 6ab - b^2 - 9) - (-5a^2 + 2ab + 3b^2 - 4) =$
$7a^2 + 6ab - b^2 - 9 + 5a^2 - 2ab - 3b^2 + 4 =$
$(7 + 5)a^2 + (6 - 2)ab + (-1 - 3)b^2 + (-9 + 4) = 12a^2 + 4ab - 4b^2 - 5$

**Solution 2**
$$
\begin{array}{l}
7a^2 + 6ab \ - \ b^2 - 9 \\
-5a^2 + 2ab + 3b^2 - 4
\end{array}
\rightarrow
\left\{
\begin{array}{l}
\text{change to the} \\
\text{opposite and add}
\end{array}
\right\}
\rightarrow
\begin{array}{l}
7a^2 + 6ab \ - \ b^2 - 9 \\
+5a^2 - 2ab - 3b^2 + 4 \\
\hline
12a^2 + 4ab - 4b^2 - 5
\end{array}
$$

## Oral Exercises

1. **a.** State the degree of the monomial $8x^2yz^4$ in each variable.
   **b.** What is the degree of the monomial?

**State the degree of each polynomial. If the polynomial is a binomial or a trinomial, state this fact.**

2. $5x^2 - 7x - 4$

3. $x^2 + 3x^3 + 7 + 4x$

4. $x^4 + y^3$

5. $ab + ab^2 + ab^3 + ab^4$

6. $r^3t^2 - r^2t$

7. $5y^3 - 7y^2x + 6x^2$

**Name the similar monomials.**

**8.** $5x,\ 3xy,\ 4y,\ -xy,\ 7y,\ 2x$

**9.** $3x^3y^2,\ 4x^2y^3,\ 5x^3y^2,\ 3xy,\ -x^2y^3$

**Add.**

**10.** $3a - 2$
$\phantom{3}4a + 7$

**11.** $4a + 9b$
$\phantom{4}5a - \phantom{9}b$

**12.** $\phantom{-}7x - 3y$
$-2x - 5y$

**13.** $4x^2 - 3x - 7$
$\phantom{4}2x^2 + 5x + 9$

**14.** $\phantom{3}y^2 - 7y - 2$
$3y^2 \phantom{{}- 7y} + 8$

**15.** $\phantom{-4}2n^2 - 5n - 7$
$-4n^2 + 3n$

**16.** $\phantom{2}r^2 - 2rs + 3s^2$
$2r^2 + 5rs - \phantom{3}s^2$

**17.** $-3a - 2b + 5c$
$-4a + 2b - 7c$

**18.** $5 - 3x$
$8 - 7x + 4x^2$

**19–27.** In Exercises 10–18, state the opposite of the lower polynomial. Then, subtract by adding that opposite to the upper polynomial.

**Simplify.**

**28.** $(5x - 3y + 7) + (2x - 5y - 8)$

**29.** $(4a - 3) - (a + 7)$

**30.** $(8a - 4b) - (5a - 2b)$

**31.** $(5x - 3y - 2) - (4x - 5)$

## Written Exercises

**Copy each polynomial and underline similar terms in the same way as in Example 1 on page 143. Then simplify the polynomial.**

**A**
**1.** $2a - 3b + 4a + 7b$

**2.** $7x - 5y - 3y + 4x$

**3.** $7x^2 - 3xy + 5xy - 4x^2$

**4.** $5mn + m^2n - 4mn + 2m^2n$

**5.** $x^2y + xy^2 - 3x^2y + xy$

**6.** $3a^3 - 7a^2b + a^3 - ab^2 - 4a^3$

**Add.**

**7.** $3a - 2$
$\phantom{3}5a + 7$

**8.** $\phantom{-}5n + 3$
$-2n - 7$

**9.** $\phantom{-}3x - 4y + 2$
$-3x + 7y + 3$

**10.** $\phantom{-}8n - 4p + 7$
$-5n + 8p - 1$

**11.** $3a^2 - 5a - 7$
$4a^2 - 2a + 9$

**12.** $7x^2 - 3xy + 4y^2$
$2x^2 - \phantom{3}xy - \phantom{4}y^2$

**13.** $\phantom{-5}3a^2 - 2ab - 7b$
$-5a^2 \phantom{{}- 2ab} - \phantom{7}b$

**14.** $\phantom{-3}4c^2 - 5cd$
$-3c^2 + 6cd - d^2$

**15.** $5x - 3y - 4z + 2$
$2x - \phantom{3}y + 3z$
$\phantom{2x - {}}2y - 5z + 6$

**16.** $8a - 3b \phantom{- 5c} + 7$
$4a \phantom{- 3b} - 5c - 3$
$-a - \phantom{3}b + 8c + 5$

**17–24.** In Exercises 7–14, subtract the lower polynomial from the upper one.

**Simplify.**

**25.** $(5a - 3b + 2) + (7a - 6b - 3)$    **26.** $(x - 5y - 7) + (4x - 3y - 8)$

**27.** $(3a^2 + 4a - 7) + (5a^2 - 2a - 1)$    **28.** $(5x^2 - 7x + 2) + (-x^2 + 4x + 5)$

**29.** $(xy^2 - 3xy^2 + y^3) + (2xy^2 - y^3 + xy^2)$    **30.** $(a^2b - 3ab^2 - ab^3) + (5ab^2 - 6ab^3)$

**31.** $(3a - 5) - (a + 2)$    **32.** $(6n - 3) - (4n + 1)$

**33.** $(4x - 7y) - (3x - 5y)$    **34.** $(8a - 7b) - (a - 4b)$

**35.** $(3x^2 - 5x - 2) - (-x^2 - 5x + 9)$    **36.** $(a^2 - 5a - 7) - (-a^2 - 8a + 7)$

**37.** $(2n^2 - 3m^2) - (n^2 + 6m^2 - mn)$    **38.** $(3c^2 - 4cd) - (cd + c^2 - d^2)$

**Solve.**

**B**  **39.** $8x - (2x - 6) = 12$    **40.** $y - (6y - 4) = 9$

**41.** $(2a - 5) - (5a + 4) = 7 - 7a$    **42.** $(3x - 2) - (11x - 5) = 19$

**43.** $(5n - 3) - (6 - 8n) = 5(3 - n)$    **44.** $9a - (3a - 8) = 2(6a - 5)$

**45.** $8(5 - x) = (x - 10) - (3x - 2)$    **46.** $3(4a - 6) = 2(4a - 3) - (a - 8)$

**47.** $(y^2 + 3y + 1) - (y^2 + 5y + 3) = 4$    **48.** $5 - (a^2 - 2a - 9) = 10 - (2a + a^2)$

**C**  **49.** $7 + x(x + 5) = x^2 - (7 - 5x)$    **50.** $3x(x - 2) - 4 = 3x - (9x - 3x^2 + 4)$

---

## Problems

**Solve.**

**A**  **1.** Find two consecutive integers whose sum is 51.

**2.** Find three consecutive integers whose sum is $-171$.

**3.** Find four consecutive even integers whose sum is 244.

**4.** Find four consecutive odd integers whose sum is 0.

**5.** The sum of the least and greatest of three consecutive integers is 44. What is the middle integer?

**6.** The sum of the least and greatest of three consecutive odd integers is 166. What are the integers?

**7.** The greater of two consecutive integers is 7 less than twice the lesser. Find the integers.

**8.** The greater of two consecutive odd integers is 13 less than twice the lesser. Find the integers.

**B**  **9.** Find three consecutive odd integers such that the sum of the greatest and twice the least is 25.

**10.** Find four consecutive integers such that the sum of the two greatest subtracted from twice the sum of the two least is 15.

---

**11.** Find four consecutive integers such that five times the third decreased by twice the fourth is 55.

**12.** Find four consecutive odd integers such that the third is the sum of the fourth and twice the second.

**13.** The measures in meters of two adjacent sides of a rectangle are consecutive odd integers. The perimeter is 96 m. What are the dimensions of the rectangle?

## Computer Exercises

*For students with some programming experience*

Given the polynomial $3x^3 + x^2 - 6x - 2$:

**1.** Write a BASIC program to find the value of this polynomial for a given value of $x$ that is entered with an INPUT statement.

**2.** Use the program you wrote in Exercise 1 to find a value of $x$ for which the value of the polynomial is between $-0.01$ and $0.01$.

# Self-Test 1

*Vocabulary*
power (p. 137)
base (p. 137)
exponent (p. 137)
factored form (p. 138)
exponential form (p. 138)
monomial (p. 143)
constant (p. 143)
polynomial (p. 143)

binomial (p. 143)
trinomial (p. 143)
coefficient (p. 143)
similar terms (p. 143)
polynomial in simplest form
(p. 143)
degree of a monomial (p. 143)
degree of a polynomial (p. 144)

**Write in exponential form.**

**1.** $a \cdot a \cdot a$      **2.** The cube of the product of $x$ and $y$      Obj. 4-1, p. 137

**Simplify.**

**3.** $(-1)^4$      **4.** $(4 - 6)^3$

**a. Add the polynomials.**
**b. Subtract the lower polynomial from the upper one.**

**5.** $5x^2 + 6x - 8$      **6.** $x^2y - 3xy^2 + 7$      Obj. 4-2, p. 143
    $x^2 - 6x - 4$         $-9x^2y + 3xy^2 - 4$

**7.** Find three consecutive odd integers such that the greatest is 15 less than twice the smallest.

Check your answers with those at the back of the book.

# Multiplication

## 4-3 Multiplying Monomials

**Objective**  To multiply monomials.

When you multiply two powers having the same base, you add the exponents as shown below.

$$x^2 \cdot x^5 = x^{2+5} = x^7$$
$$y^9 \cdot y^3 = y^{9+3} = y^{12}$$

You can understand why you add exponents if you remember that an exponent indicates the number of times the base is used as a factor.

$$\underset{\text{7 factors}}{\underbrace{x^2 \cdot x^5 = \overbrace{(x \cdot x)}^{\text{2 factors}} \cdot \overbrace{(x \cdot x \cdot x \cdot x \cdot x)}^{\text{5 factors}}}} = x^7$$

$$\underset{m + n \text{ factors}}{\underbrace{a^m \cdot a^n = \overbrace{(a \cdot a \cdot \cdots \cdot a)}^{m \text{ factors}} \cdot \overbrace{(a \cdot a \cdot \cdots \cdot a)}^{n \text{ factors}}}} = a^{m+n}$$

The following general rule applies when two powers to be multiplied have the same base.

### Rule of Exponents for Multiplication

For all positive integers $m$ and $n$,

$$a^m \cdot a^n = a^{m+n}$$

When you multiply two monomials, you use the rule of exponents along with the commutative and associative axioms for multiplication.

**Example 1**  $(3x^3y^4)(-7xy^5) = [3 \cdot (-7)](x^3 \cdot x)(y^4 \cdot y^5)$  Commutative and associative axioms for multiplication

$$= -21x^4y^9$$  Rule of exponents for multiplication

**Example 2**  $(2a^5b)(-4ab^3) + (3a^3b^2)(a^3b^2) = -8a^6b^4 + 3a^6b^4$
$$= -5a^6b^4$$

## Oral Exercises

**Simplify.**

1. $a^3 \cdot a^5$
2. $b^3 \cdot b^7$
3. $x^6 \cdot x \cdot x^2$
4. $y^4 \cdot y^2 \cdot y$

5. $a^n \cdot a^n$
6. $b^n \cdot b^{3n}$
7. $5^a \cdot 5^b$
8. $3^x \cdot 3^2$

9. $4^x \cdot 4$
10. $6^3 \cdot 6^y$
11. $(2c)(3c)$
12. $(5n)(2n)$

13. $(4n^4)(7n^7)$
14. $(3a^3)(5a^5)$
15. $(-2x^7)(-3x)$
16. $(4c^2)(-2c^3)$

17. $(x^2y)(2xy^3)$
18. $(a^2b^2)(3ab^4)$
19. $(-2rst)(-4r^2s)$
20. $-x^2 \cdot (-x)^2$

## Written Exercises

**Simplify.**

A
1. $b^5 \cdot b^3 \cdot b^2$
2. $a^4 \cdot a^7 \cdot a$
3. $(3a^3)(5a^5)$

4. $(6x^6)(3x^3)$
5. $(-2x^2y)(-3xy^2)$
6. $(4a^3b)(-2ab^2)$

7. $(4ab)(2a^2b)(3b^2)$
8. $(7x^3y)(2xy^2)(3x^2)$
9. $(4cd^5)(-2c^3)(3cd^2)$

10. $(5r^4s^2)(-3rt^2)(-2st^3)$
11. $\left(\frac{9}{4}a^4b\right)\left(\frac{8ab^8}{3}\right)$
12. $\left(\frac{14x^3y}{5}\right)\left(\frac{-15y^3x^2}{7}\right)$

13. $(7x^3)\left(\frac{1}{7}x^3\right)$
14. $(6a)\left(\frac{2}{3}a^3\right)$
15. $(5y^2)\left(\frac{4}{5}y^2\right)\left(\frac{1}{2}y\right)$

16. $(8n^2 - a)\left(-\frac{1}{4}an^2\right)$
17. $(3p^2r)(6p^3)\left(\frac{2}{9}r^2\right)$
18. $(-ab^2)(-bc^2)(-ac^2)$

19. $b^n \cdot b^3$
20. $x^4 \cdot x^a$
21. $2^k \cdot 2^{4-k} \cdot 2$

22. $3^p \cdot 3^{p+1} \cdot 3^2$
23. $(ay^7)(7y^a)$
24. $(cx^4)(4x^c)$

B
25. Evaluate $(-x)^3(-x)^4$ and $(-x^3)(-x^4)$ if $x = 2$.
26. Evaluate $(-x)^4(-x)^7$ and $(-x^4)(-x^7)$ if $x = -1$.

**Simplify.**

27. $(2a)(3a^3) + (4a^2)(5a^2)$
28. $(3b^2)(4b^3) + 7b^3 \cdot b^2$

29. $(3x^7)(2x^2) - (5x^3)(4x^6)$
30. $(4y^4)(2y^6) - (4y)(2y^9)$

31. $(3x^2y)(4xy^2) - (7x^2)(2xy^3)$
32. $(3ab^5)(5ab) - (3a^2b)(2b^5)$

33. $(5x^2y^6)(2x^3) - (-2x^4y^4)(-xy^2)$
34. $(7r^2s^3)(-3rs^4) - (-2r^2s)(5rs^6)$

**Find the perimeter and area of each shaded region.**

(Area of rectangle = length × width.)

**35.**

3ab

2ab

**36.**

3x

2x

x

3x

**37.**

4a

a

a

a

a

a

a

**Find the total surface area of each solid.**

(The total surface area of a solid is the sum of the areas of all its faces.)

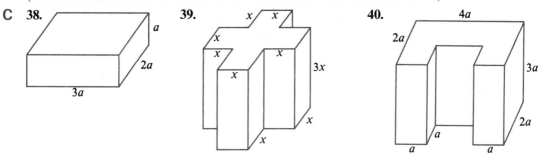

**C 38.**

a

2a

3a

**39.**

x   x

x

x

x

3x

x

x

**40.**

4a

2a

3a

2a

a   a

**41–43.** Find the volume of each solid above. (The volume can be found by multiplying the area of the bottom or top of the solid by the height.)

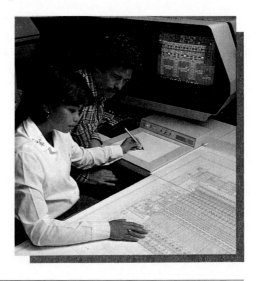

# 4-4 Powers of Monomials

**Objective**  To find powers of a monomial.

To find a power of a monomial that is itself a power, you can apply the definition of a power and the rule of exponents for multiplication.

**Example 1**  $(x^3)^2 = x^3 \cdot x^3 = x^{3+3} = x^6$

Note that $(x^3)^2 = x^6$, or $x^{3 \times 2}$. In general:

$$\underbrace{a^m \text{ is a factor } n \text{ times} \qquad n \text{ terms}}_{}$$

$$(a^m)^n = \overbrace{(a^m)(a^m) \cdots (a^m)} = a^{m+m+\cdots+m} = a^{mn}$$

Thus, *to find a power of a power, you multiply the exponents.*

---

### Rule of Exponents for a Power of a Power

For all positive integers $m$ and $n$,

$$(a^m)^n = a^{mn}.$$

---

**Example 2**  $(y^5)^4 = y^{20}$    **Example 3**  $[(-a)^4]^5 = (-a)^{20} = a^{20}$

  To find a power of a product, you can apply the definition of a power and the commutative and associative axioms for multiplication.

**Example 4**  $(3x)^2 = 3x \cdot 3x = 3 \cdot 3 \cdot x \cdot x = 3^2 \cdot x^2 = 9x^2$

Note that *both* the 3 and the $x$ are squared when the product $3x$ is squared. In general:

$$\overbrace{\qquad}^{\substack{ab \text{ is a factor} \\ m \text{ times}}} \quad \overbrace{\qquad}^{m \text{ factors}} \overbrace{\qquad}^{m \text{ factors}}$$

$$(ab)^m = (ab)(ab) \cdots (ab) = (a \cdot a \cdots \cdot a)(b \cdot b \cdot \cdots \cdot b) = a^m b^m$$

Thus, *to find a power of a product, you find the power of each factor and then multiply.*

---

### Rule of Exponents for a Power of a Product

For every positive integer $m$,

$$(ab)^m = a^m b^m.$$

---

*Example 5* $(5b)^4 = 5^4 \cdot b^4 = 625b^4$

*Example 6* $(-3y)^3 = (-3)^3 \cdot y^3 = -27y^3$

Both rules of exponents for powers are applied in the following example.

*Example 7* $(-3x^5y^3)^3 = (-3)^3 \cdot (x^5)^3 \cdot (y^3)^3 = -27x^{15}y^9$

## Oral Exercises

**Simplify.**

1. $(x^4)^2$      2. $(y^3)^5$      3. $(a^2)^6$      4. $(b^4)^4$

5. **a.** $(c^3)^2$   **b.** $c^3 \cdot c^2$      6. **a.** $(d^5)^3$   **b.** $d^5 \cdot d^3$

7. **a.** $(t^4)^3$   **b.** $t^4 \cdot t^3$      8. **a.** $s^5 \cdot s^4$   **b.** $(s^5)^4$

9. $(3a^3)^2$      10. $(5a^4)^2$      11. $(2x^5)^3$      12. $(3y^2)^3$

13. $(-x^3)^2$      14. $(-y^4)^3$      15. $(-3a^6)^2$      16. $(-3a^6)^3$

17. $[(-1)^3]^5$      18. $[(-x)^5]^2$      19. $(x^3y^6)^2$      20. $(2ab^4)^3$

21. **a.** $(b^x)^2$   **b.** $b^x \cdot b^x$      22. **a.** $(a^y)^3$   **b.** $a^y \cdot a^y \cdot a^y$

23. **a.** $(x^ny^m)^2$   **b.** $(x^ny^m)(x^ny^m)$      24. **a.** $-(b^2)y$   **b.** $[(-b)^2]y$

25. Evaluate $(ab)^2$ and $a^2b^2$ if $a = 2$ and $b = 3$.

26. Evaluate $3x^2$ and $(3x)^2$ if $x = 2$.

## Written Exercises

**Simplify.**

**A**   1. **a.** $(x^4)^3$   **b.** $(x^3)^4$   **c.** $x^3 \cdot x^4$      2. **a.** $(a^7)^2$   **b.** $(a^2)^7$   **c.** $a^2 \cdot a^7$

    3. **a.** $a^n \cdot a^n$   **b.** $(a^n)^2$   **c.** $a^2 \cdot a^n$      4. **a.** $b^t \cdot b^t \cdot b^t$   **b.** $(b^t)^3$   **c.** $b^t \cdot b^3$

**Evaluate if $x = 2$ and $y = 3$.**

5. **a.** $4x^2$   **b.** $(4x)^2$   **c.** $4^2 \cdot x^2$      6. **a.** $5x^3$   **b.** $(5x)^3$   **c.** $5^3 \cdot x^3$

7. **a.** $xy^2$   **b.** $(xy)^2$   **c.** $x^2y^2$      8. **a.** $yx^3$   **b.** $(yx)^3$   **c.** $y^3x^3$

**Simplify.**

9. $(8n)^2$      10. $(3a)^3$      11. $(2x)^5$      12. $(6a)^4$

13. $(3n^2)^4$      14. $(8b^6)^2$      15. $\left(\frac{1}{10}x^{10}\right)^3$      16. $\left(\frac{1}{2}x^3\right)^4$

17. $(2ab^2)^4$      18. $(3x^2y)^3$      19. $(2a^2b^6)^3$      20. $(5x^4y^2)^3$

**21. a.** $(-3x^5)^2$    **b.** $-(3x^5)^2$      **22. a.** $(-2n^6)^4$    **b.** $-(2n^6)^4$

**23. a.** $(-3x^5)^3$    **b.** $-(3x^5)^3$      **24. a.** $(-2n^6)^5$    **b.** $-(2n^6)^5$

**B**   **25.** $(2a)^2(2a)^3$      **26.** $(10x)^2(10x)^4$      **27.** $(5b)^4(2b)^4$      **28.** $(4n)^3\left(\dfrac{5}{2}n\right)^3$

**29.** $(3x^2y)^3 \cdot 4xy^3$      **30.** $(2a^2b)^3(-4ab^2)^2$      **31.** $(-2c^3d)^5\left(\dfrac{1}{4}d\right)^3$      **32.** $\left(\dfrac{1}{2}a^4\right)^3(-4a)^3$

**33.** $(2a^n)^3(3a^n)^2$      **34.** $(x^n)^5(2x^n)^3$      **35.** $(y^m)^n \cdot 2y^{mn}$      **36.** $(b^x)^y \cdot (b^y)^x$

**37.** $x^2(xy^3)^2 + y^2(x^2y^2)^2$                **38.** $x^3(xy^2)^2 + x(-xy)^4$

**39.** $(2c)^3(cd)^2 + (2cd)^2(-c)^3$       **40.** $(2a^2b^3)^2 - a(ab^2)^3$

**C**   **41. a.** Find the volumes of the two cubes shown.

     **b.** How many times larger is the volume of the bigger cube than that of the smaller cube?

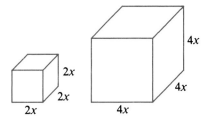

**42.** If $a = (3^3)^3$ and $b = 3^{(3^3)}$, is $a$ larger or is $b$? How many times larger is it?

**43.** Show that $16^x \cdot (4^x)^2 = 2^{8x}$.

## Computer Exercises        *For students with some programming experience*

   **1.** Write a BASIC program using READ . . . DATA statements to evaluate the expression $\dfrac{x^2}{2^x}$ for the following values of $x$: 1, 2, 3, 4, 5, 10, 50, 100, 1000, 2000. What appears to be happening to this expression as $x$ becomes larger?

   **2.** Repeat Exercise 1, this time using the program to evaluate the expression $\left(1 + \dfrac{1}{x}\right)^x$ for the given values of $x$.

## Challenge

What is wrong with the following "proof" that $2 = 1$?

$$r = s$$
$$r^2 = rs$$
$$r^2 - s^2 = rs - s^2$$
$$(r + s)(r - s) = s(r - s)$$
$$r + s = s$$
$$s + s = s$$
$$2s = s$$
$$2 = 1$$

## 4-5 Multiplying a Polynomial by a Monomial

**Objective**   To multiply a polynomial by a monomial.

The distributive axiom and the rules of exponents enable you to multiply any polynomial by a monomial. For example:

$$4a(3a^2 - 4a + 3) = 4a(3a^2) + 4a(-4a) + 4a(3) = 12a^3 - 16a^2 + 12a$$

You may multiply either horizontally or vertically:

$$-3xy(3xy + 5x - y) = -9x^2y^2 - 15x^2y + 3xy^2 \quad \text{or} \quad$$

$$\begin{array}{r} 3xy + 5x - y \\ \hline -3xy \\ \hline -9x^2y^2 - 15x^2y + 3xy^2 \end{array}$$

Recall that to simplify an expression containing more than one grouping symbol, you work with the expression within the innermost grouping symbol first.

**Example 1**   Simplify $20 - 5[3x + 2(1 - 6x)]$.

**Solution**
$$20 - 5[3x + 2(1 - 6x)] \quad \longleftarrow \text{ Simplify } 2(1 - 6x) \text{ first.}$$
$$20 - 5[3x + 2 - 12x] \quad \longleftarrow \text{ Then simplify } 5[3x + 2 - 12x].$$
$$20 - 15x - 10 + 60x$$
$$10 + 45x$$

**Example 2**   Solve $20x^2 - 2[4x - 2x(1 - 5x)] = 8$.

**Solution**
$$\begin{aligned} 20x^2 - 2[4x - 2x(1 - 5x)] &= 8 \\ 20x^2 - 2[4x - 2x + 10x^2] &= 8 \\ 20x^2 - 8x + 4x - 20x^2 &= 8 \\ -4x &= 8 \\ x &= -2 \end{aligned}$$

The check is left for you.

∴ the solution is $-2$.   **Answer**

## Oral Exercises

**Multiply.**

**1.** $2(x + 3)$

**2.** $4(a - 5)$

**3.** $5(3y + 4)$

**4.** $7(2a - 3)$

**5.** $x(x + 8)$

**6.** $y(2 - y)$

**7.** $-a(a - 8)$

**8.** $x(y + z)$

**9.** $3a(a^2 - 5a)$

**10.** $-ab(a^2 - b^2)$

**11.** $2a^2(a^3 - 3a^2 - 5a + 4)$

## Written Exercises

**Multiply.**

**A**

**1.** $5(a + 2)$      **2.** $6(n - 5)$      **3.** $-8(a - 3)$      **4.** $-5(1 + 3n)$

**5.** $4x(x + 2)$      **6.** $7y(3y - 5)$      **7.** $-3b(2 - 5b)$      **8.** $-4c(5c + 2)$

**9.** $5x(x^2 - 2x - 3)$      **10.** $4y(2y^2 - 3y - 7)$

**11.** $-8x^2(2x^2 - 3x + 4)$      **12.** $-3a^3(2a^2 - 5a - 4)$

**13.** $\frac{1}{2}a(4a^2 - 2ab + 8b^2)$      **14.** $\frac{1}{3}xy^2(9x^2 - 6xy + y^2)$

**15.** $\dfrac{2b^2 - 5b - 9}{3b}$      **16.** $\dfrac{4a^2 - 7a - 8}{5a}$

**17.** $\dfrac{3n^2 - 4n - 6}{-2n^2}$      **18.** $\dfrac{x^2y - 3xy^2 + y^3}{-2xy}$

**Simplify.**

**19.** $3x(x - 5) + 2x(4x + 3)$      **20.** $5a(3a - 5) + 7a(1 - 5a)$

**21.** $4y^2(2y - 3) - y(6y^2 - 12y)$      **22.** $3n^3(2n - 6) - 2n^2(2n^2 - 9n)$

**23.** $3x(5x^2 - 4x) - (x + 2)x^2$      **24.** $4b^2(b - 3) - (2b - 5)b^2$

**25.** $-[3x - 2(5x - 3)]$      **26.** $-4[8a - 3(7 - 4a)]$

**Solve.**

**27.** $3(a - 1) + 2 = 8$      **28.** $2(y - 2) + 1 = 7$

**29.** $4 - 5(n - 2) = 19$      **30.** $4(x - 9) + 18 = 6$

**31.** $\frac{1}{3}(6n - 3) - 4(3n + 6) = 0$      **32.** $\frac{2}{5}(5a - 10) - 3(1 - a) = 3$

**B**

**33.** $2(5x - 4) - 3(x - 5) = 8(2x - 7)$      **34.** $\frac{1}{2}(6n + 4) - \frac{2}{3}(9 - 3n) = 2\left(n + \frac{5}{2}\right)$

**35.** $3x\left(5 - \frac{1}{3}x\right) - (15 - x^2) = 0$      **36.** $4(a - 7) - 2(1 - 3a)a = 6a^2$

**37.** $2x - 5[3x - 4(1 - x)] = -2$      **38.** $4 - [8(x - 3) - 5(2x + 9)] = 13$

**39.** A hockey team gets 2 points for every game won and 1 point for every game tied. No points are given for a game lost. Complete the table.

| Games played | 50 | 50 | 50 | 60 | $G$ |
|---|---|---|---|---|---|
| Games won | 30 | 30 | $W$ | $W$ | $W$ |
| Games lost | 16 | $L$ | $L$ | $L$ | $L$ |
| Total points | ? | ? | ? | ? | ? |

**40.** There are 60 multiple-choice questions on a standardized mathematics test. Each person taking the test is given 200 points at the start of the test. For each correct answer 10 points are added; for each incorrect answer 2.5 points are subtracted. No points are gained or lost for answers that are omitted.

| Number of questions answered | 60 | 50 | 50 | $a$ | $a$ |
|---|---|---|---|---|---|
| Number correct | 56 | 42 | $r$ | 40 | $r$ |
| Test score | ? | ? | ? | ? | ? |

**Find the area of each shaded region.**

**41.**

**42.**

**43.**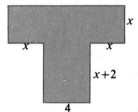

**C 44.** Find the total surface area and the volume of the solid shown.

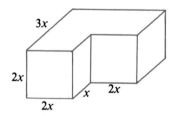

**Simplify. Each variable in an exponent represents a positive integer.**

**45.** $x^n(2x^n - 3x + 4)$    **46.** $a^{n+1}(a^n + a)$    **47.** $(2b^{n+1} + 3b^2)b^{n+1}$    **48.** $(-s)^{2n}(s^{2n} - 1)$

## Challenge

Find the value of $x$ such that the sum of the expressions is the same in each row, column, or diagonal.

| $x$ | 5 | $x - 2$ |
|---|---|---|
| $x - 5$ | 9 | 11 |
| 8 | $x + 1$ | $x - 6$ |

# 4-6 Multiplying Two Polynomials

**Objective**  To multiply polynomials.

You have learned to use the distributive axiom to multiply a polynomial by a monomial:

$$(4x + 3)(3x) = 4x(3x) + 3(3x)$$

If you replace $3x$ in the example above by the polynomial $3x + 4$, the distributive axiom can still be applied:

$$(4x + 3)(3x + 4) = 4x(3x + 4) + 3(3x + 4)$$
$$= 12x^2 + 16x + 9x + 12$$
$$= 12x^2 + 25x + 12$$

Here is another example in which a polynomial is multiplied by a polynomial, but the work is done in vertical form.

*Step 1*  Multiply by $3a$.

$$
\begin{array}{r}
5a^2 - 3a - 7 \\
3a + 2 \\
\hline
15a^3 - 9a^2 - 21a
\end{array}
$$

*Step 2*  Multiply by 2.

$$
\begin{array}{r}
5a^2 - 3a - 7 \\
3a + 2 \\
\hline
15a^3 - 9a^2 - 21a \\
10a^2 - 6a - 14
\end{array}
$$

*Step 3*  Add.

$$
\begin{array}{r}
5a^2 - 3a - 7 \\
3a + 2 \\
\hline
15a^3 - 9a^2 - 21a \\
10a^2 - 6a - 14 \\
\hline
15a^3 + a^2 - 27a - 14
\end{array}
$$

It is often helpful to rearrange the terms of a polynomial so that their degrees in a particular variable are in either decreasing or increasing order.

In order of decreasing degree in $x$:   $5x^4 + 5x^3 - 2x + 4$

In order of increasing degree in $x$:   $4 - 2x + 5x^3 + 5x^4$

In order of decreasing degree in $a$
and increasing degree in $b$:    $-7a^3 + a^2b + 2ab^2 + 3b^3$

To see the advantage of rearranging terms, first multiply the polynomials at the left below. Then compare your work with that shown at the right, where the terms of both polynomials have been rearranged.

$$
\begin{array}{l}
a^3 - ab^2 + 3b^3 + 2a^2b \\
b + a \\
\hline
\end{array}
$$

Rearrange in order
of decreasing degree
in $a$.

$$
\begin{array}{r}
a^3 + 2a^2b - ab^2 + 3b^3 \\
a + b \\
\hline
a^4 + 2a^3b - a^2b^2 + 3ab^3 \\
a^3b + 2a^2b^2 - ab^3 + 3b^4 \\
\hline
a^4 + 3a^3b + a^2b^2 + 2ab^3 + 3b^4
\end{array}
$$

# Oral Exercises

**Arrange in order of decreasing degree in the variable indicated in color.**

1. $2x + x^2 + 5$; $x$
2. $5x^2 - 3x^3 - 4 + 7x$; $x$
3. $a^2b + 2a^3 - ab^2 + 4b^3$; $a$
4. $a^2b + 2a^3 - ab^2 + 4b^3$; $b$

**Arrange in order of increasing degree in the variable indicated in color.**

5. $5y^3 - 3y^2 + y^4 + 7$; $y$
6. $s + s^2t^2 + 3s^3t - s^3t^3$; $t$

**Complete.**

7. $(5x + 3)(2x + 1) = 5x(\underline{?}) + 3(\underline{?})$
8. $(8a - 7)(3a + 2) = 8a(\underline{?}) - 7(\underline{?})$
9. $(4z + 2)(z^2 + z - 5) = 4z(\underline{?}) + 2(\underline{?})$
10. $(2t + 3)(t^2 + 5t + 1) = 2t(\underline{?}) + (\underline{?})(\underline{?})$
11. $(2y + 5)(y + 1) = 2y(y + 1) + 5(y + 1) = (\underline{?})y^2 + (\underline{?})y + (\underline{?})$
12. $(3x + 4)(x - 1) = 3x(x - 1) + 4(x - 1) = (\underline{?})x^2 + (\underline{?})x + (\underline{?})$

# Written Exercises

**Multiply. Use the horizontal form.**

A

1. $(a + 3)(a + 5)$
2. $(b + 4)(b + 7)$
3. $(c + 2)(c - 5)$
4. $(x - 4)(x + 9)$
5. $(2a - 3)(a + 6)$
6. $(5n - 3)(2n - 1)$
7. $(3t - 2)(4t + 5)$
8. $(5y + 6)(4y - 3)$
9. $(x + 2)(x^2 + 3x + 4)$
10. $(y - 1)(2y^2 + 5y + 6)$
11. $(2a - 1)(a^2 + 3a + 7)$
12. $(7n + 2)(2n^2 - 5n + 1)$
13. $(8x - 5)(3x^2 - x + 4)$
14. $(2b - 5)(3b^2 - 6b - 4)$
15. $(2 - t)(4 + 2t + 3t^2)$

**Multiply. Use the vertical form.**

16. $2a + 3$
    $a + 7$

17. $3n + 9$
    $2n - 5$

18. $4x^2 + x - 5$
    $x + 6$

19. $8y^2 - 5y - 2$
    $2y - 3$

20. $4x - 7y$
    $5x - 2y$

21. $3c - 7d$
    $2c + d$

22. $a^2 + ab + b^2$
    $a + b$

23. $2x^2 - 3xy + y^2$
    $2x + y$

24. A rectangular region is subdivided into four smaller regions with dimensions shown.
    a. Find the areas of these four regions.
    b. Show that the sum of the areas of the four small regions equals the product of the length and width of the original rectangle.

**25.** Use the figure at the right.
  **a.** Find the areas of these four regions.
  **b.** Show that the sum of the areas of the four small regions equals the product of the length and width of the original rectangle.

**Multiply using either the horizontal or the vertical form. Arrange the terms in each factor in order of decreasing or increasing degree in some variable.**

**B** **26.** $(3x + 5)(2x^2 + 7 - 3x)$

**27.** $(4n + 2)(6 - 5n + 4n^2)$

**28.** $(4a - 5)(3a + 6 - a^2)$

**29.** $(7 - 5y)(4y^2 + 2 - 9y)$

**30.** $(2x - 3y)(x^2 + y^2 - 4xy)$

**31.** $(c - 7d)(8c^2 - d^2 + cd)$

**32.** $(5a + 4b)(2ab - b^2 + a^2)$

**33.** $(8x - 4y)(2xy - y^2 + 3x^2)$

**34.** $(4a^2 - 3a + 2)^2$

**35.** $(2y^2 - 3yz + z^2)(y^2 + yz + 2z^2)$

**Solve.**

**36.** $(x - 3)(x + 2) = (x + 1)(x + 5)$

**37.** $(3n - 1)(2n + 1) - n(6n - 2) = 0$

**38.** $(3r - 2)(r - 2) - (r + 1)(3r - 1) = 0$

**39.** $(a + 7)(a + 4) - a(a + 3) = 68$

**40.** $(x - 5)(x^2 - 3x + 4) = x(x^2 - 8x + 6)$

**41.** $(2y - 4)(y^2 - 3y) - y(2y^2 - 10y + 2) = 46$

**42.** Find the square of $4a^2 - 3a + 2$. Express as a polynomial.

**43.** Find the cube of $x + 3$. Express as a polynomial.

**44.** Suppose you know that $(2 + y)^3 = 8 + 12y + 6y^2 + y^3$. Find $(2 + y)^4$.

**45.** Subtract the product of $2x + y$ and $3x - y$ from $x^2 + y^2$.

**46.** When a certain polynomial is divided by $x + 2$, the quotient is $x^2 - 5x + 4$. Find the polynomial.

**C** **47. a.** Multiply:
  (1) $(x + 1)(x^2 - x + 1)$
  (2) $(x + 1)(x^3 - x^2 + x - 1)$
  (3) $(x + 1)(x^4 - x^3 + x^2 - x + 1)$

  **b.** Using your answers to part (a), predict answers for these products.
  (4) $(x + 1)(x^5 - x^4 + x^3 - x^2 + x - 1)$
  (5) $(x + 1)(x^6 - x^5 + x^4 - x^3 + x^2 - x + 1)$

---

## Computer Exercises
*For students with some programming experience*

Write a BASIC program to add and subtract two polynomials. The coefficients of each polynomial should be entered with INPUT statements in order from least to greatest degree. Each set of coefficients should be stored in an array. Use the program to find the sum and the difference of each of the following pairs of polynomials.

**1.** $3 + 4x + 5x^2$ and $1 + 7x - 2x^2$

**2.** $-5 - 6x^2$ and $2x^2 + x^4$

**3.** $4x + 9x^2$ and $5x^3$

**4.** $7 + 2x + x^3$ and $-3 + 4x + x^2$

# Self-Test 2

**Simplify.**

1. $-2x^3x^4$

2. $(-6a^7)(-9a)\left(\frac{1}{3}a\right)$     **Obj. 4-3, p. 148**

3. $126a\left(-\frac{1}{7}a\right)\left(\frac{1}{9}a^3\right)$

4. $4^2 \cdot 4^x \cdot 4^{x-2}$

5. $(-2x^4)^3$

6. $-(2x^4y)^3$     **Obj. 4-4, p. 151**

7. $-(2x^3y)^4$

8. $(-2x^3)^4$

9. $-4c(8 - c)$

10. $\frac{1}{7}xy^2(56x^2 - 49xy + y^2)$     **Obj. 4-5, p. 154**

11. Solve $4 - \frac{2}{3}(6a - 15) = -38$.

**Multiply.**

12. $(7a - 6)(a - 8)$

13. $(9 - 7t)(7 - 6t + 8t^2)$     **Obj. 4-6, p. 157**

Check your answers with those at the back of the book.

## Biographical Note / *Hypatia*

Because so little is known about women mathematicians who may have lived before Hypatia (A.D. 370–415), she is generally regarded as the first woman mathematician. She was born in Alexandria, Egypt, at a time when that city was one of the greatest centers of learning in the world. Hypatia studied mathematics, science, art, literature, and philosophy. Highly regarded as a mathematician and as an astronomer, Hypatia became a professor of mathematics and philosophy at the university in Alexandria, where she lectured on Plato, Aristotle, astronomy, geometry, Diophantine algebra, and the conics of Appollonius. She wrote several mathematical commentaries and has been credited by some with the invention of the astrolabe and the planisphere, two instruments used in the study of astronomy. Hypatia also invented apparatus for distilling water, measuring the level of water, and determining the specific gravity of liquids.

After her death in A.D. 415, no significant progress in the mathematics taught by Hypatia was made for centuries. Unfortunately, most of her work has either been lost or destroyed. Except for a portion of one of her papers that was found in the fifteenth century, our knowledge of Hypatia is based on the letters of her contemporaries and students.

# Problem Solving

## 4-7 Transforming Formulas

**Objective**   To transform formulas.

Many applications of mathematics require the use of known formulas. In using a formula, it is often desirable to transform the formula to express a particular variable in terms of the other variables.

**Example 1**   The formula $A = \frac{1}{2}h(a + b)$ gives the area of a trapezoid with bases $a$ units and $b$ units long and with height $h$ units. Use this formula to solve for the variable $a$ in terms of $A$, $h$, and $b$.

**Solution**

$$A = \frac{1}{2}h(a + b)$$

$$2A = h(a + b)$$

$$\frac{2A}{h} = a + b$$

$$\therefore a = \frac{2A}{h} - b \quad \textbf{Answer}$$

**Example 2**   To compute the total piston displacement, $P$, in an automobile engine, a mechanic used the formula $P = 0.7854d^2sn$, where $d$ is the diameter of each cylinder, $s$ is the length of the stroke, and $n$ is the number of cylinders. Use this formula to solve for the variable $s$ in terms of $P$, $d$, and $n$.

**Solution**   $P = 0.7854d^2sn$
Dividing both sides of the formula by $0.7854d^2n$, you obtain

$$s = \frac{P}{0.7854d^2n}. \quad \textbf{Answer}$$

Note that the formula for $s$ obtained in Example 2 is meaningful only if $d \neq 0$ and $n \neq 0$. Of course, neither $d$ nor $n$ will be zero since the engine must have cylinders and each cylinder must have a diameter.

## Oral Exercises

**Solve each equation for x.**

1. $x - a = b$

2. $ax = b$

3. $y = kx$

4. $ax + b = c$

**Solve each equation for the variable shown in color.**

5. $P = a + b + c$; $b$

6. $V = Bh$; $B$

7. $A = \frac{1}{2}bh$; $h$

8. $d = rt$; $t$

9. $I = Prt$; $r$

10. $V = \pi r^2 h$; $h$

11. $R = \frac{kl}{d^2}$; $l$

12. $C = \frac{mv^2}{r}$; $r$

## Written Exercises

**Solve for the variable shown in color. State the restrictions, if any, for the formula obtained to be meaningful.**

**A**

1. $C = 2\pi r$; $r$

2. $F = ma$; $a$

3. $s = \frac{gt^2}{2}$; $g$

4. $V = \frac{b^2 h}{3}$; $h$

5. $2a - z = a$; $z$

6. $2b + y = b$; $y$

7. $A = \frac{1}{2}h(b + c)$; $h$

8. $s = vt + 16t^2$; $v$

9. $C = \frac{5}{9}(F - 32)$; $F$

10. $S = \frac{n}{2}(a + 50)$; $a$

11. $A = P + Prt$; $t$

12. $A = 2(l + w)$; $w$

**B**

13. $A = \frac{a + b + c + d}{4}$; $d$

14. $v^2 = u^2 + 2as$; $a$

15. $2ax + 1 = ax + 5$; $x$

16. $3by - 2 = 2by + 1$; $y$

17. $3aw + 1 = aw - 7$; $w$

18. $6bct - 1 = 4bct + 1$; $t$

19. $s = \frac{1}{2}n(a + l)$; $l$

20. $l = a + (n - 1)d$; $n$

21. $a = \frac{180(n - 2)}{n}$; $n$

22. $A = P(1 + rt)$; $r$

23. $(a + b)(u - 2) = (u + 2)(b - a)$; $u$

24. $(2x + b)(2x - b) = 4x(x - 1)$; $x$

25. $s = \frac{rL - a}{r - 1}$; $L$

26. $G = \frac{v(P - r)}{f - r}$; $P$

**C**

27. $A = P + Prt$; $P$

28. $R = \frac{r}{1 - r}$; $r$

29. $C = K\frac{Rr}{R - r}$; $R$

30. $F = \frac{ef}{e + f - d}$; $f$

# 4-8 Distance-Rate-Time Problems

**Objective**   To solve some problems involving uniform motion.

An object is said to be in **uniform motion** when it moves without changing its speed, or rate. The three examples that follow illustrate three types of problems involving uniform motion. Each is solved using a chart, a sketch, and the formula:

$$\text{distance} = \text{rate} \times \text{time}$$

$$d = rt$$

In your work use the symbols s for seconds, min for minutes, and h for hours.

**Example 1**   (Motion in opposite directions)
Two planes leave Chicago's O'Hare Airport at the same time, one traveling east and the other west. The average speed of the eastbound plane is 60 km/h more than the speed of the westbound plane. After 2.5 h of flying time, the planes are 4150 km apart. What are their speeds?

## Solution

*Step 1*   The problem asks for the speeds of the two planes. Make a sketch.

*Step 2*   Let $x$ = speed of the westbound plane. Make a chart of the given facts and use it to label your sketch.

|  | Rate | $\times$ Time = | Distance |
|---|---|---|---|
| Westbound | $x$ | 2.5 | $2.5x$ |
| Eastbound | $x + 60$ | 2.5 | $2.5(x + 60)$ |

*Step 3*   The sketch will help you write the equation.

*Step 4*   $2.5x + 2.5(x + 60) = 4150$
$$2.5x + 2.5x + 150 = 4150$$
$$5x + 150 = 4150$$
$$5x = 4000$$
$$x = 800$$
$$x + 60 = 860$$

*Step 5*   *Check:*   In 2.5 h, the westbound plane flies $2.5 \cdot 800 = 2000$ km.
In 2.5 h, the eastbound plane flies $2.5 \cdot 860 = 2150$ km.
$2000 + 2150 = 4150$ km   $\checkmark$

∴ the planes fly at 800 km/h and 860 km/h, respectively.   *Answer*

***Example 2*** (Motion in the same direction)

Exactly 12 minutes after the Costanzas head north on the expressway, the Carrs set out from the same point to overtake them. The Costanzas travel at a steady 45 mph (miles per hour); the Carrs travel at 54 mph. How long does it take the Carrs to overtake the Costanzas?

**Solution**

*Step 1* The problem asks for the Carrs' driving time. Make a sketch.

*Step 2* Let $x$ = the Carrs' time. Make a chart of the given facts and use it to label your sketch. Remember that 12 minutes must be written as $\frac{1}{5}$ *hour* because the speeds are given in miles per *hour*.

| | Rate | × Time | = Distance |
|---|---|---|---|
| Costanzas | 45 | $x + \frac{1}{5}$ | $45\left(x + \frac{1}{5}\right)$ |
| Carrs | 54 | $x$ | $54x$ |

*Step 3* When the Carrs overtake the Costanzas, the distances will be equal. This fact gives us the equation

$$45\left(x + \frac{1}{5}\right) = 54x.$$

*Step 4*
$$45x + 9 = 54x$$
$$9 = 9x$$
$$1 = x$$

*Step 5* *Check:* In 1 hour, the Carrs travel $54 \cdot 1 = 54$ miles. In $\left(1 + \frac{1}{5}\right)$ hours, the Costanzas travel $45\left(1 + \frac{1}{5}\right) = 54$ miles.

∴ the Carrs overtake the Costanzas in 1 hour.  ***Answer***

***Example 3*** (Round trip)

Gregory jogs to baseball practice at 10 km/h and gets a ride back home at 60 km/h. The ride home took 15 min less than his jogging. How far did he jog and for how long?

**Solution**

*Step 1* The problem asks for the jogging distance and time. Make a sketch.

*Step 2* Let $x$ = the jogging time. Then $10x$ = jogging distance. Make a chart of the given facts and use it to label your sketch. Remember 15 min is 0.25 h.

|      | Rate × | Time  | = Distance |
|------|--------|-------|------------|
| Jog  | 10     | $x$   | $10x$      |
| Ride | 60     | $x - 0.25$ | $60(x - 0.25)$ |

*Step 3* In round-trip problems, the two distances are equal.

$$60(x - 0.25) = 10x$$

*Step 4*
$$60x - 15 = 10x$$
$$50x = 15$$
$$x = \frac{15}{50} = \frac{3}{10}$$
$$x = 0.3$$
$$10x = 3$$

*Step 5* The check is left to you.

$\therefore$ Gregory jogs 0.3 h, or 18 min, for a distance of 3 km. **Answer**

Notice in Examples 2 and 3 that the time, originally given in *minutes,* was changed to *hours*. This was done in order to make the units of time compatible with the speeds, which were given in terms of miles per *hour* and kilometers per *hour.*

## Oral Exercises

**Classify each problem as (1) a problem with motion in opposite directions, (2) a problem with motion in the same direction, or (3) a round-trip problem. Then complete the chart and give an equation.**

1. Maria can average 30 km/h on her 10-speed racing bike, but Cooper cannot go that fast on his 3-speed bike. When Maria finished a race from Boston to Worcester, 90 km away, Cooper was still 18 km from the finish line. What is Cooper's average speed?

|        | Rate × | Time = | Distance |
|--------|--------|--------|----------|
| Maria  | ?      | ?      | ?        |
| Cooper | $x$    | ?      | ?        |

**2.** Rip skates across a frozen lake at 10 mph and returns at 5 mph. If his total skating time is one hour, how wide is the lake?

|  | Rate | × Time | = Distance |
|---|---|---|---|
| Going | ? | $x$ | ? |
| Returning | ? | ? | ? |

**3.** Ann leaves Avon at noon biking to Batavia at 16 km/h. At 1 P.M. Bill leaves Batavia and bikes toward Avon at 20 km/h. If the distance between Avon and Batavia is 70 km, at what time do Ann and Bill meet?

|  | Rate | × Time | = Distance |
|---|---|---|---|
| Ann | ? | $x$ | ? |
| Bill | ? | ? | ? |

**4.** Tracy leaves for work at 8 A.M. traveling at 36 mph. Sarah finds that Tracy has forgotten her briefcase, so she leaves at 8:05 chasing after her at 50 mph. At what time will Sarah catch Tracy?

|  | Rate | × Time | = Distance |
|---|---|---|---|
| Tracy | ? | $x$ | ? |
| Sarah | ? | ? | ? |

## Problems

**A 1–4.** Complete the solutions of Oral Exercises 1–4.

**5.** Two jets leave St. Louis at 2 P.M., one traveling north at 850 km/h and the other south at 750 km/h. At what time will they be 4000 km apart?

**6.** Lisa can bike 6 km/h faster than Wendy. At noon, each girl leaves her house, traveling toward the other. If the distance between their houses is 20 km and they meet in 0.5 h, what is each girl's rate?

**7.** It takes a train 90 min longer to go from Farmington to Allentown at 60 km/h than it does to return at 80 km/h. What is the distance between these towns?

8. A car travels 418 km in 6 h. One hour of the trip is in the city, where its average speed is just half of what the car averaged on the turnpike for the rest of the trip. What was the car's average city speed?

**B** 9. Kelly rode her bike from home to the repair shop and then walked home. She spent 10 min riding, 5 min talking to the attendant, and 20 min walking. If Kelly's walking speed is 12 km/h less than her biking speed, find the distance from her house to the repair shop.

10. Because Chip can run 1 m/s faster than Dean, he is able to run across a field in 20 s, a full 2.5 s quicker than Dean. How fast can Chip run?

11. Laura can run at 8 m/s and Mary at 7.5 m/s. On a race track, Mary is given a 25 m head start and the race ends in a tie. How long is the track?

12. At 1:30 P.M., George left Exeter for Portsmouth, cycling at 20 km/h. At 2:00 P.M., Luke left Portsmouth for Exeter, cycling at 24 km/h. If the distance from Exeter to Portsmouth is 32 km, at what time did the boys meet?

13. At 2:00 P.M., a small plane had been flying 1 h when a change of wind direction doubled its average ground speed. If the entire trip of 860 km took 2.5 h, how far did the plane travel in the first hour?

14. A ship must average 22 knots (nautical miles per hour) to make its 10-hour run on schedule. During the first four hours, bad weather caused it to reduce its average speed to 16 knots. What should its average speed be for the rest of the trip to maintain its schedule?

**C** 15. A boy walking $r$ km/h has a head start of $b$ km on his friend who is walking at the rate of $s$ km/h ($r < s$). How long will it take the second boy to overtake the first?

16. One station is $d$ miles due west of a second station. From the first of these stations a train traveling west at $r$ mph leaves $a$ hours before a train traveling east at $v$ mph leaves the second station. How far apart will the trains be $t$ hours after the departure of the second train?

17. It usually takes a bus 20 min to travel the 12 miles from City Hall to the airport. However, from 4:00 P.M. to 6:00 P.M., the bus will travel only 10 miles in the same length of time. If a bus leaves City Hall on the hour and every 15 min after that, and if it takes 20 min to get from a bus to an airplane, what is the last bus Sam can take from City Hall to get on a plane leaving at 5:50 P.M.?

# 4-9 Area Problems

**Objective**  To solve some problems involving area.

To solve some problems involving area, you will need to multiply and add or subtract polynomials. Sketches are especially helpful in solving such problems.

The metric units of square measure that you will use most often are square centimeters ($cm^2$) and square meters ($m^2$).

A photograph 8 cm wide and 10 cm long is surrounded by a border 3 cm wide. To find the area of the border, you subtract the areas of the two rectangles.

Area of border
= Area of outer rectangle
    − Area of inner rectangle
= $(10 + 6)(8 + 6) - 10 \cdot 8$
= $(16)(14) - 80 = 144$

Thus, the area of the border is $144 \ cm^2$.

**Example**  A photograph is twice as long as it is wide. It is mounted so that a border 3 cm wide completely surrounds the photograph. Find the dimensions of the photograph if the area of the border is $216 \ cm^2$.

**Solution**

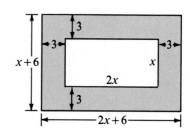

*Step 1*  The problem asks for the dimensions of the photograph.
Make a sketch.

*Step 2*  Let $x$ = width of the photograph.
Show the other dimensions on the sketch.

*Step 3*

Area of border = Area of photograph and border − Area of photograph

$$216 = (2x + 6)(x + 6) - (2x)(x)$$

*Step 4*  $216 = 2x^2 + 18x + 36 - 2x^2$
$216 = 18x + 36$
$180 = 18x$
$10 = x$

Step 5 *Check:* Area of photograph and border

$$= (2x + 6)(x + 6) = (26)(16) = 416$$
$$\text{Area of photograph} = (2x)(x) = (20)(10) = 200$$
$$\text{Area of border} = 416 - 200 = 216 \quad \sqrt{}$$

$\therefore$ the dimensions of the photograph are 20 cm and 10 cm.  *Answer*

## Problems

**A**  **1.** A rectangle is 5 m longer than it is wide. If its length is increased by 1 m and its width is increased by 1 m, the area is increased by 14 m². Find the original dimensions.

|  | Length × Width = Area | | |
|---|---|---|---|
| First rectangle | ? | $x$ | ? |
| New rectangle | ? | ? | ? |

**2.** A rectangle is twice as long as it is wide. If the length and width are both increased by 3, the area of the rectangle is increased by 45. Make a chart like the one in Exercise 1 and find the dimensions of the original rectangle.

**3.** A baker has two pans with the same area. One is a square and the other is a rectangle 5 cm longer than the square but 4 cm less wide than the square. Find the total area of each pan.

**4.** A photo is 10 cm longer than it is wide. It is mounted in a frame 2 cm wide. The area of the frame is 112 cm². Find the dimensions of the photo.

**5.** A poster is 20 cm longer than it is wide. It is mounted on a piece of cardboard so that there is a 10 cm border on all sides. If the area of the border is 2800 cm², what is the area of the poster?

**6.** A brick patio is twice as long as it is wide. It is bordered on all sides by a garden one meter wide. If the area of the garden is 40 m², find the dimensions of the patio.

**7.** A rectangular swimming pool is 5 m longer than it is wide. If a concrete walk 2 m wide is placed around the pool, the area covered by the pool and the walk is 156 m² greater than the area covered by the pool alone. What are the dimensions of the pool?

**B** **8. a.** If a circle has radius $r$, then its area $A$ is given by the formula $A = \pi r^2$. Use this formula to find a formula for the area of the shaded region in the figure at the right.

    **b.** If the area of the shaded region is 11 cm², find the radius $r$.

$$\left(\text{Use } \tfrac{22}{7} \text{ as an approximation for } \pi.\right)$$

**9.** A circular swimming pool is surrounded by a walkway 2 m wide. Find the radius of the pool if the area of the walkway is 88 m². (*Hint:* See Exercise 8a.)

**C** **10.** A running track 4 m wide goes around a rectangular soccer field that is twice as long as it is wide. At each end of the soccer field the track is a semicircle with radius $r$. Find a formula for the area of the track in terms of $r$.

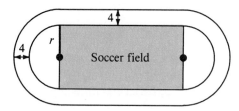

**11. a.** Suppose you plan to run once around the track described in Exercise 10. If you run staying 0.5 m from the inside edge of the track, find a formula for the distance that you would run. (*Hint:* The circumference of a circle is $C = 2\pi r$. Your answer will be in terms of $\pi$ and $r$.)

    **b.** Suppose a friend runs staying 0.5 m from the outer edge of the track. How much farther does your friend run than you?

## Computer Key-In

It is very useful to include descriptive statements, called REMARK statements, in your programs. Such statements begin with the letters REM. The computer prints these statements in a LISTing but ignores them in a RUN. Thus, additional information about the program can be given, as shown in the program on the next page.

    This program will find the cost of a number of items, the prices of which are stored on a file. Again, we use READ and DATA statements to represent this situation. The READ statement in line 130 READs the entire set of DATA. In order to READ through a second time as in line 220, a RE-STORE statement (line 200) must be given to tell the computer to start back at the beginning.

The value of N and the dimension statement DIM S(N) are also used in the program. S(N) represents an *array*, or list, of numbers. In this program, lines 120–160 allow values of S(1), S(2), S(3), and S(4) to be INPUT. The dimension statement is not needed unless you wish to use more than 10 values.

```
10   REM: DATA ON FILE
20   REM: ITEM ID NO., PRICE
30   DATA 2341,8.25
40   DATA 7204,10.95
50   DATA 3475,9.68
60   DATA 5068,11.49
70   REM---N = NUMBER OF ITEMS
80   REM---S(N) IS ARRAY OF NO.
90   REM---OF EACH ITEM SOLD
100  LET N=4
105  DIM S(4)   (not needed here—see text)
110  PRINT "INPUT NO. SOLD:"
120  FOR I=1 TO N
130  READ T,P
140  PRINT T;", HOW MANY SOLD";
150  INPUT S(I)
160  NEXT I
170  PRINT
180  PRINT "SUMMARY"
190  PRINT "ITEM";TAB(7);"NO. SOLD";
195  PRINT TAB(17);"PRICE";TAB(24);"COST"
200  RESTORE
210  FOR I=1 TO N
220  READ T,P
230  PRINT T;TAB(7);S(I);TAB(17);P;
235  PRINT TAB(24);S(I)*P
240  NEXT I
250  END
```

Stored data

INPUT data

Computation and OUTPUT

This program prints the OUTPUT as a table, using TAB statements as shown in lines 190, 195, 230, and 235. The TAB statement tells the computer in which column to print the OUTPUT. To see how TAB works, observe the positions of the OUTPUT.

## Exercises

1. RUN the given program. Use 7, 4, 12, and 15 as the numbers of items.

2. Modify the program to compute the total cost. RUN the program to find the total cost of the items in Exercise 1.

# 4-10 Problems without Solutions

**Objective** To recognize problems that do not have solutions.

Does every problem have a solution? Consider the following situation.

**Example** At Green's Country Restaurant, a shrimp salad cost as much as a roast beef sandwich and a glass of milk together. What was the price of each item if the sandwich cost three times as much as the milk and the salad cost one dollar less than four times as much as the milk?

**Solution**

Step 1 The problem asks for the price of each item: the sandwich, the glass of milk, and the shrimp salad.
The problem tells how the price of the sandwich relates to the price of the milk (*three times as much*) and how the price of the salad relates to the price of the milk (*one dollar less than four times as much*).

Step 2 Let $p$ = price of the glass of milk in dollars.

Then $3p$ = price of the sandwich, and $4p - 1$ = price of the salad.

Step 3 $\underbrace{\text{cost of salad}}$    is the same as    $\underbrace{\text{cost of milk and sandwich}}$

$$4p - 1 \qquad\qquad = \qquad\qquad p + 3p$$

Step 4 $$4p - 1 = 4p$$
$$-1 = 0$$

The equation obtained in Step 3 is equivalent to the false statement $-1 = 0$ and, therefore, has no solution. This means that the facts of the problem contain a contradiction and the problem has no solution!

In reading a problem, you should be on the lookout for facts that contradict each other. You should also be alert to recognize problems in which not enough facts are given for you to obtain a definite answer. Some of the problems in the following set can be solved; others fail to have solutions either because their facts are contradictory or because they contain too few facts.

## Problems

**Solve each problem if it has a solution. If a problem has no solution, explain why.**

A  **1.** Fred has just as many dimes as quarters. His quarters and dimes total $8. How many coins of each type has he?

2. Kandy buys more twenty-cent stamps than fifteen-cent stamps. How many of each of these kinds of stamps does she buy if the total cost of the stamps is $7.20?

3. In the course of a year, the sum of an investor's gains and losses was $1000. What were her gains that year? her losses?

4. Find two consecutive integers whose sum is 54.

5. A messenger left a drilling site and traveled by jeep at 60 km/h. Forty-five minutes after she left, it was discovered that she had been given the wrong parcel. How fast must a second messenger travel in order to overtake her in 1.5 h?

6. For the first half hour of his trip, Al Martinez drove at his normal speed, but then traffic forced him to slow to three fourths of his normal speed for the rest of his journey. Still, he made the trip in 2 hours. Find his normal driving speed.

7. Don is three times as old as Barbara. Six years ago the sum of their ages was 8. How old was Barbara 6 years ago?

8. The sponsor of a time-share vacation condominium plans to sell the permanent use of an apartment for 50 weeks of each year. Each week is designated to be either "prime" or "off-season." If each prime week sells for $7000 and each off-season week for $4000, and all weeks are sold, how many weeks must be prime in order for the sponsor to receive a total of $260,000 for the apartment?

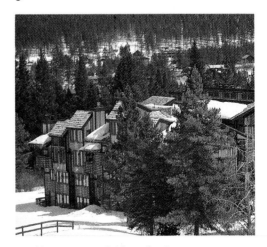

9. Find three consecutive integers whose sum is 36 more than the greatest of the integers.

10. A truck left town at noon and traveled at a uniform rate of 45 mph. At 1:00 P.M. the same day, a sedan set out from the same place at a uniform rate 10 mph greater. At what time did the sedan overtake the truck?

11. In going to a medical meeting, Dr. Lloyd made a trip of 500 miles. She traveled by train for $1\frac{1}{2}$ hours and by automobile for the rest of the trip. The average speed of the train was 15 miles per hour more than that of the automobile. Find the average speed of the automobile.

**B**  **12.** A square window is framed by two rectangular shutters. Each shutter is as long as one side of the window and the width of each shutter is 40 cm less than its length. If the area covered by one of the shutters is 4500 cm² less than the area of the window, find the dimensions of a shutter.

**13.** The edge of a certain cube is 1 cm longer then the edge of another cube. The total surface area of the first cube exceeds the total surface area of the smaller cube by 78 cm². Find the edge of the larger cube.

**14.** Eighteen-karat gold contains 18 parts by mass of gold to 6 parts of other metals. Fourteen-karat gold contains 14 parts of gold and 10 parts of other metals. How much eighteen-karat gold must be mixed with fourteen-karat gold to obtain 80 kg of an alloy containing 17 parts of gold and 7 parts of other metals?

**15.** Ella is 9 years older than Rick, and Rick is 8 years older than Donna. The sum of their ages 2 years ago was 10. How old is Ella?

**16.** Jack and Jill, together, have 19 paperback books. If Jack lost 3 of his books, but Jill doubled her supply, the two of them, together, would have 40 books. How many does each have now?

# Self-Test 3

***Vocabulary***     uniform motion (p. 163)

**1.** Solve the formula $\dfrac{PV}{T} = k$ for $V$.                    **Obj. 4-7, p. 161**

**Solve each problem. If a problem has no solution, explain why.**

**2.** At 9:00 A.M. two river boats are 210 km apart, and heading toward one another. At 3:00 P.M. the same day, they both pass Catfish Heights. If the northbound boat steams at a uniform rate of 15 km/h, find the rate of the southbound boat.          **Obj. 4-8, p. 163**

**3.** A rectangular swimming pool is 7 ft longer than it is wide. A wooden walk 1 ft wide is placed around the pool. The area covered by the pool and the walk is 58 square feet greater than the area covered by the pool alone. What are the dimensions of the pool?          **Obj. 4-9, p. 168**

**4.** A bank teller was asked to cash a check for $140 so as to give equal numbers of $5 bills and $10 bills. How many of each kind of bill did she count out?          **Obj. 4-10, p. 172**

Check your answers with those at the back of the book.

# Chapter Summary

1. The expression $b^n$ is an abbreviation for $\underbrace{b \cdot b \cdot b \cdot \,\cdots\, \cdot b.}_{n \text{ factors}}$

   The base is $b$ and the exponent is $n$.

2. To simplify expressions that contain powers, the steps listed on page 138 are followed.

3. To add (or subtract) polynomials, you add (or subtract) their similar terms. Similar terms have the same variables to the same powers.

4. Rules of Exponents

$$a^m \cdot a^n = a^{m+n} \qquad (a^m)^n = a^{mn} \qquad (ab)^m = a^m b^m$$

5. Polynomials can be multiplied in a vertical or horizontal form by applying the distributive axiom (p. 64). Before multiplying, it is wise to rearrange the terms of each polynomial in order of increasing or decreasing degree in one variable.

6. A formula may be transformed to express a particular variable in terms of the other variables.

7. A three-column chart can be used to solve problems about distances or areas. The formulas which head these columns are:

$$\text{rate} \times \text{time} = \text{distance}$$
$$\text{length} \times \text{width} = \text{area of rectangle}$$

8. Problems may fail to have solutions due to contradictory facts or due to too few facts.

# Chapter Review

**Give the letter of the correct answer.**

1. Express the square of $(x + y)$ in exponential form.      4-1
   - **a.** $x^2 + y^2$
   - **b.** $x^2 y^2$
   - **c.** $2x^2 y^2$
   - **d.** $(x + y)^2$

2. Evaluate $8 - 3^3$.
   - **a.** 125
   - **b.** $-125$
   - **c.** $-1$
   - **d.** $-19$

3. Simplify $xy^2 + 4x^2 y - 6 + (5xy^2 - 5x^2 y - 7)$.      4-2
   - **a.** $6xy^2 - 9x^2 y - 1$
   - **b.** $6xy^2 - x^2 y - 13$
   - **c.** $5xy^2 - 13$
   - **d.** $6xy^2 - x^2 y - 1$

4. Solve $x - (15x - 6) = 104$.
   - **a.** $-7$
   - **b.** $-6\frac{1}{8}$
   - **c.** $-6\frac{7}{8}$
   - **d.** 7

5. Simplify $8x^5\left(-\frac{1}{8}x^5\right)$.      4-3
   - **a.** $-64x^5$
   - **b.** $-x^5$
   - **c.** $-x^{25}$
   - **d.** $-x^{10}$

**6.** Evaluate $x^5 \cdot x^6$ if $x = -1$.
    **a.** 30                **b.** $-30$             **c.** $-1$                **d.** 1

4-4

**7.** Simplify $(-3x^2y^4)^3$.
    **a.** $9x^5y^7$           **b.** $-9x^5y^7$          **c.** $27x^6y^{12}$        **d.** $-27x^6y^{12}$

**8.** Simplify $8n^3\left(\dfrac{1}{2}n\right)^4$.

    **a.** $32n^7$           **b.** $\dfrac{1}{2}n^7$          **c.** $4n^{12}$         **d.** $32n^{12}$

4-5

**9.** Simplify $-6[16a - 8(2a - 2)]$.
    **a.** 12                **b.** $-96a$          **c.** 0               **d.** $-96$

**10.** Solve $6 - 2(n - 3) = 12$.
    **a.** 0                **b.** 6                **c.** $-6$            **d.** $-4\dfrac{1}{2}$

4-6

**11.** Multiply $(3c - 1)(3c + 1)$.
    **a.** $6c^2 - 6c - 2$     **b.** $9c^2 - 1$       **c.** $9c^2 - 6c - 1$     **d.** $6c^2 - 2$

**12.** Multiply $(c - 6)(c - 7)$.
    **a.** $2c + 42$        **b.** $c^2 - c + 42$     **c.** $c^2 - 13c + 42$     **d.** $c^2 - 42c - 13$

**13.** Multiply $(a - b)(a^2 + ab + b^2)$.
    **a.** $a^3 - b^3$                 **b.** $a^3 + a^2b + ab^2$
    **c.** $a - a^2b - ab^2 - b^3$       **d.** $a^3 + 2a^2b + 2ab^2 - b^3$

4-7

**14.** Solve for $b$ in the equation $ax + b = c$.
    **a.** $b = \dfrac{c - x}{a}$     **b.** $b = ax - c$     **c.** $b = c + ax$     **d.** $b = c - ax$

**15.** Solve for $y$ in the equation $\dfrac{xy + z}{2} = a$.

    **a.** $y = \dfrac{2a + z}{x}$           **b.** $y = \dfrac{2a - z}{x}$
    **c.** $y = 2ax - zx$           **d.** $y = 2ax + zx$

**16.** Erin ran a certain distance at $0.4$ km/min and returned to her starting
point at $0.3$ km/min. If her total running time was 21 min, how far did
she run in all?
    **a.** 9 km           **b.** 18 km         **c.** 3.6 km       **d.** 7.2 km

4-8

**17.** A rug is 1 m longer than it is wide. It is centered in a room so that it
is surrounded by a border of hardwood floor 0.5 m wide. Find the dimensions of the room if the area of the border is $8$ m$^2$.
    **a.** 3 m by 4 m            **b.** 4 m by 5 m
    **c.** 5 m by 6 m            **d.** 7 m by 8 m

4-9

**18.** Esteban has 16 coins that total $3.00. If he has only nickels and quar-
ters, how many quarters does he have?
    **a.** no solution—not enough facts       **b.** no solution—facts contradict
    **c.** 5                                          **d.** 11

4-10

# Chapter Test

**Rewrite each expression in exponential form.**

4-1

**1.** The quantity $xy$ squared.

**2.** The sum of the squares of $x$ and $y$.

**3.** Simplify $(4^2 - 3 \times 1 - 3^2) \div [0 - (-2)^2]$.

**In Exercises 4 and 5:**
**a. Add the polynomials.**
**b. Subtract the lower polynomial from the upper one.**

4-2

**4.**   $6x^2 - 5x - 1$
$\phantom{xx}-6x^2 + 5x + 1$

**5.**   $x^2 + 2xy + 3y^2$
$\phantom{xx}5x^2 - \phantom{x}xy - \phantom{x}y^2$

**Simplify.**

4-3

**6.** $-15c^2(-7cd)$

**7.** $(12a^2)\left(\frac{2}{3}a^3\right)$

**8.** $7^2 \cdot 7^a$

**Simplify.**

4-4

**9.** $(2a^2)^6$

**10.** $3^4 x^4$

**11.** $4n^3\left(\frac{1}{2}n\right)^4$

**Multiply.**

4-5

**12.** $-5(16 - 9n)$

**13.** $-3xy(7x^2 - 8xy + 9y^2)$

**14.** Solve $\frac{5}{6}(12x - 6) - 4(3x - 1) = 0$.

**Multiply.**

4-6

**15.** $(a - 1)(2a^2 - 5a - 1)$

**16.** $(2c + d)(9c^2 - 8cd + d^2)$

**Solve for the variable shown in color.**

4-7

**17.** $F = \frac{9}{5}C + 32;$ $C$

**18.** $D = \frac{a}{2}(2t - 1);$ $a$

4-8

**19.** Lynn swims at an average speed of 3.6 km/h. If Becky swims 2.25 km in the same time Lynn swims 1.8 km, what is Becky's average speed?

4-9

**20.** Elrod is mowing a rectangular lawn. The lawn is 5 m shorter than it is long. If Elrod mows a strip 0.5 m wide around the outside, the area of this border will be 28 m. Find the dimensions of the uncut lawn.

4-10

**21.** Solve the following problem if it has a solution. If it does not, explain why.

Dirk is twice as old as Meghan. If Meghan is 8 years old, in how many years will their ages be 4 years apart?

# Cumulative Review (Chapters 1–4)

**Simplify.**

**1.** $-4|3 - 21|$

**2.** $\frac{1}{2}(101 - 43)$

**3.** $-2.2 + 3.8 - 5.6 + 4$

**4.** $15s - (2s - 9)$

**5.** $-29 - (-45) \div 3$

**6.** $-\frac{3}{5} + 4\frac{5}{8} - \frac{2}{5} + 7\frac{1}{8}$

**7.** $3^3 + 42 \div 3 + 4$

**8.** $(9a - 5) + (4a + 7)$

**9.** $(12z - 2) - (4z + 3)$

**10.** $(6x^6)(4x^4) - 5(3x^3)(x^7)$

**11.** $(4a^n)^3(5a^n)^2$

**12.** $5(3z^2 - 2z + 4)$

**13.** $-4x^2(3x^2 - 2x - 5)$

**14.** $(4a - 1)(2a + 3)$

**15.** $(5 - 4x)(3 + 2x)$

**Evaluate each expression if $a = -2$, $b = -1$, $c = 2$, and $d = \frac{1}{4}$.**

**16.** $d(3a + c)$

**17.** $d(ab - c)$

**18.** $(ac + b)^3$

**19.** $(4 + a^2b)^2$

**Solve. If the equation is an identity or has no solution, state that fact.**

**20.** $|-t| = 5$

**21.** $|y - 1| + 4 = 0$

**22.** $|x| + 5 = 5$

**23.** $c - (-4) = -8$

**24.** $\frac{1}{5}x = 90$

**25.** $42z = -42$

**26.** $\frac{1}{3}t + 2 = 0$

**27.** $4z + 2 = -10$

**28.** $7y - 4 = 6y + 6$

**29.** $(7y - 5) + (6 - 5y) = 23$

**30.** $(11x - 3) - (4 + 2x) = 11$

**31.** $(2n + 9) + (5n - 4) = 6n + 9$

**32.** $5(2 - 3z) = -4(4z + 9)$

**33.** $-3(m + 7) - 5 = 4$

**34.** $(2x - 3)(3x + 1) = (3x - 4)(2x + 2)$

**35.** Solve for $m$: $am - bn = c$

**Solve.**

**36.** One third of the sum of two consecutive odd integers is 5 less than the smaller integer. Find both integers.

**37.** Frank has 24 dimes and nickels. Rick has $\frac{2}{3}$ as many nickels and $1\frac{1}{2}$ times as many dimes as Frank has. If Rick and Frank have the same amount of money, how much does each of them have?

**38.** Jessica and Amy left school at the same time and began walking in opposite directions. Jessica walked at a rate of 3.6 km/h and Amy walked at a rate of 4.2 km/h. How far apart were they after 10 min?

**39.** A rectangular piece of cardboard is trimmed to make a square by cutting a 4-cm strip off the top and a 2-cm strip off one side. If the area of the original piece is 74 cm² greater than the area of the square, find the dimensions of the rectangle.

# Maintaining Skills

**Simplify.**

*Example 1* $614 - (821 - 911)$

*Solution* $614 - (821 - 911) = 614 - (-90) = 614 + 90 = 704$

1. $1921 + (-876)$
2. $181 + 97 - 64$
3. $(55 - 82) + (91 - 108)$
4. $-78 - 84 - (-92)$
5. $(28 - 86) - (46 - 81)$
6. $284 - (93 - 165)$
7. $35 - (58 + 62)$
8. $-325 + (-726) + 922$
9. $\frac{7}{8} - \left(-\frac{1}{4} + \frac{1}{2}\right)$
10. $\left(\frac{3}{5} - \frac{2}{3}\right) - \frac{5}{9}$
11. $17.6 - (8.05 - 9.6)$
12. $112.72 + (92.04 - 87.6)$

*Example 2* $-53(28) + 27(-40)$

*Solution* $-53(28) + 27(-40) = -1484 + (-1080)$
$$= -2564$$

*Example 3* $(-814 + 776) \div (-19)$

*Solution* $(-814 + 776) \div (-19) = -38 \div (-19)$
$$= 2$$

13. $-12(-16) + 5(-24)$
14. $27(20) - 60(48)$
15. $-65 - (412 - 385)$
16. $-4(-50) + 8(25)$
17. $9.25(-2.3)$
18. $-6.06(-5.4)$
19. $-82.05 \div (-25)$
20. $-\frac{24}{35} \div \frac{9}{14}$
21. $7.24 \div (-0.25)$
22. $-\frac{12}{25} \times \left(-\frac{35}{42}\right)$
23. $-\frac{18}{35} \times \frac{49}{54}$
24. $-\frac{15}{64} \times \left(-\frac{40}{27}\right)$
25. $-2\frac{3}{8} \div \left(-2\frac{1}{8}\right)$

*Example 4* $82 + (-14)^2 \div 7 + 6$

*Solution* $82 + (-14)^2 \div 7 + 6 = 82 + 196 \div 7 + 6$
$$= 82 + 28 + 6$$
$$= 116$$

26. $7 \times 8^2 - 6 \times 3 - 12 \div 2$
27. $(29 + 7) \div 3^2 + 13 - 2^2$
28. $(0.6)^2 - 1.2^2 \div 8 + 0.27 \div 0.3$
29. $-2(0.35 + 0.55)^2 \div 1.8 \div 2$
30. $1\frac{4}{5} \div 9 \times \frac{1}{2} - \left(\frac{1}{3} + \frac{1}{2}\right)^2$
31. $-\frac{5}{7}\left[-\left(1\frac{1}{3} - \frac{3}{4}\right)\right] + \frac{1}{3} \div 4$

# Mixed Review
## Skills and Problem Solving

**Solve. If the equation is an identity or has no solution, state that fact.**

1. $3n - 1 = 11$

2. $(2y - 2)(y + 1) = 2(y - 3)(y + 4)$

3. $|b| = \dfrac{20 - 5^2}{3}$

4. $\dfrac{1}{2}(q + 3) = 10$

**Simplify.**

5. $(x + 3)(2x - 4)$

6. $(x + 3) - (2x - 4)$

7. $(x + 3) + (2x - 4)$

8. $(x^2 + 3^2) - (x + 3)^2$

9. Brian is 8 years older than Maura and Maura is 8 years older than Pete. The sum of their ages is 27. How old is Pete?

10. Solve $|x - 2| - 2 = 2$ if $x \in \{-3, -2, -1, 0, 1, 2, 3, 4, 5, 6, 7\}$.

**Write the axiom illustrated in each of the following statements.**

11. $6 \cdot \dfrac{2}{2} = 6$

12. $(7 + 4) + 3 = 3 + (7 + 4)$

13. $(8a)c = 8(ac)$

14. $3(m + 2) = 3m + 6$

15. $(5z + 3) + 0 = 5z + 3$

16. If $x = -2$, then $x + 11 = 9$.

17. Evaluate $(-ab^2c)^2 - (ab)^2c$ if $a = -2$, $b = -1$, and $c = 2$.

18. Write the numbers $-\left(\dfrac{1}{2}\right)^2$, $-2$, $3$, $\left(-\dfrac{1}{3}\right)^2$, $-1$, $|-2|$ in order from least to greatest.

19. Sarah finished second in a 10-km road race. If she could have increased her average speed by 1.25 km/h, she would have won with a time of 30 min. What was her average speed?

20. A bag contains 44 nickels, dimes, and quarters. There are twice as many dimes as nickels and 8 more quarters than nickels. How much money is in the bag?

21. The area of a trapezoid is given by the formula $A = \dfrac{1}{2}h(b_1 + b_2)$, where $h$ is the height and $b_1$ and $b_2$ are the lengths of the bases. Solve this equation for $h$. State the restrictions, if any, for the new formula to be meaningful.

22. Write an inequality for the following. The opposite of the sum of negative two and $a$ is greater than the difference of $a$ and the opposite of four.

23. Four consecutive odd integers are such that the product of the second and fourth minus the product of the first and third is 48. Find the integers.

# Preparing for College Entrance Exams

**Decide which is the best of the choices given and write the corresponding letter on your answer sheet.**

1. *ABCD* is a rectangle. Each of the longer sides is 3 cm shorter than twice a shorter side. The perimeter of the rectangle is 24 cm. Find the length of a longer side.
   **(A)** 11 cm      **(B)** 7 cm      **(C)** 5 cm      **(D)** 9 cm

2. Twice the sum of two consecutive integers is 10 less than 5 times the smaller integer. Find the larger integer.
   **(A)** 12      **(B)** 14      **(C)** 13      **(D)** −6      **(E)** −8

3. Jess is twice as old as Phil and Phil's age is three fourths of Megan's age. Four years ago Jess's age was the same as Phil's and Megan's ages together. Find the sum of the ages of these three people now.
   **(A)** 48      **(B)** 52      **(C)** 60      **(D)** 44

4. The Hawks' baseball park has reserved seats and bleacher seats. There are four times as many reserved seats as bleacher seats. Reserved seats cost $4 more than bleacher seats. Which of the following is (are) sufficient to determine the amount of money collected on a sellout day?
   I.   the number of bleacher seats     II. the cost of a bleacher seat
   III. the total number of seats
   **(A)** I only      **(B)** II only      **(C)** III only      **(D)** I and II only

5. Evaluate the expression $(a + b)^2 \div (2a) - b^2$ if $a = 6$ and $b = 4$.
   **(A)** $-\frac{23}{3}$      **(B)** $-13$      **(C)** $-25$      **(D)** $\frac{25}{16}$

6. Find $(2n^3)^2$ if $(n + 2)(n + 3) = (4 - n)(12 - n)$.
   **(A)** 144      **(B)** 128      **(C)** 256      **(D)** 784

7. Solve for $p$ in the equation $q = 1 + \frac{p}{100}$.
   **(A)** $p = 100q - 1$      **(B)** $p = \frac{q - 1}{100}$      **(C)** $p = 100(q - 1)$      **(D)** $p = 1 + \frac{q}{100}$

8. On the 16-km trip to the ball field, Lea ran for 20 min, then walked the rest of the way. Her walking speed was 18 km/h slower than her running speed. How long did the trip take?
   **(A)** 30 min      **(B)** 40 min      **(C)** 50 min      **(D)** 60 min
   **(E)** Cannot be determined from the given information

# 5  Factoring Polynomials

Fireworks produce spectacular displays of light, noise, and smoke. The curved path of fireworks at a given time ($t$) can be represented by a polynomial in the form $at^2 + bt + c$.

# Quotients and Factoring

## 5-1 Factoring Integers

**Objective** To factor integers.

When you write

$$72 = 9 \cdot 8 \quad \text{or} \quad 72 = (2)(36),$$

you have *factored* 72. In the first case the factors are 9 and 8; in the second case they are 2 and 36. You could also write $72 = (\frac{1}{2})(144)$ and call $\frac{1}{2}$ and 144 factors of 72. Usually, however, you are interested only in factors drawn from a specified set. The given number is then said to be **factored** over the given set, called the **factor set.** In this text, *integers will be factored over the set of integers* unless some other set is specified. Such factors are called *integral* factors.

You can find factors by dividing. If the remainder is zero, the divisor is a factor. For example,

$-5$ is a factor of 110 because $110 \div (-5) = -22$

but 8 is not a factor of 110 because $110 \div 8 = 13 \text{ R}6.$

You can find the *positive factors* of a positive integer by dividing it by the positive integers in succession until a previous factor is repeated. Thus:

$$72 = (1)(72) = (2)(36) = (3)(24) = (4)(18) = (6)(12) = (8)(9)$$

A set of numbers useful in factoring is the set of *prime numbers,* or *primes.* A **prime number,** or **prime,** is an integer *greater than* 1 that has no positive integral factor other than itself and 1. The first ten prime numbers are:

$$2, 3, 5, 7, 11, 13, 17, 19, 23, 29$$

A systematic way to find the prime factors of positive integers is to try the primes, in order, as divisors. You divide by each prime as many times as possible before going on to the next. This technique is illustrated at the right. The final result is

$$588 = 2 \cdot 294$$
$$= 2 \cdot 2 \cdot 147$$
$$= 2 \cdot 2 \cdot 3 \cdot 49$$
$$= 2 \cdot 2 \cdot 3 \cdot 7 \cdot 7$$
$$= 2^2 \cdot 3 \cdot 7^2$$

$$588 = 2^2 \cdot 3 \cdot 7^2.$$

This factorization shows that the prime factors of 588 are 2, 3, and 7. The expression of a positive integer as a product of prime factors is called the **prime factorization** of the integer.

It can be proved by advanced methods that the prime factorization of an integer is *unique* (one and only one) except for the order in which the factors are written. (If 1 were to be considered a prime factor, the factorization would not be unique because 1 could be considered to be a factor any number of times.)

A factor of two or more integers is called a **common factor** of the integers. The greatest integer that is a factor of two or more integers is called the **greatest common factor (GCF) of the integers.**

The following example shows how you can use the prime factorization of two integers to find their greatest common factor.

**Example**     Find the GCF of 594 and 693.

**Solution**     First find the prime factorization of each integer. Then form the product of the smaller powers of each common prime factor.

$$594 = 2 \cdot 3^3 \cdot 11 \qquad 693 = 3^2 \cdot 7 \cdot 11$$

The common prime factors are 3 and 11.
The smaller powers of 3 and 11 are $3^2$ and 11, respectively.
The greatest common factor of 594 and 693 is $3^2 \cdot 11$, or 99.   *Answer*

## Oral Exercises

**Give all the positive factors of each number.**

| | | | | | |
|---|---|---|---|---|---|
| **1.** 14 | **2.** 41 | **3.** 57 | **4.** 70 | **5.** 1 | **6.** 45 |

**State whether or not the number is prime. Find the prime factorization of the number.**

| | | | | | |
|---|---|---|---|---|---|
| **7.** 32 | **8.** 117 | **9.** 97 | **10.** 125 | **11.** 121 | **12.** 43 |
| **13.** 36 | **14.** 89 | **15.** 59 | **16.** 147 | **17.** 84 | **18.** 107 |

**Find the GCF of each pair of numbers.**

| | | | |
|---|---|---|---|
| **19.** 36 and 48 | **20.** 27 and 54 | **21.** 22 and 35 | **22.** 17 and 39 |

## Written Exercises

**List all the pairs of integral factors of each integer.**

**Example**     50

**Solution**     (1)(50), (2)(25), (5)(10), $(-1)(-50)$, $(-2)(-25)$, $(-5)(-10)$

| **A** | **1.** 18 | **2.** 30 | **3.** 37 | **4.** 63 | **5.** 64 |
|---|---|---|---|---|---|
| | **6.** 49 | **7.** 101 | **8.** 68 | **9.** 83 | **10.** 65 |

**11–20.** List all the pairs of factors of the opposites of the integers in Exercises 1–10.

**Give the prime factorization of each number.**

| **B** | **21.** 99 | **22.** 120 | **23.** 104 | **24.** 128 | **25.** 189 |
|---|---|---|---|---|---|
| | **26.** 250 | **27.** 476 | **28.** 539 | **29.** 408 | **30.** 576 |
| | **31.** 242 | **32.** 280 | **33.** 455 | **34.** 1024 | **35.** 600 |

**Give the GCF of each group of numbers.**

| **36.** 78, 90 | **37.** 28, 182 | **38.** 147, 275 | **39.** 144, 180 |
|---|---|---|---|
| **40.** 315, 350 | **41.** 252, 288 | **42.** 693, 882 | **43.** 1925, 2100 |
| **44.** 28, 56, 70 | **45.** 105, 110, 132 | **46.** 80, 96, 135 | **47.** 65, 91, 143 |

## Computer Exercises

*For students with some programming experience*

1. Write a BASIC program that uses the INT function to test whether an integer entered with an INPUT statement is even or odd.

2. Write a BASIC program that uses the INT function to test whether one integer is a factor of another integer. Both integers should be entered with an INPUT statement.

3. Write a BASIC program that uses the INT function to test whether two integers entered with INPUT statements have any factors in common other than 1. (Two integers whose only common factor is 1 are called *relatively prime*.)

## Challenge

The Coles are racing the Browns in the annual Fourth of July canoe race across Eagle Pond and back. Sixty meters before the Browns reach the opposite shore, they meet the Coles, who have already reached the opposite shore and are on their way back. It takes the Browns 40 seconds before they reach the opposite shore and return to the point where they met the Coles. Thirty-five seconds later the Coles win the race, 195 meters ahead of the Browns. Find the speed of each canoe and the width of the pond. (Assume no time is lost on the turn around.)

BASIC has a function, INT(N), that will enable you to find factors of integers. INT(N) will give the greatest integer *less than or equal to N*.

$$INT(4) = 4, \; INT(4.9) = 4, \; INT(-4.9) = -5$$

This function can be used to find factors, since

$$INT(12/3) = 12/3, \text{ but } INT(12/5) \neq 12/5.$$

The following program will PRINT pairs of factors of a positive integer. (*F* and *Q* represent the factors.)

```
 10  PRINT "TO FIND PAIRS OF FACTORS"
 20  PRINT "OF A POSITIVE INTEGER:"
 30  PRINT "WHAT IS YOUR POSITIVE INTEGER";
 40  INPUT W
 50  LET C=0
 60  FOR F=1 TO W/2
 70  LET Q=W/F
 80  IF Q <> INT(Q) THEN 110
 90  PRINT F;" AND ";Q;" ARE FACTORS OF ";W;"."
100  LET C=C+1
110  NEXT F
120  IF C>1 THEN 140
130  PRINT W;" IS PRIME,"
140  END
```

Lines 60–70: No additional factors will be found between *W*/2 and *W*.

Line 80: $\neq$ is written $<>$ in BASIC.

### Exercises

**1. a.** RUN the program for the following values of *W*.
   30, 31, 32, 33, 34, 35, 36, 37, 38, 39, 40
   **b.** Which of the numbers in part (a) are prime?
   **c.** Which number has a pair of equal factors?

**2.** Explain the purpose of lines 50, 100, and 120.

**3.** Insert these lines into the program and RUN it for *W* = 36.

```
91  FOR I = 1 TO F
92  FOR J = 1 TO Q
93  PRINT "*";
94  NEXT J
95  PRINT
96  NEXT I
```

Notice that the J-loop is inside the I-loop, which is inside the F-loop. Such loops are called *nested loops*.

*Note:* The program above can be used to do Exercises 1–10 on page 185.

# 5-2 Dividing Monomials

**Objective**  To divide and factor monomials.

There are three basic rules that are used to simplify fractions and quotients of monomials. The property of quotients (proved in Exercise 45 on page 190) enables you to express a fraction as a product.

---

**Property of Quotients**

If $c$, $d$, $x$, and $y$ are any real numbers, $d \neq 0$, and $y \neq 0$, then

$$\frac{cx}{dy} = \frac{c}{d} \cdot \frac{x}{y}.$$

---

**Example 1**  $\dfrac{14}{45} = \dfrac{2 \cdot 7}{9 \cdot 5} = \dfrac{2}{9} \cdot \dfrac{7}{5}$

If you let $d = c$ in the quotient rule, you derive the cancellation rule stated below. (This rule is proved in Exercise 46 on page 190.)

---

**Cancellation Rule for Fractions**

If $c$, $x$, and $y$ are any real numbers, $c \neq 0$, and $y \neq 0$, then

$$\frac{cx}{cy} = \frac{x}{y}.$$

---

The cancellation rule enables you to divide the numerator and denominator of a fraction by the same nonzero number. In the following examples, assume that no denominator equals 0.

**Example 2**  $\dfrac{3xy}{15x} = \dfrac{\cancel{3x} \cdot y}{\cancel{3x} \cdot 5} = \dfrac{y}{5}$  $\qquad \begin{cases} \text{The red marks indicate that both the} \\ \text{numerator and the denominator are} \\ \text{divided by } 3x. \end{cases}$

The cancellation rule can be used to simplify a quotient of two powers of the same number.

**Example 3**  Simplify:  **a.** $\dfrac{y^8}{y^5}$  **b.** $\dfrac{z}{z^7}$  **c.** $\dfrac{x^4}{x^4}$

**Solution**  **a.** $\dfrac{y^8}{y^5} = \dfrac{\cancel{y^5} \cdot y^3}{\cancel{y^5}} = y^3$  **b.** $\dfrac{z}{z^7} = \dfrac{\cancel{z}}{\cancel{z} \cdot z^6} = \dfrac{1}{z^6}$  **c.** $\dfrac{x^4}{x^4} = x^4 \cdot \dfrac{1}{x^4} = 1$

Example 3 illustrates the following rule of exponents for division.

---

### Rule of Exponents for Division

When $m$ and $n$ are positive integers and $a$ is a real number not equal to 0:

If $m > n$:

$$\frac{a^m}{a^n} = a^{m-n}$$

If $n > m$:

$$\frac{a^m}{a^n} = \frac{1}{a^{n-m}}$$

If $n = m$:

$$\frac{a^m}{a^n} = 1$$

---

In short, the rule above says that when you divide powers you subtract the smaller exponent from the larger exponent if the exponents are different. You have already seen that when you multiply powers you add the exponents.

A quotient of monomials is said to be *simplified* when each base appears only once, when there are no powers of powers, and when all fractions have been expressed in simplest form. Examples 4 and 5 show that all three rules presented in this section may be needed to simplify quotients of monomials.

**Example 4** $\quad \dfrac{18t^5}{-3t^6} = \dfrac{18}{-3} \cdot \dfrac{t^5}{t^6} = -6 \cdot \dfrac{1}{t} = -\dfrac{6}{t}, \ (t \neq 0)$

**Example 5** $\quad \dfrac{21ab^{10}}{49a^7b^9c} = \dfrac{21}{49} \cdot \dfrac{1}{a^{7-1}} \cdot b^{10-9} \cdot \dfrac{1}{c}$

$$= \frac{3}{7} \cdot \frac{1}{a^6} \cdot b \cdot \frac{1}{c} = \frac{3b}{7a^6c}, \ (a \neq 0, \ b \neq 0, \ c \neq 0)$$

The **greatest common factor of two or more monomials** is defined to be the common factor that has the greatest coefficient and the greatest degree in each variable. Example 6 shows how to find the greatest common factor of two monomials.

**Example 6**  Find the greatest common factor of $30xz^4$ and $100x^3y^2z^8$.

**Solution**   Form the product of the GCF of the numerical coefficients and the smaller power of each variable that appears in *both* monomials.

GCF of 30 and 100: 10     Smaller power of $x$: $x$
Smaller power of $z$: $z^4$     $y$ is not a common factor.

The greatest common monomial factor of $30xz^4$ and $100x^3y^2z^8$ is $10xz^4$. *Answer*

## Oral Exercises

**Simplify each expression, assuming that no denominator equals zero.**

1. $\dfrac{3x}{x}$  2. $\dfrac{8a^2}{2a}$  3. $\dfrac{5bc}{10b^6}$  4. $\dfrac{3c^2d^5}{cd^3}$  5. $\dfrac{-8x^3}{2x}$

6. $\dfrac{3^{10}}{3^8}$  7. $\dfrac{a^8b^4}{a^3b^4}$  8. $-\dfrac{12t^7}{9t^9}$  9. $\dfrac{(st)^7}{(st)^5}$  10. $\dfrac{a-b}{(a-b)^{12}}$

11. $\dfrac{4.8 \times 10^5}{2.4 \times 10^2}$  12. $\dfrac{6x^{12}y^2}{2x^8y}$  13. $\dfrac{7r^3s^2}{49r^3s}$  14. $\dfrac{2u^4v^{10}}{-u^5v^5}$  15. $\dfrac{-12c^{12}}{-4c^4}$

**Find the greatest common factor of the given monomials.**

16. $8x,\ 2xy$  17. $3a^2,\ 6a$  18. $5x^2y,\ 10xy^2$  19. $12u^3v^2,\ 5uv^3$

20. $14s^5t^2,\ 21s^3t^3$  21. $36x^2y^4,\ 15x^3y^5$  22. $2a^2b,\ ab^2c$  23. $4r^6s^7,\ 6r^6s^4$

## Written Exercises

**Simplify each expression, assuming that no denominator equals zero.**

A  1. $\dfrac{9a^4}{3a}$  2. $\dfrac{-18r^3t}{12rt^5}$  3. $\dfrac{-8xy}{-24xy^3}$  4. $\dfrac{13a^4b^9}{26a^2b^2}$

5. $\dfrac{6(xy)^5}{8(xy)^3}$  6. $\dfrac{-36u^5v^4}{27uv^6}$  7. $\dfrac{-16a^5b^3}{-24a^5b^7}$  8. $\dfrac{14x^2yz^3}{35xy^3z}$

9. $\dfrac{(x^2)^4}{(x^3)^3}$  10. $\dfrac{(3a)^3}{3a^3}$  11. $\dfrac{(3y)^2}{(3y)^3}$  12. $\dfrac{5k^3}{(5k)^3}$

13. $\dfrac{(2x)^4}{2x^4}$  14. $\dfrac{(-x)^8}{-x^6}$  15. $\dfrac{(-2y)^3}{(y^2)^3}$  16. $\dfrac{(a^5)^3}{(a^4)^4}$

17. $\dfrac{(4ab^2)^3}{(2a^2b)^4}$  18. $\dfrac{(3a^5)(2a^4)}{(6a^3)^2}$  19. $\dfrac{(13c^4d)^2}{(13cd^2)^3}$  20. $\dfrac{-(8x^2y)^4}{(8x^2y)^5}$

**Find the missing factor.**

**Example**  $36a^5b^8 = (12a^3b^2)(\underline{\ ?\ })$   **Solution**  $\dfrac{36a^5b^8}{12a^3b^2} = 3a^2b^6$  **Answer**

21. $9a^5 = (3a)(\underline{\ ?\ })$  22. $12a^2b = (3a)(\underline{\ ?\ })$

23. $-4c^3d^3 = (2cd^2)(\underline{\ ?\ })$  24. $35u^5v^6 = (7uv)(\underline{\ ?\ })$

25. $24x^6y^4 = (-3x^2y^2)(\underline{\ ?\ })$  26. $-18x^3y^5 = (-9x^2y)(\underline{\ ?\ })$

27. $98a^7b^4 = (\underline{\ ?\ })(14a^7b)$  28. $156k^3z^5n = (-13k^2z)(\underline{\ ?\ })$

B  29. $(a^2b)^6 = (a^2b)^4(\underline{\ ?\ })$  30. $(3xy)^5 = (3xy)^4(\underline{\ ?\ })$

31. $144x^6y^3 = (-12xy)^2(\underline{\ ?\ })$  32. $42x^4y^5 = (3x^2y)(2xy)(\underline{\ ?\ })$

33. $36a^8b^5 = (6ab^2)(3a^4b)(\underline{\ ?\ })$  34. $72x^5y^8 = (3xy^2)^2(2y^3)(\underline{\ ?\ })$

**Find the greatest common factor of the given monomials.**

**35.** $16rs^2t^3$, $40r^3s^3t^2$      **36.** $18k^2m^4n$, $27km^2n$      **37.** $25ab^2$, $15ab^2$, $36a^2b^2$

**38.** $21m^3n^2$, $14m^2n^3$; $35m^4n$     **39.** $(x+y)(x-y)^3$, $2(x+y)^4$   **40.** $4r^8(r+1)^7$, $9r^2(r-1)$

**Simplify each expression, assuming that $x \neq 0$, $y \neq 0$, and $n$ is a positive integer.**

**C**   **41.** $\dfrac{152x^n}{133x}$      **42.** $\dfrac{162y^{2n+2}}{54y^{2n+3}}$      **43.** $\dfrac{x^{3n}y^{n+1}}{-x^ny}$      **44.** $\dfrac{667x^{5n+2}y^{2n}}{460(xy)^{2n}}$

**Give a reason for each step in the proofs of the property of quotients and the cancellation rule for fractions. Assume that $c$, $d$, $x$, and $y$ are real numbers, $c \neq 0$, $d \neq 0$, and $y \neq 0$. Once you prove the property of quotients, you may use it in the proof of the cancellation rule.**

**45.** Property of quotients: $\dfrac{cx}{dy} = \dfrac{c}{d} \cdot \dfrac{x}{y}$         **46.** Cancellation rule for fractions: $\dfrac{cx}{cy} = \dfrac{x}{y}$

$\dfrac{cx}{dy} = cx\left(\dfrac{1}{dy}\right)$    (1) ___?___

$= cx\left(\dfrac{1}{d} \cdot \dfrac{1}{y}\right)$    (2) ___?___

$= \left(c \cdot \dfrac{1}{d}\right)\left(x \cdot \dfrac{1}{y}\right)$    (3) ___?___ ; ___?___

$= \dfrac{c}{d} \cdot \dfrac{x}{y}$    (4) ___?___

$\dfrac{cx}{cy} = \dfrac{c}{c} \cdot \dfrac{x}{y}$    (1) ___?___

$= \left(c \cdot \dfrac{1}{c}\right) \cdot \dfrac{x}{y}$    (2) ___?___

$= 1 \cdot \dfrac{x}{y}$    (3) ___?___

$= \dfrac{x}{y}$    (4) ___?___

## Calculator Key-In

When you use a calculator to divide one number by another, the remainder, if any, is always given as a decimal. You can see what the remainder is and what fraction the decimal represents by using the following method.

1. Subtract the whole number part of the quotient from the entire quotient.
2. Multiply the decimal that remains from the subtraction by the divisor and round to the nearest integer.

The number that results from Step 2 is the remainder. Using this number as the numerator and the divisor as the denominator gives the value of the decimal as a fraction.

Find the remainder. Then give the value of the decimal as a fraction.

**1.** $354 \div 13$       **2.** $621 \div 7$       **3.** $753 \div 11$

**4.** $1258 \div 15$     **5.** $3698 \div 36$     **6.** $5829 \div 45$

# 5-3 Monomial Factors of Polynomials

**Objective**  To divide a polynomial by a monomial and to find a monomial factor of a polynomial.

The following result was proved earlier (see page 83):
If $a$, $b$, and $c$ are real numbers and $c \neq 0$,

$$\frac{a + b}{c} = \frac{a}{c} + \frac{b}{c}.$$

This result is also true when $a$, $b$, and $c$ are monomials and $c \neq 0$. It suggests a technique for dividing a polynomial by a monomial.

> To divide a polynomial by a monomial, divide each term of the polynomial by the monomial, and then add the quotients.

The examples below illustrate this technique. In these examples assume that no denominator equals 0.

**Example 1**  $\dfrac{4x^4 + 8x^3y - 12x^2y^2}{4x^2} = \dfrac{4x^4}{4x^2} + \dfrac{8x^3y}{4x^2} - \dfrac{12x^2y^2}{4x^2}$

$$= x^2 + 2xy - 3y^2$$

**Example 2**  $\dfrac{x^2y^2 + x - y}{xy} = \dfrac{x^2y^2}{xy} + \dfrac{x}{xy} - \dfrac{y}{xy}$

$$= xy + \frac{1}{y} - \frac{1}{x}$$

One polynomial is said to be **evenly divisible,** or simply **divisible,** by another polynomial if the quotient is also a polynomial. Example 1 shows that $4x^4 + 8x^3y - 12x^2y^2$ is evenly divisible by $4x^2$. Example 2 shows that $x^2y^2 + x - y$ is not evenly divisible by $xy$, since $\dfrac{1}{y}$ and $\dfrac{1}{x}$ are not polynomials.

You *factor* a polynomial by expressing it as a product of other polynomials. Unless otherwise stated, the *factor set for a polynomial having integral coefficients is the set of all polynomials having integral coefficients.*

You can use division to test for factors of a polynomial. Example 1 shows that you can factor $4x^4 + 8x^3y - 12x^2y^2$ as $4x^2(x^2 + 2xy - 3y^2)$. Notice that 4, $x^2$, and $4x^2$ are all factors of $4x^4 + 8x^3y - 12x^2y^2$. In general, you find the greatest monomial factor of a polynomial. The **greatest monomial factor of a polynomial** is the greatest common monomial factor of its terms. This process is illustrated in Examples 3 and 4 on the following page.

***Example 3*** Factor $4a^3b^2c - 12b^2c^3$.

***Solution***　1. The greatest monomial factor of $4a^3b^2c - 12b^2c^3$ is $4b^2c$.

2. Divide: $\dfrac{4a^3b^2c - 12b^2c^3}{4b^2c} = \dfrac{4a^3b^2c}{4b^2c} - \dfrac{12b^2c^3}{4b^2c} = a^3 - 3c^2$

3. $4a^3b^2c - 12b^2c^3 = 4b^2c(a^3 - 3c^2)$　***Answer***

***Example 4*** Factor $30x^5 + 45x^3 - 10x$.

***Solution***　1. The greatest monomial factor of $30x^5 + 45x^3 - 10x$ is $5x$.

2. Divide: $\dfrac{30x^5 + 45x^3 - 10x}{5x} = \dfrac{30x^5}{5x} + \dfrac{45x^3}{5x} - \dfrac{10x}{5x} = 6x^4 + 9x^2 - 2$

3. $30x^5 + 45x^3 - 10x = 5x(6x^4 + 9x^2 - 2)$　***Answer***

You should check your factorizations by multiplying the resulting factors. The checks for Examples 3 and 4 are left for you.

## *Oral Exercises*

**Divide. Assume that no denominator equals zero.**

**1.** $\dfrac{6a + 12}{6}$　　　**2.** $\dfrac{9x - 6y}{3}$　　　**3.** $\dfrac{6c - 18}{6}$　　　**4.** $\dfrac{33ab - 22b}{11b}$

**5.** $\dfrac{27a - 18b + 9c}{9}$　　**6.** $\dfrac{4a^3 - 10a^2 + 6a}{2a}$　　**7.** $\dfrac{6x^2y - 4xy^2}{2xy}$　　**8.** $\dfrac{9a^3b - 12ab^4}{3ab}$

**Find the greatest monomial factor. Then factor the polynomial.**

**9.** $9ab - 6$　　　　**10.** $8a^2 + 4a$　　　　**11.** $16xy + 12yz$　　　　**12.** $14ab - 21bc$

**13.** $3a^3 - 9ac$　　　**14.** $\pi r^2 + 2\pi r$　　　**15.** $x^2yz - wyz^2$　　　**16.** $5cd - 15ce$

## *Written Exercises*

**Divide. Assume that no denominator equals zero.**

A　**1.** $\dfrac{3a + 6}{3}$　　　　**2.** $\dfrac{18a - 12}{6}$　　　　**3.** $\dfrac{30x - 15}{5}$

**4.** $\dfrac{9a + 6b + 3}{3}$　　**5.** $\dfrac{4x - 8y + 12}{4}$　　**6.** $\dfrac{x^3 + 4x^2 + x}{x}$

**7.** $\dfrac{10xy - 15x^2}{5x}$　　**8.** $\dfrac{6a - 12a^2 - 18a^3}{6a}$　　**9.** $\dfrac{14y - 21y^2 - 7y^3}{7y}$

**10.** $\dfrac{9a^2b - 6ab^2}{3ab}$　　**11.** $\dfrac{24cd^3 - 18c^2d - 12c}{-6c}$　　**12.** $\dfrac{25x^4y^3 - 15x^2y^5}{5xy}$

**13.** $\dfrac{42s^4t^4 - 35st^2}{7st^2}$

**14.** $\dfrac{8yz^2 - 24y^3z - 32yz}{-8yz}$

**15.** $\dfrac{45d^4k^2 - 75d^3k + 30d^4}{15d^2}$

**16.** $\dfrac{32k^4z^2 - 96k^2z^4 - 48k^6z^2}{16k^2z^2}$

**Evaluate by factoring.**

*Example 1*  $4 \times 21 + 4 \times 79 = 4(21 + 79)$
$$= 4(100) = 400$$

**17.** $3 \times 78 + 7 \times 78$

**18.** $28 \times 43 - 18 \times 43$

**19.** $13 \times 19 + 4 \times 19 + 3 \times 19$

**20.** $9 \times 11^2 - 9 \times 11$

**21.** $81^2 + 81 \times 19$

**22.** $(18)^2 - 4 \times 9$

**23.** $32 \times 17 + 17^2 + 17$

**24.** $216 + 2 \times 36 + 5 \times 6$

**25.** $22 \times 14 \times 25 - 11 \times 21 \times 30$

**26.** $39 \times 21 \times 2 - 26 \times 7 \times 4$

**Express each polynomial as the product of its greatest monomial factor and another polynomial.**

**27.** $9p - 6q + 3$

**28.** $4x - 8y + 16$

**29.** $15a^2 - 9a$

**30.** $6x^2 + 12$

**31.** $4a^3 + 8a^2$

**32.** $12x^3 - 6x^2 + 24x$

**33.** $10y^3 - 5y^2 + 15y$

**34.** $\pi r^2 h + 2\pi r^2$

**35.** $\dfrac{1}{2}bh - \dfrac{1}{2}ah$

**36.** $14s^2 + 7st$

**B**  **37.** $24a^4x - 18a^3x + 12a^2x^2$

**38.** $7s^2y - 21xy^2$

**39.** $8a^2b - 16ab - 24a$

**40.** $25c^3d - 15c^2d^2 + 5cd^3$

**41.** $-40r^8s^6 - 16r^9s^5$

**42.** $21e^3k - 49e^2k^2 + 84k^3$

**43.** $126w^2x^3yz + 210w^3y^4z^2$

**44.** $231a^4b^3c^2d - 143ab^2c^3$

**Simplify.**

*Example 2*  $\dfrac{5x - 10}{5} - \dfrac{12x - 9}{3} = (x - 2) - (4x - 3)$
$$= x - 2 - 4x + 3$$
$$= -3x + 1$$

**45.** $\dfrac{3x - 6}{3} - \dfrac{4 - 8x}{2}$

**46.** $\dfrac{15a - 5}{5} - \dfrac{9a - 12}{3}$

**47.** $\dfrac{24x - 18}{6} + \dfrac{14x + 7}{7}$

**48.** $\dfrac{12a^2b - 6ab^2}{3ab} + \dfrac{4a^2 + 10ab}{2a}$

**49.** $\dfrac{a^2b + 2a^2b^2}{ab} - \dfrac{2a^3 - 6a^2b}{2a}$

**50.** $\dfrac{a^4b^3 - b^2a^3}{a^3b} + \dfrac{b^3c - ab^3c}{bc}$

# Problems

**Write an expression in factored form for the area $A$ of each shaded region.**

*Example*

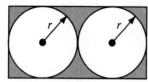

*Solution*

$A$ = Area of rectangle − 2 · area of circle
$= (4r \cdot 2r) - 2\pi r^2$
$= 2r^2(4 - \pi)$  *Answer*

**A**

**1.**

**2.**

**3.**

**4.**

**5.**

**B**

**6.**

**7.**

**8.**

**9.**

**10.**

# Self-Test 1

**Vocabulary**    factored (p. 183)
factor set (p. 183)
prime number (p. 183)
prime factorization (p. 183)
common factor (p. 184)
greatest common factor
of integers (p. 184)

greatest common factor
of monomials (p. 188)
divisible (p. 191)
greatest monomial factor
of a polynomial (p. 191)

**1.** Find the prime factorization of 72.                              Obj. 5-1, p. 183

**2.** Find all pairs of integral factors of 44.

**3.** Find the greatest common factor of 72 and 44.

**Simplify, assuming that no denominator equals zero.**

**4.** $-\dfrac{21x^2y^5}{7xy^6}$                **5.** $\dfrac{8k^2m^7}{32k^3m^3}$                Obj. 5-2, p. 187

**Find the missing factor.**

**6.** $-84t^3 = -7t(\underline{\ \ ?\ \ })$                **7.** $-35a^2b^5 = (7ab)(\underline{\ \ ?\ \ })$

**8.** Simplify $\dfrac{21t^4 + 15t^3 - 9t^2}{3t^2}$, $(t \neq 0)$.                Obj. 5-3, p. 191

**9.** Factor $4x^4y^3 - 8x^2y^2 + 6xy^2$.

Check your answers with those at the back of the book.

# Products and Factors

## 5-4 Multiplying Binomials Mentally

**Objective**   To find the product of two binomials mentally.

Study the multiplication below and notice how the three terms of the product are formed. Do you see where the distributive axiom is used?

$$
\begin{array}{r}
4x \ + \ 7 \\
2x \ - \ 3 \\
\hline
8x^2 + 14x \\
\ - \ 12x \ - \ 21 \\
\hline
8x^2 \ + \ \ 2x \ - \ 21
\end{array}
$$

$$
\begin{aligned}
(4x + 7)(2x - 3) &= (4x + 7)2x - (4x + 7)3 \\
&= 8x^2 + 14x - 12x - 21 \\
&= 8x^2 + 2x - 21
\end{aligned}
$$

You can use the following short method to multiply binomials.

Think:   $8x^2 \quad -21$

$(4x + 7)(2x - 3)$

$14x$

$-12x$

Write the product: $8x^2 + 2x - 21$

To find the terms in the trinomial product of two binomials $(ax + b)(cx + d)$:

1. Multiply the first terms of the binomials.
2. Multiply the first term of each polynomial by the last term of the other and add these products.
3. Multiply the last terms of the binomials.

Each term of a trinomial like $8x^2 + 2x - 21$ has a standard name. A **quadratic term** is a term of degree two. A **linear term** is a term of degree one. As defined earlier, a *constant term* is a numerical term with no variable factor. The trinomial itself is called a **quadratic polynomial** since its term of greatest degree is quadratic.

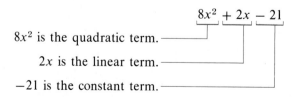

$8x^2 + 2x - 21$

$8x^2$ is the quadratic term.

$2x$ is the linear term.

$-21$ is the constant term.

## Oral Exercises

**State the two terms of the product that form the linear term. Then state the linear term, the quadratic term, the constant term, and the product.**

*Example*   $(k - 9)(k + 8)$

*Solution*   $8k$ and $-9k$; linear term, $-k$; quadratic term, $k^2$; constant term, $-72$; product, $k^2 - k - 72$

**1.** $(x + 1)(x + 3)$    **2.** $(y + 4)(y + 2)$    **3.** $(z - 3)(z - 4)$    **4.** $(a - 5)(a - 1)$

**5.** $(b - 4)(b - 6)$    **6.** $(c - 9)(c - 2)$    **7.** $(r + 4)(r - 2)$    **8.** $(s - 6)(s + 1)$

**9.** $(t + 3)(t - 4)$    **10.** $(g + 8)(g - 2)$    **11.** $(h - 5)(h + 3)$    **12.** $(k - 1)(k + 7)$

**13.** $(a + 5)(2a + 1)$    **14.** $(3a + 1)(a + 2)$    **15.** $(y - 1)(2y - 1)$    **16.** $(x - 3)(2x - 5)$

## Written Exercises

**Write each product as a trinomial.**

A    **1.** $(x + 7)(x + 2)$      **2.** $(y + 3)(y + 2)$      **3.** $(a - 4)(a - 5)$

     **4.** $(b - 7)(b - 6)$      **5.** $(c + 3)(c + 7)$      **6.** $(k - 3)(k - 11)$

     **7.** $(a - 5)(a - 9)$      **8.** $(1 + x)(2 + x)$      **9.** $(2a + 1)(a + 5)$

     **10.** $(4x + 3)(x + 5)$      **11.** $(2a + 9)(a - 3)$      **12.** $(3a - 1)(2a - 1)$

     **13.** $(x - 9)(x + 7)$      **14.** $(a - 5)(a + 7)$      **15.** $(b - 3)(b + 8)$

     **16.** $(c - 7)(c + 8)$      **17.** $(3k + 1)(2k + 5)$      **18.** $(4a - 5)(2a - 3)$

     **19.** $a(7a - 5)(5a - 7)$      **20.** $b(3b + 2)(7b + 8)$      **21.** $2x(2x - 5)(3x + 1)$

     **22.** $n(4n - 7)(3n + 6)$      **23.** $k(2k - 5)(7k + 4)$      **24.** $3n(n - 3)(2n + 7)$

**Express each product as a trinomial.**

*Example*   $(5x + 2y)(4x - 3y)$

*Solution*   $20x^2 + (-15xy + 8xy) - 6y^2 = 20x^2 - 7xy - 6y^2$

B    **25.** $(2x + 4y)(3x + 2y)$      **26.** $(3x - 2y)(4x + y)$      **27.** $(9a - 2b)(3a - 5b)$

     **28.** $(x^2 + y^2)(x^2 + 3y^2)$      **29.** $(a^2 - 3)(2a^2 + 7)$      **30.** $(r^2 - 2s)(3r^2 + s)$

     **31.** $(x^4 + 7x^2)(x^2 - 3)$      **32.** $(x^3 - 2y)(3x^3 + 4y)$      **33.** $(3a^4 - 5b^2)(a^4 - 2b^2)$

**Solve and check.**

     **34.** $(x + 5)(x - 3) = (x - 4)(x + 9)$        **35.** $(a - 4)(a + 4) = (a + 7)(a - 6)$

     **36.** $(6y - 5)(6y + 5) = (4y + 3)(9y - 7)$        **37.** $(y + 1)(2y - 1) = (y - 1)^2 + (y + 1)^2$

**Solve and check.**

**38.** $(3a - 4)(4a + 5) = (6a - 2)(2a + 10)$      **39.** $2(x + 1)(2x + 5) = (x + 3)(4x + 3)$

**40.** Show that $(ax + by)(cx + dy) = acx^2 + (ad + bc)xy + bdy^2$.

**41.** If $(ax + b)(2x - 3) = 18x^2 - 23x + c$, find the values of $a$, $b$, and $c$.

**Write each product as a trinomial, assuming that $n$ represents a positive integer.**

**C**   **42.** $(x^n + 2y^n)(x^n - y^n)$          **43.** $(x^n + 4y^n)(x^n - 4y^n)$

     **44.** Show that the square of an odd integer is odd.

---

## Computer Exercises     *For students with some programming experience*

Write a BASIC program to find the product of $(AX + B)(CX + D)$, where $A$, $B$, $C$, and $D$ are entered with INPUT statements. Use the program to find the following products. Check the computer's answers by multiplying the binomials mentally.

**1.** $(x + 3)(x + 5)$                    **2.** $(x - 4)(2x + 1)$

**3.** $(4x + 3)(2x - 5)$              **4.** $(2x + 7)^2$

**5.** $(3x - 2)(3x + 2)$              **6.** $(6x - 7)(6x - 7)$

---

## Calculator Key-In

You can use a calculator to evaluate a polynomial for a given value of the variable. One way is to evaluate the polynomial term by using the calculator's memory to store the partial sums.

     Another way is to express the polynomial in a form that suggests a sequence of steps on the calculator. For example, to evaluate $5x^2 - 3x + 6$ you could first rewrite it as follows:

$$5x^2 - 3x + 6 = (5x - 3)x + 6$$

     To evaluate the polynomial for a particular value, you can just work through the rewritten expression from left to right substituting the appropriate value for $x$.

Evaluate the polynomial for the given value of the variable.

**1.** $4x^2 + 5x - 7$; 3      **2.** $6z^2 + 8z - 9$; 4      **3.** $2x^2 + 4x + 5$; $-3$

**4.** $y^2 - 4y - 3$; 2.5      **5.** $9k^2 - 35k + 50$; 10      **6.** $40y^2 - 25y + 70$; 14

**7.** $18x^2 - 15x - 10$; $-6$      **8.** $4y^2 + 4y - 5$; 0.4      **9.** $20z^2 - 15z + 5$; $-0.5$

# 5-5 Differences of Squares

**Objective**  To simplify products of the form $(a + b)(a - b)$ and to factor differences of squares.

Observe what happens when you simplify the product $(a + b)(a - b)$.

$$\begin{array}{r} a + b \\ a - b \\ \hline a^2 + ab \\ - ab - b^2 \\ \hline a^2 \qquad - b^2 \end{array}$$

Two of the terms are opposites, so the product is just a difference of two squares. This result is so useful that you should remember it in either of the following forms.

---

$$(a + b)(a - b) = a^2 - b^2$$

$$\begin{bmatrix}\text{Sum of two} \\ \text{numbers}\end{bmatrix} \cdot \begin{bmatrix}\text{Difference of} \\ \text{the numbers}\end{bmatrix} = [\text{First number}]^2 - [\text{Second number}]^2$$

---

**Example 1**  Express each product as a binomial.

   **a.** $(a + 4)(a - 4)$   **b.** $(2x + 7)(2x - 7)$   **c.** $\left(\frac{1}{2}r^2 - 3s\right)\left(\frac{1}{2}r^2 + 3s\right)$

**Solution**
   **a.** $(a + 4)(a - 4) = a^2 - 16$
   **b.** $(2x + 7)(2x - 7) = (2x)^2 - 7^2 = 4x^2 - 49$
   **c.** $\left(\frac{1}{2}r^2 - 3s\right)\left(\frac{1}{2}r^2 + 3s\right) = \left(\frac{1}{2}r^2\right)^2 - (3s)^2 = \frac{1}{4}r^4 - 9s^2$

You can use the symmetric property of equality to write the statement $(a + b)(a - b) = a^2 - b^2$ in a form useful for factoring the difference of two squares.

$$a^2 - b^2 = (a + b)(a - b)$$

**Example 2**  Factor.   **a.** $t^2 - 100$   **b.** $25a^2 - 121b^2$

**Solution**
   **a.** $t^2 - 100 = (t + 10)(t - 10)$
   **b.** $25a^2 - 121b^2 = (5a)^2 - (11b)^2 = (5a + 11b)(5a - 11b)$

In Example 2(b) it was important to recognize that both monomials were *squares*. A monomial is a *square* if the exponents of all powers in it are even and the numerical coefficient is the square of an integer. You can use the table of squares at the back of the book or a calculator to determine whether or not an integer is a square. For example, the table shows that 625 is the square of 25.

**Example 3**  Factor $81y^4 - 625$.

**Solution**   $81y^4 - 625 = (9y^2)^2 - 25^2$
$$= (9y^2 + 25)(9y^2 - 25)$$
$$= (9y^2 + 25)(3y + 5)(3y - 5)$$

Example 3 shows that you should continue factoring until the polynomial is factored completely.

## Oral Exercises

**Square each monomial.**

**Example**   $-4k^2$     **Solution**   $(-4k^2)^2 = 16k^4$

**1.** $3x$

**2.** $-4z$

**3.** $6m^4$

**4.** $-2r^2$

**5.** $7x^2y$

**6.** $-\dfrac{1}{5}a^2b^3$

**Express each product as a binomial.**

**7.** $(x + 2)(x - 2)$

**8.** $(a + 5)(a - 5)$

**9.** $(s - t)(s + t)$

**10.** $(4b + 3)(4b - 3)$

**11.** $(2n - 3)(2n + 3)$

**12.** $(5x - 7)(5x + 7)$

**Tell whether or not each binomial is the difference of two squares. If it is, factor it.**

**13.** $x^2 - 16$

**14.** $a^2 - 10$

**15.** $k^3 - 4$

**16.** $t^8 + 64$

**17.** $4y^2 - 81$

**18.** $a^4 - 1$

**19.** $b^2 + 9$

**20.** $c^6 - 25d^2$

## Written Exercises

**Express each product as a binomial.**

**A**  **1.** $(a - 3)(a + 3)$

**2.** $(2 - x)(2 + x)$

**3.** $(3b - 5)(3b + 5)$

**4.** $(7x - y)(7x + y)$

**5.** $(9a - 7)(9a + 7)$

**6.** $(8 + 3x)(8 - 3x)$

**7.** $(8a - 5b)(8a + 5b)$

**8.** $(x^2 - 5)(x^2 + 5)$

**9.** $(3u^2 + v)(3u^2 - v)$

**10.** $(2a^2 - 5b^2)(2a^2 + 5b^2)$

**11.** $(rs + t^2)(rs - t^2)$

**12.** $(a^7 - b^4)(a^7 + b^4)$

**Multiply using the form $(a + b)(a - b)$.**

**Example 1** $83 \times 77 = (80 + 3)(80 - 3) = 6400 - 9 = 6391$

**13.** $17 \times 23$  **14.** $28 \times 32$  **15.** $62 \times 58$  **16.** $45 \times 55$

**17.** $51 \times 49$  **18.** $102 \times 98$  **19.** $204 \times 196$  **20.** $70 \times 130$

**Factor. Use the table of squares.**

**21.** $25y^2 - 9$  **22.** $49a^2 - 16$  **23.** $144 - x^2$  **24.** $169b^2 - 49c^2$

**25.** $9a^2 - b^2c^2$  **26.** $121 - 400r^2$  **27.** $x^6 - y^6$  **28.** $a^4 - 100$

**29.** $-144 + 25t^6$  **30.** $-361 + 4x^4$  **31.** $225 - a^2b^4$  **32.** $16x^4 - 3721$

**B** **33.** $a^4b^4 - c^8$  **34.** $x^8 - 256$  **35.** $a^{16} - 1$  **36.** $81k^8 - n^8$

**Factor each expression as the difference of two squares. Simplify.**

**Example 2** $(y + 3)^2 - y^2 = [(y + 3) - y][(y + 3) + y]$
$= 3(2y + 3)$

**37.** $(x + 3)^2 - x^2$

**38.** $y^2 - (y - 1)^2$

**39.** $(a + 1)^2 - (a - 1)^2$

**40.** $9(x + 1)^2 - 4(x - 1)^2$

**Factor completely.**

**Example 3** $3x^3 - 75x = 3x(x^2 - 25)$
$= 3x(x + 5)(x - 5)$

**41.** $36x^2 - 81y^2$  **42.** $2x^3 - 18x$  **43.** $2xy - 72x^3y$  **44.** $324 - 4k^4$

**45.** $81t^9 - 9t$  **46.** $16r^2 - r^6$  **47.** $450a^5 - 8a$  **48.** $27x^3 - 363xy^2$

**Factor, assuming that $n$ is a positive integer.**

**Example 4** $x^{2n} - y^2 = (x^n)^2 - y^2$
$= (x^n - y)(x^n + y)$

**C** **49.** $x^{2n} - y^{2n}$  **50.** $a^{2n} - 9$  **51.** $b^{2n} - c^{4n}$  **52.** $2x^{2n} - 98$

**53.** $a^{4n} - b^{6n}$  **54.** $x^{2n+1} - x$  **55.** $y^{2n+3} - y^3$  **56.** $ab^{4n} - a$

**57.** Show that the absolute value of the difference of the squares of two consecutive integers is equal to the absolute value of the sum of the integers.

**58.** Show that the absolute value of the difference of the squares of two consecutive even integers is equal to twice the absolute value of the sum of the integers.

# *Extra* / *Sums and Differences of Cubes*

Both sums and differences of cubes can be factored, as shown by the factoring patterns below.

$$x^3 + y^3 = (x + y)(x^2 - xy + y^2)$$
$$x^3 - y^3 = (x - y)(x^2 + xy + y^2)$$

**Example**   Factor $m^3 - 27$.

**Solution**   $(m - 3)(m^2 + 3m + 9)$

## Exercises

1. Verify the factoring pattern for the sum of two cubes by multiplying $(x + y)(x^2 - xy + y^2)$.

2. Verify the factoring pattern for the difference of two cubes by multiplying $(x - y)(x^2 + xy + y^2)$.

Factor.

3. $w^3 + 8$      4. $a^3 - 64$      5. $n^3 + 125$      6. $27 - 216e^3$

7. **a.** Factor $z^6 - 1$ as a difference of cubes to show that
$$z^6 - 1 = (z - 1)(z + 1)(z^4 + z^2 + 1).$$

   **b.** Factor $z^6 - 1$ as a difference of squares to show that
$$z^6 - 1 = (z - 1)(z + 1)(z^2 + z + 1)(z^2 - z + 1).$$

   **c.** Show that the factorizations given in parts (a) and (b) are equivalent by writing
$$z^4 + z^2 + 1 = (z^4 + 2z^2 + 1) - z^2$$
   and then factoring the difference of squares on the right.

# *Challenge*

According to the legend, the inventor of the game of chess asked to be rewarded by having one grain of wheat put on the first square of a chessboard, two grains on the second, four grains on the third, eight grains on the fourth, and so on. The total number of grains would be $2^{64} - 1$, which is several thousand times the world's annual wheat yield.

1. To find out how large $2^{64}$ is approximately, you could enter the number 2 on the calculator and press the squaring button a number of times. How many times?

2. Factor $2^{64} - 1$ as a difference of squares to show that it is divisible by 3, 5, and 17.

# 5-6 Squares of Binomials

**Objective**  To find squares of binomials and to factor trinomial squares.

Note what happens when you square the binomial $a + b$.

$$\begin{array}{r} a + b \\ a + b \\ \hline a^2 + ab \\ ab + b^2 \\ \hline a^2 + 2ab + b^2 \end{array}$$

1. Square of the first term.

2. Twice the product of the two terms.

3. Square of the last term.

When you square the binomial difference $a - b$, the middle term in the product is preceded by a minus sign.

$$\begin{array}{r} a - b \\ a - b \\ \hline a^2 - ab \\ - ab + b^2 \\ \hline a^2 - 2ab + b^2 \end{array}$$

1. Square of the first term.

2. Twice the product of the two terms.

3. Square of the last term.

These results may be expressed as these two useful formulas.

$$(a + b)^2 = a^2 + 2ab + b^2$$
$$(a - b)^2 = a^2 - 2ab + b^2$$

These formulas can be used to write squares of binomials as trinomials.

**Example 1**  $(x + 5)^2 = x^2 + 2 \cdot x \cdot 5 + 5^2 = x^2 + 10x + 25$

**Example 2**  $(2m - 1)^2 = (2m)^2 - 2 \cdot 2m \cdot 1 + 1^2 = 4m^2 - 4m + 1$

**Example 3**  $(7s - 4t)^2 = 49s^2 - 2(28st) + 16t^2 = 49s^2 - 56st + 16t^2$

**Example 4**  $(6x^2 - y^3)^2 = 36x^4 - 12x^2y^3 + y^6$

The symmetric property of equality enables you to rewrite the formulas for squaring a binomial in a form useful for factoring.

$$a^2 + 2ab + b^2 = (a + b)^2$$
$$a^2 - 2ab + b^2 = (a - b)^2$$

The expressions on the left sides of the two equations above are called **trinomial squares,** since each expression has three terms and is the square of a binomial.

To determine whether or not a trinomial is a trinomial square, ask the three questions illustrated in the next examples.

**Example 5**  Is $81x^2 - 36x + 4$ a trinomial square?

**Solution**
1. Is the first term a square?       Yes, $81x^2 = (9x)^2$
2. Is the last term a square?        Yes,    $4 = 2^2$
3. Is the middle term, neglecting the sign, twice the product of $9x$ and 2?    Yes,  $36x = 2(9x \cdot 2)$
Thus, $81x^2 - 36x + 4$ is a trinomial square and $81x^2 - 36x + 4 = (9x - 2)^2$.  **Answer**

**Example 6**  Is $100c^2 + 30cd + 9d^2$ a trinomial square?

**Solution**
1. Is the first term a square?       Yes, $100c^2 = (10c)^2$
2. Is the last term a square?        Yes,    $9d^2 = (3d)^2$
3. Is the middle term twice the product of $10c$ and $3d$?     No,   $30cd \neq 2(10c \cdot 3d)$
Thus, $100c^2 + 30cd + 9d^2$ is not a trinomial square.  **Answer**
(It would be a trinomial square if the linear term were $60cd$.)

## Oral Exercises

**Express each square as a trinomial.**

**1.** $(k - 5)^2$       **2.** $(x - y)^2$       **3.** $(a + 6)^2$       **4.** $(b - 8)^2$

**5.** $(3x + 1)^2$      **6.** $(2k + 1)^2$      **7.** $(d^2 + 3)^2$     **8.** $(5z^2 - 3)^2$

**Decide whether or not each polynomial is a trinomial square. If so, factor it.**

**9.** $x^2 + 14x + 49$       **10.** $a^2 - 6a + 9$        **11.** $b^2 - 8b + 16$

**12.** $y^2 + 2y + 4$        **13.** $9n^2 - 12n + 4$      **14.** $25x^2 - 10xy + 4y^2$

**15.** $v^2 + vt + t^2$      **16.** $h^2 - 4h + 2$        **17.** $j^4 - 2j^2 + 1$

**18.** Find the square of 31 by thinking of it as $(30 + 1)^2$.

**19.** Find the square of 49 by thinking of it as $(50 - 1)^2$.

# Written Exercises

**Express each square as a trinomial.**

A
1. $(x + 2)^2$
2. $(y - 3)^2$
3. $(a - 4)^2$
4. $(b + 9)^2$
5. $(2x + 3)^2$
6. $(3y + 8)^2$
7. $(4k - 5)^2$
8. $(7k - 2)^2$
9. $(4p + 3q)^2$
10. $(8x - 5y)^2$
11. $(3x + 7y)^2$
12. $(2a - 9b)^2$
13. $(ab - 5)^2$
14. $(x^2 + 4)^2$
15. $(2st - 7)^2$
16. $(2x^2 - y^2)^2$
17. $(-3 + 5a)^2$
18. $(-7 - 6b)^2$
19. $(-8x^2 + 1)^2$
20. $(-11a^2 - b^2)^2$

**Factor each trinomial as the square of a binomial if possible. If it is not possible, write "not factorable."**

21. $n^2 - 2n + 1$
22. $k^2 + 6k + 9$
23. $r^2 - 4r + 4$
24. $a^2 + 12a + 24$
25. $81 - 18b + b^2$
26. $49 - 7k + k^2$
27. $4x^2 + 4x + 1$
28. $9 + 12y + 4y^2$
29. $36 - 60a + 25a^2$
30. $25d^2 - 50d + 100$
31. $64x^2 - 16xy + y^2$
32. $81n^2 + nt + 9t^2$

B
33. $x^4 + 2x^2 + 1$
34. $y^4 + 10y^2 + 25$
35. $a^2b^2 - 12ab + 36$
36. $25t^2 + 55t + 121$
37. $a^4 - 24a^2 + 144$
38. $(x + 1)^2 + 2(x + 1) + 1$
39. **a.** Express $(5x - 2)^2$ and $(2 - 5x)^2$ as trinomials.
    **b.** Explain why $(5x - 2)^2 = (2 - 5x)^2$ although $5x - 2 \neq 2 - 5x$.
40. Show that $a^4 - 8a^2 + 16$ can be factored as $(a - 2)^2(a + 2)^2$.
41. Show that $x^4 - 18x^2 + 81$ can be factored as $(x - 3)^2(x + 3)^2$.

**Factor completely.**

*Example 1*   $12x^3 + 36x^2 + 27x = 3x(4x^2 + 12x + 9) = 3x(2x + 3)^2$

42. $6x^2 + 12x + 6$
43. $3z^2 + 18z + 27$
44. $a^3 - 10a^2 + 25a$
45. $18y^2 - 12y + 2$
46. $24b - 24b^2 + 6b^3$
47. $20x^4 + 60x^2 + 45$
48. $2a^6 - 24a^4 + 72a^2$
49. $16k^5 - 48k^3 + 36k$
50. $3v^8 - 48v^5 + 192v^2$

*Example 2*   $x^2 - 4x + 4 - y^2 = (x - 2)^2 - y^2 = [(x - 2) + y][(x - 2) - y]$
$= (x + y - 2)(x - y - 2)$

51. $w^2 + 6w + 9 - 4q^2$
52. $s^2t^2 - 2st + 1 - z^2$
53. $25c^2 - 4d^2 - 4d - 1$

**Solve and check.**

54. $(x + 3)(x + 5) = (x + 1)^2 + 13x$
55. $(2x + 1)^2 - (2x - 1)^2 = (x + 6)^2 - x^2$
56. $(2x - 1)^2 - (4x - 3)(x + 2) = 1 - 7x$
57. $(5x + 4)^2 - (3x + 2)^2 = (4x + 4)(4x - 4)$

**58.** The length of a rectangular flower garden is four times its width. If the width is increased by 4 m and the length is decreased by 4 m, the area will be increased by 32 m². Find the dimensions of the original garden.

**59.** The sum of the squares of three consecutive integers is 22 less than three times the product of the two greater integers. Find the integers.

**Show that each diagram illustrates the statement below it.**

*Example 3*

$$(a+b)^2 \quad = \quad a^2 \quad + \quad 2ab \quad + \quad b^2$$

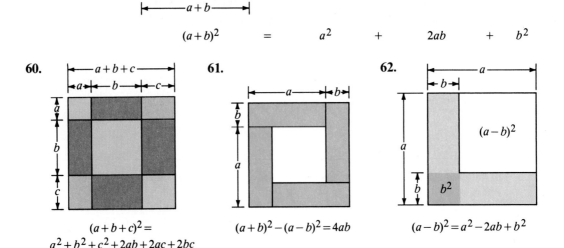

**60.**

$$(a+b+c)^2 =$$
$$a^2+b^2+c^2+2ab+2ac+2bc$$

**61.**

$$(a+b)^2-(a-b)^2=4ab$$

**62.**

$$(a-b)^2=a^2-2ab+b^2$$

**C** **63.** The square of a two-digit number ending in 5 always ends in 25. The digits before the 25 are found by multiplying the tens digit by one more than the tens digit, as shown at the right.

$$25^2 = 625$$
$$2 \times 3$$

**a.** Use this rule to find the squares of 35, 55, and 85.

**b.** Prove the rule works by letting $10t + 5$ represent a two-digit number ending in 5. Square this number and show that the result equals $[t(t + 1) \times 100] + 25$.

# Self-Test 2

**Vocabulary**    quadratic term (p. 196)        quadratic polynomial (p. 196)
                       linear term (p. 196)             trinomial square (p. 204)

**Express each product as a polynomial.**

**1.** $(3y + 5)(2y - 6)$           **2.** $2x(x - 4)(3x - 2)$       **Obj. 5-4, p. 196**

**3.** $(x - 7)(x + 7)$              **4.** $(9a + 2b)(9a - 2b)$     **Obj. 5-5, p. 199**

**Factor.**

**5.** $4x^2 - 49$                  **6.** $36x^4 - 81$

**Express each square as a trinomial.**

**7.** $(2y + 5)^2$                  **8.** $(3z - 5k)^2$           **Obj. 5-6, p. 203**

**Factor.**

**9.** $9a^2 + 12a + 4$           **10.** $16m^2 - 24mn + 9n^2$

Check your answers with those at the back of the book.

## *Career Note* / *Nutritionist*

Schools, hospitals, and other large institutions rely on nutritionists to plan for groups and individuals in their organizations. Sometimes nutritionists are needed to plan special menus for individuals in need of a salt-free, a low-cholesterol, or a high-protein diet. A nutritionist must plan appealing meals that supply the nutrients needed to maintain good health. Once a menu has been planned, a nutritionist may also be involved with the preparation and serving of the food.

    Nutritionists may need to teach people about sound nutritional practices. Thus, they should be able to work well with people. The minimum requirement for a career as a nutritionist is a bachelor's degree with coursework in physiology, food and nutrition, bacteriology, and chemistry. A scientific aptitude is also helpful. Nutritionists often continue their training after graduation with an internship in a hospital.

# 5-7 Factoring Pattern for $x^2 + bx + c$, c positive

**Objective** To factor quadratic trinomials whose quadratic coefficient is 1 and whose constant term is positive.

In this section you will study trinomials that can be factored as a product of the form $(x + r)(x + s)$ where $r$ and $s$ are both positive or both negative. First look at some products of this form to see what clues they give you for factoring the trinomial.

**Example 1** $(x + 4)(x + 3) = x^2 + 7x + 12$

sum of        product of
4 and 3        4 and 3

**Example 2** $(x - 5)(x - 6) = x^2 - 11x + 30$

sum of        product of
$-5$ and $-6$    $-5$ and $-6$

**Example 3** $(x + r)(x + s) = x^2 + (r + s)x + rs$

Example 3 suggests the following technique for factoring polynomials with quadratic coefficient 1 and positive constant term.

1. List the pairs of factors that have a product equal to the constant term.
2. Find the pair of factors in the list that have a sum equal to the coefficient of the linear term.

Examples 1 and 2 suggest that in Step 1 you can just look at the factors with the same sign as the linear term.

**Example 4** Factor $a^2 + 13a + 30$.

**Solution**
1. Since the coefficient of the linear term is 13, which is positive, list the pairs of positive factors of 30.
2. Find the factors that have a sum of 13: 3 and 10
3. $a^2 + 13a + 30 = (a + 10)(a + 3)$ **Answer**

| 30 | |
|---|---|
| 1 | 30 |
| 2 | 15 |
| 3 | 10 |
| 5 | 6 |

As you gain experience with factoring, you will learn to review the factors of the constant term mentally instead of writing them down.

**Example 5** Factor $z^2 - 16z + 28$.

**Solution**
1. Since $-16 < 0$, think of the negative factors of 28.
2. Select the factors of 28 with sum $-16$: $-2$ and $-14$
3. $z^2 - 16z + 28 = (z - 14)(z - 2)$ **Answer**

A polynomial that cannot be rewritten as a product of polynomials of lower degree is called **irreducible**. An irreducible polynomial whose greatest monomial factor is 1 is a **prime polynomial**.

**Example 6**  Factor $x^2 - x + 10$.

**Solution**  1. List the pairs of negative factors of 10: $-1, -10; -2, -5$
2. Neither of these pairs of factors has a sum of $-1$.
3. Thus, $x^2 - x + 10$ cannot be factored. It is irreducible and prime.  **Answer**

## Oral Exercises

**Find two integers with the given sum and product.**

|         | 1. | 2. | 3. | 4. | 5. | 6. | 7. | 8. |
|---------|----|----|----|----|----|----|----|----|
| sum     | 5  | -6 | -5 | -7 | 11 | 19 | -9 | 9  |
| product | 4  | 9  | 6  | 6  | 18 | 18 | 18 | 18 |

**For each trinomial, tell which two factors of the constant term have a sum equal to the coefficient of the linear term.**

**Example**   $x^2 - 10x + 21$      **Solution**   $(-3)(-7) = 21$ and $-3 + (-7) = -10; -3$ and $-7$

9. $x^2 + 10x + 9$   10. $y^2 - 5y + 4$   11. $z^2 - 4z + 4$
12. $t^2 + 7t + 10$   13. $a^2 - 3a + 2$   14. $b^2 - 9b + 14$
15. $c^2 + 2c + 1$   16. $d^2 + 17d + 16$   17. $v^2 - 21v + 20$
18. $h^2 + 9h + 20$   19. $j^2 - 12j + 20$   20. $k^2 + 12k + 20$

## Written Exercises

**Factor. Check by multiplying the factors. If the polynomial is not factorable, write "prime."**

A  1. $x^2 + 6x + 5$      2. $y^2 + 7y + 6$      3. $a^2 - 4a + 3$
4. $b^2 - 10b + 16$      5. $r^2 + 9r + 18$      6. $v^2 - 20v + 51$
7. $k^2 - 11k + 28$      8. $x^2 - 13x + 22$      9. $z^2 - 13z + 42$
10. $y^2 + 15y + 44$      11. $a^2 - 17a + 50$      12. $b^2 - 14b + 45$
13. $y^2 + 16y + 55$      14. $d^2 - 14d + 32$      15. $p^2 - 17p + 72$
16. $72 - 38z + z^2$      17. $20 - 12c + c^2$      18. $40 - 15a + a^2$

**Example 1** $a^2 - 8ab + 12b^2$

**Solution**     $a^2 - 8ab + 12b^2 = (a - \quad)(a - \quad)$
$$= (a - 2b)(a - 6b) \quad \textit{Answer}$$

19. $x^2 - 12xy + 35y^2$       20. $a^2 - 11ab + 24b^2$       21. $s^2 - 11st + 30t^2$
22. $c^2 - 19cd + 48d^2$       23. $b^2 + 13bc + 40c^2$       24. $x^2 + 15xy + 50y^2$
25. $s^2 - 13st + 42t^2$       26. $a^2 + 10ab + 25b^2$       27. $k^2 - 18ka + 36a^2$
28. $y^2 - 14yz + 49z^2$       29. $d^2 + 12de + 27e^2$       30. $y^2 - 28yz + 75z^2$

B  31. $a^2 - 23a + 120$       32. $y^2 + 22y + 96$       33. $108 - 21a + a^2$
   34. $180 - 41b + b^2$       35. $98n^2 - 21nx + x^2$       36. $112y^2 - 22yz + z^2$

**Determine all integral values for $k$ for which the trinomial can be factored.**

**Example 2** $x^2 + kx + 35$

**Solution**     35 can be factored as a product of two integers in these ways:
$$1 \cdot 35 \quad 5 \cdot 7 \quad (-1)(-35) \quad (-5)(-7)$$
The corresponding values of $k$ are 36, 12, $-36$, $-12$.  **Answer**

37. $x^2 + kx + 10$       38. $y^2 + ky + 4$       39. $z^2 + kz + 15$
40. $u^2 + ku + 21$       41. $r^2 + kr + 12$       42. $n^2 + kn + 18$

**Factor. Check by multiplying the factors.**

C  43. $(x + 2)^2 + 5(x + 2) + 4$       44. $(y - 2)^2 + 7(y - 2) + 10$
   45. $(a + b)^2 - 6(a + b) + 8$       46. $(z + 4)^2 - 8(z + 4) + 16$
   47. $a^4 - 10a^2 + 9$       48. $b^4 - 26b^2 + 25$
   49. $c^4 - 12c^2 + 27$       50. $x^5 - 13x^3 + 36x$
   51. Factor $x^{2n} - 42x^n y^{2n} + 437y^{4n}$, where $n$ is a positive integer.

## Computer Exercises     *For students with some programming experience*

Write a BASIC program to test whether a monomial entered with an
INPUT statement is a perfect square. (*Note:* In BASIC, the function
SQR(N) gives the square root of the number $N$.) Use the program to test
whether each of the following monomials is a perfect square.

1. 36       2. $4x^2$       3. $16y$
4. $m^2n^4$       5. $2xy^6$       6. $25w^9$

# 5-8 Factoring Pattern for $x^2 + bx + c$, $c$ negative

**Objective**   To factor quadratic trinomials whose quadratic coefficient is 1 and whose constant term is negative.

The factoring that you did in the last section had this form:

$$x^2 + bx + c = (x + r)(x + s)$$

positive    $r$ and $s$ both positive
or both negative

By contrast, the factoring that you will do in this section has the following form:

$$x^2 + bx + c = (x + r)(x + s)$$

negative    $r$ and $s$ have
opposite signs

The procedure that you will use in this section is the same as before. You find two numbers $r$ and $s$ whose product is $c$ and whose sum is $b$.

If a quadratic polynomial of the form $x^2 + bx + c$ ($c$ negative) can be factored, its factors will be of the form

$$(x + r)(x + s)$$

where one of $r$ and $s$, say $r$, is negative and $s$ is positive.

**Example 1**   Factor $a^2 - a - 12$.

**Solution**   1. List the factors of $-12$.
2. Find the pair of factors with a sum of $-1$: $-4$ and $3$
3. $a^2 - a - 12 = (a - 4)(a + 3)$   *Answer*
You should check by multiplying $a - 4$ and $a + 3$.

| $-12$ | |
|---|---|
| 1 | $-12$ |
| $-1$ | 12 |
| 2 | $-6$ |
| $-2$ | 6 |
| 3 | $-4$ |
| $-3$ | 4 |

It is usually faster to review the factors of the constant term mentally.

**Example 2**   Factor $b^2 + 31bc - 32c^2$.

**Solution**   1. The factoring pattern is $(b + \ \ )(b - \ \ )$.
2. Find the pair of factors of $-32$ with a sum of 31: 32 and $-1$.
3. $b^2 + 31bc - 32c^2 = (b + 32c)(b - c)$   *Answer*

## Oral Exercises

**Find two integers with the given sum and product.**

| | 1. | 2. | 3. | 4. | 5. | 6. | 7. | 8. |
|---|---|---|---|---|---|---|---|---|
| sum | $-1$ | $4$ | $-19$ | $-1$ | $8$ | $0$ | $6$ | $-15$ |
| product | $-2$ | $-12$ | $-20$ | $-20$ | $-20$ | $-16$ | $-16$ | $-16$ |

**For each trinomial, tell which two factors of the constant term have a sum equal to the coefficient of the linear term.**

***Example***     $x^2 - 7x - 8$

***Solution***     $(1)(-8) = -8$ and $1 + (-8) = -7$; $1$ and $-8$

**9.** $a^2 + 3a - 4$             **10.** $x^2 + 2x - 3$             **11.** $t^2 + 5t - 6$

**12.** $y^2 + y - 6$             **13.** $y^2 - y - 6$             **14.** $b^2 - 8b - 9$

**15.** $b^2 + 8b - 9$            **16.** $u^2 - 3u - 10$          **17.** $r^2 + 5r - 14$

## Written Exercises

**Factor. Check by multiplying the factors. If the polynomial is not factorable, write "prime."**

**A**    **1.** $a^2 + 4a - 5$           **2.** $x^2 - 2x - 3$          **3.** $y^2 - 5y - 6$

      **4.** $b^2 + 2b - 15$         **5.** $c^2 - 11c - 10$       **6.** $r^2 + 16r - 28$

      **7.** $x^2 - 6x - 18$         **8.** $y^2 - 10y - 24$       **9.** $a^2 + 2a - 35$

    **10.** $k^2 - 2k - 20$        **11.** $z^2 + 5z - 36$        **12.** $r^2 - 3r - 40$

    **13.** $p^2 - 4p - 21$        **14.** $a^2 + 3a - 54$        **15.** $y^2 - 5y - 30$

    **16.** $z^2 - z - 72$           **17.** $a^2 - ab - 30b^2$     **18.** $y^2 - 2yz - 3z^2$

    **19.** $p^2 - 5pq - 50q^2$     **20.** $a^2 - 4ab - 77b^2$     **21.** $k^2 - 11kd - 60d^2$

    **22.** $s^2 + 14st - 72t^2$     **23.** $x^2 - 9xy - 22y^2$     **24.** $p^2 - pq - 72q^2$

**B**   **25.** $1 - 8ab - 20a^2b^2$     **26.** $1 - 7pq - 60p^2q^2$     **27.** $1 - ab - 56a^2b^2$

    **28.** $n^2 + 13nm - 48m^2$     **29.** $r^2 - 18r - 144$       **30.** $a^2 + 19a - 150$

    **31.** $800 - 20b - b^2$        **32.** $a^2 + 3a - 270$        **33.** $320 - 32x - x^2$

**Find all the integral values of $k$ for which the given polynomial can be factored.**

    **34.** $x^2 + kx - 45$          **35.** $y^2 + ky - 28$         **36.** $15 - kz - z^2$

**Find two negative values for $k$ for which the given trinomial can be factored. (There are many possible values.)**

C  **37.** $x^2 - 3x + k$        **38.** $y^2 + 2y + k$        **39.** $z^2 + 4z + k$

    **40.** $k - 6x - x^2$        **41.** $n^2 + 11n + k$        **42.** $k + 4m - m^2$

**Factor.**

**43.** $(x + 1)^2 - 2(x + 1) - 15$        **44.** $(a + b)^2 - 3(a + b) - 70$

**45.** $(2x - y)^2 + 4(2x - y) - 60$        **46.** $4(a^2 - 1) - x^2(a^2 - 1)$

**47.** $x^4 - 8x^2 - 9$        **48.** $2x^4 - 30x^2 - 32$

**49.** $3a^4 - 63a^2 - 300$        **50.** $(3a + b)^4 - (a + b)^4$

---

## Historical Note / *The Sieve of Eratosthenes*

Although Eratosthenes (276–194 B.C.) is best known for determining the diameter and circumference of Earth, one of his greatest contributions to mathematics was his sieve, a method of "sifting out" the primes from the set of positive integers.

    The sieve of Eratosthenes can be used as follows. First, write a given number of consecutive integers greater than 1. Then, circle 2 and cross out all numbers in the list that are multiples of 2. Next, circle 3 and cross out every number that is a multiple of 3. Continue in this manner until only the circled numbers remain. These are the prime numbers.

$$
\begin{array}{cccccccccc}
& ② & ③ & \cancel{4} & ⑤ & \cancel{6} & ⑦ & \cancel{8} & \cancel{9} & \cancel{10} \\
⑪ & \cancel{12} & ⑬ & \cancel{14} & \cancel{15} & \cancel{16} & ⑰ & \cancel{18} & ⑲ & \cancel{20} \\
\cancel{21} & \cancel{22} & ㉓ & \cancel{24} & \cancel{25} & \cancel{26} & \cancel{27} & \cancel{28} & ㉙ & \cancel{30} \\
㉛ & \cancel{32} & \cancel{33} & \cancel{34} & \cancel{35} & \cancel{36} & ㊲ & \cancel{38} & \cancel{39} & \cancel{40} \\
�ог & \cancel{42} & ㊸ & \cancel{44} & \cancel{45} & \cancel{46} & ㊼ & \cancel{48} & \cancel{49} & \cancel{50}
\end{array}
$$

You may find it helpful to know that a number is prime if it is not divisible by any prime number less than or equal to its square root. For example, to find out if 101 is a prime number, check to see if 101 is divisible by each prime number less than or equal to $\sqrt{101}$, that is, each prime number less than 10. If 101 is not divisible by 2, 3, 5, or 7, then it is prime.

# 5-9 Factoring Pattern for $ax^2 + bx + c$

**Objective**   To factor quadratic trinomials when the coefficient of the quadratic term is an integer greater than 1.

If $ax^2 + bx + c \ (a > 1)$ can be factored, the factors will have the pattern

$$(px + r)(qx + s).$$

**Example 1**  Factor $3x^2 + x - 4$.

**Solution**

*First clue:*     Because the trinomial has a negative constant term, one of $r$ and $s$ will be negative and the other will be positive.

*Second clue:*   You can determine the possible factors of the quadratic term, $3x^2$, and the constant term, $-4$, as shown at the right.

| Factors of $3x^2$ | Factors of $-4$ | |
|---|---|---|
| $3x$ and $x$ | 1, $-4$ | $-1, 4$ |
| | 2, $-2$ | $-2, 2$ |
| | 4, $-1$ | $-4, 1$ |

Test the possibilities to see which produces the correct linear term, $x$.

| Possible factors | Linear term | | Possible factors | Linear term |
|---|---|---|---|---|
| $(3x + 1)(x - 4)$ | $(-12 + 1)x = -11x$ | | $(3x - 1)(x + 4)$ | $(12 - 1)x = 11x$ |
| $(3x + 2)(x - 2)$ | $(-6 + 2)x = -4x$ | | $(3x - 2)(x + 2)$ | $(6 - 2)x = 4x$ |
| $(3x + 4)(x - 1)$ | $(-3 + 4)x = x$ | | $(3x - 4)(x + 1)$ | $(3 - 4)x = -x$ |

Since $(3x + 4)(x - 1)$ yields the correct linear term,

$$3x^2 + x - 4 = (3x + 4)(x - 1). \quad \textit{Answer}$$

**Example 2**  Factor $10d^2 - 37d + 7$.

**Solution**

*First clue:*     Because the trinomial has a positive constant term and a negative linear term, both $r$ and $s$ will be negative.

*Second clue:*   Consider the possible factors of the quadratic term, $10d^2$, and the possible *negative* factors of the constant term, 7.

| Factors of $10d^2$ | | Negative factors of 7 | |
|---|---|---|---|
| $10d, d$ | $5d, 2d$ | $-7, -1$ | $-1, -7$ |

Test the possibilities to see which produces the correct linear term, $-37d$.

| Possible factors | Linear term | | Possible factors | Linear term |
|---|---|---|---|---|
| $(10d - 7)(d - 1)$ | $(-10 - 7)d = -17d$ | | $(5d - 7)(2d - 1)$ | $(-5 - 14)d = -19d$ |
| $(10d - 1)(d - 7)$ | $(-70 - 1)d = -71d$ | | $(5d - 1)(2d - 7)$ | $(-35 - 2)d = -37d$ |

The last possibility gives the correct linear term.

$$10d^2 - 37d + 7 = (5d - 1)(2d - 7) \quad \textit{Answer}$$

As you practice factoring, you will become able to select the correct factors without writing all the possibilities.

**Example 3**  Factor $7x^2 - 16xy - 15y^2$.

**Solution**
$$\begin{aligned}
7x^2 - 16xy - 15y^2 &= (7x \quad )(x \quad ) \\
&= (7x + \quad )(x - \quad ) \\
&= (7x + 5y)(x - 3y) \quad \textbf{\textit{Answer}}
\end{aligned}$$

*Note:* If you had written $(7x - \quad )(x + \quad )$ as the second step, you would have found that no such combination of factors would produce the desired term, $-16xy$.

When the coefficient of the quadratic term is negative, it may be help-ful to begin by factoring $-1$ from each term.

**Example 4**  Factor $5 + 7s - 6s^2$.

**Solution**  First, rearrange the polynomial in order of decreasing degree.

$$5 + 7s - 6s^2 = -6s^2 + 7s + 5$$

Then factor $-1$ from each term.

$$-6s^2 + 7s + 5 = -(6s^2 - 7s - 5)$$

Now factor $6s^2 - 7s - 5$.

$$6s^2 - 7s - 5 = (3s - 5)(2s + 1)$$

$$\therefore 5 + 7s - 6s^2 = -(6s^2 - 7s - 5) = -(3s - 5)(2s + 1) \quad \textbf{\textit{Answer}}$$

*Note:* If you had factored $5 + 7s - 6s^2$ directly, you would have found $(5 - 3s)(1 + 2s)$. Since both $(5 - 3s)(1 + 2s)$ and $-(3s - 5)(2s + 1)$ equal $5 + 7s - 6s^2$, the two answers are equivalent.

## Oral Exercises

**For each quadratic polynomial, tell whether its factorization will have the form**

$$(px + r)(qx + s), \quad (px + r)(qx - s), \quad \text{or} \quad (px - r)(qx - s),$$

**where $p$, $q$, $r$, and $s$ represent positive integers.**

1. $3x^2 - 22x + 7$          2. $3x^2 + 4x - 7$          3. $3x^2 + 10x + 7$

4. $5x^2 + 19x - 4$          5. $5x^2 - x - 4$          6. $4x^2 - 12x + 4$

7. $6x^2 + x - 2$          8. $6x^2 + 13x + 2$          9. $6x^2 - 7x + 2$

## Written Exercises

**Factor. Check by multiplying the factors. If the polynomial is not factorable, write "prime."**

**A**
1. $2x^2 + 5x + 3$
2. $2n^2 + 7n + 3$
3. $5a^2 + 6a + 1$
4. $8n^2 + 6n + 1$
5. $7n^2 - 8n + 1$
6. $14k^2 - 9k + 1$
7. $5y^2 - 16y + 3$
8. $7y^2 - 18y + 8$
9. $3k^2 - 5k + 1$
10. $3z^2 + z - 2$
11. $2t^2 - t - 6$
12. $3a^2 + 2a - 5$
13. $8y^2 - y - 9$
14. $9a^2 + 3a - 2$
15. $7k^2 + 19k - 6$
16. $3x^2 - 7x + 6$
17. $3 + b - 6b^2$
18. $10 + 3y - 2y^2$
19. $10 + y - 2y^2$
20. $6 - 23a - 4a^2$
21. $a^2 + ab - 2b^2$
22. $x^2 - xy - 56y^2$
23. $9r^2 - 25rs - 6s^2$
24. $3a^2 - 5ab - 12b^2$

**B**
25. $25a^2 + 10ab - 3b^2$
26. $36d^2 - 5d - 24$
27. $12x^2 + 19xy - 18y^2$
28. $20k^2 + 27k - 8$
29. $21 + 4x - 12x^2$
30. $15 - 31a - 24a^2$
31. $-48c^2 + 29c + 15$
32. $-21b^2 + 4b + 12$
33. $108x^2 + 15x - 7$
34. $6x^2 - 17x - 45$
35. $42y^2 + 41y + 9$
36. $40a^2 - 7a - 21$

**C**
37. $2(y + 4)^2 - (y + 4) - 3$
38. $3(a + b)^2 - 17(a + b) - 6$
39. $(x^2 - 1)^2 - 14(x^2 - 1) - 15$
40. $(x^2 - 5x - 1)^2 - 25$
41. $10(a - b)^2 - 11(a - b) - 6$
42. $14(2 - x)^2 - 15(2 - x) - 11$

43. Show that the product of $6x^2 - 13x - 5$, $15x^2 - 16x - 7$, and $10x^2 - 39x + 35$ is a *perfect square* by showing that it is the square of another polynomial.

44. Factor $60a^{4n+2}b + 25a^{2n+2}b^{4n+1} - 360a^2b^{8n+1}$, where $n$ is a positive integer.

# Self-Test 3

*Vocabulary*      irreducible polynomial (p. 209)          prime polynomial (p. 209)

**Factor.**

1. $y^2 + 8y + 15$
2. $x^2 - 10x + 16$
3. $n^2 - 3n - 28$
4. $v^2 + 9vt - 36t^2$
5. $6x^2 - 19x + 15$
6. $3x^2 + 10xy - 8y^2$

Obj. 5-7, p. 208
Obj. 5-8, p. 211
Obj. 5-9, p. 214

Check your answers with those at the back of the book.

In order to factor a quadratic trinomial of the form

$$Ax^2 + Bx + C,$$

you need to find positive and negative factors of the integer $C$, including 1, $C$, $-1$, and $-C$.

The program given below will find the positive and negative factors of any integer $N$. Since the values of $F$ in line 40 must increase, you need to use the absolute value of $N$. In BASIC this is written ABS(N). Line 70 will stop the loop after a pair of equal factors (if any) have been passed. This avoids duplications.

If $N$ is negative, then $Q$ will be negative. Lines 100 and 110 will give the opposite pairs of factors.

This program uses a *subroutine* for the OUTPUT. Line 90 GOSUB 160 sends the execution of the program to line 160. Line 170 RETURN ends the subroutine and sends the execution back to line 100. Line 120 also sends the program to the subroutine, although this time line 170 returns it to line 130.

```
10   PRINT "TO FACTOR AN INTEGER (ABS(N)>1):"
20   PRINT "WHAT IS YOUR INTEGER";
30   INPUT N
40   FOR F=1 TO ABS(N)/2
50   LET Q=N/F
60   IF Q <> INT(Q) THEN 130
70   IF ABS(Q)<ABS(F) THEN 180
80   LET F1=F
90   GOSUB 160
100   LET F1=-F
110   LET Q=-Q
120   GOSUB 160
130   NEXT F
140   GOTO 180
150   REM---SUBROUTINE
160   PRINT F1;" AND ";Q;" ARE FACTORS OF ";N
170   RETURN
180   END
```

### Exercises

1. RUN the program for 36 and $-36$.

2. RUN the program for 120 and $-120$.

3. RUN the program for 87 and $-87$.

# General Factoring and Its Application

## 5-10 Factoring by Grouping

**Objective** To factor a polynomial by grouping terms.

One of the key tools in factoring is the distributive axiom:

$$ab + ac = a(b + c).$$

This axiom holds not only when $a$ represents a monomial, but also when $a$ represents any polynomial. If $a = 5 + x$,

$$(5 + x)b + (5 + x)c = (5 + x)(b + c).$$

If $a = p - 4q + r$,

$$(p - 4q + r)b + (p - 4q + r)c = (p - 4q + r)(b + c).$$

It will help you in factoring if you learn to recognize factors that are opposites of each other.

| Factor | Opposite |
|--------|----------|
| $a - b$ | $-(a - b)$, or $-a + b$, or $b - a$ |
| $4z - y$ | $-(4z - y)$, or $-4z + y$, or $y - 4z$ |
| $5 - p - 2q$ | $-(5 - p - 2q)$, or $-5 + p + 2q$, or $p + 2q - 5$ |

**Example 1** Factor $7(r - 4) - 3r(4 - r)$.

**Solution** Notice that $r - 4$ and $4 - r$ are opposites.
$$\begin{aligned}
7(r - 4) - 3r(4 - r) &= 7(r - 4) - 3r[-(r - 4)] \\
&= 7(r - 4) + 3r(r - 4) \\
&= (7 + 3r)(r - 4) \\
&= (3r + 7)(r - 4) \quad \textbf{\textit{Answer}}
\end{aligned}$$

In Example 2, you first group terms and then factor each group of terms.

**Example 2** Factor $rq - 2rp + 5q - 10p$.

**Solution 1**

$\underbrace{(rq - 2rp)} + \underbrace{(5q - 10p)} =$

$r(q - 2p) + 5(q - 2p) =$

$(r + 5)(q - 2p)$

**Solution 2**

$\underbrace{(rq + 5q)} - \underbrace{(2rp + 10p)} =$

$q(r + 5) - 2p(r + 5) =$

$(q - 2p)(r + 5)$

Example 3 applies what you know about factoring trinomial squares and differences of squares.

**Example 3**  Factor $16j^2 - 81k^2 + 18k - 1$.

**Solution**
$$16j^2 - 81k^2 + 18k - 1 = 16j^2 - (81k^2 - 18k + 1)$$
$$= (4j)^2 - (9k - 1)^2$$
$$= (4j + 9k - 1)[4j - (9k - 1)]$$
$$= (4j + 9k - 1)(4j - 9k + 1) \quad \textbf{\textit{Answer}}$$

## Oral Exercises

**Factor.**

**1.** $5(x + y) + w(x + y)$
**2.** $6(a - 2b) - 4(a - 2b)$
**3.** $r(p - 2q) - (p - 2q)$
**4.** $7k(k - 6) + 4(6 - k)$
**5.** $z(z - 5) + 5(5 - z)$
**6.** $9(2u + v) + 5(v + 2u)$
**7.** $(3r - s) - t(s - 3r)$
**8.** $(m^2 - m) + (m - 1)$
**9.** $(ab - ac) + (b - c)$

## Written Exercises

**Factor. Check by multiplying the factors.**

**A**
**1.** $2t(n - 3) - (3 - n)$
**2.** $(c + 3d) - e(3d + c)$
**3.** $2(x + y) - y(y + x) + (x + y)$
**4.** $(s - r) - 3(r - s) + q(r - s)$
**5.** $x^2(2d - e + f) + (f - e + 2d)$
**6.** $(2a - b + 3c) + x(b - 2a - 3c)$
**7.** $(gz - g) + (hz - h)$
**8.** $(gz + hz) - (g + h)$
**9.** $(2x - 2y + 4z) + (x^2 - xy + 2xz)$
**10.** $(j^2 - 4j^2p) + (k - 4kp)$
**11.** $(2mp - 8mr) - (4nr - np)$
**12.** $(4x - 4xr) - (ry - y)$
**13.** $(2wz^2 - 12w) + (6 - z^2)$
**14.** $(6a - 3ay) + (7y - 14)$
**15.** $(2rs - 12r) - (30 - 5s)$
**16.** $(x^2 + xy) + (xz + yz)$
**17.** $2p + ap + 2q + aq$
**18.** $y^2 - 3y + yz - 3z$
**19.** $pq + 2qr + 2r^2 + pr$
**20.** $6x - 3y + 2zx - yz$
**21.** $ab - 2b + ac - 2c$
**22.** $x^3 - 2x^2 + 3x - 6$
**23.** $2x^3 + x^2 + 8x + 4$
**24.** $2ac - 6bc - 3a + 9b$
**25.** $4x^2 - 8xy - 3x + 6y$
**26.** $3rs - s + 12r - 4$
**27.** $4y^2 + 8ay - y - 2a$
**28.** $2a^3 - a^2 - 10a + 5$
**29.** $4x^2 - 2xy - 7yz + 14xz$
**30.** $2x^3 - 6x^2 - 5x + 15$

**Factor each expression as a difference of two squares.**

**B**
**31.** $a^2 - (2b + 3c)^2$
**32.** $(p - q)^2 - r^2$
**33.** $36k^2 - (2a - c)^2$
**34.** $25 - (5x - y)^2$
**35.** $(x - 4y)^2 - 9$
**36.** $(a + b)^2 - (c + d)^2$

*Factoring Polynomials*   **219**

**Factor each expression as a difference of two squares.**

**37.** $x^2 + 6x + 9 - y^2$  **38.** $p^2 - 2pq + q^2 - 4$  **39.** $h^2 - 12h + 36 - k^2$

**40.** $a^2 - x^2 - 2x - 1$  **41.** $25 - a^2 - 4ab - 4b^2$  **42.** $4a - 4a^2 + 49k^2 - 1$

**43.** $16y^2 + 8y + 1 - 16z^2$  **44.** $k^2 + 2kt + t^2 - n^2 - 8n - 16$

**Factor.**

**45.** $8b - 4 + a^2 - 4b^2$  **46.** $x^2 - 16y^2 - 6x + 9$

**47.** $a^2 - b^2 - 10bc - 25c^2$  **48.** $8yz - 4y^2 - 4z^2 + x^2$

**49.** $9a^2 + 9b^2 - 9c^2 - 18ab$  **50.** $x^4 - 8x^2 + 16 - 16y^2$

**51.** $a^2 - 2ab + b^2 - 3a + 3b$  **52.** $x^2 - 16y^2 + 2x + 8y$

**C** **53.** Factor $4x^4 + 1$ by writing it as $4x^4 + 4x^2 + 1 - 4x^2$, a difference of two squares.

**54.** Factor $64y^4 + 1$.

**55.** Factor $a^{3n+1} + 2b^{2n+1} - ab - 2a^{3n}b^{2n}$, where $n$ is a positive integer.

## Biographical Note / *Hsien Wu*

Hsien Wu was born in Foochow, China, in 1893. He received his formal schooling in China and in 1911 came to the United States to attend the Massachusetts Institute of Technology. Upon graduation, he enrolled at Harvard University, where he received his Ph.D. in biochemistry in 1917.

While at Harvard, Wu developed techniques that permitted small samples of blood to be analyzed for use in testing and research. This was a major breakthrough as previous methods required large samples, a procedure that was not very advantageous for either the patient or the doctor.

Upon completion of his work at Harvard, Wu returned to China where in 1924 he was appointed to head the biochemistry department at Peking Union Medical College. While there, Wu conducted numerous studies in nutrition, eating habits and health, and food composition. His more than 150 research papers made Wu the foremost nutrition scientist in China, as well as a leading scientific figure worldwide. He was appointed to a number of international scientific committees and was made director of the Nutrition Institute of China.

# 5-11 Using More than One Method of Factoring

**Objective**   To factor polynomials completely.

A polynomial is said to be **factored completely** when it is expressed as the product of prime polynomials and a monomial. The following guidelines will help you factor polynomials completely.

---

### Guidelines for Factoring

1. Factor out the greatest monomial factor first.
2. Look for a difference of squares.
3. Look for a trinomial square.
4. If a trinomial is not a square, look for a pair of binomial factors.
5. If a polynomial has four or more terms, look for a way to group the terms in pairs or in a group of three terms that is a trinomial square.
6. Make sure that each factor is prime. Check your work by multiplying the factors.

---

In each of the following examples the given polynomial is factored completely.

**Example 1**   Factor $30x^3 + 51x^2 + 9x$.

**Solution**
  1. Factor out the greatest monomial factor, $3x$.                      $3x(10x^2 + 17x + 3)$
  2. Find the binomial factors of $10x^2 + 17x + 3$.                      $3x(5x + 1)(2x + 3)$

**Example 2**   Factor $25y^4 - 100y^2$.

**Solution**
  1. Factor out the greatest monomial factor, $25y^2$.                    $25y^2(y^2 - 4)$
  2. Factor $y^2 - 4$ as the difference of squares.                       $25y^2(y + 2)(y - 2)$

**Example 3**   Factor $12rs - 3s^2 - 12r^2$.

**Solution**
  1. Factor out $-3$ to give a positive quadratic coefficient.           $-3(4r^2 - 4rs + s^2)$
  2. Notice that $4r^2 - 4rs + s^2$ is a trinomial square.                $-3(2r - s)^2$

---

*Factoring Polynomials*   **221**

## Oral Exercises

**State the greatest monomial factor of each polynomial.**

**1.** $5a^2 + 10ab + 5b^2$

**2.** $-x^3 + 9xy^2$

**3.** $-14z^3 + 21z + 35z^2$

**4.** $32r^4 - 48r^3 + 18r^2$

**5.** $56x^2 + 40x^3 - 16x$

**6.** $6(m + 1)^2 - 24$

**Factor completely.**

**7.** $3ab^2 - 27a^3$

**8.** $-a + 4a^3$

**9.** $-8x + 8x^2 - 2$

## Written Exercises

**A** **1–6.** Factor the polynomials in Oral Exercises 1–6 completely.

**Factor completely.**

**7.** $t^4 - 3t^2 - 2t^3$

**8.** $175 - 140w + 28w^2$

**9.** $xy + 5y - 2x - 10$

**10.** $24y - 9y^2 - 64$

**11.** $144z^3 - 36zq^2$

**12.** $40j^2k - 76jk^2 + 24k^3$

**13.** $x^4 - y^4$

**14.** $a^3x - 4ax^3$

**15.** $2x^4 - 162$

**16.** $a^2b - 9b + 3a^2 - 27$

**17.** $a^2 - 1 - 4b^2 - 4b$

**18.** $9a^2 - b^2 - 4b - 4$

**19.** $y^4 - 5y^2 + 4$

**20.** $x^4 - 26x^2 + 25$

**21.** $b^4 - 18b^2 + 81$

**22.** $2x^4 - 6x^2 - 8$

**23.** $10k^3 - 25k - 15k^2$

**24.** $-x^2 + 6xy - 9y^2$

**B** **25.** $2x^2 - 8y^2 + 16y - 8$

**26.** $x^2 - 9y^2 - 2x + 6y$

**27.** $4(a - 3)^2 - 4$

**28.** $x^8 - y^8$

**29.** $x^3 - x^2 - 4x + 4$

**30.** $a^3 + 2a^2 - 9a - 18$

**31.** $m^2 + m - k^2 - k$

**32.** $2pa + 2pr + r^2 - a^2$

**33.** $a^2c - 4abc - 9c^3 + 4b^2c$

**34.** $n(n + 1)(n + 2) - 3n(n + 1)$

**35.** $a(x^2 - a^2) + x(a - x)$

**36.** $2x^2(x + 1)(x + 3) - 6x^2$

**37.** $a^2(b - 3c) + 9b^2(3c - b)$

**38.** $(a - b)^3 + 4(b - a)$

**39.** $2 - 2y^2 - 8x^2 - 8xy$

**40.** $a^2 - 2ab + b^2 - 3a + 3b$

**41.** $x(x^2 - 1) - 2(x + 1)$

**42.** $x(x - 5)(x - 2) + 6(x - 2)$

**43.** $ax + 2ay - 3x^2 + 12y^2$

**44.** $2c^{16} - 2d^{16}$

**45.** $2p(p + 1)(p - 6) + 16(p + 1)$

**46.** $4a^2(2a - 1) - 4a(2a - 1) + (2a - 1)$

**47.** $p^2 - 4pq + 4q^2 - r^2 + 4sr - 4s^2$

**48.** $16a^2 - 16b^2 - 64bc - 64c^2$

**49.** $45x^2 - 177xy - 12y^2$

**C** **50.** $(a^2 - 4)^2 - (a - 2)^2$

**51.** $4b^2c^2 - (b^2 + c^2 - a^2)^2$

**52.** $(a^2 - 9)^2 - (3 - a)^2$

**53.** $(a + 3b)^2 - (a^2 - 9b^2)^2$

**54.** $x^2(x^2 - 4) + 4x(x^2 - 4) + 4(x^2 - 4)$

**55.** $x^2 + 4x^2y^2 + y^2 + 2xy - x^4 - 4y^4$

**56.** $t^3 + t^2 - t - 1$

**57.** $x^3 - x^2 - 4x + 4$

# 5-12 Solving Equations by Factoring

**Objective**   To solve polynomial equations by factoring.

The **converse** of a statement in if-then form is obtained by interchanging the "if" and "then" parts of the statement. The converse of a true statement is not necessarily true.

By the multiplicative property of zero you know that for any two real numbers $a$ and $b$:

$$\text{If } a = 0 \text{ or } b = 0, \text{ then } ab = 0.$$

You can show (see Exercise 52 on page 225) that the converse of the statement above is also true.

$$\text{If } ab = 0, \text{ then } a = 0 \text{ or } b = 0.$$

You can use the words *if and only if* to combine a statement and its converse. The *zero-product property* below combines the multiplicative property of zero and its converse into a single statement.

---

### Zero-Product Property

For all real numbers $a$ and $b$,

$$ab = 0 \text{ if and only if } a = 0 \text{ or } b = 0.$$

---

The zero-product property is true for any number of factors. *A product of factors is equal to zero if and only if one or more of the factors is zero.* This property can be used to solve certain equations.

**Example 1**   Solve $(x + 3)(x - 7) = 0$.

**Solution**   One of the factors on the left side must equal zero. Thus,

$$x + 3 = 0 \quad \text{or} \quad x - 7 = 0$$
$$x = -3 \quad \text{or} \quad x = 7$$

Of course, you might have seen without writing the equations that when $x = -3$ or $x = 7$ one of the factors will be 0. Either method gives the solution set $\{-3, 7\}$.   *Answer*

A **polynomial equation** is an equation whose sides are both polynomials. Polynomial equations may be named by the term of highest degree. When $a \neq 0$:

$$
\begin{array}{ll}
ax + b = 0 & \text{is a } \textbf{linear equation.} \\
ax^2 + bx + c = 0 & \text{is a } \textbf{quadratic equation.} \\
ax^3 + bx^2 + cx + d = 0 & \text{is a } \textbf{cubic equation.}
\end{array}
$$

---

Many polynomial equations can be solved by factoring and then applying the zero-product property. Often, the first step in solving such an equation is to transform it into **standard form** in which one side is 0 and the other side is a simplified polynomial arranged in descending powers of the variable.

**Example 2** Solve the quadratic equation $3x^2 + 2x = 8$.

**Solution**

1. Transform the equation into standard form.
2. Factor the left side.
3. Set each factor equal to zero and solve.
4. Check the solutions in the original equation $3x^2 + 2x = 8$, as shown below.

$$3x^2 + 2x - 8 = 0$$
$$(3x - 4)(x + 2) = 0$$
$$3x - 4 = 0 \quad \text{or} \quad x + 2 = 0$$
$$3x = 4 \qquad\qquad x = -2$$
$$x = \frac{4}{3}$$

$$3\left(\frac{4}{3}\right)^2 + 2\left(\frac{4}{3}\right) \stackrel{?}{=} 8 \qquad\qquad 3(-2)^2 + 2(-2) \stackrel{?}{=} 8$$

$$3\left(\frac{16}{9}\right) + \frac{8}{3} \stackrel{?}{=} 8 \qquad\qquad 3(4) + (-4) = 12 + (-4) = 8 \quad \checkmark$$

$$\frac{16}{3} + \frac{8}{3} = \frac{24}{3} = 8 \quad \checkmark$$

$\therefore$ the solution set is $\left\{\frac{4}{3}, -2\right\}$. *Answer*

**Example 3** Solve the cubic equation $27x^3 + 3x + 18x^2 = 0$.

**Solution**

1. Transform the equation into standard form.
2. Factor completely.

$$27x^3 + 18x^2 + 3x = 0$$
$$3x(9x^2 + 6x + 1) = 0$$
$$3x(3x + 1)(3x + 1) = 0$$

3. Solve by inspection or by equating each factor to zero.

$$x = 0 \quad \text{or} \quad x = -\frac{1}{3} \quad \text{or} \quad x = -\frac{1}{3}$$

4. The check is left for you.

$\therefore$ the solution set is $\left\{0, -\frac{1}{3}\right\}$. *Answer*

The factorization in Example 3 produced two identical factors. Since the factor $3x + 1$ occurs twice in the factored form of the equation, $-\frac{1}{3}$ is a **double** or **multiple root.** Note, however, that $-\frac{1}{3}$ is listed only once in the solution set.

**Caution!** Never transform an equation by dividing by an expression containing a variable. Notice that in Example 3, the solution 0 would have been lost if both sides of $3x(9x^2 + 6x + 1) = 0$ had been divided by $3x$.

## Oral Exercises

**Solve each equation by inspection or by setting each factor equal to 0.**

**1.** $a(a - 7) = 0$
**2.** $3b(b + 2) = 0$
**3.** $(c + 8)(c - 7) = 0$
**4.** $-5d(4d - 1) = 0$
**5.** $(6e + 1)(3e - 2) = 0$
**6.** $(f + 5)(2f + 9) = 0$
**7.** Describe how you would solve the equation $2x^3 + 9x^2 = 5x$.

## Written Exercises

**Solve.**

**A**
**1.** $(n + 17)(n + 7) = 0$
**2.** $(y - 15)(y - 100) = 0$
**3.** $35n(n - 35) = 0$
**4.** $(3x - 1)(2x + 5) = 0$
**5.** $(4k + 2)(k - 3) = 0$
**6.** $(4z + 5)5z = 0$
**7.** $3n(n - 4)(2n + 7) = 0$
**8.** $2x(2x - 5)(5x + 2) = 0$
**9.** $m(3m - 8)(3m + 1) = 0$
**10.** $x^2 - 13x + 36 = 0$
**11.** $y^2 + 2y - 63 = 0$
**12.** $z^2 + 2z - 8 = 0$
**13.** $x^2 - 5x + 6 = 0$
**14.** $x^2 - x - 6 = 0$
**15.** $x^2 + 25 = 10x$
**16.** $n^2 - 5n = 24$
**17.** $k^2 + 9 = 10k$
**18.** $y^2 - 16y = 0$
**19.** $y^2 - 16 = 0$
**20.** $4x^2 - 9 = 0$
**21.** $a^2 - 4a + 4 = 0$
**22.** $3x^2 + 2x - 1 = 0$
**23.** $a^3 - a = 0$
**24.** $n^3 - 4n = 0$
**25.** $x^2 - x - 30 = 0$
**26.** $2x^2 - 5x - 3 = 0$
**27.** $y^3 - 10y^2 + 25y = 0$
**28.** $n^2 = 36$
**29.** $4x^2 = 8x + 5$
**30.** $3y^2 + 2y = 1$
**31.** $a^2 = 24 - 5a$
**32.** $4a^2 = 8a$
**33.** $6x^2 = x + 1$
**34.** $6x^2 + x = 77$
**35.** $3x^2 - 6x = 9$
**36.** $6x^2 + 17x + 12 = 0$
**37.** $4y^2 + 7 = 29y$
**38.** $6y^2 = 22y + 40$
**39.** $6z^2 + 11z = 72$

**B**
**40.** $x^3 - 12x^2 + 32x = 0$
**41.** $y^3 + 49y = 14y^2$
**42.** $y^4 - 13y^2 + 36 = 0$
**43.** $t^3 + t^2 = 4t + 4$
**44.** $a^4 - 2a^2 + 1 = 0$
**45.** $2x^4 - 20x^2 + 18 = 0$
**46.** $9t^3 - 9t^2 - 9t + 9 = 0$
**47.** $y^3 + 45y = 14y^2$
**48.** $y^5 = 25y^3$
**49.** $(x - 2)(x + 3) = 6$
**50.** $(a - 5)(a - 2) = 28$
**51.** $4x^4 = 64$

**C** **52.** Give the missing reasons in the proof of the statement: If $ab = 0$, then
$a = 0$ or $b = 0$.
If $a = 0$, then there is nothing to prove.
If $a \neq 0$:

$ab = 0$      (1) Given

There is a unique

real number $\dfrac{1}{a}$.      (2) __?__

$\dfrac{1}{a}(ab) = \dfrac{1}{a}(0)$      (3) __?__

$\dfrac{1}{a}(ab) = 0$      (4) __?__

$\left(\dfrac{1}{a} \cdot a\right)b = 0$      (5) __?__

$(1)b = 0$      (6) __?__
$b = 0$      (7) __?__

A quadratic trinomial $Ax^2 + Bx + C$ can be thought of as

$$(A1 \times A2)x^2 + [(A1 \times C2) + (A2 \times C1)]x + (C1 \times C2)$$

where $A1$ and $A2$ are factors of $A$ and $C1$ and $C2$ are factors of $C$.

A chart of the program is shown at the right.

In BASIC, an exponent is expressed by using an upward arrow or some similar symbol. For example,

$$x^2 \text{ is written } X\uparrow 2.$$

The factors of $C$ will need to be tested in both orders. This is done in lines 360–380.

| INPUT |
|---|
| LOOP to factor $A = A1 \times A2$ |
| LOOP to factor $C = C1 \times C2$ |
| Subroutine to test for value of $B$. If $A1 \times C2 + A2 \times C1 = B$ then OUTPUT |
| NEXT $C1$ |
| NEXT $A1$ |
| OUTPUT |

```
10    PRINT "TO FIND FACTORS OF"
15    PRINT
20    PRINT "AX↑2 + BX + C:"
25    PRINT
30    PRINT "INPUT A (>0),B,C (<>0)";
40    INPUT A,B,C
50    IF A <= 0 THEN 30
60    PRINT
70    REM---FIND THE FACTORS
80    REM---OF A WHERE
90    REM---A IS THE
100   REM---COEFFICIENT
110   REM---OF X↑2
120   FOR A1=1 TO A
130   LET A2=A/A1
140   IF A2 <> INT(A2) THEN 410
150   IF A2<A1 THEN 540
160   PRINT
170   PRINT "A1 = ";A1,"A2 = ";A2
180   PRINT
190   REM---FIND THE FACTORS
200   REM---OF C WHERE
210   REM---C IS THE
220   REM---CONSTANT TERM
230   REM---OF THE TRINOMIAL
240   FOR C1=1 TO ABS(C)
250   LET C2=C/C1
260   IF C2 <> INT(C2) THEN 400
270   IF ABS(C2)<ABS(C1) THEN 410
```

```
280   LET K=0
290   LET C3=C1
300   GOSUB 460
310   LET C3=-C3
320   LET C2=-C2
330   GOSUB 460
340   IF K=1 THEN 400
350   LET K=1
360   LET T=C2
370   LET C2=C3
380   LET C3=T
390   GOTO 300
400   NEXT C1
410   NEXT A1
420   GOTO 540
430   REM---SUBROUTINE
440   REM---COMPUTE AND PRINT
450   REM---POSSIBLE MIDDLE TERMS
460   PRINT A1;" X ";C2;" + ";
470   PRINT A2;" X ";C3;" = ";
480   LET M=A1*C2+A2*C3
490   PRINT M;" B = ";B
500   IF M=B THEN 560
510   PRINT
520   RETURN
530   REM---OUTPUT
540   PRINT "PRIME"
550   GOTO 580
560   PRINT "(";A1;"X + (";C3;"))";
570   PRINT "(";A2;"X + (";C2;"))"
580   END
```

## Exercises

1. Explain the use of the temporary variable $T$ in lines 360 and 380.

2. If you can print out a copy of the program, use colored pencils to mark the loops for factoring $A$ and $C$.

RUN the program to factor the following trinomials.

3. $x^2 + 11x + 28$     4. $x^2 - x + 10$     5. $4x^2 + 20x + 21$

6. $7x^2 - 16x - 15$     7. $6x^2 - 7x - 5$     8. $35x^2 + 12x - 36$

9. When does the program give duplicate values of $M$?

10. Which lines would you need to change or delete in order to print just the answer?

*Note:* The program above can be used to do Exercises 1–36 on page 216.

# 5-13 Solving Problems by Factoring

**Objective**  To solve problems involving quadratic equations.

The problems in this section all lead to polynomial equations that can be solved by factoring. Sometimes a solution of the equation may not satisfy some of the conditions of the problem. For example, a negative number could not be a length or a width. You simply discard solutions that do not make sense for the problem.

**Example 1**  A pool is surrounded by a deck of uniform width. The area of the pool is 180 m². If the dimensions of the pool plus the deck are 16 m by 24 m, find the width of the deck.

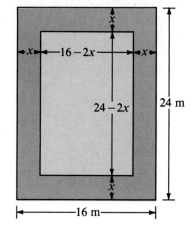

**Solution**

*Step 1*  The problem asks for the width of the deck.

*Step 2*  Let $x$ = width of the deck (in meters). Then the length of the pool = $24 - 2x$ and the width of the pool = $16 - 2x$.

*Step 3*  Area of the pool = 180.
$$(16 - 2x)(24 - 2x) = 180$$

*Step 4*
$$384 - 80x + 4x^2 = 180$$
$$4x^2 - 80x + 204 = 0$$
$$x^2 - 20x + 51 = 0$$
$$(x - 3)(x - 17) = 0$$

$$x - 3 = 0 \quad | \quad x - 17 = 0$$
$$x = 3 \quad | \quad x = 17$$

*Step 5*  *Check:* When $x = 3$ the area of the pool is $(16 - 2x)(24 - 2x) = (10)(18) = 180$. When $x = 17$, the width $16 - 2x$ and the length $24 - 2x$ are negative. Because negative widths and lengths are meaningless, we must reject $x = 17$ as an answer.

∴ the width of the deck is 3 m.  *Answer*

You may wonder how the equation in Step 3 can produce a solution, 17, that does not check. The reason is that the equation in Step 3 gives only one of the requirements of the problem. The requirements that the pool have a positive width ($16 - 2x > 0$) and a positive length ($24 - 2x > 0$) were not written down. Usually, it is easier to write only the equation and then check its solutions against the other conditions stated in the problem.

In the next example, both solutions of the equation satisfy the conditions of the problem.

You can use the formula $h = rt - 4.9t^2$ to obtain a good approximation of the height $h$ in meters that an object will reach in $t$ seconds when it is projected upward with an initial speed of $r$ meters per second (m/s).

## Example 2

A ball is thrown upward with an initial speed of 19.6 m/s. When is it directly opposite a balcony that is 14.7 m high?

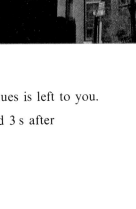

### Solution

Step 1   The problem asks for the time when the ball is opposite the balcony.

Step 2   Let  $t$ = number of seconds after being thrown that the ball is opposite the balcony,

$h$ = height of ball
$= 14.7$ (meters),

and $r$ = initial speed
$= 19.6$ (meters per second).

Step 3   $h = rt - 4.9t^2$
$14.7 = 19.6t - 4.9t^2$

$$\frac{14.7}{4.9} = \frac{19.6t}{4.9} - \frac{4.9t^2}{4.9}$$

Step 4   $3 = 4t - t^2$
$t^2 - 4t + 3 = 0$
$(t - 3)(t - 1) = 0$
Completing the solution and checking the values is left to you.

∴ the ball is opposite the balcony both 1 s and 3 s after being thrown.   **Answer**

## Problems

**Solve.**

A   **1.** The sum of a number and its square is 72. Find the number.

**2.** The sum of a positive number and its square is 90. Find the number.

**3.** A negative number is 42 less than its square. Find the number.

**4.** Find two consecutive negative integers whose product is 110.

5. The square of a number is 20 more than 8 times the number. Find the number.

6. The squares of two consecutive positive even integers total 100. Find the integers.

7. The length of a rectangle is 9 cm more than its width. Its area is 112 cm². Find the dimensions of the rectangle.

8. The length of a rectangle is 4 cm more than twice its width. If the area of the rectangle is 160 cm², find its dimensions.

9. A rectangle has perimeter 42 m and area 104 m². Find the dimensions of the rectangle. (*Hint:* If the width is *w*, the length is 21 − *w*.)

10. The dimensions of a rectangle were 5 cm by 9 cm. When both dimensions were increased by equal amounts, the area of the rectangle increased by 120 cm². Find the dimensions of the new rectangle.

11. A square field has 4 m added to its length and 2 m added to its width, thereby creating a field with an area of 195 m². Find the dimensions of the original field.

12. The sum of two numbers is 20, and the sum of their squares is 218. Find the numbers. (*Hint:* If one number is *x*, the other will be 20 − *x*.)

13. Find two numbers that total 13 and whose squares total 229.

14. I am thinking of three consecutive integers. The square of the largest one equals the sum of the squares of the other two. Find the integers.

**In Problems 15–19, use the formula $h = rt - 4.9t^2$. Notice that all numbers appearing are integral multiples of 4.9.**

15. A ball is thrown upward with an initial speed of 24.5 m/s. When is it 29.4 m high? (Two answers)

16. A projectile is fired upward with an initial speed of 2940 m/s. After how many minutes does it hit the ground?

**B** 17. A signal flare is fired upward with an initial speed of 245 m/s. A stationary balloonist at a height of 1960 m sees the flare pass on its way up. How long will it be before the flare passes the balloonist again on its way down?

18. A ball is thrown upward from the top of a 98 m tower with an initial speed of 39.2 m/s. When does it hit the ground? (*Hint:* If *h* is the height of the ball above the top of the tower, then $h = -98$ when the ball hits the ground.)

19. A ball is thrown upward with an initial speed of 29.4 m/s.
    a. When is the ball 44.1 m high?
    b. Explain why 44.1 m is the greatest height attained by the ball.

20. The height of a box is 8 cm and the total surface area of the box is 114 cm². Find the length of a side of the base of the box if the base is a square.

21. The bottom of a box is a rectangle with dimensions in centimeters of $x$ and $x + 2$. The height of the box is 5 cm and its total surface area is 236 cm². Find $x$.

22. A rug placed in a room 12 m long and 9 m wide covers half the floor area and leaves a uniform strip of bare floor around the edges. What are the dimensions of the rug?

23. A garden plot 4 m by 12 m has one side along a fence as shown below. The area of the garden is to be doubled by digging up a border of uniform width on the other three sides. What should be the width of the border?

Ex. 23

Ex. 24

24. The diagram above shows a rectangular enclosure formed by a wall and 20 m of fencing. If the area of the enclosure is 48 m², find its dimensions.

25. A rectangular garden 40 m by 30 m has two paths crossing through it as shown. If the width of each path in meters is $x$ and the area covered by the paths is 325 m², find $x$.

26. The side of one cube is 2 cm more than the side of another cube. The volumes of the cubes differ by 152 cm³. Find the lengths of the sides of each cube.

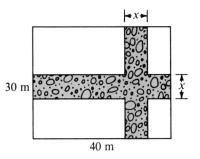

Ex. 25

C 27. A rectangular piece of cardboard is 20 cm longer than it is wide. Squares, 10 cm on a side, are cut from the corners of the cardboard, and the sides are folded up to make an open box whose volume is 8 L. Find the dimensions of the original piece of cardboard. (*Remember:* 1 L = 1000 cm³)

Ex. 27

## Self-Test 4

***Vocabulary***    factor completely (p. 221)           quadratic equation (p. 223)
                         converse (p. 223)                      cubic equation (p. 223)
                         polynomial equation (p. 223)     standard form of a
                         linear equation (p. 223)                   polynomial equation (p. 224)

**Factor completely.**

**1.** $5a - 2ac + 5b - 2bc$          **2.** $n^2 - 2n + 1 - 100t^4$         **Obj. 5-10, p. 218**

**3.** $18a^3 - 12a^2 + 2a$            **4.** $21xy - 18x^2 - 6y^2$           **Obj. 5-11, p. 221**

**Solve.**

**5.** $k^2 - 4k = 32$                 **6.** $3g^2 + 12g + 12 = 0$       **Obj. 5-12, p. 223**

**7.** $w^3 = 121w$                   **8.** $z^3 = z^2 + 30z$

**9.** The lengths of the legs of a right triangle are consecutive integers and the area is 66 cm². Find the length of the shorter leg.      **Obj. 5-13, p. 228**

Check your answers with those at the back of the book.

## Chapter Summary

1. Prime factors of positive integers can be found systematically by using the primes in order as divisors. The *prime factorization* of a positive integer is the expression of the integer as a product of prime factors.

2. The *greatest common factor (GCF) of two or more integers* is the greatest integer that divides all of them evenly. The *greatest common factor of two or more monomials* is the common factor that has the greatest coefficient and the greatest degree in each variable.

3. The *cancellation rule for fractions* (page 187) and the *rule of exponents for division* (page 188) can be used to simplify quotients of monomials.

4. A method for *multiplying binomials mentally* is given on page 196.

5. The following factoring patterns are useful in factoring polynomials:

$$a^2 + 2ab + b^2 = (a + b)^2 \qquad a^2 - b^2 = (a + b)(a - b)$$
$$a^2 - 2ab + b^2 = (a - b)^2$$

6. Guidelines for *factoring polynomials completely* are given on page 221.

7. The *zero-product property* (page 223) is useful in solving *polynomial equations*.

# Chapter Review

**Give the letter of the correct answer.**

5-1

1. List all the pairs of integral factors of $-111$.
   **a.** $(-1)(-111), (-3)(-37)$     **b.** $(-1)(111), (-3)(37)$
   **c.** $(-1)(111), (1)(-111),$     **d.** $(1)(111), (-1)(-111),$
      $(3)(-37), (-3)(37)$          $(3)(37), (-3)(-37)$

2. Give the prime factorization of 72.
   **a.** $1 \cdot 2^3 \cdot 3^2$     **b.** $2^2 \cdot 3 \cdot 6$     **c.** $2^2 \cdot 3^3$     **d.** $2^3 \cdot 3^2$

3. Give the GCF of 12 and 36.
   **a.** 2     **b.** 6     **c.** 12     **d.** 36

5-2

4. Simplify $\dfrac{(-4a)^3}{-4a^3}$.
   **a.** 1     **b.** $-1$     **c.** 3     **d.** 16

5. Find the missing factor: $-105x^3y^6 = (7xy^2)(\underline{\ ?\ })$
   **a.** $-112x^3y^3$     **b.** $-15x^3y^3$     **c.** $-15x^2y^4$     **d.** $-25x^2y^4$

5-3

6. Divide: $\dfrac{24a^2 - 48a + 8}{8}$
   **a.** $3a^2 - 6a$     **b.** $6a^2 - 7a + 1$     **c.** $3a^2 - 6a + 1$     **d.** 3

7. Express $18x^3 - 63x^2 + 9x$ as the product of its greatest monomial factor and another polynomial.
   **a.** $9(2x^3 - 7x^2 + x)$         **b.** $9x(2x^2 - 7x)$
   **c.** $9x(2x^2 - 7x + x)$         **d.** $9x(2x^2 - 7x + 1)$

5-4

8. Express $(k - 1)(k - 1)$ as a polynomial.
   **a.** $k^2 + 1$     **b.** $2k + 1$     **c.** $k^2 - 2k + 1$     **d.** $k^2 + 2k + 1$

9. Express $(7x + 3y)(x + 3y)$ as a polynomial.
   **a.** $7x^2 + 6y^2$         **b.** $7x^2 + 9y^2$
   **c.** $7x^2 + 24xy + 6y^2$         **d.** $7x^2 + 24xy + 9y^2$

5-5

10. Express $(x^3 + 1)(x^3 - 1)$ as a polynomial.
    **a.** $x^6 - 1$     **b.** $x^9 - 1$     **c.** $2x^3 - 1$     **d.** $x^6 - 2x - 1$

11. Factor $196 - x^{16}$.
    **a.** $(x^4 + 14)(x^4 - 14)$         **b.** $(14 + x^8)(14 - x^8)$
    **c.** $(x^8 + 14)(x^8 - 14)$         **d.** $(14 - x^4)(14 + x^4)$

**12.** Express $(4a - 7b)^2$ as a polynomial.  5-6
    **a.** $16a^2 + 49b^2$            **b.** $16a^2 - 49b^2$
    **c.** $16a^2 + 56ab - 49b^2$     **d.** $16a^2 - 56ab + 49b^2$

**13.** Factor $a^2 - 2a + 1$.
    **a.** not possible           **b.** $(a - 1)^2$
    **c.** $(a + 1)^2$              **d.** $(a - 2)^2$

**14.** Factor $a^2 + ab + b^2$.
    **a.** not possible           **b.** $(a + b)^2$
    **c.** $(a - b)^2$             **d.** $(a + b)(a - b)$

**15.** Factor $m^2 - 5m + 6$.  5-7
    **a.** not possible           **b.** $(m - 6)(m - 1)$
    **c.** $(m + 1)(m - 6)$      **d.** $(m - 2)(m - 3)$

**16.** Factor $x^2 + 16x + 48$.
    **a.** $(x + 6)(x + 8)$       **b.** $(x + 3)(x + 16)$
    **c.** $(x + 2)(x + 24)$     **d.** $(x + 4)(x + 12)$

**17.** Factor $x^2 + 14x - 32$.  5-8
    **a.** $(x - 8)(x + 4)$       **b.** $(x + 8)(x - 4)$
    **c.** $(x + 16)(x - 2)$     **d.** $(x - 16)(x + 2)$

**18.** Factor $x^2 - 14x - 48$.
    **a.** not possible           **b.** $(x - 6)(x - 8)$
    **c.** $(x - 16)(x + 2)$     **d.** $(x + 4)(x - 12)$

**19.** Factor $6x^2 - 19x + 3$.  5-9
    **a.** $(2x - 3)(3x - 1)$     **b.** $(6x - 1)(x - 3)$
    **c.** $(x - 1)(6x - 3)$      **d.** $(3x - 3)(2x - 1)$

**20.** Factor $6x^2 - 5x - 6$.
    **a.** $(3x + 2)(3x - 3)$     **b.** $(3x - 2)(2x + 3)$
    **c.** $(3x - 1)(2x + 6)$     **d.** $(2x - 3)(3x + 2)$

**21.** Factor $7t(n - 4) - (4 - n)$.  5-10
    **a.** $7t(n - 4)$          **b.** $(n - 4)(7t + 1)$
    **c.** $7t(2n - 8)$         **d.** $(n - 4)(7t - 1)$

**22.** Factor $4t^2 + 36$ completely.  5-11
    **a.** $(2t + 6)^2$           **b.** $4(t^2 + 9)$
    **c.** $4(t + 3)^2$          **d.** $4(t + 3)(t - 3)$

**23.** Solve $3x(2x - 1)(3x + 2) = 0$.  5-12
    **a.** $\left\{0, \frac{1}{2}, -\frac{2}{3}\right\}$       **b.** $\left\{0, 2, -\frac{2}{3}\right\}$
    **c.** $\left\{0, 2, -\frac{3}{2}\right\}$       **d.** $\left\{0, \frac{1}{2}, -\frac{3}{2}\right\}$

**24.** I am thinking of four consecutive integers. The sum of the squares of  5-13
the second and third is 61. Find the integers.
    **a.** $\{4, 5, 6, 7\}$          **b.** $\{-10, -9, -8, -7\}$
    **c.** $\{-4, -5, -6, -7\}$    **d.** no solution
       or $\{4, 5, 6, 7\}$

# Chapter Test

**List all the pairs of integral factors of each integer.**

**1.** 91                                   **2.** $-87$                                **5-1**

**Give the prime factorization of each number.**

**3.** 168                                   **4.** 420

**Simplify each expression assuming that no denominator equals zero.**

**5.** $\dfrac{-80ux^6}{-48ux^8}$                          **6.** $\dfrac{(-2y)^4}{-36y}$                     **5-2**

**7.** $\dfrac{49ab^2 - 56ab^8}{7ab^2}$               **8.** $\dfrac{-65r^6 + 78r^4 - 52r^2}{-13r^2}$        **5-3**

**Evaluate by factoring.**

**9.** $79 \times 15 - 79 \times 8$                   **10.** $64^2 - 64 \times 56$

**Express each product as a polynomial.**

**11.** $(6a - 1)(7a - 6)$               **12.** $(6a - b)(9a + 8b)$           **5-4**

**13.** $(8 + 9x)(8 - 9x)$               **14.** $(a^5 - b^3)(a^5 + b^3)$           **5-5**

**15.** $(a - 16)^2$                        **16.** $(5p - 7q)^2$                   **5-6**

**Factor each trinomial as the square of a binomial, if possible. If it is not possible, write "not factorable."**

**17.** $k^2 + 14k - 49$        **18.** $16x^2 - 8x + 1$        **19.** $a^2 - 9ab + 81b^2$

**Factor completely. If the polynomial is not factorable, write "prime."**

**20.** $b^2 - 3b + 2$       **21.** $x^2 - 2x + 4$       **22.** $a^2 - 6ab + 8b^2$      **5-7**

**23.** $a^2 - 6a - 40$       **24.** $z^2 + z - 3$          **25.** $x^2 + 22xy - 48y^2$     **5-8**

**26.** $4a^2 - a - 5$         **27.** $6y^2 + y - 15$       **28.** $7 - 23r + 6r^2$        **5-9**

**29.** $2r - 6 - 6r + 18$           **30.** $ax + 2x + a + 2$           **5-10**

**31.** $x^4 - 1$                        **32.** $x^2y - y^3$                     **5-11**

**33.** $9x^3 - 63x^2 + 108x$         **34.** $x^2 + x + xy + y$

**Solve.**

**35.** $3x^2 - 41x = -60$      **36.** $3a^2 = 57a$        **37.** $4a^2 = 1$        **5-12**

**38.** A rectangle has perimeter 34 cm and area 60 cm². Find the dimensions      **5-13**
of the rectangle.

# Cumulative Review (Chapters 1–5)

**Simplify. Assume that no denominator equals zero.**

1. $-2.1 + (-31.4) + 20.8$

2. $-\frac{3}{5}\left(-\frac{9}{17}\right) + \frac{8}{5}\left(-\frac{9}{17}\right)$

3. $\frac{-180t}{36}$

4. $(-4)^2 \div 2 + 2 - 8$

5. $(2z - 3) + (3z - 4)$

6. $(2z - 3) - (3z - 4)$

7. $(2a^2b)^3(3a^2b)^3$

8. $\frac{-35x^2yz^3}{21xyz}$

9. $\frac{27x^3y^2 - 9x^2y + 8xy}{9xy}$

10. $(7ab - 9c)(7ab + 9)$

11. $(5y + 6)^2$

12. $-t(3t + 5)(2t - 5)$

**Evaluate if $a = -\dfrac{1}{2}$, $b = 2$, $c = 0$, and $d = -3$.**

13. $\dfrac{(d - 2a) - b}{-c + 1}$

14. $\dfrac{1}{a}(bc - d)$

15. $(2b + d)^b$

16. Find the prime factorizations of 90 and 756 and then find their GCF.

**Factor completely. If the polynomial cannot be factored write "prime."**

17. $6p^3 - 2p^3r^2 + 8p^2r^3st$

18. $28z^2t - 7t$

19. $4a^2 + 12ab + 9b^2$

20. $d^2 + 13d + 22$

21. $m^2 - 9m + 18$

22. $t^2 - t - 20$

23. $6y^2 + 13y - 5$

24. $x^2 + 4xy + 4y^2 - 16$

25. $a^3 + a^2b - ab^2 - b^3$

**Solve. If the equation is an identity or has no solution, state that fact.**

26. $5t - 3 = 12$

27. $|t| - 4 = 2$

28. $\frac{3}{4}y = 21$

29. $7(x - 1) = 4x + 5$

30. $\frac{1}{4}x = -3$

31. $9 - b = -1$

32. $3m - 2 = \frac{1}{2}(8m + 6) - (m + 5)$

33. $4y^2 - 36 = 0$

34. $(x + 7)(x + 1) = (x + 2)^2 + 5x$

35. $x^2 - 6x + 15 = 6$

36. $x^3 - 9x^2 + 20x = 0$

37. $8b^2 - 10b = 3$

38. I have 20 dimes and nickels. I have $1\frac{1}{2}$ times as many nickels as I do dimes. How many nickels and how many dimes do I have?

39. The 42 km drive from Fairview to Middletown usually takes 28 min. Because of highway construction and a reduced speed limit, the trip now takes 14 min longer. Find the reduced speed limit in kilometers per hour.

40. The sum of the squares of two consecutive integers is 9 greater than 8 times the smaller integer. Find the integers.

41. The length of a rectangle is 5 greater than 3 times its width. The area of the rectangle is 22 cm². Find the length and width of the rectangle.

# Maintaining Skills

**Express each fraction as a decimal to the nearest hundredth.**

*Example 1* $\frac{11}{13}$      *Solution* $13\overline{)11.000}$ (quotient $0.846$)    $\frac{11}{13} \approx 0.85$

1. $\frac{23}{25}$    2. $\frac{35}{20}$    3. $\frac{10}{4}$    4. $\frac{49}{50}$    5. $\frac{81}{25}$    6. $\frac{5}{3}$

7. $\frac{51}{30}$    8. $\frac{7}{8}$    9. $\frac{14}{6}$    10. $\frac{41}{24}$    11. $\frac{15}{22}$    12. $\frac{21}{17}$

**Express each percent as a fraction in simplest form.**

*Example 2* $4.8\%$      *Solution* $\frac{4.8}{100} = \frac{48}{1000} = \frac{6}{125}$

13. $62\%$    14. $12\%$    15. $85\%$    16. $0.5\%$    17. $0.03\%$    18. $9.2\%$

**Express each decimal as a percent.**

*Example 3* $0.73$      *Solutions* (1) $0.73 = \frac{73}{100} = 73\%$      (2) $0.73 = 73\%$

19. $0.91$    20. $0.07$    21. $0.8$    22. $12$    23. $0.032$    24. $1.23$

**Find each number.**

*Example 4* $24\%$ of $35$      *Solution* $0.24 \times 35 = 8.4$

25. $32\%$ of $85$      26. $12\%$ of $80$      27. $0.2\%$ of $40$

28. $15.6\%$ of $50$      29. $130\%$ of $40$      30. $312\%$ of $20$

**Find the value of each variable.**

*Example 5* $35\%$ of $x = 7$      *Solution* $0.35x = 7;\ x = \frac{7}{0.35} = \frac{700}{35} = 20$

*Example 6* $n\%$ of $75 = 33$      *Solution* $\frac{n}{100} \times 75 = 33;\ \frac{n}{100} = \frac{33}{75};\ n = 44$

31. $30\%$ of $z = 21$      32. $15\%$ of $m = 6$      33. $5\%$ of $y = 0.6$

34. $52\%$ of $x = 39$      35. $24\%$ of $t = 108$      36. $45\%$ of $b = 81$

37. $p\%$ of $50 = 30$      38. $a\%$ of $45 = 18$      39. $t\%$ of $105 = 21$

40. $28 = n\%$ of $112$      41. $51 = x\%$ of $150$      42. $j\%$ of $35 = 14$

# 6 Fractions

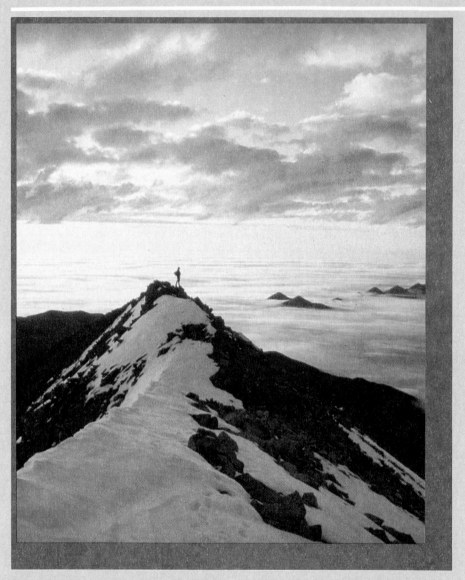

The temperature, $T$, in degrees Celsius, at a height of $h$ meters is given by the equation $T = t - \dfrac{h}{100}$, where $t$ is the ground surface temperature in degrees Celsius.

# Algebraic Fractions

## 6-1 Simplifying Fractions

**Objective**   To simplify algebraic fractions.

The procedure for simplifying a quotient of polynomials is the same procedure you learned for simplifying a quotient of monomials. Just factor the numerator and denominator and apply the cancellation rule for fractions. When the numerator and denominator have no common factor other than 1 and $-1$, the quotient is said to be in *simplest form*.

**Example 1**   Express $\dfrac{4a^2 - b^2}{4a^2 - 4ab + b^2}$ in simplest form.

**Solution**   $\dfrac{4a^2 - b^2}{4a^2 - 4ab + b^2} = \dfrac{(2a + b)\cancel{(2a - b)}}{(2a - b)\cancel{(2a - b)}} = \dfrac{2a + b}{2a - b} \quad (2a \neq b)$

Recall that you cannot divide by zero. Thus, you must restrict the variables in a denominator so that the denominator does not equal zero. In Example 1, $2a$ cannot equal $b$.

The next example shows that you must be alert to factors that have the same value, but whose terms are written in a different order.

**Example 2**   Express $\dfrac{12x^2 + 34x + 24}{(2x + 10)(3 + 2x)}$ in simplest form.

**Solution**   $\dfrac{12x^2 + 34x + 24}{(2x + 10)(3 + 2x)} = \dfrac{2(2x + 3)(3x + 4)}{2(x + 5)(3 + 2x)} \quad \left\{ \begin{array}{l} 2x + 3 \text{ and } 3 + 2x \\ \text{have the same value.} \end{array} \right.$

$= \dfrac{\cancel{2}\cancel{(2x + 3)}(3x + 4)}{\cancel{2}(x + 5)\cancel{(3 + 2x)}} = \dfrac{3x + 4}{x + 5} \quad \left( x \neq -5, x \neq -\dfrac{3}{2} \right)$

Example 3 shows that you must be alert to factors that are opposites of each other.

**Example 3**   Express $\dfrac{2x^2 + x - 15}{20 - 3x - 2x^2}$ in simplest form.

**Solution**   $\dfrac{2x^2 + x - 15}{20 - 3x - 2x^2} = \dfrac{(2x - 5)(x + 3)}{(5 - 2x)(4 + x)} \quad \{ 2x - 5 \text{ and } 5 - 2x \text{ are opposites.}$

$= \dfrac{-\cancel{(5 - 2x)}(x + 3)}{\cancel{(5 - 2x)}(x + 4)}$

$= \dfrac{-(x + 3)}{x + 4} = -\dfrac{x + 3}{x + 4} \quad \left( x \neq -4, x \neq \dfrac{5}{2} \right)$

## Oral Exercises

**Express in simplest form, noting any restrictions on the variable.**

1. $\dfrac{a^2 - 1}{a - 1}$
2. $\dfrac{b^2 - 4}{b + 2}$
3. $\dfrac{x^2 - 2x + 1}{x - 1}$
4. $\dfrac{x + 6}{36 - x^2}$

5. $\dfrac{2b + 4}{b + 2}$
6. $\dfrac{3x - 6}{4x - 8}$
7. $\dfrac{2c - 2d}{2c + 2d}$
8. $\dfrac{(2y - 8)^2}{(2y - 8)^3}$

9. $\dfrac{a - 7}{7 - a}$
10. $\dfrac{(x - 2)(x + 3)}{3 + x}$
11. $\dfrac{9 - 3c}{c - 3}$
12. $\dfrac{(4 - x)(x^2 - 9)}{(x - 4)(x - 3)}$

**Which of the following fractions *cannot* be simplified?**

13. $\dfrac{4x - 6y}{4x + 6y}$
14. $\dfrac{4x - 7y}{4x + 7y}$
15. $\dfrac{4x^2 - y^2}{2x - y}$
16. $\dfrac{4x^2 + y^2}{2x + y}$

## Written Exercises

**Express in simplest form, noting any restrictions on the variable.**

A
1. $\dfrac{3a - 6}{a - 2}$
2. $\dfrac{4n + 12}{n + 3}$
3. $\dfrac{3n + 1}{9n + 3}$
4. $\dfrac{6x - 6y}{6x + 6y}$

5. $\dfrac{2x - 2}{x^2 - 1}$
6. $\dfrac{2y + 14}{49 - y^2}$
7. $\dfrac{2xy}{x^2y - y^2x}$
8. $\dfrac{4p^3}{4p^2 - 8p}$

9. $\dfrac{a^2 + 8a + 16}{16 - a^2}$
10. $\dfrac{b^2 - 25}{b^2 - 12b + 35}$
11. $\dfrac{4y + 20}{4y^2 - 100}$
12. $\dfrac{6x + 8y}{16y^2 + 9x^2}$

13. $\dfrac{2 - y}{y^2 - 4y + 4}$
14. $\dfrac{(a - 5)^2}{25 - a^2}$
15. $\dfrac{(2x - y)^3}{(y - 2x)^4}$
16. $\dfrac{(4n - 3)^5}{(3 - 4n)^5}$

17. $\dfrac{x^2 + xy}{x^2 - xy}$
18. $\dfrac{2ab + 2ac + 4a^2}{4b + 4c + 8a}$
19. $\dfrac{(x - 2)(2x + 5)}{(5 + 2x)(x + 2)}$
20. $\dfrac{(3r + 7)^2(2r - 1)}{(1 - 2r)(7 + 3r)}$

21. $\dfrac{2n^2 - 5n - 3}{4n^2 - 8n - 5}$
22. $\dfrac{2z^2 + z - 6}{2z + 4}$
23. $\dfrac{3x^2 - 15x}{3x^2 - 16x + 5}$
24. $\dfrac{4n^2 - 6n}{4n^2 + 8n - 21}$

25. $\dfrac{10 - 7a + a^2}{a^2 - 4}$
26. $\dfrac{2y^2 - 9y + 4}{2y^2 - 8y}$
27. $\dfrac{x^2 - y^2}{x^2 + 2xy - 3y^2}$
28. $\dfrac{a^2 - b^2}{a^2 + 5ab + 4b^2}$

**Solve for $x$. Use the following steps. Assume no denominator is 0.**

*Step 1* Collect all terms with $x$ on one side of the equation and all other terms on the other side.

*Step 2* Factor both sides of the equation.

*Step 3* Divide both sides of the equation by the coefficient of $x$.

B
29. $cx + dx = c^2 - d^2$
30. $ax + bx = a^2 + 2ab + b^2$
31. $ax - a^2 = bx - b^2$
32. $2ax + 1 = 4a^2 + x$

**33.** $5kx - x = 25k^2 - 10k + 1$

**34.** $4x - 4 = b^2 + 5b - bx$

**35.** $cx - dx = c^2 - 3cd + 2d^2$

**36.** $x + 4p = 3p^2 + 3px + 1$

**37.** $a(x - a) + 6(x + 6) = 0$

**38.** $2n(x - n) = x - 5n + 2$

**39.** To evaluate $\dfrac{9x^2 - 4y^2}{3x - 2y}$ when $x = 4$ and $y = 5$, Stan first simplifies the fraction to $3x + 2y$. Then he substitutes $x = 4$ and $y = 5$, getting 22 for his answer. To evaluate $\dfrac{9x^2 - 4y^2}{3x - 2y}$ when $x = 4$ and $y = 6$, Stan substitutes these values in the simplified form $3x + 2y$, getting 24. One of his answers is correct and the other is not. Give the correct answer. Explain why the other answer is not correct.

**If the given values of the variables make the denominator zero, indicate that the fraction cannot be evaluated. Otherwise, evaluate the fraction by first simplifying it, and then substituting the given values of the variables.**

**40.** $\dfrac{4x^2 - y^2}{2x + y}$    **a.** $x = 4, y = -8$    **b.** $x = 4, y = 8$    **c.** $x = -\dfrac{1}{4}, y = \dfrac{1}{2}$

**41.** $\dfrac{x^3y - xy^3}{x^2y + xy^2}$    **a.** $x = 3, y = 3$    **b.** $x = 53, y = 49$    **c.** $x = 8, y = -8$

**42.** $\dfrac{n^2 - 9m^2}{n^2 - 5nm + 6m^2}$    **a.** $n = 8, m = -4$    **b.** $n = 6, m = 3$    **c.** $n = 9, m = -3$

**Simplify.**

**43.** $\dfrac{16x^2 - 49y^2}{16x^2 - 56xy + 49y^2}$

**44.** $\dfrac{4x^2 + 16xy + 15y^2}{2x^2 + xy - 10y^2}$

**45.** $\dfrac{6a^3 + 10a^2}{36a^3 - 100a}$

**46.** $\dfrac{8a^2 + 6ab - 5b^2}{16a^2 - 25b^2}$

**47.** $\dfrac{a - b + x(a - b)}{a - b}$

**48.** $\dfrac{a^4 - 4}{a^2(a + 2) + 2(a + 2)}$

**C 49.** $\dfrac{2x^3 - 13x^2 + 15x}{15x - 7x^2 - 2x^3}$

**50.** $\dfrac{x^4 - 10x^2 + 9}{3 - 2x - x^2}$

**51.** $\dfrac{a^2 - 9b^2 - 2a + 6b}{(a + 3b)^2 - 4}$

**52.** $\dfrac{x^3 + 6x^2 - 4x - 24}{x^3 - 2x^2 - 36x + 72}$

**53.** $\dfrac{a^2 - 6ab + 9b^2 - 9}{3a - 9b - 9}$

**54.** $\dfrac{(a - b)^3 + 4(b - a)}{(a - b)^2 + 4(b - a) + 4}$

**For which value(s) of $x$ do the given fractions equal zero? (*Hint:* A fraction is equal to zero only if its numerator equals zero.)**

**55.** $\dfrac{x^2 - 3x}{x^2 - 2x - 3}$

**56.** $\dfrac{x^2 - 2x - 8}{x^2 - 4x}$

**57.** $\dfrac{x^2 - 2x - 15}{x^2 + 3x - 40}$

**58.** $\dfrac{x^4 - x^2}{x^3 + x^2 - 2x}$

**59.** $\dfrac{2x^3 - x^2 - 10x}{x^3 - 2x^2 - 8x}$

**60.** $\dfrac{3x^4 + 27x^3 + 60x^2}{6x^2 + 6x - 72}$

## Computer Exercises
*For students with some programming experience*

**1. a.** Write a BASIC program to evaluate each of the following algebraic fractions for $x = 10, 20, 30, 40, 50$.

(1) $\dfrac{3x + 4}{4x^3 + x}$ (2) $\dfrac{5x^2 + 2x}{2x^2 - 9}$ (3) $\dfrac{3 - 2x^4}{x^3 + x^2}$

**b.** As the value of $x$ increases, what happens to the value of each of these algebraic fractions? Can you explain why?

**2. a.** Write a BASIC program that uses READ . . . DATA statements to evaluate the algebraic fraction $\dfrac{x^5 + 1}{x^4 - x^3 + x^2 - x + 1}$ for the following values of $x$: 2, 13, 22, 50, 99.

**b.** On the basis of your results in part (a), guess a general formula $\dfrac{x^5 + 1}{x^4 - x^3 + x^2 - x + 1} = \underline{\quad ? \quad}$ for all values of $x$.

---

# Application / Energy Consumption

Power is associated with the flow of electricity in a circuit. Electrical power is measured in watts (W). The amount of power that is used depends on the number of volts of the source of electricity and on the current. Current is the rate of flow of electrical charge. It is measured in amperes.

When $P$ watts of power are used for $t$ hours, the energy consumed, measured in watt-hours (W·h), is $e = Pt$.

Electric companies base their bills on a larger unit, the kilowatt-hour (kW·h), that is equal to one thousand watt-hours.

**Example 1** An air conditioner uses 1330 W in 6 hours.
 **a.** How much energy is consumed?
 **b.** If electricity costs 7.3 cents per kilowatt-hour, find the cost of operating the air conditioner.

**Solution** **a.** Use the formula $e = Pt$.
$$e = 1330 \times 6 = 7980$$
∴ the amount of energy consumed is 7980 W·h, or 7.98 kW·h.

**b.** Cost $= 7.3 \times 7.98 = 58.254$
∴ the cost of energy is about 58 cents.

It has been estimated that appliances account for as much as two fifths of total home energy consumption. Thus, consumers can save money by using energy-efficient appliances. Some appliances have a tag that shows the estimated yearly energy cost. Such tags make it easy for consumers to compare the energy efficiency of different models.

If you know the annual cost ($c$) as given on the energy cost tag and the expected lifetime ($l$) of the appliance, you can estimate the energy cost for the life of the machine. For example, suppose the appliance whose tag is shown is expected to last 15 years. The lifetime operating cost of this appliance is

$$c \cdot l = \$91 \cdot 15 = \$1365.$$

The total cost of an appliance is the sum of the purchase price and the cost of energy for the lifetime of the machine.

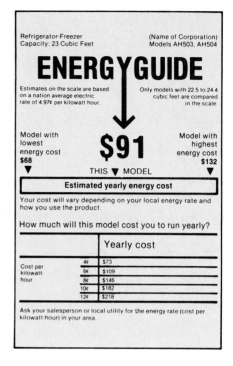

| Refrigerator-Freezer<br>Capacity: 23 Cubic Feet | (Name of Corporation)<br>Models AH503, AH504 |
|---|---|

# ENERGYGUIDE

| Estimates on the scale are based on a nation average electric rate of 4.97¢ per kilowatt hour. | Only models with 22.5 to 24.4 cubic feet are compared in the scale. |
|---|---|

| Model with lowest energy cost<br>$68 ▼ | $91 | Model with highest energy cost<br>$132 ▼ |
|---|---|---|

THIS ▼ MODEL

**Estimated yearly energy cost**

Your cost will vary depending on your local energy rate and how you use the product.

How much will this model cost you to run yearly?

| | | Yearly cost |
|---|---|---|
| Cost per kilowatt-hour | 4¢ | $73 |
| | 6¢ | $109 |
| | 8¢ | $146 |
| | 10¢ | $182 |
| | 12¢ | $218 |

Ask your salesperson or local utility for the energy rate (cost per kilowatt-hour) in your area.

**Example 2** Television A can be purchased for $225 and costs $58 per year to operate. Television B can be purchased for $275 and costs $45 per year to operate. If both have an expected lifetime of eight years, calculate the lifetime operating cost for each. Which is the least expensive?

**Solution** Use the formula to find the operating costs.

**Television A**

$$c \cdot l = \$58 \cdot 8 = \$464$$

Total cost to consumer:
$225 + $464 = $689

**Television B**

$$c \cdot l = \$45 \cdot 8 = \$360$$

Total cost to consumer:
$275 + $360 = $635

Television B costs less to operate over the eight-year lifetime.

## Exercises

1. A television uses 200 W per hour. If electricity costs 7.3¢ per kW·h, how much does it cost to watch a three-hour movie?

2. An oven uses 12,200 W per hour. At 7.3¢ per kW·h, how much does it cost to roast a turkey for five hours?

3. How many kilowatt-hours does a dishwasher use in a year if it costs $31 per year to operate at a cost of 8¢ per kilowatt-hour? What is the cost of energy over the lifetime of the dishwasher if its operating lifetime is 12 years?

4. Room air conditioner A can be purchased for $225 and costs $109 per year to operate. Room air conditioner B can be purchased for $350 and costs $95 per year to operate. Each is expected to last nine years. Which is the least expensive appliance over the length of the expected lifetime?

# 6-2 Multiplying Fractions

**Objective**  To multiply algebraic fractions.

The property of quotients states that

$$\frac{cx}{dy} = \frac{c}{d} \cdot \frac{x}{y}.$$

The symmetric property of equality makes it possible to rewrite this result as the multiplication rule for fractions, shown below. This rule enables you to express a product of two fractions as a quotient.

---

**Multiplication Rule for Fractions**

If $c$, $d$, $x$, and $y$ are any real numbers such that $d \neq 0$ and $y \neq 0$, then

$$\frac{c}{d} \cdot \frac{x}{y} = \frac{cx}{dy}.$$

---

**Example 1**  Multiply: $\dfrac{3x}{4} \cdot \dfrac{6}{2y}$

**Solution 1**  $\dfrac{3x}{4} \cdot \dfrac{6}{2y} = \dfrac{3x \cdot 6}{4 \cdot 2y} = \dfrac{\overset{9}{\cancel{18x}}}{\underset{4}{\cancel{8y}}} = \dfrac{9x}{4y}$   $(y \neq 0)$

**Solution 2**  $\dfrac{3x}{\cancel{4}} \cdot \dfrac{\overset{3}{\cancel{6}}}{\underset{2}{} 2y} = \dfrac{9x}{4y}$

**Example 2**  Multiply: $\dfrac{x^2 + 2x - 8}{x^2 + 3x} \cdot \dfrac{x^2 - 9}{x + 4}$

**Solution**

$\dfrac{x^2 + 2x - 8}{x^2 + 3x} \cdot \dfrac{x^2 - 9}{x + 4} = \dfrac{(x - 2)(x + 4)}{x(x + 3)} \cdot \dfrac{(x - 3)(x + 3)}{(x + 4)}$   $\left\{\begin{array}{l}\text{Factor the numerators} \\ \text{and denominators.}\end{array}\right.$

$\phantom{xxxxxxxxxxxxxxxxxxxxx} = \dfrac{(x - 2)\cancel{(x + 4)}}{x\cancel{(x + 3)}} \cdot \dfrac{(x - 3)\cancel{(x + 3)}}{\cancel{(x + 4)}}$   $\left\{\begin{array}{l}\text{Divide by common} \\ \text{factors.}\end{array}\right.$

$\phantom{xxxxxxxxxxxxxxxxxxxxx} = \dfrac{(x - 2)(x - 3)}{x}$   $(x \neq 0, x \neq -3, x \neq -4)$   *Answer*

Another way to write the answer to Example 2 is $\dfrac{x^2 - 5x + 6}{x}$. The factored form of the answer, as shown in Example 2, is the one you should use unless otherwise directed.

If you study the denominators in the first step in Example 2, you will

---

see that there will be a zero denominator when $x$ equals 0, $-3$, or $-4$. Thus the answer is restricted to values of $x$ other than 0, $-3$, and $-4$.

*Hereafter, it will be assumed that the domains of the variables include no value for which any denominator is zero.* Hence, it will not be necessary to show the excluded values of the variables.

In Chapter 4, you learned the rule of exponents for a power of a product:

For every positive integer $m$, $(ab)^m = a^m b^m$.

The rule of exponents for a power of a quotient is similar.

---

### Rule of Exponents for a Power of a Quotient

For every positive integer $m$,

$$\left(\frac{a}{b}\right)^m = \frac{a^m}{b^m}.$$

---

**Example 3** $\left(\dfrac{c}{4}\right)^3 = \dfrac{c^3}{4^3} = \dfrac{c^3}{64}$

**Example 4** Simplify $\left(\dfrac{x}{3}\right)^2 \cdot \dfrac{9}{8x}$.

**Solution** $\left(\dfrac{x}{3}\right)^2 \cdot \dfrac{9}{8x} = \dfrac{x^2}{9} \cdot \dfrac{9}{8x} = \dfrac{x}{8}$ **Answer**

Power of a quotient

---

## Oral Exercises

**Express each product as a fraction in simplest form.**

1. $\dfrac{2}{5} \cdot \dfrac{3}{8}$

2. $\dfrac{4}{7} \cdot \dfrac{14}{5}$

3. $\dfrac{-3}{4} \cdot \dfrac{8}{9}$

4. $\dfrac{a}{b} \cdot \dfrac{b}{a}$

5. $\dfrac{3}{x} \cdot \dfrac{x}{6}$

6. $\dfrac{n}{2} \cdot \dfrac{8}{n}$

7. $\dfrac{5y^2}{3} \cdot \dfrac{6}{y^2}$

8. $\dfrac{2a}{3} \cdot \dfrac{a}{4}$

9. $(2x)^2 \cdot \dfrac{1}{x}$

10. $\dfrac{a}{b} \cdot \dfrac{b^2}{c}$

11. $\dfrac{(x-1)^2}{8} \cdot \dfrac{4}{x-1}$

12. $\dfrac{3n-2}{n^2} \cdot \dfrac{n^4}{2-3n}$

**Complete.**

13. $\dfrac{x^2}{9y^2} = \left(\dfrac{?}{?}\right)^2$

14. $\left(\dfrac{5a}{b}\right)^2 = \dfrac{?}{?}$

15. $\left(\dfrac{n}{2s}\right)^3 = \dfrac{?}{?}$

---

*Fractions* 245

## Written Exercises

**Express each product as a fraction in simplest form.**

A  **1.** $\dfrac{4}{7} \cdot \dfrac{21}{8}$  **2.** $\dfrac{4}{9} \cdot \dfrac{3}{16}$  **3.** $\dfrac{15}{2} \cdot \dfrac{6}{25}$  **4.** $\dfrac{-3}{14} \cdot \dfrac{35}{6}$

**5.** $\dfrac{3}{5} \cdot \dfrac{5}{7} \cdot \dfrac{7}{9}$  **6.** $\dfrac{9}{5} \cdot \dfrac{2}{3} \cdot \dfrac{15}{18}$  **7.** $\left(\dfrac{-3}{4}\right)^2 \cdot \dfrac{8}{27}$  **8.** $\left(\dfrac{-3}{5}\right)^3 \cdot \dfrac{-25}{27}$

**9.** $\dfrac{4}{x} \cdot \dfrac{x^2}{8}$  **10.** $\dfrac{3y}{2} \cdot \dfrac{6}{5y}$  **11.** $\dfrac{a}{b} \cdot \dfrac{b}{c} \cdot \dfrac{c}{d}$  **12.** $\dfrac{4}{x^2} \cdot \dfrac{7x}{8}$

**13.** $\dfrac{p^2}{2q} \cdot \dfrac{q^2}{2p}$  **14.** $\dfrac{5ac^2}{3b^2} \cdot \dfrac{6b}{15a^2}$  **15.** $\dfrac{4d^2e}{9ef} \cdot \dfrac{f^2}{6d}$  **16.** $\dfrac{2rs^2}{3t} \cdot \dfrac{9t^2}{4rs}$

**Simplify, using the rules of exponents for the power of a product and the power of a quotient.**

**17.** $(3a^5)^2$  **18.** $(5n^2)^3$  **19.** $\left(\dfrac{a}{6}\right)^2$  **20.** $\left(\dfrac{4x}{3}\right)^2$

**21.** $\left(\dfrac{5a}{3b^2}\right)^3$  **22.** $\left(\dfrac{3n^2}{4}\right)^3$  **23.** $\left(\dfrac{-x^2}{10}\right)^4$  **24.** $-\left(\dfrac{5b^4}{6}\right)^2$

**25.** $\left(\dfrac{a}{b}\right)^2 \cdot \dfrac{b}{a}$  **26.** $\left(\dfrac{3x}{y}\right)^3 \cdot \dfrac{y^2}{9}$  **27.** $\left(\dfrac{2x}{5}\right)^3 \cdot \dfrac{75}{x^2}$  **28.** $\left(\dfrac{5a}{b}\right)^2 \cdot \dfrac{2ab}{15}$

**29.** Find the area of a square if each side has length $\dfrac{2x}{7}$ in.

**30.** Find the volume of a cube if each edge has length $\dfrac{4n}{5}$ in.

**31.** A rectangle has length $\dfrac{5x}{4}$ and width $\dfrac{2x}{15}$. What is the area?

**32.** If you travel for $\dfrac{9h}{2}$ hours at $\dfrac{80r}{3}$ mph, how far have you gone?

B  **33.** Find the total dollar cost of $\dfrac{4y}{3}$ eggs if they cost $d$ dollars per dozen.

**34.** Find the total dollar cost of $n$ dozen pencils if each pencil costs $\dfrac{2c}{3}$ cents.

**Simplify.**

**35.** $\dfrac{y + 3}{y} \cdot \dfrac{y^2}{y^2 - 9}$  **36.** $\dfrac{a + b}{a - b} \cdot \dfrac{a^2 - b^2}{2a + 2b}$  **37.** $\dfrac{a^2 - x^2}{a^2} \cdot \dfrac{a}{3x - 3a}$

**38.** $\dfrac{(1 - x)^3}{5} \cdot \dfrac{10}{(x - 1)^2}$  **39.** $\dfrac{x^2 - 4}{x^2 + 4x} \cdot \dfrac{x^2 - 16}{x^2 + 2x}$  **40.** $\dfrac{2a + 1}{3a^2 + 15a} \cdot 3a^3 - 75a$

**41.** $\dfrac{3x - xy}{6x^2y} \cdot \dfrac{3}{9 - y^2}$  **42.** $\left(\dfrac{x - 2}{2}\right)^2 \cdot \left(\dfrac{2}{2 - x}\right)^3$  **43.** $\left(\dfrac{2n - 1}{3}\right)^4 \cdot \left(\dfrac{9}{1 - 2n}\right)^2$

**44.** $\dfrac{x^2 + 4x - 21}{x^2 - 6x - 16} \cdot \dfrac{x^2 - 8x + 15}{x^2 + 9x + 14}$  **45.** $\dfrac{4x^2 - 2ax}{x^2 - 4ax + 4a^2} \cdot \dfrac{(2a - x)^3}{2x - a}$

**46.** $\dfrac{n^2 - 3n + 2}{n^2 + 3n + 2} \cdot \dfrac{8n + 8}{4n - 8}$

**47.** $\dfrac{3c^2 - 9c + 6}{2c^2 - 10c + 12} \cdot \dfrac{6 - 2c}{3 - 3c}$

**48.** $\left(\dfrac{x - y}{x + y}\right)^2 \cdot \dfrac{x^2 + y^2}{x^2 - y^2}$

**49.** $\dfrac{4a^2 - b^2}{4c^2 - d^2} \cdot \left(\dfrac{d - 2c}{b - 2a}\right)^2$

**C**  **50.** $\dfrac{4z^2 - 4}{1 + z^2} \cdot \dfrac{1 - z}{2z} \cdot \dfrac{1 - 2z^2 + z^4}{2 + 2z}$

**51.** $\dfrac{x^2 - x - 2}{x^2} \cdot \dfrac{x^2 + x - 2}{9x} \cdot \dfrac{54x^3}{x^4 - 5x^2 + 4}$

**52.** $\dfrac{x^3 + 3x^2 - 4x - 12}{2x^2 - 18} \cdot \dfrac{x^3 - 3x^2 + 3x - 9}{3x^3 - 12x}$

**53.** $\dfrac{a^2 - (b - c)^2}{2a - 2b + 2c} \cdot \dfrac{6a - 6b + 6c}{b^2 - (a - {}'c)^2}$

**54.** Use the multiplication rule for fractions to derive the rule of exponents for the power of a quotient.

## Computer Key-In

To find the prime numbers less than a given number *N*, you look for numbers that *do not* have factors other than 1 and *N*. Compare line 80 in the program given below with line 80 in the program given on page 186.

```
10   PRINT "TO FIND PRIME NUMBERS"
20   PRINT "LESS THAN N:"
30   PRINT "INPUT N";
40   INPUT N
45   PRINT "2 ";
50   FOR W=2 TO N
60   FOR F=2 TO W/2
70   LET Q=W/F
80   IF Q=INT(Q) THEN 140
110  NEXT F
130  PRINT W;" ";
140  NEXT W
150  END
```

### Exercises

**1.** Why does the loop in the program above begin with 2 instead of 1?

**2.** Use the program to print the prime numbers less than 100, 500, and 1000.

**3.** FOR-NEXT loops can use numbers other than 1 as increments by specifying a STEP. Copy and RUN the following program, which will print the odd numbers from 1 to 25.

```
10   FOR N=1 TO 25 STEP 2
20   PRINT N;" ";
30   NEXT N
40   END
```

# 6-3 Dividing Fractions

**Objective**   To divide algebraic fractions.

The rule for division of real numbers states that to divide by a real number, you multiply by its reciprocal. For example,

$$\frac{5}{8} \div \frac{2}{9} = \frac{5}{8} \cdot \frac{9}{2} = \frac{45}{16}.$$

In algebra, division by fractions obeys the same rule.

---

**Division Rule for Fractions**

$$\frac{a}{b} \div \frac{c}{d} = \frac{a}{b} \cdot \frac{d}{c}$$

---

**Example 1**   Divide: $\dfrac{x^2 + 3x - 10}{2x + 6} \div \dfrac{x^2 - 4}{x^2 - x - 12}$

**Solution**

$$\frac{x^2 + 3x - 10}{2x + 6} \div \frac{x^2 - 4}{x^2 - x - 12} = \frac{x^2 + 3x - 10}{2x + 6} \cdot \frac{x^2 - x - 12}{x^2 - 4} \quad \left\{ \begin{array}{l} \text{Multiply by} \\ \text{the reciprocal.} \end{array} \right.$$

$$= \frac{(x + 5)(x - 2)}{2(x + 3)} \cdot \frac{(x + 3)(x - 4)}{(x - 2)(x + 2)} \quad \left\{ \text{Factor.} \right.$$

$$= \frac{(x + 5)\cancel{(x - 2)}}{2\cancel{(x + 3)}} \cdot \frac{\cancel{(x + 3)}(x - 4)}{\cancel{(x - 2)}(x + 2)} \quad \left\{ \begin{array}{l} \text{Divide by} \\ \text{common factors.} \end{array} \right.$$

$$= \frac{(x + 5)(x - 4)}{2(x + 2)}$$

When simplifying an expression that involves both multiplication and division, do the operations in order from left to right, unless parentheses indicate a different order. Remember that you can change each division sign to a multiplication sign if you replace the fraction immediately following the division sign by its reciprocal.

**Example 2**   Simplify $\dfrac{z}{z + 3} \div \dfrac{3z^2}{3z + 9} \cdot \dfrac{z^2 + 4z + 3}{z^2 - 9}.$

**Solution**   $\dfrac{z}{z + 3} \div \dfrac{3z^2}{3z + 9} \cdot \dfrac{z^2 + 4z + 3}{z^2 - 9} = \dfrac{z}{z + 3} \cdot \dfrac{3z + 9}{3z^2} \cdot \dfrac{z^2 + 4z + 3}{z^2 - 9}$

$$= \frac{\cancel{z}}{\cancel{z + 3}} \cdot \frac{\cancel{3}\cancel{(z + 3)}}{\cancel{3} \cdot \cancel{z} \cdot z} \cdot \frac{(z + 1)\cancel{(z + 3)}}{(z - 3)\cancel{(z + 3)}}$$

$$= \frac{z + 1}{z(z - 3)}$$

## Oral Exercises

**Simplify.**

**1.** $\dfrac{2}{5} \div \dfrac{3}{5}$      **2.** $\dfrac{2}{3} \div \dfrac{1}{4}$      **3.** $\dfrac{1}{4} \div \dfrac{2}{3}$      **4.** $-\dfrac{4}{7} \div \dfrac{2}{5}$

**5.** $\dfrac{a}{b} \div \dfrac{c}{d}$      **6.** $\dfrac{x}{y} \div \dfrac{y}{x}$      **7.** $2a \div \dfrac{a}{b}$      **8.** $\dfrac{1}{bc} \div \dfrac{1}{b+c}$

**9.** $\dfrac{y^2}{3} \div \dfrac{y}{6}$      **10.** $-\dfrac{x}{2} \div \dfrac{1}{x^2}$      **11.** $\dfrac{1}{2} \cdot \dfrac{1}{3} \div \dfrac{1}{4}$      **12.** $\dfrac{a}{b} \div \dfrac{c}{d} \cdot \dfrac{e}{f}$

## Written Exercises

**Divide. Express the answers in simplest form.**

**A**

**1.** $\dfrac{5}{8} \div \dfrac{3}{4}$      **2.** $\dfrac{2}{9} \div \dfrac{4}{3}$      **3.** $\dfrac{a}{6} \div \dfrac{a}{3}$      **4.** $\dfrac{x^2}{5} \div \dfrac{x}{15}$

**5.** $\dfrac{ab}{3} \div \dfrac{b}{a}$      **6.** $\dfrac{x}{2y} \div \dfrac{xy}{4}$      **7.** $\dfrac{3n^2}{5} \div \dfrac{9n}{10}$      **8.** $\dfrac{a}{b^2} \div \dfrac{a^2}{b}$

**9.** $\dfrac{4x^2}{3y} \div (2x)$      **10.** $\dfrac{9a^2}{2b} \div (6ab)$      **11.** $1 \div \left(\dfrac{3x}{5}\right)^2$      **12.** $4 \div \left(\dfrac{2}{n}\right)^3$

**13.** $\dfrac{a+b}{3} \div \dfrac{2a+2b}{6}$      **14.** $\dfrac{x^2-1}{2} \div \dfrac{x-1}{4}$      **15.** $\dfrac{2n-5}{4} \div \dfrac{6n-15}{8}$

**16.** $\dfrac{a^2-b^2}{a^2+b^2} \div (a+b)$      **17.** $\dfrac{a-b}{cd^2} \div \dfrac{ab}{c^2d}$      **18.** $\dfrac{1}{8-2a} \div \dfrac{1}{3a-12}$

**19.** $\dfrac{3-3x}{3+3x} \div (x^2-1)$      **20.** $\dfrac{2x+2y}{x^2} \div \dfrac{x^2-y^2}{4x}$      **21.** $\dfrac{a^2+b^2}{c+d} \div \dfrac{5a+5b}{5c+5d}$

**22.** $\dfrac{3}{n^2-9} \div \dfrac{3n-9}{n+3}$      **23.** $\dfrac{3-3n}{n^2+2n-3} \div (2n-2)$      **24.** $\dfrac{x^2-4}{x^2-x-6} \div (2-x)$

**Simplify.**

**25. a.** $\dfrac{1}{2} \div \dfrac{1}{5} \cdot \dfrac{3}{4}$    **b.** $\dfrac{1}{2} \div \left(\dfrac{1}{5} \cdot \dfrac{3}{4}\right)$    **c.** $\dfrac{r}{5} \div \dfrac{t}{r} \cdot \dfrac{5}{t^2}$

**26. a.** $\dfrac{3}{8} \cdot \left(\dfrac{2}{3} \div \dfrac{1}{4}\right)$    **b.** $\dfrac{3}{8} \cdot \dfrac{2}{3} \div \dfrac{1}{4}$    **c.** $\dfrac{x}{y^2} \cdot \dfrac{2}{x^2} \div \dfrac{x}{y}$

**27. a.** $\left(\dfrac{n}{2}\right)^2 \div \dfrac{n}{4} \cdot \dfrac{n}{3}$    **b.** $\left(\dfrac{n}{2}\right)^2 \div \left(\dfrac{n}{4} \cdot \dfrac{n}{3}\right)$    **c.** $\left(\dfrac{n}{2}\right)^2 \div \left(\dfrac{n}{4}\right)^2$

**28. a.** $\left(\dfrac{x}{y}\right)^3 \div \dfrac{x}{2y} \cdot \dfrac{x}{4y}$    **b.** $\left(\dfrac{x}{y}\right)^3 \div \left(\dfrac{x}{2y} \cdot \dfrac{x}{4y}\right)$    **c.** $\left(\dfrac{x}{y}\right)^3 \div \left(\dfrac{x}{2y}\right)^3$

**B**   **29.** $2a^2 \div 3a^3 \div 4a^4$      **30.** $\dfrac{6n}{6n-14} \div \dfrac{21}{9n-21} \div \dfrac{n^2}{35}$

**Simplify.**

**31.** $\dfrac{4x^2 - 25}{x^2 - 16} \div \dfrac{12x + 30}{2x^2 + 8x}$

**32.** $\dfrac{2x - y}{2y - x} \div \dfrac{4x^2 - y^2}{4y^2 - x^2}$

**33.** $\dfrac{a^4 - b^4}{3a - 3b} \div \dfrac{a^2 + b^2}{3}$

**34.** $\dfrac{8 - 2x^4}{3x^4} \div \dfrac{2 + x^2}{6x^2}$

**35.** $\dfrac{c - d}{c + 2d} \cdot \dfrac{2d + c}{d + c} \div \dfrac{d - c}{d + c}$

**36.** $\dfrac{r^2}{r^2 - s^2} \cdot \dfrac{r - s}{r + s} \div \left(\dfrac{r}{r + s}\right)^2$

**37.** $\left(\dfrac{3n - 5}{4}\right)^3 \div \left(\dfrac{5 - 3n}{2}\right)^4$

**38.** $\dfrac{4a - 6}{9} \div \left(\dfrac{3 - 2a}{3}\right)^2$

**C  39.** $\dfrac{s^2 - 2s}{s^2 - 3s - 4} \cdot \dfrac{s^2 - 25}{s^2 - 4s - 5} \div \dfrac{s^2 + 5s}{5s^2 + 10s + 5}$

**40.** $\dfrac{b^2 + 6b - 7}{6b^2 - 7b - 20} \cdot \dfrac{2b^2 + b - 15}{b^2 + 2b - 3} \div \dfrac{b^2 + 5b - 14}{3b^2 - 2b - 8}$

**41.** $\dfrac{a^3 + 5a^2 - 9a - 45}{2a^2 - 9a + 9} \div \dfrac{a^2 + 10a + 25}{12 - 14a + 4a^2} \cdot \dfrac{a + 5}{a^2 - 4a + 4}$

**42.** $\dfrac{x^2 - 6xy + 9y^2 - 9}{x^4 - 81y^4} \cdot \dfrac{3x - 9y}{3x - 9y + 9} \div \dfrac{x - 3y - 3}{3x^2 + 27y^2}$

---

# Self-Test 1

**Express in simplest form, noting any restrictions on the variable.**

**1.** $\dfrac{-3a^2 + 6a}{a^2 - 2a}$

**2.** $\dfrac{4a^2 - 9}{6a^2 + 13a + 6}$

Obj. 6-1, p. 239

**Express in simplest form.**

**3.** $\dfrac{-3b}{4a^2c} \cdot \dfrac{-5a}{45b^3}$

**4.** $\left(\dfrac{2x}{3}\right)^3 \cdot \dfrac{27}{48x}$

Obj. 6-2, p. 244

**5.** $\dfrac{1}{56 - 8a} \div \dfrac{1}{4a - 28}$

**6.** $\dfrac{2}{15}\left(\dfrac{1}{4r} \div \dfrac{r}{10}\right)$

Obj. 6-3, p. 248

Check your answers with those at the back of the book.

---

## *Challenge*

The following problem is from the Egyptian Rhind papyrus:

There are seven houses; in each are seven cats. Each cat kills seven mice. Each mouse would have eaten seven ears of spelt [wheat]. Each ear of spelt will produce seven hekats of grain. What is the total of these? [That is, how much grain was saved?]

---

# Adding and Subtracting Fractions

## 6-4 Least Common Denominators

**Objective**   To express two or more fractions with their least common denominator.

The cancellation rule for fractions states that if $c \neq 0$

$$\frac{cx}{cy} = \frac{x}{y}.$$

This rule enables you to express a fraction in simpler form by dividing its numerator and denominator by the same nonzero number. Using the symmetric property of equality you can rewrite this rule as

$$\frac{x}{y} = \frac{cx}{cy} \quad (c \neq 0).$$

In this form, it enables you to express a fraction in a different form by multiplying its numerator and denominator by the same number.

**Example 1**   $\dfrac{5}{8} = \dfrac{?}{24}$ ————————— 8 must be multiplied by 3 to get 24.

Therefore, multiply 5 by 3 to get 15.

$$\frac{5}{8} = \frac{5 \cdot 3}{8 \cdot 3} = \frac{15}{24}$$

**Example 2**   $\dfrac{7}{3c} = \dfrac{?}{12c^2}$ ————————— $3c$ must be multiplied by $4c$ to get $12c^2$.

Therefore, multiply 7 by $4c$ to get $28c$.

$$\frac{7}{3c} = \frac{28c}{12c^2}$$

**Example 3**   $\dfrac{5}{x-7} = \dfrac{?}{(x-7)(x+3)}$ ————— $(x-7)$ must be multiplied by $(x+3)$ to get $(x-7)(x+3)$.

Therefore, multiply 5 by $(x+3)$.

$$\frac{5}{x-7} = \frac{5(x+3)}{(x-7)(x+3)}$$

The technique shown in the examples above is used to rewrite two or more fractions so that they have equal denominators. For example, you can express $\frac{1}{4}$ and $\frac{5}{6}$ as fractions having a common denominator of 12, 24, 36, or any other positive *multiple* of 12. (The product of a number and an integer is called a **multiple** of the number.) Usually, it is convenient to use the **least common denominator (LCD)** of the fractions. To determine the least common denominator of several fractions, find the **least common multiple** of the denominators.

## Finding the Least Common Denominator

1. Factor each denominator into primes.
2. Form the product of the greatest power of each prime factor occurring in the denominators.

**Example 4** What is the LCD of the fractions $\dfrac{3}{25}$, $\dfrac{11}{30}$, and $\dfrac{7}{40}$?

**Solution**    1. Factor each denominator into primes.

$$25 = 5^2 \qquad 30 = 2 \cdot 3 \cdot 5 \qquad 40 = 2^3 \cdot 5$$

2. Greatest power of 2: $2^3$
   Greatest power of 3: $3^1$
   Greatest power of 5: $5^2$

$$2^3 \cdot 3^1 \cdot 5^2 = 600$$

$\therefore$ the LCD is 600.   **Answer**

When the denominators of the fractions contain variables, the LCD will be the simplest of the common multiples of the denominators.

**Example 5** What is the LCD of $\dfrac{3}{5x - 20}$ and $\dfrac{8}{9x - 36}$?

**Solution**    1. Factor each denominator completely.

$$5x - 20 = 5(x - 4)$$
$$9x - 36 = 3^2(x - 4)$$

2. Form the product of the greatest power of each prime factor.

$$3^2 \cdot 5(x - 4) = 45(x - 4)$$

$\therefore$ the LCD is $45(x - 4)$.   **Answer**

**Example 6** Express $\dfrac{5}{c^2 + 2c - 15}$ and $\dfrac{9}{c^2 - 6c + 9}$ with their least common denominator.

**Solution**    Since $c^2 + 2c - 15 = (c + 5)(c - 3)$ and $c^2 - 6c + 9 = (c - 3)^2$, the LCD is $(c + 5)(c - 3)^2$.

$$\frac{5}{c^2 + 2c - 15} = \frac{5}{(c + 5)(c - 3)} = \frac{5(c - 3)}{(c + 5)(c - 3)(c - 3)} = \frac{5(c - 3)}{(c + 5)(c - 3)^2}$$

$$\frac{9}{c^2 - 6c + 9} = \frac{9}{(c - 3)^2} = \frac{9(c + 5)}{(c - 3)^2(c + 5)} = \frac{9(c + 5)}{(c + 5)(c - 3)^2}$$

## Oral Exercises

**Find the missing numerator.**

**1.** $\dfrac{2}{5} = \dfrac{?}{10}$      **2.** $\dfrac{3}{8} = \dfrac{?}{40}$      **3.** $\dfrac{x}{7} = \dfrac{?}{21}$      **4.** $\dfrac{a}{3} = \dfrac{?}{12}$

**5.** $\dfrac{2x}{3} = \dfrac{?}{9}$      **6.** $\dfrac{a}{b} = \dfrac{?}{b^2}$      **7.** $\dfrac{5}{2n} = \dfrac{?}{6n^2}$      **8.** $\dfrac{1}{ab} = \dfrac{?}{a^2b^3}$

**9.** $\dfrac{3}{x-1} = \dfrac{?}{(x-1)(x+2)}$      **10.** $\dfrac{4}{n+2} = \dfrac{?}{n^2-4}$

**Find the LCD for each group of fractions.**

**11.** $\dfrac{1}{4}, \dfrac{5}{6}$      **12.** $\dfrac{3}{8}, \dfrac{4}{7}$      **13.** $\dfrac{5}{18}, \dfrac{5}{12}$      **14.** $\dfrac{1}{2}, \dfrac{1}{3}, \dfrac{1}{4}$

**15.** $\dfrac{2}{x}, \dfrac{3}{xy}$      **16.** $\dfrac{4}{ab}, \dfrac{3}{a^2}$      **17.** $\dfrac{1}{n-2}, \dfrac{3}{2-n}$      **18.** $\dfrac{2}{3a-b}, \dfrac{5}{6a-2b}$

**19.** $\dfrac{4}{x^2-1}, \dfrac{3}{x+1}, \dfrac{7}{x-1}$      **20.** $\dfrac{2y}{(y-3)^2}, \dfrac{y^2}{5(y-3)(y+1)}$

## Written Exercises

**Find the missing numerator.**

A   **1.** $\dfrac{3}{7} = \dfrac{?}{35}$      **2.** $\dfrac{4}{9} = \dfrac{?}{27}$      **3.** $\dfrac{2x}{5} = \dfrac{?}{15}$      **4.** $\dfrac{4a}{13} = \dfrac{?}{39}$

**5.** $\dfrac{x-3}{4} = \dfrac{?}{12}$      **6.** $\dfrac{2n-5}{5} = \dfrac{?}{25}$      **7.** $\dfrac{4-a}{4} = \dfrac{?}{20}$      **8.** $\dfrac{2x-y}{9} = \dfrac{?}{45}$

**9.** $\dfrac{a}{b} = \dfrac{?}{a^2b}$      **10.** $\dfrac{x}{2y} = \dfrac{?}{6xy}$      **11.** $\dfrac{2n}{3m} = \dfrac{?}{6m^2n}$      **12.** $\dfrac{7}{2a} = \dfrac{?}{8a^3}$

**13.** $\dfrac{5}{2n-3} = \dfrac{?}{(2n-3)^2}$      **14.** $\dfrac{4}{a-1} = \dfrac{?}{2a-2}$      **15.** $\dfrac{4}{a-1} = \dfrac{?}{1-a}$

**16.** $\dfrac{6}{2x-5} = \dfrac{?}{10-4x}$      **17.** $\dfrac{2}{x+1} = \dfrac{?}{x^2-1}$      **18.** $\dfrac{5}{n-3} = \dfrac{?}{n^2-9}$

**19.** $\dfrac{3}{y-2} = \dfrac{?}{y^2-2y}$      **20.** $\dfrac{x}{x+5} = \dfrac{?}{x^2+5x}$      **21.** $\dfrac{6}{x+1} = \dfrac{?}{x^2+3x+2}$

**22.** $\dfrac{7}{a+b} = \dfrac{?}{a^2+2ab+b^2}$      **23.** $\dfrac{1}{x-5} = \dfrac{?}{2x^2-50}$      **24.** $\dfrac{3}{2-a} = \dfrac{?}{8-2a^2}$

**Find the LCD for each group of fractions.**

**25.** $\dfrac{1}{6}, \dfrac{5}{9}$      **26.** $\dfrac{3}{8}, \dfrac{2}{5}, \dfrac{4}{3}$      **27.** $\dfrac{1}{3}, \dfrac{2}{9}, \dfrac{3}{4}$

**28.** $\dfrac{2}{5}, \dfrac{3}{7}, \dfrac{1}{10}$      **29.** $\dfrac{1}{2}, \dfrac{2}{3}, \dfrac{3}{4}$      **30.** $\dfrac{n-3}{20}, \dfrac{n+4}{15}$

**Find the LCD for each group of fractions.**

**31.** $\dfrac{3x + 2}{8}, \dfrac{x - 4}{12}$

**32.** $\dfrac{2a - b}{4}, \dfrac{2a + b}{6}$

**33.** $\dfrac{2 - y}{20}, \dfrac{y + 3}{25}$

**B** **34.** $\dfrac{1}{3n^2m}, \dfrac{2}{nm^2}$

**35.** $\dfrac{1}{x - 2}, \dfrac{-3}{6 - 3x}$

**36.** $\dfrac{3}{4x - 2y}, \dfrac{5}{y - 2x}$

**37.** $\dfrac{5}{8x^2}, \dfrac{4}{3xy}, \dfrac{1}{16y^3}$

**38.** $\dfrac{9}{a + b}, \dfrac{4}{a}, \dfrac{3}{b}$

**39.** $\dfrac{1}{x - 1}, \dfrac{2}{x + 1}, \dfrac{3}{2x^2 - 2}$

**40.** $\dfrac{1}{2xy}, \dfrac{3}{x^2}$

**41.** $\dfrac{3}{4a^2b}, \dfrac{5}{8b^2}$

**42.** $\dfrac{3x}{2x - 4}, \dfrac{1}{x^2 - 4}$

**43.** $\dfrac{1}{y^2 - 3y}, \dfrac{1}{y^2 + 3y}$

**44.** $\dfrac{3}{x^2 - x - 2}, \dfrac{1}{x^2 - 4}$

**45.** $\dfrac{a^2}{a - 1}, \dfrac{a}{a + 1}, \dfrac{1}{a^2 - 1}$

**C** **46.** $\dfrac{1}{16a^4 - 16b^4}, \dfrac{y + 3}{(2a - 2b)^2}$

**47.** $\dfrac{y + 3}{y^2 + 6y + 8}, \dfrac{-5}{3y^2 + 21y + 36}, \dfrac{7y}{4y + 12}$

**48.** The product of the first $n$ positive integers, denoted by $n!$, is called **$n$ factorial**.

   **a.** Find $4!$, $5!$, and $6!$.

   **b.** What is the LCD of the fractions $\dfrac{1}{4!}$, $\dfrac{1}{5!}$, and $\dfrac{1}{6!}$?

   **c.** What is the LCD of the fractions $\dfrac{1}{n!}$ and $\dfrac{1}{(n + 1)!}$?

   **d.** True or false?  $(n!)^2 = (n^2)!$

---

## Computer Exercises

*For students with some programming experience*

In the Computer Exercises on pages 140–141, you wrote a BASIC program to compute $n!$ for a value of $n$ entered with an INPUT statement.

**1.** Write a BASIC program to find the following.

$$1 + \frac{1}{1!} + \frac{1}{2!}$$

$$1 + \frac{1}{1!} + \frac{1}{2!} + \frac{1}{3!}$$

$$1 + \frac{1}{1!} + \frac{1}{2!} + \frac{1}{3!} + \frac{1}{4!}$$

$$1 + \frac{1}{1!} + \frac{1}{2!} + \frac{1}{3!} + \frac{1}{4!} + \frac{1}{5!}$$

$$1 + \frac{1}{1!} + \frac{1}{2!} + \frac{1}{3!} + \frac{1}{4!} + \frac{1}{5!} + \frac{1}{6!}$$

$$1 + \frac{1}{1!} + \frac{1}{2!} + \frac{1}{3!} + \frac{1}{4!} + \frac{1}{5!} + \frac{1}{6!} + \frac{1}{7!}$$

**2.** Based upon your results from Exercise 1 guess what happens to the sum $1 + \dfrac{1}{1!} + \dfrac{1}{2!} + \dfrac{1}{3!} + \cdots + \dfrac{1}{n!}$ as $n$ becomes larger and larger.

# 6-5 Adding and Subtracting Fractions

**Objective**  To add and subtract algebraic fractions.

The results proved in Exercises 30 and 31 on page 83 can be used to show how to add and subtract fractions with the same denominator. Rewriting those results using the symmetric property of equality gives the following rules.

---

**Addition Rule for Fractions**

$$\frac{a}{c} + \frac{b}{c} = \frac{a + b}{c}$$

**Subtraction Rule for Fractions**

$$\frac{a}{c} - \frac{b}{c} = \frac{a - b}{c}$$

---

To add fractions with the same denominator, you add their numerators. To subtract fractions with the same denominator, you subtract their numerators.

**Example 1**  $\dfrac{5a}{7} + \dfrac{3a}{7} = \dfrac{5a + 3a}{7} = \dfrac{8a}{7}$

**Example 2**  $\dfrac{5x + 7}{9} - \dfrac{2x - 5}{9} + \dfrac{11x}{9} = \dfrac{(5x + 7) - (2x - 5) + 11x}{9}$

$$= \frac{5x + 7 - 2x + 5 + 11x}{9}$$

$$= \frac{14x + 12}{9} = \frac{2(7x + 6)}{9}$$

To add or subtract fractions with different denominators, you must first express the fractions with a common denominator.

**Example 3**  $\dfrac{2x - 3}{16} - \dfrac{2 - x}{8} + \dfrac{3x}{4} = \dfrac{2x - 3}{16} - \dfrac{2(2 - x)}{16} + \dfrac{12x}{16}$

$$= \frac{(2x - 3) - 2(2 - x) + 12x}{16}$$

$$= \frac{2x - 3 - 4 + 2x + 12x}{16}$$

$$= \frac{16x - 7}{16}$$

To simplify an expression involving fractions means to express it as a fraction in simplest form.

**Example 4** Simplify $\dfrac{a+10}{a^2-2a} + \dfrac{2}{a} - \dfrac{6}{a-2}$.

**Solution**

$$\dfrac{a+10}{a^2-2a} + \dfrac{2}{a} - \dfrac{6}{a-2} = \dfrac{a+10}{a(a-2)} + \dfrac{2}{a} - \dfrac{6}{a-2}$$

$$= \dfrac{a+10}{a(a-2)} + \dfrac{2(a-2)}{a(a-2)} - \dfrac{6a}{a(a-2)}$$

$$= \dfrac{(a+10) + 2(a-2) - 6a}{a(a-2)}$$

$$= \dfrac{a+10+2a-4-6a}{a(a-2)}$$

$$= \dfrac{-3a+6}{a(a-2)} = \dfrac{-3(a-2)}{a(a-2)} = -\dfrac{3}{a}$$

## Oral Exercises

**Simplify.**

**1.** $\dfrac{4}{5} + \dfrac{3}{5}$  **2.** $\dfrac{7}{9} - \dfrac{4}{9}$  **3.** $\dfrac{x}{6} + \dfrac{2x}{6}$  **4.** $\dfrac{5a}{8} - \dfrac{a}{8}$

**5.** $\dfrac{4}{x} - \dfrac{1}{x}$  **6.** $\dfrac{7}{2x} + \dfrac{3}{2x}$  **7.** $\dfrac{4}{1+x} + \dfrac{x}{1+x}$  **8.** $\dfrac{n}{n-2} - \dfrac{1}{n-2}$

**9.** $\dfrac{3}{x-5} - \dfrac{1}{5-x}$  **10.** $\dfrac{4}{a-b} + \dfrac{1}{b-a}$  **11.** $\dfrac{1}{a} + \dfrac{1}{a^2}$  **12.** $\dfrac{3}{n^3} - \dfrac{1}{n}$

**13.** $\dfrac{x}{2} + \dfrac{x}{8}$  **14.** $\dfrac{2x}{2} - \dfrac{x+1}{2}$  **15.** $\dfrac{4y}{3} - \dfrac{2y-5}{3}$  **16.** $\dfrac{n^2}{5} - \dfrac{n^2-3n+2}{5}$

## Written Exercises

**Simplify.**

A  **1.** $\dfrac{2}{n} + \dfrac{3}{n} - \dfrac{4}{n}$  **2.** $\dfrac{5}{3x} + \dfrac{9}{3x} - \dfrac{2}{3x}$  **3.** $\dfrac{8}{2a} - \dfrac{9}{2a} + \dfrac{3}{2a}$

**4.** $\dfrac{a}{5} - \dfrac{2a+3}{5}$  **5.** $\dfrac{2x}{3} - \dfrac{x-1}{3}$  **6.** $\dfrac{y-3}{4} - \dfrac{3y-5}{4}$

**7.** $\dfrac{x+4}{2} - \dfrac{3x+6}{2}$  **8.** $\dfrac{x}{x-5} + \dfrac{1}{x-5} - \dfrac{10-x}{x-5}$  **9.** $\dfrac{1}{n-2} - \dfrac{3n-2}{n-2} + \dfrac{n}{n-2}$

**10.** $\dfrac{3}{x-5} - \dfrac{2}{5-x}$  **11.** $\dfrac{4}{2y-7} - \dfrac{1}{7-2y}$  **12.** $\dfrac{4a}{a-b} + \dfrac{4b}{b-a}$

**13.** $\dfrac{2}{x} + \dfrac{3}{x^2}$

**14.** $\dfrac{5}{ab} - \dfrac{3}{ab^2}$

**15.** $\dfrac{4}{3x} - \dfrac{1}{6x^2}$

**16.** $\dfrac{1}{2ab} - \dfrac{5}{6a}$

**17.** $\dfrac{2n - 1}{2n^3} + \dfrac{5}{n^2}$

**18.** $\dfrac{4}{5(x + 1)} + \dfrac{x}{x + 1}$

**19.** $\dfrac{x - 1}{2} + \dfrac{2x - 3}{6}$

**20.** $\dfrac{2b - 3}{4} + \dfrac{b - 5}{6}$

**21.** $\dfrac{3y - 2}{6} - \dfrac{y - 3}{9}$

**22.** $\dfrac{a - 6}{15} - \dfrac{4 - a}{10}$

**23.** $\dfrac{2x + 4}{5} - \dfrac{x}{6} + \dfrac{3x - 2}{10}$

**24.** $\dfrac{x - 3}{5} - \dfrac{x + 2}{15} + \dfrac{2}{3}$

**25.** $\dfrac{5n - 2}{12} - \dfrac{3(n - 3)}{8}$

**26.** $\dfrac{3(a - b)}{20} - \dfrac{5(a + b)}{12}$

**27.** $\dfrac{2a - b}{3} - \dfrac{b}{6} - \dfrac{2b - 3a}{4}$

**Find the perimeter and the area of each figure.**

**B   28.**

**29.**

**30.**

**31.**

**Simplify.**

**32.** $\dfrac{1}{x - 1} + \dfrac{1}{x}$

**33.** $\dfrac{2}{x - 3} + \dfrac{4}{x + 3}$

**34.** $\dfrac{5}{a - 2} - \dfrac{1}{a + 1}$

**35.** $\dfrac{4}{x + 1} - \dfrac{1}{x - 2}$

**36.** $\dfrac{x}{x^2 - 1} + \dfrac{4}{x + 1}$

**37.** $\dfrac{2y}{y^2 - 25} - \dfrac{y}{y - 5}$

**Simplify.**

**38.** $\dfrac{a+1}{a} - \dfrac{a}{a+1}$

**39.** $\dfrac{x}{x+y} + \dfrac{y}{x-y}$

**40.** $\dfrac{y}{2y-4} + \dfrac{8}{4-y^2}$

**41.** $\dfrac{x}{x-5} + \dfrac{5}{5-x}$

**42.** $\dfrac{3a}{a-2b} + \dfrac{6b}{2b-a}$

**43.** $\dfrac{z}{z-z^2} - \dfrac{1}{z-z^3}$

**44.** $\dfrac{1}{n(n+5)} - \dfrac{10}{(n+5)^3}$

**45.** $\dfrac{a}{ab-b^2} - \dfrac{b}{a^2-ab}$

**46.** $\dfrac{1}{a^2+4a+4} + \dfrac{1}{a^2-4}$

**47.** $\dfrac{2n}{n^3-5n^2} + \dfrac{2}{n^2+5n}$

**48.** $\dfrac{b+2}{b^2+3b} - \dfrac{b-2}{b^2-3b}$

**49.** $\dfrac{3c}{c^2+3c+2} - \dfrac{3c-6}{c^2+4c+4}$

**C** **50.** $\dfrac{x^2+1}{x^2-1} + \dfrac{1}{x+1} + \dfrac{1}{x-1}$

**51.** $\dfrac{x}{2x-1} + \dfrac{x-1}{2x+1} - \dfrac{2x}{4x^2-1}$

**52.** $\dfrac{a+2}{a^2+5a+6} - \dfrac{2+a}{4-a^2} + \dfrac{2-a}{a^2+a-6}$

**53.** $\dfrac{x-3}{2x+6} - \dfrac{x+3}{3x-9} - \dfrac{5x^2+27}{6x^2-54}$

**54.** $\dfrac{b+1}{(b-1)^2} + \dfrac{2-2b}{(b-1)^3} + \dfrac{1}{b-1}$

**55.** $\dfrac{4}{c^2-4cd} - \dfrac{1}{cd-4d^2} - \dfrac{2}{cd}$

**56.** $\dfrac{1}{(a-b)(a-c)} + \dfrac{1}{(b-c)(b-a)} + \dfrac{1}{(c-a)(c-b)}$

**57.** $\dfrac{2}{y^2-1} - \dfrac{1}{(y+1)^2} - \dfrac{1}{(1-y)^2}$

**58.** Show that the following are true. (*Hint:* See Exercise 48, page 254.)

**a.** $4 \cdot 9! + 6 \cdot 9! = 10!$      **b.** $\dfrac{9!}{3!6!} + \dfrac{9!}{4!5!} = \dfrac{10!}{4!6!}$

---

# Self-Test 2

***Vocabulary***     multiple (p. 251)                least common denominator (p. 251)
                            least common multiple (p. 251)

**Find the missing numerators.**

**1.** $\dfrac{5a}{28b} = \dfrac{?}{84ab^3}$

**2.** $\dfrac{5}{1-a} = \dfrac{?}{a^2-a}$

Obj. 6-4, p. 251

**Express each group of fractions with their LCD.**

**3.** $\dfrac{3}{4x-8y}, \dfrac{-12}{2y-x}$

**4.** $\dfrac{2}{x}, \dfrac{3}{y}, \dfrac{5}{x+y}$

**Simplify.**

**5.** $\dfrac{25a+1}{5a} - \dfrac{5a-4}{5a}$

**6.** $\dfrac{4}{3ab} - \dfrac{8}{7ab^2}$

Obj. 6-5, p. 255

**7.** $\dfrac{x}{x-y} + \dfrac{y}{y-x}$

**8.** $\dfrac{x}{x-1} - \dfrac{1}{9(x-1)}$

Check your answers with those at the back of the book.

# Historical Note / *Broken Numbers*

The word "fraction" comes from the Latin verb *frangere,* meaning "to break." A fraction is thus a "broken number," or a part of a number.

The Babylonians used special symbols to represent commonly used fractions such as $\frac{1}{2}$, $\frac{1}{3}$, and $\frac{2}{3}$. However, sexagesimals, fractions having denominators of base sixty, were used consistently in astronomical calculations and in mathematical texts. Because the denominators of the fractions were restricted to a certain base, a positional notation was used to represent these fractions. Thus, ◀◀ intended as a fraction meant $\frac{20}{60}$. These sexagesimals were arranged in tables that ex-

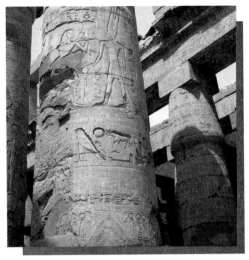

pressed the reciprocals of counting numbers as sexagesimal fractions. (The denominators were understood.) For instance, in these tables "igi 2 gál-bi 30" stood for "the reciprocal of 2 is $\frac{30}{60}$." The numerous integer divisors of sixty made it easier to simplify fractional computations. Sexagesimal fractions were also used by the ancient Greeks. In fact, they were used in Europe until the sixteenth century, when they were replaced by decimals.

Like the Babylonians the Egyptians had special symbols for commonly used fractions. In hieroglyphics the elliptical symbol ⬭ was placed over the symbol for a whole number to express its reciprocal. This symbol was replaced by a dot in cursive hieratic writing and was later adopted by the English who wrote $\dot{2}$ for $\frac{1}{2}$. The Egyptians attempted to avoid computational difficulties by expressing fractions in terms of unit fractions, that is, fractions having a numerator of one. Like the Babylonians, the Egyptians found it necessary to construct lengthy tables. The Egyptians expressed fractions as sums of unit fractions. There were numerous rules for forming unit fractions, but no one rule was used consistently. Thus, $\frac{2}{43}$ might have been expressed in any of the following ways:

$$\frac{1}{24} + \frac{1}{258} + \frac{1}{1032}$$

$$\frac{1}{30} + \frac{1}{86} + \frac{1}{645}$$

$$\frac{1}{36} + \frac{1}{86} + \frac{1}{645} + \frac{1}{172} + \frac{1}{774}$$

$$\frac{1}{40} + \frac{1}{860} + \frac{1}{1720}$$

$$\frac{1}{42} + \frac{1}{86} + \frac{1}{129} + \frac{1}{301}$$

These unit fractions, also used by the ancient Greeks, became known as simple fractions during the Middle Ages and were used as late as the seventeenth century.

# Polynomial Division

## 6-6 Mixed Expressions

**Objective**  To write mixed expressions as fractions in simplest form.

A mixed number like $4\frac{2}{5}$ denotes the sum of an integer and a fraction. Recall that $4\frac{2}{5}$ may be expressed as a fraction as follows:

$$4\frac{2}{5} = \frac{4}{1} + \frac{2}{5} = \frac{20}{5} + \frac{2}{5} = \frac{22}{5}$$

A sum or difference of a polynomial and a fraction is called a **mixed expression.** The following example shows that a mixed expression may be expressed as a fraction in simplest form.

**Example**  Express as a fraction in simplest form.

  **a.** $b + \dfrac{4}{b}$   **b.** $3 - \dfrac{n-4}{n+1}$

**Solution**  **a.** $b + \dfrac{4}{b} = \dfrac{b}{1} + \dfrac{4}{b} = \dfrac{b^2}{b} + \dfrac{4}{b} = \dfrac{b^2 + 4}{b}$

  **b.** $3 - \dfrac{n-4}{n+1} = \dfrac{3}{1} - \dfrac{n-4}{n+1}$

$$= \frac{3(n+1)}{n+1} - \frac{n-4}{n+1}$$

$$= \frac{3n + 3 - n + 4}{n+1}$$

$$= \frac{2n + 7}{n+1}$$

## Oral Exercises

**State each expression as a fraction in simplest form.**

**1.** $2\dfrac{1}{8}$    **2.** $5\dfrac{2}{3}$    **3.** $-3\dfrac{4}{7}$    **4.** $-8\dfrac{3}{4}$

**5.** $1 + \dfrac{1}{x}$    **6.** $2 + \dfrac{4}{a}$    **7.** $n + \dfrac{2}{n}$    **8.** $4 - \dfrac{1}{y}$

**9.** $2 - \dfrac{a}{b}$    **10.** $3 - \dfrac{1}{x+1}$    **11.** $\dfrac{3x}{x+2} - 1$    **12.** $\dfrac{b}{2b-3} + 2$

**13.** $2 + \dfrac{3}{x+1}$    **14.** $4 - \dfrac{1}{y+3}$    **15.** $\dfrac{2n}{2n+1} - 1$    **16.** $\dfrac{5a}{a-3} + 2$

## Written Exercises

**Write each expression as a fraction in simplest form.**

A  **1.** $4\frac{1}{5}$          **2.** $2\frac{3}{8}$          **3.** $6 + \frac{1}{x}$          **4.** $5 + \frac{2}{a}$

**5.** $3a - \frac{2}{a}$          **6.** $5x - \frac{3}{x}$          **7.** $\frac{a}{b} + 2$          **8.** $\frac{c}{d} - 7$

**9.** $5 - \frac{4}{x+2}$          **10.** $8 + \frac{y}{y-1}$          **11.** $\frac{x}{x+3} - 5$          **12.** $\frac{a+2}{a} - 4$

**13.** $6x - \frac{x}{x+1}$          **14.** $4y + \frac{y}{2y-5}$          **15.** $3 - \frac{n+2}{n^2-1}$          **16.** $8k - \frac{3k-2}{3k+2}$

**17.** $n - \frac{2}{n+1}$          **18.** $a + \frac{a-5}{2a+3}$          **19.** $a + \frac{3a+2}{a+2}$          **20.** $2y - \frac{y-4}{y+4}$

B  **21.** $x - \frac{8}{x+1} - \frac{6x-2}{x+1}$          **22.** $y - \frac{4(y+1)}{y+2} - \frac{4}{y+2}$          **23.** $\frac{x}{x+1} - \frac{x+1}{x} + 2$

**24.** $\frac{a}{a+3} + \frac{a}{a-3} - 2$          **25.** $4 - \frac{1}{x+1} - \frac{3}{x+1}$          **26.** $\frac{y}{x+y} + \frac{x}{y-x} + 1$

**27.** $a + 1 - \frac{a^2-a-18}{a-3}$          **28.** $5a + b - \frac{5a^2-b^2}{5a-b}$          **29.** $3x - \frac{x^2}{2x+3} - 2$

**30.** $(x+4)\left(\frac{4}{x} - 1\right)$          **31.** $\left(a + \frac{2}{a}\right)\left(a - \frac{4}{a}\right)$          **32.** $\left(2x - \frac{1}{x}\right)\left(x - \frac{3}{x}\right)$

**33.** $\left(\frac{a+b}{a} - 1\right)\left(\frac{a}{b} + 1\right)$          **34.** $\left(y - \frac{2}{y+1}\right)\left(1 - \frac{1}{y+2}\right)$          **35.** $\left(a - \frac{b^2}{a}\right) \div \left(1 + \frac{b}{a}\right)$

**36.** $\left(4 - \frac{1}{c^2}\right) \div (2c+1)$          **37.** $\left(1 - \frac{2}{a}\right) \div \left(1 - \frac{4}{a^2}\right)$          **38.** $1 + \frac{2x}{2x-1} - \frac{8x^2}{4x^2-1}$

**39.** As an algebra exercise, Sue, Bob, and Julie were asked to simplify
$1 - \frac{8x}{x^2-x} - \frac{2x}{1-x}$. Sue used a common denominator of
$x(x-1)(1-x)$. Bob used $x(x-1)$. Julie showed that the exercise
could be done with a common denominator of $x - 1$. Explain why all
three denominators could be used.

**40.** Jim bought $n$ baseballs for a total of
$30. He then sold all but 2 of them
for $1 more per ball than he paid.
How much did he receive for the
balls that he sold? (*Hint:* Make a
chart. Answer in terms of $n$.)

**41.** It took Roz $y$ hours to drive 200 km.
If she had increased her speed by
10 km/h and driven for 2 h less, how
far could she have gone? (*Hint:* Make
a chart. Answer in terms of $y$.)

**Write the expression as a fraction in simplest form.**

C  42. $\left(1 - \dfrac{b^2 + c^2 - a^2}{2bc}\right) \div \left(1 - \dfrac{a^2 + b^2 - c^2}{2ab}\right)$

43. $\left(2 - \dfrac{n}{n + 1} + \dfrac{n}{1 - n}\right) \div \left(\dfrac{1}{n - 1} - \dfrac{1}{n + 1}\right)$

44. Find constants $A$ and $B$ such that $\dfrac{4}{x^2 - 4} = \dfrac{A}{x + 2} + \dfrac{B}{x - 2}$.

45. Find constants $C$ and $D$ such that $\dfrac{6x}{x^2 - x - 2} = \dfrac{C}{x - 2} + \dfrac{D}{x + 1}$.

46. Simplify: $\left(1 - \dfrac{1}{2}\right)\left(1 - \dfrac{1}{3}\right)\left(1 - \dfrac{1}{4}\right)\left(1 - \dfrac{1}{5}\right) \cdots \left(1 - \dfrac{1}{n}\right)$

## Computer Key-In

The following program will find the LCD for two denominators.

```
10   PRINT "TO FIND THE LEAST"
20   PRINT "COMMON DENOMINATOR;"
30   PRINT "INPUT D1, D2:";
40   INPUT D1,D2
50   FOR M=1 TO D1
60   LET Q=D2*M/D1
70   IF Q=INT(Q) THEN 90
80   NEXT M
90   PRINT "LCD(";D1;",";D2;") = ";
100  PRINT D2;" X ";M;" = ";D2*M
110  END
```

### Exercises

RUN this program for the following denominators.

**1.** $D1 = 24$, $D2 = 36$      **2.** $D1 = 36$, $D2 = 24$

**3.** $D1 = 13$, $D2 = 15$      **4.** $D1 = 15$, $D2 = 13$

**5–8.** In order to see how the program works, insert

```
65 PRINT D2*M;"/";D1;"=";D2*M/D1
```

and RUN the program again for the data in Exercises 1–4.

**9.** Compare the RUNs when you put the smaller denominator first and then second. Which requires fewer steps of computation?

**10.** Explain how to find the least common denominator for the three denominators 27, 36, and 30.

*Note:* The program above can be used to do Exercises 25–33 on pages 253–254.

# 6-7 Polynomial Long Division

**Objective**  To divide polynomials.

Division of one polynomial by another is very much like ordinary long division. Compare the long division and the polynomial division shown below.

**Long Division**

Step 1
$$31\overline{)688}$$
with $2$ above, $\underline{62}$, $68$

Step 2
$$31\overline{)688}$$
with $22$ above, $\underline{62}$, $68$, $\underline{62}$, $6$

*Check:*  $688 \overset{?}{=} 22 \cdot 31 + 6$

$688 \overset{?}{=} 682 + 6$

$688 = 688 \ \checkmark$

$\therefore \dfrac{688}{31} = 22\dfrac{6}{31}$

**Polynomial Division**

Step 1
$$3x + 1\overline{)6x^2 + 8x + 8}$$
with $2x$ above, $\underline{6x^2 + 2x}$, $6x + 8$

Step 2
$$3x + 1\overline{)6x^2 + 8x + 8}$$
with $2x + 2$ above, $\underline{6x^2 + 2x}$, $6x + 8$, $\underline{6x + 2}$, $6$

*Check:*  $6x^2 + 8x + 8 \overset{?}{=} (2x + 2)(3x + 1) + 6$

$6x^2 + 8x + 8 \overset{?}{=} (6x^2 + 8x + 2) + 6$

$6x^2 + 8x + 8 = 6x^2 + 8x + 8 \ \checkmark$

$\therefore \dfrac{6x^2 + 8x + 8}{3x + 1} = (2x + 2) + \dfrac{6}{3x + 1}$

In both divisions above, the answer was expressed in the following form:

$$\frac{\text{Dividend}}{\text{Divisor}} = \text{Quotient} + \frac{\text{Remainder}}{\text{Divisor}}$$

The following identity was used to check both divisions:

$$\text{Dividend} = \text{Quotient} \times \text{Divisor} + \text{Remainder}$$

When you divide polynomials, always make sure that the terms in each polynomial are arranged in order of decreasing degree in the variable.

***Example 1*** Divide $13x - 35 + 12x^2$ by $4x - 5$.

***Solution*** First rewrite $13x - 35 + 12x^2$ as $12x^2 + 13x - 35$.

$$
\begin{array}{r}
3x \phantom{xx} + 7 \phantom{x} \\
4x - 5 \overline{) 12x^2 + 13x - 35} \\
\underline{12x^2 - 15x} \phantom{xxxxx} \\
28x - 35 \\
\underline{28x - 35} \\
0
\end{array}
$$

*Check:* $(3x + 7)(4x - 5) \overset{?}{=} 12x^2 + 13x - 35$

$(3x + 7)(4x - 5) = 12x^2 - 15x + 28x - 35$

$= 12x^2 + 13x - 35 \ \checkmark$

$\therefore \dfrac{12x^2 + 13x - 35}{4x - 5} = 3x + 7$  ***Answer***

Notice that in Example 1 the remainder is 0. Thus, both $4x - 5$ and $3x + 7$ are factors of $12x^2 + 13x - 35$.

***Example 2*** Divide: $\dfrac{3a^3 + 5}{a - 2}$. Write the answer as a mixed expression.

***Solution*** Rewrite $3a^3 + 5$ in order of decreasing degree in $a$, inserting terms with 0 coefficients as shown below.

$$
\begin{array}{r}
3a^2 + 6a \phantom{x} + 12 \phantom{x} \\
a - 2 \overline{) 3a^3 + 0a^2 + 0a + 5} \\
\underline{3a^3 - 6a^2} \phantom{xxxxxxx} \\
6a^2 + 0a \phantom{xxx} \\
\underline{6a^2 - 12a} \phantom{xxx} \\
12a + 5 \\
\underline{12a - 24} \\
29
\end{array}
$$

*Check:* $(3a^2 + 6a + 12)(a - 2) + 29 \overset{?}{=} 3a^3 + 5$

$(3a^2 + 6a + 12)(a - 2) + 29 = 3a^3 + 6a^2 + 12a - 6a^2 - 12a - 24 + 29$

$= 3a^3 + (6a^2 - 6a^2) + (12a - 12a) - 24 + 29$

$= 3a^3 + 5 \ \checkmark$

$\therefore \dfrac{3a^3 + 5}{a - 2} = 3a^2 + 6a + 12 + \dfrac{29}{a - 2}$  ***Answer***

The division process ends when the remainder is either 0 or of lesser degree than the divisor.

**Show how you would arrange the divisor and dividend before actually doing the long division. Do not divide.**

1. Divide $x^2 + 3x^3 + 5x - 2$ by $x + 1$.
2. Divide $x^3 + 8$ by $x + 2$.
3. Divide $5 + 4x^3 - 17x$ by $2x - 5$.

**Use the given information to find the dividend.**

4. divisor $= 4$
   quotient $= 7$
   remainder $= 3$

5. divisor $= x - 2$
   quotient $= x$
   remainder $= 5$

6. divisor $= x^2 + 1$
   quotient $= 2x$
   remainder $= 7x + 5$

7. When $x^3 - x - 6$ is divided by $x - 2$, the quotient is $x^2 + 2x + 3$ and the remainder is 0.
   This means that __?__ and __?__ are factors of __?__.

## Written Exercises

**Divide. Write your answer as a polynomial or mixed expression.**

A 1. $\dfrac{x^2 + 8x + 15}{x + 3}$

2. $\dfrac{x^2 - 5x - 36}{x - 4}$

3. $\dfrac{n^2 - 3n - 54}{n - 9}$

4. $\dfrac{n^2 - 11n - 26}{n + 2}$

5. $\dfrac{y^2 + 6y + 10}{y + 2}$

6. $\dfrac{a^2 - 4a - 6}{a + 2}$

7. $\dfrac{x^2 - 3x - 9}{x - 3}$

8. $\dfrac{z^2 - 8z - 12}{z + 4}$

9. $\dfrac{8 + n^2 - 3n}{n - 5}$

10. $\dfrac{s^2 + 6 - 4s}{s + 4}$

11. $\dfrac{x^2 + 4}{x + 2}$

12. $\dfrac{y^2 - 9}{y + 9}$

13. $\dfrac{2x^2 - 7x + 5}{2x - 1}$

14. $\dfrac{3a^2 + 8a + 5}{3a + 2}$

15. $\dfrac{8 + 4x^2}{2x + 1}$

16. $\dfrac{9y^2 + 6}{3y - 1}$

17. $\dfrac{n^3 + n^2 - n - 1}{n - 1}$

18. $\dfrac{a^3 - 4a^2 + a + 6}{a - 2}$

19. $\dfrac{a^3 + 8}{a + 2}$

20. $\dfrac{n^3 - 1}{n - 1}$

21. $\dfrac{24x^3 + 2x^2 - 15}{3x - 2}$

22. $\dfrac{6n^3 + 5n^2 - 13n + 10}{3n - 5}$

B 23. $\dfrac{a^3 + 7a^2b + 3ab^2 - 14b^3}{a + 2b}$

24. $\dfrac{3x^3 + 5x^2y - xy^2}{3x + 2y}$

25. $\dfrac{4x^4 - 8x^3 - 3x^2 + 13x - 6}{2x - 3}$

26. $\dfrac{6x^4 - 2x^3 + 6x^2 - 5x + 3}{3x - 1}$

27. $\dfrac{2n^4 - n^3 - 2n + 1}{2n - 1}$

28. $\dfrac{z^4 + 16}{z + 2}$

29. $\dfrac{n^4 + 3n^3 + 3n^2 - 3n - 4}{n^2 - 1}$

30. $\dfrac{3x^3 - 4x^2 + 2x + 4}{x^2 - 2x + 2}$

**31.** The volume of a rectangular solid is $12n^3 + 8n^2 - 3n - 2$. The length of the solid is $2n + 1$ and the width is $2n - 1$. Find the height.

**32.** Divide $a^4 + a^2 - 20$ by $a - 2$.
   **a.** Use long division.
   **b.** Factor $a^4 + a^2 - 20$ first. Then divide by $a - 2$.
   **c.** Show that your answers to parts (a) and (b) are the same.

**33.** Factor $3n^3 - 7n^2 + 4$ completely given that $3n + 2$ is one of its factors.

**34.** Factor $x^3 + 4x^2 + x - 6$ given that $x - 1$ is one of its factors.

**35.** Factor $4x^3 - 12x^2 - 37x - 15$ given that $2x + 1$ is a factor.

**36.** Factor $2x^3 - 7x^2 + 4x + 4$ given that $(x - 2)^2$ is a factor.

**C** **37.** Find the value of $k$ for which $2x + 3$ is a factor of $6x^2 + 5x + k$.

**38.** Find the value of $k$ for which $x + 3$ is a factor of $2x^3 + 11x^2 + 13x + k$.

**39.** Find the value of $k$ for which $y - 2$ is a factor of $y^3 - 4y^2 + ky + 6$.

**40.** When $6x^4 - 5x^3 - 37x^2 + 46x + n$ is divided by $2x - 5$, the remainder is 5. Find the value of $n$.

**41. a.** Divide $x^{100} - 1$ by $x - 1$.   **b.** Divide $x^n - 1$ by $x - 1$.

**42. a.** Divide $x^{100} + 1$ by $x + 1$.   **b.** Divide $x^n + 1$ by $x + 1$, where $n$ is even.

**43. a.** Divide $x^{101} + 1$ by $x + 1$.   **b.** Divide $x^n + 1$ by $x + 1$, where $n$ is odd.

# Self-Test 3

***Vocabulary***    mixed expression (p. 260)

**Write each expression as a fraction in simplest form.**

**1.** $9 + \dfrac{a}{b}$          **2.** $4x - \dfrac{1}{x}$          **3.** $a - \dfrac{a-1}{a+1}$          Obj. 6-6, p. 260

**Divide. Write your answer as a polynomial or mixed expression.**

**4.** $\dfrac{-20 + 2x^2 + 3x}{x + 4}$          **5.** $\dfrac{2b^3 + b^2 + b + 16}{b + 2}$          Obj. 6-7, p. 263

Check your answers with those at the back of the book.

# Extra / Complex Fractions

A complex fraction is a fraction whose numerator or denominator contains one or more fractions. To express a complex fraction as a simple fraction, use one of the methods below.

Method 1: Simplify the numerator and denominator. Express the fraction as a quotient using the ÷ sign. Multiply by the reciprocal of the divisor.

Method 2: Find the LCD of all the simple fractions. Multiply the numerator and the denominator of the complex fraction by the LCD.

**Example** Simplify $\dfrac{\frac{1}{a} + \frac{1}{b}}{\frac{b}{2a} - \frac{a}{2b}}$.

**Solution** Method 1:

$$\frac{\frac{1}{a} + \frac{1}{b}}{\frac{b}{2a} - \frac{a}{2b}} = \frac{\frac{b + a}{ab}}{\frac{b^2 - a^2}{2ab}}$$

$$= \frac{b + a}{ab} \div \frac{b^2 - a^2}{2ab}$$

$$= \frac{\cancel{b + a}}{\cancel{ab}} \cdot \frac{2a\cancel{b}}{\cancel{(b + a)}(b - a)}$$

$$= \frac{2}{b - a}$$

Method 2:

The LCD of all the simple fractions is $2ab$.

$$\frac{\frac{1}{a} + \frac{1}{b}}{\frac{b}{2a} - \frac{a}{2b}} = \frac{\left(\frac{1}{a} + \frac{1}{b}\right)2ab}{\left(\frac{b}{2a} - \frac{a}{2b}\right)2ab}$$

$$= \frac{2b + 2a}{b^2 - a^2}$$

$$= \frac{2\cancel{(b + a)}}{\cancel{(b + a)}(b - a)} = \frac{2}{b - a}$$

## Exercises

In the following exercises you can use either Method 1 or Method 2 to simplify the fractions. Most people find Method 2 preferable, especially when simplifying more involved complex fractions.

Simplify.

**A**

**1.** $\dfrac{\frac{m}{8}}{\frac{5m}{8}}$

**2.** $\dfrac{\frac{3a}{4}}{\frac{15a}{12}}$

**3.** $\dfrac{\frac{u}{v^2}}{\frac{u}{v}}$

**4.** $\dfrac{6e}{\frac{3}{7e}}$

**5.** $\dfrac{\frac{1}{4} + \frac{1}{8}}{\frac{1}{4} - \frac{1}{8}}$

**6.** $\dfrac{\frac{1}{6} + \frac{1}{3}}{\frac{1}{2} + \frac{1}{5}}$

**7.** $\dfrac{\frac{5}{6} - \frac{5}{7}}{\frac{5}{6} + \frac{5}{7}}$

**8.** $\dfrac{\frac{3}{x}}{\frac{1}{x} - \frac{1}{3x}}$

**9.** $\dfrac{\frac{9c^2}{5d^4}}{\frac{3c^2}{10d^3}}$

**10.** $\dfrac{\frac{n^2 - 25}{n}}{n - 5}$

**11.** $\dfrac{\frac{r}{s} + 2}{1 - \frac{r}{s}}$

**12.** $\dfrac{\frac{2w}{3} + 2}{\frac{5w}{3} - \frac{15}{x}}$

Simplify.

**B** 13. $\dfrac{z - \dfrac{5z}{z + 5}}{z + \dfrac{5z}{z - 5}}$

14. $\dfrac{1 - \dfrac{6}{s^2 + 2}}{\dfrac{4s + 2}{s^2 + 2} + 1}$

15. $\dfrac{k + \dfrac{k - 3}{k + 1}}{k - \dfrac{2}{k + 1}}$

16. $\dfrac{\dfrac{1}{c} - \dfrac{1}{3 - 3c}}{\dfrac{1}{1 - c} - \dfrac{3}{c}}$

17. $\dfrac{\dfrac{e}{e - f} - \dfrac{f}{e + f}}{\dfrac{f}{e - f} + \dfrac{e}{e + f}}$

18. $\dfrac{1 - 2u}{1 + \dfrac{1}{2u}} \div \dfrac{1 + 2u}{1 - \dfrac{1}{2u}}$

19. $\dfrac{\dfrac{2}{z + 1} - 2}{\dfrac{2 - z}{z^2 - 1} - 2}$

20. $\dfrac{\dfrac{m - n}{m + n} + \dfrac{n}{m}}{\dfrac{m}{n} - \dfrac{m - n}{m + n}}$

21. If $x = \dfrac{y - 1}{y + 1}$ and $y = \dfrac{1}{1 - z}$, express $x$ in terms of $z$.

22. If $a = \dfrac{b - c}{1 + bc}$ and $b = \dfrac{1}{z - 1}$ and $c = \dfrac{1}{z + 1}$, find $a$ in terms of $z$.

23. Sam drives $d$ km at 50 km/h and returns the same distance at 30 km/h. Show that the average speed is 37.5 km/h. (*Hint:* Average speed = total distance divided by total time.)

24. A cyclist travels 12 km on a level road at $x$ km/h and then goes 9 km on a downhill road at $2x$ km/h. Find her average speed in terms of $x$. (See Hint for Exercise 23.)

25. If $n$ items can be purchased for 50 cents, how many items can be purchased for 50 cents after the price per item is decreased by 10 cents?

26. If $a = \dfrac{1 - c}{1 + c}$ and $c = \dfrac{1 + b}{1 - b}$, show that $a + b = 0$.

Simplify.

27. $\left(\dfrac{w}{6} - \dfrac{6}{w}\right) \div \left(\dfrac{6}{w} - 4 + \dfrac{w}{2}\right)$

28. $\left(\dfrac{x}{4 - x^2} + \dfrac{1}{x - 2}\right) \div \left(1 - \dfrac{2}{2 + x}\right)$

29. $\left(\dfrac{1}{n - n^2} - \dfrac{1}{n^2 + n}\right) \div \left(\dfrac{1}{n^2 + 1} - \dfrac{1}{n^2 - 1}\right)$

30. $\left(\dfrac{c^2 + d^2}{cd} - 2\right) \div \left(\dfrac{4c^2 - 4d^2}{2cd}\right)$

31. $\left(\dfrac{9e^2 - 5}{e - 1} - \dfrac{1}{6}\right) \div \left(1 - \dfrac{e - 9e^2}{e - 1}\right)$

32. $\left(\dfrac{u^2 + v^2}{u^2 - v^2}\right) \div \left(\dfrac{u - v}{u + v} - \dfrac{u + v}{u - v}\right)$

**C** 33. $\dfrac{r}{2}\left(\dfrac{r^2 - s^2}{r^2s + rs^2}\right)\left(\dfrac{1}{r - s}\right)\left(\dfrac{1}{r + s}\right) \div \dfrac{1}{r + s}$

34. $\left(\dfrac{4x^2 - y^2}{3xy}\right) \div \left(\dfrac{2x^2 - y^2}{xy} + 1\right)$

35. $1 - \dfrac{1}{1 - \dfrac{1}{c - 2}}$

36. $2 + \dfrac{1}{1 + \dfrac{2}{a + \dfrac{1}{a}}}$

# Chapter Summary

1. A fraction can be simplified by factoring its numerator and its denominator and dividing each by their common factors.

2. The *rule of exponents for a power of a quotient* (page 245) is often useful in simplifying fractions.

3. The following rules are used for combining fractions.

Multiplication Rule

$$\frac{c}{d} \cdot \frac{x}{y} = \frac{cx}{dy}$$

Division Rule

$$\frac{a}{b} \div \frac{c}{d} = \frac{a}{b} \cdot \frac{d}{c}$$

Addition Rule

$$\frac{a}{c} + \frac{b}{c} = \frac{a+b}{c}$$

Subtraction Rule

$$\frac{a}{c} - \frac{b}{c} = \frac{a-b}{c}$$

4. When adding or subtracting fractions with different denominators, rewrite the fractions using their *least common denominator* (*LCD*). Then apply the appropriate rule. (See the method and the examples on pages 255–256.)

5. A sum or difference of a polynomial and a fraction is called a *mixed expression*. A mixed expression can be expressed as a fraction in simplest form.

6. When dividing polynomials, arrange the terms of the *divisor* and *dividend* in order of decreasing degree in a variable. Insert zero coefficients where the dividend is missing a power.

# Chapter Review

**Give the letter of the correct answer.**

1. Express $\dfrac{9x^2 - 9}{x^2 + 1}$ in simplest form.    6-1

   **a.** 0

   **b.** $-9$

   **c.** $\dfrac{9(x+1)(x-1)}{x^2+1}$

   **d.** $\dfrac{9(x-1)}{x+1}$

2. Express $\dfrac{8xy}{12x^2y - xy^2}$ in simplest form.

   **a.** $\dfrac{2}{3(x-y)}$     **b.** $\dfrac{8}{12x-y}$     **c.** $\dfrac{3}{2(x-y)}$     **d.** $\dfrac{8}{11y}$

3. Express $\left(-\dfrac{3}{4}\right)^3\left(-\dfrac{16}{9}\right)$ in simplest form.    6-2

   **a.** $\dfrac{3}{4}$     **b.** $-\dfrac{4}{3}$     **c.** $-\dfrac{3}{4}$     **d.** $\dfrac{4}{3}$

**4.** Express $\dfrac{5xy}{12} \cdot \dfrac{32}{3xy^2}$ in simplest form.

    **a.** $\dfrac{40}{3y}$         **b.** $\dfrac{40}{3y^2}$         **c.** $\dfrac{40}{9y}$         **d.** $40y$

**5.** Express $5ab^2 \div \dfrac{10a}{b}$ in simplest form.                     6-3

    **a.** $\dfrac{1}{2}b$         **b.** $\dfrac{b^3}{2}$         **c.** $\dfrac{50a^2}{b}$         **d.** $2b^3$

**6.** Express $\dfrac{x^2 - 16}{4x + 16} \div (4 - x)$ in simplest form.

    **a.** $-4$         **b.** $4$         **c.** $\dfrac{1}{4}$         **d.** $-\dfrac{1}{4}$

**7.** Find the missing numerator in $\dfrac{2}{x - y} = \dfrac{?}{x^2 - 2xy + y^2}$.       6-4

    **a.** $2$         **b.** $2(x + y)$         **c.** $2xy$         **d.** $2(x - y)$

**8.** Find the LCD for $\dfrac{4n}{9n - 6}$ and $\dfrac{2n}{15(3n - 2)^2}$.

    **a.** $15(3n - 2)$                **b.** $45(3n - 2)^2$

    **c.** $15(3n - 2)^2$              **d.** $5(3n - 2)$

**9.** Simplify $\dfrac{5a}{a - 1} + \dfrac{5}{1 - a}$.                       6-5

    **a.** $5$         **b.** $\dfrac{5a + 5}{a - 1}$         **c.** $-5$         **d.** $\dfrac{5a - 5}{1 - a}$

**10.** Simplify $\dfrac{n - 9}{36} - \dfrac{n - 35}{108}$.

    **a.** $\dfrac{n - 2}{27}$         **b.** $\dfrac{n + 4}{54}$         **c.** $2n + 8$         **d.** $\dfrac{n - 31}{54}$

**11.** Write $3 - \dfrac{a + 1}{a - 1}$ as a fraction in simplest form.       6-6

    **a.** $2$         **b.** $\dfrac{2a}{a - 1}$         **c.** $\dfrac{a - 2}{a - 1}$         **d.** $\dfrac{2a - 4}{a - 1}$

**12.** Simplify $z + 3 + \dfrac{1}{z - 3}$.

    **a.** $\dfrac{z^2 - 8}{z - 3}$         **b.** $\dfrac{z + 4}{z - 3}$         **c.** $\dfrac{z^2 - 8}{z^2 - 9}$         **d.** $\dfrac{z^2 - 10}{z - 3}$

**13.** When $x^3 - 3x^2 + 3x + 4$ is divided by $x - 2$, what is the remainder?     6-7
    **a.** $2$         **b.** $4$         **c.** $6$         **d.** $8$

**14.** Divide $\dfrac{8x^3 + 27}{2x + 3}$. Write your answer as a polynomial or mixed expression.

    **a.** $4x^2 + 9$                **b.** $4x^2 + 6x - 9 + \dfrac{54}{2x + 3}$

    **c.** $4x^2 - 6x + 9$             **d.** $4x^2 + 6x + 9$

# Chapter Test

**Express in simplest form, noting any restrictions on the variable.**

6-1

**1.** $\dfrac{4x - 32}{64 - x^2}$

**2.** $\dfrac{49 - a^2}{a^2 - 14a + 49}$

**3.** $\dfrac{3x^2 - 6x - 24}{3x^2 + 2x - 8}$

**4.** $\dfrac{15y^2 - 30y - 45}{5y^2 + 10y - 15}$

**Express in simplest form.**

6-2

**5.** $\left(-\dfrac{x^2}{5}\right)^3$

**6.** $\dfrac{(2x)^3}{6} \cdot \dfrac{x^3}{6}$

**7.** $\left(\dfrac{3a}{b}\right)^3 \cdot \dfrac{7ab}{54}$

6-3

**8.** $\dfrac{5}{9} \div \dfrac{5}{9}$

**9.** $\dfrac{7}{8} \div \dfrac{8}{7}$

**10.** $\dfrac{3a^2}{8b} \div 24ab$

**11.** $18 \div \left(\dfrac{3n}{2}\right)^3$

**12.** $\dfrac{6a + 36}{6a} \div \dfrac{a^2 - 36}{a^2}$

**13.** $\dfrac{y}{2x^3} \div \left(\dfrac{y}{2x}\right)^3$

**Find the missing numerator.**

6-4

**14.** $\dfrac{7n}{16m} = \dfrac{?}{144m^2n}$

**15.** $\dfrac{3}{x + 5} = \dfrac{?}{3x^2 - 75}$

**Express each group of fractions with their LCD.**

**16.** $\dfrac{2}{7x^2}, \dfrac{3}{14xy}, \dfrac{7}{8y^2}$

**17.** $\dfrac{2 - y}{16}, \dfrac{y + 1}{18}$

**Simplify.**

6-5

**18.** $\dfrac{x}{x - 9} + \dfrac{1}{x - 9} - \dfrac{19 - x}{x - 9}$

**19.** $\dfrac{x - 1}{3} + \dfrac{3 - 2x}{6}$

**20.** $\dfrac{2}{y^2 - 2y} - \dfrac{3}{y^2 - y - 2}$

**21.** $\dfrac{4a}{a - 2b} + \dfrac{8b}{2b - a}$

**Write each expression as a fraction in simplest form.**

6-6

**22.** $\dfrac{a}{b} - 6$

**23.** $5y + \dfrac{3 - y}{y - 3}$

**24.** $\dfrac{3}{4 - x} - 2$

**25.** $\dfrac{x}{x + 2} + \dfrac{2}{x - 2} + 1$

**Divide. Write your answer as a polynomial or mixed expression.**

6-7

**26.** $\dfrac{45 - 13n + n^2}{n - 5}$

**27.** $\dfrac{2x^3 - x^2 - 5x - 2}{2x + 1}$

**28.** Use long division to decide whether or not $x - 2$ is a factor of $x^3 + 6x^2 - x - 30$.

# Cumulative Review (Chapters 1–6)

**Perform the indicated operations. Express the answers in simplest form. Assume that no denominator is zero.**

**1.** $0.6(-0.8)^2 + 0.4(-0.8)^2$

**2.** $\dfrac{45x^3y^2z^5}{-30(xyz)^2}$

**3.** $(-3a^2b^3c^4)^3$

**4.** $(3m - 9n) + (2m + 11n)$

**5.** $(5x - 3)(4x + 3)$

**6.** $-2x(4x^3 - 3x^2 + 9)$

**7.** $(-13t + 6s) - (4t + 9s)$

**8.** $(-2b + 7c)^2$

**9.** $(4t^2s - 9)(4t^2s + 9)$

**Evaluate if $a = -1$, $b = 1$, $c = -2$, and $d = 3$.**

**10.** $\dfrac{a + b}{c} - cd$

**11.** $(a + b)^2 \div (c^2 + d)$

**12.** $(a^2 + b^2) \div c^2 + d$

**Factor completely. If the polynomial cannot be factored, write "prime."**

**13.** $6a^3b + 5a^3b^2 - 3a^2b^2$

**14.** $81x^2 + 18xy + y^2$

**15.** $8t^3 - 56t^2 + 98t$

**16.** $z^4 + 11z^3 + 18z^2$

**17.** $m^2 + 12m + 30$

**18.** $t^2 - 13t + 22$

**19.** $y^3 + 4y^2 - 32y$

**20.** $10z^2 + 16z - 8$

**21.** $4x^2 - y^2 + 2y - 1$

**Solve. If the equation is an identity or has no solution, state that fact.**

**22.** $8z - 1 = 23$

**23.** $\frac{1}{3}y - 5 = 7$

**24.** $6 - \frac{3}{4}d = -3$

**25.** $(n + 2)^2 = (n + 4)(n - 2)$

**26.** $10m^2 - m^3 = 25m$

**27.** $18c^2 - 32 = 0$

**28.** $t^2 + 12t + 15 = -5$

**29.** $x^2 - 6x = 7$

**30.** $6y^3 + 13y^2 - 5y = 0$

**Perform the indicated operations. Express the answers in simplest form. Assume that no denominator is zero.**

**31.** $\dfrac{2a^2 + 9a + 4}{2a^2 + 3a + 1} \cdot \dfrac{a + 1}{a^2 + 8a + 16}$

**32.** $\dfrac{3x}{5x - 10} + \dfrac{x + 2}{x^2 - 3x + 2}$

**33.** $\dfrac{u^2 - b^2}{(cd)^3} \div \dfrac{a + b}{c^2d}$

**34.** $\dfrac{3}{a^2 + 6a + 9} - \dfrac{a + 1}{a^2 - 9}$

**35.** $\dfrac{6b^3 - 13b^2 + 8b - 11}{2b - 3}$

**36.** $\left(x - \dfrac{y}{x}\right)\left(2x + \dfrac{y^2}{x}\right)$

**37.** Ted and Tina are twins. Their mother was 24 years old when they were born. Eight years ago she was 4 times their age. How old are all three now?

**38.** Maggie has 24 quarters and half dollars. If she had twice as many half dollars and half as many quarters, she would have $2 more. How much money does she have?

**39.** It took Len 25 min to ride his bicycle to the repair shop and 1 h 15 min to walk back home. If Len can ride his bicycle 8 km/h faster than he can walk, how far is the repair shop from his house?

**40.** Find two numbers whose sum is 15 and whose squares total 113.

# Maintaining Skills

Review the five-step problem-solving method described in Section 1-6.

**Example**    The length of a rectangle is 28 cm less than 5 times the width. If the perimeter is 1.12 m, find the dimensions.

**Solution**

Step 1   Read the problem carefully a few times. It asks for the length and width of the rectangle. Make a sketch.

Step 2   Choose a variable and use it with the given facts to represent the numbers described in the problem.
Let $w$ = the width.
Then $5w - 28$ = the length.

Step 3   Write an open sentence based on the given facts:

The perimeter    is   1.12 m.

$$2w + 2(5w - 28) = \quad 112 \quad (1.12 \text{ m} = 112 \text{ cm})$$

Step 4   Solve the open sentence and find the required numbers:

$$12w - 56 = 112$$
$$12w = 168$$
$$w = 14; \; 5w - 28 = 5(14) - 28 = 42$$

Step 5   Check your results with the words of the problem. Give the answer. The check is left to you.

∴ the length is 42 cm and the width is 14 cm. **Answer**

**Use the five-step plan to solve each problem.**

1. The length of a rectangle is 10 cm greater than twice its width. The area of the rectangle is 28 cm². Find the dimensions of the rectangle.

2. Three consecutive integers are such that the square of the greatest is 32 less than the sum of the squares of the other two. Find the integers.

3. The bottom of a box is a rectangle with length 3 cm more than the width. The height of the box is 6 cm and its volume is 324 cm³. Find the dimensions of the bottom of the box.

4. A painting is 10 cm longer than it is wide. The painting is to be surrounded by a mat that is 3 cm wide and covered by a piece of glass with area 816 cm². Find the dimensions of the painting.

5. Cynthia and George paddled a canoe downstream from a boat landing to a picnic area and back. They averaged 24 km/h downstream and 16 km/h less upstream. The whole trip took 50 min. How far was it from the boat landing to the picnic area?

# Mixed Review

## Skills and Problem Solving

1. The length of a rectangle is 1 cm longer than 3 times the width. If both dimensions of the rectangle are increased by 3 cm, the area is increased by 36 cm². Find the dimensions of the original rectangle.

2. Factor the polynomial $128r^2s^8 - 2r^2t^4$ completely.

3. Choose a point on a number line and label it "0." Then graph the numbers $-4$, 6, 2, $-1$, and 3.

**Solve. Assume that no denominator is zero. If the equation is an identity or has no solution, state that fact.**

4. $\dfrac{(n + 1)^2}{3} \div \dfrac{n + 1}{n} = n + 1$

5. $-\dfrac{1}{2}|x - 1| = 6$

6. $15b^2 + 7b - 2 = 0$

7. $(z + 1)^2 - (z + 2)^2 = 3$

8. Write $\dfrac{2x - 2y}{x^2 - y^2} + \dfrac{4}{x^2 + 2x + y^2} + \dfrac{1}{x + y}$ as a fraction in simplest form.

9. The home team scored 50 points more than half the number scored by the visitors. Their scores totaled 194 points. Who won the game and by how many points?

**Express the answers in simplest form. Assume that no denominator is zero.**

10. $-\dfrac{1}{5}(140x)\left(\dfrac{3x}{4} + \dfrac{5x}{7}\right)$

11. $(2a + b)^2 - (a - 2b)^2$

12. $\dfrac{c - d}{c + d} \div \dfrac{d}{c - d}$

13. $-\left|-108 \div \left(\dfrac{15}{4^2 - 11}\right)^2\right|$

14. Divide $6x^3 + 9x^2 - 7x + 16$ by $2x + 5$. Write the answer as a polynomial or a mixed expression.

15. Express $x^2 + 5x - (1 - 3x^2) + 4 + 3x$ as the product of two binomials.

16. Solve the equation $x^3 + 3x^2 - 9x = 27$ if
$$x \in \{-5, -4, -3, -2, -1, \ 0, 1, 2, 3, 4, 5\}.$$

17. Find two numbers whose sum is 2 and whose squares total 164.

18. A bag contains $9.75 in quarters and half dollars. The number of half dollars is 8 less than twice the number of quarters. How many coins of each type are in the bag?

**Evaluate if $q = -7$, $r = -4$, $s = -0.75$, $t = 2$, and $u = 3$.**

19. $2rs - qt^2$

20. $(2q + rt + 1) \div q$

21. $2r^2 \div 4 + 3rt$

# Preparing for College Entrance Exams

## Strategy for Success

In some types of problems, especially those involving length and width, area, perimeter, or relative position, it may be helpful to draw a sketch. Use any available space in the test booklet. Be careful to make no assumptions in drawing the figure. Use only the information specifically given in the problem.

**Decide which is the best of the choices given and write the corresponding letter on your answer sheet.**

1. How many integral values of $k$ are there for which $x^2 + kx + 24$ is factorable?

   **(A)** 0      **(B)** 2      **(C)** 4      **(D)** 6      **(E)** 8

2. Which of the polynomials is prime?

   **(A)** $35x^2 + 76x + 33$      **(B)** $4x^2 - 26x + 13$

   **(C)** $121y^2 + 176$      **(D)** $21x^2 + 40x - 21$

3. How many distinct roots does the equation $10x^3 - 7x^2 - 12x = 0$ have?

   **(A)** none      **(B)** one      **(C)** two      **(D)** three

4. A rectangular pool is to be built in a rectangular yard 12 m by 16 m. The pool will be positioned so that a uniform strip of land will be left around the pool. If the pool will take up half the area of the yard, find the perimeter of the pool.

   **(A)** 20 m      **(B)** 22 m      **(C)** 24 m      **(D)** 40 m      **(E)** 44 m

5. Express $\dfrac{4t + v}{t + v} - \dfrac{4t^2 - v^2}{t^2 - v^2}$ in simplest form. Assume that no denominator is zero.

   **(A)** $\dfrac{2tv}{t^2 - v^2}$      **(B)** $\dfrac{8tv + 2v^2}{v^2 - t^2}$      **(C)** $\dfrac{5tv}{t^2 - v^2}$      **(D)** $\dfrac{3tv}{v^2 - t^2}$

6. Which of the following are factors of $6x^3 + 29x^2 - 7x - 10$?

   I. $3x - 1$      II. $2x + 2$      III. $x + 5$

   **(A)** I only      **(B)** II only      **(C)** III only      **(D)** I and III only

   **(E)** II and III only

7. Express $\dfrac{(3n - 5)^4}{(2n + 1)^2} \div \dfrac{(5 - 3n)^4}{2n^2 + 7n + 3}$ in simplest form. Assume that no denominator is zero.

   **(A)** $\dfrac{(3n - 5)^4(n + 3)}{(5 - 3n)^4(2n + 1)}$      **(B)** $\dfrac{n + 3}{2n + 1}$      **(C)** $\dfrac{2n + 1}{n + 3}$

   **(D)** $\dfrac{(3n - 5)^4(2n + 1)}{(5 - 3n)^4(n + 3)}$      **(E)** $n + 3$

# 7 Applying Fractions

Io is the third largest of the known moons of Jupiter. Astronomical distances are often expressed in scientific notation and can be compared by using ratios.

# Ratio and Proportion

## 7-1 Ratios

**Objective**   To solve problems involving ratios.

The distance from Earth to the moon is approximately 240,000 miles. The distance from Jupiter to one of its moons, Io, is approximately 260,000 miles. Although these distances differ by 20,000 miles, they are approximately the same. This relationship is indicated by the quotient, or ratio, of the distances:

$$\frac{240,000}{260,000} = \frac{12}{13}$$

The **ratio** of one number to another is the quotient of the first number divided by the second. You can express the ratio of 7 to 4 as:

1. an indicated quotient using the division sign ÷          $7 \div 4$

2. an indicated quotient using the ratio sign :          $7:4$

3. a fraction          $\frac{7}{4}$

4. a decimal          $1.75$

When working with ratios, you must be certain that all distances, masses, and other measures are *expressed in the same units*. For example, if you wish to find the ratio of the height of a 4 m tree to the height of a 50 cm sapling, you express 4 m as 400 cm and divide to find the ratio

$$\frac{400}{50} \text{ or } 8:1.$$

---

To find the ratio of two quantities of the same kind:

1. Express the measures in the same unit.
2. Then divide them.

---

The ratio $\frac{9}{6}$ can be expressed in simplest form as $\frac{3}{2}$. When solving certain problems involving ratios, you need to express a ratio in a different form. If you know that two numbers are in the ratio 3:2, you can represent the numbers as $3x$ and $2x$ for some nonzero $x$ because the cancellation rule for fractions gives

$$\frac{3x}{2x} = \frac{3}{2}.$$

## Example

A farmer plants alfalfa and wheat in the ratio 3:5. How many acres of the 160-acre farm are planted with alfalfa and how many acres with wheat?

## Solution

*Step 1* The problem asks for the number of acres of alfalfa and the number of acres of wheat.

*Step 2* Let $3x$ = the number of acres of alfalfa and $5x$ = the number of acres of wheat.

*Step 3* $3x + 5x = 160$

*Step 4* $8x = 160$
$x = 20$

Number of acres of alfalfa = $3x = 3 \cdot 20 = 60$
Number of acres of wheat = $5x = 5 \cdot 20 = 100$

*Step 5* The check is left to you.

∴ there are 60 acres of alfalfa and 100 acres of wheat. *Answer*

Saying that three numbers are in the ratio 3:7:11 means that the ratio of the first to the second is 3:7 and the ratio of the second to the third is 7:11.

## *Oral Exercises*

**State each ratio in simplest form.**

**1.** 5:15

**2.** 18:24

**3.** 75:50

**4.** 8:24:16

**5.** $4x:6x$

**6.** $20t:35t$

**7.** $4a^2:8a$

**8.** $20n:30n:15n$

**9.** $\dfrac{4a^2b}{12ab^2}$

**10.** $\dfrac{(3n)^2}{9n^2}$

**11.** $\dfrac{(8x)^2}{8x^2}$

**12.** $\dfrac{1}{2}:\dfrac{3}{4}$

**13.** 45 min to 2 h

**14.** 3 m to 60 cm

**15.** 4 h to 20 min

**16.** 10 cm to 2 m

**17.** 8 wk to 16 d

**18.** 1 kg to 50 g

**19.** If a problem states that two numbers are in the ratio 5:6, how would you represent those numbers using a variable?

## Written Exercises

**State each ratio in simplest form.**

**A**
1. 20 min : 2 h
2. 6 m : 120 cm
3. 4 cm : 4 m
4. 150 g : 3 kg
5. 6 wk : 3 d
6. 5 km : 450 cm

7. The student-teacher ratio in a school with 3300 students and 150 teachers.

8. The ratio of rainy days to rainless days in a year having 365 days of which 245 are rainless.

9. The ratio of new airplanes to old airplanes in a fleet of 720 planes of which 240 are old.

10. The ratio of seniors taking a math course to seniors not taking a math course if 105 out of 270 seniors are taking math.

11. The ratio of wins to losses to ties for a hockey team that played 48 games, winning 24 and tying 6.

12. The ratio of whole-wheat flour to milk to nuts in a recipe calling for $2\frac{1}{4}$ cups of flour, 1 cup of milk, and $1\frac{1}{2}$ cups of nuts.

**Find the ratio of (a) the perimeters and (b) the areas of each pair of figures.**

13. A rectangle with sides 8 cm and 6 cm and one with sides 10 cm and 9 cm.

14. A rectangle with length 12 cm and perimeter 30 cm and one with length 10 cm and perimeter 30 cm.

15. A rectangle with sides 4 m and 80 cm and one with sides 3 m and 80 cm.

16. A rectangle with sides 50 cm and 1.5 m and a similar rectangle whose sides are 3 times as long.

**Find the ratio of $x$ to $y$ determined by each equation.**

*Example*    $3x = 7y$      *Solution*    $3x = 7y$

$$x = \frac{7}{3}y$$

$$\frac{x}{y} = \frac{7}{3} \text{ or } x : y = 7 : 3 \quad \textit{Answer}$$

**B**
17. $8x = 5y$
18. $14x = 12y$
19. $18y = 9x$
20. $ax = by$
21. $4(x + y) = 8(x - y)$
22. $8(2x - 3y) = 6(x + y)$
23. $8x - 4y = 2cx - cy$
24. $ax + by = cx + dy$
25. $ax - a^2y = bx - b^2y$

(*Hint:* In Exercises 23–25, collect $x$ terms on one side and $y$ terms on the other. Then factor.)

**Find the ratio of $x$ to $y$ determined by each equation.**

C  **26.** $x^2 + 2y^2 = 2xy + y^2$    **27.** $x^2 - 4xy + 4y^2 = 0$    **28.** $25x^2 + 36y^2 = 60xy$

(*Hint:* In Exercises 26–28, collect terms on one side of the equation. Then factor the resulting polynomial.)

## Problems

A   **1.** Two numbers are in the ratio $3:8$ and their sum is 66. What are the numbers?

**2.** There are a total of 180 players and coaches in the town soccer league. If the player-coach ratio is $9:1$, how many players are there?

**3.** The freshman class of 700 students has a boy to girl ratio of $17:18$. How many girls are there?

**4.** The perimeter of a rectangle is 96 cm. Find the length and width if their ratio is $7:5$.

**5.** Three numbers are in the ratio $5:6:7$ and their total is 720. Find the numbers.

**6.** The measures of the angles of a triangle are in the ratio $1:2:3$. Find these measures. (*Hint:* The measures of the angles of a triangle total $180°$.)

**7.** Concrete can be made by mixing cement, sand, and gravel in the ratio $3:6:8$. How many cubic meters of each ingredient are needed to make 850 m³ of concrete?

**8.** A new alloy is made by mixing 8 parts of iron with 3 parts of zinc and 1 part of tungsten. How much of each metal is needed to make 420 m³ of the alloy?

B   **9.** Two cars leave from the same place at the same time, traveling in opposite directions at speeds that are in the ratio $4:3$. After 2 h, the cars are 308 km apart. What are their speeds? (*Hint:* Make a rate-time-distance chart.)

**10.** The ratio of Alex's cycling speed to Bart's cycling speed is $6:5$. Bart leaves school at 3 P.M. and Alex leaves at 3:10 P.M. By 3:30, Alex is only 2 km behind Bart. How fast is each boy going?

**11.** In a collection of dimes and nickels worth $3.20, the ratio of the number of dimes to the number of nickels is $3:2$. Find the number of each type of coin. (*Hint:* Make a coin value chart.)

**12.** In a collection of nickels, dimes, and quarters worth $20.30, the ratio of the numbers of nickels, dimes, and quarters is $5:4:9$. Find the number of each type of coin.

13. The College Bookstore purchased a supply of mechanical pencils and ball-point pens. The ratio of pencils to pens is 5:9. If the pencils cost $1 each, the pens 25 cents each, and the total bill was $290, find the number of pencils purchased. (*Hint:* Make a number-price-cost chart.)

14. The ratio of Sue's age to her father's age is 2:7. In three years, their ages will total 60. How old is each now?

C 15. There are 2820 cars in Farmington. The ratio of intermediates to compacts is 7:5 and the ratio of compacts to full-size cars is 8:9. How many full-size cars are there?

16. Find two numbers such that their sum, their difference, and their product have the ratio 3:2:5.

## Biographical Note / *Juan de la Cierva*

Juan de la Cierva was born in Murcia, Spain, in 1895. He attended school in Murcia and Madrid and later graduated from the Special Technical College in Madrid.

Juan de la Cierva was interested from childhood in the design and building of aircraft. In 1912, at the age of seventeen, de la Cierva and two friends assembled a biplane using the wreckage from a French aircraft. This airplane became the first Spanish-built plane to fly. De la Cierva later designed and built a monoplane, as well as the world's second trimotor, a plane powered by three engines.

It was the crash of the trimotor that started de la Cierva on the road to designing a new type of aircraft, the autogiro. This aircraft resembled a cross between a helicopter and an airplane, although the large rotor at the top of the plane was not powered, but moved due to the passage of air over the blades. De la Cierva hoped that this design would eliminate a major problem of airplanes of his day, that of crashes caused by engines stalling at low speeds. He constructed a number of autogiros from 1920 to 1922, continually refining the concept until in 1923 a successful autogiro took to the air. By 1928 the design had been perfected to the point that de la Cierva was able to fly an autogiro across the English Channel, a feat that brought him numerous honors. The concept of the autogiro reached its high point in 1933 with the model C.30, a craft that could take off in a space of six yards and was capable of a speed of 100 miles per hour. At the time of his death in 1936, Juan de la Cierva was recognized, along with the Wright brothers, as one of the creative forces in modern aviation.

## 7-2 Proportion

**Objective**   To solve problems involving proportion.

An equation that states that two ratios are equal is called a **proportion.** You can write proportions in several different ways.

$2:3 = 4:6$   read, "2 is to 3 as 4 is to 6."

$\frac{x}{12} = \frac{9}{4}$   read, "$x$ divided by 12 equals 9 divided by 4."

In the proportion

$$a:b = c:d \quad \text{or} \quad \frac{a}{b} = \frac{c}{d},$$

$a$ and $d$ are called the **extremes** and $b$ and $c$ are called the **means.** You can use the multiplication property of equality to show that in any proportion *the product of the extremes equals the product of the means.* (See Oral Exercise 9.) Thus, if $a:b = c:d$, you have $ad = bc$ (and by the commutative axiom for multiplication, $da = cb$). This fact can be used to solve proportions.

**Example 1**   Solve: $\frac{3}{x} = \frac{5}{4}$

**Solution**
$$\frac{3}{x} = \frac{5}{4}$$
$$3 \cdot 4 = 5x$$
$$12 = 5x$$
$$\frac{12}{5} = x$$

$\therefore$ the solution is $\frac{12}{5}$.   **Answer**

**Example 2**   Solve: $\frac{2n - 3}{5} = \frac{n + 2}{6}$

**Solution**
$$\frac{2n - 3}{5} = \frac{n + 2}{6}$$
$$6(2n - 3) = 5(n + 2)$$
$$12n - 18 = 5n + 10$$
$$7n = 28$$
$$n = 4$$

$\therefore$ the solution is 4.   **Answer**

**Example 3**   Solve the formula $I = \frac{E}{R}$ for $R$.

**Solution**   Rewrite the formula as the proportion $\frac{I}{1} = \frac{E}{R}$.

$$\frac{I}{1} = \frac{E}{R}$$
$$IR = E$$
$$R = \frac{E}{I} \quad \textbf{Answer}$$

The following examples illustrate two of the many types of problems that can be solved by proportions.

**Example 4** A recipe for making 30 bran muffins requires 1200 g of flour. If you have only 1000 g of flour, how many muffins can you make?

### Solution

Step 1 The problem asks for the number of muffins.

Step 2 Let $x$ = the number of muffins.

Step 3 1200 g makes 30 muffins.
1000 g makes $x$ muffins.

$$\frac{1200}{1000} = \frac{30}{x}$$

Step 4 Solve.

$$\frac{12}{10} = \frac{30}{x}$$
$$12x = 300$$
$$x = 25$$

Step 5 The check is left to you.

∴ you can make 25 bran muffins. **Answer**

**Example 5** Nick Massey drove 352 miles on 11 gallons of gas. How many additional miles can he drive on the 4 gallons remaining in his car's gas tank?

### Solution

Step 1 The problem asks for the number of additional miles he can drive.

Step 2 Let $x$ = the number of additional miles.

Step 3 352 miles on 11 gallons
$x$ miles on 4 gallons

$$\frac{352}{11} = \frac{x}{4}$$

Step 4 Solve.

$$\frac{352}{11} = \frac{x}{4}$$
$$352 \cdot 4 = 11x$$
$$128 = x$$

Step 5 The check is left to you.

∴ he can drive 128 additional miles. **Answer**

## Oral Exercises

**State the equation that results when you equate the product of the extremes and the product of the means in the following proportions.**

**1.** $\dfrac{5}{3} = \dfrac{2}{x}$  **2.** $\dfrac{3}{y} = \dfrac{7}{8}$  **3.** $\dfrac{2x}{7} = \dfrac{3}{5}$  **4.** $\dfrac{-3}{2n} = \dfrac{5}{-6}$

**5.** $\dfrac{y-3}{4} = \dfrac{5}{2}$  **6.** $\dfrac{4}{9} = \dfrac{a-2}{3}$  **7.** $\dfrac{2}{2d-1} = \dfrac{4}{7}$  **8.** $\dfrac{3}{x-5} = \dfrac{4}{x+5}$

**9.** If you multiply both sides of the proportion $\dfrac{a}{b} = \dfrac{c}{d}$ by $bd$, what equation do you get?

## Written Exercises

**Solve.**

**A** **1.** $\dfrac{x}{5} = \dfrac{3}{4}$  **2.** $\dfrac{y}{3} = \dfrac{4}{7}$  **3.** $\dfrac{9}{2x} = \dfrac{6}{4}$  **4.** $\dfrac{2}{3} = \dfrac{8}{2n}$

**5.** $\dfrac{3n}{7} = \dfrac{4}{5}$  **6.** $\dfrac{8}{5k} = \dfrac{2}{5}$  **7.** $\dfrac{9}{4} = \dfrac{3a}{5}$  **8.** $\dfrac{4}{3} = \dfrac{12}{7k}$

**9.** $\dfrac{18x}{13} = \dfrac{36}{39}$  **10.** $\dfrac{15x}{64} = \dfrac{45}{32}$  **11.** $\dfrac{81}{49} = \dfrac{27y}{14}$  **12.** $\dfrac{25}{17a} = \dfrac{125}{51}$

**13.** $\dfrac{15a}{36} = \dfrac{45}{12}$  **14.** $\dfrac{81}{64} = \dfrac{27n}{40}$  **15.** $\dfrac{17}{25b} = \dfrac{34}{75}$  **16.** $\dfrac{36}{24} = \dfrac{12x}{36}$

**17.** $\dfrac{4}{x} = 5$  **18.** $\dfrac{5}{2n} = 3$  **19.** $\dfrac{3r}{7} = -6$  **20.** $-2 = \dfrac{4y}{5}$

**21.** $\dfrac{x-5}{4} = \dfrac{3}{2}$  **22.** $\dfrac{y-3}{8} = \dfrac{3}{4}$  **23.** $\dfrac{2n-1}{5} = 7$  **24.** $\dfrac{1-4n}{5} = 9$

**25.** $\dfrac{5n-3}{4} = \dfrac{5n+3}{6}$  **26.** $\dfrac{6x-2}{7} = \dfrac{5x+7}{8}$  **27.** $\dfrac{4y-3}{7} = \dfrac{2y-1}{3}$

**28.** $\dfrac{3n-11}{5} = \dfrac{1+5n}{18}$  **29.** $\dfrac{4x}{5} = \dfrac{2x}{7}$  **30.** $\dfrac{4x+12}{8} = \dfrac{x+3}{2}$

**B** **31.** $\dfrac{25(x-3)}{28} = \dfrac{75}{14}$  **32.** $\dfrac{36}{2x-3} = \dfrac{72}{2x+3}$  **33.** $\dfrac{15}{x+7} = \dfrac{45}{x+21}$

**Find the ratio of $x$ to $y$.**

**34.** $\dfrac{3x+2y}{5} = \dfrac{4x-7y}{6}$  **35.** $\dfrac{8x-y}{4} = \dfrac{x+y}{3}$  **36.** $\dfrac{x-2y}{17} = \dfrac{x+2y}{34}$

**37.** $\dfrac{cy}{d-c} = \dfrac{dx}{d^2-c^2}$  (Give your answer in terms of $c$ and $d$.)

**38.** Solve the formula $\frac{F}{m} = a$ for $F$. Then solve for $m$.

**39.** Solve the formula $F = \frac{mr^2}{r}$ for $m$. Then solve for $r$.

**40.** Solve $\frac{p}{t} = \frac{P}{T}$ for $P$. Then solve for $T$.

**41.** Solve $\frac{PV}{T} = K$ for $V$. Then solve for $T$.

When the means of a proportion are the same, the mean is called the **mean proportional** between the two extremes. For example, since $4:6 = 6:9$, 6 is the mean proportional between 4 and 9.

**Find the mean proportional between the following.**

C   **42.** 3 and 27            **43.** 4 and 64            **44.** $a$ and $b$, if both are positive

## *Problems*

A   **1.** Three cans of tuna cost $3.51. How much will five cans cost?

      **2.** A plane can fly 1800 km in 2 h. How far can it fly in 3 h?

      **3.** A truck uses 8 L of gasoline to go 120 km. How much will it use to go 300 km?

      **4.** A car that sold for $7200 had a sales tax of $240. How much is the tax on a car that sells for $9000?

      **5.** A recipe for $2\frac{1}{2}$ dozen whole-wheat muffins requires 600 g of flour. How many muffins can be made with 900 g of flour?

      **6.** A pump can fill a 2400-liter water tank in 50 min. How much water can it pump in half an hour?

      **7.** An advertisement claims that in a recent poll, three out of four dentists recommended brushing with Cleanteeth toothpaste. If there were 92 dentists polled, how many favored Cleanteeth?

B   **8.** In a town with 18,000 homes, a survey was taken to determine the number with cable television. Of the 360 homes surveyed, 135 had cable television. Estimate the number of homes in the town that have cable television.

      **9.** A 25-acre field yields 550 bushels of wheat annually. How many additional acres should be planted so that the annual yield will be 660 bushels?

10. A photograph 20 cm by 15 cm is enlarged so that its length becomes 28 cm. **a.** What does the width become? **b.** Find these ratios:

$$\frac{\text{new length}}{\text{old length}}, \quad \frac{\text{new perimeter}}{\text{old perimeter}}, \quad \frac{\text{new area}}{\text{old area}}$$

11. On a map, 1 cm represents 10 km, and Wyoming is a rectangle 44.5 cm by 59.1 cm. Find the area of Wyoming in square kilometers.

C 12. Mahogany weighs 33.94 pounds per cubic foot, whereas pine weighs 23.45 pounds per cubic foot. Which weighs more: a mahogany board with dimensions $5\frac{1}{2}$ in. by 1 in. by 6 ft or a pine board with dimensions $3\frac{1}{2}$ in. by $1\frac{1}{2}$ in. by 8 ft?

# Self-Test 1

***Vocabulary***    ratio (p. 277)                    proportion (p. 282)
means (p. 282)                   extremes (p. 282)

**Express each ratio in simplest form.**

1. 36 min : 1 h                    2. 2 dollars : 5 cents                    **Obj. 7-1, p. 277**

3. The ratio of the number of questions Tony answered correctly on a test to the total number of questions on the test was 9 : 11. If the test consisted of 77 questions, how many questions did Tony answer correctly?

**Solve.**

4. $\dfrac{x}{150} = \dfrac{9}{25}$           5. $\dfrac{3}{4r} = 12$           6. $\dfrac{x+2}{4} = \dfrac{x-5}{3}$           **Obj. 7-2, p. 282**

Check your answers with those at the back of the book.

# *Computer Exercises*          *For students with some programming experience*

1. Write a BASIC program that converts the ratio of two integers entered with INPUT statements to a decimal number. Use the program to convert the following ratios to decimal form.

   **a.** $\dfrac{2}{3}$           **b.** $\dfrac{15}{6}$           **c.** $\dfrac{5}{11}$           **d.** $\dfrac{5}{37}$

2. Write a BASIC program that converts a repeating decimal number to the ratio of two integers. Use the program to convert the following decimal numbers to ratios.

   **a.** $0.\overline{4}$           **b.** $0.0\overline{3}$           **c.** $0.\overline{9}$           **d.** $0.\overline{123}$

The following program will print out several ratios equal to $\frac{A}{B}$.

```
10   PRINT "TO PRINT OUT EQUAL RATIOS:"
20   PRINT "INPUT A,B";
30   INPUT A,B
40   PRINT
50   FOR I=1 TO 10
60   PRINT I*A
70   PRINT "-----"
80   PRINT I*B
90   PRINT
100  NEXT I
110  END
```

### Exercises

RUN the program for the following.

**1.** $A = 3, B = 5$                 **2.** $A = 5, B = 7$

Make these changes in the program.

```
10   PRINT "TO PRINT PROPORTIONAL RECTANGLES:"
50   FOR I=1 TO 5
55   PRINT "RECTANGLE ";I
60   FOR J=1 TO I*A
65   FOR K=1 TO I*B
70   PRINT "*";
75   NEXT K
80   PRINT
85   NEXT J
```

RUN the revised program for the following.

**3.** $A = 3, B = 5$                 **4.** $A = 2, B = 6$

Let the number of asterisks represent the area of each rectangle.

**5.** What is the area of each of the five rectangles?

What is the ratio of the following?

**6.** The area of rectangle 2 to the area of rectangle 1.

**7.** The area of rectangle 5 to the area of rectangle 1.

**8.** If you can print out the results of Exercises 3 and 4, draw lines to mark off rectangles equivalent to rectangle 1 on each of the other rectangles.

# Fractional Equations

## 7-3 Equations with Fractional Coefficients

**Objective**   To solve equations with fractional coefficients.

You can solve equations with fractional coefficients by using the least common denominator of all the fractions in the equation. Transform the equation by multiplying both sides by the least common denominator. Then solve the transformed equation.

**Example**   Solve: $\dfrac{n+1}{10} - \dfrac{n}{3} = \dfrac{19}{15}$

**Solution**   The LCD of the fractions is 30.

$$30\left[\left(\frac{n+1}{10}\right) - \left(\frac{n}{3}\right)\right] = 30\left[\frac{19}{15}\right]$$

$$30\left(\frac{n+1}{10}\right) - 30\left(\frac{n}{3}\right) = 30\left[\frac{19}{15}\right]$$

$$3(n+1) - 10n = 2[19]$$

$$3n + 3 - 10n = 38$$

$$-7n + 3 = 38$$

$$-7n = 35$$

$$n = -5$$

∴ the solution is $-5$.   **Answer**

## Oral Exercises

**State the least common denominator of the fractions in each equation. Then state the equation that results when both sides are multiplied by the LCD.**

1. $\dfrac{x}{3} + \dfrac{x}{2} = 1$

2. $\dfrac{3y}{8} + \dfrac{y}{4} = 10$

3. $\dfrac{n}{2} + \dfrac{n}{3} = \dfrac{20}{6}$

4. $\dfrac{3a}{5} - \dfrac{a}{2} = \dfrac{1}{20}$

5. $\dfrac{x+1}{6} + \dfrac{x+5}{4} = 1$

6. $\dfrac{y}{2} - \dfrac{y+5}{3} = 0$

7. $\dfrac{x}{4} - \dfrac{2x-1}{3} = -3$

8. $\dfrac{1}{4}(n+2) - \dfrac{1}{6}(n-2) = \dfrac{3}{2}$

9. $\dfrac{3(x+1)}{2} - \dfrac{5(x+1)}{4} = \dfrac{1}{2}$

# Written Exercises

**A** **1–9.** Solve the equations in Oral Exercises 1–9.

**Solve.**

**10.** $\dfrac{5n}{18} - \dfrac{4n}{9} = \dfrac{1}{12}$

**11.** $2a + \dfrac{a}{3} = \dfrac{a}{4} + 5$

**12.** $x + \dfrac{x}{4} = 14 - \dfrac{x}{2}$

**13.** $\dfrac{x - 2}{3} = \dfrac{x + 1}{4}$

**14.** $\dfrac{17x}{25} = \dfrac{51}{50}$

**15.** $x + \dfrac{x + 2}{4} = 0$

**16.** $\dfrac{y + 2}{3} + \dfrac{y - 1}{6} = 5$

**17.** $\dfrac{4y + 1}{3} - \dfrac{2y + 1}{5} = \dfrac{3}{5}$

**18.** $\dfrac{x + 2}{15} - \dfrac{x - 3}{5} = \dfrac{2}{3}$

**19.** $\dfrac{5y}{3} = \dfrac{y}{6}$

**20.** $\dfrac{3y - 9}{6} = \dfrac{2y - 6}{4}$

**21.** $\dfrac{n + 3}{3} - \dfrac{n}{4} = \dfrac{n - 2}{5}$

**B** **22.** $\dfrac{2}{3}(x - 1) - \dfrac{1}{5}(x - 2) = \dfrac{x + 2}{3}$

**23.** $\dfrac{1}{4}(y - 1) - \dfrac{1}{6}(y - 3) = \dfrac{2}{3}$

**24.** $\dfrac{x + 2}{4} - \dfrac{x + 3}{3} + \dfrac{2x - 3}{6} = 0$

**25.** $\dfrac{2}{3}(x - 1) - \dfrac{1}{5}(2x - 3) = 1$

**26.** $\dfrac{6b - 4}{3} - 2 = \dfrac{18 - 4b}{3} + b$

**27.** $2 - \dfrac{7c - 1}{6} = 3c - \dfrac{19c + 3}{4}$

**28.** $\dfrac{3}{4}(x + 4) - \dfrac{2}{5}(x + 5) = x + 1$

**29.** $\dfrac{1}{3}(x + 6) - 1 = \dfrac{1}{6}(9 - x)$

**C** **30.** $\dfrac{1}{4}\left(y - \dfrac{1}{3}\right) - \dfrac{1}{6}(y - 3) = \dfrac{2}{3}$

**31.** $\dfrac{1}{2}\left(x + \dfrac{2}{3}\right) - \dfrac{1}{6}\left(7x - \dfrac{1}{3}\right) = \dfrac{1}{6}$

**32.** $\dfrac{1}{5}(2x - 3) - \dfrac{2}{3}\left(x - \dfrac{1}{2}\right) = \dfrac{7}{15}$

**33.** $\dfrac{3}{4}(x - 2) - \dfrac{2}{3}\left(x - \dfrac{1}{2}\right) = \dfrac{x + 1}{2}$

**Solve for $x$ in terms of the other variable.**

**34.** $\dfrac{x + 3a}{10} - \dfrac{x - a}{2} = \dfrac{x}{5}$

**35.** $\dfrac{x - n}{5} - \dfrac{7x - n}{10} = \dfrac{2n - x}{15}$

**36.** $\dfrac{1}{5}(2x - 3c) - \dfrac{1}{3}\left(x - \dfrac{c}{2}\right) - \dfrac{x}{6} = 0$

**37.** $\dfrac{a^2 + 6a + 9}{x} = a^2 + 3a$

# Problems

**A** **1.** One third of a number is 10 more than one eighth of the number. Find the number.

**2.** One fourth of a number is 4 less than one third of the number. Find the number.

**3.** Two numbers are in the ratio $5:2$. One half of their sum is $10\frac{1}{2}$. Find the numbers.

4. Three numbers are in the ratio $2:3:4$. One fourth of their sum is 5 more than the smallest number. Find the numbers.

5. Jack is 3 years older than Jill. Three years ago Jill's age was four fifths of Jack's age. How old is each now?

6. Tom is two years older than Jerry. Next year Tom will be one and a half times as old as Jerry. How old is each now?

7. A rectangle is 9 cm longer than it is wide. The width is one seventh of the perimeter. Find the length and width.

8. The lengths of the sides of a triangle are consecutive integers. Half of the perimeter is 14 more than the length of the longest side. Find the perimeter.

**B** 9. Erica hiked up a mountain trail at 3 km/h and returned at 4 km/h. The entire trip took 5 h 10 min, including the half hour she spent at the top. How long was the trail?

10. Consuela walks from her house to the recreation center at 6 km/h, stays for 45 min, and then gets a ride back home at 48 km/h. If she arrives home 1.5 h after she started out, find the distance from her home to the recreation center.

11. Three fourths of a pile of coins are quarters and the rest are dimes. If the total value is $6.80, how many of each type of coin are there?

12. Two thirds of a pile of coins are nickels, one fourth are dimes, and the rest are quarters. If the total value is $4.75, how many of each type of coin are there?

13. Liann bought several apples at the rate of 3 apples for 35 cents. She sold nine tenths of them at 25 cents each, making a profit of $6.50. How many apples did Liann fail to sell?

**C** 14. Diophantus was a famous Greek mathematician, who lived and worked in Alexandria, Egypt, probably in the third century A.D. After he died, someone described his life in this puzzle:

He was a boy for $\frac{1}{6}$ of his life.

After $\frac{1}{12}$ more, he acquired a beard.

After another $\frac{1}{7}$, he married.

In the fifth year after his marriage
his son was born.
The son lived half as many years as
his father.
Diophantus died 4 years after his son.

How old was Diophantus when he died?

# 7-4 Fractional Equations

**Objective**   To solve fractional equations.

An equation that has a variable in the denominator of one or more terms is called a **fractional equation.** You can use the multiplication property of equality to solve fractional equations.

**Example**   Solve: $1 + \dfrac{2}{b-1} = \dfrac{2}{b^2 - b}$

**Solution**   1. Factor all the denominators to determine the LCD.

$$1 + \frac{2}{b-1} = \frac{2}{b(b-1)}$$

The LCD is $b(b-1)$; note that $b \neq 0$ or 1.

2. Multiply both sides of the equation by the LCD.

$$b(b-1)\left[1 + \frac{2}{b-1}\right] = b(b-1)\left[\frac{2}{b(b-1)}\right]$$
$$b(b-1) + 2b = 2$$
$$b^2 - b + 2b = 2$$
$$b^2 + b - 2 = 0$$
$$(b-1)(b+2) = 0$$
$$b = 1 \quad \text{or} \quad b = -2$$

3. Recall that 1 is not permissible as a solution to the original equation. Check $-2$ in the original equation.

$$1 + \frac{2}{-2-1} \stackrel{?}{=} \frac{2}{(-2)^2 - (-2)}$$
$$1 + \left(-\frac{2}{3}\right) \stackrel{?}{=} \frac{2}{6}$$
$$\frac{1}{3} = \frac{1}{3} \quad \checkmark$$

∴ the solution is $-2$.   *Answer*

In the preceding example you saw that 1 was not a solution of the original equation even though it satisfied the transformed equation. Notice that multiplying the equation by $b(b-1)$ led to an equation that was *not equivalent* to the given one. This new equation had the extra root 1, a number for which the multiplier $b(b-1)$ represents *zero*.

In general, multiplying both sides of an equation by a variable expression that can represent zero may produce an equation that is not equivalent to the original equation. Therefore, *you must check each root of the resulting equation to see that it satisfies the original equation.*

**State the least common denominator of the fractions in each equation. Then state the equation that results when both sides are multiplied by the LCD.**

1. $\dfrac{1}{4} + \dfrac{2}{x} = \dfrac{3}{4}$

2. $\dfrac{3}{x} + \dfrac{1}{2} = 1$

3. $\dfrac{3}{y} - \dfrac{1}{4} = \dfrac{1}{12}$

4. $\dfrac{1}{a} + \dfrac{3}{2a} = \dfrac{1}{6}$

5. $\dfrac{n}{n-2} = \dfrac{6}{5}$

6. $\dfrac{1+b}{1-b} = \dfrac{4}{3}$

## Written Exercises

**A** **1–6.** Solve the equations in Oral Exercises 1–6.

**Solve and check. If the equation has no solution, write "no solution."**

7. $\dfrac{3}{4n} + \dfrac{1}{n} = \dfrac{7}{8}$

8. $\dfrac{2}{3n} + \dfrac{4}{n} = \dfrac{7}{9}$

9. $\dfrac{6-x}{4-x} = \dfrac{3}{5}$

10. $\dfrac{9}{4+3x} = \dfrac{5}{3-3x}$

11. $\dfrac{2x-5}{8x-5} = \dfrac{1}{4}$

12. $\dfrac{n-3}{6n-18} = \dfrac{1}{6}$

13. $\dfrac{x-4}{x-2} = 2$

14. $\dfrac{2x-4}{x-2} = 2$

15. $\dfrac{2x-4}{x-2} = 3$

16. $\dfrac{y-6}{y-2} = 3$

17. $\dfrac{3y-6}{y-2} = 3$

18. $\dfrac{3y-6}{y-2} = 2$

19. $\dfrac{1+y}{3y} = \dfrac{1}{y}$

20. $\dfrac{a-5}{2} = \dfrac{3}{a}$

21. $\dfrac{1}{x} - \dfrac{2x}{x+1} = 0$

22. $\dfrac{3}{2a+1} - \dfrac{3}{2a-1} = 0$

23. $\dfrac{3}{2n+1} - \dfrac{6}{4n+2} = 0$

24. $\dfrac{3}{2x-1} = \dfrac{7}{4x-2}$

**B** 25. $\dfrac{3x+5}{6} - \dfrac{10}{x} = \dfrac{x}{2}$

26. $\dfrac{4}{x+1} - \dfrac{1}{x} = 1$

27. $\dfrac{5}{1+y} - \dfrac{3}{1-y} = 2$

28. $\dfrac{2}{a+1} - \dfrac{1}{1-a} = 1$

29. $\dfrac{1}{y-3} = \dfrac{6}{y^2-9}$

30. $\dfrac{4}{a^2-4a} + \dfrac{1}{4-a} = 0$

31. $\dfrac{n+1}{3n-1} + \dfrac{n}{n-1} = \dfrac{4}{3}$

32. $\dfrac{y+2}{y-3} - \dfrac{y-3}{y+2} = \dfrac{5}{6}$

33. $\dfrac{n-2}{n} - \dfrac{n-3}{n-6} = \dfrac{1}{n}$

34. $\dfrac{5}{y-5} - \dfrac{3}{y+5} = \dfrac{2}{y}$

35. $\dfrac{1}{2x-1} - \dfrac{3}{4x^2-1} = 0$

36. $\dfrac{1}{y^2-y} + \dfrac{1}{1-y} = \dfrac{1}{2}$

37. $\dfrac{1}{x-4} + \dfrac{2}{x^2-16} = \dfrac{3}{x+4}$

38. $\dfrac{3a}{a-1} - \dfrac{4}{a+1} = \dfrac{4}{a^2-1}$

39. $\dfrac{8}{b-1} + \dfrac{30}{1-b^2} = \dfrac{6}{b+1}$

40. $\dfrac{1}{y} - \dfrac{2}{1-y} = \dfrac{8}{y^2-y}$

**C**  **41.** $\dfrac{x-2}{x^2-x-6} = \dfrac{1}{x^2-4} + \dfrac{3}{2x+4}$

**42.** $\dfrac{x}{x+1} - \dfrac{x+1}{x-4} = \dfrac{5}{x^2-3x-4}$

**43.** $\dfrac{n-4}{2n^2+5n-3} + \dfrac{2n+7}{8n^2-2n-1} = \dfrac{4n-1}{4n^2+13n+3}$

**44.** $\dfrac{2x^2}{1-x^2} = \dfrac{x}{x-1} - \dfrac{x}{x+1} - 3$

## Problems

**A**  **1.** The sum of a number and its reciprocal is $\frac{13}{6}$. Find the number.

**2.** The sum of the reciprocals of two consecutive even integers is $\frac{11}{60}$. Find the integers.

**3.** The numerator of a fraction is 1 more than the denominator. If the numerator and the denominator are both increased by 2, the new fraction will be $\frac{1}{4}$ less than the original fraction. Find the original fraction.

**4.** The denominator of a fraction is 4 more than the numerator. The sum of the fraction and its reciprocal is $\frac{5}{2}$. Find the fraction.

**5.** The sum of two numbers is 40. If twice the larger number is divided by the smaller, the quotient is 3 and the remainder is 10. Find the numbers.

**6.** Two numbers differ by 20. If the larger number is divided by the smaller, the quotient is 2 and the remainder is 5. Find the numbers.

**B**  **7.** Dale hikes 15 km up a mountain trail. Her return trip along the same trail takes 30 min less because she is able to increase her speed by 1 km/h. How long does it take her to climb up and down the mountain?

| | Rate | $\times$ Time | = Distance |
|---|---|---|---|
| Up | $x$ | $\dfrac{15}{x}$ | 15 |
| Down | ? | ? | ? |

**8.** If I increase my usual driving speed by 10 km/h, I can drive the 255 km trip to Nashville in 24 min less than usual. How fast do I usually drive?

**9.** The cost of a bus excursion was $180. This amount was to have been shared equally by all those who said they wished to go. However, 6 people failed to show up so that those who did go each had to pay $1.50 more. How many people actually went on the trip?

| | Number | $\times$ Price | = Cost |
|---|---|---|---|
| Original plan | $x$ | $\dfrac{180}{x}$ | 180 |
| Later plan | ? | ? | ? |

**10.** The $75 cost for a party was to be shared equally by all those attending. Since 5 more people attended than was expected, the price per person dropped by 50 cents. How many people attended the party?

**11.** Fifteen minutes after Cindy and Dave leave the dock to canoe downstream, Tammy leaves by motor boat with the supplies. Since the motor boat goes twice as fast as the canoe, it catches up with the canoe 3 km from the dock. How fast does the motor boat go?

**12.** A plumber made $600 for working on a certain job. His apprentice who makes $3 per hour less, also made $600, but he worked 10 hours more than the plumber. How much does the plumber make per hour?

---

## Computer Exercises

*For students with some programming experience*

Write a BASIC program to find the least common denominator for a pair of integers that are entered through INPUT statements. Use the program to find the LCD for each of the following pairs of denominators.

**1.** 12 and 15      **2.** 31 and 17      **3.** 5 and 50      **4.** 252 and 98

---

# Self-Test 2

**Vocabulary**    fractional equation (p. 291)

**Solve.**

**1.** $\dfrac{5n}{48} - \dfrac{2n}{9} = \dfrac{17}{18}$

**2.** $x + \dfrac{x-2}{8} = 20$

**3.** $\dfrac{5a+2}{3} = \dfrac{a-1}{2}$

**4.** $\dfrac{n+6}{6} - \dfrac{n}{9} = \dfrac{2}{3}$

**Obj. 7-3, p. 288**

**Solve and check. If the equation has no solution, write "no solution."**

**5.** $\dfrac{3x-1}{x+1} = 4$

**6.** $\dfrac{2}{x-3} - \dfrac{1}{2x-6} = 0$

**Obj. 7-4, p. 291**

**7.** Find two consecutive integers such that the sum of their reciprocals is $\dfrac{5}{6}$.

Check your answers with those at the back of the book.

# Percent Problems

## 7-5 Percents

**Objective**  To work with percents.

The ratio of one number to another can be expressed as a percent. The word **percent** (usually denoted %) means "hundredths" or "divided by 100." For example,

$$\frac{29}{100} \text{ is called "29 percent" and written 29\%.}$$

**Example 1**  Express each number as a percent.

a. $\frac{3}{5}$    b. $\frac{1}{3}$    c. 4.7

**Solution**

a.  $\dfrac{x}{100} = \dfrac{3}{5}$

   $5x = 300$

   $x = 60$

   $\therefore \dfrac{3}{5} = 60\%$

b.  $\dfrac{x}{100} = \dfrac{1}{3}$

   $3x = 100$

   $x = 33\dfrac{1}{3}$

   $\therefore \dfrac{1}{3} = 33\dfrac{1}{3}\%$

c.  $\dfrac{x}{100} = 4.7$

   $x = 470$

   $\therefore 4.7 = 470\%$

In problems involving percent, the word "of" indicates multiplication and the word "is" indicates equality. The next three examples illustrate these ideas.

**Example 2**  15% of 180 is what number?

**Solution**  $\dfrac{15}{100} \cdot 180 = x$

   $27 = x$

   $\therefore$ 15% of 180 is 27.  *Answer*

When finding a percent of a number, it is often convenient to express the percent as a decimal and then multiply. Example 2 can be worked as follows:

$$15\% = 0.15 \qquad 15\% \text{ of } 180 = 0.15 \times 180 = 27$$

**Example 3** 23 is 25% of what number?

**Solution**

$$23 = \frac{25}{100} \cdot x$$

$$2300 = 25x$$
$$92 = x$$
$\therefore$ 23 is 25% of 92.  **Answer**

**Example 4** What percent of 64 is 48?

**Solution**

$$\frac{x}{100} \cdot 64 = 48$$

$$64x = 4800$$
$$x = 75$$
$\therefore$ 75% of 64 is 48.  **Answer**

When solving an equation containing coefficients expressed as decimals, it is helpful to multiply both sides of the equation by a power of 10 to obtain an equivalent equation with integral coefficients.

**Example 5** Solve: $1.2x = 36 + 0.4x$

**Solution** $\quad 10(1.2x) = 10(36 + 0.4x)$ $\quad \left\{ \begin{array}{l} \text{Multiply both sides by 10 to} \\ \text{eliminate decimals.} \end{array} \right.$
$$12x = 360 + 4x$$
$$8x = 360$$
$$x = 45 \quad \textbf{Answer}$$

**Example 6** Solve: $94 = 0.15x + 0.08(1000 - x)$

**Solution** $\quad 100 \cdot [94] = 100[0.15x + 0.08(1000 - x)]$ $\quad \left\{ \begin{array}{l} \text{Multiply both sides by 100 to} \\ \text{eliminate decimals.} \end{array} \right.$
$$9400 = 15x + 8(1000 - x)$$
$$9400 = 15x + 8000 - 8x$$
$$1400 = 7x$$
$$200 = x \quad \textbf{Answer}$$

## Oral Exercises

**Express as a percent.**

1. 0.83

2. 0.07

3. 1.50

4. 0.085

5. 0.003

6. $\frac{1}{2}$

7. $\frac{3}{4}$

8. $\frac{2}{5}$

9. $1\frac{1}{4}$

10. $\frac{9}{50}$

**Express as a fraction in simplest form.**

**11.** 10%　　　　**12.** 30%　　　　**13.** 6%　　　　**14.** $\frac{1}{2}$%　　　　**15.** $37\frac{1}{2}$%

**Express as a mixed number and then as a fraction.**

**16.** 150%　　　　**17.** 250%　　　　**18.** 175%　　　　**19.** 325%　　　　**20.** 360%

**Express as a decimal.**

**21.** 35%　　　　**22.** 4%　　　　**23.** 115%　　　　**24.** 0.4%　　　　**25.** $9\frac{1}{2}$%

**Tell whether you would multiply by 10, 100, or 1000 to eliminate the decimals in each equation. Then give the equation that would result if you did the multiplication.**

**26.** $0.3x = 1.2 + 2.3x$　　　**27.** $0.08x = 1.5(8 - x)$　　　**28.** $4.5x - 0.02 = 0.075(100 - x)$

**29.** $15.2(1000 - x) = 2.8$　　　**30.** $0.1x - 0.01x = .001$　　　**31.** $0.125x = 7$

## Written Exercises

**Express as a fraction in simplest form.**

A　**1.** 25%　　　　**2.** 40%　　　　**3.** $33\frac{1}{3}$%　　　　**4.** 75%

　　**5.** 60%　　　　**6.** $66\frac{2}{3}$%　　　　**7.** $12\frac{1}{2}$%　　　　**8.** 80%

　　**9.** 4%　　　　**10.** $2\frac{1}{2}$%　　　　**11.** 125%　　　　**12.** 240%

**Evaluate.**

**13.** 32% of 300　　　**14.** 6% of 145　　　**15.** $9\frac{1}{2}$% of 2000　　　**16.** $8\frac{1}{4}$% of 4000

**17.** $\frac{1}{2}$% of 12　　　**18.** 9.2% of 180　　　**19.** 17.8% of 500　　　**20.** 35% of 84

**21.** 28% of 483 + 72% of 483　　　**22.** $7\frac{1}{2}$% of 15,500 + $12\frac{1}{2}$% of 15,500

**23.** $33\frac{1}{3}$% of 6200 + $33\frac{1}{3}$% of 2800　　　**24.** $66\frac{2}{3}$% of 7650 − $66\frac{2}{3}$% of 1650

**25.** 8 is 20% of what number?　　　**26.** 15 is 25% of what number?

**27.** 27 is 15% of what number?　　　**28.** 78 is 15% of what number?

**29.** 4.2 is 75% of what number?　　　**30.** 32.4 is 45% of what number?

**31.** What percent of 75 is 60?　　　**32.** What percent of 48 is 12?

**33.** What percent of 150 is 3?　　　**34.** What percent of 36 is 45?

**35.** What percent of 63 is 21?　　　**36.** What percent of 800 is 120?

**Complete the tables.**

|      | Original Price | % Discount | Price Decrease | New Price |
|------|----------------|------------|----------------|-----------|
| **37.** | $ 12 | 25% | ? | ? |
| **38.** | $ 18 | 20% | ? | ? |
| **39.** | $160 | 15% | ? | ? |
| **40.** | $120 | $33\frac{1}{3}\%$ | ? | ? |

|      | Original Price | % Markup | Price Increase | New Price |
|------|----------------|----------|----------------|-----------|
| **41.** | $ 44 | 25% | ? | ? |
| **42.** | $ 85 | 20% | ? | ? |
| **43.** | $180 | $66\frac{2}{3}\%$ | ? | ? |
| **44.** | $ 15 | 40% | ? | ? |

**Solve.**

**B**  **45.** $1.8x = 36$   **46.** $0.06x = 120$   **47.** $0.4n = 7.2 - 0.5n$

**48.** $0.4n = 1.2(8 - n)$   **49.** $0.75y + 1.3y = 41$   **50.** $0.05a + 0.5a = 4.4$

**51.** $0.025x + 0.05 = 0.3$   **52.** $0.06y - 0.035y = 9$   **53.** $90 - x = 0.04(180 - x)$

**54.** $0.4x + 0.24(x - 5) = 0.08$   **55.** $0.025y - 0.05(20 - 2y) = 0.2$

**56.** $0.08x + 0.09(6000 - x) = 530$   **57.** $0.06(1000 - x) + 0.05x = 700$

**58.** $0.1x - 0.01(10 - x) + 0.01(100 - x) = 19$   **59.** $\dfrac{0.3x - 1}{5} = 0.12x + 3.2$

**Complete the table below in which interest rates are given as decimals.**

|      | Principal | × Annual interest rate | = One year's interest |
|------|-----------|------------------------|-----------------------|
| **60.** | $ 5000 | 0.085 | ? |
| **61.** | $12,000 | 0.1025 | ? |
| **62.** | $ 1000 | ? | $105 |
| **63.** | $ 2500 | ? | $275 |
| **64.** | ? | 0.15 | $135 |
| **65.** | ? | 0.09 | $180 |

# Problems

**A** 1. The Chess Club has a goal of 25 new members. So far, they have 15. What percent of the club's goal have they achieved?

2. Laura makes an 8% commission on each of her sales. How much does she make when she sells a $180 camera?

3. The fund drive has raised $18,700. That is 22% of its goal. What is its goal?

4. Because an item is slightly damaged a storekeeper reduces the price by $6. This represents a 30% reduction. What was the original price?

5. Roger Carlson makes a 2% commission on each of his sales. When he sold a new car, he made $190. How much did the car cost?

6. A weed killer is to be diluted with water so that the weed killer is just 1% of the solution. How much water should be mixed with 5 cm³ of weed killer?

7. Where Sondra lives, there is a 3% state sales tax, a $1\frac{1}{2}$% county sales tax, and a 1% municipal sales tax. How much tax would Sondra pay if she bought a $340 bicycle?

8. Molly Pritchard invests $4000 in bonds paying $11\frac{1}{2}$% simple interest and $5000 in bank accounts paying 9.1% simple interest. Which investment yields more interest in one year? How much more?

**B** 9. A $52 sweater is marked down 25%. What is the new price?

10. A sporting goods dealer estimates that an $85 tennis racket will cost 6% more next year. What will be the new price?

11. A $160 pair of skis is on sale at a 25% discount. If there is a 5% sales tax, how much will the skis cost?

12. A dealer buys a new car for $8400. How much do you have to pay for the car if the dealer makes a 20% profit and there is a 5% sales tax?

13. In a nation of 221 million people, the urban population is 2.25 times the rural population. Find the rural and urban populations.

14. Sam Goddard is 112 lb heavier than his daughter. He also figures that he is 2.4 times as heavy as she is. How much does each person weigh?

15. For lunch Roberto had a sandwich and two glasses of milk for a total of 660 calories. The sandwich had 2.4 times as many calories as a glass of milk. How many calories were in the sandwich?

# 7-6 Percent Problems

**Objective:** To solve problems involving percents.

Whenever a price increases or decreases, the percent change is based on the original price and is given by the following formula.

$$\frac{\text{percent change}}{100} = \frac{\text{change in price}}{\text{original price}}$$

**Example 1** The annual membership fee in the Film Club increased from \$25 to \$27. What was the percent increase?

**Solution**

*Step 1* The problem asks for the percent increase.

*Step 2* Let $x$ = the percent increase.

*Step 3* $\dfrac{\text{percent change}}{100} = \dfrac{\text{change in price}}{\text{original price}}$

$$\frac{x}{100} = \frac{27 - 25}{25}$$

*Step 4* $\qquad \dfrac{x}{100} = \dfrac{2}{25}$

$$25x = 200$$
$$x = 8$$

*Step 5* The check is left to you.

$\therefore$ there was an 8% increase. **Answer**

**Example 2**

Ricardo pays \$76.50 for ice skates that are on sale at a 15% discount. What was the original price of the skates?

**Solution**

*Step 1* The problem asks for the original price.

*Step 2* Let $x$ = the original price.

*Step 3* $\dfrac{\text{percent change}}{100} = \dfrac{\text{change in price}}{\text{original price}}$

$$\frac{15}{100} = \frac{x - 76.50}{x}$$

*Step 4*   $15x = 100x - 7650$
$$7650 = 85x$$
$$90 = x$$

*Step 5* The check is left to you.

∴ the original price was $90.   ***Answer***

In the last example, the 15% discount was written as the fraction $\frac{15}{100}$, but it also could have been written as the decimal 0.15. In the next example the percents are expressed as decimals. Example 3 uses the following formula.

Principal × Annual Interest Rate = Annual Simple Interest

***Example 3*** Selma Peterson invests part of her $6000 in bank accounts that pay 7% annual simple interest and the rest in bonds that pay 13% annual simple interest. Her total annual income from these investments is $540. How much money is invested in bank accounts and how much money in bonds?

**Solution**

*Step 1* The problem asks for the amounts invested in bank accounts and in bonds.

*Step 2* Let $x$ = amount invested in bank accounts. Then $6000 - x$ = amount invested in bonds.

|  | Principal × Rate = Interest | | |
|---|---|---|---|
| Bank Accounts | $x$ | 0.07 | $0.07x$ |
| Bonds | $6000 - x$ | 0.13 | $0.13(6000 - x)$ |

*Step 3* Since the total interest is $540, we have:
$$0.07x + 0.13(6000 - x) = 540$$

*Step 4* $100[0.07x + 0.13(6000 - x)] = 100(540)$ {Multiply both sides by 100 to eliminate decimals.

$$7x + 13(6000 - x) = 54{,}000$$
$$7x + 78{,}000 - 13x = 54{,}000$$
$$-6x = -24{,}000$$
$$x = 4000$$
$$6000 - x = 2000$$

*Step 5* The check is left to you.

∴ she invested $4000 in bank accounts and $2000 in bonds.   ***Answer***

# Oral Exercises

**Complete each table.**

| | Item | Original price | New price | Price increase | Percent increase |
|---|---|---|---|---|---|
| **1.** | Jeans | $25.00 | $30.00 | ? | ? |
| **2.** | School lunch | $ 1.60 | $ 2.00 | ? | ? |
| **3.** | Shirt | $14.00 | $15.40 | ? | ? |
| **4.** | Sandwich | $ 2.00 | $ 2.10 | ? | ? |

| | Item | Original price | Sale price | Price decrease | Percent decrease |
|---|---|---|---|---|---|
| **5.** | Sweater | $ 60 | $ 45 | ? | ? |
| **6.** | Fly rod | $ 20 | $ 15 | ? | ? |
| **7.** | Hiking boots | $120 | $108 | ? | ? |
| **8.** | Bike | $300 | $210 | ? | ? |

**State the equation you would use to find x.**

| | Original price | New price | Percent change |
|---|---|---|---|
| **9.** | $x$ | $88 | 10% price increase |
| **10.** | $x$ | $75 | 25% price increase |
| **11.** | $x$ | $36 | 10% price decrease |
| **12.** | $x$ | $72 | 20% price decrease |

# Written Exercises

**Complete each table.**

| | | Item | Original price | New price | Percent increase |
|---|---|---|---|---|---|
| **A** | **1.** | Sneakers | $ 30.00 | $ 33.00 | ? |
| | **2.** | Record album | $ 12.00 | $ 15.00 | ? |
| | **3.** | Hat | $ 8.00 | $ 8.40 | ? |
| | **4.** | Shoes | $ 36.00 | $ 37.80 | ? |

|     | Item | Original price | New price | Percent increase |
|-----|------|----------------|-----------|------------------|
| 5.  | Paint | $ 20.00 | $ 22.50 | ? |
| 6.  | Skis | $220.00 | $253.00 | ? |
| 7.  | Movie ticket | $ 3.50 | $ ? | 4% |
| 8.  | Tank of gas | $ 23.20 | $ ? | 5% |
| 9.  | Hammer | $ ? | $ 8.00 | 25% |
| 10. | Saw | $ ? | $ 22.00 | 10% |
| 11. | Airplane ticket | $ ? | $ 51.00 | 2% |
| 12. | Paperback book | $ ? | $ 3.36 | 12% |

|     | Item | Original price | Sale price | Percent decrease |
|-----|------|----------------|------------|------------------|
| 13. | Shirt | $ 25.00 | $ 20.00 | ? |
| 14. | Pants | $ 36.00 | $ 27.00 | ? |
| 15. | Belt | $ 8.00 | $ 6.80 | ? |
| 16. | Camera | $240.00 | $168.00 | ? |
| 17. | Soccer ball | $ 32.00 | $ ? | 20% |
| 18. | Spaghetti sauce | $ 2.20 | $ ? | 15% |
| 19. | Souvenir | $ ? | $ 6.30 | 10% |
| 20. | Shovel | $ ? | $ 15.00 | 20% |
| 21. | Skates | $ ? | $ 59.50 | 15% |
| 22. | Math book | $ ? | $ 13.30 | 5% |

## Problems

A  1. The population of Houston increased from 1.2 million in 1970 to 1.6 million in 1980. What was the percent increase?

2. Elaine Poro bought 100 shares of stock at $25 per share and sold them at $31 per share. What was her percent profit?

3. Michael Quigley's home was reassessed at a value of $162,000. It had previously been assessed at $150,000. What was the percent increase in the assessment?

4. While traveling during her last vacation, Luann noted that a $3.25 breakfast actually cost $3.38 because of the sales tax. What is the sales tax rate?

5. A $60 sweater is on sale for $48. What is the percent of discount?

6. The number of paid subscribers to *The Groundhog Quarterly* has declined from 3240 people to 2430 people. What is the percent of decrease?

7. Yvonne Gregory paid $11,448 for a new automobile. This amount included the 6% sales tax. What was the price of the automobile without the tax?

8. The selling price of a house includes the 6% real-estate commission. If the Lings' house was sold for $159,000, how much did the Lings receive and how much did the real estate broker receive?

9. At the Runner's Shop anniversary sale, running shoes were on sale at a 15% discount. If Hector Gonzalez paid $35.70 for a pair of running shoes, what was the original price?

10. The population in Dogwood is now 115 people. This represents an 8% decline from last year. What was the population last year?

11. Sondra Warren invests $6000. Some of the money is invested in stocks paying 6% a year and some in bonds paying 11% a year. She receives a total of $580 each year from these investments. How much money is invested in stocks and how much money in bonds?

12. Bob Cornell invested $8000 in bank certificates and bonds. The certificates pay 7% interest and the bonds pay 10% interest. His interest income is $725 each year. How much money was invested in bank certificates?

B 13. The Dalton Arts Fund must raise $2500 next year by investing $30,000 in federal notes paying 9% and in municipal bonds paying 8%. The treasurer wants to invest as much as possible in the bonds, even though they pay less, because the bonds are for projects in the Dalton area. How much should the treasurer invest in bonds?

14. Eric Steel invested in company stock paying a $10\frac{1}{2}\%$ dividend. Marie Steel invested $4000 more than Eric in tax-free bonds paying $7\frac{1}{2}\%$ annual simple interest. If Marie's income from the investment is $75 more than Eric's, find how much money each invested.

15. Beatrice Roberts invested $2000 more in stocks than in bonds. The bonds paid 7.2% interest and stocks paid 6%, yet the income from each was the same. How much annual interest did she receive?

16. Half of Bill Lee's money is invested at 12% interest, one third at 11%, and the rest at 9%. If the total annual income is $1340, how much money has Bill invested?

## Computer Exercises

1. Suppose that you deposit $100 in a bank account that pays 6% interest per year. At the end of one year, you will have $(100 + 100 \cdot \frac{6}{100}) = \$106$. At the end of the second year, you will have $(106 + 106 \cdot \frac{6}{100})$ dollars. Write a BASIC program that will display in chart form how much money you will have at the end of 1, 2, 3, 4, . . . , 10 years.

2. Write a BASIC program that will store a set of DATA entered with INPUT statements in an array. The program should then calculate and print out the percent of increase or decrease between each consecutive pair of data. If the percent of increase (or decrease) is the same for each consecutive pair, we say that the data are growing (or decaying) exponentially. RUN the program for the following sets of data.

   **a.**

   | No. of yr after 1984 | Population of Muddville |
   | --- | --- |
   | 1 | 207 |
   | 2 | 200 |
   | 3 | 193 |
   | 4 | 186 |
   | 5 | 179 |

   **b.**

   | No. of hr observing a bacteria colony | No. bacteria present |
   | --- | --- |
   | 1 | 500 |
   | 2 | 705 |
   | 3 | 1000 |
   | 4 | 1410 |
   | 5 | 1988 |

# Self-Test 3

*Vocabulary*    percent (p. 295)

**Express as a fraction in simplest form.**

1. 56%    2. $87\frac{1}{2}\%$    3. 105%                              Obj. 7-5, p. 295

4. Find 16% of 85.          5. 3.75 is 60% of what number?

6. What percent of 90 is 225?    7. What percent of 300 is 75?

8. Last year an accountant earned $18,000. This year she received a 12% raise. How much was the raise?

9. A suit that sold for $162 is now on sale for $108. What is the percent of discount?          Obj. 7-6, p. 300

Check your answers with those at the back of the book.

# Mixture and Work Problems

## 7-7 Mixture Problems

**Objective**   To solve mixture problems.

A merchant often mixes goods of two or more kinds in order to sell a blend at a given price. Similarly, a chemist often mixes solutions of different strengths of a chemical to obtain a solution of desired strength. Charts can be helpful in solving mixture problems.

**Example 1**   A convenience store owner wishes to mix together raisins and roasted peanuts to produce a high energy snack for hikers. The raisins sell for $3.50 per kilogram and the nuts sell for $4.75 per kilogram. How many kilograms of each should be mixed together to obtain 20 kg of this snack worth $4.00 per kilogram?

**Solution**

*Step 1*   The problem asks for the number of kilograms of raisins and the number of kilograms of nuts.

*Step 2*   Let $x$ = number of kilograms of raisins.
Then $20 - x$ = number of kilograms of nuts.

|  | Number $\times$ Price $=$ Cost | | |
|---|---|---|---|
| Raisins | $x$ | 3.50 | $3.5x$ |
| Nuts | $20 - x$ | 4.75 | $4.75(20 - x)$ |
| Mixture | 20 | 4.00 | 80 |

*Step 3*   Cost of raisins + cost of nuts = cost of mixture
$$3.5x + 4.75(20 - x) = 80$$

*Step 4*   Multiply both sides of the equation by 100.
$$350x + 475(20 - x) = 8000$$
$$350x + 9500 - 475x = 8000$$
$$-125x = -1500$$
$$x = 12$$
$$20 - x = 8$$

*Step 5*   The check is left to you.

$\therefore$ 12 kg of raisins and 8 kg of nuts are needed.   **Answer**

***Example 2*** An auto mechanic has 300 g of battery acid solution that is 60% acid. He must add water to this solution in order to dilute it so that it is only 45% acid. How much water should be added?

***Solution***

*Step 1* The problem asks for the number of grams of water to be added.

*Step 2* Let $x$ = number of grams of water to be added.

| | Total amount $\times$ % acid $=$ Amount of acid | | |
|---|---|---|---|
| Original solution | 300 | 60% | 0.60(300) |
| Added water | $x$ | 0% | 0 |
| New solution | $300 + x$ | 45% | $0.45(300 + x)$ |

*Step 3* Original amount of acid + added acid = new amount of acid

$$0.60(300) + \quad 0 \quad = 0.45(300 + x)$$

*Step 4* $60(300) = 45(300 + x)$ {Multiply both sides of the equation by 100.

$18{,}000 = 13{,}500 + 45x$

$4500 = 45x$

$100 = x$

*Step 5* The check is left to you.

$\therefore$ 100 g of water should be added. ***Answer***

Although Examples 1 and 2 may at first glance appear to be quite different, they are very much alike. You can see the similarities in the charts and in Step 3 of each solution. In fact, mixture problems are very much like investment problems, coin problems, and certain distance problems. The Oral Exercises will help to point out these similarities.

## Oral Exercises

**Read each problem and complete each chart. Use the chart to give an equation, but do not solve the equation.**

1. The owner of the Fancy Food Shoppe wishes to mix cashews selling at $8.00 per kilogram and pecans selling at $7.00 per kilogram. How much of each kind of nut should be mixed to get 8 kg worth $7.25 per kilogram?

| | Number of kilograms $\times$ Price per kilogram $=$ Total cost | | |
|---|---|---|---|
| Cashews | $x$ | ? | ? |
| Pecans | ? | ? | ? |
| Mixture | ? | ? | ? |

**2.** A chemist has 40 g of a solution that is 50% acid. How much water should she add to make a solution that is 10% acid?

| | Total amount | × % acid = | Amount of acid |
|---|---|---|---|
| Original solution | ? | ? | ? |
| Added water | $x$ | ? | ? |
| New solution | ? | ? | ? |

**3.** A chemist has 800 g of a solution that is 15% salt. How much salt should be added to make a solution that is 20% salt?

| | Total amount × % salt = Amount of salt | | |
|---|---|---|---|
| Original solution | ? | ? | ? |
| Added salt | $x$ | ? | ? |
| Mixture | ? | ? | ? |

**4.** A chemist mixes together 20 L of a solution that is 60% acid and 30 L of a solution that is 20% acid. What is the acid percentage of the mixture?

| | Total amount | × % acid = | Amount of acid |
|---|---|---|---|
| Solution $A$ | 20 | 60% | ? |
| Solution $B$ | ? | ? | ? |
| Mixture | ? | $x$% | ? |

**5.** A grocer mixes together four pounds of peanuts costing $2 per pound with two pounds of walnuts costing $5 per pound. What should the price per pound of this mixture be?

| | Number of pounds | × | Cost per pound = | Total cost |
|---|---|---|---|---|
| Peanuts | 4 | | 2 | ? |
| Walnuts | ? | | ? | ? |
| Mixture | ? | | $x$ | ? |

**6.** Sam Daniels drives for 2 h at 85 km/h and then for one more hour at 70 km/h. What is his average speed?

| | Time × Rate = Distance | | |
|---|---|---|---|
| 1st part of trip | 2 | ? | ? |
| 2nd part of trip | ? | ? | ? |
| Whole trip | ? | $x$ | ? |

**7.** Sally Chou has $100 earning 10% interest and $300 earning 14% interest. What is her average rate of return?

|  | Principal × Rate = Interest | | |
|---|---|---|---|
| Investment $A$ | $100 | ? | ? |
| Investment $B$ | ? | ? | ? |
| Total Investments | ? | $x$ | ? |

**8.** Lucy has a pile of 50 dimes and nickels worth $4.30. How many of each coin does she have?

|  | Number of coins × Value per coin = Total value | | |
|---|---|---|---|
| Dimes | $x$ | ? | ? |
| Nickels | ? | ? | ? |
| Mixture | 50 |  | ? |

*Note:* The bottom row of the chart in Exercise 8 is usually omitted. However, it is included here so that you will see that coin problems are another type of mixture problem. The missing middle entry in the bottom row of the chart stands for the average value per coin of the 50 coins. It is similar to the $x$ in Exercise 7 that stands for the average rate of interest, or the $x$ in Exercise 6 that stands for the average speed. What kinds of averages do the $x$'s stand for in Exercises 4 and 5?

## Problems

**A  1–8.** Solve the problems presented in Oral Exercises 1–8.

**Solve.**

**9.** How many grams of water must be added to 50 g of a 30% acid solution in order to produce a 20% acid solution?

**10.** How many kilograms of water must be added to 80 kg of a 60% iodine solution in order to dilute it to a 40% iodine solution?

**11.** How many kilograms of salt must be added to 30 kg of a 20% salt solution in order to increase the salt content to 25%?

**12.** A grocer mixes two kinds of nuts. One kind costs $5.00 per kilogram and the other $5.80 per kilogram. How many kilograms of each type are needed to make 40 kg of a blend worth $5.50 per kilogram?

13. A health food store makes a mixture of dried fruits by mixing dried apples costing $6.00 per kilogram with dried apricots costing $8.00 per kilogram. How many kilograms of each are needed to produce 20 kg of a mixture worth $7.20 per kilogram?

14. A grocer mixes two types of juice. How much should he charge if he mixes 24 L of juice worth 80 cents per liter with 16 L of juice worth $1.00 per liter?

15. If you drive for 2 h at 80 km/h, how fast must you drive during a third hour in order to have an average speed of 75 km/h?

16. When Julia works overtime, she is paid $1\frac{1}{2}$ times as much per hour as she normally is. After working her usual 40 hours last week, she worked an additional 8 hours overtime. If she made $520 last week, find her normal hourly wage.

B 17. A chemist wishes to mix some pure acid with some water to produce 8 L of a solution that is 40% acid. How much pure acid and how much water should be mixed?

18. How many kilograms of water must be evaporated from 10 kg of a 40% salt solution to produce a 50% salt solution?

19. How many kilograms of water must be evaporated from 12 kg of a 20% salt solution to produce a 60% solution?

20. A wholesaler has 100 kg of mixed nuts that sell for $4.00 per kilogram. In order to make the price more attractive, the wholesaler plans to mix in some cheaper nuts worth $3.20 per kilogram. If the wholesaler wants to sell the mixture for $3.40 per kilogram, how many kilograms of the cheaper nuts should be used?

21. A securities broker advised a client to invest $14,000 in bonds paying 12% interest and in certificates of deposit paying $5\frac{1}{2}$% interest. The annual income from these investments is $1127.50. Find out how much is invested at each rate.

22. A collection of 50 coins is worth $5.20. There are 12 more nickels than dimes and the rest of the coins are quarters. How many of each kind of coin is in the collection?

23. a. If you bike for 2 h at 30 km/h and then for 2 h at 20 km/h, what is your average speed for the whole trip?
    b. If you bike for 60 km at 30 km/h and then return at 20 km/h, what is your average speed for the whole trip?

24. The ratio of nickels to dimes to quarters is $3:8:1$. If all the coins were dimes, the amount of money would be the same. Show that there are an infinite number of solutions to this problem.

**Write a formula for each of the following.**

**C** **25. a.** The total distance traveled if you go for $x$ hours at $r$ km/h and $2x$ hours at $s$ km/h.
   **b.** The average speed for this trip.

**26. a.** The total amount of salt in a solution formed by mixing $n$ grams of salt with 100 g of a solution that is 10% salt.
   **b.** The percent of salt in the mixture.

**27. a.** The total annual income from investing $a$ dollars in bank accounts that pay 5% simple interest and $b$ dollars in bonds that pay 10% simple interest.
   **b.** The average interest rate from these two investments.

**28. a.** The total value of a mixture of $j$ kg of peanuts costing $5 per kilogram with $k$ kg of walnuts costing $8 per kilogram.
   **b.** The price at which the mixture should be sold to make a 25% profit.

## Calculator Key-In

If your calculator does not have a percent key, you can divide by 100 when entering percents. For example, you can find 9.5% of 3000 as follows:

$$9.5 \div 100 \times 3000 = 285$$

**1.** Find 5.24% of 18,500.  **2.** Find 4.4% of 6600.

**3.** Find 7.5% of 8500.  **4.** Find 11.32% of 4500.

**5.** Find $6\frac{1}{2}$% of 25,000.  **6.** Find $\frac{1}{2}$% of 550.

**7.** Helen Fong purchased a computer at a sale offering a 15.5% discount off the original price. If the original price of the computer she bought was $2038 and the sales tax rate was 5.5%, how much did she pay in all?

## Challenge

Two horses approach each other along the same country road, one walking at 5.5 km/h and the other at 4.5 km/h. At the time they are 10 km apart, a horsefly leaves one horse and flies at 30 km/h to the other horse. No sooner does he reach that horse than the fly turns around (losing no time on the turn) and returns to the first horse. If the fly continues to fly back and forth between the approaching horses, how far has the fly flown when the horses meet?

# 7-8 Work Problems

**Objective**   To solve work problems.

The following formula is used to solve work problems.

$$\text{work rate} \times \text{time} = \text{work done}$$

$$rt = w$$

Work rates are often expressed in terms of the job to be done. For example, if it takes you 4 days to do a job, then your rate is $\frac{1}{4}$ job per day.

Notice in the following examples that the fractional parts of a job must have a sum of 1.

**Example 1**   Eldridge can split a cord of wood in 4 days and his father can do it in 3 days. How long would it take them if they worked together?

**Solution**

Step 1   The problem asks for the number of days it will take if they both work together.

Step 2   Let $x$ = number of days required to do the job together. Since Eldridge can do the whole job in 4 days, his work rate is $\frac{1}{4}$ job per day. Similarly, his father's work rate is $\frac{1}{3}$ job per day.

|  | Work rate | × Time | = Work done |
|---|---|---|---|
| Eldridge | $\frac{1}{4}$ | $x$ | $\frac{x}{4}$ |
| Father | $\frac{1}{3}$ | $x$ | $\frac{x}{3}$ |

Step 3   $\dfrac{\text{Part of job}}{\text{Eldridge does}} + \dfrac{\text{Part of job}}{\text{father does}} = \text{Whole job}$

$$\frac{x}{4} \quad + \quad \frac{x}{3} \quad = \quad 1$$

Step 4
$$12\left(\frac{x}{4} + \frac{x}{3}\right) = 12(1)$$
$$3x + 4x = 12$$
$$7x = 12$$
$$x = \frac{12}{7}$$

Step 5   The check is left to you.

$\therefore$ it would take $\frac{12}{7}$, or $1\frac{5}{7}$, days to do the job together.   **Answer**

## Example 2

It will take a Type A robot 6 min to weld a fender, but a Type B robot would take only $5\frac{1}{2}$ min. If the robots work together for 2 min, how long will it take the Type B robot to finish welding by itself?

## Solution

Step 1 The problem asks for the time needed for a Type B robot to finish welding.

Step 2 Let $x$ = number of minutes for a Type B robot to finish. Since a Type B robot's work rate is

$$\frac{1}{5\frac{1}{2}} = \frac{1}{\frac{11}{2}} = \frac{2}{11}, \text{ we}$$

have the chart at the right.

|  | Work rate × Time = Work done | | |
|---|---|---|---|
| Type A robot | $\frac{1}{6}$ | 2 | $\frac{2}{6}$ or $\frac{1}{3}$ |
| Type B robot | $\frac{2}{11}$ | $2 + x$ | $\frac{2}{11}(2 + x)$ |

Step 3 $\dfrac{\text{Part of job}}{\text{done by A}} + \dfrac{\text{Part of job}}{\text{done by B}} =$ Whole job

$$\frac{1}{3} + \frac{2}{11}(2 + x) = 1$$

Step 4
$$11 + 6(2 + x) = 33$$
$$11 + 12 + 6x = 33$$
$$6x = 10$$
$$x = \frac{5}{3}$$

Step 5 The check is left to you.

∴ it will take $1\frac{2}{3}$ min for a Type B robot to finish welding. **Answer**

The charts used for work problems look similar to the charts used for other problems. The reason is that work problems are just another type of mixture problem. The following equations will help to show the similarities between several types of problems that you have studied.

work done by $A$ + work done by $B$ = total work done

acid in solution $A$ + acid in solution $B$ = total acid in mixture

interest from banks + interest from bonds = total interest

distance traveled by bike + distance traveled by car = total distance traveled

# Oral Exercises

**State the work rate.**

**Example**   Pete can rake the lawn in 2 hours.

**Solution**   rate = $\frac{1}{2}$ job per hour

**1.** Beatrice can wallpaper the room in 8 hours.

**2.** Mary can edit a book in 10 months.

**3.** Sandy can tune a car in 30 minutes.

**4.** A drain pipe can empty a full tank in 3 hours.

**Complete the charts. Do not solve the problems.**

**5.** Using a ride-on lawn mower, Abby can mow the lawn in 2 hours. Her sister Carla takes 3 hours using an older mower. How long will it take them if they work together?

|  | Work rate × Time = Work done | | |
|---|---|---|---|
| Abby | ? | $x$ | ? |
| Carla | ? | ? | ? |

**6.** Phil can paint the garage in 12 hours and Rick can do it in 10 hours. They work together for 3 hours. How long will it take Rick to finish the job alone?

|  | Work rate × Time = Work done | | |
|---|---|---|---|
| Phil | ? | 3 | ? |
| Rick | ? | $x + 3$ | ? |

**7.** Bill usually takes 50 minutes to groom the horses. After working for 10 minutes, he was joined by Ann and they finished the grooming in 15 minutes. How long would it have taken Ann working alone?

|  | Work rate × Time = Work done | | |
|---|---|---|---|
| Bill | ? | ? | ? |
| Ann | $\frac{1}{x}$ | ? | ? |

# *Problems*

**A**  **1.** Selby takes 5 hours to type a report. What part of the typing can she do in 2 hours? in $x$ hours?

**2.** Lincoln can do a job in 8 hours and Dave can do it in 6 hours. What part of the job can they do by working together for 2 hours? for $x$ hours?

**3.** Jake can wallpaper a room in 5 hours and Maura can do it in 6 hours. What part of the job can they do by working together for 1.5 hours? for $x$ hours?

**4.** One drain pipe can empty a swimming pool in 6 hours. Another pipe takes 3 hours. If both pipes are used simultaneously to drain the pool, what part of the job is completed in 2 hours? in $x$ hours?

**5–7.** Solve the problems stated in Oral Exercises 5–7.

**8.** It takes Ruth 60 minutes to pick the apples from her backyard tree. Bud can do it in 40 minutes. How long will it take them if they pick together?

**9.** It takes Gary 1 hour to milk all of the cows, and it takes Dana 1.5 hours. How long will it take to do the job together?

**10.** A roofing contractor estimates that he can shingle a house in 20 hours and that his assistant can do it in 30 hours. How long will it take for the two of them together to shingle the house?

**11.** Stan can load the truck in 40 minutes. If I help him, it takes us 15 minutes. How long will it take me alone?

**12.** One printing machine works twice as fast as another. When both machines are used, they can print a magazine in 3 hours. How many hours would each machine require to do this printing alone?

**B**  **13.** Art can do a job in 30 minutes, Bob can do it in 40 minutes, and Carl can do it in 60 minutes. How long will it take them if they work together?

**14.** It takes my father 3 hours to plow our cornfield with his new tractor. Using the old tractor it takes me 5 hours. If we both plow for 1 hour before I go to school, how long will it take Dad to finish the plowing?

**15.** Ingrid can rake our lawn in 90 minutes and I can do it in 60 minutes. If Ingrid rakes for 15 minutes before I join her, how long will it take us to finish?

16. One pump can fill a water tank in 40 minutes and another pump takes 30 minutes. When the tank was empty, both pumps were turned on for 10 minutes and then the slower pump was turned off. How much longer did the faster pump have to run before the tank was filled?

17. A pipe can fill a swimming pool in 6 hours. After it has been filling the empty pool for 3 hours, a second pipe is also used, with the result that the pool is filled in another 2 hours. How long will it take the second pipe alone to fill the pool?

18. Vanessa can do a job in 12 days. After she has worked for 4 days, she is joined by Susan, and they finish the job together in 2 more days. How long would it have taken Susan to do the whole job herself?

19. The fill pipe for a tank can fill the tank in 4 hours, and the drain pipe can drain it in 2 hours. If both pipes are accidentally opened, how long will it take to empty a half-filled tank?

C 20. Miranda and Sally are addressing invitations to the junior class party. Miranda can address one every 30 seconds and Sally can do one every 40 seconds. How long will it take them to address 140 invitations?

21. Sam Bordner can dig his garden in 4 hours and Elsie Bordner takes the same amount of time. After working together for an hour, their son Gregory helps them finish in just half an hour. How long would it have taken Gregory to dig the garden by himself?

22. If three pipes are all opened, they can fill an empty swimming pool in 3 hours. The largest pipe alone takes one third the time that the smallest pipe takes and half the time the other pipe takes. How long will each pipe take by itself?

# Self-Test 4

**Solve.**

1. How many kilograms of water must be evaporated from 40 kg of a 10% salt solution to produce a 25% salt solution?

Obj. 7-7, p. 306

2. How many kilograms of raisins must be added to 1.8 kg of plain bran muffin batter to produce a batter that is 10% raisins?

3. Jean can make a quilt in 9 days. If Donna helps her, they can make the quilt in 6 days. How long will it take Donna to make the quilt alone?

Obj. 7-8, p. 312

4. The main engine on a rocket can consume the fuel supply in 60 s. The auxiliary engine can consume the fuel supply in 80 s. How long can both engines be fired together?

Check your answers with those at the back of the book.

# Problems Involving Exponents

## 7-9 Scientific Notation

**Objective**   To use scientific notation.

Some numbers are so large or so small that they are difficult to read or to write. For example, consider the following:

diameter of the solar system: 118,000,000,000 km

diameter of a silver atom: 0.00000000000025 km

*Scientific notation* makes it easier to read and to calculate with such numbers.

Scientific notation is based on positive and negative powers of 10. You are familiar with the positive powers of 10. The negative powers are defined below.

**Positive Powers of 10**

$10^1 = 10$

$10^2 = 100$

$10^3 = 1000$

$10^4 = 10,000$

and so on

**Negative Powers of 10**

$10^{-1} = \frac{1}{10^1} = \frac{1}{10} = 0.1$

$10^{-2} = \frac{1}{10^2} = \frac{1}{100} = 0.01$

$10^{-3} = \frac{1}{10^3} = \frac{1}{1000} = 0.001$

$10^{-4} = \frac{1}{10^4} = \frac{1}{10,000} = 0.0001$

and so on

A number is written in **scientific notation** when it is expressed as a product of a number greater than or equal to 1, but less than 10, and an integral power of 10.

118,000,000,000   $= 1.18 \times 10^{11}$    decimal point moved 11 places

4,709,000,000    $= 4.709 \times 10^9$    decimal point moved 9 places

0.000152     $= 1.52 \times 10^{-4}$    decimal point moved 4 places

0.00000000000025 $= 2.5 \times 10^{-13}$    decimal point moved 13 places

***Example 1*** Express each number in scientific notation.

  **a.** 58,120,000,000    **b.** 0.00000072

***Solution***  **a.** The decimal point must be moved 10 places to get a number between 1 and 10.

$$58,120,000,000 = 5.812 \times 10^{10}$$

10

  **b.** The decimal point must be moved 7 places to get a number between 1 and 10.

$$0.00000072 = 7.2 \times 10^{-7}$$

7

***Example 2*** Express each number without using scientific notation.

  **a.** $4.95 \times 10^{8}$    **b.** $7.63 \times 10^{-5}$

***Solution***  **a.** The decimal point must be moved 8 places.

$$4.95 \times 10^{8} = 495,000,000$$

8

  **b.** The decimal point must be moved 5 places.

$$7.63 \times 10^{-5} = 0.0000763$$

5

Example 3 shows that it is easier to compare large or small numbers and to calculate with them if they are expressed in scientific notation.

***Example 3*** The distances from the sun to Pluto and from the sun to Mercury are $5.9 \times 10^{9}$ km and $6 \times 10^{8}$ km, respectively. Find the ratio of these distances.

***Solution***
$$\frac{\text{sun to Pluto}}{\text{sun to Mercury}} = \frac{5.9 \times 10^{9}}{6 \times 10^{8}} = \frac{59 \times 10^{8}}{6 \times 10^{8}}$$

$$= \frac{59}{6} \times \frac{10^{8}}{10^{8}} = \frac{59}{6}$$

Numbers written in scientific notation can be multiplied and divided easily by using the rules of exponents. For example:

$$(3.2 \times 10^{7})(2.0 \times 10^{4}) = (3.2 \times 2.0)(10^{7} \times 10^{4})$$
$$= 6.4 \times 10^{11} \quad \{\text{Add exponents when multiplying.}$$

$$\frac{3.2 \times 10^{7}}{2.0 \times 10^{4}} = \frac{3.2}{2.0} \times \frac{10^{7}}{10^{4}} = 1.6 \times 10^{3} \quad \begin{cases} \text{Subtract exponents when} \\ \text{dividing.} \end{cases}$$

$$(2.5 \times 10^{3})(6.0 \times 10^{2}) = (2.5 \times 6.0)(10^{3} \times 10^{2})$$
$$= 15 \times 10^{5} = 1.5 \times 10^{6}$$

Positive and negative powers of 10 are used in our decimal number system, as well as in scientific notation, since every digit of a number can be associated with an integral power of 10. For convenience, the zero power of 10, written $10^0$, is defined as 1. The following numbers are written in **expanded notation.**

$$8572 = 8 \cdot 10^3 + 5 \cdot 10^2 + 7 \cdot 10^1 + 2 \cdot 10^0$$
$$0.3946 = 3 \cdot 10^{-1} + 9 \cdot 10^{-2} + 4 \cdot 10^{-3} + 6 \cdot 10^{-4}$$
$$25.307 = 2 \cdot 10^1 + 5 \cdot 10^0 + 3 \cdot 10^{-1} + 0 \cdot 10^{-2} + 7 \cdot 10^{-3}$$

The metric system of measurement is also based on powers of 10. Conversions from one metric unit to another simply involve multiplying by a power of 10. For example:

To convert from meters to kilometers, multiply by $10^{-3}$.

To convert from kilometers to meters, multiply by $10^3$.

## Oral Exercises

**Express each of the following numbers in scientific notation.**

**1.** 38,500

**2.** 4,070,000

**3.** 18,050,000,000

**4.** 0.003

**5.** 0.000028

**6.** 0.0000000902

**7-12.** Express each number in Exercises 1–6 in expanded notation.

**Simplify each expression to a power of 10.**

**13.** $10^3 \cdot 10^4 \cdot 10^8$

**14.** $\dfrac{10^5 \cdot 10^4}{10^2}$

**15.** $\dfrac{10^8}{10^6 \cdot 10^6}$

**16.** $\dfrac{10^5}{10^{-2}}$

**17.** $\dfrac{10^{-4}}{10^{-6}}$

**18.** $\dfrac{10^4 \cdot 10^{-2}}{10^{-1}}$

**Express each in scientific notation.**

**19.** $(2 \times 10^5)(4 \times 10^6)$

**20.** $\dfrac{6 \times 10^7}{2 \times 10^2}$

**21.** $(4 \times 10^6)(3 \times 10^2)$

**22.** $\dfrac{8 \times 10^6}{2 \times 10^{-3}}$

**23.** $\dfrac{9 \times 10^{-5}}{3 \times 10^{-3}}$

**24.** $\dfrac{(4 \times 10^4)(9 \times 10^{-2})}{2 \times 10^5}$

## Written Exercises

**Rewrite each number without using scientific notation.**

A **1.** The speed of light is $3.0 \times 10^8$ m/s.

**2.** The diameter of the sun is about $1.39 \times 10^9$ m.

**Rewrite each number without using scientific notation.**

3. The mass of the sun is about $2.0 \times 10^{30}$ kg.

4. The frequency of an AM radio wave is $1.4 \times 10^6$ cycles per second.

5. The wavelength of ultraviolet light is $1.36 \times 10^{-6}$ cm.

6. The wavelength of gamma rays is $3.0 \times 10^{-10}$ cm.

7. The diameter of the nucleus of a hydrogen atom is $5.0 \times 10^{-17}$ cm.

8. The mass of an atom of helium is $6.65 \times 10^{-24}$ g.

**Complete each statement by writing a power of 10.**

9. a. 1 kg = __?__ g
   b. 1 g = __?__ kg

10. a. 1 m = __?__ cm
    b. 1 cm = __?__ m

11. a. 1 kg = __?__ mg
    b. 1 mg = __?__ kg

12. 1 mm = __?__ cm

13. 1 km = __?__ mm

14. 1 g = __?__ mg

**Express each of the following numbers in (a) scientific notation and (b) expanded notation.**

15. 4700

16. 395,000

17. 908,100,000

18. 87,060,000

19. 0.00021

20. 0.0000039

21. 0.0000000102

22. 0.000000606

23. $99\dfrac{44}{100}\%$

B  24. 4.5 million

25. 17 billion

26. 108 trillion

**Perform the indicated operations.**

27. $\dfrac{6 \times 10^8}{3 \times 10^2}$

28. $(1.5 \times 10^7)(3 \times 10^4)$

29. $(8 \times 10^4)(2 \times 10^4)$

30. $\dfrac{(5 \times 10^7)(9 \times 10^{-3})}{3 \times 10^{-2}}$

31. $\dfrac{(2 \times 10^5)^2}{(8 \times 10^{-3})(5 \times 10^{12})}$

32. $\dfrac{(4 \times 10^{-5})^3}{(2 \times 10^{-7})^2}$

## *Problems*

**Give your answers in scientific notation.**

A  1. Find the number of kilometers in a light year. A light year is the distance that light travels in one year. Light travels at the rate of $3.0 \times 10^5$ km/s.

2. The Andromeda galaxy is approximately $1.5 \times 10^6$ light years from Earth. Find the distance in kilometers.

3. The distance from Earth to the star Alpha Centauri is about $4.07 \times 10^{13}$ km. Use the result of Problem 1 to find how long it takes light from this star to reach Earth.

4. How long does it take light from the sun to reach Earth? The sun is $1.5 \times 10^8$ km from Earth.

5. A sheet of paper is 0.015 cm thick. Suppose that you tear this paper in half, place the two halves together and tear them in half. Then you take the four pieces, place them together and rip them in half. If it were possible to continue this process of stacking the ripped pieces together and tearing them apart for 50 times, the stack would have $2^{50}$ pieces in it. How high would the stack reach? Would it be higher than your room? Higher than the tallest redwood tree (83 m)? Higher than the world's tallest building (443.18 m)? Higher than the moon (384,432 km)? Higher than the sun ($1.5 \times 10^8$ km)?

6. The diagram shows the repetitive pattern of an electromagnetic wave. The frequency of such a wave is the number of repetitions, or cycles, per second. A typical television wave could have a frequency of $1.3 \times 10^8$ cycles per second. The wavelength, $L$, is the distance from the peak of one wave to the peak of the next. The frequency, $F$, and wavelength, $L$, in centimeters, are related by the following formula:

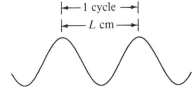

$$F \cdot L = 3.0 \times 10^{10} = \text{speed of light in cm/s}$$

Use this formula to complete the table below.

|  | Television | Red light | Violet light | x rays |
|---|---|---|---|---|
| Frequency $F$ | $1.3 \times 10^8$ | $4.0 \times 10^{14}$ | ? | ? |
| Wavelength $L$ | ? | ? | $1.3 \times 10^{-8}$ | $1 \times 10^{-11}$ |

Computers are programmed to switch over to scientific notation to give approximate values for very large and very small numbers. The actual format depends on the number of digits the computer handles.

In BASIC

$\times 10^3$ is written E+03   and   $\times 10^{-3}$ is written E−03.

To explore when and how your computer uses scientific notation for large numbers, RUN the program given below.

```
10   LET N=1
20   FOR I=1 TO 39
30   LET N=N*10
40   PRINT N,
50   NEXT I
60   END
```

Change line 30 to 30 LET N = N/10 to see how your computer uses scientific notation for small numbers.

### Exercises

Change the program above by deleting line 30 and changing line 40 to PRINT I, N↑I. RUN the program for the following values of N.

**1.** 2        **2.** 5        **3.** −3        **4.** −7

**5–6.** In Exercises 1 and 2, find the largest power for which your computer gives an exact value.

**7.** In the program on page 58, you used a negative number to end the loop. What kind of number can you use to end the loop if you want to add a list of positive and negative numbers?

To display very large numbers, most calculators use a form of exponential notation similar to scientific notation. Try this on a calculator:

Press the 9 key until the display is filled with 9's. Next, estimate what the answer would be if you were to multiply this large number by 2. Write your estimate on paper. Now go ahead and multiply by 2 on the calculator. Compare the displayed answer with your estimate. They should be two different forms of the same number.

Enter 9's again. Predict what the calculator will display when you multiply by 20. Try it. Were you right? What will be displayed if you multiply by 400 instead of 20?

# 7-10 Negative Exponents

**Objective**   To use negative exponents.

You have seen negative powers of 10 used in scientific notation. Negative powers of other numbers are defined in the same way as negative powers of 10.

$$10^{-2} = \frac{1}{10^2} = \frac{1}{100} \qquad 10^{-3} = \frac{1}{10^3} = \frac{1}{1000}$$

$$5^{-2} = \frac{1}{5^2} = \frac{1}{25} \qquad 5^{-3} = \frac{1}{5^3} = \frac{1}{125}$$

$$4^{-2} = \frac{1}{4^2} = \frac{1}{16} \qquad 4^{-3} = \frac{1}{4^3} = \frac{1}{64}$$

In general, you have the following rule.

## Rule for Negative Exponents

If $a \neq 0$ and $n$ is a positive integer,

$$a^{-n} = \frac{1}{a^n}.$$

You can understand why $a^{-n}$ is defined as $\frac{1}{a^n}$ by considering the Rule of Exponents for Division (page 188). This rule states that for $m > n$, $\frac{a^m}{a^n} = a^{m-n}$. To apply the rule when $m < n$, that is, when $m - n$ is a negative number, we must give meaning to raising to a power when the exponent is negative. We apply this rule as follows:

$$\frac{a^7}{a^3} = a^{7-3} = a^4 \qquad \frac{a^3}{a^7} = a^{3-7} = a^{-4}$$

Since $\frac{a^7}{a^3}$ and $\frac{a^3}{a^7}$ are reciprocals, $a^4$ and $a^{-4}$ must be reciprocals; that is,

$$a^4 = \frac{1}{a^{-4}} \text{ and } a^{-4} = \frac{1}{a^4}.$$

In order to define $a^0$ we again refer to the Rule of Exponents for Division. In the first two parts of this rule $m \neq n$. However, if you were to apply these two rules to evaluate $\frac{a^m}{a^m}$, you would obtain these expressions:

$$\frac{a^m}{a^m} = a^{m-m} = a^0 \qquad \frac{a^m}{a^m} = \frac{1}{a^{m-m}} = \frac{1}{a^0}$$

Since $\frac{a^m}{a^m} = a^0$, and also, by the third part of the Exponent Rule for Division, $\frac{a^m}{a^m} = 1$, we can state the following rule for $a^0$.

## Rule for a Zero Exponent

If $a$ is a real number not equal to zero,

$$a^0 = 1.$$

We shall not use the expression $0^0$.

Since all the rules of positive exponents continue to hold for zero and negative exponents, we have the following.

## Summary of Rules for Exponents

1. Multiplication: $\qquad\qquad b^m b^n = b^{m+n}$
2. Division: $\qquad\qquad\quad b^m \div b^n = b^{m-n}$
3. Power of a Power: $\qquad (b^m)^n = b^{mn}$
4. Power of a Product: $\qquad (ab)^m = a^m b^m$
5. Power of a Quotient: $\qquad \left(\dfrac{a}{b}\right)^m = \dfrac{a^m}{b^m}$

**Example 1** Simplify. Give answers in terms of positive exponents.

        **a.** $\dfrac{5}{5^{-3}}$     **b.** $(b^{-1})^{-3}$     **c.** $(3x^{-1})^2$

**Solution**     **a.** $\dfrac{5^1}{5^{-3}} = 5^{1-(-3)} = 5^4$      (Rule 2)

              **b.** $(b^{-1})^{-3} = b^{(-1)(-3)} = b^3$    (Rule 3)

              **c.** $(3x^{-1})^2 = 9x^{-2}$          (Rules 4 and 3)

                          $= \dfrac{9}{x^2}$           (Definition of negative exponents)

Positive and negative exponents are often used in problems dealing with population growth, interest, or energy consumption. These quantities are said to grow exponentially when the equations that describe the growth involve exponents.

**Example 2** The population of a city has been growing exponentially. It is estimated that in $t$ years the population $P$ will be

$$P = 2(1.03)^t \text{ million people.}$$

    **a.** What will the population be in 2 years?
    **b.** What is the population now?
    **c.** What was the population last year?

**Solution**    **a.** Let $t = 2$.    $P = 2(1.03)^2 = 2(1.0609)$ million $= 2,121,800$

**b.** Let $t = 0$.    $P = 2(1.03)^0 = 2(1) = 2$ million

**c.** Let $t = -1$.    $P = 2(1.03)^{-1} = \dfrac{2}{1.03}$ million $\approx 1,941,748$

## Oral Exercises

**Evaluate.**

**1.** $10^{-1}$

**2.** $6^{-1}$

**3.** $7^{-1}$

**4.** $3^{-1}$

**5.** $10^{-2}$

**6.** $6^{-2}$

**7.** $7^{-2}$

**8.** $3^{-3}$

**9.** $2^{-3}$

**10.** $4^{-3}$

**11.** $3^{-4} \cdot 3^2$

**12.** $5^6 \cdot 5^{-8}$

**13.** $(3^{-1})^2$

**14.** $(3^{-1})^{-2}$

**15.** $\dfrac{5}{5^{-1}}$

**16.** $\dfrac{4^{-3}}{4^{-6}}$

**17.** $\left(\dfrac{1}{2} - \dfrac{1}{4}\right)^{-1}$

**18.** $\left(\dfrac{1}{2} \cdot \dfrac{1}{4}\right)^{-1}$

**19.** $(2 + 3^{-1})^{-1}$

**20.** $(2 \cdot 5^{-1})^{-1}$

**Simplify. Give answers in terms of positive exponents.**

**21.** $a^{-1}b^2$

**22.** $\dfrac{c^{-2}}{d^{-3}}$

**23.** $(2x^{-1})^3$

**24.** $(3y^{-2})^{-1}$

**25.** The electrical energy consumption in a city has been increasing. In $n$ years it is estimated that the annual electrical consumption will be $C = 1.3(1.07)^n$ billion kilowatts. What value of $n$ should be substituted to find the value of $C$ (a) now? (b) 10 years from now? (c) 10 years ago?

## Written Exercises

**Evaluate.**

A    **1.** $5^{-1}$

**2.** $4^{-1}$

**3.** $5^{-2}$

**4.** $4^{-2}$

**5.** $9^{-2}$

**6.** $8^{-2}$

**7.** $9^{-3}$

**8.** $8^{-3}$

**9.** $2^{-4}$

**10.** $3^{-4}$

**11.** $2^{-5}$

**12.** $3^{-5}$

**13.** $4^{-2} \cdot 4^5$

**14.** $3^7 \cdot 3^{-9}$

**15.** $(3^{-2})^{-2}$

**16.** $(5^{-1})^{-3}$

**17.** $\dfrac{3}{3^{-2}}$

**18.** $\dfrac{6^{-2}}{6^{-3}}$

**19.** $\dfrac{8 \cdot 8^{-2}}{8^{-3}}$

**20.** $\dfrac{7^{-2} \cdot 7^5}{7^3}$

**21.** $\left(\dfrac{3^{-1}}{3}\right)^2$

**22.** $\left(\dfrac{8^4}{8^{-4}}\right)^0$

**23.** $\left(\dfrac{9^3 \cdot 9}{9^5}\right)^{-3}$

**24.** $\dfrac{(4^{-2} \cdot 3)^3}{4^{-6}}$

**Evaluate.**

25. a. $(2^{-1} + 2^{-2})^{-1}$　　b. $(2^{-1} \cdot 2^{-2})^{-1}$　　26. a. $(2 + 3^{-1})^{-2}$　　b. $(2 \cdot 3^{-1})^{-2}$

27. a. $(3^0 \cdot 2^{-2})^{-2}$　　b. $(3^0 - 2^{-2})^{-2}$　　28. a. $(2^{-1} \div 2^{-2})^3$　　b. $(2^{-1} - 2^{-2})^3$

29. Why is $b^{-3}$ not defined when $b = 0$?

30. Suppose that you did not know that $b^0 = 1$. Explain how you could deduce this fact by using the laws of exponents to simplify $b^2 \cdot b^0 = b^2$.

**Simplify. Give answers in terms of positive exponents.**

31. $7x^{-1}$　　　　32. $8a^{-2}$　　　　33. $x^{-1}y^2$　　　　34. $a^{-2}b^{-3}$

35. $(a^{-2})^3$　　　36. $(b^{-1})^{-3}$　　　37. $(3x^{-2})^3$　　　38. $(4n^{-1})^2$

**B**　39. $x^3 \cdot x^{-5}$　　40. $y^3 \cdot y^{-3}$　　41. $(a^2 \cdot a^{-5})^2$　　42. $(b^5 \cdot b^{-7})^3$

43. $\dfrac{a^5}{a^{-3}}$　　　44. $\dfrac{b^7}{b^{-7}}$　　　45. $\dfrac{c^{-5}}{c^2}$　　　46. $\dfrac{d^{-3}}{d^{-5}}$

47. $\left(\dfrac{x^{-2}}{x^{-4}}\right)^3$　　48. $\left(\dfrac{a^{-1}}{a^4}\right)^2$　　49. $\left(\dfrac{n^{-3}}{n}\right)^{-2}$　　50. $\left(\dfrac{y^5}{y^{-2}}\right)^{-3}$

**Use the table of powers of 5 to evaluate the expressions below.**

*Example*　$\dfrac{3125}{0.008} = \dfrac{5^5}{5^{-3}} = 5^8 = 390{,}625$

| | |
|---|---|
| $5^1 = 5$ | $5^{-1} = 0.2$ |
| $5^2 = 25$ | $5^{-2} = 0.04$ |
| $5^3 = 125$ | $5^{-3} = 0.008$ |
| $5^4 = 625$ | $5^{-4} = 0.0016$ |
| $5^5 = 3125$ | $5^{-5} = 0.00032$ |
| $5^6 = 15{,}625$ | $5^{-6} = 0.000064$ |
| $5^7 = 78{,}125$ | $5^{-7} = 0.0000128$ |
| $5^8 = 390{,}625$ | $5^{-8} = 0.00000256$ |

51. $15{,}625 \times 0.0016$　　52. $0.00032 \times 3125$

53. $(78{,}125)^{-1}$　　54. $(0.0016)^{-2}$

55. $\dfrac{0.008}{625}$　　56. $\dfrac{125}{0.00032}$

57. $\dfrac{(3125)^2}{15{,}625}$　　58. $(0.0000128)^3(390{,}625)^2$

**Exponents can be fractions as well as integers. Exercises 59–63 will help you see how fractional exponents can be defined.**

**C**　59. If Rule 1 for integral exponents were to hold for fractional exponents, then $9^{\frac{1}{2}} \cdot 9^{\frac{1}{2}} = 9^{\frac{1}{2}+\frac{1}{2}} = 9^1$.
Therefore, $9^{\frac{1}{2}}$ ought to be defined as the number ___?___.

60. If Rule 1 for integral exponents were to hold for fractional exponents, then $16^{\frac{1}{2}} \cdot 16^{\frac{1}{2}} = 16^1$.
Therefore, $16^{\frac{1}{2}}$ ought to be defined as the number ___?___.

61. If Rule 3 for integral exponents were to hold for fractional exponents, then $(8^{\frac{1}{3}})^3 = 8^{\frac{1}{3} \cdot 3} = 8^1$.
Therefore, $8^{\frac{1}{3}}$ ought to be defined as the number ___?___.

62. Guess how $x^{\frac{1}{2}}$ and $x^{\frac{1}{3}}$ are defined.

63. Guess how $x^{-\frac{1}{2}}$ and $x^{-\frac{1}{3}}$ are defined.

## Problems

A 1. If you have 1 kg of radioactive iodine, it will gradually decay (decrease in amount) so that $d$ days later you will have $1.09^{-d}$ kg. Find how many kilograms you will have 4 days later and 8 days later.

2. The value, $V$, of a new $10,000 automobile $y$ years after it is purchased is given by the formula $V = 10,000(1.3)^{-y}$. Copy and complete the table below.

| Years | 0 | 1 | 2 | 3 | 4 | 5 |
|-------|---|---|---|---|---|---|
| Value ($V$) | ? | ? | ? | ? | ? | ? |

3. The population of a certain state $t$ years from now is predicted to be $P = 15(1.04)^t$ million. Estimate to the nearest million the population (a) now, (b) 10 years from now, and (c) 10 years ago.

4. The cost of living in a large metropolitan area has been increasing in such a way that an item costing one dollar today will cost $(1.08)^t$ dollars in $t$ years. (a) How much will today's one-dollar item cost in 3 years? (b) How much in 9 years? (c) How much did today's one-dollar item cost 9 years ago?

5. A microbiologist has a bacteria culture whose growth rate can be described by $N = n(2.72)^{2t}$, where $n$ is the original number of bacteria, and $N$ is the number after $t$ hours. If the number of bacteria at noon is 100 find (a) the number at 2 P.M., (b) the number at 10 A.M., (c) the number at 6 P.M., and (d) the number at 6 A.M.

# Self-Test 5

***Vocabulary***    scientific notation (p. 317)            expanded notation (p. 319)

**Express each of the following numbers in scientific notation.**

1. 150 million            2. 0.000000009            **Obj. 7-9, p. 317**

**Evaluate.**

3. $(3^0)^{-5}$            4. $\dfrac{2^{-3}}{2^0}$            5. $-\dfrac{2}{2^{-3}}$            **Obj. 7-10, p. 323**

**Simplify. Give answers in terms of positive exponents.**

6. $x^{-5}$            7. $4a^{-2}$            8. $(3a^{-4})^2$

Check your answers with those at the back of the book.

## Historical Note / *The Rule of Three*

The Rule of Three was the forerunner of the
statement "The product of the means equals
the product of the extremes." However, because the rule was used primarily by merchants,
and because the terms were not written in
ratio form, its relationship to ratio and proportion
was not realized until the end of the fifteenth
century. Although no explanation was ever
given as to why the rule worked, merchants
knew the first and third terms had to be meas-
ured in the same units and that the product of the second and third terms
divided by the first term gave the quantity they wanted to find.

The Rule of Three was stated in various forms. For instance, the
seventh-century mathematician Brahmagupta wrote, "In the Rule of Three,
Argument, Fruit, and Requisition are the names of the terms. The first and
last terms must be similar. Requisition multiplied by Fruit, and divided by
Argument is the Produce." In the twelfth century Bhāskara asked, "Two
palas and a half of saffron are purchased for three sevenths of a niska, how
many palas will be purchased for nine niskas?" Other application problems
can be found in the Egyptian Rhind mathematical papyrus (1550 B.C.), the
Chinese *K'iu—ch'ang Suan-shu,* or *Arithmetic in Nine Sections* (second mil-
lennium B.C.), and the *Treviso Arithmetic* published in Italy (A.D. 1478).

In the early nineteenth century the Rule of Three was listed among the
requirements for admission to Harvard College and Princeton University.

## *Calculator Key-In*

You can use a calculator to evaluate algebraic fractions for given values of
their variables. First evaluate the denominator and store its value in the calculator's memory. (You may want to review the method for evaluating a polynomial given on page 198.) Then evaluate the numerator and divide by the
value of the denominator.

Evaluate each fraction for the given value of the variable.

1. $\dfrac{9}{x + 3}$; $x = 12$

2. $\dfrac{2y + 5}{8}$; $y = 9$

3. $\dfrac{5n - 16}{2n}$; $n = 5$

4. $\dfrac{7a + 20}{3a}$; $a = 4$

5. $\dfrac{7x^2 + 4x + 12}{x}$; $x = 9$

6. $\dfrac{4z^2 + 11z - 60}{2z + 8}$; $z = -6$

7. $\dfrac{a^2 + 8a - 10}{2a}$; $a = 0.5$

8. $\dfrac{5y^2 - 22y + 30}{6y - 10}$; $y = -2$

# Chapter Summary

1. A *ratio* of two numbers is their quotient. The ratio 6 to 8 can be written as 6:8 or more simply as 3:4, 3 ÷ 4, $\frac{3}{4}$, or 0.75. If you are told that the ratio of two numbers is 5:7, you can represent the numbers as $5x$ and $7x$.

2. A *proportion* is an equation stating that two ratios are equal. In a proportion the product of the means is equal to the product of the extremes. Thus,

$$\text{if } \frac{a}{b} = \frac{c}{d}, \text{ then } ad = bc.$$

3. You can eliminate fractions from equations with fractional coefficients and from *fractional equations* by multiplying both sides of the equation by the LCD. Similarly, you can eliminate decimals from equations by multiplying each term by a suitable power of 10.

4. *Percent* means "hundredths." Percent problems usually involve finding a percent of a number, finding what percent one number is of another, or finding a number when a percent of the number is known (see the examples on pages 295–296). When solving word problems involving percents, it is often convenient to express the percent as a decimal. For example:

$$7\frac{1}{2}\% = 7.5\% = 0.075$$

5. Many word problems are very much alike. The similarities that exist among mixture, coin, investment, work, and distance problems can be seen in the charts and equations used to solve them.

6. Expressing very large or very small numbers in *scientific notation* makes these numbers easier to read and to use in calculations.

7. Exponents can be positive, negative, or zero. The rules for positive exponents continue to hold for zero and negative exponents.

# Chapter Review

1. State the ratio 52 wk:28 d in simplest form.        7-1

   **a.** $\frac{13}{7}$        **b.** $\frac{7}{13}$        **c.** $\frac{12}{1}$        **d.** $\frac{13}{1}$

2. In a ceramics class the ratio of students making projects that they intend to give as gifts to students making projects that they intend to keep is 5:3. If there are 24 students in the class, how many of the students intend to keep the projects that they are making?

   **a.** 3        **b.** 12        **c.** 9        **d.** 15

**3.** Solve for $x$: $\dfrac{x}{60} = \dfrac{45}{25}$

7-2

   **a.** 108      **b.** $\dfrac{12}{25}$      **c.** $\dfrac{25}{12}$      **d.** 21

**4.** Elena is drawing a map. If she lets 1.5 cm represent 125 km, how long should she draw a segment that represents 875 km?
   **a.** 12 cm      **b.** 10.5 cm      **c.** 7.5 cm      **d.** 7 cm

**5.** Solve for $x$: $x - \dfrac{x + 3}{3} = 0$

7-3

   **a.** 0      **b.** $-\dfrac{3}{2}$      **c.** $\dfrac{2}{3}$      **d.** $\dfrac{3}{2}$

**6.** Solve for $a$: $\dfrac{1}{a - 1} + \dfrac{3}{3a - 1} = 0$

7-4

   **a.** $\dfrac{2}{3}$      **b.** 0      **c.** $\dfrac{3}{2}$      **d.** no solution

**7.** Express $166\frac{2}{3}\%$ as a fraction in simplest form.

7-5

   **a.** $\dfrac{8}{3}$      **b.** $\dfrac{5}{3}$      **c.** $\dfrac{20}{3}$      **d.** $\dfrac{7}{3}$

**8.** Find 56% of 56.

   **a.** 1      **b.** 100      **c.** $\dfrac{14}{25}$      **d.** 31.36

**9.** 18 is 6% of what number?

   **a.** 3      **b.** 300      **c.** 1.08      **d.** $\dfrac{3}{50}$

**10.** What percent of 36 is 27?

   **a.** $\dfrac{4}{3}\%$      **b.** $\dfrac{3}{4}\%$      **c.** 75%      **d.** 7.5%

**11.** A team won 63 games and lost 21. What percent did the team win?
   **a.** 75%      **b.** 3%      **c.** 30%      **d.** 70%

**12.** Monty saves 20% by buying a record on sale for $6.36. What was the original price of the record?

7-6

   **a.** $7.95      **b.** $9.54      **c.** $7.99      **d.** $8.48

**13.** A chemist has 10 cm³ of a 20% salt solution. How many cubic centimeters of water should she add to produce a 5% salt solution?

7-7

   **a.** 13 cm³      **b.** 18 cm³      **c.** 22 cm³      **d.** 30 cm³

**14.** Veronica can clean the house in 5 hours. If Eduardo helps her, they can clean the house in 3 hours. How long would it take Eduardo to clean the house alone?

7-8

   **a.** $3\dfrac{3}{5}$ hours      **b.** $7\dfrac{1}{2}$ hours      **c.** $5\dfrac{1}{3}$ hours      **d.** 6 hours

**15.** Express 163 million in scientific notation.

7-9

   **a.** $1.63 \times 10^2$      **b.** $1.63 \times 10^6$      **c.** $1.63 \times 10^8$      **d.** $1.63 \times 10^{-8}$

**16.** Simplify $(2^{-1} - 2^0)^3$.

7-10

   **a.** $-\dfrac{1}{8}$      **b.** $\dfrac{1}{8}$      **c.** 8      **d.** $-8$

# Chapter Test

**Express each ratio in simplest form.**

1. $42 \text{ min}:2 \text{ h}$

2. $63 \text{ cm}:0.9 \text{ m}$

7-1

3. The ratio of time Lionel spent writing an essay to the time he spent revising it was $3:1$. If he spent a total of 2 hours writing and revising the essay, how long did it take him to write it?

**Solve.**

4. $\dfrac{91}{x} = \dfrac{7}{3}$

5. $\dfrac{16}{3y} = \dfrac{12}{5}$

7-2

6. $\dfrac{3x}{10} = \dfrac{5x}{6}$

7. $\dfrac{2n - 1}{3} = \dfrac{n - 4}{5}$

8. $a + \dfrac{a}{3} = 18 - \dfrac{a}{6}$

9. $\dfrac{3y + 5}{2} - \dfrac{3y + 2}{5} = \dfrac{3}{10}$

7-3

10. $\dfrac{1}{b} + \dfrac{3b}{5b - 2} = 0$

11. $\dfrac{c - 1}{6c} = \dfrac{1}{c}$

7-4

**Express as a fraction in simplest form.**

12. $35\%$

13. $62\frac{1}{2}\%$

14. $510\%$

7-5

15. Find $20\%$ of $83\frac{1}{2}$.

16. Find $37\%$ of 68.

17. 48 is $32\%$ of what number?

18. What percent of 675 is 225?

19. On Saturday night the attendance at the senior play was $15\%$ higher than it had been Friday night. If 340 people attended the play Friday night, how many people attended that play on Saturday night?

7-6

20. How many liters of apple juice must be added to 16 L of cranberry juice to produce a drink that is $36\%$ apple juice?

7-7

21. Working alone, Sally Jillson can correct a set of examinations in 7 hours. It would take Ellen Ryan 3 hours to correct the same set of examinations. If they work together, how long will it take them to correct the examinations?

7-8

22. Express 0.000128 in scientific notation.

7-9

**Evaluate.**

23. $2^{-3} \cdot 2^{-2}$

24. $\dfrac{4^0}{4^{-2}}$

25. $(3 + 2^{-1})^{-1}$

7-10

**Simplify. Give answers in terms of positive exponents.**

26. $14x^{-7}$

27. $(a^{-2})^{-3}$

28. $(n^{-4})^2$

# Cumulative Review (Chapters 1–7)

**Perform the indicated operations. Express the answers in simplest form using only positive exponents. Assume that no denominator is zero.**

**1.** $24 \div 2 + 2^2 - 4^3 \div 2^4$

**2.** $\frac{16}{32}\left(\frac{2}{19}\right) + \frac{1}{2}\left(\frac{2}{19}\right)$

**3.** $(-2m^3n^4)(8m^5n^3)$

**4.** $xy^2(-2x^2y - 3xy^3 + 12)$

**5.** $(-5a^3bc^4)^2$

**6.** $(10b + 9)^2$

**7.** $(6tv^2 - 5)^2$

**8.** $(3bc - 4)(5bc + 6)$

**9.** $(2x - y)(x^2 - 5xy + 3y^2)$

**10.** $\dfrac{t^2 - 10s + 25s^2}{t - s} \cdot \dfrac{t^2 - s^2}{t^2 - 4ts - 5s^2}$

**11.** $\dfrac{3z - 1}{xyz^3} \div \dfrac{9xz^2 - x}{yz^2}$

**12.** $\dfrac{x}{x + 5} + \dfrac{x + 2}{x^2 + 4x - 6}$

**13.** $\dfrac{10b^2 - 9b - 9}{2b - 3}$

**14.** $\left(\dfrac{y^3}{y - 4}\right)^3$

**15.** $\left(\dfrac{x^{-7}}{x - 4}\right)^{-2}$

**16.** What percent of 400 is 336?

**17.** 72 is what percent of 600?

**Factor completely. If the polynomial cannot be factored, write "prime."**

**18.** $-42s^3t + 14s^2t^2 + 21st^3$

**19.** $49z^2 - 28z + 4$

**20.** $-49y^2 + 100t^2$

**21.** $6b^2 + 23b + 21$

**22.** $18t^2 + 27t + 12$

**23.** $12x^2 + 47x - 4$

**Solve. If the equation is an identity or has no solution, state that fact.**

**24.** $8x + 9 = -39$

**25.** $\frac{2}{3}t - 8 = 12$

**26.** $(n + 4)^2 = (n + 2)^2 + 4(n + 3)$

**27.** $4y^2 + 36y + 81 = 0$

**28.** $m^2 + 14 + 9m = 0$

**29.** $y^3 - 12y^2 + 11y = 0$

**30.** $0.02(700 - x) + 0.5x = 20$

**31.** $\dfrac{n - 2}{n + 2} + \dfrac{1}{n - 2} = \dfrac{4}{n^2 - 4}$

**Express in scientific notation.**

**32.** 112 billion

**33.** 0.000074

**34.** $(8.2 \times 10^6)(2.0 \times 10^{-3})$

**35.** The product of two consecutive even integers is 32 less than the square of the greater integer. Find the integers.

**36.** Three numbers are in the ratio 3:4:5 and their sum is 144. Find the numbers.

**37.** A video cassette recorder that normally costs $625 at Fenton's would cost an employee $550. What is the percent of the employee's discount?

**38.** How many liters of water should be added to 15 L of a 40% acid solution to make a solution that is 10% acid?

**39.** One pipe can fill a tank in 2 hours. A second pipe can fill it in $1\frac{3}{4}$ hours. How long will it take to fill the tank with both pipes open?

# Maintaining Skills

**Simplify.**

***Example 1***  $-5(a + 3b) - 4(-2a + b) = -5a - 15b + 8a - 4b = 3a - 19b$

1. $7a^2 + 2 - 5a + 2a^2 + 6$

2. $-4c + 2d - 3 - 5d + 3c - 6$

3. $(12 - 2x) + (-8x + 5x)$

4. $(3m - 2n) - (-4m + 3n)$

5. $4(x - 3z) - 8(-x + z)$

6. $-2(5y^2 - 2y) + 3(-3y + 1)$

7. $-2(5x + 3) + 4(3x - 2y)$

8. $-3(5x - y) + 5x(2y + 2)$

9. $\frac{3}{4}(8a - 2b) - \frac{2}{3}(9a + b)$

10. $\frac{2}{3}(-12j - k) + \frac{1}{6}(18j + 8k)$

***Example 2***  $(-4x^2yz)(-5xy^4z^3) = [(-4)(-5)](x^2 \cdot x)(y \cdot y^4)(z \cdot z^3) = 20x^3y^5z^4$

11. $(-2a^2b^2)(3ab^2c)$

12. $(4st^2)(-s^3t)(-2s^2t^2)$

13. $(4m^2np)\left(-\frac{1}{4}m^3np^2\right)$

14. $(-5a^2b^3)(2a^3b^2) + (a^4b)(6ab^4)$

***Example 3***  $(-9a^3b^2)^3 = (-9)^3(a^3)^3(b^2)^3 = -729a^9b^6$

15. $(2x^2y^3)^4$

16. $(-11m^4n^3)^2$

17. $(r^3s^2t)^4(rst)^3$

18. $-9(fg^3)^2(-2f^3g)^2$

19. $(2c^2d^2e)^6 + (-2c^4d^4r^2)^3$

20. $-ab(a^3b^2)^4 + a^3b^4(-a^2b)^5$

**Multiply.**

***Example 4***  $5x^2y(3x^2 - 4xy + 2y^2) = 15x^4y - 20x^3y^2 + 10x^2y^3$

21. $3ab^2(a^2 - ab + b^2)$

22. $-4m^2n(3mn^2 - 2m + n^3)$

23. $c^2d^3(d^4 - 2d^2c + c^3)$

24. $-xy(5x^3y^2 - 2x^2y + 7y^5)$

***Example 5***  $(2r - 5s)(-3r + 2s) = 2r(-3r + 2s) - 5s(-3r + 2s)$
$$= -6r^2 + 4rs + 15rs - 10s^2$$
$$= -6r^2 + 19rs - 10s^2$$

25. $(z - 3)(z + 8)$

26. $(2d + 7)(7d - 2)$

27. $(y - 2)(y + 10)$

28. $(2t - 5)(5t - 3)$

29. $(4z + 1)(3z - 3)$

30. $(3c + 4)(5c + 3)$

31. $(9d - 3)(9d + 3)$

32. $(4t + 5)^2$

33. $(x^2 - 6)(x^2 + 6)$

34. $(y - 3)(3y^2 - 4y + 1)$

35. $(b - 7)(-2b^2 + 5b - 2)$

# 8 Linear Equations and Systems

Like many other planned cities, Chicago, Illinois, is laid out in a grid pattern. This pattern suggests a coordinate plane, which you will study in this chapter.

# Using Two Variables

## 8-1 Equations in Two Variables

**Objective** To solve equations in two variables over given domains of the variables.

In previous chapters, the equations you have solved have contained only one variable. In this chapter, you will learn how to solve some equations containing two variables.

| One-variable equations | Two-variable equations |
|:---:|:---:|
| $2x - 3 = 7$ | $4x + 3y = 10$ |
| $y = 9$ | $xy = 6$ |

The solutions to equations in one variable are numbers; the solutions to equations in two variables are *pairs* of numbers. For example, the pair of numbers $x = 1$ and $y = 2$ is a **solution** of the equation

$$4x + 3y = 10 \quad \text{because} \quad 4 \cdot 1 + 3 \cdot 2 = 10.$$

The solution $x = 1$ and $y = 2$ is usually written as $(1, 2)$, with the $x$-value written first. A pair of numbers, such as $(1, 2)$, for which the order of the numbers is important, is called an **ordered pair.**

The ordered pair $(1, 2)$ is not the only solution of the equation $4x + 3y = 10$.

$(4, -2)$ is a solution because $\quad 4 \cdot 4 + 3 \cdot (-2) = 10.$

$(-2, 6)$ is a solution because $\quad 4 \cdot (-2) + 3 \cdot 6 = 10.$

$\left(\dfrac{3}{2}, \dfrac{4}{3}\right)$ is a solution because $\quad 4 \cdot \dfrac{3}{2} + 3 \cdot \dfrac{4}{3} = 10.$

$(3, -1)$ is *not* a solution because $4 \cdot 3 + 3 \cdot (-1) \neq 10.$

The equation $4x + 3y = 10$ has many solutions. However, if both $x$ and $y$ are required to be whole numbers, then $(1, 2)$ is the only solution. When you find the set of all solutions of an equation, whether it is a one- or two-variable equation, you are said to have **solved** the equation.

**Example 1** Solve $2x + y = 3$ if $x$ and $y$ are whole numbers.

**Solution** If $x = 0$, then $2(0) + y = 3$ and $y = 3$. $(0, 3)$

If $x = 1$, then $2(1) + y = 3$ and $y = 1$. $(1, 1)$

If $x \geq 2$, then $2x \geq 4$ and there are no more solutions.

$\therefore$ the solutions are $(0, 3)$ and $(1, 1)$. *Answer*

**Example 2** Solve $xy = 4 - x$ if $x$ and $y$ are whole numbers.

**Solution** 1. Solve the given equation for $y$ in terms of $x$.

$$xy = 4 - x$$
$$y = \frac{4 - x}{x}$$

2. Replace $x$ with successive whole numbers and calculate the corresponding values of $y$. If $y$ is a whole number, you have found a solution pair.

$\therefore$ the solutions are $(1, 3)$, $(2, 1)$, and $(4, 0)$. **Answer**

| $x$ | $y = \dfrac{4 - x}{x}$ | Solution |
|---|---|---|
| 0 | denominator $= 0$ | No |
| 1 | $\dfrac{4 - 1}{1} = 3$ | $(1, 3)$ |
| 2 | $\dfrac{4 - 2}{2} = 1$ | $(2, 1)$ |
| 3 | $\dfrac{4 - 3}{3} = \dfrac{1}{3}$ | No |
| 4 | $\dfrac{4 - 4}{4} = 0$ | $(4, 0)$ |
| Values of $x$ greater than 4 give negative values of $y$. | | |

**Example 3** Dana spent $13 on posters and notebooks. The posters cost $2 each and the notebooks cost $3 each. How many of each did she buy?

**Solution**

*Step 1* The problem asks for the number of posters and the number of notebooks Dana bought.

*Step 2* Let $p$ = number of posters, and $n$ = number of notebooks.

*Step 3* Since the total cost is $13, you have: $2p + 3n = 13$

*Step 4* Solve for $p$: $2p = 13 - 3n$
$$p = \frac{13 - 3n}{2}$$

Both $n$ and $p$ must be whole numbers because Dana cannot buy a negative or fractional number of posters or notebooks.

*Step 5* Check that $(1, 5)$ and $(3, 2)$ are solutions of the problem:

$$2(5) + 3(1) = 13$$
$$2(2) + 3(3) = 13$$

$\therefore$ Dana bought either 1 notebook and 5 posters or 3 notebooks and 2 posters. **Answer**

|  | Number $\times$ Price $=$ Cost | | |
|---|---|---|---|
| Posters | $p$ | 2 | $2p$ |
| Notebooks | $n$ | 3 | $3n$ |

| $n$ | $p = \dfrac{13 - 3n}{2}$ | Solution |
|---|---|---|
| 1 | $\dfrac{13 - 3}{2} = 5$ | $(1, 5)$ |
| 2 | $\dfrac{13 - 6}{2} = \dfrac{7}{2}$ | No |
| 3 | $\dfrac{13 - 9}{2} = 2$ | $(3, 2)$ |
| 4 | $\dfrac{13 - 12}{2} = \dfrac{1}{2}$ | No |
| Values of $n$ greater than 4 give negative values of $p$. | | |

When solving equations in two variables, it is customary to give the numbers in a solution pair in the alphabetical order of the variables. Therefore, in Example 3 the solutions were given as $(n, p)$ instead of $(p, n)$.

## Oral Exercises

**State whether each ordered pair of numbers is a solution of the given equation.**

**1.** $x - y = 5$
$(9, 4), (7, 3)$

**2.** $x + 2y = 8$
$(3, 3), (0, 4)$

**3.** $3x + y = 6$
$(2, 0), (3, -1)$

**4.** $12 - y = 3x$
$(5, -3), \left(\frac{1}{3}, 11\right)$

**5.** $y = x^2$
$(-3, 9), (4, 2)$

**6.** $x^2 + y^2 = 10$
$(1, 3), (-3, -1)$

**7.** $st = 6$
$(3, -2), \left(\frac{9}{2}, \frac{4}{3}\right)$

**8.** $a^2 - 4b^2 = 0$
$(-2, 1), (1, 2)$

**Solve each equation for $y$ in terms of $x$.**

**9.** $2x + y = 4$     **10.** $3x - y = 7$     **11.** $x = 4 + 3y$     **12.** $2x + 5y = 9$

**Solve each equation if $x$ and $y$ are whole numbers.**

**13.** $x + y = 3$     **14.** $x + 2y = 7$     **15.** $2xy = 8$     **16.** $x^2 = -y^2$

## Written Exercises

**State whether each ordered pair is a solution of the given equation.**

**A**

**1.** $2x + 3y = 13$
$(5, 1), (11, -3)$

**2.** $5x - 4y = 9$
$(7, 6), (-3, -6)$

**3.** $3a - 4b = 11$
$\left(\frac{1}{3}, -\frac{5}{2}\right), \left(-\frac{5}{3}, -4\right)$

**4.** $3m - 2n = 6$
$(0, 3), \left(\frac{5}{3}, -\frac{1}{2}\right)$

**5.** $2x^2 - 4y^2 = 4$
$(4, -3), (0, -1)$

**6.** $x^2 + y^2 = 50$
$(-7, -1), (5, -5)$

**7.** $3st = t^2$
$(-3, -9), \left(\frac{1}{6}, -\frac{1}{2}\right)$

**8.** $ab = a^2 - a$
$(4, 3), (0, 37.2)$

**Solve each equation for $y$ in terms of $x$.**

**9.** $3x - 2y = 7$     **10.** $4y - 3x = 1$     **11.** $7x^2 - 3y = 4$

**12.** $x^2y = 3$     **13.** $\dfrac{8}{x + y} = 6$     **14.** $\dfrac{2}{x} = \dfrac{3}{y + 7}$

**Solve for the variable indicated in color.**

**15.** $2a - 3b = 7$     **16.** $5n + 3m = 7$     **17.** $4p - 3q = 0$

**18.** $5s - 7t = 8$     **19.** $\dfrac{a - 2b}{3} = \dfrac{a}{4}$     **20.** $\dfrac{3n - 2}{5} - \dfrac{1 - m}{4} = \dfrac{1}{2}$

**Solve the following equations if all the variables represent whole numbers.**

**B**  **21.** $x + 2y = 9$  **22.** $3x + y = 7$  **23.** $5x + 2y = 27$  **24.** $3a + 2b = 24$

**25.** $x^2 + y^2 = 25$  **26.** $2s^2 + t^2 = 9$  **27.** $5nm = 30$  **28.** $y^2t = 4$

**29.** Mona bought several 45 rpm records costing $2 each and several LP records costing $8 each. If she spent $34, how many of each kind of record did she buy? (There is more than one solution.)

**30.** Hank and Jill Arbor spent $100 for some spruce trees. Some were blue spruce priced at $20 each, and the rest were green spruce priced at $10 each. How many of each kind of spruce did the Arbors buy? (There is more than one solution.)

**31.** Ed Haley spent $280 for some baby pigs and some chickens. The pigs cost $40 each and the chickens $3 each. If Ed bought more than one pig, how many pigs and how many chickens did he buy?

**32.** The perimeter of the figure at the right is 60. Find $x$ and $y$ if they represent positive integers.

**In Exercises 33–36, find an ordered pair that is a solution of both equations.**

**C**  **33.** $y = 3x$; $2x + y = 15$  **34.** $x = y - 2$; $x + 4y = 18$

**35.** $a + b = 27$; $a - b = 11$  **36.** $3r - s = 2$; $2r + s = 8$

**37.** Solve for $y$: $\dfrac{1}{x} + \dfrac{1}{y} = \dfrac{1}{2}$

**38.** If $a$ and $b$ are positive two-digit integers, how many solutions are there of the equation $2a + 3b = 100$?

## Computer Exercises

*For students with some programming experience*

Write a BASIC program that checks whether an ordered pair entered with an INPUT statement is a solution to a given equation. RUN the program for the following equations with the given ordered pairs.

**1.** $3x - 2y = 1$; $(3, 4)$  **2.** $4x + y = 10$; $(-3, 2)$

**3.** $xy + y^2 = 6$; $(1, 2)$  **4.** $x^2 + y^2 = 25$; $(-4, -3)$

**5.** $x^2y + xy^2 = 0$; $(-1, -1)$  **6.** $x^2 + (xy)^2 = 45$; $(3, -2)$

# 8-2 Points, Lines, and Their Graphs

**Objective** To graph ordered pairs and linear equations in two variables.

You know how to graph a number as a point on a number line. Ordered pairs are graphed as points in a "number plane." You can construct a "number plane" as follows:

1. Draw a horizontal number line, called the **horizontal axis.**
2. Draw a second number line intersecting the first at right angles so that both number lines have the same zero point, or **origin** (*O*). The second number line is called the **vertical axis.**
3. Indicate the positive direction on each axis by an arrowhead. The positive direction is usually to the right on the horizontal axis and upward on the vertical axis, as shown in the first diagram.

The horizontal axis is usually labeled with an *x* and is referred to as the **x-axis.** The vertical axis is usually labeled with a *y* and is referred to as the **y-axis.**

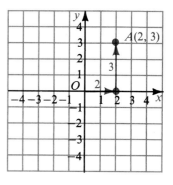

The diagram at the right shows a point *A* that is the **graph of the ordered pair** (2, 3). Point *A* is located by moving 2 units to the right of the origin and 3 units up. The numbers 2 and 3 are called the **coordinates** of point *A*; 2 is the **x-coordinate,** or **abscissa,** of *A* and 3 is the **y-coordinate,** or **ordinate,** of *A*. Although there is a difference between the ordered pair of numbers (2, 3) and the point *A*, it is customary to stress the association between the two by referring to the point *A*(2, 3).

The diagrams below illustrate how to locate, or **plot,** the points *B*(−2, 4), *C*(4, −2), and *D*(−3, −1).

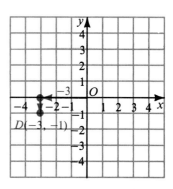

The $x$- and $y$-axes are sometimes referred to as **coordinate axes** and the number plane is then called a **coordinate plane.** The coordinate axes separate a coordinate plane into four **quadrants** as shown in the figure at the right. Points on the coordinate axes are not considered to be in any quadrant.

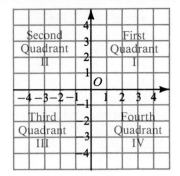

The **graph of an equation** in two variables consists of all the points that are associated with the solutions of the equation. For example, the equation $x + 2y = 6$ has as some of its solutions the ordered pairs $(0, 3)$, $(2, 2)$, $(4, 1)$, $(6, 0)$, and $(-2, 4)$. These solutions are graphed at the left below. Of course, the equation $x + 2y = 6$ has many other solutions too; for example, $(1, 2\frac{1}{2})$ and $(6.2, -0.1)$. The graphs of all solutions lie on the straight line shown at the right below. This line is the graph of the equation $x + 2y = 6$.

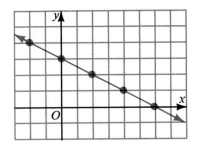

The equation $x + 2y = 6$ is an example of a **linear equation,** so named because its graph is a line. All linear equations in the variables $x$ and $y$ can be written in the form

$$ax + by = c$$

where $a$, $b$, and $c$ are real numbers with $a$ and $b$ not both zero. If $a$, $b$, and $c$ are integers, the equation is said to be in **standard form.**

| Linear equations in standard form | Linear equations not in standard form | Nonlinear equations |
|---|---|---|
| $2x - 5y = 7$ | $\frac{1}{2}x + 4y = 12$ | $x^2y + 3y = 4$ |
| $4x + 9y = 0$ | $y = 3x - 2$ | $xy = 6$ |
| $y = 3$ | $x + y - 1 = x - y + 1$ | $\frac{1}{x} + 3y = 1$ |

Since two points determine a line, you need to find only two solutions of a linear equation in order to graph it. However, it is a good idea to find a third solution as a check. The most convenient solutions to use are those where the line crosses the $x$-axis ($y = 0$) and the $y$-axis ($x = 0$).

**Example 1**  Graph $2x - 3y = 6$ in a coordinate plane.

**Solution**    Let $y = 0$:                          Let $x = 0$:
$$2x - 3(0) = 6$$                    $$2(0) - 3y = 6$$
$$2x = 6$$                          $$-3y = 6$$
$$x = 3;\ Solution\ (3, 0)$$        $$y = -2;\ Solution\ (0, -2)$$

Any third solution, such as $(6, 2)$, can be used as a check.

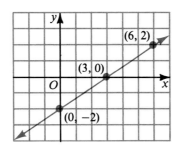

**Example 2**  **a.** Graph $x = 2$ in a coordinate plane.
**b.** Graph $y = -3$ in a coordinate plane.

**Solution**   **a.** The equation places no restriction on $y$. All points with
$x$-coordinate 2 are graphs of solutions. The graph of
$x = 2$ is a vertical line.

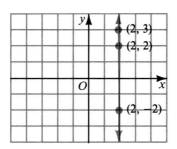

**b.** The equation places no restriction on $x$. All points with
$y$-coordinate $-3$ are graphs of solutions. The graph of
$y = -3$ is a horizontal line.

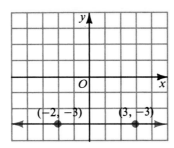

# Oral Exercises

**Exercises 1–20 refer to the diagram below.**

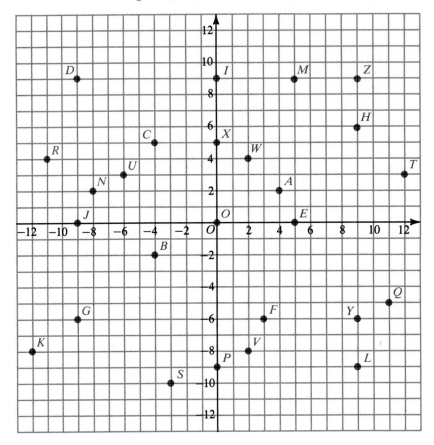

**Name the point that is the graph of each ordered pair.**

1. $(2, 4)$
2. $(4, 2)$
3. $(-6, 3)$
4. $(3, -6)$
5. $(9, 6)$
6. $(9, -6)$
7. $(0, -9)$
8. $(-9, 0)$
9. $(0, 9)$
10. $(11, -5)$
11. $(-11, 4)$
12. $(-3, -10)$

**Give the coordinates and the quadrant (if any) of each point.**

13. $M$
14. $L$
15. $D$
16. $B$
17. $E$
18. $V$
19. $G$
20. $X$

**Describe the graphs of the following equations.**

21. **a.** $x = 2$      **b.** $x = -1$      **c.** $x = 0$
22. **a.** $y = -3$      **b.** $y = 4$      **c.** $y = 0$

Give the coordinates of the points where each graph crosses the $x$-axis and the $y$-axis.

**23.** $2x + y = 8$ **24.** $3x - y = 9$ **25.** $2x + 3y = 12$

Classify each equation as a linear equation in standard form, a linear equation not in standard form, or a nonlinear equation.

**26.** $5x + 3y = 2$ **27.** $\dfrac{5}{x} + \dfrac{3}{y} = 2$ **28.** $\dfrac{x}{5} + \dfrac{y}{3} = 2$

**29.** $4x^2 + y^2 = 4$ **30.** $x + y = x - y$ **31.** $xy = 4$

## Written Exercises

Plot the graph of each of the given points.

A  **1.** $A(5, 3)$ **2.** $B(7, 2)$ **3.** $C(-5, -3)$ **4.** $D(-7, -2)$
   **5.** $E(-8, 0)$ **6.** $F(0, -8)$ **7.** $G(-6, 4)$ **8.** $H(4, -6)$
   **9.** $O(0, 0)$ **10.** $P(-3, 5)$ **11.** $R(7, -2)$ **12.** $S(-4, -6)$

Plot the points $A$, $B$, $C$, and $D$. Then connect $A$ to $B$, $B$ to $C$, $C$ to $D$, and $D$ to $A$. Is the resulting figure best described as a square, a rectangle, a parallelogram, or a trapezoid?

**13.** $A(-3, -4)$, $B(5, -2)$, $C(6, 4)$, $D(-2, 2)$  **14.** $A(-2, 0)$, $B(0, -4)$, $C(4, -2)$, $D(2, 2)$
**15.** $A(-4, -1)$, $B(-6, 5)$, $C(3, 8)$, $D(5, 2)$  **16.** $A(-1, 4)$, $B(0, 1)$, $C(4, -1)$, $D(7, 0)$

Refer to the diagram on the previous page. Name the point(s) described.

**17.** The point is on the positive $x$-axis.  **18.** The point is on the negative $y$-axis.
**19.** The $x$-coordinate equals the $y$-coordinate.
**20.** The $x$-coordinate is the opposite of the $y$-coordinate.
**21.** The $x$-coordinate is zero.
**22.** The $y$-coordinate is zero.
**23.** This point in Quadrant III is nearest the $x$-axis.
**24.** This point in Quadrant IV is nearest the $y$-axis.

Graph each equation.

**25.** $x = 3$ **26.** $y = 5$ **27.** $y = -2$ **28.** $x = -5$
**29.** $x - y = 6$ **30.** $x + y = 8$ **31.** $y = 2x + 3$ **32.** $y = -2x + 3$
**33.** $2x + y = 6$ **34.** $x - 3y = 9$ **35.** $4x - 3y = 12$ **36.** $2x + 5y = 10$

B  **37.** $\dfrac{x}{2} = \dfrac{y}{3}$ **38.** $\dfrac{x}{4} + y = 0$ **39.** $\dfrac{x - y}{2} = \dfrac{x + y}{4}$ **40.** $\dfrac{y}{4} - \dfrac{x}{3} = \dfrac{1}{2}$

**41.** In one coordinate plane, graph the following six equations.

    **a.** $y = x$  **b.** $y = 2x$  **c.** $y = 3x$  **d.** $y = -x$  **e.** $y = -2x$  **f.** $y = -3x$

**42.** In one coordinate plane, graph the following four equations.

    **a.** $y = x + 1$    **b.** $y = x + 3$    **c.** $y = x - 1$    **d.** $y = x - 3$

**In Exercises 43 and 44, (a) graph both equations in the same coordinate plane, (b) give the point that the graphs have in common, and (c) check that the coordinates of this point satisfy both equations.**

**43.** $3x - y = 9$ and $3x - 5y = -15$            **44.** $2x - 3y = 12$ and $3x + 2y = 5$

---

## Computer Exercises      *For students with some programming experience*

**1.** Modify the BASIC program you wrote for the Computer Exercises on page 338 so that it will check whether an ordered pair entered with an INPUT statement is a solution to a pair of linear equations $Ax + By = C$ and $Dx + Ey = F$. $A$, $B$, $C$, $D$, $E$, and $F$ should also be entered with INPUT statements. RUN the program for the following pairs of linear equations.

  **a.** $x + 2y = 5$  $(-3, 4)$      **b.** $5x - y = 7$  $(1, -2)$      **c.** $x = -5$  $(-5, 3)$
       $x + y = 1$                $3x + 2y = 1$               $y = 3$

**2.** Write a BASIC program that will find the points where a linear equation $Px + Qy = R$ will cross the x-axis and the y-axis, where $P$, $Q$, and $R$ are entered with INPUT statements. The program should report if the graph does not cross either the x-axis or the y-axis. RUN the program for the following linear equations.

  **a.** $2x - 3y = 6$                 **b.** $8x + y = 12$
  **c.** $7x + 0y = -14$             **d.** $0 - 5y = 2$
  **e.** $3x + 3y = 8$                **f.** $6x - 4y = 9$

---

# Self-Test 1

**Vocabulary**      solution (p. 335)                 abscissa (p. 339)
                       ordered pair (p. 335)        y-coordinate (p. 339)
                       horizontal axis (p. 339)     ordinate (p. 339)
                       vertical axis (p. 339)       plot (p. 339)
                       origin (p. 339)               coordinate axes (p. 340)
                       x-axis (p. 339)              coordinate plane (p. 340)
                       y-axis (p. 339)              quadrants (p. 340)
                       graph of an ordered pair (p. 339)     graph of an equation (p. 340)
                       coordinates (p. 339)         linear equation (p. 340)
                       x-coordinate (p. 339)       standard form (p. 340)

**State whether or not each ordered pair of numbers is a solution of the given equation.**

**1.** $2x + 4y = 12$

$(2, 2),\ \left(7, \dfrac{1}{2}\right)$

**2.** $3x + 5y = 30$    Obj. 8-1, p. 335

$(3, 5),\ (10, 0)$

**Solve each equation for $y$ in terms of $x$.**

**3.** $2x - 3y = 6$

**4.** $5y + 2x = 10$

**Plot the graph of each of the given ordered pairs.**

**5.** $(3, 7)$        **6.** $(-2, 4)$        **7.** $(-5, -2)$        Obj. 8-2, p. 339

**Graph the equation.**

**8.** $y = 4$        **9.** $x + y = 6$        **10.** $2x + 3y = 12$

Check your answers with those at the back of the book.

## Computer Key-In

### Exercises

**1. a.** Write a program that will print out ordered pairs of integers that can be used to graph $Ax + By = C$ when $A$ and $B$ are not zero. Let $X$ vary from $-5$ to $5$.

   **b.** RUN the program for $2x + 3y = 6$ and $2x - 3y = 6$.

**2. a.** Change the program that you wrote for part (a) of Exercise 1 to print out pairs of whole numbers. Let $x$ vary from 0 to 10.

   **b.** RUN this program for $2x + 3y = 6$ and $2x - 3y = 6$.

**3. a.** Change the program that you wrote for part (a) of Exercise 1 to print out pairs of integers for $xy = k$. Avoid $x = 0$.

   **b.** RUN the program for $xy = 12$ and $xy = -12$.

*Note:* The programs of Exercises 1 and 2 above can be used to do Exercises 29–36 on page 343.

## Challenge

Find the smallest positive integer that when divided by 2, 3, and 7 leaves remainders of 1, 2, and 6, respectively.

# Solving Systems of Linear Equations

## 8-3 The Graphic Method

**Objective**   To use graphs to solve systems of linear equations.

Two equations in the same variables form a **system of equations. A solution of a system** of two equations in two variables is an ordered pair of numbers that satisfies each of the equations. For example, consider the system

$$x - y = 4 \quad \text{and} \quad 2x + y = 5.$$

The ordered pair $(3, -1)$ is a solution of this system because, when you substitute 3 for $x$ and $-1$ for $y$, you obtain

$$3 - (-1) = 4 \quad \text{and} \quad 2 \cdot 3 + (-1) = 5.$$

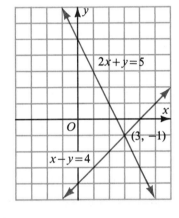

The graphs of $x - y = 4$ and $2x + y = 5$ are shown at the right. Notice that the point $(3, -1)$ is the **intersection point** of the graphs. Since no other point lies on both of these lines, $(3, -1)$ is the only solution.

Not all systems of equations have a solution, and some have more than one solution. The diagram at the right shows the graphs of the equations:

$$x + 3y = \phantom{-}6$$
$$x + 3y = -3$$

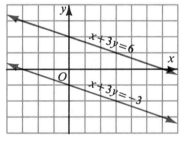

The graphs do not intersect. Lines in the same plane that do not intersect are **parallel lines.** This system has *no solution.*

The next diagram shows the graphs of:

$$x - 2y = \phantom{1}4$$
$$3x - 6y = 12$$

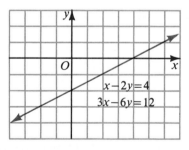

The graphs *coincide.* Every solution of either equation is a solution of the other. The equations are equivalent (divide both sides of the second equation by 3). The coordinates of every point on the line shown form a solution. This system has an unlimited, or *infinite,* number of solutions.

Because a system of two equations imposes two conditions on the variables at the same time, the system is often called a **system of simultaneous equations.** When you find all the solutions of a system of simultaneous equations, you have **solved the system,** or **found the solution set.** The method of solving a system by using graphs is called the **graphic method.**

## The Graphic Method

To solve a system of linear equations in two variables, draw the graph of each linear equation in the same coordinate plane.

1. If the lines intersect, the coordinates of the intersection point give the solution of the system.
2. If the lines are parallel, there is no solution.
3. If the lines coincide, there are an infinite number of solutions.

## Oral Exercises

**State whether the given ordered pair is a solution of the system.**

**1.** $(3, 1)$
$$3x - y = 8$$
$$x + y = 4$$

**2.** $(-1, 4)$
$$4x + 3y = 8$$
$$3x + y = 0$$

**3.** $(3, -3)$
$$7x = 12 - 3y$$
$$y = 2x - 9$$

**State the solution of each system.**

**4.**

**5.**

**6.**

**7.**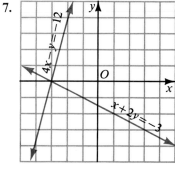

**8.** Suppose the graphs of a pair of linear equations appear to intersect in the point $(3, -2)$. How can you check whether $(3, -2)$ really is a solution of the system?

**9.** If a system of linear equations has no solution, what do you know about the graphs of the equations?

**10.** Suppose $(1, 5)$ and $(3, 7)$ are known to be solutions of a system of two linear equations. Are there any other solutions?

## Written Exercises

**Solve each system by the graphic method.**

A
**1.** $y = x$
$y = 9 - 2x$

**2.** $y = -x$
$y = x + 4$

**3.** $x + y = 2$
$y = 2x + 5$

**4.** $3x + y = 1$
$y = x - 3$

**5.** $x - y = 6$
$2x + y = 0$

**6.** $2x - y = -1$
$3x + y = 6$

**7.** $3x - 9y = 0$
$3y + 3 = x$

**8.** $y = 3x$
$x + y = 8$

**9.** $y = \frac{1}{2}x + 1$
$x + 2 = 2y$

**10.** $2y - x = 2$
$x - 2y = 8$

**11.** $y - 2x = -5$
$y - x = -3$

**12.** $6x - 3y = 9$
$\dfrac{y + 3}{2} = x$

**Solve each system graphically. Estimate the coordinates of the intersection point to the nearest half unit.**

B
**13.** $x + y = 3$
$x - y = 4$

**14.** $2x + y = -2$
$2x - 3y = 15$

**15.** $3x + 5y = 15$
$x - y = 4$

**16.** $3y - 2x = 6$
$3y + 2x = 15$

The graphic method of solving a system of equations is particularly useful when the equations are not linear. Estimate the solutions of each nonlinear system below by studying the graphs. Check whether your estimate satisfies both equations.

**17.** $y = x^2$ and $y = 8 - x^2$

**18.** $y = x^2 - 4x$ and $y = -x^2 + 10x - 20$

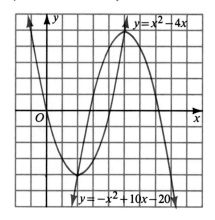

348     *Chapter 8*

19. Where on the graph of $5x - 2y = 15$ is the $x$-coordinate equal to the $y$-coordinate?

20. Where on the graph of $3x - y = 12$ are the $x$- and $y$-coordinates opposites of each other?

21. Where on the graph of $4x + y + 12 = 0$ is the $y$-coordinate twice the $x$-coordinate?

**C** 22. The triangular region is enclosed by the $x$-axis and by the graphs of $y = \frac{1}{2}x$ and $x + y = 9$. Find the area of this region. (*Hint:* Area of a triangle $= \frac{1}{2} \times$ base $\times$ height.)

23. Find the area of the triangular region enclosed by the $y$-axis and the graphs of $x + 3y = 12$ and $x - 3y = 0$.

24. Find the area of the triangular region whose vertices are the points of intersection of the graphs of $2x + y = 5$, $y = x - 4$, and $y = 5$.

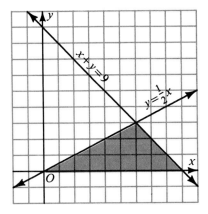

---

# *Career Note* / *Accountant*

A company is considering opening a branch office. Before making a decision, the managers of the company will analyze financial reports prepared by an accountant. Accountants are responsible for recording and analyzing financial information. Some accountants specialize in a particular area of financial management, such as tax matters or budgeting. Accountants may serve as consultants to management or they may audit records, examining them for accuracy.

Accountants may work for the public, for government, or for industry. Certification is valuable in each of these fields, but it is a necessity for anyone considering work as a certified public accountant. To become certified, a candidate must pass an intensive four-part examination. Many states require an accountant to have a college degree and some states require additional college work beyond a bachelor's degree. Persons considering accounting as a career should be able to interpret facts and figures and to communicate clearly.

# 8-4 The Substitution Method

**Objective**  To use the substitution method to solve systems of linear equations in two variables.

When the solution of a system of equations is an ordered pair that is not located near the origin or that does not contain whole numbers, the graphic method will not be useful. There are several algebraic methods of solving a system of equations without using their graphs. One of these is the **substitution method** illustrated in the examples below.

**Example 1**  Solve:  $x + y = 14$
$$3x + 2y = 48$$

**Solution**

1. Solve the first equation for $y$.

$$x + y = 14$$
$$y = 14 - x$$

2. Substitute this expression for $y$ in the other equation, and solve for $x$.

$$3x + 2y = 48$$
$$3x + 2(14 - x) = 48$$
$$3x + 28 - 2x = 48$$
$$x + 28 = 48$$
$$x = 20$$

3. Substitute this value for $x$ in the equation of Step 1, and find $y$.

$$y = 14 - x$$
$$y = 14 - 20$$
$$y = -6$$

4. Check in *both* equations.

$$x + y = 14 \qquad\qquad\qquad 3x + 2y = 48$$
$$20 + (-6) \overset{?}{=} 14 \qquad 3(20) + 2(-6) \overset{?}{=} 48$$
$$14 = 14 \ \checkmark \qquad\qquad\qquad 48 = 48 \ \checkmark$$

∴ the solution is $(20, -6)$.  **Answer**

In the first step of Example 1, it would have been just as easy to solve for $x$ as it was for $y$. In the first step of Example 2 below, however, it is easier to solve the second equation for $x$ than for $y$.

**Example 2**  Solve: $3x + 2y = 11$
$$x + 4y = 2$$

**Solution**

1. Solve the second equation for $x$ (since its coefficient is 1).

$$x + 4y = 2$$
$$x = 2 - 4y$$

2. Substitute this expression for $x$ in the other equation, and solve for $y$.

$$3x + 2y = 11$$
$$3(2 - 4y) + 2y = 11$$
$$6 - 12y + 2y = 11$$
$$-10y = 5$$
$$y = -\frac{1}{2}$$

3. Substitute this value for $y$ in the
equation of Step 1, and find $x$.

$$x = 2 - 4y$$
$$x = 2 - 4\left(-\frac{1}{2}\right)$$
$$x = 4$$

4. The check in *both* equations is left to you.

$\therefore$ the solution is $\left(4, -\frac{1}{2}\right)$. **Answer**

The substitution method is most convenient to use when the coefficient of one of the variables is 1 or $-1$. The method is used to find an *equivalent system* of equations whose solution is readily seen. An **equivalent system** of equations is one with the same solution set as another system.

## The Substitution Method

To solve a system of linear equations in two variables:

1. Solve one equation for one of the variables.
2. Substitute this expression in the other equation and solve.
3. Find the corresponding value of the other variable.
4. Check in both equations.

## Oral Exercises

**For each system, solve one of the equations for one of the variables.**

**1.** $y - 5x = 0$
$x + y = 12$

**2.** $2x - 3y = 5$
$x + y = 0$

**3.** $5s + 3t = 1$
$3s - t = 9$

**4.** $3a + 2b = 13$
$4a = b + 19$

**5.** $2n + 5m = 14$
$\dfrac{n}{2} = \dfrac{m}{4}$

**6.** $3p - 10 = 4q$
$\dfrac{p}{6} + \dfrac{q}{3} = 0$

**Solve by the substitution method.**

**7.** $x = 3$
$y = x - 2$

**8.** $y = x - 8$
$y = 4$

**9.** $m = -2$
$2n = m$

**10.** $y = 4x$
$x + y = 10$

**11.** $y = 3x$
$x + y = 20$

**12.** $y = x - 2$
$x + y = 12$

**13.** $x = y + 1$
$4y + x = 6$

**14.** $x = 3y$
$5y - x = 8$

**15.** $a = b + 8$
$5b = a$

**16.** $2x - 3y = 5$
$x + 3y = -2$

**17.** $5v + u = -17$
$3u = 4v + 6$

**18.** $4a = 3b + 15$
$2b - a = 0$

## Written Exercises

**Solve by the substitution method.**

**A**
**1.** $y = 5x$
$x + y = 30$

**2.** $y = x + 2$
$2x + y = 17$

**3.** $x = 4y$
$2x + 5y = 26$

**4.** $3y - x = 4$
$x = 7 + 2y$

**5.** $b - 3a = 1$
$4b = 16a$

**6.** $3n - m = 13$
$2m + 3n = 16$

**7.** $4p + 2q = 10$
$p - 5q = 8$

**8.** $r = 3s - 5$
$s = 4r - 2$

**9.** $5c - 2d = 0$
$6d = 1 + c$

**10.** $3a + 5b = 7$
$b - 6 = 4a$

**11.** $3s - t = 1$
$2s + 3t = 5$

**12.** $2x + 3z = 0$
$x + 5 = 6z$

**13.** $p - 5q = 6$
$3p - 2q = 5$

**14.** $10d + 25q = 335$
$d + q = 20$

**15.** $2a - b = 1$
$a = \frac{3}{5}b$

**16.** $3x + 2y = 550$
$x = \frac{4}{5}y$

**17.** $c - d = 8$
$\frac{c}{5} = d + 4$

**18.** $\frac{x}{2} - t = 1$
$x + t + 7 = 0$

**19.** $\frac{a}{3} + \frac{b}{3} = 2$
$2a + 3b = 10$

**20.** $\frac{n}{2} + \frac{m}{2} = 7$
$3n + 2m = 48$

**21.** $\frac{x + y}{2} = 10$
$2x = 3y$

**22.** $\frac{1}{6}(x + y) = 2$
$\frac{1}{4}(x - y) = 2$

**23.** $\frac{r}{2} + \frac{s}{3} = 1$
$\frac{r}{4} + \frac{2s}{3} = -1$

**24.** $\frac{c}{2} - \frac{d}{5} = -4$
$\frac{2c}{3} - \frac{3d}{5} = -7$

**B 25.** $\frac{3x + y}{4} = \frac{x + 1}{2}$
$\frac{x - y}{4} = 1$

**26.** $\frac{3a - b}{4} = a + 1$
$\frac{5a + b}{2} = a$

**27.** $2x - \frac{y + 2}{2} = 22$
$3x + \frac{y + 2}{3} = 7$

**Determine whether each of the following systems has no solution or an infinite number of solutions. If there is an infinite number of solutions, give three of them.**

**28.** $3y - x = 4$
$x = 7 + 3y$

**29.** $3y - 6x = 24$
$8 + 2x = y$

**30.** $2x = 14y$
$\frac{x - y}{3} = \frac{x + y}{4}$

**In each exercise, two equivalent systems of linear equations are given. Find the values of $A$ and $B$.**

**31.** $x + y = 14$     $Ax + y = 30$
$x - y = 2$     $2x + By = 10$

**32.** $2x + y = 6$     $x + By = -4$
$3x - 2y = 2$     $Ax + 3y = 10$

33. Without drawing the graphs, show that the graphs of $3x - y = 7$ and $6x - 2y = 5$ are parallel lines.

34. The graphs of the equations $ax + 4y = 6$ and $x + by = -8$ intersect at $(-2, 3)$. Find $a$ and $b$.

35. The graphs of $ax + by = 13$ and $ax - by = -3$ intersect at $(1, 4)$. Find $a$ and $b$.

**C** 36. The graphs of $x + 2y = 7$, $4x - y = 1$, and $6x + ay = 0$ intersect at the same point. Find $a$.

37. Determine whether the lines $3x - 5y = -1$, $x - y = 3$, and $2x - 3y = 1$ intersect at the same point.

**Use the substitution method to solve each system.**

38. $x + y + z = 180$
$y = 3x$
$z = 5x$

39. $a + b + c = 62$
$a = 2c - 5$
$b = 3c - 5$

40. $x + y + 2z = 1$
$x - y = 1$
$x - z = 2$

41. $x - 2y + 3z = 13$
$x - 3z = -1$
$y + z = 1$

42. $c - a = b + 6$
$a + 5 = \frac{1}{2}c$
$a - 5 = \frac{1}{3}(b + 5)$

43. $a + b + c + d = 2$
$a - c = -2$
$b + c = 5$
$c - d = 7$

---

## Computer Exercises  *For students with some programming experience*

Write a BASIC program to print out a table of ordered pairs for each of two linear equations $Ax + By = C$ and $Dx + Ey = F$, where $A$, $B$, $C$, $D$, $E$, and $F$ are entered with INPUT statements. The values of $x$ should be a set of consecutive integers. If the two equations have an ordered pair in common, the program should report that the ordered pair is a solution of the system of equations. RUN the program for the given pairs of equations.

1. $2x - 7y = 9$
   $x + y = 0$
   $x = \{0, 1, 2, 3, 4, 5\}$

2. $x + 3y = 1$
   $\frac{1}{2}x - 4y = -5$
   $x = \{-3, -2, -1, 0, 1\}$

3. $4x - 3y = 0$
   $2x + y = 2$
   $x = \{0, 1, 2, 3, 4\}$

4. $3x - 4y = -6$
   $3x - 2y = 0$
   $x = \{-2, -1, 0, 1, 2\}$

# 8-5 Solving Problems with Two Variables

**Objective**  To use systems of linear equations in two variables to solve problems.

You have learned to solve problems using equations in one variable. Now you can solve problems with equations in two variables. Example 1 compares these two methods.

**Example 1**  June has 20 coins, all nickels and dimes, worth $1.45. How many nickels and how many dimes does June have?

**Solution 1** (one variable)

*Step 1*  The problem asks for the number of nickels and the number of dimes.

*Step 2*  Let $x$ = the number of nickels. Then $20 - x$ = the number of dimes. Make a chart.

|  | Number $\times$ Value per coin = Total Value | | |
|---|---|---|---|
| Nickels | $x$ | 5 | $5x$ |
| Dimes | $20 - x$ | 10 | $10(20 - x)$ |

*Step 3*  The only fact not recorded in this chart is the total value of the coins, $1.45. Use this fact to write an equation.

$$5x + 10(20 - x) = 145$$

*Step 4*  
$$5x + 200 - 10x = 145$$
$$-5x = -55$$
$$x = 11$$
$$20 - x = 9$$

*Step 5*  The check is left to you.
∴ June has 11 nickels and 9 dimes. **Answer**

**Solution 2** (two variables)

*Step 1*  The problem asks for the number of nickels and the number of dimes.

*Step 2*  Let $n$ = the number of nickels and $d$ = the number of dimes. Make a chart.

|  | Number $\times$ Value per coin = Total Value | | |
|---|---|---|---|
| Nickels | $n$ | 5 | $5n$ |
| Dimes | $d$ | 10 | $10d$ |

*Step 3* The two facts not recorded in the chart are the total number of coins, 20, and the total value, $1.45. Use these facts to write a system of equations.

$$n + d = 20$$
$$5n + 10d = 145$$

*Step 4* $d = 20 - n$         {Find $d$ in terms of $n$.
$$5n + 10(20 - n) = 145 \quad \text{\{Substitute.}$$
$$5n + 200 - 10n = 145$$
$$-5n = -55$$
$$n = 11$$
$$d = 20 - n = 20 - 11 = 9$$

*Step 5* The check is left to you.
∴ June has 11 nickels and 9 dimes. **Answer**

It may appear that the two-variable solution involves more work than the one-variable solution. However, the two-variable solution has the advantage that the variables $n$ and $d$ remind you of nickels and dimes, so that you can write the equations $n + d = 20$ and $5n + 10d = 145$ more easily than the one-variable equation. Example 2 also shows that a wise choice of variables can make it easier to write equations that will solve the problem. Here $A$ and $B$ represent Al's money and Bob's money, respectively.

**Example 2**   Al and Bob together have $80. Al has $5 more than twice Bob's amount. How much money does each have?

**Solution**

*Step 1* The problem asks for the amount of money each person has.

*Step 2* Let $A$ = the amount of Al's money and $B$ = the amount of Bob's money.

*Step 3* $A + B = 80$
$$A = 5 + 2B$$

*Step 4* $(5 + 2B) + B = 80$   {Substitute $5 + 2B$ for $A$.
$$5 + 3B = 80$$
$$3B = 75$$
$$B = 25$$
$$A = 5 + 2(25) = 55$$

*Step 5* *Check:*   $A + B = 80$
$$A = 5 + 2B$$
$$55 + 25 \overset{?}{=} 80; \quad 80 = 80 \;\checkmark$$
$$55 \overset{?}{=} 5 + 50; \quad 55 = 55 \;\checkmark$$
∴ Bob has $25 and Al has $55. **Answer**

## Oral Exercises

**Give a system of equations that can be used to solve each problem.**

**In Problems 1–4 use *n*, *d*, and *q* for the number of nickels, the number of dimes, and the number of quarters, respectively.**

1. May has 30 nickels and dimes worth $2.40. How many nickels does May have?

2. Ed has 24 dimes and quarters worth $3.60. How many quarters does Ed have?

3. Peg has $5.50 in dimes and quarters. She has 8 more quarters than dimes. How many quarters does she have?

4. Luis and Julia have the same number of coins. Luis has only dimes and Julia has only quarters. If Julia has $1.80 more than Luis does, how much does each have?

**In Problems 5–8, use *C*, *D*, *S*, and *T* for the amounts of money that Connie, Dick, Steve, and Tracy have, respectively.**

5. Dick and Connie together have $36. Connie has $17 more than Dick. How much does each have?

6. Steve has three times as much money as Dick. Together they have $72. How much does each have?

7. Tracy has $12 more than Connie. If Tracy had $8 more, she would have twice as much as Connie. How much does each have?

8. Steve has $3 more than twice as much as Tracy. Together they have $57. How much does each have?

**In Exercises 9–14, use whatever variables seem appropriate.**

9. Pat and Mike purchased a radio for $88. Pat paid $17 more than Mike. How much did each pay?

10. Sylvia sold twice as many tickets as Frank. They sold 54 tickets in all. How many did each sell?

11. The length of a rectangle is 1 cm less than twice its width. If the perimeter is 40 cm, find the dimensions.

12. Pea Porridge Pond was stocked with 2000 fish, all bass and trout. The ratio of bass to trout was 3 to 2. How many of each kind of fish were put in the pond?

**13.** A person invests $5000 in treasury notes and bonds. The notes pay 8% annual interest and the bonds pay 10% annual interest. If the annual income is $480, how much is invested in treasury notes?

**14.** Adult tickets to a play cost $5 and student tickets cost $2. In all, 720 tickets were sold for a total of $2640. How many student tickets were sold?

## Problems

**A  1-14.** Solve the problems given in Oral Exercises 1-14.

**Solve, using two equations in two variables.**

**B  15.** The sum of two numbers is 38. Four times the smaller number exceeds three times the larger number by 12. Find the numbers.

**16.** One number is 5 more than half of another number. The sum of the numbers is 47. Find the numbers.

**17.** Alan Keme paid $2.94 for a liter of milk and two liters of fruit juice. He wanted to buy two liters of milk and one liter of fruit juice, but this would have cost $3.12 and Alan only had $3. How much does a liter of milk cost?

**18.** The length of a rectangle exceeds its width by 3 m. The perimeter is 58 m. Find the dimensions.

**19.** Elma Lincoln invested $4000 more in bonds paying 12% annual interest than she did in stocks paying dividends of 5% per year. Her total annual income from these investments is $814.90. How much did she invest in bonds?

**20.** A grocer wants to mix together some cashews costing $8 per kilogram with some Brazil nuts costing $10 per kilogram. The grocer wants to sell 12 kg of the mixture for $8.50 per kilogram. How many kilograms of cashews are needed?

**21.** One number is 16 more than another. If the smaller number is subtracted from two thirds of the larger number, the result is one fourth of the sum of the two numbers. Find the numbers.

**Solve each problem by using a system of three equations in three variables.**

**C  22.** I have 30 coins, all nickels, dimes, and quarters, worth $4.60. There are three times as many quarters as nickels and two more dimes than quarters. How many of each kind of coin do I have?

**23.** Carl, Diane, and Ed together have $46. Carl has half as much as Diane, and Diane has $2 more than Ed. How much does each have?

# 8-6 The Addition-or-Subtraction Method

**Objective**    To use addition or subtraction to solve systems of linear equations in two variables.

When solving a system of two equations, you can sometimes add or subtract the equations to obtain a new equation with just one variable. This method is called the *addition-or-subtraction* method.

**Example 1**          Solve: $3x - y = 8$
(The Addition Method)          $2x + y = 7$

## Solution

1. Add similar terms of the two equations.

$$\begin{array}{r} 3x - y = 8 \\ 2x + y = 7 \\ \hline 5x \quad\;\; = 15 \end{array}$$
$\left\{ \begin{array}{l} \text{The } y\text{-terms are} \\ \text{eliminated.} \end{array} \right.$

2. Solve the resulting equation.

$$x \quad = 3$$

3. Substitute $x = 3$ in either of the original equations to find $y$.

$$\begin{array}{r} 2x + y = 7 \\ 2 \cdot 3 + y = 7 \\ y = 1 \end{array}$$

4. Check in both original equations:

$$\begin{array}{c} 2x + y = 7 \\ 2 \cdot 3 + 1 \overset{?}{=} 7 \\ 7 = 7 \; \checkmark \end{array} \qquad \begin{array}{c} 3x - y = 8 \\ 3 \cdot 3 - 1 \overset{?}{=} 8 \\ 8 = 8 \; \checkmark \end{array}$$

∴ the solution is (3, 1). **Answer**

**Example 2**          Solve: $4s + 5t = 6$
(The Subtraction Method)          $4s - 2t = -8$

## Solution

1. Subtract similar terms of the two equations.

$$\begin{array}{r} 4s + 5t = 6 \\ 4s - 2t = -8 \\ \hline 7t = 14 \end{array}$$
$\left\{ \begin{array}{l} \text{The } s\text{-terms are} \\ \text{eliminated.} \end{array} \right.$

2. Solve the resulting equation.

$$t = 2$$

3. Substitute $t = 2$ in either of the original equations to find $s$.

$$\begin{array}{r} 4s + 5t = 6 \\ 4s + 5 \cdot 2 = 6 \\ 4s = -4 \\ s = -1 \end{array}$$

4. The check in both original equations is left to you.

∴ the solution is $(-1, 2)$. **Answer**

The addition-or-subtraction method is based on the addition property of equality. Note that in Example 2 the coefficients of $s$ are the *same*, and in Example 1 the coefficients of $y$ are *opposites*. Whenever two equations have the same or opposite coefficients for one of their terms, the addition-or-subtraction method can be used.

### The Addition-or-Subtraction Method

To solve a system of linear equations in two variables:

1. Add or subtract the equations to eliminate one variable.
2. Solve the resulting equation for the other variable.
3. Substitute in either original equation to find the value of the first variable.
4. Check in both equations.

## Oral Exercises

**Use the addition method to solve for x.**

1. $3x + 2y = 7$
   $5x - 2y = 1$

2. $x - 5y = 1$
   $2x + 5y = 17$

3. $4y + 3x = 9$
   $-4y - x = 7$

**Use the subtraction method to solve for s.**

4. $3t + 5s = 10$
   $3t + s = 2$

5. $4s - 5t = 7$
   $2s - 5t = 3$

6. $3s + 4t = 18$
   $-2s + 4t = 8$

**Use the addition-or-subtraction method to solve for one of the variables.**

7. $3a + 2b = 11$
   $2a - 2b = 4$

8. $3p + 2q = 19$
   $3p - 5q = 5$

9. $-4s + 7t = 10$
   $4s - 2t = 8$

## Written Exercises

**Solve by the addition-or-subtraction method.**

**A**

1. $x + y = 9$
   $x - y = 1$

2. $a - b = 17$
   $a + b = 7$

3. $2r - 3s = 17$
   $2r + 3s = -1$

4. $2a - b = 3$
   $4a + b = 9$

5. $2p - 5q = 30$
   $2p + 7q = 6$

6. $7m + 8n = -10$
   $7m + 2n = 8$

7. $2r - 5s = 14$
   $2r + 3s = 10$

8. $2k - 5p = 17$
   $6k - 5p = 1$

9. $3x - 2y = 13$
   $4x + 2y = 8$

**Solve by the addition-or-subtraction method.**

**10.** $4n - 7m = 13$
$2n - 7m = 3$

**11.** $6a + 9b = 4$
$6a + 3b = 0$

**12.** $-4x + y = 7$
$4x + 3y = 5$

**13.** Without drawing the graphs, state where the lines $2x + 4y = 2$ and $6x - 4y = 2$ intersect.

**14.** State on which coordinate axis the two lines $5x - y = 3$ and $10x - y = 3$ intersect.

**Express each equation in standard form. Then solve by either the substitution method or the addition-or-subtraction method.**

**B** **15.** $a = 6b + 3$
$a + 2b = 5$

**16.** $x - 5y = 2$
$2x + y = 4$

**17.** $c - 2d = 7$
$c + 3d = 2$

**18.** $4(x - 2y) = 8$
$x + 6y = 2$

**19.** $4(a - 2b) = 8$
$2(a + 4b) = -8$

**20.** $n = 2 - 6m$
$\frac{1}{2}n - m = 1$

**21.** $\frac{1}{2}(c + d) + 1 = 0$
$\frac{1}{2}(c - d) - 2 = 0$

**22.** $\frac{1}{3}a - \frac{2}{3}b = 1$
$a + b + 7 = 0$

**23.** $y = \frac{2}{3}x$
$x + 6y = 30$

**24.** $\frac{5a}{6} - \frac{b}{3} = 6$
$a + 2b = 0$

**25.** $3n + 1 = \frac{k}{4}$
$n = \frac{k + 1}{15}$

**26.** $\frac{x + y}{3} - \frac{x - y}{2} = 42$
$\frac{x - y}{9} + \frac{x}{2} = 5$

**27.** The graphs of $ax + by = 18$ and $ax - by = 6$ intersect at $(3, -2)$. Find $a$ and $b$.

**C** **28.** The graphs of $5x - 3y = 35$, $7x - 3y = 43$, and $4x - ay = 61$ all intersect in the same point. Find $a$.

**29.** Show that the graphs of $\frac{x - 2y}{x + 2y} = \frac{1}{3}$ and $\frac{x - y}{x + y} = \frac{3}{5}$ coincide.

## Problems

**Solve using two equations in two variables. Use either the substitution method or the addition-or-subtraction method.**

**A** **1.** The sum of two numbers is 21 and their difference is 5. What are the numbers?

**2.** The sum of two numbers is 64. Twice the smaller number is 10 less than the larger number. Find the numbers.

**3.** There are 812 students in a school. There are 36 more girls than boys. How many girls are there?

**4.** The ratio of the total number of animals in a zoo to the number of bears is 22:1. If the total number of animals minus the number of bears is 315, find the number of bears.

**B** **5.** At an amusement park you get 5 points for each bull's eye you hit, but you lose 10 points for every miss. After 30 tries, Yolanda lost 90 points. How many bull's eyes did she have?

**6.** Since my uncle's farmyard appeared to be overrun with chickens and dogs, I asked him how many of each he had. Being a puzzler as well as a farmer, my uncle replied that his dogs and chickens had a total of 148 legs and 60 heads. How many dogs and how many chickens does my uncle have?

**7.** If Linda Chu walks for 1 h and cycles for 2 h, she can travel 68 km. But if she walks for 2 h and cycles for 1 h, Linda travels 46 km. What are her walking and cycling speeds?

**8.** Daniel is ten years older than Gregory. Two years ago, he was twice as old as Gregory was then. How old is each now?

**C** **9.** If Tom gives Maria 30 cents, they will have equal amounts of money. But if Maria then gives Tom 50 cents, he will have twice as much money as she does. How much money does each have now?

**10.** Five years ago, Megan's age was 5 years less than twice Tony's age. In three years, one third of Tony's age will be 12 years less than Megan's age. How old are they now?

**11.** A shipment of 18 cars, some weighing 3,000 pounds apiece and the others 5,000 pounds each, has a total weight of 30 tons. Find the number of each kind of car.

## *Challenge*

The following ''Problem of a Hundred Fowl'' dates to sixth-century China:

If a rooster is worth 5 yuan, a hen is worth 3 yuan, and 3 chicks are worth 1 yuan, how many of each, 100 in all, would be worth 100 yuan? Assume that at least 5 roosters are required.

# 8-7 Multiplication with the Addition-or-Subtraction Method

**Objective**   To use multiplication with the addition-or-subtraction method to solve systems of linear equations.

To solve a system such as

$$5x - 9y = 17$$
$$4x + 3y = 1,$$

you cannot apply the addition-or-subtraction method immediately. Neither the terms in $x$ nor the terms in $y$ are the same or opposites. See what happens, however, when you multiply both sides of the second equation by 3:

$$5x - 9y = 17 \longrightarrow 5x - 9y = 17$$
$$3(4x + 3y) = 3(1) \longrightarrow 12x + 9y = 3$$

You now have an equivalent system that can be solved by the addition-or-subtraction method, since the terms in $y$ are opposites.

Sometimes you may need to transform both equations by multiplication before you can apply the addition-or-subtraction method, as shown in Example 1.

**Example 1**   Solve: $3a + 4b = -25$
$$2a - 3b = 6$$

**Solution**

1. Transform both equations by multiplication so that the terms in $a$ are the same.

$$2(3a + 4b) = 2(-25) \longrightarrow 6a + 8b = -50$$
$$3(2a - 3b) = 3(6) \longrightarrow \underline{6a - 9b = \phantom{-}18}$$

2. Subtract similar terms.

$$17b = -68$$

3. Solve the resulting equation.

$$b = -4$$

4. Substitute in either of the *original* equations to find the corresponding value of the other variable.

$$3a + 4b = -25$$
$$3a + 4(-4) = -25$$
$$3a - 16 = -25$$
$$3a = -9$$
$$a = -3$$

5. The check in both original equations is left to you.
   $\therefore$ the solution is $(-3, -4)$.   **Answer**

To solve a system of linear equations involving fractions, it is usually convenient to clear the equations of fractions first, as shown in Example 2.

**Example 2** Solve: $\dfrac{5x}{4} + y = \dfrac{11}{2}$

$$x + \dfrac{y}{3} = 3$$

## Solution

1. Transform each equation by multiplying by the LCD of its denominators.

$$4\left(\dfrac{5x}{4} + y\right) = 4\left(\dfrac{11}{2}\right) \longrightarrow 5x + 4y = 22$$

$$3\left(x + \dfrac{y}{3}\right) = 3(3) \longrightarrow 3x + y = 9$$

2. Multiply the second equation by 4 so that the terms in $y$ are the same.

$$
\begin{array}{rcl}
5x + 4y = 22 & \longrightarrow & 5x + 4y = \phantom{0}22 \\
4(3x + y) = 4(9) & \longrightarrow & 12x + 4y = \phantom{0}36 \\
\hline
& & -7x \phantom{+4y} = -14
\end{array}
$$

3. Subtract similar terms.

4. Solve the resulting equation.
$$x = 2$$

5. Substitute in either of the original equations to find the value of $y$.

$$x + \dfrac{y}{3} = 3$$

$$2 + \dfrac{y}{3} = 3$$

$$\dfrac{y}{3} = 1$$

$$y = 3$$

6. The check is left to you.
   $\therefore$ the solution is $(2, 3)$. *Answer*

## Oral Exercises

**Explain how to use multiplication with the addition-or-subtraction method to solve each system by answering these questions:**
**a.** Which equation(s) will you transform by multiplication?
**b.** By what number(s) will you multiply?
**c.** Will you then add or subtract similar terms?

**1.** $2x + y = 8$
$3x - 2y = 5$

**2.** $3a + 5b = 3$
$a + 2b = 13$

**3.** $3x - 2t = 4$
$2x + t = 5$

**4.** $3c - 8d = 7$
$c + 2d = -7$

**5.** $3a + b = 4$
$a - 2b = 6$

**6.** $x + y = 7$
$3x - 2y = 11$

**7.** $4x - 3y = 7$
$5x - y = 6$

**8.** $4p - q = 6$
$2p - 3q = 8$

**9.** $4x - 3y = 8$
$2x + y = 14$

**Explain how to use multiplication with the addition-or-subtraction method to solve each system by answering questions (a)–(c) on page 363.**

**10.** $5p - 2q = 1$
$4p + 5q = 47$

**11.** $2c - 3d = -1$
$3c - 4d = -3$

**12.** $3r - 2s = 15$
$7r - 3s = 15$

**13.** $2a + 3b = 7$
$3a + 4b = 10$

**14.** $5a - 2b = 7$
$2a + 7b = -5$

**15.** $\frac{1}{2}x + 3y = 5$
$x - 2y = 2$

**16.** $\frac{1}{3}a + \frac{2}{3}b = 8$
$a - b = -3$

**17.** $3p + 7q + 18 = 0$
$5p - 2q + 30 = 0$

**18.** $3x + 4z + 2 = 0$
$2x - 3z - 10 = 0$

## Written Exercises

**A**  **1–18.** Solve each system in the Oral Exercises by using multiplication with the addition-or-subtraction method.

**Express each equation in standard form. Then solve.**

**B**  **19.** $\frac{a}{4} + \frac{b}{3} = 2$
$\frac{a}{2} - b = -1$

**20.** $\frac{x}{2} - y = 9$
$x + \frac{y}{2} = 8$

**21.** $\frac{a}{6} + \frac{b}{4} = \frac{3}{2}$
$\frac{2a}{3} = \frac{b}{2}$

**22.** $\frac{p}{8} + \frac{q}{6} = 1$
$\frac{p}{q} = \frac{-2}{3}$

**23.** $0.3x + 0.5y = 31$
$0.2x - 0.1y = -1$

**24.** $0.05x + 0.06y = 215$
$x + y = 4000$

**25.** $\frac{a+b}{3} - \frac{a-b}{5} = -4$
$\frac{2a}{3} + \frac{b-1}{5} = 2$

**26.** $c - 1 + \frac{d-4}{2} = 14$
$\frac{d+2}{2} - \frac{c-3}{5} = 3$

**27.** Determine whether the graphs of $3x - 4y = 3$, $6x + 6y = 13$, and $9x + 2y = 16$ intersect in a single point.

**28.** The point $(8, -3)$ is the intersection of the graphs of $ax + by = 25$ and $3ax - 5by = 3$. Find $a$ and $b$.

**Solve for $x$ and $y$ by whatever method you prefer.** (*Hint:* These equations are not linear in $x$ and $y$. However, if you let $\frac{1}{x} = a$ and $\frac{1}{y} = b$, the equations become linear in $a$ and $b$.)

**C**  **29.** $\frac{1}{x} + \frac{1}{y} = 1$
$\frac{3}{x} - \frac{2}{y} = 8$

**30.** $\frac{1}{x} + \frac{1}{y} = 5$
$\frac{3}{x} - \frac{5}{y} = -9$

**31.** $\frac{8}{x} + \frac{15}{y} = 33$
$\frac{4}{x} - \frac{35}{y} = -43$

**Solve for $x$ and $y$ in terms of $a$ and $b$.**

**32.** $ax + y = 5$
$3ax - 2y = 0$

**33.** $ax + by = 1$
$3ax - 2by = 4$

**34.** $ax - by = 1$
$bx + ay = 1$

**Solve for $x$, $y$, and $z$.** (*Hint:* Eliminate one variable from the first two equations and then eliminate the same variable from the second two equations. This will give two new equations in two variables.)

**35.** $x + y + z = 7$
$2x - y + z = 4$
$3x + 2y + z = 11$

**36.** $x + y + z = 4$
$2x - y + z = 0$
$x - y + 2z = -3$

**37.** $x + 2y - z = 10$
$3x + y + 2z = 20$
$2x + y + z = 14$

## Mixed Practice

**Solve by the graphic method.**

A  **1.** $y - x = 5$
$y = 2x + 4$

**2.** $x + y = 0$
$3x + y = -8$

**3.** $3x + 4y = 10$
$x - y = 1$

**Solve by the substitution method.**

**4.** $a = 3b$
$a - 5b = 16$

**5.** $2c - d = 5$
$4c + 5d = 17$

**6.** $4p = 3q$
$3p - q = 15$

**Solve by the addition-or-subtraction method.**

**7.** $2a + 3b = -1$
$a - 3b = 4$

**8.** $5x - 9y = -3$
$4x - 3y = 6$

**9.** $2p + 3q + 1 = 0$
$3p + 5q + 2 = 0$

**Solve by whatever method you prefer.**

B  **10.** $y = x + 2$
$2x + y = 11$

**11.** $x + y = 8$
$x - 3y = 4$

**12.** $3x - 2y = 1$
$4y = 7 + 3x$

**13.** $x - 5y = 2$
$2x + y = 4$

**14.** $2a - 4b = 6$
$7 + a = -3b$

**15.** $r - s = 4$
$r - 6 = 2(s - 6)$

**16.** $a - 2b = 10$
$a + b = 2(b + 6)$

**17.** $t + u = 11$
$(10t + u) - (10u + t) = 27$

**18.** $u - t = 5$
$10t + u = 3(t + u)$

**19.** $3x + 2y = 21$
$7x - 5y = 20$

**20.** $2a + 3b = 7$
$3a + 4b = 10$

**21.** $5n - 2m = 1$
$4n + 5m = 47$

**22.** $0.04x - 0.06y = 40$
$x + y = 6000$

**23.** $2.4 = 0.3x + 0.4y$
$5x = 2 + 6y$

**24.** $2x - \dfrac{5}{2}y = 13$

$\dfrac{x}{3} + \dfrac{y}{3} = \dfrac{14}{15}$

**25.** $3a + 2b = 4$
$\dfrac{1}{3}(2a + b) = 1$

**26.** $\dfrac{1}{3}(3a - 2b) = -3$

$3(a - b) = -9$

**27.** $\dfrac{x}{2} + \dfrac{y}{3} = -4$

$x + y = -10$

**Solve.** (*Hint:* See Exercises 35–37 on page 365.)

**C** **28.** $x - y + z = 7$
$z = x - 3$
$y = -2z$

**29.** $r + s + t = 180$
$r = s + t$
$s = 4t$

**30.** $a + b + c = 8$
$b = \dfrac{a - c}{2}$
$b = \dfrac{a + c}{3}$

**31.** $\dfrac{3}{2x} + \dfrac{2}{y} = 16$
$\dfrac{2}{x} - \dfrac{1}{5y} = 7$

**32.** $\dfrac{3}{x} + \dfrac{4}{y} = 1$
$\dfrac{2}{x} - \dfrac{2}{y} = 10$

**33.** $x + y + z = 0$
$x - 2y + 3z = 18$
$2x + 2y + 5z = 20$

## Problems

**Solve by whatever method you prefer.**

**A** **1.** The sum of two numbers is 50 and their difference is 18. Find the numbers.

**2.** One number is 18 more than three times another number. The difference in the numbers is 54. Find the numbers.

**3.** Al is 13 years older than Jack. Next year the ratio of their ages will be 3:2. How old is each now?

**4.** Last year Sue was three times as old as Pablo. Next year she will be twice as old as Pablo is. How old is each now?

**5.** The length of a rectangle is 20 cm greater than its width. The perimeter is 360 cm. What is the area?

**6.** A rectangle is four times as long as it is wide. If it were 6 m shorter and 6 m wider, it would be a square. What are the dimensions?

**7.** Sally has $21.40 in dimes and quarters, for a total of 100 coins. How many of each kind of coin does Sally have?

**8.** Elizabeth Chin has twice as many dimes as quarters and four more quarters than nickels. If Elizabeth has $7.80, how many coins does she have?

**9.** The ratio of boys to girls at a school dance was 5:3. There would have been an equal number of boys and girls if there had been 3 more girls and 3 fewer boys. How many boys and how many girls were at the dance?

**10.** Thomas takes 40 minutes to wash the family car and Joanna takes 60 minutes. How long will it take Thomas and Joanna to wash the car if they work together?

**11.** A movie theater charges $4 for an adult ticket and $2 for a child's ticket. One night 380 tickets were sold for a total of $1320. How many children attended the movie that night?

**12.** A chemist has 500 g of a solution that is 40% acid. How many grams of water must be added to reduce the acidity to 25%?

**13.** A chemist has 800 g of a dye solution that is 20% of its original strength. How much dye must be added to increase the strength to 50%?

**14.** Five pens and four pencils cost $2.55. But four pens and five pencils cost $2.40. How much do the pens cost and how much do the pencils cost?

**15.** Becky's bill for 6 cans of grape juice and 4 cans of orange juice was $13.20. When she got home, she found that she should have bought 4 cans of grape juice and 6 cans of orange juice. Although she mixed up the order, Becky did save 60 cents. How much does each can cost?

**16.** Joe Tyson is the place kicker for his college football team. Last season he kicked 38 times and never missed. Each field goal scored 3 points and each point after touchdown scored 1 point for a total of 70 points. How many field goals did Joe kick?

**B** **17.** In a concrete mixture, the ratio of cement to sand to water is $4:3:2$. How much of each ingredient is needed to make 630 kg of concrete?

**18.** The equation $2x + 6y = 35$ has no whole number solutions. Why not?

**19.** Find the area enclosed between the $x$-axis and the graphs of $x + y = 20$ and $3x - 2y = 0$.

**20.** A car traveled at a steady speed for 120 km. Due to a mechanical problem, it returned at half that speed. If the total time for the round trip was 4 h 30 min, find the two speeds.

**21.** Edna Britten's income from two stocks each year totals $280. Stock A pays dividends at the rate of 5% and stock B at the rate of 6%. If she has invested a total of $5000, how much is invested in each stock?

**22.** Luann Bailey usually takes 75 minutes to grade her students' algebra quizzes. After working for 30 minutes, another math teacher helps her finish the job in 15 minutes. How long would the second teacher take to grade the quizzes alone?

**23.** Before last weekend's hiking trip, Juanita mixed 3 kg of peanuts and raisins as an energy snack. The peanuts cost $4.25 per kilogram and the raisins cost $3.50 per kilogram. The whole mix cost $12. How many kilograms of peanuts did Juanita have?

**24.** Phil has 48 words to spell for a puzzle. As an incentive, his mother offers to pay him 10 cents for each word he spells correctly if Phil will pay her 6 cents for each word he spells incorrectly. If Phil makes $1.92, how many words does he spell correctly?

*Linear Equations and Systems* **367**

**25.** Beatrice Robinson receives $375 per year from a $6000 investment in stocks and bonds. The bonds pay 10% interest and the stocks pay 5% in dividends. How much is invested in stocks?

**26.** Several ball bearings and cubes are balanced in a simple pan balance as shown. How many bearings does it take to balance one cube?

**C** **27.** On a simple pan balance, 3 apples and 1 banana exactly balance 10 plums. Also, 1 apple and 6 plums balance 1 banana. How many plums will balance one banana?

**28.** Roger, Sue, and Tim have $155 between them. Roger has $5 more than Sue and Tim together. If Sue gives Tim $5, he will have twice as much as she does. How much does each have?

**29.** If the length of a rectangle is increased by 12 and the width is decreased by 8, the area is unchanged. The area is also unchanged if the original length is increased by 5 and the original width is decreased by 4. Find the original dimensions of the rectangle.

**30.** If Alexandra increases her usual driving speed by 15 km/h, it will take her 2 h less to make a trip. If she decreases her usual speed by 15 km/h, it will take her 3 h more than usual to make the trip. How long is the trip?

## Computer Key-In

### Exercises

**1.** Use multiplication with the addition-or-subtraction method to verify that the solution of the system

$$\begin{matrix} Ax + By = C \\ Dx + Ey = F \end{matrix} \quad \text{is} \quad \left( \frac{CE - BF}{AE - BD}, \frac{AF - CD}{AE - BD} \right).$$

**2. a.** Using the result in Exercise 1, write a program to solve a system of linear equations in two variables. Provide for the case $AE - BD = 0$.

**b.** RUN the program for each of the following.

| | | | |
|---|---|---|---|
| $3x + 4y = -25$ | $5x + 4y = 22$ | $2x + 4y = 11$ | $2x + y = 8$ |
| $2x - 3y = 6$ | $3x + y = 9$ | $3x + 6y = 17$ | $3x - 2y = 5$ |

*Note:* The program of Exercise 2 above can be used to do Exercises 1–18 on pages 363–364.

# Self-Test 2

**Vocabulary** system of equations (p. 346)   system of simultaneous
solution of a system (p. 346)   equations (p. 346)
intersection point (p. 346)   solution set (p. 346)
parallel lines (p. 346)   equivalent system (p. 351)

**Solve each system by the graphic method.**

1. $x + y = 8$
   $x - y = 4$

2. $x - 2y = 3$      **Obj. 8-3, p. 346**
   $2x - 3y = 4$

**Solve by the substitution method.**

3. $3a - b = 14$
   $a = 2b - 2$

4. $m - 2n = -8$      **Obj. 8-4, p. 350**
   $m + n = 4$

5. Solve by using two equations in two variables: The treasurer of      **Obj. 8-5, p. 354**
   the school play knows that 900 tickets were sold for a certain
   performance. If orchestra tickets sold for $3 each and balcony
   tickets for $2 each, and if the total receipts were $2300, how
   many of each kind of ticket were sold?

**Solve by the addition-or-subtraction method.**

6. $a - 2b = 0$
   $a + 2b = 12$

7. $3c + 5d = 20$      **Obj. 8-6, p. 358**
   $-2c + 5d = 20$

**Solve by using multiplication with the addition-or-subtraction method.**

8. $3r - 8s = 7$
   $r + 2s = -7$

9. $2a + 3b = 12$      **Obj. 8-7, p. 362**
   $3a + 2b = 13$

Check your answers with those at the back of the book.

## Calculator Key-In

If you used multiplication with the addition-or-subtraction method to solve

$$Ax + By = C$$
$$Dx + Ey = F,$$

you would obtain    $x = \dfrac{CE - BF}{AE - BD}$   and   $y = \dfrac{CD - AF}{BD - AE}$.

When the values of $A$, $B$, . . . , $F$ are decimals, it is convenient to solve the
system by using a calculator. Use a calculator and this method to solve the
following systems.

1. $1.2x + 4.6y = 16.2$
   $3.1x + 2.1y = 12.5$

2. $2.3x + 1.6y = 14.9$
   $4.1x + 3.2y = 28.3$

# Reading Algebra / Problem-Solving Strategies

If you are to be a successful problem solver, you must first master the art of reading word problems. Before you begin solving a set of problems, be sure you have read the accompanying lesson in your textbook and have worked through all the text examples. Then, for each problem, read the problem slowly and carefully. Do not begin writing until you have determined what you are being asked to find and until you have chosen a strategy for finding it. Be sure the strategy that you have chosen is appropriate and that any formulas involved are correct. When you have found an answer, check it to be sure that it makes sense and that it is correct. The time you spend on planning and checking will be well worthwhile. Planning and checking will improve your chances of achieving success on the first try and will help you to develop a sound problem-solving strategy.

If you find that you are having trouble understanding a word problem or figuring out how to begin solving it, there are a number of things you can do. The first is rereading. Perhaps you overlooked something when you first read the problem. Then, attempt to break the problem down. You may be able to use the parts that you understand to make sense of the parts that you do not. It may also help to organize the information in a table or chart, or to draw a diagram.

## Exercises

1. A coin box contains $26.50 in dimes and quarters. There are 157 coins altogether. How many of each type of coin are in the box?

2. The length of a rectangle is 4 cm more than twice the width. The perimeter is 56 cm. Find the length and the width.

3. Two planes leave an airport at the same time flying in opposite directions. The first plane is traveling at a speed of 1100 km/h. After 4 h, the planes are 7600 km apart. Find the speed of the second plane.

4. The trip from Arquette to Carver takes 8 min longer during rush hour, when the average speed is 75 km/h, than in off-peak hours, when the average speed is 90 km/h. Find the distance between the two towns.

5. A rectangle is 5 cm longer than it is wide. If the length is doubled and the width is tripled, the area is increased by 420 cm². Find the original dimensions.

6. The sum of two numbers is 11 and the sum of their squares is 65. Find the numbers.

7. The edges of one cube are 2 cm longer than the edges of another. The volume of the smaller cube is 152 cm³ less than the volume of the larger cube. Find the lengths of the edges of each cube.

8. A soccer league signed up 440 players. The ratio of returning players to new players was 4:7. How many players were new?

# Applications

## 8-8 Wind and Water Current Problems

**Objective**   To use systems of equations to solve wind and water current problems.

Suppose that you can paddle a canoe at the rate, or speed, of 3 mph in still water. If you paddle downstream on a river with a current of 1 mph, your speed is increased to 3 + 1, or 4 mph. If you paddle upstream against the current, your speed is reduced to 3 − 1, or 2 mph. Since the current increases your speed downstream by as much as it decreases your speed upstream, you might think that the current has no effect on the total time for the round trip. However, the calculations below show that the current increases the total time.

Suppose that the trip is 12 miles downstream and 12 miles back upstream. The time for the trip downstream and the trip back upstream can be found in each case by using the relationship:

$$\text{Time} = \text{Distance} \div \text{Rate}$$

**No current**                          **1 mph current**

|  | Rate × Time = Distance | | | Rate | × | Time | = Distance |
|---|---|---|---|---|---|---|---|
| Downstream | 3 | 4 | 12 | 3 + 1 = 4 | | 12 ÷ 4 = 3 | 12 |
| Upstream | 3 | 4 | 12 | 3 − 1 = 2 | | 12 ÷ 2 = 6 | 12 |

Total Time $= 4 + 4 = 8$ h          Total Time $= 3 + 6 = 9$ h

Average Speed $= \dfrac{\text{Total distance}}{\text{Total time}} = \dfrac{24}{8} = 3$ mph       Average Speed $= \dfrac{24}{9} = 2\dfrac{2}{3}$ mph

The principles illustrated above apply with wind currents as well as water currents. Thus, if

   $r =$ the rate of a plane when there is no wind

and

   $w =$ the rate of wind,

then

   $r + w =$ the rate of the plane flying with the wind

and

   $r - w =$ the rate of the plane flying against the wind.

The basic formula for wind and water current problems is:

$$\text{Distance} = \text{Rate} \times \text{Time}$$

***Example*** A jet can travel the 6000 km distance between Washington, D.C. and London in 6 h with the wind. The return trip against the same wind takes 7.5 h. Find the rate of the jet in still air and the rate of the wind.

**Solution**

*Step 1* The problem asks for the rate of the jet in still air and the rate of the wind.

*Step 2* Let $r$ = the rate of jet in km/h and let $w$ = the rate of wind in km/h.

| | | Rate $\times$ Time $=$ Distance | | |
|---|---|---|---|---|
| With the wind | $r + w$ | 6 | 6000 |
| Against the wind | $r - w$ | 7.5 | 6000 |

*Step 3* Use the information in the chart to write two equations:

$$6(r + w) = 6000, \quad \text{or} \quad r + w = 1000$$
$$7.5(r - w) = 6000, \quad \text{or} \quad r - w = 800$$

*Step 4*
$$\begin{aligned} r + w &= 1000 \\ \underline{r - w} &= \underline{800} \\ 2r\phantom{+w} &= 1800 \\ r &= 900 \\ 900 + w &= 1000 \\ w &= 100 \end{aligned}$$

*Step 5* The check is left to you.

∴ the rate of the jet is 900 km/h and the rate of the wind is 100 km/h. ***Answer***

## *Oral Exercises*

**Complete the table. All rates are in km/h.**

| | Rate of plane in still air | Rate of wind | Rate of plane with wind | Rate of plane against wind |
|---|---|---|---|---|
| **1.** | 700 | 50 | ? | ? |
| **2.** | 825 | 100 | ? | ? |
| **3.** | 900 | $w$ | ? | ? |
| **4.** | $p$ | $w$ | ? | ? |

The following rates are given in km/h.

$$r = \text{rate of a rowboat in still water}$$
$$s = \text{rate of a swimmer in still water}$$
$$c = \text{rate of the current}$$

**What rate does each expression represent?**

**5.** $r + c$  **6.** $r - c$  **7.** $s + c$  **8.** $s - c$

**Using the variables $r$, $s$, and $c$ above, write an equation that expresses the given fact.**

**9.** The rate of the rowboat going downstream is 12 km/h.

**10.** The rate of the rowboat going upstream is 8 km/h.

**11.** The rate of the swimmer going downstream is 3 km/h.

**12.** The rate of the swimmer going upstream is 1 km/h.

**13.** Use the information in Exercises 11 and 12 to find the rate of the swimmer in still water and the rate of the current.

**14.** Use the information in Exercises 9 and 10 to find the rate of the rowboat in still water and the rate of the current.

## Problems

**Solve.**

**A**  **1.** Suppose a motorboat travels at 10 km/h in still water. The boat makes a trip 30 km downstream and back.
Complete each table.

**No current**

|  | Rate | × Time | = Distance |
|---|---|---|---|
| Downstream | ? | ? | 30 |
| Upstream | ? | ? | 30 |

Total time = ___?___
Average speed = ___?___

**5 km/h current**

| Rate | × Time | = Distance |
|---|---|---|
| ? | ? | 30 |
| ? | ? | 30 |

Total time = ___?___
Average speed = ___?___

**2.** Suppose you can paddle a canoe in still water at 5 km/h and that you are going to travel 6 km up a river and 6 km back. If the river current is 1 km/h, find your total time and your average speed for the round trip.

**3.** Sam can paddle in still water at 6 mph. The Saco River is flowing at 2 mph. How far downstream can Sam travel if he must return in two hours?

*Linear Equations and Systems* **373**

4. A powerboat has a four-hour supply of gasoline. How far can this boat travel from the marina if the rate out against the current is 40 km/h and the rate back in with the current is 60 km/h?

5. A boat travels with the current at 22 km/h and travels against the current at 12 km/h. What is the rate of the boat in still water? What is the rate of the current?

6. Hal can swim upstream at 1 m/s and downstream at 2.5 m/s. How fast can he swim in still water? How fast is the current?

7. An airplane takes 3 h to fly 1200 km against the wind. The return trip takes 2 h. What would the speed of the plane be if there were no wind? What is the wind speed?

8. A boat can go 20 km downstream in 2 h. The return trip takes 5 h. What would the speed of the boat be if there were no current? What is the speed of the current?

9. The 4200 km trip from New York to San Francisco takes 6 h flying against the wind but only 5 h returning. Find the speed of the plane in still air and the wind speed.

10. The 1080 km trip from Madrid to Paris takes 2 h flying against the wind and 1.5 h flying with the wind. Find the speed of the plane in still air and the wind speed.

B  11. A motorboat goes 36 km downstream in the same amount of time that it takes to go 24 km upstream. If the current is flowing at 3 km/h, what is the rate of the boat in still water?

12. The rate of the current in the Susquehanna River is 4 km/h. If a canoeist can paddle 5 km downstream in the same amount of time that she can paddle 1 km upstream, how fast can she paddle in still water?

13. The steamboat River Queen travels at the rate of 30 km/h in still water. If it can travel 45 km upstream in the same amount of time that it takes to go 63 km downstream, what is the rate of the current?

14. An airplane whose speed in still air is 760 km/h can travel 2000 km with the wind in the same amount of time that it takes to fly 1800 km against the wind. What is the wind speed?

C  15. A plane has a speed of $p$ km/h in still air. It makes a round trip flying with and against a wind of $w$ km/h. Show that its average speed is
$$\frac{p^2 - w^2}{p} \text{ km/h.}$$

# 8-9 Digit, Age, and Fraction Problems

**Objective**   To use systems of equations to solve digit, age, and fraction problems.

Digit problems are based on our decimal system of numeration.
Note the value of the number with digits $h$, $t$, and $u$ shown below.

|  | Hundreds digit | Tens digit | Units digit | Value |
|---|---|---|---|---|
| $537 =$ | 5 | 3 | 7 | $5 \cdot 100 + 3 \cdot 10 + 7 \cdot 1$ |
| $604 =$ | 6 | 0 | 4 | $6 \cdot 100 + 0 \cdot 10 + 4 \cdot 1$ |
| $htu =$ | $h$ | $t$ | $u$ | $h \cdot 100 + t \cdot 10 + u \cdot 1$ |

**Example 1**   (Digit Problem)

The sum of the digits in a two-digit number is 15. The new number obtained when the digits are reversed is 27 more than the original number. Find the original number.

**Solution**

*Step 1*   The problem asks for the original number.

*Step 2*   Let $t =$ the tens digit of the original number.
Let $u =$ the units digit of the original number.

|  | Tens | Units | Value |
|---|---|---|---|
| Original number | $t$ | $u$ | $10t + u$ |
| Number with digits reversed | $u$ | $t$ | $10u + t$ |

*Step 3*   Use the facts of the problem to write two equations.
Sum of digits of original number is 15:  $\qquad t + u = 15$

Difference of the numbers is 27:   $(10u + t) - (10t + u) = 27$
$$10u + t - 10t - u = 27$$
$$9u - 9t = 27$$
$$9(u - t) = 27$$
$$u - t = 3$$

*Step 4*
$$u + t = 15$$
$$\underline{u - t = 3}$$
$$2u = 18$$
$$u = 9$$

Substitute $u = 9$ in the second equation. $\Big\}$   $9 - t = 3$
$$t = 6$$

*Step 5*   The check is left to you.
$\therefore$ the solution is 69.   **Answer**

The technique of organizing the given facts of a problem in a chart is also useful when solving age problems involving two variables.

### Example 2 (Age problem)

Five years ago, Janet was only $\frac{1}{5}$ of the age of her mother. Now she is $\frac{1}{3}$ of her mother's age. Find their ages now.

### Solution

**Step 1** The problem asks for Janet's age and her mother's age now.

**Step 2** Let $j$ = Janet's age now and let $m$ = her mother's age now. Make a chart.

| Age | Now | 5 years ago |
|-----|-----|-------------|
| Janet | $j$ | $j - 5$ |
| Mother | $m$ | $m - 5$ |

**Step 3** Use the facts of the problem to write two equations.

Five years ago: $j - 5 = \frac{1}{5}(m - 5)$

Now: $j = \frac{1}{3}m$

**Step 4** Simplify the equations.

$$j - 5 = \tfrac{1}{5}(m - 5) \longrightarrow 5j - 25 = m - 5$$
$$j = \tfrac{1}{3}m \longrightarrow 3j = m$$

Substitute $3j$ for $m$ and solve.

$$5j - 25 = 3j - 5$$
$$2j - 25 = -5$$
$$2j = 20$$
$$j = 10$$
$$m = 3j = 30$$

**Step 5** The check is left to you.

$\therefore$ Janet is 10 years old and her mother is 30. **Answer**

### Example 3 (Fraction problem)

The denominator of a fraction is 4 more than the numerator. If 2 is subtracted from each, the value of the resulting fraction is $\frac{1}{5}$. Find the original fraction.

### Solution

**Step 1** The problem asks for the original fraction.

**Step 2** Let $n$ = numerator of the original fraction and $d$ = denominator of the original fraction. Then $\frac{n}{d}$ = the original fraction.

Step 3 Use the facts of the problem to write two equations.

$$d = n + 4$$

$$\frac{n-2}{d-2} = \frac{1}{5}, \quad \text{or} \quad 5(n-2) = d - 2$$

Step 4 Simplify the equations and solve.

$$d = n + 4 \longrightarrow -n + d = 4$$
$$5(n-2) = d - 2 \longrightarrow \underline{\phantom{-}5n - d = 8}$$
$$4n = 12$$
$$n = 3$$

Substitute $n = 3$.   $-3 + d = 4$
$$d = 7$$

Step 5 The check is left to you.

$\therefore$ the original fraction is $\frac{3}{7}$. **Answer**

## Oral Exercises

**A two-digit number has tens digit *t* and units digit *u*. Express the following in terms of *t* and *u*.**

1. The value of the two-digit number.
2. The value of the two-digit number obtained by reversing the digits.
3. The tens digit exceeds the units digit by 5.
4. The units digit exceeds the tens digit by 8.
5. The tens digit is one half the units digit.

**A three-digit number has hundreds digit *h*, tens digit *t*, and units digit *u*. Express the following as equations.**

6. The sum of the digits is 12.
7. The tens digit is twice the sum of the other two digits.
8. The units digit is the difference of the tens digit minus the hundreds digit.
9. The number obtained by reversing the order of the digits exceeds the original number by 99.

**Let *b* = Bob's age now and *c* = Claire's age now. Express the following in terms of *b* and *c*.**

10. Bob's age in 6 years.
11. Claire's age in 6 years.
12. Bob's age 2 years ago.
13. Claire's age 2 years ago.
14. The sum of their ages in 6 years.
15. The sum of their ages 2 years ago.

**A fraction is represented by $\frac{n}{d}$. Express in terms of $n$ and $d$ the new fractions obtained by following the given directions.**

**16.** Increase both the numerator and the denominator by 4.

**17.** Decrease both the numerator and the denominator by 7.

**18.** Interchange the numerator and the denominator.

**19.** Increase the numerator by 5 and decrease the denominator by 3.

## Problems

**Solve each of the following problems about two-digit numbers.**

A **1.** The sum of the digits of a two-digit number is 11. If the digits are reversed, the number is increased by 45. What is the original number?

**2.** A two-digit number is four times the sum of its digits. If its digits are reversed, the new number is 36 more than the original number. What is the original number?

**3.** If 18 is added to a two-digit number, the digits are reversed. The sum of the digits is 16. Find the original number.

**4.** The sum of the digits of a two-digit number is 6. If the digits are reversed, the number is decreased by 36. What is the original number?

**5.** A number is 8 times the sum of its digits. The tens digit is 5 greater than the units digit. Find the number.

**6.** The sum of the digits is 13. If the number represented by reversing the digits is subtracted from the original number, the result is 27. Find the original number.

**Solve by using a system of two equations in two variables.**

**7.** Alicia is 7 years older than Bruce. Next year she will be twice as old as he will be. How old is she now?

**8.** In 1943 the Brooklyn Bridge was 10 times as old as the Golden Gate Bridge. That same year, the difference in their ages was 54 years. Find the year of completion for each bridge.

**9.** Karen's mother is twice as old as Karen is. Eleven years ago she was 3 times as old as Karen was. Find Karen's present age.

**10.** Two years ago, Al's age was 1 year less than twice Ed's. Four years from now, Al's age will be 8 years more than half Ed's. How old is Al?

**11.** In 1984, the Eiffel Tower was $\frac{19}{20}$ as old as the Washington Monument. If the Washington Monument was built 5 years earlier than the Eiffel Tower, find the age of each in 1984.

**12.** Anita is $\frac{3}{4}$ as old as Judy. Four years ago Anita was $\frac{2}{3}$ as old as Judy. How old is each?

**13.** The denominator of a fraction is 8 more than the numerator. If 3 is added to both the numerator and the denominator, the value of the resulting fraction is $\frac{1}{2}$. What is the original fraction?

**14.** The denominator of a fraction is 9 more than the numerator. If the numerator is decreased by 3 and the denominator is increased by 3, the value of the resulting fraction is $\frac{1}{4}$. What is the original fraction?

**15.** If 1 is subtracted from the numerator of a fraction, the value of the resulting fraction is $\frac{1}{2}$. However, if 7 is added to the denominator of the original fraction the value of the resulting fraction is $\frac{1}{3}$. Find the original fraction.

**16.** If the numerator of a fraction is increased by 4, the value of the resulting fraction is $\frac{3}{4}$. If the denominator of the original fraction is increased by 2, the value of the resulting fraction is $\frac{1}{2}$. Find the original fraction.

**17.** A fraction has value $\frac{2}{3}$. When 15 is added to its numerator, the resulting fraction equals the reciprocal of the value of the original fraction. Find the original fraction.

**18.** A fraction's value is $\frac{4}{5}$. When its numerator is increased by 9, the new fraction equals the reciprocal of the value of the original fraction. Find the original fraction.

**Solve each of the following problems about three-digit numbers.**

**B** **19.** A number between 300 and 400 is forty times the sum of its digits. The tens digit is 6 more than the units digit. Find the number.

**20.** The sum of the three digits is 12. The tens digit exceeds the hundreds digit by the same amount that the units digit exceeds the tens digit. If the digits are reversed, the new number exceeds the original number by 198. Find the original number.

**21.** The sum of the three digits is 9, and the tens digit is 1 more than the hundreds digit. When the digits are reversed, the new number is 99 less than the original number. Find the original number.

**Solve by using a system of two equations in two variables.**

**22.** A father, being asked his age and that of his son, said, "If you add 4 to my age and divide the sum by 4, you will have my son's age. But 6 years ago I was $7\frac{1}{2}$ times as old as my son." Find their ages.

**Solve by using a system of two equations in two variables.**

**23.** James said, "If I were $\frac{1}{2}$ as old as I am, and Noriko were $\frac{3}{4}$ as old as she is, the sum of our ages would be 3 years more than my age alone. But if I were $\frac{2}{3}$ as old as I am, and Noriko were $\frac{1}{4}$ as old as she is, together our ages would be 2 years younger than I am alone." How old is James?

**24.** Laura is 3 times as old as Maria was when Laura was as old as Maria is now. In 2 years, Laura will be twice as old as Maria was 2 years ago. Find their present ages.

**25.** The two digits in the numerator of a fraction whose value is $\frac{2}{9}$ are reversed in its denominator. The reciprocal of the fraction is the value obtained when 27 is added to the original numerator and 71 is subtracted from the original denominator. Find the original fraction.

**26.** The numerator equals the sum of the two digits in the denominator. The value of the fraction is $\frac{1}{4}$. When both numerator and denominator are increased by 3, the resulting fraction has the value $\frac{1}{3}$. Find the original fraction.

**27.** The two digits in the numerator of a fraction are reversed in its denominator. If 1 is subtracted from both the numerator and the denominator, the value of the resulting fraction is $\frac{1}{2}$. The fraction whose numerator is the difference and whose denominator is the sum of the units and tens digits equals $\frac{2}{5}$. Find the original fraction.

**C**  **28.** Find a two-decimal-place number between 0 and 1 such that the sum of its digits is 9 and such that if the digits are reversed the number is increased by 0.27.

**29.** The numerator of a fraction is a two-digit number and the denominator is that number with the digits reversed. The value of the fraction is $\frac{7}{4}$. Find the fraction. (*Hint:* There are four possible answers.)

**30.** Cindy's age equals the sum of Paul's age and Sue's age. Two years ago, Cindy was 4 times as old as Sue was, and two years from now, Cindy will be 1.4 times as old as Paul will be. How old is each now? (*Hint:* Use a system of three equations in three variables.)

**31.** A man is three times as old as his son was at the time when the father was twice as old as his son will be two years from now. Find the present age of each person if the sum of their ages is 55 years.

---

## *Challenge*

Solve if $a$, $b$, and $c$ are positive integers:
$$4a - 11b + 12c = 22$$
$$a + 5b - 4c = 17$$

# Biographical Note / *Emily Warren Roebling*

Emily Warren Roebling (1843–1903), who helped supervise the completion of the Brooklyn Bridge, was born in Cold Spring, New York. She was married to Washington Roebling, an engineer whose father, John Roebling, was commissioned to build the Brooklyn Bridge. In order to prepare for the construction, Emily and Washington Roebling went to Europe, where Washington studied the experimental method of using pneumatic caissons, or watertight chambers of compressed air, to sink underwater foundations. Within months of their return to the United States, John Roebling was injured at the bridge site and died three weeks later. Washington Roebling, who had assisted his father on several previous bridge-building projects, became chief engineer, but was incapacitated by caisson disease (the bends) ten years before the bridge was completed.

In order to continue the project, Emily Roebling studied calculus, the details of cable construction, and the procedures involved in bridge building. She learned how to read bridge specifications, how to determine the stress various materials could tolerate, and how to calculate catenary curves. As surrogate chief engineer, she negotiated with the representatives of various construction supply firms, made daily visits to the bridge to inspect the work, and delivered explicit instructions to the assistant engineers. She kept her husband informed of the progress made each day.

Nine months before the completion of the bridge the board of trustees tried to displace Washington Roebling as chief engineer. As a result of a presentation Emily Roebling made before the American Society of Civil Engineers, Roebling secured the backing of the engineering profession and retained his position. Throughout 1882 and 1883 articles that she wrote regarding the project appeared in Brooklyn newspapers.

As was stated at the opening-day ceremonies on May 24, 1883, the bridge is a tribute to Emily Roebling's intense and sustained involvement. A plaque in her honor was placed on the bridge in 1950 by The Brooklyn Engineers Club.

After the completion of the bridge, Emily Roebling involved herself in a number of social, political, and philanthropic works. She was involved with the management of the 1893 World's Fair and traveled extensively in Europe. Emily Roebling later planned and was the general contractor for the Roeblings' home in Trenton, New Jersey. Eventually she studied law at New York University, graduating in 1899 with an award-winning essay.

# Self-Test 3

**Solve by using a system of two equations in two variables.**

1. A boat travels upstream at 16 km/h. The same boat travels downstream at 30 km/h. What is the rate of the boat in still water? What is the rate of the current?

   Obj. 8-8, p. 371

2. The sum of the digits in a two-digit number is 15. If the digits are reversed, the number is decreased by 27. What is the number?

   Obj. 8-9, p. 375

3. Six years ago Ella was twice as old as her brother Sanford. Six years from now Sanford will be as old as Ella is now. Find their current ages.

4. The numerator of a fraction is 3 less than the denominator. If 5 is added to each, the value of the resulting fraction is $\frac{3}{4}$. Find the original fraction.

Check your answers with those at the back of the book.

## *Extra* / *Proving Divisibility Tests*

You may have learned the following divisibility tests in an earlier course.

| Divisibility by | Test |
|---|---|
| 2 | Number must end in 0, 2, 4, 6, or 8 |
| 3 | Sum of digits must be divisible by 3 |
| 4 | Last two digits must be divisible by 4 (81,736 is divisible by 4 because 36 is.) |
| 5 | Number must end in 0 or 5 |
| 6 | Number must pass tests for both 2 and 3 |
| 8 | Last 3 digits must be divisible by 8 (145,320 is divisible by 8 because 320 is.) |
| 9 | Sum of digits must be divisible by 9 |

These tests rely on our decimal system of numeration. They can be proved by writing expressions for the values of the numbers involved.

**Example**  Prove the divisibility test for 9 for a three-digit number.

**Solution**  A three-digit number with digits $h$, $t$, and $u$ has a value of $100h + 10t + u = (99h + 9t) + (h + t + u)$. Since $99h + 9t$ is divisible by 9, the entire right-hand side of the equation is divisible by 9 if and only if the sum of the digits, $h + t + u$, is divisible by 9.

## Exercises

1. Prove the test for divisibility by 3 for a three-digit number.

2. The number $87,154,316$ can be written as $(871,543) \cdot 100 + 16$. Explain why you need look only at the last two digits to see if the original number is divisible by 4.

3. Prove the test for divisibility by 4 for a six-digit number.

4. Prove the test for divisibility by 8 for a six-digit number. (*Hint:* See Exercise 3.)

5. Prove that a six-digit number is divisible by 11 if and only if the sum of the first, third, and fifth digits minus the sum of the second, fourth, and sixth digits is divisible by 11.

6. Devise a test to check whether eleven-digit numbers are divisible by 11.

---

## Chapter Summary

1. The solution set of a linear equation in two variables is the set of all ordered pairs of numbers that make the equation into a true statement.

2. Ordered pairs of real numbers can be graphed as points in a coordinate plane. The graph of a linear equation in two variables is a line.

3. The solutions of pairs of linear equations in two variables can be estimated by graphing, and computed by the substitution method or the addition-or-subtraction method. Multiplication may have to be used with the addition-or-subtraction method.

4. Systems of linear equations in two variables may be used to solve word problems involving wind, water current, age, fractions, and digits, as well as other types.

---

## Chapter Review

**Give the letter of the correct answer.**

1. Which ordered pair is a solution of $2x - 3y = -5$?      8-1
   **a.** $(1, 1)$      **b.** $(4, 1)$      **c.** $(-1, 1)$      **d.** $(-4, 1)$

2. Solve $2x - 3y = 9$ for $y$ in terms of $x$.
   **a.** $y = \frac{2}{3}x - 9$      **b.** $y = \frac{2}{3}x - 3$
   **c.** $x = \frac{3}{2}y + \frac{9}{2}$      **d.** $x = \frac{2}{3}y + \frac{2}{9}$

---

3. In which quadrant is the graph of $(-3, 5)$? 8-2
   a. I    b. II    c. III    d. IV

4. Where is the graph of $(-3, 0)$ in the coordinate plane?
   a. in Quadrant II          b. in Quadrant III
   c. on the $x$-axis          d. on the $y$-axis

5. The solution of the system $\begin{array}{l} x + 2y = 11 \\ 5x - y = 11 \end{array}$ is $(3, 4)$. 8-3

   How are the graphs of the two equations related?
   a. The graphs are parallel.
   b. The graphs coincide.
   c. The graphs intersect at $(3, 4)$.
   d. The graphs intersect at $(3, 0)$ and $(0, 4)$.

6. Solve by the substitution method: 8-4

$$2x + y = 6$$
$$3x - 2y = 2$$

   a. $(2, 2)$    b. $(-2, -2)$    c. $(3, 0)$    d. $(0, -2)$

7. Solve by using two equations in two variables: One positive integer is 8-5
   18 less than a second positive integer. If the sum of twice the greater
   and three times the smaller is 86, find each integer.
   a. 18 and 68    b. 34 and 52    c. 18 and 104    d. 10 and 28

8. Solve by the addition-or-subtraction method: 8-6

$$p - 6q = -3$$
$$3p + 6q = 15$$

   a. $(1, 3)$    b. $(3, 1)$    c. $(-3, -1)$    d. $(-1, -3)$

9. Solve by using multiplication with the addition-or-subtraction method: 8-7

$$4a + 3b = -24$$
$$5a - 2b = -7$$

   a. $(3, 4)$    b. $(4, 3)$    c. $(-3, -4)$    d. $(-4, -3)$

10. A small plane can fly 240 km in 3 h with the wind, but only 210 km in 8-8
    3 h against the wind. Find the rate of the wind.
    a. 75 km/h    b. 80 km/h    c. 5 km/h    d. 10 km/h

11. The sum of the digits of a two-digit number is 8. If the digits are re- 8-9
    versed, the number is increased by 54. Find the original number.
    a. 71    b. 17    c. 26    d. 62

12. Hector will be twice as old as Will in 5 years. Five years ago Hector
    was three times as old as Will. How old is Will now?
    a. 35    b. 20    c. 15    d. 5

13. The denominator of a fraction is 7 more than the numerator. If 5 is
    added to each, the value of the resulting fraction is $\frac{1}{2}$. Find the original
    fraction.

    a. $\frac{7}{14}$    b. $\frac{9}{2}$    c. $\frac{5}{12}$    d. $\frac{2}{9}$

# Chapter Test

**State whether each ordered pair of numbers is a solution of the given equation.**

8-1

**1.** $-3x + 2y = 12$
$(-2, 3), (4, 0)$

**2.** $7x - 5y = -3$
$(-1, -2), (-4, -5)$

**Solve each equation for $y$ in terms of $x$.**

**3.** $2x + y = 12$

**4.** $2x - 3y = -5$

**Draw a coordinate plane and plot the graph of each of the given points.**

8-2

**5.** $(5, 3)$  **6.** $(0, -6)$  **7.** $(-3, -4)$  **8.** $(-2, 5)$

**Graph each equation.**

**9.** $y = 2x - 1$  **10.** $2x + 6y = 12$

**11.** Solve by the graphic method:

8-3

$$2x + 5y = 9$$
$$3x - 2y = 4$$

**12.** Solve by the substitution method:

8-4

$$8x + y = 3$$
$$5x + 2y = -27$$

**13.** Solve, using two equations in two variables: This year, the total number of dogs and cats sold by the Animal Adoption Agency was 1216. Last year, 420 more cats and double the number of dogs were sold for a total of 2024. How many of each were sold this year?

8-5

**14.** Solve by the addition-or-subtraction method:

8-6

$$4x - 5y = 0$$
$$8x + 5y = -60$$

**15.** Solve by using multiplication with the addition-or-subtraction method:

8-7

$$-7x + y = -16$$
$$3x + 2y = 2$$

**Solve by using a system of two equations in two variables.**

**16.** A small plane can fly 2400 km in 10 h flying into the wind. With the wind behind it, the plane can fly 3200 km in 10 h. What is the speed of the plane in still air and what is the speed of the wind?

8-8

**17.** The numerator of a fraction is 3 less than the denominator. If 25 is added to each, the value of the resulting fraction is equal to $\frac{9}{10}$. Find the original fraction.

8-9

# Cumulative Review (Chapters 1–8)

**Perform the indicated operations. Express the answers in simplest form. Assume that no denominator is zero.**

1. $(28p^4q^3 + 16p^3q^2 - 84p^2q^5) \div (2pq)^2$

2. $(-3xy^3z^2)^3(x^2yz)^5$

3. $-3j^3(jk^4 - 8jk^3 + 9k^4)$

4. $(5c - 3)(2c^2 + 4c + 1)$

5. $(21z - 3)(2z + 4)$

6. $(9z^3 - 4b)(9z + 4b)$

7. $\dfrac{28t^2 + 27t + 5}{4t + 1}$

8. $\dfrac{3}{2b - 1} + \dfrac{b^2 + 2}{1 - 4b^2} + b$

9. $\dfrac{x^2 + x - 12}{x^2 - x - 6} \div \dfrac{5x^2 + 5x - 60}{x + 2}$

10. $10y^2 + 27y - 15 \div (2y + 7)$

11. $(2.4 \times 10^5)(0.3 \times 10^7)$

12. $\left(\dfrac{z^{-3}}{z^{-5}}\right)^4$

**Factor completely. If the polynomial cannot be factored, write "prime."**

13. $64z^2 + 144zy + 81y^2$

14. $64x^4 - 81y^4$

15. $40x^2 + 26x + 1$

16. $28y^2 + 37y + 12$

17. $6y^2 - 17y - 10$

18. $16y^2 - 25x^2 + 10x - 1$

**Solve. Assume that no denominator is zero. If the equation is an identity or has no solution, state that fact.**

19. $\frac{7}{8}t + 9 = 23$

20. $16 - \frac{1}{2}|m| = 5$

21. $\frac{1}{5}(x - 6) = 34 - 3x$

22. $169x^2 - 81 = 0$

23. $25b^2 + 36 = 60b$

24. $-6z^2 - 5z + 25 = 0$

25. $15y^2 + 59y - 4 = 0$

26. $\dfrac{2x + 1}{x - 3} + \dfrac{x + 3}{2x + 1} = \dfrac{2x}{3 - x}$

27. $0.4(850 - z) + 0.65z = 300$

28. Solve the system $\begin{array}{l} y = 2x \\ 5x - y = 6 \end{array}$ graphically.

**Solve algebraically.**

29. $\begin{array}{l} 4x + 3y = 12 \\ 3y - 8x = -12 \end{array}$

30. $\begin{array}{l} 3x = y + 1 \\ 4x + 3y = 10 \end{array}$

31. $\begin{array}{l} 2x + 5y = 9 \\ 3x - 2y = 4 \end{array}$

32. The sum of the digits of a two-digit number is 6. When the digits are reversed, the resulting number is 6 greater than 3 times the original number. Find the original number.

33. Flying with the wind, a jet was able to complete a 3360 km trip in 4 h. Flying against the wind, the jet made the return trip in 7 h. Find the speed of the jet in still air and the wind speed.

34. How many kilograms of nuts worth $5 per kilogram should be mixed with 6 kg of nuts worth $9 per kilogram to produce a mix worth $6.50 per kilogram?

35. The square of the sum of two consecutive odd integers is 16 times the sum of the integers. Find the integers.

# Maintaining Skills

**Factor completely. If the polynomial cannot be factored, write "prime."**

*Example 1*  $24x^2y - 60xy^4$     *Solution*     $24x^2y - 60xy^4 = 12xy(2x - 5y^3)$

**1.** $25b^2c^3 + 15b^5c^4$     **2.** $12m^3 - 15mn^2 - 8n^2$     **3.** $9u^5v + 36u^4v^2 - 15u^4v^3$
**4.** $-vt^3 + 40t^2v^3 - v^6$     **5.** $-24x^7y^5 + 32x^6y^3 - 8x^2y^4$     **6.** $20m^6n^6 - 4m^6n^5 + 24m^5n^7$

*Example 2*  $81y^4 - 16$

*Solution*     $81y^4 - 16 = (9y^2 + 4)(9y^2 - 4) = (9y^2 + 4)(3y + 2)(3y - 2)$

*Example 3*  $9y^2 + 30y + 25$

*Solution*     $9y^2 + 30y + 25 = (3y)^2 + 2(3y \cdot 5) + 5^2 = (3y + 5)^2$

**7.** $z^3 - 121z$     **8.** $27bc^2 - 12b$     **9.** $-x^6 + 49$
**10.** $9t^2 - 12t + 4$     **11.** $25m^4 + 9$     **12.** $1 - 16z^8$
**13.** $16a^2 - 40a + 25$     **14.** $4t^2 - 16t + 16$     **15.** $25x^2 + 30x + 9$

*Example 4*  $g^2 - 2g - 35$     *Solution*     $g^2 - 2g - 35 = (g + 5)(g - 7)$

**16.** $z^2 + 8z - 16$     **17.** $b^2 + 11b + 18$     **18.** $y^2 - 9y + 18$
**19.** $-c^2 + 5cd + 14d^2$     **20.** $2d^2 + 18d - 72$     **21.** $x^2 + 10x + 21$
**22.** $4c^2 - 36c + 32$     **23.** $n^2 - 5np + 6p^2$     **24.** $7f + f^2 - 30$

*Example 5*  $3cd + 21d - 2c - 14$

*Solution*     $3cd + 21d - 2c - 14 = 3d(c + 7) - 2(c + 7) = (3d - 2)(c + 7)$

**25.** $rt - 2st + 3r - 6s$     **26.** $2xy - y^2 + 6x - 3y$     **27.** $s^2 - 4t^2 - 12t - 9$
**28.** $x^2 - 10x + 25 - y^2$  **29.** $16a^2 - 9b^2 + 30b - 25$     **30.** $s^2t - 5s^2 + 5t - 2$

*Example 6*  $10p^2 - 19p - 15$

*Solution*     Test the possibilities for the first terms: $10p$ and $p$; $5p$
and $2p$.
Test the possibilities for the second terms: $-15$ and $1$; $15$
and $-1$; $-5$ and $3$; $5$ and $-3$.
$10p^2 - 19p - 15 = (5p + 3)(2p - 5)$

**31.** $3b^2 + 2b - 5$     **32.** $10t^2 + 3t - 1$     **33.** $6m^2 - 8m - 8$
**34.** $6a^2 + 7a - 3$     **35.** $25z^3 + 15z^2 + 2z$     **36.** $14 + 15y - 9y^2$
**37.** $-7y^2 - 20y + 3$     **38.** $22n + 8n^2 - 6$     **39.** $12b^2 - 14b - 10$

# Mixed Review

## Skills and Problem Solving

**1.** Solve the system $\begin{array}{l} x + 1 = y \\ 2x + y = 4 \end{array}$ graphically.

**Solve. Assume that no denominator is zero.**

**2.** $20x^2 + 32x + 3 = 0$

**3.** $\frac{1}{3}(x + 4) = 6$

**4.** $\dfrac{2}{x + 1} - \dfrac{1}{x} = \dfrac{1}{x - 1}$

**5.** $(4x - 1)(x + 3) = (2x + 1)^2 + 6x$

**6.** The sum of the digits of a two-digit number is one eighth of the number with the digits reversed. The tens digit is 5 less than the ones digit. Find the number.

**7.** On a number line, point $A$ has coordinate $-8$ and point $B$ has coordinate 16. Find the coordinate of the point two thirds of the way from $A$ to $B$.

**8.** How many kilograms of salt must be added to 12 kg of an 8% salt solution to make a solution that is 20% salt?

**Factor completely. If the polynomial cannot be factored, write "prime."**

**9.** $9x^2 + 30x + 25$

**10.** $9x^2 + 34x + 25$

**11.** A rowboat traveled 3.6 km downstream in 24 min. The return trip took 1 h 12 min. Find, in kilometers per hour, the rate of the current and the rate of the boat in still water.

**12.** The perimeter of a triangle with sides that are in the ratio $3:4:5$ is 216 cm. Find the lengths of the sides.

**13.** The sum of the squares of two consecutive odd integers is 2 more than 8 times their sum. Write an equation in one variable describing this relationship.

**14.** The Lamarques invested $8000 in accounts paying 6% annual simple interest and in bonds paying 8% annual simple interest. If they had reversed the amounts of their investments, they would have earned $80 less. How much money did they invest in each?

**Express in scientific notation.**

**15.** $1\frac{1}{4}$ million

**16.** $(6.02 \times 10^{23})(4.0 \times 10^{-12})$

**Solve.**

**17.** $\begin{array}{l} y = 7x - 16 \\ 3x + 2y = 2 \end{array}$

**18.** $\begin{array}{l} 4x - 5y = 0 \\ 8x + 5y = -60 \end{array}$

**19.** $\begin{array}{l} 6x + 2y = 3 \\ -9x + 8y = 1 \end{array}$

# Preparing for College Entrance Exams

## Strategy for Success

Depending upon how a multiple-choice test is scored, it may not be good to guess. However, if you can eliminate several of the possible answers, it may be worthwhile to guess. For example, suppose you do not know the answer to a problem, but your knowledge of algebra tells you the answer must be a positive integer. This may help you eliminate some of the choices and improve your chances of guessing correctly.

**Decide which is the best of the choices given and write the corresponding letter on your answer sheet.**

1. The inlet pipe on a water tank can fill the tank in 8 hours. When the tank was full, both the inlet pipe and the drain pipe were accidentally opened. Twenty-four hours later, the tank was empty. How many hours would it take to empty a full tank if only the drain pipe were open?
   (A) 6 hours     (B) 12 hours     (C) 9 hours     (D) 10 hours

2. A runner won a 5 km road race with a time of exactly 15 min. An observer, using a watch that was running fast, clocked the winning time at 15 min 24 s. To the nearest tenth of a minute, how many minutes does the observer's watch gain in a day?
   (A) 24.0 min     (B) 38.4 min     (C) 58.4 min     (D) 61.0 min     (E) 61.6 min

3. The length of a rectangle is 3 cm less than twice its width. A second rectangle is such that each of its dimensions is the reciprocal of the corresponding dimension of the first rectangle. The perimeter of the second rectangle is $\frac{1}{5}$ the perimeter of the first. Find the perimeter of the first rectangle.
   (A) 9 cm     (B) 6 cm     (C) 18 cm     (D) 12 cm

4. A total of $12,000 was invested in accounts earning 8% annual simple interest and in bonds earning 12% annual simple interest. If twice as much of the $12,000 had been invested in bonds, the earnings would have been $160 higher. How much was invested in bonds?
   (A) $1000     (B) $2000     (C) $4000     (D) $6000

5. A shopper paid $7.70 for 2 containers of milk and 3 containers of apple juice. It would have cost 60 cents more for 2 containers of apple juice and 3 containers of milk. How much would it cost to buy one container of each?
   (A) $2.60     (B) $2.90     (C) $3.20     (D) $3.60     (E) $3.80

6. Which method(s) could be used to solve: $\begin{array}{l} xy = 9 \\ x + y = 6 \end{array}$ ?
   I. Graphing     II. Multiplication with Addition-or-Subtraction     III. Substitution
   (A) I only     (B) II only     (C) III only     (D) I, II, and III
   (E) I and III only

# 9 Introduction to Functions

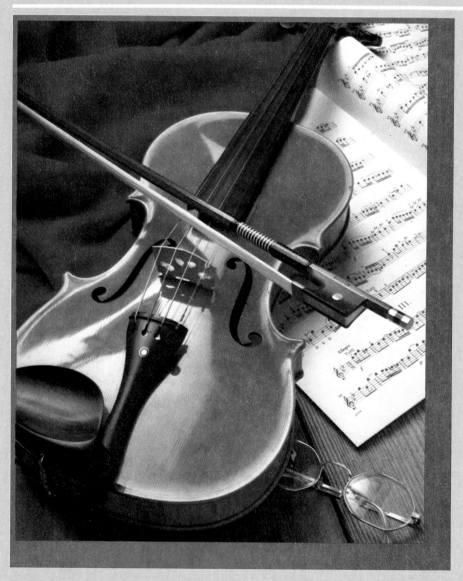

The pitch of a musical tone is determined by its frequency. The frequency of a tone played on a violin is a function of the tension, the length, and the mass of a string. (See Exercises 9–10, page 428.)

# Linear Equations

## 9-1 Slope of a Line

**Objective** To find the slope of a line.

To describe the steepness, or *slope,* of an airplane's flight path shortly after take-off, you estimate the vertical *rise* for every 100 m of horizontal *run* and calculate the ratio:

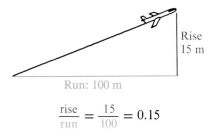

$$\frac{\text{rise}}{\text{run}} = \frac{15}{100} = 0.15$$

To describe the slope of a straight line, choose any two points on the line, count the units in the rise and the run from one point to the other, and calculate the ratio of the rise to the run.

*Example 1*                                      *Example 2*

                              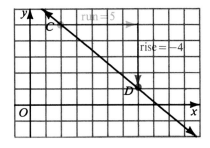

$$\text{slope} = \frac{\text{rise}}{\text{run}} = \frac{3}{9} = \frac{1}{3}$$

$$\text{slope} = \frac{\text{rise}}{\text{run}} = \frac{-4}{5} = -\frac{4}{5}$$

In Example 1, the line passes through the points $A(1, 2)$ and $B(10, 5)$. The rise, or vertical change, in moving from point $A$ to point $B$ is the difference between the $y$-coordinates: $5 - 2 = 3$. The run, or horizontal change, in moving from point $A$ to point $B$ is the difference between the $x$-coordinates: $10 - 1 = 9$.

The coordinates of a pair of points on a line can be used to calculate the slope of the line:

$$\textbf{slope} = \frac{\text{rise}}{\text{run}} = \frac{\text{vertical change}}{\text{horizontal change}} = \frac{\text{difference between } y\text{-coordinates}}{\text{difference between } x\text{-coordinates}}$$

Thus, if

$$(x_1, y_1), \text{ read "} x \text{ sub 1, } y \text{ sub 1," and}$$
$$(x_2, y_2), \text{ read "} x \text{ sub 2, } y \text{ sub 2,"}$$

are any two different points on a line,

$$\textbf{slope} = \frac{y_2 - y_1}{x_2 - x_1} \qquad (x_1 \neq x_2).$$

Notice that the differences are taken in the same order.

**Example 3** Find the slope of the line through the points $(3, 8)$ and $(5, 4)$.

**Solution** Let $x_1 = 3$, $y_1 = 8$, $x_2 = 5$, and $y_2 = 4$.

Then, slope $= \dfrac{y_2 - y_1}{x_2 - x_1} = \dfrac{4 - 8}{5 - 3} = \dfrac{-4}{2} = -2$ *Answer*

**Example 4** Find the slope of the line whose equation is $3x - 2y = 6$.

**Solution**

Find two points on the line (page 340):

If $x = 0$: $-2y = 6$ or $y = -3$.
If $y = 0$: $3x = 6$ or $x = 2$.

$(0, -3)$ and $(2, 0)$

$\therefore$ slope $= \dfrac{0 - (-3)}{2 - 0} = \dfrac{3}{2}$. *Answer*

In Example 4, two convenient points were chosen, but the slope calculated using any two points on the line would be $\frac{3}{2}$.

---

A basic property of a line is that its slope is constant.

---

**Example 5** Determine whether the points whose coordinates are given lie on the same line. If they do, find the slope of the line.
  **a.** $(-1, 9)$, $(0, 5)$, $(1, 1)$, $(2, -3)$
  **b.** $(0, 0)$, $(2, 1)$, $(4, 3)$, $(6, 4)$
  **c.** $(-2, 5)$, $(0, 6)$, $(6, 9)$, $(2, 7)$

**Solution**     *Plan:* Arrange the coordinates of the points in a table in order of increasing $x$-coordinates. Then, compute the changes in the $x$-coordinates (blue) and the $y$-coordinates (red) and the ratio, as you move from one point to the next.

**(a)**

| $x$ | $y$ |
|---|---|
| $-1$ | 9 |
| 0 | 5 |
| 1 | 1 |
| 2 | $-3$ |

$1 \{ \quad \} -4$
$1 \{ \quad \} -4$
$1 \{ \quad \} -4$

The ratio of vertical change to horizontal change is constant:

$$\frac{-4}{1} = -4.$$

The points lie on a line whose slope is $-4$.

**(b)**

| $x$ | $y$ |
|---|---|
| 0 | 0 |
| 2 | 1 |
| 4 | 3 |
| 6 | 4 |

$2 \{ \quad \} 1$
$2 \{ \quad \} 2$
$2 \{ \quad \} 1$

The ratio of vertical change to horizontal change is *not* constant. The points do *not* lie on a line.

**(c)**

| $x$ | $y$ |
|---|---|
| $-2$ | 5 |
| 0 | 6 |
| 2 | 7 |
| 6 | 9 |

$2 \{ \quad \} 1$
$2 \{ \quad \} 1$
$4 \{ \quad \} 2$

The ratio of vertical change to horizontal change is constant: $\frac{1}{2}$. The points lie on a line whose slope is $\frac{1}{2}$.

Points that lie on the same line are said to be **collinear.**

Whenever a line rises from left to right, its slope is a positive number (Examples 1 and 4). When it falls from left to right, its slope is a negative number (Examples 2 and 3). The slope of the horizontal line joining $(-3, 1)$ and $(2, 1)$ in the figure at the right is

$$\frac{1 - 1}{2 - (-3)} = \frac{0}{5} = 0.$$

In fact,

*the slope of every horizontal line is 0.*

If you use the formula on page 392 to try to compute the slope of the vertical line shown at the right, you find that the denominator is 0. Since you cannot divide by zero, the formula does not apply.

*Vertical lines have no slope.*

## Oral Exercises

**Find the slope of each line.**

**1.**

**2.**

**3.**

**4.**

**5.**

**6.**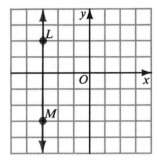

## Written Exercises

**Find the slope of the line through the given points.**

**A**
**1.** $(9, 5)$, $(7, 6)$
**2.** $(2, -4)$, $(5, -6)$
**3.** $(-8, 1)$, $(-6, 3)$

**4.** $(2, 7)$, $(4, 3)$
**5.** $(-5, 3)$, $(6, 5)$
**6.** $(3, -4)$, $(9, 4)$

**7.** $(-2, -2)$, $(0, 0)$
**8.** $(7, 2)$, $(-2, 2)$
**9.** $(1, 8)$, $(1, -2)$

**10.** $(-6, -7)$, $(-4, -4)$
**11.** $(0, -1)$, $(5, -1)$
**12.** $(0, 0)$, $(4, 10)$

**Find the slope of each line whose equation is given.**

**13.** $y = 5x - 2$
**14.** $y = 3x - 2$
**15.** $y = -3x + 8$

**16.** $2x + y = 4$
**17.** $x - y = 7$
**18.** $5x - y = 16$

**19.** $2x + 3y = 12$
**20.** $4x + 3y = 36$
**21.** $8x - 3y = 24$

**22.** $4x + 5y = 20$
**23.** $y = -5$
**24.** $y - 7 = 0$

**If the points are collinear, find the slope of the line through them.**

**25.** $(0, 4)$, $(1, 2)$, $(2, 0)$, $(3, -2)$
**26.** $(4, 3)$, $(5, 5)$, $(6, 7)$, $(7, 10)$

**27.** $(0, -1)$, $(1, -2)$, $(2, -4)$, $(-1, 0)$
**28.** $(1, -1)$, $(-1, 2)$, $(-3, 5)$, $(-5, 8)$

**Through the given point, draw a line with the given slope.**

*Example*   $P(-2, 1)$; slope $-3$

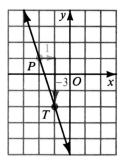

*Solution*   1. Plot point $P$.

2. Write the slope as the fraction $\frac{-3}{1}$. From $P$, measure 1 unit to the right and 3 units down to locate a second point, $T$. Draw the line through $P$ and $T$.

**29.** $A(3, 2)$; slope 4    **30.** $B(-3, 4)$; slope $-2$    **31.** $R(2, -7)$; slope 0

**32.** $N(-2, -1)$; slope $\frac{2}{7}$    **33.** $K(-5, 1)$; slope $-\frac{1}{2}$    **34.** $H(4, -3)$; slope $-\frac{3}{5}$

**B**   **35.** The vertices of a triangle are $A(-4, 6)$, $B(5, 6)$, and $C(-4, -2)$. Find the slope of each side of the triangle.

**36.** The vertices of a rectangle are $M(-2, -3)$, $N(3, 2)$, $P(10, -5)$, and $Q(5, -10)$. Find the slope of each side of the rectangle.

**37.** Determine the slope of the line through the points $(4, 6)$ and $(0, 4)$. Find the value of $y$ if $(8, y)$ lies on this line.

**38.** The slope of a line through the point $(1, 3)$ is 1.5. If the point $(-3, y)$ lies on the line, find the value of $y$.

**39.** A line with slope $-4$ passes through the points $(-7, c)$ and $(1, 3c)$. Find the value of $c$.

**40.** A line with slope $-3$ passes through the points $(-8, p)$ and $(2, 3p)$. Find the value of $p$.

**C**   **41.** The vertices of a square are $A(3, 5)$, $B(11, 3)$, $C(9, -5)$, and $D(1, -3)$. Use the idea of slope to show that the point $M(6, 0)$ lies on the diagonal joining $A$ and $C$, and on the diagonal joining $B$ and $D$.

**42.** The vertices of a right triangle are $P(-4, 2)$, $Q(-4, -6)$, and $R(6, -6)$. Use the idea of slope to show that $S(1, -2)$ lies on one of the sides of the triangle.

## *Computer Exercises*   For students with some programming experience

Write a BASIC program that prints the coordinates of points on a line when the slope and the coordinates of a given point on the line are entered with INPUT statements. RUN the program for the following data.

**1.** $m = 2$; $(-1, -3)$; 5 more points    **2.** $m = 0$; $(-4, -2)$; 3 more points

**3.** $m = -\frac{1}{2}$; $(0, 6)$; 10 more points    **4.** $m = \frac{4}{3}$; $(2, 5)$; 5 more points

# 9-2 The Slope-Intercept Form of a Linear Equation

**Objective**  To use the slope-intercept form of a linear equation.

The table shows the coordinates of a few of the points on the graph of the linear equation $y = 2x$. The graph is the straight line that has slope $\frac{2}{1}$, or 2, and that passes through the origin.

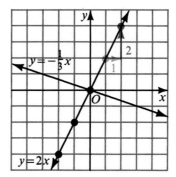

The graph of the equation $y = -\frac{1}{3}x$ is a line that has slope $-\frac{1}{3}$ and passes through the origin.

---

For every real number $m$, the graph in a coordinate plane of the equation

$$y = mx$$

is the line that has slope $m$ and passes through the origin.

---

The graphs of the linear equations

$$y = 2x \quad \text{and} \quad y = 2x + 4$$

have been drawn on the same set of axes. The lines have equal slopes, but they cross the $y$-axis at different points. The $y$-coordinate of a point where a graph intersects the $y$-axis is called the **$y$-intercept** of the graph.

To determine the $y$-intercept of a line, replace $x$ with 0 in the equation of the line:

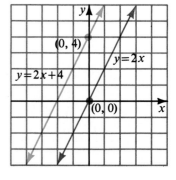

$y = 2x$
$y = 2(0)$
$y = 0$
$y$-intercept: 0

$y = 2x + 4$
$y = 2(0) + 4$
$y = 4$
$y$-intercept: 4

If you write $y = 2x$ as $y = 2x + 0$, you can see that the constant term in the following equations is the $y$-intercept of each graph:

$$y = 2x + 0 \qquad y = 2x + 4$$

For all real numbers $m$ and $b$, the graph in a coordinate plane of the equation

$$y = mx + b$$

is the line whose slope is $m$ and whose $y$-intercept is $b$. This is called the **slope-intercept form** of an equation of a line.

*Example 1* Write a linear equation in standard form whose graph has the given slope and $y$-intercept.

        **a.** $m = -4$, $b = -3$     **b.** $m = \frac{1}{5}$, $b = 2$

*Solution* First write an equation of the form $y = mx + b$. Then transform it into an equivalent equation in the form $Ax + By = C$, where $A$, $B$, and $C$ are integers.

    **a.** $y = -4x + (-3)$        **b.** $y = \frac{1}{5}x + 2$
           $4x + y = -3$   *Answer*
                                      $5y = x + 10$
                                     $-x + 5y = 10$   *Answer*

If you solve linear equations for $y$, the coefficient of $x$ is the slope of the graph of the linear equation.

*Example 2* Use only the $y$-intercept and slope to graph the equation $2x - 3y = 6$.

*Solution* Solve for $y$ to transform the equation into the form $y = mx + b$.

$$2x - 3y = 6$$
$$-3y = -2x + 6$$
$$y = \frac{2}{3}x - 2$$

Since the $y$-intercept is $-2$, plot $(0, -2)$.

Since the slope is $\frac{2}{3}$, measure 3 units to the right of $(0, -2)$ and 2 units up to locate a second point. Draw the line through the two points.

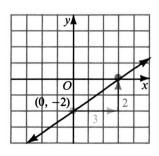

**Example 3** Show that the lines whose equations are $2x + y = 8$ and $2x + y = 6$ are parallel.

**Solution**   1. Recall (page 346) that parallel lines do not intersect. Therefore, to show that the given lines are parallel, you can show that the *system* of equations

$$2x + y = 8$$
$$2x + y = 6$$

has *no solution*.

2. Write each equation in slope-intercept form:

$$y = -2x + 8$$
$$y = -2x + 6$$

3. Use the substitution method (page 351) to solve the system in Step 2. You find

$$-2x + 8 = -2x + 6$$
or     $8 = 6$

4. Since Step 3 produces a false statement, the system has no solution.

∴ the given lines are parallel.   *Answer*

Notice that the parallel lines in Example 3 have the same slope, $-2$. In general:

---

Different lines with the same slope are parallel. Also, parallel lines that are not vertical have the same slope.

---

With this information, you can tell whether or not two nonvertical lines are parallel by inspecting the slope-intercept form of their equations.

## Oral Exercises

**State the slope and $y$-intercept of each line whose equation is given.**

**1.** $y = 4x$     **2.** $y = 5x - 3$     **3.** $y = \frac{1}{2}x + 2$     **4.** $y = -3x$

**5.** $y = -2x - \frac{1}{3}$     **6.** $y = \frac{3}{4}x + \frac{1}{2}$     **7.** $y = -\frac{2}{5}x$     **8.** $y = 6x - 1.5$

State an equation of the line that has the given slope and $y$-intercept.

**9.** $m = 3, b = 2$     **10.** $m = 3, b = 0$     **11.** $m = -2, b = -1$     **12.** $m = -1, b = 7$

## Written Exercises

Write an equation in standard form of the line that has the given slope and $y$-intercept.

A
**1.** $m = 2, b = \frac{1}{3}$

**2.** $m = -3, b = \frac{2}{3}$

**3.** $m = \frac{1}{5}, b = 4$

**4.** $m = -\frac{3}{4}, b = 2$

**5.** $m = 6, b = -\frac{3}{5}$

**6.** $m = -\frac{2}{3}, b = -1$

**7.** $m = \frac{7}{3}, b = -\frac{1}{6}$

**8.** $m = -\frac{5}{4}, b = -\frac{7}{8}$

**9.** $m = 0, b = -6$

**10.** $m = 0, b = 15$

**11.** $m = -2.1, b = -0.4$

**12.** $m = 1.8, b = -2.5$

Change each equation to the slope-intercept form. Then draw the graph, using only the slope and $y$-intercept.

**13.** $x + y = 5$

**14.** $2x - y = -3$

**15.** $x - y = 4$

**16.** $-x + 3y = 9$

**17.** $x - 2y = 6$

**18.** $2y - 3x = -6$

**19.** $2x + 3y = 0$

**20.** $4x - 3y = 12$

**21.** $-4x + 5y = 15$

**22.** $5x = 2y$

**23.** $2x - 3y - 6 = 0$

**24.** $3y = 7$

Use the slope-intercept form of the equations to determine whether each system has a solution.

B
**25.** $2x - 3y = 7$
$-2x + 3y = 4$

**26.** $x - 2y = 1$
$2x + y = 4$

**27.** $x - y = 4$
$y - x = -4$

**28.** $4x - y = 1$
$-8x + 2y = -2$

**29.** $\frac{x}{2} + \frac{y}{2} = 5$
$2x + 2y = 3$

**30.** $\frac{x}{3} - \frac{y}{3} = 2$
$3x - 3y = 1$

**31.** Write an equation of the line that has $y$-intercept $-4$ and is parallel to the graph of $y = 3x - 1$.

**32.** Write an equation of the line that is parallel to the graph of $y - 2x = 1$ and has the same $y$-intercept as the graph of $4y + 3x = 20$.

**33.** In the equation $3y + px = 5$, for what value of $p$ is the graph of the equation parallel to the graph of $x - y = 4$? the graph of $x + y = 4$?

**34.** In the equation $dy + 3x = 2$, for what value of $d$ is the graph of the equation parallel to the graph of $x - 6y = 0$? the $y$-axis?

**In Exercises 35–37, use the points $A(5, 3)$, $B(2, 6)$, and $C(-2, 0)$.**

35. Find $r$ if the line joining $A$ to $(r, 2r)$ is parallel to the line joining $B$ and $C$.

36. Find $s$ if the line joining $B$ to $(s + 4, s)$ is parallel to the line joining $A$ and $C$.

37. Find $t$ if the line joining $C$ to $(-3t, 2t + 1)$ is parallel to the line joining $A$ and $B$.

C
38. A radio beacon is located at $(-1, 0)$ and another at $(2, -1)$. A navigator's equipment tells her that the line joining her position to the first beacon has slope $-5$ and the line joining her position to the second has slope 3. What is the navigator's location?

39. Using the standard form of a linear equation, $Ax + By = C$, find a formula for the slope and a formula for the $y$-intercept in terms of the coefficients, assuming that $B \neq 0$.

## Historical Note / *The Seqt of a Pyramid*

To ensure the uniform slope of the faces of a pyramid, the ancient Egyptians determined the pyramid's *seqt*. "Seqt" was the ratio of the run to the rise. (Modern-day architects use the same ratio to describe the slope of a wall, terrace, bank, or pier.) The run was always measured in hands, while the rise was always measured in cubits. There were seven hands in a cubit.

Problems 56 and 57 of the Rhind mathematical papyrus, a collection of 85 practical problems copied from some earlier document by the scribe Ahmes about 1550 B.C., deal with the seqt of a pyramid. Problem 56 asks one to find the seqt of a pyramid 250 cubits high having a square base of 360 cubits on a side. The answer given is $5\frac{1}{25}$ hands per cubit. (Note that the measurements are not expressed in the same units.) Problem 57 asks one to find the height of a pyramid having a square base 140 cubits on a side and a seqt of 5 hands and 1 finger per cubit. (Not surprisingly, there were 4 fingers in a hand.) The answer given is $93\frac{1}{3}$ cubits.

The great pyramid of Cheops has a square base 440 cubits on a side and is 280 cubits high. Its seqt, then, is $5\frac{1}{2}$ hands per cubit.

# 9-3 Determining an Equation of a Line

**Objective**   To find an equation of a line given the slope and one point on the line, or given two points on the line.

The line shown in the diagram has slope $\frac{3}{4}$ and passes through the point $(-3, -2)$. The slope-intercept form of the equation of this line is

$$y = \frac{3}{4}x + b.$$

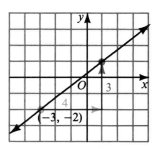

Since the point $(-3, -2)$ is on the line, its coordinates satisfy the equation. You can substitute to find the value of $b$.

$$-2 = \frac{3}{4}(-3) + b$$

$$-2 = -\frac{9}{4} + b$$

$$\frac{1}{4} = b$$

Therefore, an equation of the line with slope $\frac{3}{4}$ and passing through $(-3, -2)$ is $y = \frac{3}{4}x + \frac{1}{4}$, or in standard form, $-3x + 4y = 1$.

**Example**   Write an equation of the line passing through the points $(-2, -1)$ and $(4, 8)$.

**Solution**   $\text{slope} = \dfrac{\text{difference between } y\text{-coordinates}}{\text{difference between } x\text{-coordinates}}$

$$= \frac{8 - (-1)}{4 - (-2)} = \frac{9}{6} = \frac{3}{2}$$

∴ the slope-intercept form of the equation is

$$y = \frac{3}{2}x + b.$$

Choose one of the points, say $(4, 8)$. Since it lies on the line, its coordinates satisfy the equation. Substitute to find the value of $b$:

$$8 = \frac{3}{2}(4) + b$$

$$8 = 6 + b$$

$$2 = b$$

∴ an equation of the line is $y = \frac{3}{2}x + 2$.   ***Answer***

As shown in the text above the Example, you can find an equation of a line if you know the slope and one point on the line. To determine an equation of a line when two points on the line are given, you first find the slope and then find the $y$-intercept as shown in the Example.

## Written Exercises

Each given point is on a line whose equation is $y = \frac{3}{4}x + b$. Find each value of $b$.

**A**    **1.** $(8, 1)$        **2.** $(-8, 3)$        **3.** $(0, -7)$        **4.** $(-2, -5)$

Write an equation in standard form of the line that has the given slope and passes through the given point.

**5.** $m = 2;\ (-3, 1)$        **6.** $m = 4;\ (-2, 3)$        **7.** $m = -3;\ (4, 6)$

**8.** $m = -2;\ (3, -1)$        **9.** $m = \frac{3}{2};\ (0, 3)$        **10.** $m = \frac{4}{3};\ (1, 0)$

**11.** $m = -\frac{4}{5};\ (-1, -6)$        **12.** $m = -1;\ (5, 1)$        **13.** $m = -\frac{1}{2};\ (0, 0)$

**14.** $m = \frac{9}{7};\ (-14, 3)$        **15.** $m = 0;\ \left(\frac{1}{2}, -4\right)$        **16.** $m = 0;\ \left(-3, \frac{5}{8}\right)$

Write an equation in standard form of the line passing through the given points.

**17.** $(1, -1),\ (5, 6)$        **18.** $(4, 0),\ (-1, 2)$        **19.** $(4, 1),\ (-3, 1)$
**20.** $(-1, 2),\ (4, 7)$        **21.** $(3, 4),\ (2, 6)$        **22.** $(7, 1),\ (3, 2)$
**23.** $(3, -1),\ (6, 7)$        **24.** $(-3, -1),\ (1, -4)$        **25.** $(0, -1),\ (1, 4)$
**26.** $(-1, -2),\ (0, 3)$        **27.** $(-2, 0),\ (2, -3)$        **28.** $(3, 0),\ (-2, 5)$

Write an equation in standard form for each line described.

**B**    **29.** The line that passes through the point $(-1, 3)$ and is parallel to the graph of $3x - y = 4$.

**30.** The line that is parallel to the graph of $x - 2y + 7 = 0$ and contains the point $(-4, 0)$.

**31.** The line that passes through the point $(-4, -5)$ and has the same $y$-intercept as the graph of $x + 3y + 9 = 0$.

**32.** The line that contains the points $(7, 1)$, $(p, 0)$, and $(0, p)$ for $p \neq 0$.

**C**    **33.** The line that has slope $\frac{1}{3}$ and passes through the point of intersection of the graphs of $2x - 7y = 15$ and $x - y = 5$.

**34.** The line that has slope $\frac{1}{2}$ and passes through the point of intersection of the graphs of $x - 6y = 10$ and $x - y = 5$.

**35.** The line whose $x$-intercept is $-6$ and whose $y$-intercept is 2. (The *x-intercept* of a line is the $x$-coordinate of the point where the line crosses the $x$-axis.)

# Self-Test 1

**Vocabulary** slope (p. 392)
collinear (p. 393)
*y*-intercept (p. 396)

slope-intercept form of an
equation (p. 397)

1. Find the slope of the line that passes through the points $(2, 3)$ and $(4, 6)$.

**Obj. 9-1, p. 391**

2. Find the slope of the line $y = 7$.

3. Find the slope and *y*-intercept of the line whose equation is $3x - 7y = 28$.

**Obj. 9-2, p. 396**

4. Write an equation in standard form of the line with slope 3 that passes through the point $(-2, -1)$.

**Obj. 9-3, p. 401**

5. Write an equation in standard form of the line through the points $(5, 0)$ and $(0, -5)$.

Check your answers with those at the back of the book.

## Computer Key-In

### Exercises

1. **a.** Write a formula and then write a program to find the slope of the line between the points $(X1, Y1)$ and $(X2, Y2)$. When is there no slope?
   **b.** RUN the program for each of the following.

$$(2, 3) \text{ and } (1, 5)$$
$$(-3, 2) \text{ and } (1, 5)$$
$$(2, 3) \text{ and } (2, 5)$$
$$(2, 5) \text{ and } (-2, 5)$$

2. **a.** Using the standard form of the equation of a line, $Ax + By = C$, write formulas for the *x*-intercept, the *y*-intercept, and the slope.
   **b.** Write a program to find the items in part (a). RUN your program for $3x - 2y = 6$, $3x = 6$, and $2y = 6$.

3. **a.** Write a program to transform an equation of a line in standard form to an equation in slope-intercept form.
   **b.** RUN the program for $3x - 2y = 6$, $3x = 6$, and $2y = 6$.

*Note:* The program of Exercise 1 above can be used to do Exercises 1–12 on page 394. The program of Exercise 3 above can be used to do Exercises 13–24 on page 399.

# Functions

## 9-4 Functions Defined by Equations

***Objective*** To understand what a function is and how to find its values.

An equation such as $y = 7x + 1$ assigns to each number in the domain of the variable $x$ another number, the value of $y$. For example, if the domain of $x$ is $\{2, 4, 6\}$, the equation $y = 7x + 1$ assigns the following values to $y$:

$$y = 7 \cdot 2 + 1 = 15$$
$$y = 7 \cdot 4 + 1 = 29$$
$$y = 7 \cdot 6 + 1 = 43$$

Thus, the given equation pairs each member of $\{2, 4, 6\}$ with a single member of $\{15, 29, 43\}$, as shown by the diagram. This example illustrates the mathematical idea of a *function*.

A **function** consists of two sets, the **domain** and the **range,** and a *rule* that assigns to each member of the domain *exactly one* member of the range. Each member of the range must be assigned to *at least one* member of the domain.

In the preceding example, the rule that defines the function is the equation $y = 7x + 1$, the domain $D$ is $\{2, 4, 6\}$, and the range $R$ is $\{15, 29, 43\}$.

The rule that defines a function may also be written using an arrow notation and a single letter, such as $f$, $g$, $F$, or $H$, to name the function. The **arrow notation**

$$f: x \longrightarrow 7x + 1$$

is read "the function $f$ that assigns $7x + 1$ to $x$" or "the function $f$ that pairs $x$ with $7x + 1$." To specify a function completely, you must also describe the domain of the function. The numbers assigned by the rule then form the range.

***Example 1*** List the members of the range of

$$g: x \longrightarrow 4 + 3x - x^2$$

if the domain $D = \{-1, 0, 1, 2\}$.

***Solution*** In $4 + 3x - x^2$ replace $x$ with each member of $D$ to find the members of the range $R$.

$$\therefore R = \{0, 4, 6\} \quad \textit{Answer}$$

| $x$ | $4 + 3x - x^2$ |
| --- | --- |
| $-1$ | $4 + 3(-1) - (-1)^2 = 0$ |
| $0$ | $4 + 3(0) - 0^2 = 4$ |
| $1$ | $4 + 3(1) - 1^2 = 6$ |
| $2$ | $4 + 3(2) - 2^2 = 6$ |

Notice that the function $g$ in Example 1 assigns the number 6 to both 1 and 2. In specifying the range of $g$, however, you name 6 only once.

Members of the range of a function are called **values of the function.** Thus, in Example 1, the values of the function $g$ are 0, 4, and 6. To indicate that the function $g$ assigns to 2 the value 6, you write

$$g(2) = 6$$

which may be read "$g$ of 2 equals 6" or "the value of $g$ at 2 is 6." Notice that $g(2)$ is *not* the product of $g$ and 2. It names the number that $g$ assigns to 2.

**Example 2** Given $F: z \rightarrow z^4 - 1$ with the set of real numbers as the domain, find **a.** $F(1)$ **b.** $F(-1)$ **c.** $F(2)$.

**Solution** First write the equation: $F(z) = z^4 - 1$
Then: **a.** $F(1) = 1^4 - 1 = 0$
**b.** $F(-1) = (-1)^4 - 1 = 0$
**c.** $F(2) = 2^4 - 1 = 15$

You may use whatever variable you choose to define a function. For example, $G: t \rightarrow t^4 - 1$ with the set of real numbers as the domain is the same function as $F$ in Example 2. Both $F$ and $G$ assign to each real number its fourth power decreased by 1.

## Oral Exercises

Given the function $g: x \longrightarrow 5 - 2x$, find the following values of $g$.

**1.** $g(0)$      **2.** $g(-1)$      **3.** $g(1)$      **4.** $g(2)$

**5.** $g(-2)$      **6.** $g(5)$      **7.** $g(8)$      **8.** $g(-8)$

State the range of each function.

**9.** $f: w \rightarrow w + 3$, $D = \{0, 1, 2\}$      **10.** $g: n \rightarrow 4 - n$, $D = \{-1, 0, 1\}$

**11.** $F: p \rightarrow p^3$, $D = \left\{-\frac{1}{3}, 0, \frac{1}{3}\right\}$      **12.** $G: x \rightarrow x^2 - 1$, $D = \{-1, 0, 1\}$

**13.** $h: x \rightarrow 5x^2$, $D = \{0, 1, 2\}$      **14.** $H: a \rightarrow a^3 + 2$, $D = \left\{0, \frac{1}{2}, 1\right\}$

Complete the following statements about the function $f: x \longrightarrow x^2 - 4$.

**15.** The value of $f$ at $-2$ is __?__.      **16.** The value of $f$ at 2 is __?__.

**17.** The value of $f$ at __?__ is $-4$.      **18.** The value of $f$ at both __?__ and __?__ is 0.

## Written Exercises

**Given $f: x \rightarrow 7 - 2x$, find the following values of $f$.**

A

1. $f(0)$
2. $f(1)$
3. $f(-1)$
4. $f(-2)$

5. $f(-4)$
6. $f(5)$
7. $f\left(\frac{1}{2}\right)$
8. $f\left(-\frac{1}{2}\right)$

**Given $H(s) = s^2 + 3s$, find the following values of $H$.**

9. $H(-3)$
10. $H(0)$
11. $H(1)$
12. $H(-1)$

13. $H(-2)$
14. $H(3)$
15. $H\left(-\frac{2}{3}\right)$
16. $H\left(\frac{1}{3}\right)$

**Find all the values of each function.**

17. $g(x) = 5x + 1, D = \{-1, 0, 1\}$
18. $f(x) = 3x - 4, D = \{1, 2, 3\}$
19. $f(x) = 4 - 3x - x^2, D = \{1, 2, 4\}$
20. $m(x) = x^2 + 3x - 4, D = \{-1, -2, -4\}$
21. $G(n) = 6 + \frac{1}{n+2}, D = \{-3, -1, 0\}$
22. $F(t) = \frac{8}{3t+1}, D = \{-1, 0, 1\}$

**Find the range of each function.**

23. $s: z \rightarrow 5 - 4z, D = \{-2, 0, 2\}$
24. $h: y \rightarrow -1 - 2y, D = \{-3, 0, 1\}$
25. $r: x \rightarrow \frac{10}{x}, D = \{1, 2, -5\}$
26. $n: t \rightarrow \frac{12}{t-1}, D = \{2, 3, 4\}$
27. $K: p \rightarrow \frac{p^2 + 1}{3p - 1}, D = \{-1, 0, 1\}$
28. $M: v \rightarrow \frac{v^2 - v}{v + 1}, D = \{-2, 0, 2\}$

B

29. $g: a \rightarrow 4a^2 - 1, D = \{-1, 0, 1\}$
30. $h: b \rightarrow (b - 3)^2, D = \{0, 2, 4\}$
31. $f: z \rightarrow z^2 - 5z + 6, D = \{2, 3, 4\}$
32. $k: x \rightarrow x^3 - 5x^2 + 6x, D = \{0, 2, 3\}$
33. $G: t \rightarrow (t^2 + 2t)^2, D = \{-2, 0, 1, 2\}$
34. $F: p \rightarrow p(1 - p^2)^3, D = \{-2, -1, 0, 1\}$

**In each of Exercises 35–40, (a) find $f(0)$; (b) solve $f(x) = 0$.**

35. $f(x) = 2x - 12$
36. $f(x) = -\frac{1}{2}x + 5$
37. $f(x) = x^4 - x^2$

38. $f(x) = x - x^3$
39. $f(x) = \frac{x+1}{x-2}$
40. $f(x) = \frac{x^2 - 3x + 2}{x + 1}$

**Given that $f(x) = 3x + 4$ and $g(x) = -x^2$, find each of the following.**

41. $\frac{1}{2}g(6)$
42. $2f(5)$
43. $f(1) + g(1)$
44. $f(2) \cdot g(2)$

**In Exercises 45–47, let $f(x) = x^2$ and $g(x) = 2x$. Find each of the following. (Hint: To find $g[f(2)]$, first find $f(2)$.)**

C

45. a. $g(1)$
   b. $f(1)$
   c. $g[f(1)]$
   d. $f[g(1)]$

46. a. $g(-2)$
   b. $f(-2)$
   c. $g[f(-2)]$
   d. $f[g(-2)]$

**47.** Is there any real number $x$ for which $f[g(x)] = g[f(x)]$?
If there is such a number, find it. If there is no such number, explain
why not.

**48.** If $f(x) = x + 1$, and $g[f(x)] = x$, what is $g(x)$?

## Computer Exercises

*For students with some programming experience*

Write a BASIC program to calculate the value of a given function for values of $x$ entered with READ . . . DATA statements. Recall that the BASIC
statement that corresponds to $f(x) = x^2$ is DEF FNA(X) = X↑2. RUN the
program for the functions given below.

**1.** $f(x) = 3x - 7$;   $x = -2, 0, 1, 10$
**2.** $f(x) = x^2 + 3x + 2$;   $x = -1, -2, 0, 1$
**3.** $f(x) = 2^x$;   $x = -4, -1, 0, 1, 2, 4$
**4.** $f(x) = 9 - x^2$;   $x = -3, -1, 0, 2, 3, 4$

## *Challenge*

**1. a.** Find each sum.

$$\frac{1}{1 \cdot 2} + \frac{1}{2 \cdot 3} = \underline{\quad?\quad}$$

$$\frac{1}{1 \cdot 2} + \frac{1}{2 \cdot 3} + \frac{1}{3 \cdot 4} = \underline{\quad?\quad}$$

$$\frac{1}{1 \cdot 2} + \frac{1}{2 \cdot 3} + \frac{1}{3 \cdot 4} + \frac{1}{4 \cdot 5} = \underline{\quad?\quad}$$

**b.** If this addition pattern were continued for 100 fractions, what would
the sum be?

**c.** If this addition pattern were continued for $n$ fractions, what would
the sum be?

**2. a.** Find each sum.

$$\frac{1}{1 \cdot 3} + \frac{1}{3 \cdot 5} = \underline{\quad?\quad}$$

$$\frac{1}{1 \cdot 3} + \frac{1}{3 \cdot 5} + \frac{1}{5 \cdot 7} = \underline{\quad?\quad}$$

$$\frac{1}{1 \cdot 3} + \frac{1}{3 \cdot 5} + \frac{1}{5 \cdot 7} + \frac{1}{7 \cdot 9} = \underline{\quad?\quad}$$

**b.** If this addition pattern were continued for 50 fractions, what would
the sum be?

**c.** If this addition pattern were continued for $n$ fractions, what would
the sum be?

# 9-5 Functions Described by Tables and Graphs

**Objective**  To define functions without using equations.

The table at the right shows the number of chromosomes associated with each of several biological species. This association is a function. But, unlike the functions in Section 9-4, the chromosome function does not have a rule that can be given by an equation. Instead, the rule is incorporated in the table of ordered pairs. The domain of the function is the set of first coordinates:

{corn, domestic fowl, fruit fly, horse, human, mouse, tomato}.

The range of the function is the set of second coordinates:

{8, 24, 40, 46, 64, 78}.

| Species | Number of Chromosomes |
|---|---|
| Corn | 40 |
| Domestic fowl | 78 |
| Fruit fly | 8 |
| Horse | 64 |
| Human | 46 |
| Mouse | 40 |
| Tomato | 24 |

It is easier to compare the chromosome numbers if the facts are displayed in a *bar graph*. In the following graph, the members of the domain are listed on the left along the vertical axis. For each member of the domain a horizontal bar is drawn to represent the corresponding value in the range of the function. Notice that the scale of the bars starts at zero, so that their relative lengths are correct.

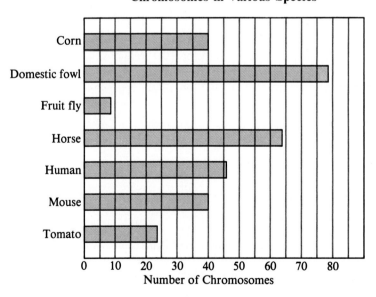

**Chromosomes in Various Species**

Number of Chromosomes

When the members of the domain of a function are in a numerical succession, it may be better to use a *broken-line graph* such as the one shown below.

**Receipts at Chuck's Chicken Restaurants**

| Fiscal Year | Receipts (in millions) |
|:-----------:|:----------------------:|
| 1975        | $250                   |
| 1977        | 265                    |
| 1979        | 246                    |
| 1981        | 280                    |
| 1983        | 300                    |
| 1985        | 370                    |

Note that in this graph the members of the domain are listed along the horizontal axis.

The line segments of the graph do *not* necessarily show the actual receipts for even-numbered years. They do, however, help you to see the trends over time.

## Oral Exercises

**State the domain and range of the function shown by each table.**

**1.**

| Tree            | Height in feet |
|-----------------|:--------------:|
| Douglas fir     | 40             |
| Juniper         | 10             |
| Oak             | 25             |
| Poplar          | 30             |
| Weeping willow  | 30             |
| Yew             | 12             |

**2.**

| Appliance       | Percent of total electrical energy used in the home |
|-----------------|:---------------------------------------------------:|
| Air-conditioner | 8                                                   |
| Clothes dryer   | 5                                                   |
| Electric range  | 15                                                  |
| Refrigerator    | 20                                                  |
| T.V.            | 9                                                   |
| Water heater    | 38                                                  |
| All others      | 5                                                   |

**State the domain and range of the function shown by each table.**

3.

| Substance | Boiling point (°C) |
|---|---|
| Acetic acid | 118 |
| Benzene | 80 |
| Bromine | 59 |
| Cyclobutane | 13 |
| Methyl chloride | −24 |
| Water | 100 |

4.

| Item | Percent change in cost over one year |
|---|---|
| Clothing | −2 |
| Food | −1 |
| Housing | 3.5 |
| Medical care | 4 |
| Utilities | 1.5 |

5.

| Cost of a Barrel of Crude Oil | | | | | | | | | | | |
|---|---|---|---|---|---|---|---|---|---|---|---|
| Year | 1970 | 1971 | 1972 | 1973 | 1974 | 1975 | 1976 | 1977 | 1978 | 1979 | 1980 |
| Cost | $1.30 | $1.68 | $1.80 | $3.44 | $10.17 | $10.37 | $11.23 | $12.37 | $12.27 | $19.49 | $31.50 |

6.

| Earnings Per Share of Common Foods Corp. | | | | | | | |
|---|---|---|---|---|---|---|---|
| Year | 1980 | 1981 | 1982 | 1983 | 1984 | 1985 | 1986 |
| Earnings per Share ($) | −0.30 | 0.75 | 0.90 | 1.12 | 1.43 | 1.65 | 2.05 |

## Written Exercises

**A** **1–4.** Make a bar graph for the function shown in each table in Oral Exercises 1–4.

**5–6.** Make a broken-line graph for each function shown in Oral Exercises 5 and 6.

**7.** Show on a broken-line graph beginning with January the average monthly temperature (°C) in Greenough:

$$-2, \ -0.5, \ 4, \ 12, \ 18, \ 23, \ 26, \ 25.5, \ 21, \ 16, \ 7, \ 1.5$$

**8.** Make a broken-line graph of the number of students with colds recorded for the months September through June:

$$10, \ 21, \ 25, \ 34, \ 32, \ 40, \ 42, \ 30, \ 24, \ 15$$

Exercises 9 and 10 require you to find data. Sources that you may use are results of experiments in your science classes, surveys that you conduct in your class or neighborhood, or reference materials in your library.

**B** 9. Find data suitable for presentation as a bar graph, and then draw the graph.

10. Find data suitable for presentation on a broken-line graph, and then draw the graph.

## *Application* / *Line of Best Fit*

Is your future income related to the number of years you attend school? Is there a correlation between achievers in mathematics and achievers in physics? Scatter graphs or diagrams often are used to show researchers whether a relationship exists between two measurements. Researchers can then base predictions on the patterns they observe in these relationships.

In the chart below are shown physics marks and mathematics marks for the same eight people. Each pair of measurements is plotted as a point $(x, y)$ on a graph. If the plotted points tend to cluster around a line (shown in color), called the *line of best fit*, since it fits closer to the points than any other line, then a clear relationship exists.

| Mathematics Marks | Physics Marks |
|---|---|
| 28 | 20 |
| 52 | 44 |
| 80 | 72 |
| 48 | 52 |
| 50 | 60 |
| 96 | 84 |
| 98 | 95 |
| 35 | 28 |

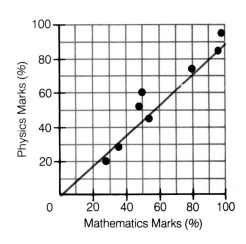

With sufficient data, mathematicians can then make predictions based on this correlation. Although you can fit a line "by eye," mathematicians have derived exact formulas for determining the line of best fit. Determining patterns in relationships is an important aspect of a mathematician's or statistician's work.

# 9-6 Linear and Quadratic Functions

**Objective**   To graph linear and quadratic functions.

The function $g$ defined by the formula

$$g(x) = 3x - 2$$

is called a *linear function*. If its domain is the set of all real numbers, then we call the straight line that is the graph of the equation

$$y = g(x) = 3x - 2$$

the **graph** of $g$. The slope of the graph is 3; the $y$-intercept is $-2$.

In general,

---

A function $f$ given by

$$f(x) = mx + b$$

is a **linear function.**
   If its domain is the set of real numbers, then its graph is the straight line with slope $m$ and $y$-intercept $b$.

---

Now, consider the function $h$ defined by the formula

$$h(x) = x^2 - 2x - 2.$$

If the domain of $h$ is the set of real numbers, then its graph is the graph of the equation

$$y = h(x) = x^2 - 2x - 2.$$

To graph this equation, find the coordinates of selected points, as shown in the table below. Then plot the points and connect them with a smooth curve.

| $x$ | $x^2 - 2x - 2 = y$ |
|---|---|
| $-2$ | $(-2)^2 - 2(-2) - 2 = \phantom{-}6$ |
| $-1$ | $(-1)^2 - 2(-1) - 2 = \phantom{-}1$ |
| $0$ | $0^2 \phantom{xx} - 2(0) \phantom{x} - 2 = -2$ |
| $1$ | $1^2 \phantom{xx} - 2(1) \phantom{x} - 2 = -3$ |
| $2$ | $2^2 \phantom{xx} - 2(2) \phantom{x} - 2 = -2$ |
| $3$ | $3^2 \phantom{xx} - 2(3) \phantom{x} - 2 = \phantom{-}1$ |
| $4$ | $4^2 \phantom{xx} - 2(4) \phantom{x} - 2 = \phantom{-}6$ |

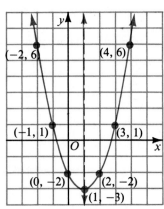

The curve shown beside the table is a **parabola.** This parabola opens upward and has a **minimum point** (lowest point): $(1, -3)$. The $y$-coordinate of this point is the least value of the function.

The vertical line $x = 1$, containing the minimum point, is called the **axis of symmetry** of the parabola. If you fold the graph along the axis of symmetry, the two halves of the parabola coincide.

Compare the parabola just seen with the graph of the function $k$ defined by the equation
$$y = k(x) = -x^2 + 2x + 2.$$

| $x$ | $-x^2 + 2x + 2 = y$ |
|---|---|
| $-2$ | $-(-2)^2 + 2(-2) + 2 = -6$ |
| $-1$ | $-(-1)^2 + 2(-1) + 2 = -1$ |
| $0$ | $-0^2 \ + \ 2(0) \ + 2 = \ \ \ 2$ |
| $1$ | $-1^2 \ + \ 2(1) \ + 2 = \ \ \ 3$ |
| $2$ | $-2^2 \ + \ 2(2) \ + 2 = \ \ \ 2$ |
| $3$ | $-3^2 \ + \ 2(3) \ + 2 = -1$ |
| $4$ | $-4^2 \ + \ 2(4) \ + 2 = -6$ |

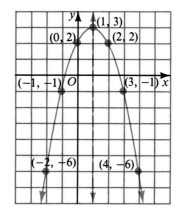

This graph is a parabola that opens downward and has a **maximum point** (highest point): $(1, 3)$. The $y$-coordinate of the maximum point is the greatest value of the function. Note that the maximum point $(1, 3)$ lies on the axis of symmetry, the line $x = 1$.

Parabolas occur in a variety of everyday settings. You can see them in bridges, arches, fountains, fireworks, and the spouts of water from a fireboat.

In general:

A function $f$ given by
$$f(x) = ax^2 + bx + c \quad (a \neq 0)$$

is a **quadratic function.**
If its domain is the set of real numbers, then its graph is a parabola.
If $a$ is positive, the parabola opens upward.
If $a$ is negative, the parabola opens downward.

The minimum or maximum point of a parabola is called the **vertex.** Notice that in the examples shown on the previous pages, the points, except the vertex, occur in *pairs that have the same y-coordinate.* Also, the average of the x-coordinates of any such pair is the x-coordinate of the vertex. For the parabola on page 413:

| Pairs of Points | | Average of *x*-coordinates |
|---|---|---|
| $(-2, -6)$ | $(4, -6)$ | |
| $(-1, -1)$ | $(3, -1)$ | |
| $(0, 2)$ | $(2, 2)$ | |

$$\frac{-2 + 4}{2} = 1$$

$$\frac{-1 + 3}{2} = 1 \longleftarrow \text{x-coordinate of vertex}$$

$$\frac{0 + 2}{2} = 1$$

The graphs at the right illustrate that the x-coordinate of the vertex is the same for equations that differ only in the constant term. Therefore, a formula for the x-coordinate of the vertex of $y = ax^2 + bx + c$ can be found using the two points where the graph of $y = ax^2 + bx$ crosses the x-axis; that is, the points where $y = 0$.

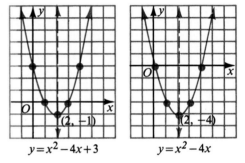

$y = x^2 - 4x + 3$      $y = x^2 - 4x$

Let $y = 0$:
$$0 = ax^2 + bx$$
$$0 = x(ax + b)$$
$$x = 0 \quad \text{or} \quad ax + b = 0$$
$$\therefore x = 0 \quad \text{or} \quad x = -\frac{b}{a}$$

The average of these x-coordinates is $\dfrac{0 + \left(-\dfrac{b}{a}\right)}{2}$, or $-\dfrac{b}{2a}$.

Therefore:

---

The x-coordinate of the vertex of the parabola
$$y = ax^2 + bx + c \quad (a \neq 0)$$
is $-\dfrac{b}{2a}$.

The axis of symmetry is the line $x = -\dfrac{b}{2a}$.

---

*Unless otherwise stated, you may assume that the domain of each linear or quadratic function is the set of real numbers.*

**Example**   Find the coordinates of the vertex of the graph of

$$H: x \longrightarrow 2x^2 + 4x - 3.$$

Use the vertex and six other points to graph $H$. Identify and draw the axis of symmetry.

**Solution**   1. $x$-coordinate of vertex $= -\dfrac{b}{2a} = -\dfrac{4}{4} = -1$

2. To find the $y$-coordinate of the vertex, substitute $-1$ for $x$.

$$y = 2x^2 + 4x - 3$$
$$y = 2(-1)^2 + 4(-1) - 3$$
$$= 2 - 4 - 3 = -5$$

∴ the vertex is $(-1, -5)$.

3. Construct a table. For values of $x$, choose three numbers greater than $-1$ and three less than $-1$ to obtain paired points with the same $y$-coordinate.

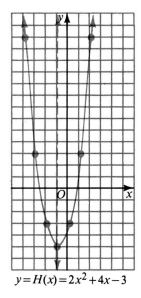

| $x$ | $2x^2 + 4x - 3 = y$ | |
|---|---|---|
| $-4$ | $2(-4)^2 + 4(-4) - 3 =$ | $13$ |
| $-3$ | $2(-3)^2 + 4(-3) - 3 =$ | $3$ |
| $-2$ | $2(-2)^2 + 4(-2) - 3 =$ | $-3$ |
| Vertex $-1$ | $2(-1)^2 + 4(-1) - 3 =$ | $-5$ |
| $0$ | $2(0)^2 + 4(0) - 3 =$ | $-3$ |
| $1$ | $2(1)^2 + 4(1) - 3 =$ | $3$ |
| $2$ | $2(2)^2 + 4(2) - 3 =$ | $13$ |

4. Plot the points, and through them draw a smooth curve.

5. The axis of symmetry is the line $x = -1$ (shown as a dashed line on the graph).

$$y = H(x) = 2x^2 + 4x - 3$$

## Oral Exercises

**State the slope and $y$-intercept of the graph of each linear function.**

**1.** $f: x \rightarrow -2x + 7$      **2.** $g: x \rightarrow 4x - 8$      **3.** $p(x) = 4 - \dfrac{5x}{2}$

**4.** $t(x) = -\dfrac{x}{2}$      **5.** $t(x) = 0$      **6.** $h(x) = 9$

**State whether the graph of each quadratic equation opens upward or downward.**

**7.** $y = x^2 - 6x + 3$       **8.** $y = -2x^2 + 3x + 1$       **9.** $y = 4 - x^2$

**10.** $x^2 - 4 = y$       **11.** $3x^2 - 3x = y$       **12.** $y = \dfrac{-x^2}{3}$

**State whether the graph of each quadratic function has a minimum or a maximum point.**

**13.** $f: x \rightarrow x^2 - 4x + 1$       **14.** $g: x \rightarrow -3 - 2x - x^2$       **15.** $h: x \rightarrow 7x^2 - x$

**16.** $P: x \rightarrow 1 - x^2$       **17.** $T: x \rightarrow -8x^2 + x - 6$       **18.** $f: x \rightarrow \dfrac{3x^2}{7}$

## Written Exercises

**Draw the graph of each function.**

**A**    **1.** $g: x \rightarrow x - 3$       **2.** $f: x \rightarrow -x + 1$       **3.** $q(x) = 2 - \dfrac{x}{3}$

     **4.** $d(x) = -\dfrac{3}{4}x$       **5.** $r(x) = -7$       **6.** $n(x) = 0$

**Find the coordinates of the vertex and the equation of the axis of symmetry of the graph of each equation. Use the vertex and at least six other points to graph the equation.**

**7.** $y = 2x^2$       **8.** $y = 4x^2$       **9.** $y = -x^2$

**10.** $y = -3x^2$       **11.** $y = \dfrac{1}{3}x^2$       **12.** $y = -\dfrac{1}{3}x^2$

**13.** $y = x^2 - 2x$       **14.** $y = -x^2 + 4x$       **15.** $y = -x^2 - 5x + 6$

**16.** $y = x^2 - 3x - 10$       **17.** $y = 2 - \dfrac{1}{2}x^2$       **18.** $y = 6 + 4x - \dfrac{1}{2}x^2$

**Find the least value of each function.**

**19.** $f: x \rightarrow x^2 + 5x$       **20.** $g: x \rightarrow x^2 + 9$       **21.** $h: x \rightarrow x^2 - x - 12$

**22.** $t: x \rightarrow 4 - 10x + 5x^2$       **23.** $G: x \rightarrow 9x^2 - 4$       **24.** $F: x \rightarrow \dfrac{1}{4}x^2$

**Find the greatest value of each function.**

**25.** $g: x \rightarrow -x^2 - 7x$       **26.** $f: x \rightarrow 4x - 2x^2$       **27.** $H: x \rightarrow -x^2 - 8x - 15$

**28.** $K: x \rightarrow 1 - 3x - 6x^2$       **29.** $f(x) = x - 2x^2$       **30.** $h(x) = 1 - \dfrac{1}{3}x^2$

**B**    **31. a.** On the same set of axes draw the graphs of $y = x^2$, $y = x^2 + 1$, and $y = x^2 - 2$.
       **b.** Use your results in part (a) to describe the changes in the graph of $y = x^2 + c$ as the value of $c$ increases; as $c$ decreases.

**32. a.** On the same set of axes draw the graphs of $y = \frac{1}{2}x^2$, $y = x^2$, and $y = 2x^2$.

**b.** On the same set of axes draw the graphs of $y = -\frac{1}{2}x^2$, $y = -x^2$, and $y = -2x^2$.

**c.** Use your results in parts (a) and (b) to describe the change in the graph of $y = ax^2$ as $|a|$ increases.

The *zeros* of a function $f$ are the values of $x$ for which $f(x) = 0$. In Exercises 33 and 34, find (a) $f(0)$; (b) the zeros of $f$.

**33.** $f(x) = x^2 + 3x - 4$          **34.** $f(x) = x^2 - 8x + 12$

**35.** Interpret the zeros of the function $f$ in terms of the graph of $f$.

**36.** Interpret $f(0)$ in terms of the graph of $f$.

# Self-Test 2

*Vocabulary*
function (p. 404)
domain of a function (p. 404)
range of a function (p. 404)
arrow notation (p. 404)
value of a function (p. 405)
linear function (p. 412)
graph (p. 412)

parabola (p. 413)
minimum point (p. 413)
axis of symmetry (p. 413)
maximum point (p. 413)
quadratic function (p. 413)
vertex (p. 414)

**1.** Given $f(x) = 5x - 1$, find $f(2)$.         **Obj. 9-4, p. 404**

**2.** Find the range of $g$ if
$g: n \rightarrow n^2 + 2n + 3$ and $D = \{-1, 0, 1, 2, 3\}$.

**3.** The table below shows a function.         **Obj. 9-5, p. 408**
**a.** State the domain and range of the function.
**b.** Graph the function by means of a bar graph or a broken-line graph, whichever is more suitable.

| Amount dissolved in 100 g of water at 20°C | | | | |
|---|---|---|---|---|
| Substance | Boric Acid | Salt | Sodium Nitrate | Sugar |
| Amount | 4.8 g | 36.0 g | 88.0 g | 203.9 g |

**4.** Find the coordinates of the vertex and the equation of the axis of symmetry of the graph of $y = 2x^2 - 4x + 1$.      **Obj. 9-6, p. 412**

**5.** Find the least value of the function
$f: x \rightarrow 1 + \frac{1}{5}x^2$.

Check your answers with those at the back of the book.

# Variation

## 9-7 Direct Variation

**Objective** To use the concept of direct variation to solve problems.

The table below shows the weight $w$ at sea level of a gold ingot whose volume is $v$ cubic centimeters.

| Volume in cubic centimeters: $v$ | Weight in grams: $w$ |
|:---:|:---:|
| 1 | 19.1 |
| 2 | 38.2 |
| 3 | 57.3 |
| 4 | 76.4 |
| 5 | 95.5 |

You can see that

$$w = 19.1\, v$$

and that this equation defines a linear function. Notice that if the volume of the ingot is doubled, the weight is doubled; if the volume is tripled, the weight is tripled, and so on. You say that the weight *varies directly as* the volume. This function is an example of a *direct variation.*

A **linear direct variation** (or simply, a **direct variation**) is a function defined by an equation of the form

$$y = kx, \text{ where } k \text{ is a nonzero constant.}$$

You can say that *y varies directly as x,* or *y varies with x.* The constant $k$ is called the **constant of variation.**

When the domain is the set of real numbers, the graph of a direct variation is a straight line with slope $k$ that passes through the origin.

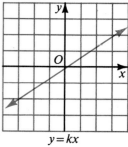

$y = kx$

**Example 1** Given that $d$ varies directly as $t$, and that $d = 86$ when $t = 2$, find the following.
  **a.** the constant of variation  **b.** the value of $d$ when $t = 3$

**Solution** Let $d = kt$.
  **a.** Substitute $d = 86$ and $t = 2$;  $86 = k \cdot 2$
  $43 = k$  ***Answer***
  **b.** Substitute $k = 43$ and $t = 3$:  $d = 43 \cdot 3 = 129$  ***Answer***

Suppose that two ordered pairs of a direct variation defined by $y = kx$ are

$$(x_1, y_1) \quad \text{and} \quad (x_2, y_2),$$

and that neither $x_1$ nor $x_2$ equals zero. The coordinates of these ordered pairs satisfy $y = kx$:

$$y_1 = kx_1 \quad \text{and} \quad y_2 = kx_2.$$

From these equations you can write the ratios

$$\frac{y_1}{x_1} = k \quad \text{and} \quad \frac{y_2}{x_2} = k.$$

Since each ratio equals $k$, the ratios are equal.

$$\frac{y_1}{x_1} = \frac{y_2}{x_2}, \quad \text{read "} y_1 \text{ is to } x_1 \text{ as } y_2 \text{ is to } x_2 \text{."}$$

This equation, which states that two ratios are equal, is a proportion (page 282). For this reason, $k$ is sometimes called the **constant of proportionality,** and $y$ is said to be *directly proportional to x.*

When you use a proportion to solve a problem, you will find it helpful to recall that the product of the extremes equals the product of the means.

**Example 2** The amount of interest earned on savings is directly proportional to the amount of money saved. If $26 interest is earned on $325, how much interest will be earned on $900 in the same period of time?

**Solution**

Step 1 The problem asks for the interest on $900, given that the interest on $325 is $26.

Step 2 Let $i$, in dollars, be the interest on $d$ dollars.

$$i_1 = 26 \qquad i_2 = \underline{\quad ? \quad}$$
$$d_1 = 325 \qquad d_2 = 900$$

Step 3 An equation can be written in the form $\dfrac{i_1}{d_1} = \dfrac{i_2}{d_2}$:

$$\frac{26}{325} = \frac{i_2}{900}$$

Step 4
$$26(900) = 325i_2$$
$$23{,}400 = 325i_2$$
$$72 = i_2$$

Step 5 The check is left to you.

∴ the interest earned on $900 will be $72.   *Answer*

Examples 1 and 2 illustrate two methods of solving problems involving direct variation. To solve Example 2 by the method shown in Example 1, first write the equation $i = kd$ and solve for the constant of variation, $k$, by using the fact that $i = 26$ when $d = 325$. Then use the resulting value of $k$ to find the value of $i$ when $d = 900$. Complete the problem this way for yourself. You will find the exercises and problems of this section easier if you understand *both* methods.

## Oral Exercises

**State whether or not the equation defines a direct variation. For each direct variation, state the constant of variation.**

**1.** $y = 5x$       **2.** $p = 7s$       **3.** $xy = 2$       **4.** $d = 2.8t$

**5.** $\frac{1}{3}x = 7$       **6.** $\frac{y}{x} = -2$       **7.** $p = \frac{7}{q}$       **8.** $C = \pi d$

**9.** $A = \pi r^2$       **10.** $\frac{c}{d} = 1$       **11.** $y = 2x^3$       **12.** $\frac{x}{y} = \frac{3}{2}$

**State whether or not the given ordered pairs are in a direct variation.**

**Example**      $(6, 8), (9, 12), (18, 24)$

**Solution**      $\frac{8}{6} = \frac{4}{3}, \frac{12}{9} = \frac{4}{3}, \frac{24}{18} = \frac{4}{3}$. Since the ratios are equal, the

ordered pairs are in the direct variation $y = \frac{4}{3}x$.

**13.** $(2, 4), (6, 12), (10, 20)$       **14.** $(1, 3), (-6, -18), (5, 15)$

**15.** $(1, 1), (2, 1), (3, 3)$       **16.** $(-1, 2), (2, -4), (4, -8)$

**17.** $(-1, 9), (2, -18), (-3, 27)$       **18.** $(0, 0), (5, -10), (-3, -6)$

**State whether or not each statement is true. If it is not true, give a reason why it is not true.**

**19.** Every linear function is a direct variation.

**20.** All direct variations are linear functions.

**21.** Some linear functions are direct variations.

**22.** No function is both a linear function and a direct variation.

**State whether or not each formula expresses direct variation.**

**23.** $\frac{x_1}{y_1} = \frac{x_2}{y_2}$       **24.** $\frac{x_1}{x_2} = \frac{y_1}{y_2}$       **25.** $\frac{y_1}{x_2} = \frac{y_2}{x_1}$       **26.** $\frac{y_2}{x_2} = \frac{y_1}{x_1}$

## Written Exercises

**In Exercises 1-6, find the constant of variation.**

A   **1.** $y$ varies directly as $x$, and $y = 13$ when $x = 52$.

     **2.** $y$ varies directly as $x$, and $y = 8$ when $x = 72$.

     **3.** $t$ varies directly as $s$, and $t = -28$ when $s = -4$.

     **4.** $h$ varies directly as $m$, and $h = 368$ when $m = -16$.

     **5.** $W$ is directly proportional to $m$, and $W = 300$ when $m = 12$.

     **6.** $P$ is directly proportional to $t$, and $P = 490$ when $t = 35$.

     **7.** If $y$ varies directly as $x$, and $y = 900$ when $x = 6$, find $y$ when $x = 10$.

     **8.** If $d$ varies directly as $z$, and $d = 12$ when $z = 48$, find $d$ when $z = 30$.

     **9.** If $h$ is directly proportional to $a$, and $h = 425$ when $a = 8.5$, find $h$ when $a = 12$.

   **10.** If $r$ is directly proportional to $A$, and $r = 14$ when $A = 87.5$, find $r$ when $A = 25$.

**In each exercise find the missing value if $(x_1, y_1)$ and $(x_2, y_2)$ are ordered pairs of the same direct variation.**

**11.** $x_1 = 15,\ y_1 = 9$
$x_2 = 40,\ y_2 = \underline{\quad?\quad}$

**12.** $x_1 = 45,\ y_1 = \underline{\quad?\quad}$
$x_2 = 60,\ y_2 = 100$

**13.** $x_1 = 3.6,\ y_1 = 3$
$x_2 = \underline{\quad?\quad},\ y_2 = 1$

**14.** $x_1 = \underline{\quad?\quad},\ y_1 = 7$
$x_2 = 7.65,\ y_2 = 9$

**15.** $x_1 = \frac{1}{10},\ y_1 = \frac{1}{6}$
$x_2 = \frac{2}{5},\ y_2 = \underline{\quad?\quad}$

**16.** $x_1 = \frac{6}{5},\ y_1 = \underline{\quad?\quad}$
$x_2 = \frac{2}{3},\ y_2 = \frac{1}{9}$

**For the direct variation described, state (a) a formula and (b) a proportion.**

**Example**    The speed, $v$, of a skydiver in free fall is directly proportional to the number, $t$, of seconds of fall. After 3 s, the speed is 29.4 m/s.

**Solution**    **a.** $v = kt$; $v = 29.4$ when $t = 3$.

$$29.4 = k(3),\ k = \frac{29.4}{3} = 9.8$$

$$v = 9.8t$$

           **b.** Let $v_1 = 29.4$ and $t_1 = 3$. $\dfrac{29.4}{3} = \dfrac{v_2}{t_2}$

B   **17.** The heat, $H$, required to melt a substance varies directly with its mass, $m$. Forty-nine calories of heat are needed to melt one gram of copper.

   **18.** The length, $L$, of the shadow of a tree at any moment varies directly with the height, $h$, of the tree. At a certain moment, a tree 40 m tall casts a shadow 28 m long.

**For the direct variation described, state (a) a formula and (b) a proportion.**

19. The weight, *M*, of an astronaut on the moon is directly proportional to the weight, *E*, on Earth. An astronaut weighing 84 kg on Earth weighs 14 kg on the moon.

20. Distance, *m*, on a map varies directly with the actual distance, *d*. On a certain map, 1 cm represents 2 km.

21. At any given temperature, the electric resistance of wire is directly proportional to its length. At 20°C, 500 m of No. 18 gauge copper wire has a resistance of 10.295 ohms.

22. Under constant pressure, the volume, *V*, of a dry gas is directly proportional to its temperature, *T*, in degrees Kelvin. A sample of oxygen occupies a volume of 5 L at 300°K.

**In Exercises 23 and 24, suppose that $(x_1, y_1)$ and $(x_2, y_2)$ are ordered pairs of a direct variation and that no coordinate is 0. Show that the given statement is true.**

C  23. $\dfrac{y_1}{x_1} = \dfrac{y_2}{x_2}$         24. $\dfrac{y_1}{y_2} = \dfrac{x_1}{x_2}$

## *Problems*

Solve.

A  1. The area covered by a painter is directly proportional to the number of hours worked. A painter covered 54 m² in the first eight hours on the job. How large an area will the painter cover in 36 h?

2. The amount of sand used in mixing mortar is directly proportional to the amount of lime used. If 2 bags of lime are mixed with 5 bags of sand, how much sand is mixed with 15 bags of lime in a shipment of this mortar?

3. Nine grams of hydrochloric acid neutralize 10 g of lye. At this rate, how many grams of lye are neutralized by 72 g of hydrochloric acid?

4. A school lunchroom buys 10 kg of ground beef to prepare 110 servings of chili. At this rate, how many servings can the lunchroom make with 25 kg of ground beef?

5. A mass of 25 g stretches a spring 10 cm. If the distance a spring is stretched is directly proportional to the mass, what mass will stretch the spring 16 cm?

6. A mass of 27 kg causes a diving board to bend 1.8 cm. If the amount of bending varies directly as the mass, what mass will cause the board to bend 1.2 cm?

7. A formula for dishwashing detergent calls for mixing 100 g of sodium metaphosphate with 300 g of trisodium phosphate. If you use this formula, how much sodium metaphosphate do you mix with 681 g of trisodium phosphate?

8. When an electric current is 32 A (amperes), the electromotive force is 288 V (volts). Find the force when the current is 45 A if the force varies directly as the current.

9. In making a monster movie, model figures were used to create the illusion of great size. What was the scale of the models if an ape that appeared to be 54 ft in height was actually a model 20 in. tall?

10. In a scale model of a sailboat, an object that is 6 feet tall is represented by a figure 8 inches high. How tall should the mast of the sailboat be in the model if the actual mast of the sailboat is 38 feet tall?

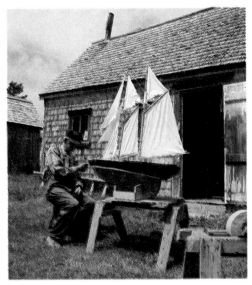

B  11. Two thermometers are exactly the same except that thermometer F is marked off into 180 equal units and thermometer C is marked off into 100 equal units. A length equal to 66.6 units on thermometer F is equal to a length of how many units on thermometer C?

12. The odometer on the Bristers' car was not measuring distance correctly. For the 220 km trip from home to the grandparents' home, the odometer registered only 216.7 km. On the return trip, the Bristers had to detour for road repairs. If the odometer registered 453.1 km for the round trip, how many actual kilometers was the detour?

13. On a map, 1 cm represents an actual distance of 75 m. Find the area of a piece of land that is represented on the map by a rectangle measuring 12.5 cm by 16 cm.

14. If the circumference of a circle varies directly as the diameter, and the diameter varies directly as the radius, show that the circumference varies directly as the radius.

# Challenge

If at least one coin of each kind is used, how can you change a dollar into 15 coins, each less than a quarter in value?

# 9-8 Inverse Variation

**Objective**  To use the concept of inverse variation to solve problems.

The table shows the time, $t$, that it takes a car to cover a distance of 60 km traveling at the rate of $r$ km/h. You can see that

$$rt = 60.$$

| Rate in km/h: $r$ | Time in hours: $t$ |
|---|---|
| 20 | 3 |
| 40 | $\dfrac{3}{2}$ |
| 60 | 1 |
| 80 | $\dfrac{3}{4}$ |

Notice that if the rate of travel is increased, the time required is decreased, so that the product is always 60. You can say that the time *varies inversely as* the rate. This example illustrates an *inverse variation*.

An **inverse variation** is a function defined by an equation of the form

$$xy = k, \text{ where } k \text{ is a nonzero constant.}$$

$$y = \frac{k}{x}, \text{ where } x \neq 0.$$

You can say that *y varies inversely as x* or *y is inversely proportional to x*. The constant $k$ is the **constant of variation.**

The graph of an inverse function is not a straight line, since the defining equation

$$xy = k$$

is not linear; the term $xy$ is of degree 2. The graph of $xy = 1$ is shown below. This graph is called a **hyperbola.**

$xy = 1$

| $x$ | $y$ |
|---|---|
| $-4$ | $-\dfrac{1}{4}$ |
| $-2$ | $-\dfrac{1}{2}$ |
| $-1$ | $-1$ |
| $-\dfrac{1}{2}$ | $-2$ |
| $-\dfrac{1}{4}$ | $-4$ |

| $x$ | $y$ |
|---|---|
| $\dfrac{1}{4}$ | 4 |
| $\dfrac{1}{2}$ | 2 |
| 1 | 1 |
| 2 | $\dfrac{1}{2}$ |
| 4 | $\dfrac{1}{4}$ |

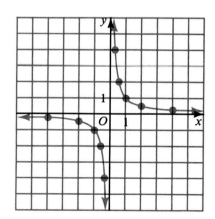

Since neither $x$ nor $y$ can have the value 0, neither of the two branches of the hyperbola intersects an axis.

For every nonzero value of $k$, the graph of $xy = k$ is a hyperbola. When $k$ is positive, the branches of the graph are in Quadrants I and III. When $k$ is negative, the graph is in Quadrants II and IV.

In some practical problems involving inverse variation, negative answers are meaningless, and the domain and the range are limited to positive numbers. The graph of such an inverse variation has only the branch in Quadrant I.

If $(x_1, y_1)$ and $(x_2, y_2)$ are ordered pairs of the same inverse variation, then the coordinates satisfy the equation $xy = k$:

$$x_1 y_1 = k \quad \text{and} \quad x_2 y_2 = k.$$

Therefore,

$$x_1 y_1 = x_2 y_2.$$

Compare:

| Direct Variation | Inverse Variation |
|:---:|:---:|
| $y = kx$ | $xy = k, \quad \text{or} \quad y = \dfrac{k}{x}$ |
| $\dfrac{y_1}{x_1} = \dfrac{y_2}{x_2}$ | $x_1 y_1 = x_2 y_2$ |

These equations can be written in other equivalent forms, but the forms shown are the easiest to remember. *For direct variation the quotients of coordinates are constant, and for inverse variation the products are constant.*

One example of inverse variation is the law of the lever. A lever is a bar pivoted at a point called the fulcrum. If masses $m_1$ and $m_2$ are placed at distances $d_1$ and $d_2$ from the fulcrum, and the lever is at balance, then

$$m_1 d_1 = m_2 d_2.$$

*Example*    If a 12 g mass is 60 cm from the fulcrum of a lever, how far from the fulcrum is a 45 g mass that balances it?

*Solution*    Let $m_1 = 12$, $d_1 = 60$, and $m_2 = 45$. $d_2 = \underline{\ ?\ }$
Use $m_1 d_1 = m_2 d_2$.
$$12(60) = 45 d_2$$
$$16 = d_2$$

∴ the distance of the 45 g mass from the fulcrum is 16 cm.   *Answer*

## Oral Exercises

State whether each equation defines an inverse variation or a direct variation ($k$ is a constant).

1. $\dfrac{y}{x} = k$

2. $y = \dfrac{k}{x}$

3. $p = \dfrac{k}{z}$

4. $xy = 45$

5. $d = 2.5t$

6. $m = \dfrac{1}{d}$

7. $\dfrac{n_1}{b_1} = \dfrac{n_2}{b_2}$

8. $a_1 b_1 = a_2 b_2$

9. $\dfrac{1}{3} = rt$

10. $\dfrac{3}{4} = \dfrac{h}{s}$

11. $\dfrac{x}{y} = \dfrac{1}{k}$

12. $kxy = 2$

Complete the ordered pairs so that they belong to the given inverse variation.

13. $xy = 24$ and $(x, y) = (2, \underline{\ ?\ })$ $(\underline{\ ?\ }, 8)$ $(-6, \underline{\ ?\ })$

14. $v = \dfrac{100}{m}$ and $(m, v) = (25, \underline{\ ?\ })$ $(\underline{\ ?\ }, 5)$ $(-2, \underline{\ ?\ })$

15. $288 = pq$ and $(p, q) = (8, \underline{\ ?\ })$ $(-3, \underline{\ ?\ })$ $(\underline{\ ?\ }, 9)$

16. $xy = -1$ and $(x, y) = (-1, \underline{\ ?\ })$ $\left(\dfrac{1}{4}, \underline{\ ?\ }\right)$ $(\underline{\ ?\ }, 2)$

17. If $rs = k$, and $r$ is tripled while $k$ remains the same, how does $s$ change?

18. If $d = rt$, and $t$ is halved while $d$ remains constant, how does $r$ change?

## Written Exercises

Graph each equation if the domain and the range are both limited to the set of positive numbers.

**A**  1. $xy = 6$

2. $4xy = 1$

3. $x = \dfrac{4}{y}$

4. $\dfrac{x}{2} = \dfrac{8}{y}$

Find the missing value if $(x_1, y_1)$ and $(x_2, y_2)$ are ordered pairs of the same inverse variation.

5. $x_1 = 3$, $y_1 = 54$, $x_2 = 2$, $y_2 = \underline{\ ?\ }$

6. $x_1 = 30$, $y_1 = 10$, $x_2 = \underline{\ ?\ }$, $y_2 = 12$

7. $x_1 = \underline{\ ?\ }$, $y_1 = 19.5$, $x_2 = 11.7$, $y_2 = 10.5$

8. $x_1 = 32$, $y_1 = \underline{\ ?\ }$, $x_2 = 8$, $y_2 = \dfrac{1}{4}$

Exercises 9 and 10 refer to the lever at balance shown on page 425. Find the missing value.

9. $m_1 = 24$, $m_2 = 8$, $d_1 = 6$, $d_2 = \underline{\ ?\ }$

10. $m_1 = \underline{\ ?\ }$, $m_2 = 40$, $d_1 = 5$, $d_2 = 7$

**For the inverse variation described, state (a) a formula and (b) a proportion.**

*Example*    The height $h$ of a right circular cylinder of fixed volume varies inversely as the area $A$ of the base. A cylinder 4 units high has a base of 10 square units.

*Solution*    **a.** $Ah = k$; $h = 4$, when $A = 10$.

$\therefore 10(4) = k$, $k = 40$

$$Ah = 40, \quad \text{or} \quad h = \frac{40}{A}$$

**b.** $A_1 h_1 = A_2 h_2$

Dividing by $h_1 h_2$, you obtain the proportion:

$$\frac{A_1}{h_2} = \frac{A_2}{h_1}$$

Let $A_1 = 10$ and $h_1 = 4$.    $\dfrac{10}{h_2} = \dfrac{A_2}{4}$

**B**   **11.** The length $l$ and width $w$ of a rectangle of given area vary inversely as each other. When the length is 15, the width is 4.

**12.** The force, $f$, needed to shift a heavy log varies inversely as the length, $l$, of the crowbar used. When the length is 2 m, the force needed is 1.5 N (newtons).

**13.** The frequency $f$ of a periodic wave is inversely proportional to the length $l$ of the wave. The frequency is 2.5 Hz (hertz) when the wavelength is 0.60 m.

**14.** The time, $t$, required to drive between two cities is inversely proportional to the average speed, $r$, of the truck. It took 3 h at an average speed of 78 km/h.

**15.** At a fixed temperature, the volume, $V$, of a gas varies inversely as the pressure, $P$. A volume of 465 cm$^3$ of a gas is at a pressure of 725 mm.

**16.** The amount of current, $I$, flowing through a circuit is inversely proportional to the amount of resistance, $R$, of the circuit. In a circuit with a resistance of 18 ohms there is a current of 0.25 A.

## *Problems*

**Solve.**

**A**   **1.** The number of days needed to pave a section of highway varies inversely as the number of people working on the job. It takes 18 days for 2 people to complete the project. If the job has to be finished in 4 days, how many people are needed?

**2.** The interest rate required to yield a given income is inversely proportional to the amount of money invested. Jane Kidd has $75,000 invested at 6%. How much money must she have invested to receive the same income if the rate of return is 7.5%?

**3.** A rectangle has length 48 cm and width 35 cm. Find the length of another rectangle of equal area whose width is 21 cm.

**4.** The winner of a race ran the distance in 45 s at an average speed of 9.6 m/s. The runner who came in last finished in 48 s. What was the last runner's average speed?

**5.** A fifteen-centimeter pulley runs at 300 rpm (revolutions per minute). How fast does the five-centimeter pulley it drives revolve, if the number of revolutions per minute varies inversely as the diameter?

**6.** A gear with 42 teeth revolves at 1200 rpm and meshes with a gear having 72 teeth. What is the speed of the second gear if the rotational speed of a gear wheel varies inversely with the number of teeth?

**7.** In buying shares of stock each month, James Halloran uses the dollar-cost averaging system. With this system the number of shares purchased varies inversely with the price per share. If Mr. Halloran bought 150 shares at $8 per share on January 2, how many shares did he purchase on February 2 when the price was $20 per share?

**8.** The number of floors in a building of given height varies inversely as the distance between the floors. If a building can contain 52 floors when the floors are 3.3 m apart, how many floors can be contained in the building if the floors are 3.9 m apart?

**9.** A string on a violin is 25.8 cm long and produces a tone whose frequency is 440 Hz. By how much should the string be shortened to produce a tone of frequency 516 Hz, if the frequency of a vibrating string is inversely proportional to its length?

**10.** The frequency of a vibrating string is inversely proportional to its diameter. A violin string with diameter 0.50 mm produces a tone of frequency 440 Hz. What is the frequency of the tone produced by a similar string whose diameter is 0.05 mm larger?

**In Exercises 11–14, apply the law of the lever.**

**11.** If Tim weighs 126 lb and Joel weighs 168 lb, how far from the seesaw support must Tim sit to balance Joel who is 2 yd from it?

**12.** One end of a pry bar is under a 700 kg boulder. The fulcrum of the bar is 15 cm from the boulder and 1.75 m from the other end of the bar. What mass at that end of the bar will balance the boulder?

15 cm

**B** **13.** A 12 g mass is placed at one end of a meter stick. A 28 g mass is placed at the other end. Where should the fulcrum be placed to have the meter stick balanced?

**14.** A lever has a 500 kg steel ball on one end and a 300 kg log on the other end. The lever is balanced, and the steel ball is 1 m closer to the fulcrum than the log. How far from the fulcrum is the log?

**For the wave motion of sound, the following formula holds:**

$$fl = v,$$

**where $f$ is the frequency (number of cycles per second), $l$ is the wavelength (in meters), and $v$ is the speed of sound (about 335 m/s in air). Use this information in the following problems.**

**15.** The frequency of a note an octave above a given note is twice that of the given note. How does the wavelength of the higher note compare with that of the lower note?

**16.** If the wavelength of a note is $\frac{3}{2}$ that of a given note, how do the frequencies compare?

**17.** An open organ pipe produces a sound wave that has a length that is twice the length of the pipe. Find the length of an open pipe that will produce the note A with the frequency 440. Give the answer to the nearest tenth of a meter.

**18.** A stopped organ pipe produces a sound wave that has a length that is four times the length of the pipe. What is the frequency of the sound produced by a stopped organ pipe 2 m long?

## Computer Exercises

*For students with some programming experience*

Write a BASIC program in which at least three ordered pairs are entered with INPUT statements. The program should then report whether the data represents a direct variation, an inverse variation, or neither. RUN the program for the following sets of ordered pairs.

**1.** (2, 3), (8, 12), (10, 15), (−24, −36)

**2.** (12, −4), (−16, 3), (−15, 3.2)

**3.** (0, 0), (3, 4), (9, 8), (−2, −3)

# 9-9 Direct and Inverse Variation Involving Squares

**Objective**  To use quadratic direct variation and variation inversely as a square in problem solving.

In the world around you, there are many examples in which a quantity varies either directly or inversely *as the square* of another quantity. For example, the area of a circle varies directly as the square of the radius: $A = \pi r^2$. This is an example of a *quadratic direct variation*.

A **quadratic direct variation** is a function defined by an equation of the form

$$y = kx^2, \text{ where } k \text{ is a nonzero constant.}$$

If $(x_1, y_1)$ and $(x_2, y_2)$ are ordered pairs of the same quadratic direct variation, and neither $x_1$ nor $x_2$ is zero, then:

$$\frac{y_1}{x_1^2} = \frac{y_2}{x_2^2}$$

You say that *y varies directly as $x^2$* or *y is directly proportional to $x^2$*.

**Example 1**  Given that $A$ varies directly as the square of $d$, and $A = 48$ when $d = 4$, find the value of $A$ when $d = 20$.

**Solution**

**Method 1**

Use $A = kd^2$.
$$48 = k(4)^2$$
$$48 = 16k$$
$$3 = k$$
$$\therefore A = 3d^2$$

For $d = 20$:
$$A = 3(20)^2$$
$$A = 1200 \quad \textbf{Answer}$$

**Method 2**

Use $\dfrac{A_1}{d_1^2} = \dfrac{A_2}{d_2^2}$.

$$\frac{48}{4^2} = \frac{A_2}{(20)^2}$$
$$\frac{48}{16} = \frac{A_2}{400}$$
$$16A_2 = 19{,}200$$
$$A_2 = 1200 \quad \textbf{Answer}$$

The intensity of sound *varies inversely as the square* of the distance of a listener from the source of sound. Thus, if you halve the distance between yourself and a drummer, the intensity of the sound that reaches your ears will be quadrupled.

An **inverse variation as the square** is a function defined by an equation of the form

$x^2y = k$, where $k$ is a nonzero constant.

This function may also be written as $y = \dfrac{k}{x^2}$, where $x \neq 0$.

You say that *y varies inversely as $x^2$* or *y is inversely proportional to $x^2$*. If $(x_1, y_1)$ and $(x_2, y_2)$ are ordered pairs of the function defined by $x^2y = k$, then

$$x_1{}^2y_1 = x_2{}^2y_2.$$

**Example 2**  Given that *h* varies inversely as the square of *r*, and that $h = 5$ when $r = 2$, find the value of *h* when $r = 8$.

**Solution**

Method 1

Use $h = \dfrac{k}{r^2}$.

$$5 = \dfrac{k}{2^2}$$

$$20 = k$$

$$\therefore h = \dfrac{20}{r^2}$$

For $r = 8$:

$$h = \dfrac{20}{8^2}$$

$$h = \dfrac{20}{64} = \dfrac{5}{16} \quad \textbf{Answer}$$

Method 2

Use $r_1{}^2h_1 = r_2{}^2h_2$.

$$2^2(5) = 8^2h_2$$

$$20 = 64h_2$$

$$h_2 = \dfrac{5}{16} \quad \textbf{Answer}$$

# Oral Exercises

**Translate each statement into a formula. Use *k* as the constant of variation where needed.**

1. The distance, *d*, that an object falls from rest is directly proportional to the square of the time, *t*.

2. The force between two point charges of static electricity is inversely proportional to the square of the distance, *d*, between them.

3. The illumination, *E*, of a surface is inversely proportional to the square of the distance, *r*, from the surface to the source of light.

4. The area, *A*, of the surface of a steel ball varies directly as the square of the radius, *r*, of the ball.

5. The quantity, *Q*, of heat energy in an electric circuit is directly proportional to the square of the current, *I*.

6. The time, *t*, required to fill a fuel tank varies inversely as the square of the diameter, *d*, of the hose.

# *Problems*

**Solve.**

**A**  **1.** The amount of material required to cover a ball is directly proportional to the square of its diameter. A ball with a diameter of 14 cm requires 616 cm$^2$ of material to cover it. How much material is needed to cover a ball with a diameter of 35 cm?

**2.** The price of a diamond varies directly as the square of its mass. If a 1.5-carat diamond costs $2025, find the price of a similar diamond 2 carats in mass.

**3.** The distance required for an automobile to come to a stop varies directly as the square of its speed. If the stopping distance for a car traveling at 80 km/h is 175 m, what is the distance required for a car traveling 48 km/h to stop?

**4.** Wind pressure on a flat surface varies directly as the square of the velocity of the wind. If the pressure from a 35 km/h wind was measured at 0.024 g/cm$^2$, find the pressure when the wind's velocity was 42 km/h.

**5.** The brightness of the illumination of an object varies inversely as the square of the distance from the object to the source of light. At a distance of 1.2 m directly in front of a light source, illumination on a page of a book was measured to be 250 lm/m$^2$ (lumens per square meter). If the page were moved 0.4 m closer to the light source, what would the illumination measure?

**6.** The time needed to fill a tank varies inversely as the square of the radius of the hose. If a hose of radius 3 cm takes 4.5 min to fill the tank, how long will it take to fill the same tank with a hose that is 2 cm greater in radius?

**B**  **7.** The strength of a radio signal is inversely proportional to the square of the distance from the source of the signal. If an observer moves from a position 50 m from the source of the signal to a position 200 m from the source, how does the strength of the signal at the second position compare with the strength at the first position?

**8.** At or above the surface of Earth, the acceleration due to gravity, $g$, is inversely proportional to the square of the distance from the center of Earth. Compare the value of $g$ at a point $1.6 \times 10^7$ m from the center of Earth with that of $g$ at a point $0.8 \times 10^7$ m from the center of Earth.

**9.** The height of a circular cylinder of given volume varies inversely as the square of the radius of the base. How much greater is the radius of a cylinder 3 m high than the radius of a cylinder 6 m high with the same volume?

**10.** The surface area of a human body is approximately directly proportional to the square of the person's height. How many times as much skin does a man 6 ft tall have compared to a child 2 ft tall?

**C  11.** The volume of a sphere varies directly as the cube of the radius. If the ratio of the radii of two spheres is 4:3, what is the ratio of the volumes of the spheres?

**12.** The heat radiated from a star is directly proportional to the fourth power of the surface temperature of the star. If the surface temperature of one star is $1\frac{1}{2}$ times as great as the surface temperature of a second star of the same size, what is the ratio of the amounts of heat radiated by the stars?

## Computer Key-In

To find ordered pairs to be used in graphing the related parabola of a quadratic function, it is convenient to compute these ordered pairs on either side of the vertex. The following program first finds the vertex and then gives a set of ordered pairs to be used in graphing.

```
10    PRINT "TO FIND COORDINATES"
20    PRINT "OF POINTS ON A GRAPH"
30    PRINT "OF Y = AX↑2 + BX + C:"
40    PRINT "INPUT A (<> 0), B, C";
50    INPUT A,B,C
60    IF A=0 THEN 40
70    LET X1=-B/(2*A)
80    LET Y1=A*X1*X1+B*X1+C
90    PRINT "VERTEX AT (";X1;",";Y1;")"
100   PRINT "X","Y"
110   LET X1=INT(X1)
120   FOR X=X1-5 TO X1+5
130   PRINT X,A*X*X+B*X+C
140   NEXT X
150   END
```

### Exercises

RUN the program for the following. Draw each graph.

**1.** $y = x^2 - 2x - 2$  **2.** $y = -x^2 + 2x + 2$  **3.** $y = x^2 - 4x + 3$

**4.** $y = x^2 - 4x$  **5.** $y = 2x^2 + 4x - 3$  **6.** $y = -x^2 - 5x + 6$

*Note:* The program above can be used to do Exercises 7–18 on page 416.

# 9-10 Joint and Combined Variation

**Objective**   To solve problems involving joint variation and combined variation.

If Wanda earns $400 next summer and puts her earnings into a savings account, the amount of simple interest she will receive depends on her bank's interest rate and on the length of time that she leaves the money in the account:

$$I = 400rt$$

The interest is directly proportional to the product of the rate and the time. You say that the interest *varies jointly as* the rate and the time.

In general, if a variable varies directly as the product of two or more other variables, the resulting relationship is called a **joint variation.** If $z$ varies jointly as $x$ and $y$, you can express the relationship in the following equations. For a nonzero constant $k$:

$$z = kxy \quad \text{and} \quad \frac{z_1}{x_1 y_1} = \frac{z_2}{x_2 y_2}$$

**Example 1**   The volume of a right circular cone varies jointly as the height, $h$, and the square of the radius, $r$. If $V = 616$ when $h = 12$ and $r = 7$, find $V$ when $h = 9$ and $r = 14$.

**Solution**   Let $V_1 = 616$, $h_1 = 12$, $r_1 = 7$, $h_2 = 9$, and $r_2 = 14$. $V_2 = \underline{\ ?\ }$

$$\frac{V_1}{h_1 r_1^2} = \frac{V_2}{h_2 r_2^2}$$

$$\frac{616}{12(7)^2} = \frac{V_2}{9(14)^2}$$

$$12(49)V_2 = 9(196)(616)$$

$$V_2 = 1848 \quad \textit{Answer}$$

If a variable varies *directly* as one variable and *inversely* as another, the resulting relationship is called a **combined variation.** For example, if $z$ varies directly as $x$ and inversely as $y$, you can express the relationship in the following equations. For a nonzero constant $k$:

$$zy = kx \quad \left(\text{or } z = \frac{kx}{y}\right) \quad \text{and} \quad \frac{z_1 y_1}{x_1} = \frac{z_2 y_2}{x_2}$$

**Example 2**   The power, $P$, of an electric current varies directly as the square of the voltage, $V$, and inversely as the resistance, $R$. If 6 volts applied across a resistance of 3 ohms produces 12 watts of power, how much power will 9 volts applied across a resistance of 6 ohms produce?

**Solution**    Let $P_1 = 12$, $V_1 = 6$, $R_1 = 3$, $V_2 = 9$, and $R_2 = 6$. $P_2 = \underline{\ ?\ }$

$$\frac{P_1 R_1}{V_1^{\,2}} = \frac{P_2 R_2}{V_2^{\,2}}$$

$$\frac{12(3)}{6^2} = \frac{P_2(6)}{9^2}$$

$$36(6)P_2 = 36(81)$$

$$P_2 = \frac{81}{6} = \frac{27}{2}$$

∴ the amount of power produced is 13.5 watts.  *Answer*

## Oral Exercises

**Translate each statement into a formula. Use *k* as the constant of variation where needed.**

1. $T$ varies jointly as $n$ and $p$.
2. $R$ varies directly as $d$ and inversely as $t$.
3. $y$ varies directly as the square of $x$ and inversely as $z$.
4. $I$ varies directly as $r$ and inversely as the square of $t$.
5. $p$ varies directly as the square of $m$ and inversely as the square of $s$.
6. $I$ varies jointly as $P$, $r$, and $t$.
7. The mass, $m$, of a rectangular block varies jointly as the length, $l$, width, $w$, and depth, $d$, of the block.
8. The area, $A$, of a triangle varies jointly as the base, $b$, and the altitude, $h$.
9. The volume, $V$, of a gas varies directly as the temperature, $T$, and inversely as the pressure, $P$.
10. The power, $P$, of an electric current varies directly as the square of the voltage, $V$, and inversely as the resistance, $R$.
11. The centrifugal force, $F$, of an object moving in a circular path is directly proportional to the square of its velocity, $v$, and inversely proportional to the radius, $r$, of its path.
12. The intensity, $I$, of illumination at any point is directly proportional to the strength, $s$, of the light source and inversely proportional to the square of the distance, $d$, from the source.
13. The lateral surface, $S$, of a cylinder varies jointly as the radius, $r$, and the height, $h$, of the cylinder.
14. The heat, $H$, generated by an electric stove element varies jointly as the resistance, $R$, and the square of the current, $C$.

## Written Exercises

**A**
1. If $y$ varies directly as $a$ and inversely as $b$, and $y = 20$ when $a = 60$ and $b = 8$, find $y$ when $a = 96$ and $b = 16$.

2. If $d$ varies jointly as $r$ and $t$, and $d = 27$ when $r = 18$ and $t = 6$, find $d$ when $r = 30$ and $t = 10$.

3. If $M$ varies jointly as $v$ and the square of $u$, and $M = 9$ when $v = 15$ and $u = 6$, find $M$ when $v = 25$ and $u = 12$.

4. If $C$ varies inversely as the square of $h$ and directly as $n$, and $C = 1$ when $h = 11$ and $n = 50$, find $C$ when $h = 2$ and $n = 6$.

5. If $y$ varies jointly as the square of $x$ and the cube of $z$, and $y = 135$ when $x = 2$ and $z = 3$, find $y$ when $x = \frac{1}{2}$ and $z = 2$.

6. If $Q$ varies directly as the square of $t$ and inversely as the cube of $r$, and $Q = 129.6$ when $t = 12$ and $r = 2$, find $Q$ when $t = 15$ and $r = 3$.

**B**
7. If $x$ varies jointly as $u$ and $v$, how does $x$ change when both $u$ and $v$ are doubled? when $u$ is doubled and $v$ is halved?

8. If $N$ varies directly as $r$ and inversely as $s$, how does $N$ change when both $r$ and $s$ are tripled? when $r$ is tripled and $s$ is halved?

9. In the formula $h = \frac{y^2 xw}{5}$, $x$ remains constant. If $y$ is doubled and $w$ is tripled, how is $h$ changed?

10. In the formula $F = \frac{\pi r t^2}{s}$, $r$ remains constant, $t$ is halved, and $s$ is doubled. How does $F$ change?

## Problems

**Solve.**

**A**
1. The volume of a pyramid varies jointly as the height and the area of the base. A pyramid 15 cm high whose base has an area of 36 cm² has a volume of 180 cm³. What is the volume if the height is 21 cm and the area of the base is 25 cm²?

2. The lateral surface area of a cylindrical column varies jointly as the radius and the height of the column. For a radius of 0.5 yd and a height of 4 yd, the surface area is 12.4 yd². What is the radius, if the surface area is 471 yd² and the height is 50 yd?

3. When a wire carries an electric current for a given time, the heat developed varies jointly as the resistance and the square of the current. If a 6 ampere current produces 130 J (joules) of heat in a wire with a resistance of 15 ohms, find the resistance in a wire carrying a current of 9 amperes, if the heat developed is 195 J.

4. The volume of a right circular cylinder varies jointly as its height and the square of its radius. If a right circular cylinder of height 10 cm and radius 4 cm has a volume of $160\pi$ cm$^3$, find the volume of one with a height of 8 cm and a radius of 3 cm.

**In Exercises 5 and 6, apply the statement: The number of persons needed to do a job varies directly as the amount of work to be done and inversely as the time in which the job must be done.**

5. If 2 students in the typing pool can type 210 pages in 3 days, how many students will be needed to type 700 pages in 2 days?

6. If 2 workers can erect 400 m of fence in 10 h, how long will it take 5 workers to erect 600 m of fence?

7. The load that can be borne by a square horizontal beam supported at its ends varies directly as the square of its depth and inversely as the length between its supports. A beam 4 m long and 0.2 m deep bears 620 kg. What load can a beam 10 m long and 0.3 m deep bear?

8. The cost of operating an appliance varies jointly as the number of watts drawn, the hours of operation, and the cost per kilowatt-hour. A 6000-watt convection oven operates for 10 minutes for 15¢ at 7.5¢ per kilowatt-hour. What is the cost of cooking two meals if each meal takes 70 minutes to cook?

**B**  9. Using the mass of the sun as the unit of mass, and measuring distance in astronomical units (AU) and time in years, the total mass of a double star is directly proportional to the cube of the maximum distance between the stars and inversely proportional to the square of the period (the time it takes each star to revolve about the other). The double star Sirius has a period of 50.0 years, a maximum distance of 41.0 AU, and a total mass of 3.45. What is the total mass of Capella if its period is 0.285 years and the maximum distance is 1.51 AU?

10. The area of a trapezoid varies jointly as the sum of the lengths of the two parallel sides and the distance between the parallel sides. When the lengths of the parallel sides are 7 cm and 9 cm and the distance between them is 4 cm, the area is 32 cm$^2$. If the area is to remain constant and the height is reduced to 0.5 cm, what is the sum of the lengths of the parallel sides?

11. The heat lost through a windowpane varies jointly as the difference of the inside and outside temperatures and the window area, and inversely as the thickness of the pane. If 49.5 joules of heat are lost through a pane 40 cm by 28 cm that is 0.8 cm thick, in one hour when the temperature difference is 44°C, how many joules are lost in one hour through a pane 0.5 cm thick having an area that is 0.25 the area of the other pane, when the temperature difference is 40°C?

**C** **12.** The heat generated by a stove element varies jointly as the resistance and the square of the current. What is the effect on the heat generated in the following cases?

  **a.** The current is unchanged but the resistance is doubled.

  **b.** The resistance is unchanged but the current is doubled.

  **c.** The current is tripled and the resistance is doubled.

**13.** The power in an electric circuit varies directly as the square of the voltage and inversely as the resistance. What is the effect on the power in the following cases?

  **a.** The resistance is constant and the voltage is doubled.

  **b.** The voltage is constant and the resistance is doubled.

  **c.** The voltage is doubled and the resistance is quadrupled.

# Self-Test 3

***Vocabulary***  linear direct variation (p. 418)
constant of variation (p. 418, 424)
constant of proportionality (p. 419)
inverse variation (p. 424)
hyperbola (p. 424)

quadratic direct variation (p. 430)
inverse variation as the square (p. 430)
joint variation (p. 434)
combined variation (p. 434)

**Solve.**

1. A worker's earnings are directly proportional to the number of hours worked. If $59.20 is earned for 8 hours of work, how much is earned for 35 hours of work?

Obj. 9-7, p. 418

2. Four friends on a ski trip pay $140 each to share the rent of a cabin. The cost per person varies inversely as the number of persons sharing the rent. How many people sharing the rent would make the cost $80 per person?

Obj. 9-8, p. 424

3. The distance that the signal from a radio station travels varies directly as the square of the number of kilowatts (kW) it produces. A 40 kW station can broadcast a distance of 64 km. How far could the station broadcast if it produced 70 kW?

Obj. 9-9, p. 430

4. The mass of a circular coin varies jointly as the thickness and the square of the radius of the coin. A silver coin 2 cm in radius and 0.2 cm thick has a mass of 26.4 g. What is the mass of a silver coin 4 cm in radius and 0.3 cm thick?

Obj. 9-10, p. 434

Check your answers with those at the back of the book.

# Application / Illumination

Suppose you had to use a flashlight to help you see an object at a very close range. You would need to hold the light close to the object to make it clearer and brighter. To see a larger area, you would put more distance between the light and the object.

Scientists have measured how illumination is related to distance and brightness. The brightness, or intensity ($I$), of a light source is measured in units called candelas (cd). A 100-watt bulb gives about 130 cd. Illumination is the amount of light energy per second that falls on a unit area. Illumination is measured in luxes (lx).

Illumination is directly proportional to the intensity of the source. If the intensity is doubled, the illumination is doubled. Illumination on a surface is also dependent on its distance from the source. The farther the light source is from the surface, the lower the illumination.

Specifically, illumination ($E$) on a surface perpendicular to a light source varies inversely as the square of the distance ($r$) from the light source:

$$E = \frac{I}{r^2}$$

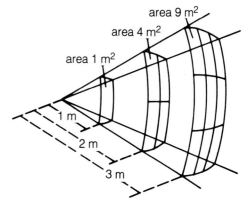

Thus, if the distance from the light source is doubled, the illumination is one fourth of what it was originally. If the distance is tripled, the illumination is one ninth. This equation is called the *law of illumination*.

**Example**  What illumination is provided on the surface of a table 3 m directly below a 99 cd lamp?

**Solution**  Use the formula to solve for $E$.

$$E = \frac{99}{3^2} = 11$$

∴ the illumination is 11 lx.

## Exercises

1. What illumination is provided on a surface 4 m from a 160 cd lamp?

2. If a light is giving 315 cd from 3 m above a desk top, what illumination is provided?

3. If a lamp gives 216 cd, how far must it be placed from a table surface to provide 24 lx of illumination?

4. What is the illumination of a 120 cd lamp at a distance of 2 m?

5. What illumination is provided on the surface of a desk 2.5 m directly below a 125 cd lamp?

# *Extra* / *Relations*

The diagram at the right shows how each number in the set

$$D = \{0, 1, 2, 3\}$$

is paired with one or more numbers in the set

$$R = \{-1, 1, 2, 3\}.$$

The same pairing is shown in the adjoining table, and in the listing of the ordered pairs of numbers.

| D | R |
|---|---|
| 0 | −1 |
| 0 | 1 |
| 1 | 1 |
| 2 | 3 |
| 3 | 2 |

$$\{(0, -1), (0, 1), (1, 1), (2, 3), (3, 2)\}$$

Notice that this pairing assigns to the number 0 in $D$ two different numbers, $-1$ and 1 in $R$. Therefore, the pairing is *not* a function with domain $D$ and range $R$. For, in a function, each member of the domain is assigned *exactly one* partner in the range. The pairing described above is an example of a *relation*.

---

A *relation* is any set of ordered pairs. The set of first coordinates in the ordered pairs is the *domain* of the relation, and the set of second coordinates is the *range*.

---

The figure at the right shows the graphs of all the ordered pairs that form the relation described above. We call this set the *graph of the relation*.

Of course, a function is a special kind of relation.

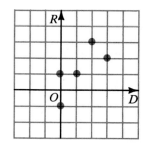

---

A function is a relation in which different ordered pairs have different first coordinates.

---

Thus, in the graph of a function, there is only one point plotted for each value in the domain.

## Exercises

State the domain and range of each relation. Is the relation a function?

**1.** $\{(3, 4), (2, 3), (3, 6), (2, 0)\}$

**2.** $\{(1, -1), (2, 3), (3, 5), (4, 8)\}$

**3.** $\{(2, -1), (3, 0), (4, 6), (1, -3)\}$

**4.** $\{(5, 0), (5, 1), (5, 2), (0, 4)\}$

**5.** $\{(-1, 1), (1, 1), (2, 4), (-2, 4)\}$

**6.** $\{(4, 2), (4, -2), (9, 3), (9, -3)\}$

Give the domain and range of the relation graphed in each diagram. Is the relation a function?

**7.**

**8.**

**9.**

**10**

**11.**

**12.**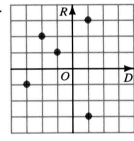

In Exercises 13–18, graph each relation and determine whether it is a function. If it is not a function, explain how that fact shows up on the graph.

**13.** $\{(-4, 2), (-1, 3), (4, 4), (4, -3)\}$

**14.** $\{(0, -1), (1, -2), (2, -3), (-1, 2)\}$

**15.** $\{(-3, 2), (0, 1), (3, -2), (-3, 0)\}$

**16.** $\{(-1, 1), (0, 0), (1, 1), (2, 4)\}$

**17.** $\{(0, 0), (1, 2), (2, 9), (-2, -7)\}$

**18.** $\{(1, 0), (2, 3), (3, -1), (1, 5)\}$

**19.** Consider the set of all ordered pairs of real numbers $(x, y)$ that satisfy the equation $|y| = |x|$. Is this set of ordered pairs a relation? a function? Justify your answers.

**20.** The circle shown at the right is the graph of the equation $x^2 + y^2 = 4$. Do the coordinates of the points of the circle form a relation? a function? Why or why not? If the points form a relation (or function), what are the domain and range?

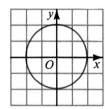

In Exercises 21–24, consider the set of all ordered pairs $(x, y)$ as described. Is the set a relation? Is it a function?

**21.** $(x, y)$, where $x$ is the name of a telephone subscriber in your town and $y$ is the subscriber's telephone number.

**22.** $(x, y)$, where $x$ is the name of each mother in your town and $y$ is the name of her child.

**23.** $(x, y)$, where $x$ is the name of each man in London, England, and $y$ is his right thumbprint.

**24.** $(x, y)$, where $x$ is any nonvertical line in the coordinate plane and $y$ is its slope.

*Introduction to Functions*    **441**

# Chapter Summary

1. The slope of a line can be found by using any two points on the line. Different lines with the same slope are parallel.

2. An equation of a line can be found from: (a) the slope and the $y$-intercept; (b) the slope and any point on the line; (c) two points on the line.

3. A function can be defined by an equation, a table, a correspondence, or a set of ordered pairs.

4. The value of a function $F$ at 2 is denoted by $F(2)$. Any value of a function can be found by replacing the variable in the function equation by the given number.

5. A linear function is defined by a linear equation. Its graph is a line.

6. A quadratic function is defined by an equation of the form $y = ax^2 + bx + c = 0$, $a \neq 0$. Its graph is a parabola that opens upward if $a$ is positive or downward if $a$ is negative.

7. Several kinds of variation have been described ($k$ is a nonzero constant):
   a. A linear direct variation is a linear function defined by an equation of the form $y = kx$.
   b. An inverse variation is a function defined by an equation of the form $xy = k \left( \text{or } y = \dfrac{k}{x} \right)$.
   c. A quadratic direct variation is a quadratic function defined by an equation of the form $y = kx^2$.
   d. An inverse variation as the square is a function defined by an equation of the form $x^2 y = k \left( \text{or } y = \dfrac{k}{x^2} \right)$.
   e. A joint variation is defined by an equation of the form $z = kxy$.
   f. A combined variation is defined by an equation of the form $zy = kx$ or $z = \dfrac{kx}{y}$.

# Chapter Review

**Give the letter of the correct answer.**

1. Find the slope of the line that passes through the points $(4, 4)$ and $(-4, 6)$.
   **a.** $-4$  **b.** $0$  **c.** $-\dfrac{1}{4}$  **d.** no slope

9-1

2. Find the slope of the line whose equation is $y - 8 = 0$.
   **a.** 8  **b.** 0  **c.** $-8$  **d.** no slope

**3.** Write an equation in standard form of the line that has slope $-\frac{1}{3}$ and 9-2

y-intercept 5.

**a.** $y = -\frac{1}{3}x + 5$         **b.** $-x + 3y = 15$

**c.** $-5x + y = -\frac{1}{3}$         **d.** $x + 3y = 15$

**4.** Find the slope and y-intercept of the line whose equation is $3x = 2y$.

**a.** $m = \frac{2}{3}, b = 0$         **b.** $m = -\frac{3}{2}, b = 0$

**c.** $m = 3, b = -2$         **d.** $m = \frac{3}{2}, b = 0$

**5.** Find $b$ given that the point $(12, -3)$ lies on the line whose equation is 9-3

$y = -\frac{4}{3}x + b$.

**a.** 13      **b.** $-19$      **c.** 8      **d.** 16

**6.** Write an equation in standard form of the line that passes through the points $(0, -7)$ and $(-7, 0)$.

**a.** $-x + y = 7$   **b.** $-x + y = -7$   **c.** $x + y = -7$   **d.** $y = -7$

**7.** Find $G(0)$ given $G(x) = 8 - 4x$. 9-4

**a.** 0      **b.** 2      **c.** 8      **d.** 4

**8.** Find $F(-1)$ given $F(x) = 6 - x^2$.

**a.** 49      **b.** 7      **c.** 4      **d.** 5

**9.** State the range of the function $\{(-1, 1), (0, 0), (1, 1), (2, 6)\}$. 9-5

**a.** $\{0, 1, 2, 3, 4, 5, 6\}$      **b.** $\{-1, 0, 1, 2\}$

**c.** $\{(-1, 1), (1, 1)\}$      **d.** $\{0, 1, 6\}$

**10.** Find the least value of the function $f: x \rightarrow x^2 + 8x + 3$. 9-6

**a.** $-13$      **b.** 3      **c.** $-4$      **d.** 8

**11.** Find the greatest value of the function $t: x \rightarrow x - x^2$.

**a.** $\frac{1}{2}$      **b.** $\frac{1}{4}$      **c.** 0      **d.** $-\frac{1}{4}$

**12.** Find the constant of variation if $y$ varies directly as $x$, and $y = 19$ 9-7
when $x = 95$.

**a.** 5      **b.** $\frac{1}{5}$      **c.** 19      **d.** 95

**13.** Find the missing value if $(75, 30)$ and $(\underline{\ ?\ }, 18)$ are ordered pairs of 9-8
the same inverse variation.

**a.** 125      **b.** 75      **c.** 45      **d.** 7.2

**14.** If $y$ varies inversely as $x^2$, and $x$ is halved, then $y$ is $\underline{\ ?\ }$. 9-9

**a.** doubled      **b.** quadrupled      **c.** divided by 4      **d.** halved

**15.** If $r$ varies directly as the cube of $t$ and inversely as the square of $s$, 9-10

and $r = \frac{1}{2}$ when $s = 6$ and $t = 2$, find $r$ when $s = 12$ and $t = 4$.

**a.** $\frac{1}{4}$      **b.** 0      **c.** $\frac{1}{2}$      **d.** 1

*Introduction to Functions*    **443**

# Chapter Test

**Find the slope of the line passing through the two given points.**

9-1

1. $(-6, 0)$, $(8, -7)$
2. $(-5, 7)$, $(8, 7)$
3. $(9, 5)$, $(9, -5)$
4. $(-2, 4)$, $(3, -1)$

**Find the slope of each line whose equation is given.**

5. $y = -3x + 2$
6. $x + y = 0$
7. $3x - 5y = 15$
8. $2x + 4y = 1$

**Write an equation in standard form of the line that has the given slope and $y$-intercept.**

9-2

9. $m = 1$; $b = 0$
10. $m = -\dfrac{5}{8}$; $b = 6$

11. $m = 0$; $b = -\dfrac{1}{3}$
12. $m = \dfrac{7}{4}$; $b = 8$

**Change each equation to the slope-intercept form. Then draw the graph using only the slope and $y$-intercept.**

13. $3x - y = 1$
14. $-x + 3y + 6 = 0$
15. $2y = 1$
16. $x + 2y - 6 = 0$

**Write an equation in standard form of the line that has the given slope and passes through the given point.**

9-3

17. $m = -3$; $(0, -1)$
18. $m = \dfrac{5}{2}$; $(-6, 7)$

19. $m = 0$; $\left(2, -\dfrac{1}{4}\right)$
20. $m = \dfrac{3}{4}$; $(-3, -4)$

21. Write an equation in standard form of the line passing through the points $(-4, -6)$ and $(4, 10)$.

**Find the range of each function.**

9-4

22. $F(t) = \dfrac{1}{1 + 3t}$, $D = \{-1, 0, 2\}$

23. $g: x \to x^2 - 1$, $D = \left\{-1, -\dfrac{1}{2}, 6\right\}$

24. $f: x \to \dfrac{2x}{3} - 1$, $D = \{-6, -3, 0, 3\}$

25. $f(x) = \dfrac{2x - 1}{3}$, $D = \{-6, -3, 0, 3\}$

**26.** The table below shows a function. 9-5

    **a.** State the domain and range of the function.

    **b.** Graph the function by means of a bar or a broken-line graph, whichever is more suitable.

| Region | % of Forested Land |
|---|---|
| Central | 18 |
| Lake States | 25 |
| Middle Atlantic | 58 |
| New England | 81 |
| Pacific Coast | 38 |
| Rocky Mountain | 25 |
| South | 39 |

**Draw the graph of each function.**

**27.** $g: x \rightarrow 1 - \dfrac{x}{2}$                         **28.** $t(x) = -1$ 9-6

**29.** Find the coordinates of the vertex and the equation of the axis of symmetry of the graph of the equation $y = 2x - x^2$. Use the vertex and at least six other points to graph the equation.

**Find the missing value if $(x_1, y_1)$ and $(x_2, y_2)$ are ordered pairs of the same direct variation.**

**30.** $x_1 = 7.2, y_1 = 3$              **31.** $x_1 = \dfrac{1}{5}, y_1 = \underline{\ \ ?\ \ }$ 9-7

    $x_2 = \underline{\ \ ?\ \ }, y_2 = 2$               $x_2 = \dfrac{3}{10}, y_2 = \dfrac{1}{6}$

**32.** The number of bolts a machine can make varies directly as the running time of the machine. If a machine can make 1000 bolts in six hours, in how many hours can it make 300 bolts?

**33.** Graph $\dfrac{x}{3} = \dfrac{4}{y}$ if the domain and the range are both limited to the set of positive numbers. 9-8

**34.** The area of a square is directly proportional to the square of its diagonal. If the area of a square having a diagonal 16 cm long is 128 cm², what is the area of a square having a diagonal 24 cm long? 9-9

**35.** If $V$ varies jointly as $B$ and $h$, and $V = 50$ when $B = 25$ and $h = 6$, find $h$ when $B = 36$ and $V = 108$. 9-10

# Cumulative Review (Chapters 1–9)

**Simplify.**

1. $(3y - 2z) - (-8z + 2y)$
2. $(8x - 4z)(2x + 3z)$
3. $2m^2n(10m^2 + 3mn + 5n^2)$
4. $(2x^3y^2z^4)^4 \div (4x^2yz^3)^2$
5. $(5b - 8c)^2$
6. $(3.2 \times 10^{-8})(1.5 \times 10^{12})$

**Factor completely.**

7. $12x^2 + 17x - 7$
8. $4y^2 - 12y + 9$
9. $3z^2 - 21z - 24$

**Express in simplest form. Assume that no denominator is zero.**

10. $\dfrac{a^2 - a - 2}{a^2 + 2a + 1}$

11. $\dfrac{x^2 + 4x + 3}{x + 1} \cdot \dfrac{(x^2 - 1)}{2x^2 + x - 1}$

12. $\dfrac{3z^2 + 8z - 3}{3z^2 + 5z - 2} \div \dfrac{z^2 + 6z + 9}{z^3 - 4z}$

13. $\dfrac{t}{t - 2} - \dfrac{t}{t + 2} - 3$

**Write an equation in standard form for each line described.**

14. The line with slope 4 that passes through $(-1, -2)$.
15. The line through $(5, 2)$ and $(2, 5)$.
16. The line that contains $(1, 3)$ and is parallel to $2x + y = 4$.
17. Find the range of the function $f: x \rightarrow x^2 - x + 1$ with domain $\{-3, -2, -1, 0, 1, 2, 3\}$.

**Graph each equation.**

18. $2x + 4y = 7$
19. $y = x^2 + x + 1$
20. Find the coordinates of the vertex and the equation of the axis of symmetry of the graph of $y = 2x^2 + 3x + 4$.

**Solve each equation or system. Assume that no denominator is zero.**

21. $3(x + 5) = 2(2x - 3)$
22. $2|x| + 1 = 5$
23. $y\%$ of $50 = 27$
24. $9a^2 - 12a + 4 = 0$
25. $36b^2 - 25 = 0$
26. $10t^2 + t = 3$

27. $\dfrac{1}{x + 1} + 1 = x + 2$

28. $\dfrac{y + 1}{y + 2} = \dfrac{y + 4}{y - 1}$

29. $\dfrac{2z}{z - 3} - \dfrac{1}{z + 1} = -1$

30. $y = x - 1$
    $2x + 3y = 7$

31. $3x + 4y = 8$
    $5x - 4y = 4$

32. $2x + 7y = 29$
    $3x - 4y = -29$

33. If $x$ varies directly as the square of $y$ and inversely as the cube of $z$, and $x = 3.6$ when $y = 3$ and $z = 2$, find $x$ when $y = 2$ and $z = \dfrac{1}{2}$.

34. For a given distance, the speed at which a car travels varies inversely as the time it travels. If it takes 1.5 h to travel a distance at 84 km/h, how long would it take to travel the same distance at 90 km/h?

# Maintaining Skills

**Simplify. Assume that no denominator is zero.**

**Example 1**  $\dfrac{5x + 15}{2x} \cdot \dfrac{4x^3}{x^2 + 6x + 9} = \dfrac{5(x + 3)}{2x} \cdot \dfrac{4x^3}{(x + 3)^2} = \dfrac{20x^3(x + 3)}{2x(x + 3)^2} = \dfrac{10x^2}{x + 3}$

**1.** $\dfrac{ab}{4a - 4b} \cdot \dfrac{a^2 - ab}{ab}$

**2.** $\dfrac{2x - 14}{-5x} \cdot \dfrac{5x^3}{3x - 21}$

**3.** $\dfrac{8f + 24g}{2f - 4g} \cdot \dfrac{4f - 8g}{2f + 6g}$

**4.** $\dfrac{m + 2}{2m - 6} \cdot \dfrac{m^2 - 5m + 6}{2m + 4}$

**5.** $\dfrac{3z - 6}{5z} \cdot \dfrac{z^2 - z - 6}{z^2 - 4}$

**6.** $\dfrac{x^2 - 4}{x^2 - 9} \cdot \dfrac{2x^2 + 6x}{x - 2}$

**7.** $\dfrac{3t^2 + 2t - 1}{5t^2 - 9t - 2} \cdot \dfrac{10t^2 - 13t - 3}{2t^2 - t - 3}$

**8.** $\dfrac{b^2 + 12b + 36}{36 - b^2} \cdot \dfrac{b^2 - 5b - 6}{2b^2 - 2b - 84}$

**Example 2**  $\dfrac{2m^2 + 5m + 2}{m^2 + 4m + 3} \div \dfrac{m + 2}{2m^2 + 7m + 3}$

**Solution**  $\dfrac{(2m + 1)(m + 2)}{(m + 3)(m + 1)} \cdot \dfrac{(2m + 1)(m + 3)}{m + 2} = \dfrac{(2m + 1)^2}{m + 1}$

**9.** $\dfrac{10a - 10b}{ab} \div \dfrac{2a - 2b}{a^2b^2}$

**10.** $\dfrac{16m^2 - n^2}{6m + 3n} \div \dfrac{4mn - n^2}{2mn + n^2}$

**11.** $\dfrac{2b^2 + 17b + 21}{b + 1} \div (b + 7)$

**12.** $\dfrac{z^2 + z}{-z^2 - 2z - 1} \div \dfrac{z^2 - 3z}{2z^2 - 2}$

**13.** $\dfrac{c^2 - c - 6}{c^2 + 2c - 15} \div \dfrac{c^2 - 4c - 5}{c^2 - 25}$

**14.** $\dfrac{6t^2 - t - 2}{12t^2 + 5t - 2} \div \dfrac{8t^2 - 6t + 1}{4t^2 - 1}$

**15.** $\dfrac{r^2 - r - 20}{r^2 - 6r + 5} \cdot \dfrac{r^2 - 36}{r^2 - 9} \div \dfrac{r^2 + 7r + 12}{r^2 + 5r - 6}$

**Example 3**  $\dfrac{b}{b - 2} - \dfrac{2}{b^2 - 4} + 1$

**Solution**  $\dfrac{b(b + 2) - 2 + (b + 2)(b - 2)}{(b + 2)(b - 2)} = \dfrac{b^2 + 2b - 2 + b^2 - 4}{(b + 2)(b - 2)} = \dfrac{2(b^2 + b - 3)}{(b + 2)(b - 2)}$

**16.** $\dfrac{2t - 3}{r^2t} + \dfrac{r - t}{r^2t}$

**17.** $\dfrac{x + 2y}{x - y} + \dfrac{x + y}{x - y}$

**18.** $\dfrac{3b + 2}{b^3} - \dfrac{2b + 2}{b^3}$

**19.** $\dfrac{w - 2}{w - 3} - \dfrac{w^2 + w}{w - 3}$

**20.** $z + \dfrac{z - 1}{z + 1} + 1$

**21.** $\dfrac{8}{v^2 - 1} + \dfrac{v}{v + 1}$

**22.** $\dfrac{s}{s - t} - \dfrac{s}{s + t}$

**23.** $\dfrac{3b}{2b - 1} - b$

**24.** $\dfrac{z + 3}{z - 1} + \dfrac{z}{z + 2}$

**25.** $\dfrac{d - 3}{2d + 1} + \dfrac{1}{d + 1}$

**26.** $\dfrac{v + 4}{v + 2} - \dfrac{v + 2}{v + 4}$

**27.** $\dfrac{t}{t^2 - 4} - \dfrac{5t}{4 - t^2}$

**28.** $\dfrac{2b}{b + 2} + \dfrac{b + 1}{b} - 1$

**29.** $\dfrac{x + 4}{x - 4} - \dfrac{x - 4}{x + 3} + 2$

**30.** $\dfrac{3a + b}{a^2 - b^2} - \dfrac{1}{a + b}$

# 10 Inequalities

Linear programming (see pages 487–490) can be used to help large-scale manufacturers of computer chips and other items make decisions related to inventory, manufacturing, and profits.

# Inequalities in One Variable

## 10-1 Order of Real Numbers

**Objective**   To review the concept of order and to graph certain inequalities.

A number line pictures order relations among real numbers.

$$-5 < 2$$
$-5$ is less than 2

$$4 > -1$$
$4$ is greater than $-1$

Recall (page 37) that on a horizontal number line any number $x$ is:

1. less than every number whose graph is to the right of the graph of $x$;
2. greater than every number whose graph is to the left of the graph of $x$.

The sentence

$-3 < x < 2$, read "$-3$ is less than $x$ and $x$ is less than 2,"

means that $x$ denotes a number *between* $-3$ and 2. You can also read the sentence as "$x$ is greater than $-3$ and less than 2." The same comparisons are stated in the sentence

$$2 > x > -3.$$

Are the following statements true?

$$\underbrace{-4 < 1 < 5}_{\text{True}} \qquad \underbrace{-4 < 8 < 5}_{\text{False}}$$

The one on the right is false because 8 is *not* less than 5 (although $-4$ is less than 8).

For a statement like $-4 < 8 < 5$ to be true *both* "less than" statements of order must be true.

Sometimes it is convenient to indicate that one number is greater than or equal to another number. This can be written

$x \geq 5$, read "$x$ is greater than or equal to 5."

Similarly, you can write $x \leq 5$ for "$x$ is less than or equal to 5." The statements

$$6 \geq 5 \quad \text{and} \quad 5 \geq 5$$

are both true since such statements are true *either* if the first number is greater than the second *or* if the first number equals the second.

Here are three *inequalities:*

$$-2 < 0 \qquad 4x - 3 > 2 \qquad y + 7 \le 9$$

the sides

An **inequality** is formed by placing an inequality symbol ($>$, $<$, $\ge$, $\le$) between numerical or variable expressions, called the **sides** of the inequality.

As in the case of equations, an inequality containing a variable is called an *open sentence* (page 10). You solve such an inequality by finding the values of the variable for which the inequality is a true statement. Such values are called **solutions of the inequality;** they make up the **solution set of the inequality.**

**Example 1**  If $y \in \{-1, 0, 1, 2, 3, 4\}$, what is the solution set of $y + 7 \le 9$?

**Solution**  Replace $y$ with each of its values in turn:

$$y + 7 \le 9$$

| | | | |
|---|---|---|---|
| $-1 + 7 \le 9$ | True | $2 + 7 \le 9$ | True |
| $0 + 7 \le 9$ | True | $3 + 7 \le 9$ | False |
| $1 + 7 \le 9$ | True | $4 + 7 \le 9$ | False |

$\therefore$ the solution set is $\{-1, 0, 1, 2\}$.  **Answer**

When you graph the numbers in the solution set of an open sentence on a number line, you say that you have drawn the **graph of the open sentence.** The graph of the inequality $y + 7 \le 9$ in Example 1 is shown below.

**Example 2**  Solve $-3 \le x < 2$ and draw its graph if the domain of $x$ is the set of real numbers.

**Solution**  For the inequality to be a true statement, $x$ must denote any number between $-3$ and $2$, including $-3$, but not $2$.

$\therefore$ the solution set is {the real numbers greater than or equal to $-3$ and less than $2$}.  **Answer**

Notice that the graph includes all the points on the number line from the graph of $-3$ up to, but not including, the graph of $2$. The open circle shows that $2$ is not a solution.

# Oral Exercises

**Classify each statement as true or false.**

1. $9 \geq -4$
2. $17 \leq 23$
3. $-14 \leq -23$
4. $-1 \geq -2$
5. $-7 < 6 < 14$
6. $4 > -4 > -1$
7. $2 > 0 > -6$
8. $-1.5 < 0.5 < 2.5$
9. $|-5| \geq 0$
10. $|-2| > |-8|$
11. $2^4 < 4^2$
12. $\left(\frac{1}{3}\right)^2 \geq \frac{1}{3}$

**Describe the numbers whose graphs appear in color. There may be more than one correct description.**

*Example 1*

*Solution*  The real numbers between $-2$ and $1$, or the real numbers greater than $-2$ and less than $1$

*Example 2*

*Solution*  The real numbers less than or equal to $2$

13.

14.

15.

16.

17.

18.

19.

20.

# Written Exercises

**Translate the statements into symbols.**

**A**

1. 6 is greater than $-7$.
2. $-8$ is less than $-4$.
3. $-12$ is less than or equal to $-9$.
4. 4 is greater than or equal to 1.
5. 3 is greater than 2 and less than 3.5.
6. 0 is greater than $-\frac{1}{2}$ and less than 1.
7. $-15$ is between $-10$ and $-20$.
8. 3 is between 4 and $-4$.
9. 2.8 is greater than 2 and 2 is greater than 0.
10. $-1.5$ is less than $-1$ and $-1$ is less than $-0.5$.

**Translate the statements into symbols.**

**11.** The absolute value of $n$ is greater than or equal to $n$.

**12.** The absolute value of $n$ is greater than or equal to the opposite of $n$.

**Classify each statement as true or false.**

**13.** $|-0.7| < -0.5$

**14.** $\left|-\frac{1}{4}\right| \geq 0$

**15.** $|-10| < |-25|$

**16.** $|4 - 1| \leq |1 - 4|$

**17.** $-6 < 1 < 7$

**18.** $8 > 0 > 3$

**Solve each inequality if $x \in \{-4, -3, -2, -1, 0, 1, 2, 3, 4\}$.**

**19.** $4x < 8$

**20.** $3x \geq 6$

**21.** $-2x < 6$

**22.** $x + 1 < 3$

**23.** $-5 - x \leq 1$

**24.** $2 - x \geq 0$

**25.** $x^2 \geq 10$

**26.** $x^2 \leq 5$

**Solve each inequality over the given domain and draw its graph.**

**B**  **27.** $21 < 7x$; {the positive numbers}

**28.** $3y < 12$; {the positive numbers}

**29.** $-5 \leq x < 1$; {the integers}

**30.** $4 \geq t \geq -1$; {the integers}

**31.** $6 > v > 0$; {the real numbers}

**32.** $-3 < m < 3$; {the real numbers}

**33.** $-5 \leq h < 1$; {the negative integers}

**34.** $5 \geq s > -6$; {the negative integers}

**For each statement in Exercises 35–38:**
**a. Find a pair of values of $x$ and $y$ for which the statement is true.**
**b. Find a pair of values of $x$ and $y$ for which the statement is false.**

**C**  **35.** If $x \geq y$, then $|x| \leq |y|$.

**36.** If $x \geq 0$ and $y < 0$, then $xy \geq 0$.

**37.** If $x > y$, then $xy > y^2$.

**38.** $|x - y| > x - y$

---

## Computer Exercises
*For students with some programming experience*

Write a BASIC program to find the solution set of an inequality in one variable for a specified domain of the variable. RUN the program to find the solution set for each of the following inequalities with the given domains.

**1.** $2x - 5 < 7$; $x \in \{0, 1, 2, \ldots, 10\}$

**2.** $x^2 - x < 6$; $x \in \{-4, -3, -2, \ldots, 1, 2, 3, 4\}$

**3.** $|4 - 5x| > 13$; $x \in \{0, 1, 2, 3, 4, 5\}$

**4.** $|x^2 + 3x| < -1$; $x \in \{0, 1, 2, 3, 4, 5\}$

**5.** $x^2 + 3x + 4 < 10$; $x \in \{-3, -2, -1, 0, 1, 2, 3\}$

**6.** $x^2 - 4x + 1 > 6$; $x \in \{0, 1, 2, 3, \ldots, 8, 9, 10\}$

# 10-2 Solving Inequalities

**Objective**   To transform inequalities in order to solve them.

Only the first of the following statements is true:

$$-6 < 5 \qquad -6 = 5 \qquad -6 > 5$$

True          False          False

In comparing real numbers, you make the following basic assumption:

---

### Axiom of Comparison

For all real numbers $a$ and $b$, one and only one of the following statements
is true:

$$a < b, \quad a = b, \quad \text{or} \quad a > b.$$

---

Now suppose you know two facts about the graphs of three numbers
$a$, $b$, and $c$.

1. The graph of $a$ is to the left of the graph of $b$: $a < b$
2. The graph of $b$ is to the left of the graph of $c$: $b < c$

Where is the graph of $a$ relative to the graph of $c$? You can see that it is to
the left of $c$: $a < c$

   In general, the following assumption is made:

---

### Transitive Axiom of Order

For all real numbers $a$, $b$, and $c$:

1. If $a < b$ and $b < c$, then $a < c$;
2. If $c > b$ and $b > a$, then $c > a$.

---

What happens when the same number is added to each side of an
inequality?

$$
\begin{array}{cc}
2 \quad < \quad 7 & \qquad 2 \quad < \quad 7 \\
\underbrace{2+3} \quad \underbrace{7+3} & \qquad \underbrace{2-3} \quad \underbrace{7-3} \\
5 \quad < \quad 10 & \qquad -1 \quad < \quad 4
\end{array}
$$

   These numerical examples suggest the axiom of order stated on the
following page. (Recall that subtracting a number is the same as adding
the opposite of that number.)

## Addition Axiom of Order

For all real numbers $a$, $b$, and $c$:

1. If $a < b$, then $a + c < b + c$;
2. If $a > b$, then $a + c > b + c$.

What happens when each side of the inequality $-3 < 2$ is multiplied by a nonzero real number?

Multiply by 5: Is it true that $5(-3) < 5(2)$?

Yes, $-15 < 10$.

Multiply by $-5$: Is it true that $-5(-3) < -5(2)$?

No, $15 > -10$.

This example suggests that multiplying each side of an inequality by a negative number *reverses the direction,* or order, of the inequality.

In general, the following assumption is made:

## Multiplication Axiom of Order

For all real numbers $a$, $b$, and $c$ such that

$c > 0$:

1. If $a < b$, then $ac < bc$;
2. If $a > b$, then $ac > bc$.

$c < 0$:

1. If $a < b$, then $ac > bc$;
2. If $a > b$, then $ac < bc$.

Multiplying both sides of an inequality by zero does not produce an inequality; the result is the identity $0 = 0$.

The axioms that have been stated guarantee that the following transformations of a given inequality always produce an **equivalent inequality,** that is, one with the same solution set.

## Transformations That Produce an Equivalent Inequality

1. Substituting for either side of the inequality an expression equivalent to that side.
2. Adding to (or subtracting from) each side the same real number.
3. Multiplying (or dividing) each side by the same positive number.
4. Multiplying (or dividing) each side by the same negative number and reversing the direction of the inequality.

To solve an inequality, you usually try to transform it into a simple equivalent inequality whose solution set can be seen at once.

*You may assume that the domain of all variables is the set of real numbers unless otherwise stated.*

**Example 1**  Solve $5x - 1 < 11 + 3x$ and draw its graph.

**Solution**

$$5x - 1 < 11 + 3x$$
$$5x - 1 + 1 < 11 + 3x + 1 \qquad \text{Add 1 to each side.}$$
$$5x < 12 + 3x$$
$$5x - 3x < 12 + 3x - 3x \qquad \text{Subtract } 3x \text{ from each side.}$$
$$2x < 12$$
$$\frac{2x}{2} < \frac{12}{2} \qquad \text{Divide each side by 2.}$$
$$x < 6$$

∴ the solution set is {the real numbers less than 6}.
The graph is:

 *Answer*

To solve an inequality, you take the same steps used to solve equations:

---

1. Simplify each side of the inequality.
2. Use the inverse operations to undo any indicated additions or subtractions.
3. Use the inverse operations to undo any indicated multiplications or divisions.

---

**Example 2**  Solve and graph $2(z - 8) + 9 \geq 3(4 - z) - 4$.

**Solution**

$$2(z - 8) + 9 \geq 3(4 - z) - 4$$
$$2z - 16 + 9 \geq 12 - 3z - 4$$
$$2z - 7 \geq 8 - 3z$$
$$5z \geq 15$$
$$z \geq 3$$

∴ the solution set is {the real numbers greater than or equal to 3}.
The graph is:

 *Answer*

*Inequalities*   **455**

## Oral Exercises

**Tell how to transform the first inequality to obtain the second one.**

**1.** $t + 3 < 7$
$t < 4$

**2.** $s - 2 > 7$
$s > 9$

**3.** $-1 < x - 2$
$1 < x$

**4.** $y + 5 < 0$
$y < -5$

**5.** $4p < 20$
$p < 5$

**6.** $2m < -16$
$m < -8$

**7.** $-6a < 18$
$a > -3$

**8.** $\frac{z}{2} > 3$
$z > 6$

**9.** $2 > \frac{v}{7}$
$14 > v$

**10.** $\frac{r}{-2} < -10$
$r > 20$

**11.** $3y < \frac{1}{2}$
$y < \frac{1}{6}$

**12.** $-\frac{t}{3} > 0$
$t < 0$

**Explain how to transform each inequality in order to solve it. Then state the transformed inequality.**

**13.** $y - 5 < 8$

**14.** $7 < x + 2$

**15.** $10p > 100$

**16.** $-8 < -4c$

**17.** $\frac{w}{2} \geq 12$

**18.** $-1 \leq -\frac{r}{4}$

## Written Exercises

**Match each inequality in Exercises 1–8 with its solution set in a–h.**

**A**

**1.** $y - 2 \geq 7$

**2.** $10 > z + 10$

**3.** $6p \neq 24$

**4.** $16 < 8v$

**5.** $-28 > -7m$

**6.** $\frac{d}{4} < -5$

**7.** $2 - g > 0$

**8.** $2 \leq \frac{w}{-3}$

**a.**

**b.**

**c.**

**d.**

**e.**

**f.**

**g.**

**h.**

**Solve each inequality and draw its graph.**

**9.** $n - 4 > 11$

**10.** $a + 5 < 14$

**11.** $-\frac{y}{2} > 4$

**12.** $3q < 15$

**13.** $36 < \frac{x}{-9}$

**14.** $-9 < \frac{s}{3}$

**15.** $-6m \geq 6$

**16.** $-5w \leq 25$

**17.** $\frac{x}{2} - 4 > -6$

**18.** $3v + 2 > 8$

**19.** $-\frac{z}{3} \geq 0$

**20.** $7 \geq 2k - 5$

**21.** $\frac{3}{2}t - 7 < 2$

**22.** $-3 \leq 3 - \frac{u}{2}$

**23.** $-1 < 9 + \frac{2}{3}g$

**24.** $5 + \frac{x}{4} \leq 8$

**25.** $12 - \frac{3}{2}c > 0$

**26.** $0 > 8 - \frac{4}{3}b$

**Solve each inequality.**

**27.** $5y < 4y + 6$

**28.** $7f - 6 > 6f + 12$

**29.** $4r - 5 < 5r + 7$

**30.** $1 + 2r > 7 - r$

**31.** $8 - 2b \geq 4 - b$

**32.** $3(x - 4) \leq 9$

**33.** $8 < 2(4 - m)$

**34.** $4(n - 6) < 2(n - 2)$

**35.** $5(1 - t) \geq 4(3 - t)$

**36.** $7(2 - v) \geq -(v - 8)$

**37.** $\frac{5}{6}r + 1 \geq \frac{4}{3}$

**38.** $\frac{1}{8} < 5 - \frac{3}{4}a$

**Solve each inequality and draw its graph.**

**B** **39.** $5(x - 1) \geq \frac{5}{4}x$

**40.** $\frac{4}{3}y \leq 8(y - 5)$

**41.** $n - \frac{5}{2} > \frac{3}{4}(n - 6)$

**42.** $4w - \frac{1}{2}(3w + 10) \geq 0$

**43.** $5(5 - k) - 7(7 + k) < 0$

**44.** $4(v - 3) > 3(v + 4) - 9$

**45.** $4\left(r - \frac{1}{2}\right) - 3 \leq 5(r - 1) + 4$

**46.** $3(t - 1) - 2(t + 2) \leq 3 - 5t$

**47.** $5 - a + 2(a - 3) \geq 5(a + 1)$

**48.** $2(2b - 1) - 3(b + 1) > 3b + 7$

**Given that $a$ and $b$ are real numbers such that $a > b$, describe the real numbers $c$ for which each statement is true.**

**C** **49.** $ac > bc$

**50.** $ac < bc$

**51.** $ac = bc$

**52.** $\frac{a}{c} > \frac{b}{c}$

**53.** $\frac{a}{c} < \frac{b}{c}$

**54.** $ac^2 > bc^2$

**55.** $\frac{a}{c^2} < \frac{b}{c^2}$

**56.** $ac^2 = bc^2$

**Classify each statement as true for all real numbers $a$ and $b$ such that $a > b > 0$ or false for some $a$ and $b$ such that $a > b > 0$. If you classify a statement as false, give an example of values for which it is false.**

**57.** $a > 0$

**58.** $a^2 > a$

**59.** $ab > 0$

**60.** $a + b > a$

**61.** $a^2 > b$

**62.** $a^2 > ab$

**63.** $ab > b^2$

**64.** $a^2 > b^2$

# Reading Algebra / *Inequalities*

When working with inequalities, it is extremely important to read both the symbols and the words slowly and carefully. Unlike equations that involve only the equals sign, $=$, inequalities can contain any of the four inequality symbols, $<$, $>$, $\leq$, $\geq$, and which of these symbols is used determines what your answer will be. For example, the equation $2x + 6 = 14$ is equivalent to $x = 4$ and the solution set is simply $\{4\}$. The inequalities $2x + 6 < 14$, $2x + 6 > 14$, $2x + 6 \leq 14$, and $2x + 6 \geq 14$, however, all have different solution sets.

> $2x + 6 < 14$ is equivalent to $x < 4$. The solution set is {the real numbers less than 4}.
>
> $2x + 6 > 14$ is equivalent to $x > 4$. The solution set is {the real numbers greater than 4}.
>
> $2x + 6 \leq 14$ is equivalent to $x \leq 4$. The solution set is {4, and the real numbers less than 4}.
>
> $2x + 6 \geq 14$ is equivalent to $x \geq 4$. The solution set is {4, and the real numbers greater than 4}.

Word problems involving inequalities also require very careful reading. An important step in solving this type of problem is determining which symbol to use when you write your inequality. Is the problem asking for a solution that is less than, greater than, less than or equal to, or greater than or equal to a particular number or expression? Before you write your inequality you should be certain that you are going to use the correct symbol.

Combined inequalities involve the words "and" and "or." These types of inequalities must be read extremely carefully, as they can involve the same numbers and symbols, but have different solutions, depending on whether they are joined by "and" or "or."

## Exercises

For each of the following:

**a.** Determine whether the inequality symbol means less than, greater than, less than or equal to, or greater than or equal to.

**b.** Determine whether the graph has a closed circle or an open circle and whether the graph goes to the right or the left of that circle.

**c.** Solve and graph the solution.

**1.** $x - 3 > 12$

**2.** $3y + 1 > 7$

**3.** $5 \geq 2y - 3$

**4.** $12 + y \leq 24$

**5.** $-9 < 21 + 2m$

**6.** $-6 \leq 6 - k$

**7.** $18 - 3y > 0$

**8.** $1 + 3r \geq 5 - r$

**9.** $2x - 3 < 4x + 5$

**10.** $21 - 15x < -8x - 7$

**11.** $4(t - 2) > 5(t - 3)$

**12.** $6(z - 5) \leq 15 + 5(7 - 2z)$

# 10-3 Solving Problems Involving Inequalities

**Objective**  To solve problems that involve inequalities.

**Example 1**  The width of a rectangular
computer screen is 20 cm
less than twice the length.
The perimeter is more than
56 cm. Find the minimum
dimensions of the screen,
if each dimension, in centimeters, is an integer.

**Solution**

*Step 1*  The problem asks for the
minimum length, $l$, and
width, $w$, in centimeters.
We are told that:
a. $l$ and $w$ are integers;
b. $w$ is 20 cm less than twice $l$;
c. the perimeter $(2l + 2w)$ is more than 56 cm.

*Step 2*  Let $l$ = length in centimeters.
Then $2l - 20$ = width in centimeters.

*Step 3*  The perimeter  is more than  56 cm.

*Step 4*
$$2l + 2(2l - 20) > 56$$
$$2l + 4l - 40 > 56$$
$$6l - 40 > 56$$
$$6l > 96$$
$$l > 16$$

∴ the minimum length is 17 cm.
The minimum width is $2(17) - 20$, or 14 cm.

*Step 5*  *Check:* (1) Is the width 20 cm less than twice the length?
$$14 \stackrel{?}{=} 2(17) - 20$$
$$14 = 14 \ \checkmark$$

(2) Is the perimeter more than 56 cm?
$$2(17) + 2(14) = 34 + 28 = 62; \ 62 > 56 \ \checkmark$$

(3) Are the dimensions the least possible? Suppose the length
were the next smaller integer, 16. Then, the width would be
$2(16) - 20$, or 12 cm. The perimeter would be $2(16) + 2(12)$,
or 56 cm, which is *not* greater than 56 cm.

∴ the dimensions are 17 cm and 14 cm.  ***Answer***

**Example 2** Find all sets of three positive consecutive odd integers such that twice the sum of the first two is less than three times the third.

**Solution**

*Step 1* The problem asks for three consecutive odd integers that are positive.

*Step 2* Let the first of these integers be $n$. Then, in natural order, the other two are $n + 2$ and $n + 4$.

*Step 3* Twice the sum of the first two is less than three times the third.

$$2[n + (n + 2)] \qquad < \qquad 3(n + 4)$$

*Step 4*
$$2(2n + 2) \qquad < \qquad 3n + 12$$
$$4n + 4 \qquad < \qquad 3n + 12$$
$$4n \qquad < \qquad 3n + 8$$
$$n \qquad < \qquad 8$$

Since the least number in the set must be positive, odd, and less than 8, there are only four choices: 1, 3, 5, and 7.

∴ the four sets are $\{1, 3, 5\}$, $\{3, 5, 7\}$, $\{5, 7, 9\}$, and $\{7, 9, 11\}$.

*Step 5* *Check:* Is twice the sum of the first two consecutive odd integers less than three times the greatest?

Check for $\{1, 3, 5\}$: $2(1 + 3) \overset{?}{<} 3(5)$
$$8 < 15 \;\checkmark$$

Check for $\{3, 5, 7\}$: $2(3 + 5) \overset{?}{<} 3(7)$
$$16 < 21 \;\checkmark$$

Check for $\{5, 7, 9\}$: $2(5 + 7) \overset{?}{<} 3(9)$
$$24 < 27 \;\checkmark$$

Check for $\{7, 9, 11\}$: $2(7 + 9) \overset{?}{<} 3(11)$
$$32 < 33 \;\checkmark$$

To show that these four sets of integers are *all* the solutions, check the next possible set of three consecutive odd integers, $\{9, 11, 13\}$, to see whether the condition is satisfied.

$$2(9 + 11) \overset{?}{<} 3(13)$$
$$40 < 39 \quad \text{False}$$

∴ the required sets are $\{1, 3, 5\}$, $\{3, 5, 7\}$, $\{5, 7, 9\}$, and $\{7, 9, 11\}$.

*Answer*

To translate phrases such as "is at least" and "is no less than" or "is at most" and "is no more than" into mathematical terms, you use the symbols $\geq$ or $\leq$. For example:

| | |
|---|---|
| The age of the tree is at least 70 years: | $a \geq 70$ |
| The rent is no less than \$400 per month: | $r \geq 400$ |
| The price of the paperback book is at most \$5.95: | $p \leq 5.95$ |
| Her time in the 10 km race was no more than 40 min: | $t \leq 40$ |

## Written Exercises

**For each of the following:**
**a. Choose a variable to represent the number indicated in color.**
**b. Use the variable to write an inequality based on the given information. (Do not solve.)**

**A** **1.** Isabel, who is not yet 21 years old, is two years older than Ida. (Ida's age)

**2.** After typing 15 pages of manuscript, a typist had fewer than 36 pages left to type. (the number of pages of manuscript the typist had originally)

**3.** A sales executive traveled a certain number of kilometers by airplane and then one tenth as far by automobile. Her total trip was more than 3000 km.

**4.** The number of County Community College students enrolled in liberal arts is one half the number enrolled in applied arts and sciences. The total number of students in these programs is at least 8000.

**5.** In a marathon, Fred ran 15 more kilometers than half the number Jim ran. Fred ran at most 36 km.

**6.** A homeowner figures that the total of the monthly mortgage payment and the home's operating expenses is no more than $900. The mortgage payment is $100 more than twice the operating expenses.

**7.** The sum of three consecutive odd integers is no less than 51. (the middle integer)

**8.** The product of two consecutive even integers is at most 360. (the greater integer)

**9.** A coin bank containing only quarters, dimes, and nickels has twice as many dimes as nickels and half as many quarters as nickels. In all the bank contains no more than $11.40. (the number of nickels)

**10.** Two trucks start from the same point at the same time, but travel in opposite directions. One truck travels at 86 km/h, the other at 78 km/h. After some hours of traveling, the trucks are at least 650 km apart.

**B** **11.** If a motorist drove 10 km/h faster, then in 3 h he would travel farther than he does in 4 h at his present speed.

**12.** Eight years from now, Violette will be more than twice as old as she is now. (her age now)

**For each of the following:**
**a. Choose a variable to represent the number indicated in color.**
**b. Use the variable to write an inequality based on the given information. (Do not solve.)**

13. A dowel 25 cm long is cut into two pieces. One piece is at least 1 cm longer than twice as long as the other piece. (the length of the shorter piece)

14. At a school cafeteria, a student paid 90 cents for a whole-wheat muffin and a glass of milk. The milk cost less than two thirds of the cost of the muffin.

15. The smaller of two consecutive odd integers is no less than 15 more than one fourth of the greater.

16. The greater of two consecutive even integers is no more than 50 less than five times the smaller.

17. There are three consecutive integers such that five times the greatest diminished by the second is at least nine more than twice the least.

18. Three consecutive odd integers are such that their sum is more than 57 decreased by twice the greatest of the three integers.

**In Exercises 19–20, express in symbols the property that is stated in words.**

C 19. The absolute value of the sum of two real numbers is no greater than the sum of the absolute values of the numbers.

20. The square of the sum of two nonnegative real numbers is at least as great as 4 times the product of the numbers.

## Problems

**Solve.**

A 1. A bakery makes bread in which the ratio of whole-wheat flour to white flour is 5:2. How much white flour is used in making a batch of bread containing at least 35 kg of flour?

2. Dimes minted before 1965 contained copper and silver in the ratio 1:9. At least how much silver was in a sack of those coins, weighing no less than 100 kg?

3. The sum of two consecutive integers is less than 75. Find the pair of integers with the greatest sum.

4. The sum of two consecutive even integers is less than 500. Find the pair with the greatest sum.

5. Of all pairs of consecutive odd integers whose sum is greater than 80, find the pair whose sum is least.

**6.** Of all pairs of consecutive integers whose sum is no more than 100, find the pair whose sum is greatest.

**7.** Between them, Terry and Jane have 50 cassettes. If Jane has more than two thirds as many cassettes as Terry, at least how many cassettes does Jane have? At most how many does Terry have?

**8.** A bag contains 100 marbles, some red, the rest blue. If there are no more than $1\frac{1}{2}$ times as many red marbles as blue ones in the bag, at most how many red marbles are in the bag? At least how many blue ones are in the bag?

**9.** Two sides of a triangle have the same length. The third side is 20 cm longer than each of the other sides. The perimeter is no less than 95 cm. At least how long are the sides of the triangle?

**10.** There are 3 exams in a marking period. A student received grades of 74 and 83 on the first two exams. What grade must the student get on the last exam to obtain an average for the marking period of no less than 80?

**11.** Peter is 3 years older than Diane. Twenty years ago Peter was at least twice as old as Diane was. At most how old is Diane?

**12.** Cheryl's father is 7 times as old as Cheryl. Two years ago he was at most 9 times as old as Cheryl was. At least how old is Cheryl?

**B**  **13.** At 1 P.M. two trains, traveling toward each other, leave from towns that are 312 km apart. One train averages at most 82 km/h, and the other at most 74 km/h. What is the earliest possible time for them to meet?

**14.** If Marva were able to increase her average cycling speed by 3.5 km/h, she would be able to cover in 2 h a distance at least as great as that which now takes her 3 h. What is the best average speed she achieves at present?

**15.** A brine solution contains 90 kg of water and 6 kg of salt. At least how much salt must be added to obtain a solution that is no less than 10% salt?

**16.** At least how many grams of copper must be alloyed with 380 g of pure silver to produce an alloy that is no more than 89.1% pure silver?

**17.** A pair of consecutive integers has the property that 6 times the smaller is less than 5 times the greater. Find the greatest such integers.

**18.** The sum of four consecutive integers decreased by 18 is greater than twice the smallest of the four. What are the four smallest such integers?

**19.** The units digit of a certain two-digit number is 5 more than the tens digit. Thirty-six times the tens digit is greater than the number with the digits reversed. Find the least possible value of the original number.

**20.** If the digits of a certain two-digit number are reversed, the resulting number is 9 less than the original number. The sum of the digits is at most 7. Find the greatest possible value of the original number.

21. Mike walked at the rate of 5.2 km/h in a straight path from his campsite to a ranch. He returned immediately on horseback at the rate of 7.8 km/h. Upon his return, he found that he had been gone no more than 3.5 h. At most how far is it from his campsite to the ranch?

22. The length of a rectangle exceeds the width by 8 cm. If each dimension were 4 cm greater, the area would be no less than 128 cm² more. Find the least possible dimensions of the rectangle.

C 23. During the first week of their vacation trip, the Gomez family spent $200 more than three fifths of their vacation money and had more than $400 less than half of it left. If they started their trip with a whole number of dollars, what was the greatest amount of vacation money they could have had?

24. Two consecutive odd integers have the property that three times their product is at least 11 more than the sum of their squares. Find the greatest such negative integers.

25. Three consecutive integers have the property that the difference of the squares of the greatest and least integers exceeds the middle integer by more than 126. Find the smallest three consecutive integers having this property.

26. Verna decided to sell her collection of paperback books. To Fred, she sold 2 books, and one fifth of what was left. Later, to Joan she sold 6 books, and one fifth of what then remained. If she sold more books to Fred than to Joan, what was the least possible number of books in her original collection?

# Self-Test 1

***Vocabulary***   inequality (p. 450)
sides of an inequality (p. 450)
solutions of an inequality
   (p. 450)

solution set of an inequality
   (p. 450)
graph of an open sentence (p. 450)
equivalent inequalities (p. 454)

1. Translate the statement "−2 is between −5 and −1" into symbols.   **Obj. 10-1, p. 449**

2. Solve $4x + 7 \leq 15$ if the domain of $x$ is $\{-3, -2, -1, 0, 1, 2, 3\}$.

**Solve and graph.**

**3.** $r - 9 < -1$                       **4.** $5 - 3t \leq 20$                 **Obj. 10-2, p. 453**

**Solve.**

**5.** A purse contains 20 coins, some of which are dimes and the      **Obj. 10-3, p. 459**
rest nickels. Altogether, the coins are worth more than $1.40.
At least how many dimes are in the purse?

Check your answers with those at the back of the book.

# *Extra* / Intersection and Union of Sets

The diagrams below show how shading can be used to represent the relationships among the sets:

$$A = \{1, 2, 3, 4, 5\}$$
$$B = \{2, 4, 6\}$$
$$C = \{7, 8\}$$

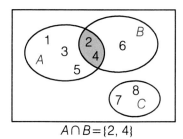

$A \cap B = \{2, 4\}$

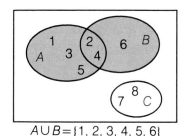

$A \cup B = \{1, 2, 3, 4, 5, 6\}$

    To find the *intersection* of $A$ and $B$, we shade the region consisting of those members and only those members *common to both* set $A$ and set $B$. From the diagram at the left above, you can see that the intersection of $\{1, 2, 3, 4, 5\}$ and $\{2, 4, 6\}$ is $\{2, 4\}$. This is written

$$\{1, 2, 3, 4, 5\} \cap \{2, 4, 6\} = \{2, 4\}.$$

    Notice in the diagrams that the regions $A$ and $C$ do not overlap. Two sets, such as $A$ and $C$, that have no members in common are called *disjoint sets*. Their intersection is the empty set: $A \cap C = \emptyset$.

    In the diagram at the right above, we shade the region consisting of the members that belong to *at least one* of the sets $A$ and $B$, in order to find the *union* of $A$ and $B$. This diagram shows that the union of $\{1, 2, 3, 4, 5\}$ and $\{2, 4, 6\}$ is $\{1, 2, 3, 4, 5, 6\}$. This is written

$$\{1, 2, 3, 4, 5\} \cup \{2, 4, 6\} = \{1, 2, 3, 4, 5, 6\}.$$

## Exercises

Refer to the diagram and list the members of each of the following sets.

**1.** $D \cap E$          **2.** $D \cup E$

**3.** $E \cup F$         **4.** $E \cap F$

**5.** $(D \cap E) \cap F$    **6.** $D \cup (E \cap F)$

**7.** $D \cap (E \cup F)$    **8.** $(D \cup E) \cup F$

**9.** $(D \cap F) \cup (E \cap F)$

**10.** Express $\{6, 7, 8, 9\}$ in terms of $D$, $E$, and $F$.

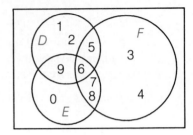

Specify the union and the intersection of the given sets. If the sets are disjoint, say so.

**11.** $\{-2, -3, -4\}$, $\{-3, -2, -1, 0\}$      **12.** $\{-1, 0, 1\}$, $\{0, 1, 2, 3\}$

**13.** $\{3, 5, 7\}$, $\{4, 6, 8\}$      **14.** $\{6, 8\}$, $\{5, 6, 7, 8, 9\}$

**15.** $\{3, 4, 6, 8, 12\}$, $\{2, 4, 6, 8, 10\}$      **16.** $\{-5, -4, -3\}$, $\{-2, -1, 0\}$

In Exercises 17–24, refer to the number lines shown and describe each set.

> $P = \{$the real numbers greater than $-1\}$
> $Q = \{$the real numbers between $-3$ and $3\}$
> $R = \{$the real numbers less than $2\}$

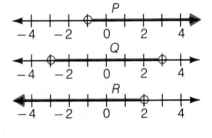

**17.** $P \cap R$     **18.** $P \cap Q$     **19.** $P \cup Q$

**20.** $P \cup R$     **21.** $Q \cap R$     **22.** $Q \cup R$

**23.** $P \cap (Q \cap R)$      **24.** $P \cup (Q \cap R)$

For each of Exercises 25 and 26, make two copies of the diagram shown at the right. On your copies shade the regions representing the sets named.

**25.** $X \cap (Y \cup Z)$; $(X \cap Y) \cup (X \cap Z)$

**26.** $X \cup (Y \cap Z)$; $(X \cup Y) \cap (X \cup Z)$

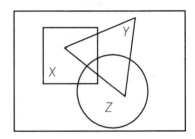

**27.** State a "distributive axiom" that appears to be true on the basis of Exercise 25.

**28.** State a "distributive axiom" that appears to be true on the basis of Exercise 26.

**29.** Copy the diagram at the right and write in the remaining members of these sets:

> $J = \{1, 3, 5, 7, 9\}$
> $K = \{-3, -1, 1, 3, 4\}$
> $L = \{1, 2, 3, 4, 5, 6, 7\}$
> $M = \{3, 4, 5, 6, 7\}$

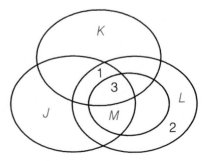

## Biographical Note / *Daniel Hale Williams*

Daniel Hale Williams (1856–1931) was a pioneer in heart surgery. After serving as a surgeon's apprentice for almost two years, Williams attended Chicago Medical College and received his diploma in 1883. Dr. Williams opened a medical practice in Chicago's South Side, where he often performed successful surgery in his office or in patients' homes. Realizing a need for a hospital that would admit and give quality care to all and provide training for nurses, Williams was instrumental in founding Provident Hospital, the first interracial hospital established in the United States. Because the hospital contained only twelve beds, only the seriously ill or those in need of surgery could be admitted. Still, the percentage of recoveries at the hospital was far higher than average. Williams' colleagues, impressed by his extraordinary techniques and skill, often observed him as he performed surgery.

Dr. Williams' most famous case occurred on July 9, 1893. A young man who had been stabbed in the chest was admitted to the hospital. Risking his career and reputation, Williams opened the chest cavity, something no one had done before, cleansed the wound, rejoined an artery, and stitched the membrane surrounding the heart. The successful operation saved the life of the patient and won Williams the praise of the medical world. The following year he was appointed chief surgeon of Freedmen's Hospital in Washington, D.C. Williams completely reorganized and modernized the hospital, adding departments in bacteriology and pathology and instituting training programs for nurses and interns. In addition to the many honors he received, he was elected vice president of the National Medical Association, which he had actively helped to organize.

## *Challenge*

What is wrong with the following "proof" that $0 > 3$?

$$a > 3$$
$$3a > 3(3)$$
$$3a - a^2 > 9 - a^2$$
$$a(3 - a) > (3 - a)(3 + a)$$
$$a > 3 + a$$
$$\therefore 0 > 3$$

# Combining Open Sentences

## 10-4 Solving Combined Inequalities

**Objective**   To find the solution sets of combined inequalities.

Each of the four sentences below involves one or two inequalities.

| **Sentence** | **Graph** |
|---|---|
| (a) $-3 < x$ |  |
| (b) $x < 2$ | |
| (c) $-3 < x$  and  $x < 2$ | |
| (d) $-3 < x$  or  $x < 2$ | |

The sentence in (c) is formed by joining the sentences in (a) and (b) by the word and. Such a sentence is called a **conjunction.** To **solve a conjunction** of two open sentences in a given variable, you find the values of the variable for which *both* sentences are true. Note that the conjunction in (c) can be written in the compact form

$$-3 < x < 2.$$

The graph consists of the points that belong to *both* the graph of $-3 < x$ and the graph of $x < 2$.

In (d) above, the inequalities in (a) and (b) have been joined by the word or. A sentence formed by joining two sentences by the word *or* is called a **disjunction.** To **solve a disjunction** of two open sentences, you find the values of the variable for which *at least one* of the sentences is true (that is, one or the other or both are true). Notice that *every* real number is a solution of the disjunction in (d).

Recall (page 449) that the disjunction

$$y > 2 \quad \text{or} \quad y = 2$$

is usually written "$y \geq 2$." Similarly, when you write "$y \leq 2$," you mean

$$y < 2 \quad \text{or} \quad y = 2.$$

**Example 1**   What is the solution set of the
**a.** conjunction:   $t < 5$   and   $t \geq 5$?
**b.** disjunction:   $t < 5$   or   $t \geq 5$?

*Solution*   **a.** The empty set.

**b.** The set of all real numbers.   *Answer*

To solve conjunctions and disjunctions of inequalities, you use the transformations listed on page 454.

*Example 2*   Find the solution set of $-4 \le x - 2 < 3$, and draw its graph.

*Solution*   To solve the inequality $-4 \le x - 2 < 3$, you solve the conjunction

$$
\begin{array}{ccc}
-4 \le x - 2 & \text{and} & x - 2 < 3 \\
-4 + 2 \le x - 2 + 2 & \big| & x - 2 + 2 < 3 + 2 \\
-2 \le x & \text{and} & x < 5
\end{array}
$$

$$-2 \le x < 5$$

∴ the solution set is $\{-2$, and the real numbers between $-2$ and $5\}$.
The graph is:

Below is a more compact way of transforming the conjunction in Example 2:

$$
\begin{array}{c}
-4 \le x - 2 < 3 \\
-4 + 2 \le x - 2 + 2 < 3 + 2 \\
-2 \le x < 5
\end{array}
$$

*Example 3*   Solve the following disjunction and draw its graph:

$$4w - 1 < 3 \quad \text{or} \quad 3w \ge w + 8$$

*Solution*

$$
\begin{array}{ccc}
4w - 1 < 3 & \text{or} & 3w \ge w + 8 \\
4w - 1 + 1 < 3 + 1 & & 3w - w \ge w - w + 8 \\
4w < 4 & & 2w \ge 8 \\
\dfrac{4w}{4} < \dfrac{4}{4} & & \dfrac{2w}{2} \ge \dfrac{8}{2} \\
w < 1 & \text{or} & w \ge 4
\end{array}
$$

∴ the solution set is $\{4$, and the real numbers greater than 4 or less than $1\}$.
The graph is:

## Oral Exercises

**In Exercises 1–7, match each graph with one of the open sentences in a–g.**

1.

2.

3.

4.

5.

6.

7.

**a.** $t > 3$

**b.** $t \geq 3$ or $t < -3$

**c.** $-3 < t < 3$

**d.** $t \leq 3$

**e.** $t \leq -3$ or $t > 3$

**f.** $t < 3$

**g.** $-3 \leq t \leq 3$

**In Exercises 8–12, match each open sentence with an equivalent inequality in a–e.**

**8.** $x < 4$ and $x > -1$       **a.** $x \geq 4$

**9.** $x = 4$ or $x < 4$       **b.** $-1 < x \leq 4$

**10.** $x \leq 4$ and $x > -1$       **c.** $x \leq 4$

**11.** $x = 4$ or $x > 4$       **d.** $-1 < x \leq 4$

**12.** $x \leq 4$ and $x \geq -1$       **e.** $-1 < x < 4$

## Written Exercises

**Draw the graph of each open sentence.**

**A**   **1.** $-4 < t \leq 1$                **2.** $r > 3$ or $r \leq -2$

   **3.** $2 \leq n \leq 6$                **4.** $s < -2$ or $s \geq 0$

**Solve each open sentence and graph each solution set that is not empty.**

   **5.** $-1 < a + 2 < 4$              **6.** $-2 < y - 2 \leq 1$

   **7.** $-5 < -5 + z \leq 3$          **8.** $-6 \leq 3 + r < 4$

**9.** $-3 \le 2a + 1 < 7$

**10.** $-2 < 2b - 1 \le 5$

**11.** $-7 \le 3m - 1 < 2$

**12.** $-8 < 3n + 7 \le 1$

**13.** $y - 1 < -3$ or $y - 1 \ge 3$

**14.** $h + 5 \le -2$ or $h + 5 \ge 2$

**15.** $3x + 2 \le -4$ or $3x + 2 \ge 4$

**16.** $1 + 2y < -9$ or $1 + 2y > 9$

**17.** $2n - 1 \le -5$ or $5 \le 2n - 1$

**18.** $2d - 5 < -7$ or $7 < 2d - 5$

**B 19.** $-5 \le -x \le 3$

**20.** $-8 \le -2x \le 6$

**21.** $-3 \le 1 - t < 4$

**22.** $-2 < 3 - y \le 1$

**23.** $-9 < 1 - 2x \le 7$

**24.** $-7 < -1 - 3x \le 8$

**25.** $-3m < 12$ and $8 + 2m < 0$

**26.** $-6r < 18$ or $12 + 4r > 0$

**27.** $-8 \le -3 - s < -1$

**28.** $-9 < -10 - p \le -4$

**29.** $7 - v > 8$ or $v - 7 > 8$

**30.** $t - 5 \ge 2$ or $5 - t \ge 2$

**31.** $9 - 2p > 11$ or $9 - 2p < -1$

**32.** $7 - 3g \ge 10$ or $-2 \ge 7 - 3g$

**33.** $2d - 7 \ge -10$ and $2d - 7 \le d - 5$

**34.** $9 - y \le 3 - 2y$ and $-1 - 2y \ge -5$

**C 35.** $8 - c < 2c + 5 \le 9 + c$

**36.** $5 - d \le 3 - 2d$ or $d + 2 > 3d - 2$

**37.** $3(1 - w) \ge 6$ or $3w - 7 \le 2w - 1$

**38.** $1 - 4m \le 3 - 5m \le m - 3$

**39.** Find all sets of four consecutive even integers whose sum is between $-6$ and 14.

**40.** Aaron is three years older than Ben and Ben is three years older than Chris. The sum of their ages in years is between 12 and 21. How old are Aaron, Ben, and Chris if the product of their ages is 80?

**41.** Find an example of real values of $a$, $b$, $c$, and $d$ for which the following statement is **(a)** true; **(b)** false.

$$\text{If } a > b \text{ and } c > d, \text{ then } ac > bd.$$

**42.** Find a value of $k$ so that the solution set of

$$k - 5 \le x - 6 \le 3$$

will be the same as the solution set of

$$3x - 7 \le 2(1 + x) \quad \text{and} \quad 5x - 7 \ge 23.$$

## Computer Exercises

*For students with some programming experience*

The sum of two numbers must be no more than 10, but their product must be at least 9. Write a BASIC program to list all the ordered pairs $(x, y)$ that satisfy these requirements if it is known that $x$ and $y$ are both positive integers.

# 10-5 Absolute Value in Open Sentences

**Objective**   To solve equations and inequalities involving absolute value.

The figure below suggests a useful way to think about absolute value (page 35).

On a number line, the distance between the graphs of the numbers $a$ and $b$ is the absolute value of the difference of $a$ and $b$. For simplicity, we usually speak of "the distance between $a$ and $b$" instead of "the distance between the graphs of $a$ and $b$."

**Example 1**   Find the distance between:

  **a.** 5 and 11      **b.** $-7$ and 2      **c.** $-8$ and $-13$

**Solution**      **a.** $|5 - 11| = |-6| = 6$
   **b.** $|-7 - 2| = |-9| = 9$
   **c.** $|-8 - (-13)| = |-8 + 13| = |5| = 5$

**Example 2**   Solve $|y - 2| = 3$.

**Solution 1**   To satisfy the equation $|y - 2| = 3$, $y$ must be a number whose distance from $2$ is $3$. Thus, to arrive at $y$, start at $2$ and move $3$ units in either direction on the number line.

You arrive at 5 and $-1$ as the values of $y$.

$\therefore$ the solution set is $\{-1, 5\}$.   **Answer**

**Solution 2**   Another way to solve Example 2 is to note that

$$|y - 2| = 3$$

is equivalent to the disjunction

$$y - 2 = -3 \quad \text{or} \quad y - 2 = 3$$
$$y = -1 \quad \text{or} \quad y = 5$$

$\therefore$ the solution set is $\{-1, 5\}$.   **Answer**

***Example 3*** Solve and graph $|x + 1| \leq 4$.

***Solution 1*** Because $x + 1 = x - (-1)$, $|x + 1| \leq 4$ is equivalent to

$$|x - (-1)| \leq 4.$$

Hence, the distance between $x$ and $-1$ must be no more than 4.

So, starting at $-1$, the numbers up to and including 3 will satisfy the given inequality, along with the numbers down to and including $-5$. Thus, the given inequality is equivalent to

$$-5 \leq x \leq 3.$$

∴ the solution set is $\{-5, 3,$ and the real numbers between $-5$ and $3\}$. The graph is shown above. ***Answer***

***Solution 2*** Use the fact that $|x + 1| \leq 4$ is equivalent to the conjunction:

$$-4 \leq x + 1 \leq 4$$
$$-4 - 1 \leq x + 1 - 1 \leq 4 - 1$$
$$-5 \leq x \leq 3$$

∴ the solution set and graph are as given above. ***Answer***

***Example 4*** Solve and graph $|t - 3| > 2$.

***Solution 1*** The distance between $t$ and 3 must be greater than 2, as shown in the graph below.

Therefore, the given inequality is equivalent to the disjunction

$$t < 1 \quad \text{or} \quad t > 5.$$

∴ the solution set is {the real numbers less than 1 or greater than 5}, and the graph is shown above. ***Answer***

(*Solution 2 is on the next page.*)

***Solution 2*** $|t - 3| > 2$ is equivalent to the disjunction:

$$t - 3 < -2 \quad \text{or} \quad t - 3 > 2$$
$$t < 1 \quad \text{or} \quad t > 5$$

∴ the solution set and graph are as in Solution 1. ***Answer***

## *Oral Exercises*

**In Exercises 1–6, express the distance between the given numbers in terms of absolute value. Then, find the distance.**

**1.** 8 and 3          **2.** 4 and 9          **3.** 6 and $-2$

**4.** $-1$ and 10        **5.** $-2$ and $-3$       **6.** $-7$ and $-5$

**In Exercises 7–18:**
**a. Translate the sentence into a statement involving the distance between numbers.**
**b. State a conjunction or disjunction equivalent to the given sentence.**

***Example 1*** $|r + 2| > 7$

***Solution***    **a.** The distance between $r$ and $-2$ is greater than 7.
           **b.** $r + 2 > 7$   or   $r + 2 < -7$

**7.** $|x - 1| = 4$        **8.** $|y - 6| = 8$        **9.** $|r| = 5$

**10.** $|p| < 8$           **11.** $|n - 4| \le 3$       **12.** $|n - 4| > 3$

**13.** $|v + 5| \ge 2$       **14.** $|v + 5| \le 2$       **15.** $4 \le |1 - s|$

**16.** $5 \ge |3 - q|$       **17.** $1 \ge |2 + m|$       **18.** $6 \le |3 + w|$

**In Exercises 19–24, match each open sentence with its graph in a–f.**

**19.** $|x| \le 2$

**20.** $|x| \ge 2$

**21.** $|x - 3| = 2$

**22.** $|x + 2| > 2$

**23.** $|x - 1| = 2$

**24.** $|3 - x| < 2$

a.
b.
c.
d.
e.
f.

Use absolute value to state an inequality equivalent to each conjunction or disjunction.

**Example 2** $-8 \leq k - 10 \leq 8$

**Solution** $|k - 10| \leq 8$

25. $-3 < z + 7 < 3$
27. $a + 10 > 4$  or  $a + 10 < -4$
29. $-2 \leq -3 - p \leq 2$

26. $-1 \leq 9 - h \leq 1$
28. $7 + b \geq 5$  or  $7 + b \leq -5$
30. $-1 + q \leq -9$  or  $-1 + q \geq 9$

## Written Exercises

Write an equation or an inequality involving absolute value to describe each graph. Use $x$ as the variable.

A    1.

2.

3.

4.

5.

6.

Solve each open sentence and draw its graph.

7. $|m - 8| = 1$
10. $|7 - y| = 4$
13. $|y + 6| > 2$
16. $|4 - v| \geq 5$

8. $|k + 9| = 4$
11. $|r| < 2.5$
14. $|t + 3| < 4$
17. $|-2 - a| \geq 4$

9. $|6 + x| = 7$
12. $|s| \geq 1.5$
15. $|6 - p| \leq 4$
18. $|-1 - b| \leq 6$

B   19. $3|s| - 2 \geq 7$
21. $|3 - z| + 8 > 12$
23. $1 - 2|r| \geq -7$
25. $7 - |2 - p| \leq 5$

27. $2(3|a| - 1) \leq 10$

20. $4|p| - 1 < 15$
22. $|2 - q| - 3 < 1$
24. $4 - 3|y| < 1$
26. $8 - |1 - x| > 7$

28. $\dfrac{8 - 3|b|}{2} \geq 1$

C   29. $|x - 1| = \dfrac{x}{2}$

31. $|y - 3| = y - 3$
33. $|n + 5| < n + 5$

30. $|y + 1| = \dfrac{y}{3}$

32. $|t - 3| > t - 3$
34. $|n + 5| \geq n + 5$

# 10-6 Absolute Values of Products in Open Sentences

**Objective**   To extend your skill in solving open sentences that involve absolute value.

**Example 1**   Solve $|2p - 5| = 7$.

$|2p - 5| = 7$ is equivalent to the disjunction:

$$2p - 5 = -7 \qquad \text{or} \qquad 2p - 5 = 7$$
$$2p - 5 + 5 = -7 + 5 \qquad\quad 2p - 5 + 5 = 7 + 5$$
$$2p = -2 \qquad\qquad\qquad 2p = 12$$
$$\frac{2p}{2} = \frac{-2}{2} \qquad\qquad\qquad \frac{2p}{2} = \frac{12}{2}$$
$$p = -1 \qquad \text{or} \qquad p = 6$$

$\therefore$ the solution set is $\{-1, 6\}$.   **Answer**

To use a number line to solve the open sentence in Example 1, recall (page 69) that the absolute value of a product of numbers equals the product of the absolute values of the numbers. For example:

1. $|-8 \times 5| = |-40| = 40 = 8 \times 5 = |-8| \times |5|$
2. $|(-3)(-2)| = |6| = 3 \times 2 = |-3| \times |-2|$

Using this property of absolute value, you see that

$$|2p - 5| = \left|2\left(p - \frac{5}{2}\right)\right| = 2\left|p - \frac{5}{2}\right|.$$

Therefore, the open sentence in Example 1,

$$|2p - 5| = 7,$$

is equivalent to

$$2\left|p - \frac{5}{2}\right| = 7.$$

$$\therefore \left|p - \frac{5}{2}\right| = \frac{7}{2}$$

Since the distance between $p$ and $\frac{5}{2}$ on the number line must be $\frac{7}{2}$, the solutions of $|p - \frac{5}{2}| = \frac{7}{2}$ and, therefore, of $|2p - 5| = 7$ are $-1$ and $6$, as shown on the diagram above.

***Example 2*** Solve and graph $|12 - 3k| \geq 6$.

***Solution 1*** Since $|12 - 3k| = |(-3)(k - 4)| = 3|k - 4|$,

$$|12 - 3k| \geq 6$$

is equivalent to

$$3|k - 4| \geq 6.$$
$$\therefore |k - 4| \geq 2$$

The distance between $k$ and 4 must be 2 or more, as pictured above. Therefore, the given inequality is equivalent to the disjunction

$$k \leq 2 \quad \text{or} \quad k \geq 6.$$

$\therefore$ the solution set is {2, 6, and the real numbers less than 2 or greater than 6}. The graph is shown above. ***Answer***

***Solution 2*** Because $|12 - 3k| = |3k - 12|$, the given inequality is equivalent to

$$|3k - 12| \geq 6.$$

This is a compact form of the disjunction:

$$
\begin{array}{ccc}
3k - 12 \leq -6 & \text{or} & 3k - 12 \geq 6 \\
3k \leq 6 & & 3k \geq 18 \\
k \leq 2 & \text{or} & k \geq 6
\end{array}
$$

$\therefore$ the solution set and graph are as given in Solution 1. ***Answer***

## Written Exercises

**Solve each open sentence and draw its graph.**

**A**

**1.** $|2x| = 10$

**2.** $|5y| = 35$

**3.** $\left|\dfrac{y}{3}\right| \geq 1$

**4.** $\left|\dfrac{t}{3}\right| \leq 2$

**5.** $|2a - 1| = 7$

**6.** $|3b - 2| = 7$

**7.** $|4d - 9| \leq 3$

**8.** $|5h - 2| \geq 8$

**9.** $|4 + 5n| \leq 16$

**10.** $|1 + 8c| > 23$

**11.** $\left|\dfrac{y}{3} - 2\right| \geq 3$

**12.** $\left|\dfrac{x}{2} - 3\right| \leq 2$

*Inequalities* **477**

**Solve each open sentence and draw its graph.**

**B** **13.** $|1 - (2 - 3x)| < 20$        **14.** $|6 - (2y - 3)| \le 9$

**15.** $5 + 3|4g + 1| = 14$        **16.** $2|3k - 7| + 11 = 19$

**17.** $8 - 5|3 - 2t| > 23$        **18.** $21 - 4|2 - 5w| > 13$

**Classify each of the following sentences as true for all real values of the variable or false for some real value. If you classify a sentence as false, give at least one value of the variable for which it is false.**

**C** **19.** $|a^2| = a^2$        **20.** $|-a^2| = a^2$

**21.** $\left|\dfrac{a}{2}\right| = \dfrac{a}{2}$        **22.** $|a - 2| < |a + 2|$

**23.** $|a + 1| \le |a| + 1$        **24.** $|a| - 1 \le |a - 1|$

**25.** During January in Colton the absolute value of the temperature in degrees Celsius never exceeded 10°. In degrees Fahrenheit, what were the greatest and least possible temperatures in Colton that month? (*Hint:* $C = \frac{5}{9}(F - 32)$, where $C$ and $F$ are the temperatures in degrees Celsius and Fahrenheit, respectively.)

# Self-Test 2

***Vocabulary***        conjunction (p. 468)        disjunction (p. 468)
                        solve a conjunction (p. 468)        solve a disjunction (p. 468)

**Solve each open sentence and graph its solution set.**

**1.** $3x - 1 > 8$   or   $2 - x > 0$        **2.** $-2 \le y + 4 < 5$        **Obj. 10-4, p. 468**

**3.** $3m + 1 \le -5$   or   $3m - 1 \ge 5$        **4.** $-5 \le 3x + 1 < 4$

**5.** $|x - 4| = 4$        **6.** $|3 - n| \ge 2$        **Obj. 10-5, p. 472**

**7.** $|1 - y| = 1$        **8.** $|x + 1| < 2$

**9.** $|4s - 13| \le 7$        **10.** $|2p - 4| = 10$        **Obj. 10-6, p. 476**

**11.** $|2m - 1| = 5$        **12.** $|1 - 2a| < 3$

Check your answers with those at the back of the book.

## Computer Key-In

The following program will print the graph of an open sentence in one variable. Notice that the open sentence is written into the program in line 80.

```
10   PRINT "TO GRAPH AN OPEN SENTENCE,"
20   PRINT "INPUT EXTENT OF GRAPH--"
30   PRINT "M, N, INTEGERS, M<N";
40   INPUT M,N
50   IF M >= N THEN 20
60   REM---SENTENCE INSIDE LOOP
70   FOR X=M TO N
80   IF (5*X-1)<(3+3*X) THEN 110
90   PRINT "-";
100   GOTO 120
110   PRINT "*";
120   NEXT X
130   PRINT "X"
140   REM---PRINT "0"
150   FOR I=M TO N
160   IF I <> 0 THEN 190
170   PRINT "0"
180   GOTO 210
190   PRINT " ";      ⎡ Single space between
200   NEXT I          ⎣ quotation marks
210   END
```

(If possible, save this program for use in later computer sections.)

### Exercises

Use $M = -10$ and $N = 10$.
   **1.** RUN the program as it is written.
   **2.** Change line 80 to include the inequality
   $2(x - 8) + 9 \geq 3(4 - x) - 4$ and RUN the program again.

Change line 80 and RUN the program for each of the following.

   **3. a.** $-3 \leq x$    **b.** $x < 2$    **c.** $-3 \leq x$ and $x < 2$
   **4. a.** $-5 < x$    **b.** $x \leq 1$    **c.** $-5 < x$ and $x \leq 1$
   **5.** $-3 \geq x$ or $x > 2$        **6.** $-5 > x$ or $x \geq 1$
   **7.** $|x - 3| > 2$            **8.** $|x + 1| \leq 4$
   **9.** $|2x - 5| = 7$          **10.** $|12 - 3x| \geq 6$

*Note:* The program above can be used to do Exercises 1–38 on pages 470–471, Exercises 7–34 on page 475, and Exercises 1–18 on pages 477–478.

# Inequalities in Two Variables

## 10-7 Graphing Linear Inequalities

**Objective**   To graph linear inequalities in two variables.

The graph of the linear equation

$$y = x + 2$$

separates the coordinate plane into three sets of points:

the points *on* the line,
the points *above* the line,
the points *below* the line.

The regions above and below the line are called **open half-planes,** and the line is the **boundary** of each half-plane.

If you start at any point on the line, say $P(2, 4)$, and move upward from $P$, the $y$-coordinate increases. If you move downward from $P$, the $y$-coordinate decreases.

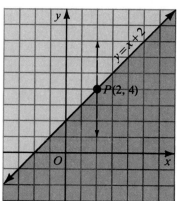

Thus, the upper open half-plane is the graph of the inequality

$$y > x + 2$$

and the lower open half-plane is the graph of the inequality

$$y < x + 2.$$

The graphs of

$$y > x + 2, \quad y = x + 2, \quad \text{and} \quad y < x + 2$$

completely cover the coordinate plane. The upper half-plane and the boundary line together form the graph of

$$y \geq x + 2.$$

The lower half-plane and the boundary line together form the graph of

$$y \leq x + 2.$$

The graph of an open half-plane and its boundary is called a **closed half-plane.**

The graphs of inequalities are shown by shading. If the boundary line is part of a graph, it is drawn as a solid line. If the boundary line is *not* part of the graph, it is drawn as a dashed line. This is shown by the figures at the top of the following page.

(a) $y > x + 2$

(b) $y \geq x + 2$

(c) $y < x + 2$

(d) $y \leq x + 2$

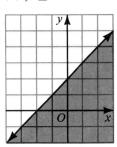

In general, you follow these steps.

To graph a linear inequality in the variables $x$ and $y$, when the coefficient of $y$ is not zero:

1. Transform the given inequality into an equivalent inequality that has $y$ alone as one side.

2. Graph the equation of the boundary. Use a solid line if the symbol $\geq$ or $\leq$ is used; use a dashed line if $>$ or $<$ is used.

3. Shade the appropriate region.

**Example 1** Graph $2x - 3y \geq -6$.

**Solution** 1. Transform the inequality:

$$2x - 3y \geq -6$$
$$-3y \geq -6 - 2x$$
$$y \leq 2 + \frac{2}{3}x$$

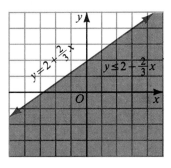

2. Draw the boundary line $y = 2 + \frac{2}{3}x$ as a *solid* line, since the symbol $\leq$ includes the equals sign.

3. Shade the region *below* the line since the symbol $\leq$ includes the less than sign.

*Check:* Choose a point of the graph not on the boundary, say $(0, 0)$. See whether its coordinates satisfy the given inequality:

$$2x - 3y \geq -6$$
$$2(0) - 3(0) \overset{?}{\geq} -6$$
$$0 \geq -6 \;\checkmark$$

Thus, $(0, 0)$ is in the solution set, and the correct region has been shaded.

**Example 2** Graph $y > 1$.

**Solution**     Graph $y = 1$ as a dashed horizontal
line. Shade the open half-plane above
the line, since $y > 1$.

The next example shows how to graph a linear
inequality in $x$ and $y$ when the coefficient of $y$ is 0.

**Example 3** Graph $x < -3$.

**Solution**     Show the graph of $x = -3$ as a
dashed vertical line. The coordinates of
any point to the left of that vertical
line satisfy $x < -3$. Therefore, the
graph of $x < -3$ is the open half-
plane to the left of the graph of
$x = -3$.

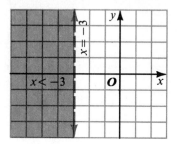

## Oral Exercises

**State whether the given points belong to the graph of the given inequality.**

**1.** $x \geq 4$; $(4, 2)$, $(-4, 5)$, $(0, 0)$
**2.** $y < -3$; $(2, -3)$, $(4, -4)$, $(0, 0)$
**3.** $y < x + 3$; $(2, 4)$, $(-2, 1)$, $(0, 0)$
**4.** $y \leq 2x - 1$; $(2, 0)$, $(1, 1)$, $(0, 0)$
**5.** $x + 2y < 0$; $(-3, 1)$, $(3, -1)$, $(0, 0)$
**6.** $x - 3y \geq -2$; $(1, -1)$, $(-1, 1)$, $(0, 0)$

**Transform each inequality into an equivalent inequality having $y$ alone as
one side. Then state the equation of the boundary of the graph.**

**7.** $x + y < 3$
**8.** $-x + y > 1$
**9.** $3x + y \geq 9$
**10.** $2x + y \leq -2$
**11.** $3x + 2y > 0$
**12.** $15x + 5y < 0$
**13.** $6y < x$
**14.** $2x > -3y$
**15.** $x - y \geq 1$
**16.** $14x - 7y \leq 0$
**17.** $x - 8y > 24$
**18.** $6 > x - y$

## Written Exercises

**Graph each inequality.**

**A**  **1.** $y \geq 3$
**2.** $y > 3$
**3.** $x < 2$
**4.** $x \leq 2$
**5.** $x > 0$
**6.** $y < 0$
**7.** $y \geq -1$
**8.** $x \leq -4$
**9.** $y < x + 2$
**10.** $y > -x + 1$
**11.** $y \leq 3 - 2x$
**12.** $y \geq 1 - 3x$

Transform each inequality into an equivalent inequality with $y$ as one side.
Then graph the inequality.

**13.** $x + y < 2$

**14.** $x - y \geq 3$

**15.** $x - 2y \leq -7$

**16.** $2x + y > -4$

**17.** $3x - y > 6$

**18.** $y - 2x \leq -3$

**19.** $3x - 2y \geq 10$

**20.** $3y - 2x < 0$

**21.** $7x + 4y \leq x - 8$

**22.** $3y - 5 > 2x - 6$

**23.** $3(x - y) \geq 4x + 7$

**24.** $5y - 8 < 2(x + 2y)$

In each of Exercises 25–33, write an inequality whose graph is shown.

**B**  **25.**

**26.**

**27.**

**28.**

**29.**

**30.**

**31.**

**32.**

**33.**

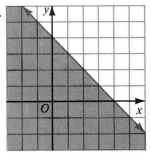

Graph each of the following in a coordinate plane.

**C**  **34.** $|y| > 2$

**35.** $|y| < 2$

**36.** $y = |x|$

**37.** $y = -|x|$

**38.** $y > |x|$

**39.** $y \leq |x|$

# 10-8 Systems of Linear Inequalities

**Objective**   To graph the solution set of a system of two linear inequalities in two variables.

You can use graphs to find the solution set of a system of linear inequalities.

**Example**   Graph the solution set of the system:

$$y - x - 3 \le 0$$
$$2x + 3y \ge -6$$

**Solution**   1. Transform each inequality into an equivalent one with $y$ as one side.

$$y - x - 3 \le 0 \quad \longrightarrow \quad y \le x + 3$$
$$2x + 3y \ge -6 \quad \longrightarrow \quad y \ge -\frac{2}{3}x - 2$$

2. Draw the graph of $y = x - 3$, the boundary for the first inequality. Use a solid line and shade the region below this line to show the graph of $y \le x - 3$ (red shading).

3. In the same coordinate system, draw the graph of $y = -\frac{2}{3}x - 2$, the boundary for the second inequality. Use a solid line, and shade the region above this line to show the graph of $y \ge -\frac{2}{3}x - 2$ (blue shading).

4. The doubly shaded region resulting from Steps 2 and 3 is the graph of the solution set of the given system.

# Oral Exercises

Give a system of two linear inequalities whose solution set is shown by the shaded region in each graph.

**1.**

**2.**

**3.**
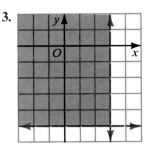

State whether or not each ordered pair is a solution of the system: $y \geq 6$ and $x < 4$.

**4.** $(0, 0)$     **5.** $(4, 6)$     **6.** $(3, 6)$     **7.** $(-2, 6)$     **8.** $(-2, -6)$

**9.** $(6, 4)$     **10.** $(5, 9)$     **11.** $(4, 3)$     **12.** $(0, 8)$     **13.** $(0, 6)$

State whether each point belongs to the graph of the solution set of the system: $y \leq 3$ and $x - y \leq 5$.

**14.** $(0, -5)$     **15.** $(9, 3)$     **16.** $(10, 3)$     **17.** $(-10, 3)$     **18.** $(-10, 4)$

**19.** $(0, 0)$     **20.** $(8, 3)$     **21.** $(0, -6)$     **22.** $(-4, -6)$     **23.** $(-9, 2)$

# Written Exercises

Graph each pair of inequalities and indicate the solution set of the system with crosshatching or shading.

**A**

**1.** $y > 0$
$x \geq 0$

**2.** $y \leq 5$
$x \geq 1$

**3.** $y > 2$
$x < -3$

**4.** $y < -4$
$x > 4$

**5.** $y < x$
$x > 2$

**6.** $y > 3x$
$x < 1$

**7.** $x \leq 4$
$y > 6 - x$

**8.** $x > -2$
$y \leq 2x + 7$

**9.** $y \leq x + 1$
$y \geq 1 - x$

**10.** $y < 4x + 4$
$y > -4x + 4$

**11.** $y > 3x - 2$
$y < 3x + 6$

**12.** $y < 5x + 5$
$y > 5 - 5x$

**B**

**13.** $x + y \leq 7$
$x - y \geq 3$

**14.** $x + y \geq 5$
$x - 2y > 8$

**15.** $3x - y > -1$
$x - y > -5$

**16.** $x - y < 7$
$x - 3y > 15$

**17.** $3x - 4y < -12$
$3x + 4y > 0$

**18.** $2x - 5y > 0$
$x - 4y \leq -6$

**Write a system of linear inequalities whose solution set is shown by the shaded region in each graph.**

**19.**

**20.**

**21.**

**22.**

*Example*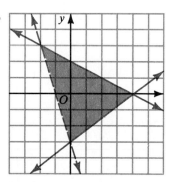

*Solution*

$$y \geq \frac{3}{4}x - 3$$

$$y > -3x - 3$$

$$y \leq -\frac{1}{2}x + 2$$

**C 23.**

**24.**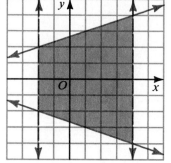

**Graph each system of inequalities. Determine exactly the *corner points* of the graph of the solution set of the system, that is, the points where boundary lines intersect.**

**25.** $y \geq x$
$\quad\;\; y \geq -x$
$\quad\;\; y < 2$

**26.** $y \geq 2x$
$\quad\;\; 3y < x$
$\quad\;\; x \geq -3$

**27.** $2x - y \geq 4$
$\quad\;\;\; x \leq -1$
$\quad\;\;\; |y| \leq 2$

**28.** $x + 3y \leq 6$
$\quad\;\;\; y \geq -1$
$\quad\;\;\; |x| \leq 3$

---

# Self-Test 3

***Vocabulary***  open half-plane (p. 480)       closed half-plane (p. 480)
boundary (p. 480)

**Graph each inequality in a coordinate plane.**

**1.** $x > 5$                         **2.** $x + 2y \leq 6$                         Obj. 10-7, p. 480

**3.** Graph the solution set of the system:                         Obj. 10-8, p. 484

$$x - y > 5$$
$$3x + y \geq -1$$

Check your answers with those at the back of the book.

---

## Calculator Key-In

You can compare two fractions with the aid of a calculator. First change each fraction to a decimal by dividing numerator by denominator. Then compare the decimals.

True or false?

**1.** $\dfrac{5}{8} > \dfrac{9}{20} > \dfrac{6}{13}$

**2.** $\dfrac{17}{23} < \dfrac{18}{24} < \dfrac{19}{25}$

**3.** $\dfrac{90}{101} > \dfrac{91}{102} > \dfrac{92}{103}$

---

## *Extra* / Linear Programming

Decisions in business and industry often aim at making certain quantities, such as profit, as large as possible, or other quantities, such as cost, as small as possible. Of course, a decision to maximize or to minimize a given quantity is usually subject to some conditions (*constraints*). When the quantity can be represented by a linear equation and the constraints can be represented by a system of linear inequalities, the decision problem can be solved by using techniques developed in a branch of mathematics called *linear programming*.

## Example

A machine shop makes two automotive parts, I and II, each requiring the use of three machines, A, B, and C. Each Part I requires 4 minutes on machine A, 4 minutes on machine B, and 5 minutes on machine C. Each Part II requires 5 minutes on machine A, 1 minute on machine B, and 6 minutes on machine C. The shop makes a profit of $8 on each Part I and $5 on each Part II. However, the number of units of Part II produced must not be less than half the number of Part I. Also, each day, the shop has available only 120 minutes of machine A, 72 minutes of machine B, and 180 minutes of machine C for the production of Parts I and II. What should the daily production of these parts be to maximize the shop's profit?

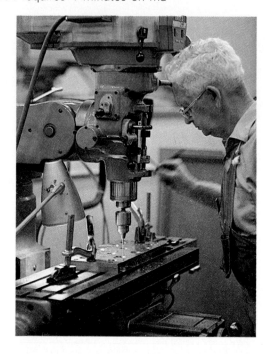

## Solution

Let $x$ = number of units of Part I

$y$ = number of units of Part II

$P$ = total profit on Parts I and II

The data in the problem are summarized in the following chart and the inequalities below.

| Part | Number | Minutes on Machine | | | Profit per Unit |
|---|---|---|---|---|---|
| | | A | B | C | |
| I | $x$ | 4 | 4 | 5 | $8 |
| II | $y$ | 5 | 1 | 6 | $5 |
| Available Time | | 120 | 72 | 180 | |

$4x + 5y \leq 120$    (Total time on machine A must not exceed 120 min)

$4x + y \leq 72$    (Total time on machine B must not exceed 72 min)

$5x + 6y \leq 180$    (Total time on machine C must not exceed 180 min)

$y \geq \frac{1}{2}x$    (Number of units of Part II must not be less than half the number of Part I)

$\left.\begin{array}{l} x \geq 0 \\ y \geq 0 \end{array}\right\}$    (A negative number of parts cannot be produced.)

We want to find values of $x$ and $y$ that maximize $P$ subject to these inequalities (constraints) where

$$P = 8x + 5y.$$

**Step 1**
Graph the solution set of this system of inequalities. The solution set is shaded and is called the *feasible region*.

**Step 2**
Find the points of the feasible region where the boundary lines intersect. These points are called *corner points*. The corner points are $(0, 0)$, $(16, 8)$, $(15, 12)$, and $(0, 24)$.

A remarkable fact, proved in more advanced mathematics courses, is that if a maximum or minimum value of a *linear expression ax + by* exists, it must occur at a corner point of the feasible region. We use this fact in the next step.

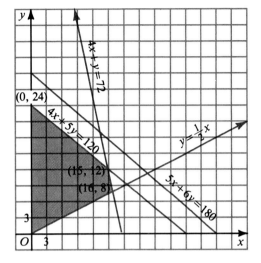

**Step 3**
Evaluate $P = 8x + 5y$ at each corner point.

$(0, 0)$:     $P = 8(0) + 5(0) = 0$
$(16, 8)$:    $P = 8(16) + 5(8) = 168$
$(15, 12)$: $P = 8(15) + 5(12) = 180$
$(0, 24)$:   $P = 8(0) + 5(24) = 120$

The maximum value of $P$ is \$180, which occurs at $(15, 12)$. Therefore, to maximize its profit, the machine shop should produce 15 units of Part I and 12 units of Part II each day.

## Exercises

**1. a.** Draw the graph of the solution set of the system of inequalities

$$x \geq 2y + 4$$
$$x + y \geq -2$$
$$4x + y \leq 4$$

   **b.** Find the corner points of the solution set.
   **c.** Find the maximum and minimum values of $4x + 7y$ subject to the inequalities in part (a).

**2.** Find $x$ and $y$ to maximize $R = x + 3y$ subject to the constraints $x \geq 2$, $y \geq 1$, $x + 2y \leq 8$, $x + y \leq 6$.

3. **a.** A farmer plants two crops, corn and soybeans. The expenses are $6 for each acre of corn planted and $12 for each acre of soybeans planted. Each acre of corn requires 12 bushels of storage, and each acre of soybeans requires 16 bushels of storage. The farmer has at most 3600 bushels of storage available and $2400 to spend on these expenses. Choose variables for the number of acres of corn and soybeans planted. Write four inequalities that express the conditions of the problem.

   **b.** Graph the solution set of the system of inequalities described in part (a). State the coordinates of the corner points for this feasible region.

   **c.** Suppose that the farmer earns a profit of $24 for each acre of corn and $48 for each acre of soybeans. Find two ways the farmer can satisfy the conditions while maximizing the profits. (Notice that a linear programming problem can have more than one solution.)

4. Each week the School Bus Service needs at least 650 L of diesel fuel, 324 L of gasoline, and 48 L of oil to keep the school buses in operation. Western Petroleum Company can deliver 130 L of diesel fuel, 36 L of gasoline, and 4 L of oil for a bulk wholesale rate of $50. A similar plan, costing $62.50, is available from Carib Oil Company for 65 L of diesel fuel, 54 L of gasoline, and 12 L of oil. How many standing orders should the School Bus Service place with each oil company to meet its weekly petroleum needs at the least cost?

# *Challenge*

The diagrams illustrate some equalities of mass among spheres, cubes, cylinders, and cones. What is the least number of objects that will balance the final scale?

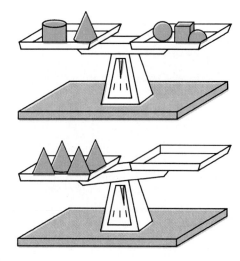

The program on page 479 can be expanded to graph equations and inequalities in two variables. First insert this line:

```
15  PRINT "IN TWO VARIABLES,"
```

Study the diagram shown at the right as you insert or change the lines listed below.

The graph will be printed from the top down. First print "Y" above the y-axis:

```
51  REM---PRINT "Y"
52  FOR I=M TO N
53  IF I <> 0 THEN 56
54  PRINT "Y"
55  GOTO 65
56  PRINT " ";
57  NEXT I
```

(Compare lines 51–57 with lines 140–200 on page 479.)

In order for the values of y to decrease, you must reverse M and N and use STEP −1:

```
65  FOR Y=N TO M STEP −1
```

Change line 80 for each open sentence. Use these lines to print the axes:

```
81  IF X=0 THEN 87          130  REM---PRINT "X"
82  IF Y=0 THEN 90          140  IF Y=0 THEN 170
84  PRINT " ";              150  PRINT
85  GOTO 120                160  GOTO 180
87  PRINT "!";              170  PRINT "X"
88  GOTO 120                180  NEXT Y
```

Delete lines 190 and 200.
(If possible, save this program for later use.)

### Exercises

**1.** Revise and LIST the program as shown above. Copy the diagram, replacing the question marks with the program line numbers.

Change line 80 in the program to graph the following.

**2.** $y > x + 2$ **3.** $y \geq x + 2$ **4.** $y = x + 2$ **5.** $y < x + 2$
**6.** $y - x \leq 3$ and $2x + 3y \geq -6$ **7.** $x + y \leq 7$ and $x - y \geq 3$

*Note:* The program of Exercise 1 above can be used to do Exercises 13–24 on page 483 and Exercises 9–18 on page 485.

# Chapter Summary

1. The symbols $>$, $<$, $\geq$, and $\leq$ are used to express inequalities. $-2 < 4 < 9$ (or $9 > 4 > -2$) means that 4 is between $-2$ and 9.
2. Open inequalities can be solved by transformations to obtain simple equivalent inequalities whose solution sets can be seen at a glance. The graph of the solution set of an inequality in one variable can be shown on a number line.
3. Sentences joined by "and" are conjunctions. A conjunction is true if and only if it is formed of true statements. Sentences joined by "or" are disjunctions. A disjunction of statements is true if at least one of the statements is true.
4. The distance between the graphs of two numbers $a$ and $b$ on a number line is the absolute value of the difference between $a$ and $b$. This concept can be used to solve open sentences involving the absolute value of a variable. These open sentences also may be written as equivalent conjunctions or disjunctions.
5. The solution set of a linear inequality in two variables is an open or closed half-plane.
6. The graph of the solution set of a system of inequalities consists of the points common to the graphs of all the inequalities in the system.

# Chapter Review

**Give the letter of the correct answer.**

1. Which statement is true?                                                    10-1
   **a.** $-7 < -10 < -12$              **b.** $8 > -6 > 4$
   **c.** $-9 < -4 < 2$                 **d.** $-5 > 3 > 0$

2. Find the solution set of $1 - x \leq 0$ if $x \in \{-4, -2, 0, 2, 4\}$.
   **a.** $\{-4, -2, 0, 2, 4\}$  **b.** $\{-4, -2\}$   **c.** $\{2, 4\}$      **d.** $\{0\}$

3. Find an inequality equivalent to $-3x < 12$.                                10-2
   **a.** $x > -36$          **b.** $x < -36$      **c.** $x > -4$      **d.** $x < -4$

4. Find an inequality equivalent to $3(3 + y) < 5(5 + y)$.
   **a.** $y < -8$            **b.** $y > -8$        **c.** $y < 8$       **d.** $y > 8$

5. Represent the statement "The product of two consecutive even integers       10-3
   is at most 80" as an inequality.
   **a.** $n(n + 1) \geq 80$             **b.** $n(n + 1) \leq 80$
   **c.** $n(n + 2) \geq 80$             **d.** $n(n + 2) \leq 80$

6. Which is the graph of the solution set of $x < 4$   or   $x > 4$?           10-4

   a.  b.  c.

7. Which is the graph of the conjunction $-6 \leq x$ and $x < 4$?

a.

$\quad -4 \quad 0 \quad 4$

b. $\quad -4 \quad 0 \quad 4$

c. $\quad -4 \quad 0 \quad 4$

d. $\quad -4 \quad 0 \quad 4$

8. Which open sentence states that the distance from $a$ to 2 is greater than 4? 10-5

   a. $a - 2 > 4$      b. $a - 2 \geq 4$      c. $|a - 2| > 4$    d. $|a - 2| \geq 4$

9. Which inequality is equivalent to $|6n - 3| < 9$? 10-6

   a. $|2n - 1| < 9$               b. $|2n - 1| < 3$

   c. $|n - 3| < 9$              d. $|2n - 1| > -3$

10. What is the equation of the boundary of the graph of the inequality $x - 2y > 4$? 10-7

   a. $y = 2x - 4$      b. $y = \frac{1}{2}x - 2$    c. $y \leq \frac{1}{2}x - 2$    d. $y \geq 2x - 4$

11. Which point belongs to the graph of the solution set of the system: 10-8

$$x > -3$$
$$y \leq 2x + 5$$

   a. $(0, 7)$          b. $(0, -7)$       c. $(-7, 0)$      d. $(-2, 7)$

# Chapter Test

1. Classify the statement as true or false: $5 > -\frac{1}{2} > -3$ 10-1

2. Find the solution set of $y + 2 < 3$ if $y \in \{-2, -1, 0, 1, 2\}$.

3. Solve the inequality $5 \geq 2x - 3$ and graph the solution set on a number line. 10-2

4. Of all pairs of consecutive odd integers whose sum is greater than 75, find the pair whose sum is the least. 10-3

**Solve each open sentence and graph its solution set.**

5. $-1 \leq 2c + 1 < 5$            6. $k + 5 \leq -3$   or   $k + 5 \geq 3$ 10-4

7. $|3 - y| = 4$                  8. $|y + 1| < 2$ 10-5

9. $|6 - 2x| = 4$                10. $|2m - 1| \leq 5$ 10-6

**Graph each inequality in a coordinate plane.**

11. $y \leq 3$                    12. $y \geq 3 - x$ 10-7

13. Graph the solution set of the system: $y < 2x + 2$ 10-8
$$y > 2 - 2x$$

# Cumulative Review (Chapters 1–10)

**Simplify. Assume that no denominator is zero.**

1. $(-7b + 4) + (3b - 8)$

2. $2x^2(8x^3 - 6x^2 + 9x)$

3. $(3x^3y^4)^5 \div (9xy^8)$

4. $(3x + 5y)(7x - 4y)$

5. $(5c - d)(3c^2 - 4cd + 8d^2)$

6. $(11t - 7v)^2$

7. $\dfrac{3x^2 - 8x - 3}{9x^2 + 9x + 2}$

8. $(12m^3n^2 - 11r^3)(12m^3n^2 + 11r^3)$

9. $\dfrac{4.8 \times 10^{21}}{2.0 \times 10^{15}}$

10. $\dfrac{z^2 + 8z + 16}{z^2 + 7z + 12} \cdot \dfrac{z^2 - 9}{z^2 + z - 12}$

11. $\dfrac{y^3 + 4y^2 + 3y}{y^2 + 5y + 6} \div \dfrac{y^2 + y}{y^3 + 2y^2}$

12. $\dfrac{z + 2}{3z + 9} + \dfrac{1}{z - 3} - 1$

**Factor completely.**

13. $30z^2 + 240z + 96$

14. $52t^2 + 31t - 6$

15. $16z^2 - y^2 - 10y - 25$

**Write an equation in standard form for each line described.**

16. The line that contains $(-4, 3)$ and $(6, 1)$.

17. The line that has slope $\dfrac{1}{2}$ and contains $(5, 6)$.

**Graph each inequality.**

18. $|x - 2| \leq 4$

19. $2y + 1 < -5$ or $3y - 5 > 1$

20. Graph the solution set of the system: $\quad x + y < 2$
$$2x - y \leq 0$$

**Solve each equation, inequality, or system. Assume that no denominator is zero.**

21. $|z| - 3 = 4$

22. $5q - 3 = 12$

23. 24% of $m = 18$

24. $b^2 - 8 = 1$

25. $5(d - 3) = 3(2d - 5)$

26. $12y^2 + 5y = 2$

27. $x^2 + 4x + 3 = 0$

28. $2b^2 + 9b - 5 = 0$

29. $3z^2 - 2z - 5 = 0$

30. $\dfrac{n - 1}{n} - \dfrac{1}{n + 1} = 1$

31. $\dfrac{b + 1}{b + 2} - \dfrac{b + 2}{b + 1} = \dfrac{1}{b + 2}$

32. $\dfrac{t}{3t + 1} + \dfrac{1}{t - 1} = \dfrac{3t + 1}{t - 1}$

33. $y = 5x - 1$
$\quad 2x + 3y = 14$

34. $3r + 2s = -4$
$\quad 4r + 2s = -8$

35. $6m + 5n = 4$
$\quad 4m + 3n = 2$

36. $5 + 4t \leq -3$

37. $3 - 5b > 9$

38. $2|3x - 1| + 1 < 5$

39. Marcy can do a job alone in 5 hours. If Mark helps her, they can do the job together in 3 hours. How long would Mark take working alone?

40. The units digit of a two-digit number is 1 less than the tens digit. Nine times the tens digit is less than the number with the digits reversed. Find the least such number.

# Maintaining Skills

**Solve. If the equation is an identity or has no solution, state that fact. Assume that no denominator is zero.**

***Example 1*** $12t^2 - 3 = 5t$

***Solution***

$$12t^2 - 5t - 3 = 0$$
$$(4t - 3)(3t + 1) = 0$$
$$4t - 3 = 0 \quad \text{or} \quad 3t + 1 = 0$$
$$4t = 3 \qquad\qquad 3t = -1$$
$$t = \frac{3}{4} \qquad\qquad t = -\frac{1}{3}$$

The check is left to you. The solution set is $\left\{\frac{3}{4}, -\frac{1}{3}\right\}$.

**1.** $t^2 - 6t - 40 = 0$      **2.** $x^2 = 15x - 56$      **3.** $y^2 + 12y + 36 = 0$

**4.** $n^2 + 400 = 40n$      **5.** $5z^2 + 4z = 1$      **6.** $10m^2 + 29m + 10 = 0$

**7.** $8 + 14z = 15z^2$      **8.** $21b^2 + 25b + 6 = 0$      **9.** $9d^2 + 7d = 16$

***Example 2*** $\dfrac{z + 3}{z + 1} + \dfrac{z}{z - 2} = \dfrac{2}{z - 2}$

***Solution***     Note that $z \neq -1$ or $z \neq 2$.

$$(z + 1)(z - 2)\left[\frac{z + 3}{z + 1} + \frac{z}{z - 2}\right] = (z + 1)(z - 2)\left(\frac{2}{z - 2}\right)$$
$$(z - 2)(z + 3) + z(z + 1) = 2(z + 1)$$
$$z^2 + z - 6 + z^2 + z = 2z + 2$$
$$2z^2 = 8$$
$$z^2 = 4$$
$$z = 2 \text{ or } z = -2$$

The check is left to you. The solution set is $\{-2\}$.

**10.** $\dfrac{1}{x} + \dfrac{3}{x} = 4$      **11.** $\dfrac{2}{3} + \dfrac{2}{t} = \dfrac{10}{3t}$      **12.** $\dfrac{5}{y} - \dfrac{4}{y} = \dfrac{1}{y}$

**13.** $\dfrac{a + 5}{a} + \dfrac{2}{a^2} = 1$      **14.** $y - \dfrac{y}{y + 1} = \dfrac{1}{y + 1}$      **15.** $\dfrac{3}{4b - 6} - \dfrac{1}{2b - 3} = 0$

**16.** $\dfrac{3x}{x + 1} - \dfrac{1}{x} = \dfrac{x + 1}{x}$      **17.** $\dfrac{b - 2}{b + 2} + \dfrac{b}{b - 2} = 2$      **18.** $\dfrac{1}{t} - \dfrac{1}{t + 1} = \dfrac{t + 2}{t^2 + t}$

**19.** $\dfrac{x^2 + 12}{x^2 - 4} - \dfrac{1}{x - 2} = \dfrac{3}{x - 2}$      **20.** $\dfrac{5}{d - 1} - \dfrac{10}{d^2 - 1} = 3$      **21.** $\dfrac{b^2 + 1}{b^2 - 1} = \dfrac{b}{b - 1} + \dfrac{2}{b + 1}$

**22.** $\dfrac{x}{x + 1} - \dfrac{5}{x^2 - 3x - 4} = \dfrac{x + 1}{x - 4}$      **23.** $\dfrac{y^2 - 2y + 2}{y^2 - 2y - 3} - \dfrac{y}{y - 3} = \dfrac{4}{y + 1}$

# Mixed Review

## Skills and Problem Solving

**Factor completely. If the polynomial cannot be factored, write "prime."**

**1.** $20b^2 - 13b - 15$

**2.** $16t^2 - 8t - 9v^2 + 1$

**3.** $3z^2 + 5z + 4$

**4.** How many groups of three consecutive integers are there such that their sum is equal to twice the second integer?

**5.** If $x$ varies directly as the square of $y$ and inversely as the cube of $z$, and $x = 5$ when $y = \frac{1}{4}$ and $z = \frac{1}{2}$, find the constant of variation.

**6.** 21 is what percent of 25?

**7.** 35% of what number is 49?

**8.** Write an equation in standard form of the line that contains $(-5, 6)$ and has $y$-intercept $-3$.

**Solve each equation, inequality, or system. Assume that no denominator is zero.**

**9.** $|3x - 4| > 2$

**10.** $\frac{2a - 5}{a + 1} - \frac{a - 3}{2a + 1} = \frac{5a + 2}{2a^2 + 3a + 1}$

**11.** $2x^2 - 4x = 30$

**12.** $\frac{t}{t + 1} + \frac{3}{t} = 1$

**13.** $x^2 + 5 = x^2 + 10x + 25$

**14.** $4x + 5y = 9$
$3x + 4y = 8$

**15.** How many liters of water must be evaporated from 84 L of a 5% acid solution to obtain a solution that is 20% acid?

**16.** The width of a rectangle is 4 cm less than half the length. The perimeter is less than 36 cm. Find the greatest possible width the rectangle could have, given that the width must be an integer.

**17.** On a boat ride, the trip upstream took 2.5 h longer than the return trip. If the whole trip took 5.8 h and covered 132 km, find the rate of the current and the speed of the boat in still water.

**Simplify. Assume that no denominator is zero. (Give the answer to Exercise 18 in scientific notation.)**

**18.** $\frac{7,000,000}{0.0035}$

**19.** $(2^{-3} - 3^{-2})^{-1}$

**20.** $\frac{n + 1}{n - 1} \div (n^2 - 1) + \frac{1}{n + 1}$

**21.** The sides of a triangle are in the ratio $5:8:11$. The perimeter is 72 m. Find the lengths of the sides.

**Graph the solution set.**

**22.** $2x - y \geq -1$
$6x + 3y \leq 3$

**23.** $\frac{1}{2}|x - 3| \geq 2$

**24.** $2x - 4y = 3$

# Preparing for College Entrance Exams

## Strategy for Success

Remember that you are asked to determine the *best* answer. More than one answer may be "right" to some degree. Do not choose the first answer that seems reasonable. Be sure to check all possible choices before determining which is the best answer.

**Decide which is the best of the choices given and write the corresponding letter on your answer sheet.**

1. Identify the point(s) on the line that contains $(-4, 3)$ and has slope $-\frac{1}{4}$.

   I. $(8, 0)$  II. $(-1, -3)$  III. $(-12, -13)$
   
   (A) I only    (B) II only    (C) III only
   
   (D) I, II, and III    (E) None of the above

2. Find an equation of the line that intersects the $y$-axis at the same point as the line containing $(2, 2)$ and $(-4, -1)$ and that is parallel to the line containing $(6, 6)$ and $(-3, 3)$.
   
   (A) $x - 3y = -3$  (B) $x - 2y = -8$  (C) $x + 2y = 8$  (D) $2x + y = 4$

3. For the function $f: x \rightarrow \dfrac{1}{x^2}$ the domain is the set of all real numbers except 0. Identify the true statement.
   
   (A) $f(x)$ varies inversely as $x$.
   (B) The function has exactly one zero.
   (C) The range of $f$ is the set of all nonnegative numbers.
   (D) $f(x)$ varies inversely as $x^2$.
   (E) The graph of $f$ is a parabola.

4. A given rectangle has area 24. The graph of the length as a function of the width:
   
   (A) is a parabola that opens upward.    (B) is a parabola that opens downward.
   (C) is a hyperbola.    (D) is one branch of a hyperbola.
   (E) cannot be determined from the given information.

5. How many sets of three consecutive positive even integers are there such that three times the sum of the first two integers is less than five times the third integer?
   
   (A) none    (B) two    (C) four    (D) six    (E) eight

6. Identify the inequality whose graph is shown at the right.
   
   (A) $x + 3y \leq 9$    (B) $x + 3y \geq 9$
   (C) $3x - y \leq 3$    (D) $3x - y \geq 3$

# 11 Rational and Irrational Numbers

Triangles are often used in construction. As you will learn in this chapter, the lengths of the sides of right triangles can be found by using the Pythagorean theorem if the lengths of two of the three sides are known.

# Rational Numbers

## 11-1 Properties of Rational Numbers

**Objective**  To learn and apply some properties of real numbers.

A real number that can be written as the quotient of two integers is called a **rational number.** Thus, the following numbers are rational numbers:

$$0 = \frac{0}{1} \qquad 5 = \frac{5}{1} \qquad 7\frac{2}{3} = \frac{23}{3} \qquad 0.48 = \frac{48}{100} \qquad -\frac{5}{9} = \frac{-5}{9}$$

Using the properties of fractions, a rational number can be expressed as a quotient of integers in an unlimited number of ways:

$$2 = \frac{4}{2} = \frac{8}{4} = \frac{-12}{-6} = \cdots \qquad -3\frac{1}{3} = \frac{-10}{3} = \frac{20}{-6} = \cdots \qquad 36\% = \frac{36}{100} = \frac{18}{50} = \cdots$$

To determine which of two rational numbers is greater, you can write the numbers with the same positive denominator and compare their numerators.

**Example 1**  Compare $\frac{11}{3}$ and $\frac{17}{5}$.

**Solution**    The LCD is 15.

$$\frac{11}{3} = \frac{55}{15} \qquad \frac{17}{5} = \frac{51}{15}$$

Because $55 > 51$, $\frac{55}{15} > \frac{51}{15}$.

Thus, $\frac{11}{3} > \frac{17}{5}$.  **Answer**

The procedure used in Example 1 may be generalized as follows:

For all integers $a$ and $b$ and all positive integers $c$ and $d$:

$$\frac{a}{c} > \frac{b}{d} \quad \text{if and only if} \quad ad > bc.$$

Similarly, $\frac{a}{c} < \frac{b}{d}$ if and only if $ad < bc$.

(See Exercise 36 on page 503 for a proof of this last statement.)

Thus, $\frac{4}{9} > \frac{3}{8}$ because $(4)(8) > (3)(9)$;

$$-\frac{5}{6} > -\frac{7}{8} \text{ because } (-5)(8) > (-7)(6).$$

**Example 2** Compare $-\frac{13}{7}$ and $-\frac{9}{5}$.

**Solution** Write $-\frac{13}{7}$ as $\frac{-13}{7}$ and $-\frac{9}{5}$ as $\frac{-9}{5}$. Then use the technique shown above to compare $\frac{-13}{7}$ and $\frac{-9}{5}$.

$(-13)(5) < (-9)(7)$ because $-65 < -63$.

Thus, $-\frac{13}{7} < -\frac{9}{5}$.  **Answer**

Rational numbers are different from integers in several ways. For example, given any integer, there is a next larger integer: $-5$ follows $-6$, 1 follows 0, 15 follows 14, and so on. There is, however, no "next larger" rational number after a given rational number. This property of rational numbers is called the *density* property.

---

### The Density Property for Rational Numbers

Between every pair of different rational numbers there is another rational number.

---

If $a$ and $b$ are rational numbers, and $a < b$, then: The number halfway from $a$ to $b$ is $a + \frac{1}{2}(b - a)$; the number one third of the way from $a$ to $b$ is $a + \frac{1}{3}(b - a)$; and so on.

Thus, the density property implies that it is possible to find an infinite number of rational numbers between two given rational numbers.

**Example 3** Find a rational number between $\frac{9}{4}$ and $\frac{17}{6}$.

**Solution** Choose, for example, the number halfway between $\frac{9}{4}$ and $\frac{17}{6}$. This number can be expressed as

$$\frac{9}{4} + \frac{1}{2}\left(\frac{17}{6} - \frac{9}{4}\right).$$

$$\frac{17}{6} - \frac{9}{4} = \frac{34}{12} - \frac{27}{12} = \frac{7}{12}$$

$$\frac{9}{4} + \frac{1}{2}\left(\frac{7}{12}\right) = \frac{9}{4} + \frac{7}{24} = \frac{54}{24} + \frac{7}{24} = \frac{61}{24}$$

*Check:* Is $\frac{9}{4} < \frac{61}{24} < \frac{17}{6}$?

$$9(24) \stackrel{?}{<} (61)(4) \qquad (61)(6) \stackrel{?}{<} (17)(24)$$
$$216 < 244 \text{ } \checkmark \qquad 366 < 408 \text{ } \checkmark$$

$\therefore$ a rational number between $\frac{9}{4}$ and $\frac{17}{6}$ is $\frac{61}{24}$. **Answer**

In Example 3, the number chosen to be found was halfway between the two given numbers. The number halfway between two numbers is also the average of the two numbers since

$$a + \frac{1}{2}(b - a) = \frac{2a}{2} + \frac{b - a}{2} = \frac{a + b}{2}.$$

## Oral Exercises

**Express each number as a ratio of integers.**

**Example**   4.35       **Solution**   $\frac{435}{100}$

**1.** 3.5

**2.** $-2.8$

**3.** $-3\frac{1}{4}$

**4.** 52%

**5.** $-9$

**6.** 25

**7.** 0

**8.** $\frac{5}{9} + \left(-\frac{7}{9}\right)$

**Which rational number in each pair is greater?**

**9.** $\frac{9}{13}, \frac{11}{13}$

**10.** $-\frac{3}{8}, -\frac{5}{8}$

**11.** $-3, \frac{1}{2}$

**12.** $-3, -\frac{1}{2}$

**13.** $\frac{7}{12}, \frac{2}{3}$

**14.** $-\frac{10}{3}, -\frac{14}{4}$

## Written Exercises

**Replace the __?__ with <, =, or > to make a true statement.**

**A**   **1.** $\frac{1}{6} \underline{\text{ ? }} \frac{6}{42}$

**2.** $\frac{2}{3} \underline{\text{ ? }} \frac{11}{15}$

**3.** $\frac{28}{43} \underline{\text{ ? }} \frac{31}{37}$

**4.** $-\frac{12}{19} \underline{\text{ ? }} -\frac{17}{24}$

**5.** $\frac{35}{72} \underline{\text{ ? }} \frac{53}{107}$

**6.** $\frac{138}{55} \underline{\text{ ? }} \frac{243}{78}$

**7.** $26\frac{4}{7} \underline{\text{ ? }} \frac{194}{8}$

**8.** $-\frac{214}{14} \underline{\text{ ? }} -15\frac{2}{3}$

**9.** $\frac{392}{9} \underline{\text{ ? }} 44\frac{5}{8}$

**Arrange each group of numbers in order from least to greatest.**

**10.** $\frac{2}{3}, \frac{3}{4}, \frac{4}{7}$

**11.** $\frac{3}{8}, -\frac{4}{9}, \frac{5}{6}$

**12.** $-3.8, -\frac{35}{8}, -3$

**13.** $5.6, \frac{107}{18}, \frac{303}{56}$

**14.** $\frac{9}{35}, \frac{7}{15}, \frac{1}{3}, \frac{8}{37}$

**15.** $-\frac{3}{7}, -\frac{3}{5}, -\frac{6}{7}, -\frac{5}{9}$

**Find the number halfway between the given numbers.**

**16.** $\frac{3}{8}, \frac{4}{9}$

**17.** $\frac{7}{11}, \frac{3}{4}$

**18.** $-\frac{11}{19}, -\frac{13}{25}$

**19.** $-\frac{37}{160}, -\frac{9}{42}$

**20.** $-4\frac{3}{5}, -5\frac{5}{6}$

**21.** $-4\frac{3}{7}, 8\frac{1}{3}$

**If $x \in \{0, 1, 2, 3\}$, state whether each fraction increases or decreases in value as $x$ takes on its values in increasing order.**

**22.** $\frac{x}{6}$

**23.** $\frac{x + 2}{5}$

**24.** $\frac{9}{x + 3}$

**25.** $\frac{8 - 3x}{5}$

**26.** $\frac{12}{8 + 3x}$

**B** **27.** Find the number one third of the way from $\frac{4}{7}$ to $1\frac{3}{4}$.

**28.** Find the number one fourth of the way from $-\frac{1}{9}$ to $-\frac{7}{8}$.

**29.** Find the number one fifth of the way from $-\frac{2}{3}$ to $\frac{3}{5}$.

**30.** Find the number two thirds of the way from $\frac{1}{4}$ to $\frac{5}{3}$.

**31.** Find a rational number between $\frac{1}{3}$ and $\frac{3}{4}$.

**32.** Find a rational number between $-\frac{1}{5}$ and $-\frac{1}{9}$.

**33.** Write an expression for the number halfway between $\frac{4a}{7}$ and $-\frac{a}{9}$.

**34.** Write an expression for the number one sixth of the way from $-\frac{9b}{7}$ to $-\frac{4b}{5}$.

**35. a.** Sue and Diane agree to share evenly the expenses of a vacation trip to the seashore. For convenience, instead of each paying half of each individual expense, they agree to take turns paying and then settle accounts at the end of the trip. During the trip, Sue paid $60 and Diane paid $80. Sue said to Diane, "I owe you half the difference, which is $10." Was Sue right?

**b.** In general, suppose Sue paid $a$ dollars and Diane paid $b$ dollars, where $b > a$. Show that if Sue gives Diane $\frac{1}{2}(b - a)$ dollars, then each will have paid exactly half the total expense.

**C** **36.** Give the reason for each statement in the proof of the following theorem: For all integers $a$ and $b$ and all positive integers $c$ and $d$, $\frac{a}{c} < \frac{b}{d}$ if and only if $ad < bc$.

Proof: If $\frac{a}{c} < \frac{b}{d}$, then $ad < bc$.

1. $\frac{a}{c} < \frac{b}{d}$          1. Given

2. $\frac{ad}{cd} < \frac{bc}{cd}$          2. ___?___

3. $ad < bc$          3. ___?___

$\therefore$ if $\frac{a}{c} < \frac{b}{d}$, then $ad < bc$.

Proof: If $ad < bc$, then $\frac{a}{c} < \frac{b}{d}$.

1. $ad < bc$          1. Given

2. $\frac{ad}{cd} < \frac{bc}{cd}$ (since $cd > 0$)          2. ___?___

3. $\frac{a}{c} < \frac{b}{d}$          3. ___?___

$\therefore$ if $ad < bc$, then $\frac{a}{c} < \frac{b}{d}$.

$\therefore \frac{a}{c} < \frac{b}{d}$ if and only if $ad < bc$.

**State conditions for $w$ and $z$ that make the following true.**

**37.** $\frac{x}{w} > \frac{x}{z}$; $x > 0$

**38.** $\frac{x}{w} < \frac{x}{z}$; $x < 0$

**39.** $\frac{x}{w - z} < \frac{x}{z - w}$; $x > 0$

**40.** $\frac{x}{w - z} > \frac{x}{z - w}$; $x < 0$

# *Challenge*

A parallelogram is a figure in geometry. Geometry is a branch of mathematics. Therefore, a parallelogram is a figure in mathematics.

No canaries are in my house. My house is in the Canary Islands. Therefore, no canaries are in the Canary Islands.

Is this reasoning logical?

# 11-2 Decimal Forms of Rational Numbers

**Objective**  To express rational numbers as decimals or fractions.

To write a common fraction as a decimal, you divide the numerator by the denominator. If the remainder is zero, the decimal is called a **terminating, ending,** or **finite decimal.** The division at the right shows that $\frac{7}{16}$ can be expressed as the terminating decimal 0.4375.

$$\frac{7}{16} = 7 \div 16 = 0.4375$$

```
      0.4375
16)7.0000
   6 4
     60
     48
    120
    112
      80
      80
       0
```

If the remainder is not zero, you continue dividing until the remainders start to repeat.

$$\frac{16}{30} \longrightarrow$$
```
      0.533
30)16.000
   15 0
    1 00
      90
     100
      90
      10
```

$$\frac{5}{11} \longrightarrow$$
```
      0.4545
11)5.0000
   4 4
     60
     55
     50
     44
     60
     55
      5
```

$$\frac{4}{7} \longrightarrow$$
```
      0.5714285
7)4.0000000
  3 5
    50
    49
    10
     7
    30
    28
    20
    14
    60
    56
    40
    35
     5
```

The decimal quotients shown above are **nonterminating, unending,** or **infinite.** They are also called **repeating** or **periodic** because the same digit or block of digits repeats unendingly.

$$\frac{16}{30} = 0.533\ldots \qquad \frac{5}{11} = 0.4545\ldots \qquad \frac{4}{7} = 0.5714285\ldots$$

The dots indicate that the decimals continue unendingly. A bar is used to indicate the block of digits that repeat, as shown below.

$$\frac{16}{30} = 0.5\overline{3} \qquad \frac{5}{11} = 0.\overline{45} \qquad \frac{4}{7} = 0.\overline{571428}$$

When you divide a positive integer $n$ by a positive integer $d$, the remainder $r$ at each step must be zero or a positive integer less than $d$. For example, if the divisor is 8, the remainders will be 0, 1, 2, 3, 4, 5, 6, or 7, and the division will terminate or begin repeating within 7 steps after only zeros remain to be brought down. In general:

For every integer $n$ and every positive integer $d$, the decimal numeral of the rational number $\frac{n}{d}$ either terminates or eventually repeats in a block of fewer than $d$ digits.

To express a terminating decimal as a common fraction, express the decimal as a common fraction with a power of ten as the denominator. This fraction is often expressed in simplest form.

$$0.34 = \frac{34}{100} = \frac{17}{50} \qquad 0.425 = \frac{425}{1000} = \frac{17}{40}$$

The following examples show how to express a repeating decimal as a common fraction.

**Example 1** Express $0.5\overline{81}$ as a common fraction.

**Solution**    Let $N$ = the number.          $N = 0.5\overline{81}$

Multiply $N$ by $10^n$, where $n$ is the number of digits in the block of repeating digits.
    Since $0.5\overline{81}$ has 2 digits in the repeating block, $n = 2$. Thus, you multiply by $10^2$, or 100.          $100N = 100(0.5\overline{81})$

Note that since $0.5\overline{81}$ means $0.5818181\ldots$, $0.5\overline{81}$ can be written as $0.58\overline{18}1$. Thus:

$$100(0.5\overline{81}) = 100(0.58\overline{181})$$
$$= 58.1\overline{81}$$

Subtract $N$ from $100N$ and solve for $N$.

$$\begin{array}{r} 100N = 58.1\overline{81} \\ N = \phantom{0}0.5\overline{81} \\ \hline 99N = 57.600 \end{array}$$

$$N = \frac{57.6}{99} = \frac{576}{990} = \frac{64}{110} = \frac{32}{55}$$

$$\therefore 0.5\overline{81} = \frac{32}{55} \quad \textbf{\textit{Answer}}$$

***Example 2*** Express $0.\overline{285}$ as a common fraction.

***Solution***    Let $N$ = the number.

$$1000\,N = 285.\overline{285}$$

Subtract    $\underline{\quad\quad N = \quad\, 0.\overline{285}}$

$$999N = 285.000$$

$$N = \frac{285}{999} = \frac{95}{333}$$

$$\therefore\ 0.\overline{285} = \frac{95}{333}\quad\textbf{\textit{Answer}}$$

---

All terminating decimals and all repeating decimals represent rational numbers that can be written in the form $\frac{n}{d}$ where $n$ is an integer and $d$ is a positive integer.

---

It is often convenient to use an approximation of a lengthy decimal. For example, you may approximate $\frac{12}{17}$ as

$$0.70588 \quad \text{or} \quad 0.706 \quad \text{or} \quad 0.71.$$

---

To round a decimal:
1. If the first digit dropped is 5 or more, add 1 to the last digit retained.
2. If the first digit dropped is less than 5, leave the retained digits unchanged.

---

The following examples show approximations of nonterminating decimals. The symbol $\approx$ means "is approximately equal to."

$$\frac{11}{12} = 0.91\overline{6} \approx 0.917 \text{ to the nearest thousandth}$$
$$\approx 0.92 \text{ to the nearest hundredth}$$

$$\frac{5}{6} = 0.8\overline{3} \approx 0.83 \text{ to the nearest hundredth}$$
$$\approx 0.8 \text{ to the nearest tenth}$$

$$\frac{95}{37} = 2.\overline{567} \approx 2.6 \text{ to the nearest tenth}$$
$$\approx 3 \text{ to the nearest unit}$$

$$\frac{176}{333} = 0.\overline{528} \approx 0.5 \text{ to the nearest tenth}$$
$$\approx 1 \text{ to the nearest unit}$$

**Round each number to the nearest tenth.**

**1.** 3.752      **2.** $-0.837$      **3.** $3.\overline{5}$      **4.** $2.37\overline{3}$      **5.** $-0.7\overline{8}$

**6–10.** Round the numbers in Exercises 1–5 to the nearest hundredth.

## Written Exercises

**Express each rational number as a terminating or repeating decimal.**

**A**    **1.** $\dfrac{3}{8}$      **2.** $\dfrac{9}{2}$      **3.** $\dfrac{5}{9}$      **4.** $-\dfrac{2}{5}$

   **5.** $\dfrac{31}{25}$      **6.** $\dfrac{11}{12}$      **7.** $\dfrac{11}{3}$      **8.** $\dfrac{3}{7}$

   **9.** $-\dfrac{5}{18}$      **10.** $\dfrac{15}{32}$      **11.** $-2\dfrac{7}{20}$      **12.** $3\dfrac{5}{11}$

   **13.** $\dfrac{82}{99}$      **14.** $-5\dfrac{3}{4}$      **15.** $-\dfrac{16}{33}$      **16.** $\dfrac{22}{37}$

**Express each rational number as a fraction in simplest form.**

   **17.** $0.66$      **18.** $0.3$      **19.** $0.\overline{5}$      **20.** $1.\overline{25}$

   **21.** $0.325$      **22.** $-0.31\overline{6}$      **23.** $4.8$      **24.** $2.3\overline{9}$

   **25.** $0.\overline{07}$      **26.** $-1.\overline{18}$      **27.** $-2.4\overline{6}$      **28.** $0.\overline{714285}$

**Find the difference of the given numbers. Then find the number halfway between them.**

**B**    **29.** $\dfrac{3}{4}$ and $0.756$      **30.** $\dfrac{1}{8}$ and $0.121$      **31.** $0.77$ and $0.\overline{7}$

   **32.** $0.59$ and $0.\overline{59}$      **33.** $\dfrac{8}{55}$ and $0.14\overline{52}$      **34.** $0.83$ and $\dfrac{5}{6}$

**Express both numbers as fractions and find their product.**

   **35.** $\dfrac{3}{4}$ and $0.5$      **36.** $0.875$ and $\dfrac{4}{7}$      **37.** $0.\overline{5}$ and $\dfrac{3}{5}$

   **38.** $-3.\overline{3}$ and $0.\overline{6}$      **39.** $0.\overline{407}$ and $0.2\overline{7}$      **40.** $0.5\overline{6}$ and $1.4\overline{27}$

**C**    **41. a.** Express $\dfrac{1}{7}$ and $\dfrac{5}{7}$ as repeating decimals.

       **b.** In the decimals that you found in part (a), what is the relationship between the blocks of digits that repeat?

       **c.** Express $\dfrac{2}{7}$, $\dfrac{3}{7}$, and $\dfrac{6}{7}$ as decimals.

**42. a.** Express $\frac{1}{9}$, $\frac{5}{9}$, and $\frac{7}{9}$ as repeating decimals.

    **b.** Express $\frac{1}{18}$, $\frac{5}{18}$, and $\frac{7}{18}$ as repeating decimals.

    **c.** What is the relationship between the decimals in part (a) and part (b)?

**43.** Since $\frac{1}{99} = 0.\overline{01}$, $\frac{n}{99} = n(0.\overline{01})$ for $n < 100$.

    **a.** Confirm the fact above by expressing $\frac{5}{99}$, $\frac{25}{99}$, and $\frac{74}{99}$ as decimals.

    **b.** Express 1 as $\frac{99}{99}$ to show that $0.\overline{9} = 1$.

## Computer Key-In

A computer will express a rational number, such as $\frac{4}{7}$, as a decimal by having it PRINT 4/7. The result will display the fixed number of decimal places for which the computer is programmed.

However, a program can be written that will compute one digit at a time just as you do when you do long division. Then the computer can find as many digits as you wish. The computation for $\frac{4}{7}$ is given below.

**As written:**

```
      0.571428
7 ) 4.000000
    3 5
      50
      49
       10
        7
        30
        28
        20
        14
         60
         56
          4
```

**As calculated:**

$4 \times 10 = 40$
$40 \div 7 = 5$, Remainder 5
$5 \times 10 = 50$
$50 \div 7 = 7$, Remainder 1
$1 \times 10 = 10$
$10 \div 7 = 1$, Remainder 3
$3 \times 10 = 30$
$30 \div 7 = 4$, Remainder 2
$2 \times 10 = 20$
$20 \div 7 = 2$, Remainder 6
$6 \times 10 = 60$
$60 \div 7 = 8$, Remainder 4

(Notice that when you "bring down a zero," you multiply the remainder by 10.)

The last remainder above, 4, is the same as the numerator. If the division is continued, the digits in the quotient will repeat in blocks. The calculation shown at the right above is the basis for the following computer program. See lines 130–170.

```
10   PRINT "TO FIND A DECIMAL FOR N/D:"
20   PRINT "INPUT N, D (0 < N < D)";
30   INPUT N,D
40   PRINT N;" /";D;" = 0 .";
50   REM---THE NUMERATOR IS
60   REM---THE FIRST "REMAINDER"
70   REM---IN THE LOOP BELOW.
80   LET R=N
90   REM---THIS LOOP COMPUTES AND
100  REM---PRINTS ONE DIGIT, Q1,
110  REM---AT A TIME.
120  FOR I=1 TO D+3
130  LET A=R*10
140  LET Q=A/D
150  LET Q1=INT(Q)
160  PRINT Q1;
170  LET R=A-Q1*D
180  IF R=0 THEN 220
190  NEXT I
200  PRINT " ..."
210  GOTO 230
220  PRINT " TERMINATES"
230  END
```

## Exercises

RUN the program given above to change each fraction to a decimal. If the decimal repeats, give the block of digits that repeats. Compare the results in each list.

1. $\dfrac{1}{7}, \dfrac{2}{7}, \dfrac{3}{7}, \dfrac{4}{7}, \dfrac{5}{7}, \dfrac{6}{7}$

2. $\dfrac{1}{2}, \dfrac{1}{20}, \dfrac{1}{3}, \dfrac{1}{30}, \dfrac{1}{4}, \dfrac{1}{40}$

3. $\dfrac{1}{14}, \dfrac{3}{14}, \dfrac{5}{14}, \dfrac{9}{14}, \dfrac{11}{14}, \dfrac{13}{14}$

4. What are the smallest whole numbers that can be used for $N$ and $D$ according to line 20 of the program?

5. Change line 20 to:   20   LET N = 1

   Change line 30 to:   30   FOR D = 2 TO 20

   Change the end of the program to complete the loop. RUN the revised program and compare the results.

*Note:* The program given above can be used to do Exercises 1–16 on page 507.

# 11-3 Rational Square Roots

**Objective**   To find the square roots of numbers that have rational square roots.

You have learned that subtracting a number is the inverse of adding that number, and that dividing by a nonzero number is the inverse of multiplying by that number. The inverse of squaring a number is finding a *square root*. If $a^2 = b$, then $a$ is called a **square root** of $b$. Because $8^2 = 64$ and $(-8)^2 = 64$, both 8 and $-8$ are square roots of 64.

The symbol $\sqrt{\phantom{x}}$ is used to denote the **principal,** or nonnegative, square root of a positive number. Thus,

$$\sqrt{64} = 8 \quad \text{and} \quad -\sqrt{64} = -8.$$

The symbol $\sqrt{\phantom{x}}$ is called the **radical sign,** and $\sqrt{64}$ is an example of a **radical.** An expression written beneath the radical sign, such as 64, is called the **radicand.** Often it is convenient to use *plus-or-minus* notation with radicals. For example:

$$\pm\sqrt{64} \text{ means the positive or negative square root of 64.}$$

In general, we have the following definition:

---

For all positive real numbers $a$, the symbol $\sqrt{a}$ denotes the principal square root of $a$.

---

It follows from the definition of square root that $(\sqrt{a})^2 = a$.

Zero has only one square root, namely zero itself; that is, $\sqrt{0} = 0$.

Because the square of every real number is either positive or zero, *negative numbers do not have square roots in the set of real numbers.*

The values of certain square roots can be seen at a glance; for example, $\sqrt{49} = 7$. You may be able to find other square roots by expressing them as a product of square roots that are familiar to you.

Notice that

$$\sqrt{9 \cdot 16} = \sqrt{144} = 12$$

and

$$\sqrt{9} \cdot \sqrt{16} = 3 \cdot 4 = 12.$$

This relationship suggests the following fact about square roots.

---

### Product Property of Square Roots

For any nonnegative real numbers $a$ and $b$:

$$\sqrt{ab} = \sqrt{a} \cdot \sqrt{b}$$

---

***Example 1*** Find $\sqrt{400}$.

***Solution***    $\sqrt{400} = \sqrt{4} \cdot \sqrt{100} = 2 \cdot 10 = 20$

If you cannot see any squares that divide the radicand, begin by factoring the radicand. (See the material on factoring integers on page 183.)

***Example 2*** Find $\sqrt{2304}$.

***Solution***
$$\sqrt{2304} = \sqrt{2^2 \cdot 3^2 \cdot 8^2}$$
$$= \sqrt{2^2} \cdot \sqrt{3^2} \cdot \sqrt{8^2}$$
$$= 2 \cdot 3 \cdot 8 = 48$$

The examples $\sqrt{\dfrac{64}{16}} = \sqrt{4} = 2$ and $\dfrac{\sqrt{64}}{\sqrt{16}} = \dfrac{8}{4} = 2$ suggest another property of square roots.

---

### Quotient Property of Square Roots

For any nonnegative real number $a$ and any positive real number $b$:

$$\sqrt{\frac{a}{b}} = \frac{\sqrt{a}}{\sqrt{b}}$$

---

***Example 3*** Find $\sqrt{\dfrac{121}{1156}}$.

***Solution***    $\sqrt{\dfrac{121}{1156}} = \dfrac{\sqrt{121}}{\sqrt{1156}} = \dfrac{11}{\sqrt{2^2 \cdot 17^2}} = \dfrac{11}{2 \cdot 17} = \dfrac{11}{34}$

---

## *Oral Exercises*

**Find the indicated square roots.**

1. $\sqrt{9}$     2. $\sqrt{36}$     3. $\sqrt{64}$     4. $\sqrt{121}$     5. $\sqrt{169}$

6. $\sqrt{12^2}$     7. $\sqrt{61^2}$     8. $\sqrt{47^2}$     9. $(\sqrt{5})^2$     10. $(\sqrt{21})^2$

11. $\sqrt{\dfrac{1}{16}}$     12. $\sqrt{\dfrac{1}{81}}$     13. $\sqrt{\dfrac{100}{36}}$     14. $\sqrt{\dfrac{81}{25}}$     15. $\sqrt{\dfrac{144}{49}}$

16. $\sqrt{\left(\dfrac{4}{7}\right)^2}$     17. $\sqrt{\left(\dfrac{12}{23}\right)^2}$     18. $\left(\sqrt{\dfrac{5}{19}}\right)^2$     19. $\sqrt{5^2 - 4^2}$     20. $\sqrt{8^2} - \sqrt{5^2}$

## Written Exercises

**Find the indicated square roots.**

**A**
1. $\sqrt{25}$
2. $\sqrt{81}$
3. $\sqrt{100}$
4. $\sqrt{225}$
5. $-\sqrt{441}$

6. $\sqrt{324}$
7. $-\sqrt{196}$
8. $\sqrt{625}$
9. $\pm\sqrt{289}$
10. $\sqrt{576}$

11. $\sqrt{1600}$
12. $\sqrt{2025}$
13. $\sqrt{1764}$
14. $\sqrt{3136}$
15. $\sqrt{8100}$

16. $\sqrt{\dfrac{49}{900}}$
17. $\pm\sqrt{\dfrac{400}{81}}$
18. $-\sqrt{\dfrac{225}{36}}$
19. $\sqrt{\dfrac{1}{256}}$
20. $\sqrt{\dfrac{121}{441}}$

21. $-\sqrt{\dfrac{729}{100}}$
22. $\sqrt{\dfrac{361}{2704}}$
23. $\sqrt{\dfrac{1024}{1849}}$
24. $\sqrt{\dfrac{676}{169}}$
25. $\pm\sqrt{\dfrac{484}{529}}$

**Example** $\quad \sqrt{0.81} = \sqrt{\dfrac{81}{100}} = \dfrac{\sqrt{81}}{\sqrt{100}} = \dfrac{9}{10} = 0.9$

26. $\sqrt{0.09}$
27. $-\sqrt{0.49}$
28. $\sqrt{1.44}$
29. $\pm\sqrt{2.25}$
30. $-\sqrt{7.84}$

31. $\sqrt{0.0169}$
32. $\sqrt{0.0324}$
33. $-\sqrt{0.2304}$
34. $\sqrt{0.0004}$
35. $\sqrt{0.0025}$

**Evaluate the expression $\sqrt{x^2 - y^2} - (\sqrt{x})^2$ for the given values of $x$ and $y$.**

36. $x = 5, y = 3$
37. $x = 13, y = 12$
38. $x = 15, y = 12$
39. $x = 20, y = 16$

**Find the indicated square roots.**

**Example** $\quad \sqrt{\dfrac{12}{75}} = \sqrt{\dfrac{3 \cdot 4}{3 \cdot 25}} = \sqrt{\dfrac{4}{25}} = \dfrac{2}{5}$

**B**
40. $\sqrt{\dfrac{18}{32}}$
41. $-\sqrt{\dfrac{12}{75}}$
42. $\sqrt{\dfrac{99}{44}}$
43. $\pm\sqrt{\dfrac{175}{28}}$
44. $\sqrt{\dfrac{5}{180}}$

45. $\pm\sqrt{\dfrac{147}{192}}$
46. $\sqrt{\dfrac{33}{132}}$
47. $\sqrt{\dfrac{200}{1152}}$
48. $-\sqrt{\dfrac{3200}{648}}$
49. $\sqrt{\dfrac{882}{20,000}}$

## Calculator Key-In

Many calculators have a square root key. It is possible to use this key to find the fourth root, eighth root, sixteenth root, and so on, of a number. For example, to find the eighth root of 32, press the square root key three times ($2^3 = 8$). The answer is 1.5422108.

Find the indicated roots of each number.

1. Fourth root of 48
2. Fourth root of 196
3. Eighth root of 150
4. Eighth root of 38
5. Sixteenth root of 164
6. Thirty-second root of 200

# Self-Test 1

**Vocabulary**    rational number (p. 499)         square root (p. 510)
terminating decimal (p. 504)    principal square root (p. 510)
repeating decimal (p. 504)        radicand (p. 510)

**Find a rational number halfway between the given numbers.**

1. $\frac{4}{7}$ and $\frac{5}{9}$
      2. $\frac{5}{4}$ and $\frac{4}{3}$
      3. $4\frac{1}{6}$ and $5\frac{1}{8}$
    **Obj. 11-1, p. 499**

**Which rational number is greater?**

4. $\frac{4}{7}$ or $\frac{3}{5}$
      5. $-\frac{33}{20}$ or $-\frac{37}{22}$
      6. $\frac{19}{18}$ or $\frac{13}{12}$

7. Express $\frac{6}{25}$ as a decimal.
                                 **Obj. 11-2, p. 504**

8. Express $\frac{11}{8}$ as a decimal.

9. Express $\frac{7}{30}$ as a decimal.

10. Express $\frac{24}{35}$ as a decimal.

11. Express $0.2\overline{02}$ as a fraction in simplest form.

**Find the indicated square roots.**

12. $\sqrt{1024}$
      13. $\sqrt{\dfrac{64}{2025}}$
      14. $\sqrt{2.56}$
    **Obj. 11-3, p. 510**

Check your answers with those at the back of the book.

# Challenge

1. On the same set of axes, graph the following line segments to draw a
   picture.

   $x = 0, 2 \leq y \leq 7$               $x = 6, 0 \leq y \leq 5$
   $x = 18, 4 \leq y \leq 9$           $x + 3y = 6, 0 \leq x \leq 6$
   $x + 3y = 21, 0 \leq x \leq 6$     $x - y = -7, 0 \leq x \leq 3$
   $x - 3y = 6, 6 \leq x \leq 18$     $x - 3y = -9, 6 \leq x \leq 18$
   $x - 3y = -27, 3 \leq x \leq 15$   $5x + 3y = 45, 3 \leq x \leq 6$
   $5x + 3y = 117, 15 \leq x \leq 18$

2. Draw a picture on graph paper using line segments. Write a set of
   equations and inequalities to describe your picture as in Exercise 1.

# Irrational Numbers

## 11-4 Irrational Square Roots

***Objective***   To simplify radicals and to find decimal approximations to irrational square roots.

You can use the Product Property of Square Roots to simplify radicals when the radicand has a factor that is the square of an integer other than 1.

***Example 1***  Simplify:   **a.** $\sqrt{196}$   **b.** $\sqrt{50}$   **c.** $3\sqrt{96}$

***Solution***
  **a.** $\sqrt{196} = \sqrt{4} \cdot \sqrt{49} = 2 \cdot 7 = 14$
  **b.** $\sqrt{50} = \sqrt{25 \cdot 2} = 5\sqrt{2}$
  **c.** $3\sqrt{96} = 3\sqrt{16 \cdot 6} = 3 \cdot 4\sqrt{6} = 12\sqrt{6}$

Parts (b) and (c) of the example above suggest that some integers, such as 2 and 6, are not squares of integers. Integers that are not squares of integers do not have rational square roots. The following proof shows that 2 does not have a rational square root.

In this proof we begin by assuming that 2 has a rational square root and then show that this assumption leads to a contradiction. Hence, the original assumption that 2 has a rational square root must be false.

1. Assume that 2 has a rational square root.

2. Then, $\sqrt{2} = \frac{a}{b}$, where $a$ and $b$ are positive integers that have no common prime factor, that is, $\frac{a}{b}$ is in simplest form. Hence, $a$ and $b$ cannot both be even integers.

3. If $\sqrt{2} = \frac{a}{b}$, then $2 = \frac{a^2}{b^2}$. Since $a^2$ has the same prime factors as $a$, and $b^2$ has the same prime factors as $b$, $a^2$ and $b^2$ have no common prime factors. Thus, $\frac{a^2}{b^2}$ is in simplest form.

4. Multiplying $\frac{a^2}{b^2} = 2$ by $b^2$, we have $a^2 = 2b^2$. Thus, $a$ must be even because its square is even. (Recall that the square of an even integer is even and that the square of an odd integer is odd.)

5. Since $a$ is even, we may write $a = 2n$ for some integer $n$. Then, substituting $2n$ for $a$ in $a^2 = 2b^2$, we have $(2n)^2 = 2b^2$, $4n^2 = 2b^2$, or $2n^2 = b^2$.

6. Since $2n^2 = b^2$, $b$ must be even because its square is even. Therefore, we may write $b = 2m$ for some integer $m$.

7. This contradicts the fact that $a$ and $b$ are not both even. Therefore, 2 does not have a rational square root.

Since integers such as 2, 6, and 11 are not squares of integers, numbers such as $\sqrt{2}$, $\sqrt{6}$, and $\sqrt{11}$ are not in the set of rational numbers. These numbers are in another major subset of the real numbers called the set of *irrational numbers*.

---

**Irrational numbers** are real numbers that cannot be expressed in the form $\dfrac{a}{b}$, where $a$ and $b$ are integers.

---

Irrational square roots are not the only irrational numbers, however. For example, $\pi$ is an irrational number.

The set of real numbers is made up of the rational numbers and the irrational numbers. The real numbers have all the properties that you have studied thus far in this course. In addition, the set of real numbers has the *property of completeness*.

---

## *Property of Completeness*

Every decimal represents a real number, and every real number can be represented as a decimal.

---

Terminating and repeating decimals represent rational numbers. Therefore, the decimals for irrational numbers neither terminate nor repeat. You can use a calculator or a table of square roots to find a decimal approximation of an irrational square root. For example, the Table of Square Roots on page 650 indicates that $\sqrt{87} \approx 9.327$. The product and quotient properties of square roots can be used with the table to approximate irrational square roots.

***Example 2*** Approximate $\sqrt{756}$ to the nearest hundredth.

***Solution*** $\sqrt{756} = \sqrt{2^2 \cdot 3^2 \cdot 21} = \sqrt{2^2} \cdot \sqrt{3^2} \cdot \sqrt{21} = 6\sqrt{21}$

From the table: $\sqrt{21} \approx 4.583$

$6\sqrt{21} \approx 6(4.583) = 27.498$

$\therefore \sqrt{756} \approx 27.50$ ***Answer***

---

**Example 3** Approximate $\sqrt{0.6}$ to the nearest ten-thousandth.

**Solution** $\sqrt{0.6} = \sqrt{\dfrac{60}{100}} = \dfrac{\sqrt{60}}{\sqrt{100}} \approx \dfrac{7.746}{10} = 0.7746$

$\therefore \sqrt{0.6} \approx 0.7746$ *Answer*

## Oral Exercises

**State whether the following represent rational or irrational numbers.**

1. $\sqrt{13}$    2. $\sqrt{15}$    3. $\sqrt{36}$    4. $\sqrt{43.8}$    5. $\sqrt{0.64}$

**Simplify.**

6. $\sqrt{75}$    7. $\sqrt{125}$    8. $\sqrt{108}$    9. $\sqrt{180}$    10. $\sqrt{220}$

**Approximate each square root to the nearest tenth. Use the table on page 650 as necessary.**

11. $\sqrt{600}$    12. $\sqrt{1100}$    13. $\sqrt{2800}$    14. $\sqrt{3700}$    15. $\sqrt{6300}$

## Written Exercises

**Simplify.**

**A**  1. $\sqrt{225}$    2. $\sqrt{40}$    3. $\sqrt{120}$    4. $2\sqrt{32}$    5. $5\sqrt{72}$
   6. $\sqrt{676}$    7. $9\sqrt{90}$    8. $\sqrt{324}$    9. $12\sqrt{50}$    10. $6\sqrt{45}$
   11. $10\sqrt{75}$    12. $4\sqrt{108}$    13. $\sqrt{128}$    14. $\sqrt{864}$    15. $\sqrt{7225}$

**In Exercises 16–30, use the table on page 650 as necessary. Approximate each square root to the nearest tenth.**

**B**  16. $\sqrt{800}$    17. $-\sqrt{4800}$    18. $-\sqrt{700}$    19. $\sqrt{9200}$    20. $\sqrt{5900}$

**Approximate each square root to the nearest hundredth.**

21. $\sqrt{86}$    22. $\sqrt{31}$    23. $-\sqrt{0.3}$    24. $\sqrt{0.73}$    25. $-\sqrt{0.08}$

**Approximate each square root to the nearest unit.**

26. $\sqrt{250,000}$    27. $\sqrt{120,000}$    28. $\sqrt{420,000}$    29. $\sqrt{520,000}$    30. $\sqrt{820,000}$

**C**  31. Prove that $\sqrt{3}$ is irrational. (*Hint:* Consider the proof for $\sqrt{2}$ being irrational.)

# 11-5 Square Roots of Variable Expressions

**Objective**  To find square roots of variable expressions and to use them to solve equations and problems.

Is it always true that $\sqrt{a^2} = a$? Recall that the symbol $\sqrt{\phantom{x}}$ stands for the principal, or nonnegative, square root of a number. Thus, when $a = -5$ you have

$$\sqrt{(-5)^2} = \sqrt{25} = 5.$$

Therefore, it is not necessarily true that $\sqrt{a^2} = a$. If $a$ is nonnegative, $\sqrt{a^2} = a$; but if $a$ is negative, then $\sqrt{a^2} = -a$. In either case, it is true that

$$\sqrt{a^2} = |a|.$$

When you are finding square roots of variable expressions, you must be careful to use absolute value signs, when needed, to ensure that your answer is nonnegative.

**Example 1**  Simplify:  **a.** $\sqrt{121y^2}$  **b.** $\sqrt{49x^8}$  **c.** $\sqrt{y^2 - 8y + 16}$

**Solution**  **a.** $\sqrt{121y^2} = 11|y|$

   **b.** $\sqrt{49x^8} = 7x^4$  ($x^4$ is always nonnegative.)

   **c.** $\sqrt{y^2 - 8y + 16} = \sqrt{(y-4)^2} = |y - 4|$

**Example 2**  Solve $x^2 = 81$.

**Solution 1**
$$x^2 = 81$$
$$x^2 - 81 = 0$$
$$(x - 9)(x + 9) = 0$$
$$x = 9 \text{ or } x = -9$$

**Solution 2**  $x^2 = 81$
$$x = \pm\sqrt{81} = \pm 9$$

*Check:* $9^2 = 81$ and $(-9)^2 = 81$ ✓

$\therefore$ the solution set is $\{9, -9\}$.  *Answer*

Solution 2 is based upon the following property:

**Property of Square Roots of Equal Numbers**

If $r$ and $s$ are any real numbers, $r^2 = s^2$ if and only if $r = s$ or $r = -s$.

## Oral Exercises

**Simplify.**

**1.** $\sqrt{36y^2}$    **2.** $\sqrt{169x^2}$    **3.** $\sqrt{81a^4}$    **4.** $\sqrt{121x^2y^2}$    **5.** $\sqrt{0.04b^6}$

**6.** $\sqrt{\dfrac{x^2}{49}}$    **7.** $\pm\sqrt{\dfrac{16}{a^4}}$    **8.** $\sqrt{\dfrac{x^4y^4}{25}}$    **9.** $\sqrt{\dfrac{r^6s^6}{64}}$    **10.** $\sqrt{\dfrac{m^{14}}{16n^8}}$

## Written Exercises

**Simplify.**

**A**  **1.** $\sqrt{144a^2}$    **2.** $\sqrt{32x^2}$    **3.** $\sqrt{75b^4}$    **4.** $\sqrt{45r^3}$    **5.** $\sqrt{80a^2b^2}$

**6.** $-\sqrt{36x^2}$    **7.** $\sqrt{81z^2}$    **8.** $-\sqrt{16a^2b^2}$    **9.** $-\sqrt{9c^4}$    **10.** $\sqrt{25d^6}$

**11.** $3\sqrt{63x^2y^3}$    **12.** $8\sqrt{90n^6}$    **13.** $\sqrt{56r^6s^4}$    **14.** $\sqrt{\dfrac{x^4y^6}{4r^2}}$    **15.** $\sqrt{\dfrac{27m^3n^2}{3mn^4}}$

**16.** $-\sqrt{144y^2z^4}$    **17.** $\sqrt{441a^6b^4}$    **18.** $\sqrt{2.25m^8n^6}$    **19.** $-\sqrt{3.24x^4}$    **20.** $\sqrt{1.96k^6}$

**21.** $\sqrt{\dfrac{4e^2}{625}}$    **22.** $\sqrt{\dfrac{100f^{10}}{121}}$    **23.** $\sqrt{\dfrac{169}{400s^{12}}}$    **24.** $\sqrt{\dfrac{49g^{18}}{6400h^{20}}}$    **25.** $\sqrt{\dfrac{169r^{50}}{25}}$

**26.** $\sqrt{y^2 + 6y + 9}$    **27.** $\sqrt{m^2 - 10m + 25}$    **28.** $\sqrt{49 + 14r + r^2}$

**Solve.**

**29.** $a^2 = 16$    **30.** $x^2 - 36 = 0$    **31.** $d^2 - 1 = 0$

**32.** $64y^2 = 9$    **33.** $4c^2 - 25 = 0$    **34.** $81z^2 - 49 = 0$

**35.** $2m^2 - 32 = 0$    **36.** $50b^2 - 200 = 0$    **37.** $27p^2 - 75 = 0$

**Find both roots of each equation to the nearest tenth.**

**B**  **38.** $x^2 = 657$    **39.** $a^2 = 164$    **40.** $r^2 = 0.29$

**41.** $c^2 - 204 = 0$    **42.** $y^2 - 4.75 = 0$    **43.** $n^2 - 11.16 = 0$

**44.** $7z^2 = 399$    **45.** $8s^2 - 154 = 0$    **46.** $6b^2 - 0.42 = 0$

**C**  **47.** $0.11m^2 = 6.38$    **48.** $7k^2 = 130$

**49.** $(x - 1)^2 + (x + 1)^2 = 150$    **50.** $(a + 3)^2 + (a - 3)^2 = 196$

## Problems

**Solve. Find each answer to the nearest tenth. Use $\pi \approx 3.14$.**

**A**  **1.** Find the length of a side of a square whose area is 200 cm².

**2.** Find the length of a side of a square whose area is the same as that of a rectangle whose dimensions are 18 cm by 24 cm.

3. The length of the base of a triangle is 3 times the length of its altitude. Find the length of the base if the area of the triangle is 54 m².

4. Find the length of a side of a square if its area is the same as the area of a triangle with an altitude of 14 cm and a base of 9 cm.

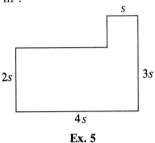

Ex. 5

5. If the area of the figure at the right is 400 mm², find s.

6. A circle inside a square just touches its sides. If the area of the circle is 266.9 cm², what is the length of a side of the square?

**B** 7. An old water pipe is to be replaced by a new one so that twice as much water can flow through the pipe. What is the ratio of the radius of the new pipe to that of the old pipe?

8. A square quilt is to be made of 150 rectangular pieces 10 cm by 15 cm. How many meters of trim are required to edge the quilt?

9. The formula $s = 4.9t^2$ gives the approximate distance traveled in $t$ seconds by an object falling from rest. How long does it take a rock falling from rest to travel 1587.6 m?

**Let $a$, $b$, and $c$ represent the lengths of the sides of a triangle, and let $s = \frac{1}{2}(a + b + c)$. Then the area, $A$, of the triangle is given by the formula $A = \sqrt{s(s - a)(s - b)(s - c)}$. Use the formula to answer the following questions. Find each answer to the nearest tenth.**

**C** 10. What is the area of a triangle whose sides are 7 cm, 9 cm, and 12 cm long?

11. What is the area of a triangle whose sides are 11 m, 16 m, and 21 m long?

## Computer Exercises    *For students with some programming experience*

Write a BASIC program that will print out the square root of a nonnegative rational number entered with an INPUT statement. If the number that is INPUT is negative, the program should ask the user for another number. If the number that is INPUT is not a perfect square, the program should print out a decimal approximation of the square root to the degree of accuracy specified by the user.

# 11-6 The Pythagorean Theorem

**Objective**  To use the Pythagorean theorem and its converse to construct lengths corresponding to irrational numbers and to solve geometric problems.

In this section you will see how the Pythagorean theorem can be used to find the lengths of sides of triangles that correspond to irrational numbers.

## The Pythagorean Theorem

In any right triangle, the square of the length of the hypotenuse equals the sum of the squares of the lengths of the other two sides. For the triangle shown,

$$a^2 + b^2 = c^2.$$

The following two diagrams suggest a proof of the theorem. Each diagram shows a square, $(a + b)$ units on a side, divided into other figures. The diagrams suggest different expressions for the area of a square $(a + b)$ units on a side. Equating these expressions leads to the equation $a^2 + b^2 = c^2$, as shown below.

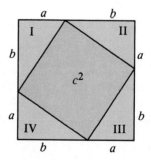

$$(a + b)^2 = a^2 + b^2 + 4\left(\frac{1}{2}ab\right) \qquad (a + b)^2 = c^2 + 4\left(\frac{1}{2}ab\right)$$

$$a^2 + b^2 + 4\left(\frac{1}{2}ab\right) = c^2 + 4\left(\frac{1}{2}ab\right)$$

$$\therefore a^2 + b^2 = c^2$$

To draw a line segment with a length of $\sqrt{2}$ units, draw a right triangle whose two shorter sides are 1 unit long, as shown in the following diagram.

Then:

$$a^2 + b^2 = c^2$$
$$1^2 + 1^2 = c^2$$
$$1 + 1 = c^2$$
$$2 = c^2$$
$$\pm\sqrt{2} = c$$

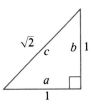

∴ the length of the hypotenuse is $\sqrt{2}$ units.

The following diagrams show that a segment $\sqrt{2}$ units long can be used to construct a segment $\sqrt{3}$ units long, that a segment $\sqrt{3}$ units long can be used to construct a segment $\sqrt{4}$ units long, and so on.

   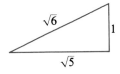

A series of such triangles can be used to locate irrational square roots such as $\sqrt{2}$, $\sqrt{3}$, and $\sqrt{5}$ on the number line. The arcs are drawn to transfer the length of the hypotenuse of each triangle to the $x$-axis. Note that $-\sqrt{2}$ is located $\sqrt{2}$ units to the left of 0.

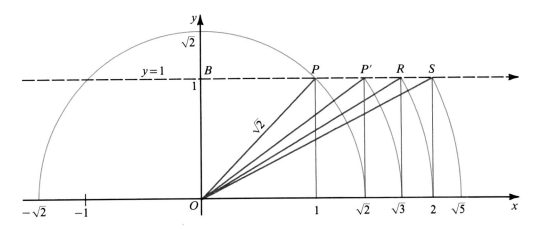

The converse of the Pythagorean theorem is also true. It can be used to see if a given triangle is a right triangle.

## Converse of the Pythagorean Theorem

If the sum of the squares of the lengths of the two shorter sides of a triangle is equal to the square of the length of the longest side, then the triangle is a right triangle. The right angle will be opposite the longest side.

***Example 1*** Is a triangle with sides 9, 40, and 41 a right triangle?

***Solution***
$$a^2 + b^2 = c^2$$
$$9^2 + 40^2 \overset{?}{=} 41^2$$
$$1681 = 1681 \ \checkmark$$

∴ a triangle with sides 9, 40, and 41 is a right triangle. ***Answer***

***Example 2*** The length of one side of a right triangle is 24 cm and the length of the hypotenuse is 25 cm. What is the length of the third side?

***Solution***
$$a^2 + b^2 = c^2 \qquad\qquad Check: \ 7^2 + 24^2 \overset{?}{=} 25^2$$
$$a^2 = c^2 - b^2 \qquad\qquad\qquad\qquad 625 = 625 \ \checkmark$$
$$a = \sqrt{c^2 - b^2}$$
$$a = \sqrt{25^2 - 24^2}$$
$$a = \sqrt{625 - 576}$$
$$a = \sqrt{49} = 7$$

∴ the length of the third side of the right triangle is 7 cm. ***Answer***

***Example 3*** What is the length of a diagonal of a rectangle whose width is 36 cm and whose length is 48 cm?

***Solution***
$$a^2 + b^2 = c^2$$
$$\sqrt{a^2 + b^2} = c$$
$$\sqrt{36^2 + 48^2} = c$$
$$\sqrt{1296 + 2304} = c$$
$$\sqrt{3600} = c$$
$$60 = c$$
$$Check: \ 36^2 + 48^2 \overset{?}{=} 60^2$$
$$3600 = 3600 \ \checkmark$$

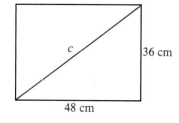

∴ the length of a diagonal of the rectangle is 60 cm. ***Answer***

## Oral Exercises

**Evaluate.**

**1.** $\sqrt{3^2 + 4^2}$
     **2.** $\sqrt{10^2 - 8^2}$
     **3.** $\sqrt{13^2 - 12^2}$

**State and solve an equation for the length of the unknown side.**

**4.**

**5.**

## Written Exercises

In Exercises 1–10, refer to the right triangle shown at the right. Find the missing length correct to the nearest hundredth.

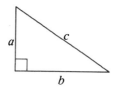

**A**    **1.** $a = 9, b = 12, c = \underline{\ ?\ }$      **2.** $a = 5, b = 12, c = \underline{\ ?\ }$

    **3.** $a = 7, b = 4, c = \underline{\ ?\ }$      **4.** $a = 11, b = 8, c = \underline{\ ?\ }$

    **5.** $a = 7, b = 7, c = \underline{\ ?\ }$      **6.** $a = 16, b = 8, c = \underline{\ ?\ }$

    **7.** $a = \underline{\ ?\ }, b = 15, c = 17$      **8.** $a = \underline{\ ?\ }, b = 12, c = 19$

    **9.** $a = 6, b = \underline{\ ?\ }, c = 40$      **10.** $a = 3, b = \underline{\ ?\ }, c = 6$

State whether or not the three numbers given could represent the lengths of the sides of a right triangle.

**11.** 5, 10, 15      **12.** 14, 48, 50      **13.** 9, 40, 41

**14.** 15, 30, 34      **15.** 15, 20, 24      **16.** 17, 35, 39

**17.** $a, 2a, 3a$      **18.** $3a, 4a, 5a$      **19.** $5a, 12a, 13a$

In Exercises 20–25, refer to the diagram for Exercises 1–10. Find the missing length correct to the nearest hundredth.

**B**   **20.** $a = b = 10, c = \underline{\ ?\ }$      **21.** $a = 9, b = \dfrac{1}{3}a, c = \underline{\ ?\ }$

    **22.** $a = 16, b = \dfrac{1}{4}a, c = \underline{\ ?\ }$      **23.** $a = \dfrac{1}{2}b, b = 12, c = \underline{\ ?\ }$

    **24.** $a = \dfrac{3}{5}b, b = 15, c = \underline{\ ?\ }$      **25.** $a = \dfrac{5}{6}b, b = 18, c = \underline{\ ?\ }$

In Exercises 26–29, refer to the diagram for Exercises 1–10. Find $a$ and $b$ correct to the nearest hundredth.

**C**   **26.** $a = b, c = 80$      **27.** $a = 3b, c = 20$

    **28.** $a = \dfrac{1}{2}b, c = 25$      **29.** $a = \dfrac{2}{3}b, c = 52$

## Computer Exercises     *For students with some programming experience*

Write a BASIC program that will report whether three numbers entered with INPUT statements could represent the lengths of the sides of a right triangle.

## Problems

**Make a sketch for each problem. Approximate each square root to the nearest hundredth.**

A

1. Find the length of a diagonal of a rectangle whose dimensions are 7 cm by 24 cm.

2. A rope 17 m long is attached to the top of a flagpole. The rope is just able to reach a point on the ground 8 m from the base of the pole. Find the height of the flagpole.

3. The diagonal of a square measures $9\sqrt{2}$ m. Find the length of a side of the square.

4. The base of an isosceles triangle is 16 cm long. The equal sides are each 22 cm long. Find the altitude ($a$) of the triangle.

B

5. A right triangle has sides whose lengths can be expressed by consecutive even integers. Determine the length of each side.

6. The dimensions of a rectangular doorway are 200 cm by 80 cm. Can a circular mirror with a diameter of 220 cm be carried through the doorway?

C

7. What is the length of the diagonal of a cube that is 30 cm on each side?

8. What is the length of the diagonal of a rectangular box having length 40 cm, width 30 cm, and height 80 cm? Would a meter stick fit in the box?

9. Ellen is standing on a dock 1.5 m above the water. She is pulling in a boat that is attached to the end of a 3.9 m rope. If she pulls in 1.4 m of rope, how far did she move the boat?

## Self-Test 2

*Vocabulary*    irrational numbers (p. 515)          Pythagorean theorem (p. 520)

**Approximate each square root to the nearest hundredth using the Table of Square Roots.**

1. $\sqrt{97}$          2. $\sqrt{1700}$          3. $-\sqrt{0.88}$          Obj. 11-4, p. 514

**Simplify.**

4. $\sqrt{81x^2y^2}$          5. $-\sqrt{144a^6b^8}$          6. $\sqrt{0.25c^4}$          Obj. 11-5, p. 517

**Solve.**

**7.** $s^2 = 49$

**8.** $w^2 - 64 = 0$

**9.** $36y^2 - 25 = 0$

**10.** Find $c$ correct to the nearest hundredth if $a = 14$ and $b = 17$.

**11.** Is a triangle with sides 9, 12, and 14 units long a right triangle?

Obj. 11-6, p. 520

Check your answers with those at the back of the book.

## *Extra* / The Distance Formula

The distance between two points on the *x*-axis or on a line parallel to that axis is the absolute value of the difference between their abscissas. Using the notation $A'B'$ to denote the distance from $A'$ to $B'$, you can write the following:

$$A'B' = |2 - 8| = |8 - 2| = 6$$
$$AB = |2 - 8| = |8 - 2| = 6$$

The distance between two points on the *y*-axis or on a line parallel to that axis is the absolute value of the difference between their ordinates.

$$A'C' = |3 - 7| = |7 - 3| = 4$$
$$AC = |3 - 7| = |7 - 3| = 4$$

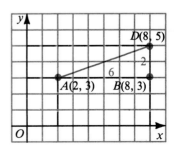

To find the distance between two points not on an axis or a line parallel to an axis, use the Pythagorean theorem:

$$AD = \sqrt{(AB)^2 + (BD)^2} = \sqrt{(8-2)^2 + (5-3)^2}$$
$$= \sqrt{6^2 + 2^2} = \sqrt{36 + 4}$$
$$= \sqrt{40} = 2\sqrt{10}$$

This method for finding the distance between any two points can be generalized as shown on the following page.

*Rational and Irrational Numbers* **525**

## The Distance Formula

For any points $P_1(x_1, y_1)$ and $P_2(x_2, y_2)$

$$P_1P_2 = \sqrt{(x_2 - x_1)^2 + (y_2 - y_1)^2}$$

**Example**  Find the distance between points $P(-3, 2)$ and $Q(5, 8)$.

**Solution 1**  $PQ = \sqrt{(-3 - 5)^2 + (2 - 8)^2}$
$= \sqrt{(-8)^2 + (-6)^2}$
$= \sqrt{64 + 36} = \sqrt{100} = 10$

**Solution 2**  $PQ = \sqrt{(5 - (-3))^2 + (8 - 2)^2}$
$= \sqrt{8^2 + 6^2}$
$= \sqrt{64 + 36} = \sqrt{100} = 10$

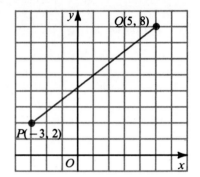

### Exercises

Use the distance formula to find the distance between the points to the nearest tenth.

**1.** $(-5, 0), (3, 0)$     **2.** $(0, 9), (0, -12)$     **3.** $(2, 3), (8, 5)$

**4.** $(10, 3), (-4, 9)$     **5.** $(-4, -2), (-9, -6)$     **6.** $(8, -1), (3, -5)$

**7.** $(-4, 6), (5, 2)$     **8.** $(-3, 7), (-9, -6)$     **9.** $(3, -3), (-8, -5)$

**10.** $(2, -5), (9, -7)$     **11.** $(-2, 1), (-8, -5)$     **12.** $(10, -1), (-9, 3)$

**13.** Show that the points $(1, 1)$, $(5, 2)$, and $(4, -2)$ are the vertices of an isosceles triangle.

**14.** Show that the point $(-2, -2)$ is the midpoint of the segment joining $(3, 8)$ and $(-7, -12)$.

## Computer Key-In

BASIC has a function, SQR(N), for finding the square root of a number. Use this function to find SQR(16), SQR(25), SQR(2), and SQR(625).

### Exercises

**1.** Write a program to find the distance between $(X1, Y1)$ and $(X2, Y2)$.

**2.** Use your program to check your answers to Exercises 1–12 above.

# Radical Expressions

## 11-7 Multiplication, Division, and Simplification of Radicals

**Objective**   To simplify products and quotients of radicals.

You can use the product and quotient properties of square roots together with the commutative, associative, and distributive axioms to multiply, divide, and simplify square-root radicals.

An expression having a square-root radical is in **simplest form** when

1. no integral radicand has a square factor other than 1,
2. no fractions are under a radical sign, and
3. no radicals are in a denominator.

**Example 1**   Simplify the following expressions.

        **a.** $3\sqrt{2} \cdot 5\sqrt{8}$    **b.** $\sqrt{3}(2 + \sqrt{3})$

**Solution**   **a.** $3\sqrt{2} \cdot 5\sqrt{8} = 3 \cdot 5 \cdot \sqrt{2} \cdot \sqrt{8} = 15\sqrt{16} = 15 \cdot 4 = 60$

        **b.** $\sqrt{3}(2 + \sqrt{3}) = 2\sqrt{3} + \sqrt{3 \cdot 3} = 2\sqrt{3} + 3$

**Example 2**   Simplify the following expressions.

        **a.** $\dfrac{3}{\sqrt{7}}$    **b.** $\sqrt{\dfrac{5}{8}}$    **c.** $\dfrac{5\sqrt{3}}{4\sqrt{5}}$

**Solution**   **a.** $\dfrac{3}{\sqrt{7}} = \dfrac{3 \cdot \sqrt{7}}{\sqrt{7} \cdot \sqrt{7}} = \dfrac{3\sqrt{7}}{(\sqrt{7})^2} = \dfrac{3\sqrt{7}}{7}$

        **b.** $\sqrt{\dfrac{5}{8}} = \dfrac{\sqrt{5}}{\sqrt{8}} = \dfrac{\sqrt{5} \cdot \sqrt{2}}{\sqrt{8} \cdot \sqrt{2}} = \dfrac{\sqrt{10}}{\sqrt{16}} = \dfrac{\sqrt{10}}{4}$

        **c.** $\dfrac{5\sqrt{3}}{4\sqrt{5}} = \dfrac{5\sqrt{3} \cdot \sqrt{5}}{4\sqrt{5} \cdot \sqrt{5}} = \dfrac{5\sqrt{3 \cdot 5}}{4(\sqrt{5})^2} = \dfrac{5\sqrt{15}}{4 \cdot 5} = \dfrac{\sqrt{15}}{4}$

The process of expressing a fraction with an irrational denominator, such as $\dfrac{3}{\sqrt{7}}$, as a fraction with a rational denominator, such as $\dfrac{3\sqrt{7}}{7}$, is called **rationalizing the denominator.**

## Oral Exercises

**Express in simplest form.**

1. $\sqrt{2} \cdot \sqrt{3}$    2. $\dfrac{\sqrt{27}}{\sqrt{3}}$    3. $\dfrac{\sqrt{32}}{\sqrt{2}}$    4. $\sqrt{5} \cdot 4\sqrt{2}$    5. $\sqrt{3} \cdot \sqrt{6}$

6. $\sqrt{2} \cdot \sqrt{12}$    7. $\dfrac{\sqrt{18}}{\sqrt{3}}$    8. $\dfrac{\sqrt{54}}{\sqrt{2}}$    9. $\sqrt{5} \cdot \sqrt{15}$    10. $\sqrt{\dfrac{4}{7}}$

## Written Exercises

**Express in simplest form.**

**A**  1. $\sqrt{2} \cdot 3\sqrt{2}$    2. $3\sqrt{7} \cdot 2\sqrt{7}$    3. $\sqrt{3} \cdot \sqrt{5} \cdot \sqrt{6}$

4. $\sqrt{5} \cdot \sqrt{5} \cdot \sqrt{9}$    5. $2\sqrt{5} \cdot \sqrt{7}$    6. $5\sqrt{2} \cdot \sqrt{5} \cdot \sqrt{8}$

7. $\sqrt{3} \cdot \sqrt{12}$    8. $\sqrt{2} \cdot \sqrt{50}$    9. $6\sqrt{288}$

10. $\sqrt{\dfrac{4}{7}} \cdot \sqrt{\dfrac{7}{4}}$    11. $\sqrt{\dfrac{4}{9}} \cdot \dfrac{18}{4}$    12. $\sqrt{\dfrac{9}{7}} \cdot \dfrac{14}{36}$

13. $\sqrt{\dfrac{3}{4}} \cdot \sqrt{\dfrac{5}{6}}$    14. $\sqrt{\dfrac{7}{3}} \cdot \sqrt{\dfrac{3}{28}}$    15. $\sqrt{\dfrac{4}{5}} \cdot \sqrt{\dfrac{10}{36}}$

16. $\sqrt{2\dfrac{2}{5}} \cdot \sqrt{1\dfrac{2}{3}}$    17. $\dfrac{1}{5}\sqrt{\dfrac{9}{2}} \cdot \dfrac{1}{2}\sqrt{\dfrac{2}{3}}$    18. $\dfrac{15\sqrt{18}}{5\sqrt{2}}$

19. $\sqrt{\dfrac{10}{13}} \cdot \sqrt{\dfrac{1}{2}}$    20. $\dfrac{9\sqrt{3}}{\sqrt{24}}$    21. $3\sqrt{\dfrac{48}{9}}$

22. $\dfrac{7\sqrt{45}}{\sqrt{35}}$    23. $\dfrac{14\sqrt{320}}{2\sqrt{5}}$    24. $\dfrac{13\sqrt{8}}{\sqrt{104}}$

**Simplify. Assume that all variables represent positive real numbers.**

**B**  25. $(5\sqrt{ab^2})(-2\sqrt{a})$    26. $(-x\sqrt{x^2y})(y\sqrt{xy^2})$

27. $\sqrt{r}(4 - \sqrt{r})$    28. $\sqrt{m}(\sqrt{m^3} + 5)$

29. $(5\sqrt{2})(-2\sqrt{8})(3\sqrt{32})$    30. $(4\sqrt{5})(-\sqrt{10})(2\sqrt{2})$

31. $(\sqrt{2x})(\sqrt{3x})(2\sqrt{6x^2})$    32. $\sqrt{27}\sqrt{3x}\sqrt{5x}$

33. $(4\sqrt{7y})^2$    34. $2n(\sqrt{5n})^2$

35. $3x\sqrt{\dfrac{x}{y}} \cdot \sqrt{\dfrac{4x}{y}}$    36. $2q\sqrt{\dfrac{3q}{2r}} \cdot \sqrt{\dfrac{q}{r}}$

**C**  37. $\sqrt{2a}(\sqrt{8a} - 3\sqrt{12a^2})$    38. $\sqrt{6m}(\sqrt{2m} - 3\sqrt{8m^2})$

39. $3\sqrt{8x^3}(2\sqrt{2x} - 5\sqrt{8x^4})$    40. $2\sqrt{10x^3}(3\sqrt{2x} - 5\sqrt{8x^4})$

41. $(3\sqrt{5y^3})^3$    42. $(2\sqrt{3y^3})^3$

43. $(\sqrt{10xy})^3(x\sqrt{5x^3y} - y\sqrt{10xy^3})$    44. $(\sqrt{12xy})^3(x\sqrt{5x^2y} + y\sqrt{6xy^2})$

# 11-8 Addition and Subtraction of Radicals

**Objective**  To simplify sums and differences of radicals.

You can use the distributive axiom to simplify the sum of $3\sqrt{6}$ and $5\sqrt{6}$ because they have $\sqrt{6}$ as a common factor.

$$3\sqrt{6} + 5\sqrt{6} = (3 + 5)\sqrt{6} = 8\sqrt{6}$$

On the other hand, terms that have unlike radicands cannot be combined.

$$3\sqrt{5} - 5\sqrt{17} + 6\sqrt{5} = 9\sqrt{5} - 5\sqrt{17}$$

By expressing each radical in simplest form, you can sometimes combine terms in sums and differences of radicals.

**Example**  Simplify $7\sqrt{3} - 6\sqrt{5} + 2\sqrt{75} - 3\sqrt{45}$.

**Solution**
$$\begin{aligned}
7\sqrt{3} - 6\sqrt{5} + 2\sqrt{75} - 3\sqrt{45} &= 7\sqrt{3} - 6\sqrt{5} + 2\sqrt{25\cdot 3} - 3\sqrt{9\cdot 5} \\
&= 7\sqrt{3} - 6\sqrt{5} + 2(5\sqrt{3}) - 3(3\sqrt{5}) \\
&= 7\sqrt{3} - 6\sqrt{5} + 10\sqrt{3} - 9\sqrt{5} \\
&= 17\sqrt{3} - 15\sqrt{5}
\end{aligned}$$

---

To simplify sums or differences of square-root radicals:

1. Express each radical in simplest form.
2. Use the distributive axiom to add or subtract radicals with like radicands.

---

## Oral Exercises

**Indicate the terms in each expression that can be expressed with the same radicand. Then state the expression in simplest form.**

1. $4\sqrt{7} + 2\sqrt{7}$

2. $8\sqrt{5} - 2\sqrt{5}$

3. $2\sqrt{13} - 6\sqrt{13}$

4. $2\sqrt{11} + 8\sqrt{3} + 5\sqrt{11}$

5. $6\sqrt{14} - 3\sqrt{14} + \sqrt{3}$

6. $2\sqrt{21} - 4\sqrt{7} + 5\sqrt{3}$

7. $8\sqrt{3} - 7\sqrt{3}$

8. $8\sqrt{15} - 5\sqrt{15} + 7\sqrt{15}$

9. $6\sqrt{17} - 2\sqrt{17} + 3\sqrt{17}$

10. $\sqrt{12} + \sqrt{3}$

11. $\sqrt{75} + \sqrt{3}$

12. $\sqrt{18} + \sqrt{2}$

## *Written Exercises*

**Simplify.**

**A** **1.** $7\sqrt{2} - 3\sqrt{2}$

**2.** $9\sqrt{3} + 8\sqrt{3}$

**3.** $-11\sqrt{23} - 5\sqrt{23}$

**4.** $4\sqrt{45} - 3\sqrt{5}$

**5.** $2\sqrt{2} + 5\sqrt{50}$

**6.** $-2\sqrt{24} - 3\sqrt{6}$

**7.** $2\sqrt{28} - 5\sqrt{63}$

**8.** $5\sqrt{18} + 7\sqrt{25}$

**9.** $4\sqrt{32} - 3\sqrt{27}$

**10.** $-4\sqrt{75} + 3\sqrt{147}$

**11.** $-11\sqrt{8} - 7\sqrt{12}$

**12.** $\sqrt{175} - 4\sqrt{112}$

**13.** $11\sqrt{19} - 7\sqrt{11} + \sqrt{19}$

**14.** $-4\sqrt{2} + 6\sqrt{72} - 8\sqrt{32}$

**15.** $5\sqrt{28} + 2\sqrt{7} - \sqrt{14}$

**16.** $-3\sqrt{54} + 5\sqrt{40} - 6\sqrt{96}$

**17.** $-\sqrt{338} - \sqrt{200} + \sqrt{162}$

**18.** $2\sqrt{80} + 7\sqrt{44} - 8\sqrt{99}$

**Simplify.**

**Example** $\quad \sqrt{21} - \sqrt{\dfrac{3}{7}} = \sqrt{21} - \dfrac{\sqrt{3}}{\sqrt{7}}$

$$= \sqrt{21} - \dfrac{\sqrt{3} \cdot \sqrt{7}}{\sqrt{7} \cdot \sqrt{7}}$$

$$= \sqrt{21} - \dfrac{\sqrt{21}}{7}$$

$$= \dfrac{7\sqrt{21} - \sqrt{21}}{7} = \dfrac{6\sqrt{21}}{7}$$

**19.** $\sqrt{6} - \sqrt{\dfrac{2}{3}}$

**20.** $\sqrt{15} - \sqrt{\dfrac{5}{2}}$

**21.** $3\sqrt{18} + \sqrt{\dfrac{2}{25}}$

**22.** $\sqrt{\dfrac{5}{7}} - \sqrt{\dfrac{7}{5}}$

**23.** $\sqrt{\dfrac{5}{6}} - \sqrt{\dfrac{3}{10}}$

**24.** $7\sqrt{\dfrac{9}{5}} - \sqrt{\dfrac{9}{8}}$

**B** **25.** $5\sqrt{5} + 2\sqrt{20} - 6\sqrt{\dfrac{9}{10}}$

**26.** $4\sqrt{\dfrac{5}{6}} - 3\sqrt{\dfrac{6}{5}} - \sqrt{30}$

**27.** $2\sqrt{\dfrac{7}{2}} + 4\sqrt{\dfrac{7}{8}} - \dfrac{1}{2}\sqrt{98}$

**28.** $2\sqrt{\dfrac{2}{3}} + \sqrt{\dfrac{5}{6}} - \dfrac{1}{3}\sqrt{40}$

**29.** $2\sqrt{3}(\sqrt{27} - 3\sqrt{6})$

**30.** $5\sqrt{2}(4\sqrt{8} - 2\sqrt{12})$

**Simplify. Assume that all variables represent positive real numbers.**

**C** **31.** $3\sqrt{36x^3} - 5\sqrt{9x^5}$

**32.** $5\sqrt{90y^4} - 3y\sqrt{160y^2}$

**33.** $\sqrt{\dfrac{x^2}{9} + \dfrac{x^2}{16}}$

**34.** $\sqrt{\dfrac{x^2}{36} - \dfrac{x^2}{100}}$

**35.** $\sqrt{\dfrac{x^2}{a^2} + \dfrac{x^2}{b^2}}$

**36.** $\sqrt{\dfrac{x}{a} + \dfrac{a}{x}}$

# 11-9 Multiplication of Binomials Containing Radicals

**Objective**  To multiply binomials containing square-root radicals.

When working with radicals, you sometimes need to use the special methods of multiplying binomials you learned in Chapter 5.

**Example 1**  Simplify $(5 + \sqrt{3})(5 - \sqrt{3})$.

**Solution**    The pattern is $(a + b)(a - b) = a^2 - b^2$.

$$(5 + \sqrt{3})(5 - \sqrt{3}) = 5^2 - (\sqrt{3})^2$$
$$= 25 - 3 = 22$$

**Example 2**  Simplify $(5 + \sqrt{7})^2$.

**Solution**    The pattern is $(a + b)^2 = a^2 + 2ab + b^2$.

$$(5 + \sqrt{7})^2 = (5)^2 + 2(5)(\sqrt{7}) + (\sqrt{7})^2$$
$$= 25 + 10\sqrt{7} + 7 = 32 + 10\sqrt{7}$$

**Example 3**  Simplify $(3\sqrt{2} - 5\sqrt{6})^2$.

**Solution**    The pattern is $(a - b)^2 = a^2 - 2ab + b^2$.

$$(3\sqrt{2} - 5\sqrt{6})^2 = (3\sqrt{2})^2 - 2(3)(5)(\sqrt{2})(\sqrt{6}) + (5\sqrt{6})^2$$
$$= 9(2) - 30\sqrt{12} + 25(6)$$
$$= 18 - 30\sqrt{4(3)} + 150 = 168 - 60\sqrt{3}$$

If $b$ and $d$ are both nonnegative, then the binomials

$$a\sqrt{b} + c\sqrt{d} \quad \text{and} \quad a\sqrt{b} - c\sqrt{d}$$

are called **conjugates** of one another. Conjugates differ only in the sign of one term. If $a$, $b$, $c$, and $d$ are all integers, then the product

$$(a\sqrt{b} + c\sqrt{d})(a\sqrt{b} - c\sqrt{d})$$

will be an integer (see Example 1). Conjugates can be used to rationalize binomial denominators that contain radicals.

**Example 4**  Rationalize the denominator of the fraction $\dfrac{2}{4 - 2\sqrt{7}}$.

**Solution**    $\dfrac{2}{4 - 2\sqrt{7}} = \left(\dfrac{2}{4 - 2\sqrt{7}}\right)\left(\dfrac{4 + 2\sqrt{7}}{4 + 2\sqrt{7}}\right) = \dfrac{8 + 4\sqrt{7}}{16 - (2\sqrt{7})^2}$

$$= \dfrac{8 + 4\sqrt{7}}{16 - 28} = \dfrac{8 + 4\sqrt{7}}{-12} = \dfrac{-2 - \sqrt{7}}{3}$$

## Oral Exercises

**Complete. Express in simplest form.**

**1.** $(\sqrt{3} + 2)(\sqrt{3} - 2) = 3 - \underline{?} = \underline{?}$      **2.** $(7 - \sqrt{5})(7 + \sqrt{5}) = 49 - \underline{?} = \underline{?}$

**3.** $(\sqrt{2} + 5)^2 = 2 + \underline{?} + 25 = 27 + \underline{?}$      **4.** $(4 - \sqrt{7})^2 = 16 - \underline{?} + \underline{?} = \underline{?}$

**State the conjugate of each binomial.**

**5.** $9 + 3\sqrt{5}$      **6.** $-8 - 5\sqrt{11}$      **7.** $-6 + 5\sqrt{7}$      **8.** $3 - 7\sqrt{11}$

## Written Exercises

**Express in simplest form.**

**A**   **1.** $(2 - \sqrt{5})(2 + \sqrt{5})$      **2.** $(4 + \sqrt{11})(4 - \sqrt{11})$

**3.** $(\sqrt{17} + 4)(\sqrt{17} - 4)$      **4.** $(\sqrt{13} - 9)(\sqrt{13} + 9)$

**5.** $(\sqrt{15} - \sqrt{3})(\sqrt{15} + \sqrt{3})$      **6.** $(\sqrt{19} + \sqrt{21})(\sqrt{19} - \sqrt{21})$

**7.** $(5 + \sqrt{3})^2$      **8.** $(7 - \sqrt{7})^2$

**9.** $(2\sqrt{2} - 3)^2$      **10.** $(\sqrt{11} + \sqrt{3})^2$

**11.** $(\sqrt{13} + 2\sqrt{5})^2$      **12.** $(2\sqrt{7} - \sqrt{2})^2$

**13.** $2\sqrt{5}(3\sqrt{10} - 4\sqrt{5})$      **14.** $5\sqrt{3}(2\sqrt{6} - 4\sqrt{15})$

**15.** $-2\sqrt{7}(3\sqrt{14} - 5\sqrt{7})$      **16.** $4\sqrt{6}(5\sqrt{3} - \sqrt{12})$

**B**   **17.** $(4\sqrt{3} - 5)(2\sqrt{3} + 3)$      **18.** $(\sqrt{2} + 5\sqrt{11})(4\sqrt{2} - 3\sqrt{11})$

**19.** $(3\sqrt{7} - 6\sqrt{5})(4\sqrt{7} + \sqrt{5})$      **20.** $(7\sqrt{13} + 2\sqrt{6})(2\sqrt{13} + 3\sqrt{6})$

**21.** $(5\sqrt{10} - 2\sqrt{3})(5\sqrt{10} + 7\sqrt{3})$      **22.** $(8\sqrt{6} - 2\sqrt{3})(2\sqrt{6} - 3\sqrt{3})$

**Rationalize the denominator of each fraction.**

**23.** $\dfrac{4}{1 + \sqrt{2}}$      **24.** $\dfrac{3}{\sqrt{5} - 2}$

**25.** $\dfrac{1}{3 - \sqrt{3}}$      **26.** $\dfrac{1 - \sqrt{2}}{2 + \sqrt{2}}$

**27.** $\dfrac{2 + \sqrt{5}}{1 - \sqrt{3}}$      **28.** $\dfrac{\sqrt{3} - 4}{\sqrt{7} + 2}$

**29.** $\dfrac{7}{3\sqrt{3} + 4}$      **30.** $\dfrac{4 + 2\sqrt{2}}{2\sqrt{5} - 3}$

**If $f(x) = x^2 - 4x + 1$, find these function values.**

**31.** $f(\sqrt{7})$      **32.** $f(\sqrt{2} + 1)$      **33.** $f(\sqrt{3} + 2)$      **34.** $f(\sqrt{5} - 1)$

**35.** Show that $(1 + \sqrt{3})$ and $(1 - \sqrt{3})$ are roots of the equation $x^2 - 2x - 2 = 0$.

**36.** Show that $5 + \sqrt{3}$ and $5 - \sqrt{3}$ are roots of the equation $x^2 - 10x + 22 = 0$.

**37.** Show that $\dfrac{1}{3} + \dfrac{\sqrt{7}}{3}$ and $\dfrac{1}{3} - \dfrac{\sqrt{7}}{3}$ are roots of the equation $3x^2 - 2x - 2 = 0$.

**C**  **38.** Write an expression in simplest form for the area of a rectangle whose base is $\dfrac{5\sqrt{2} + 3}{5}$ units and whose height is $\dfrac{3\sqrt{2} - 2}{3}$ units.

**Simplify each expression, assuming that the value of each variable is non-negative.**

**39.** $(\sqrt{x} + y)(\sqrt{x} - y)$

**40.** $(x + 2\sqrt{3})^2$

**41.** $(3r\sqrt{s} - 2q)(5r\sqrt{s} + 3q)$

**42.** $\sqrt{\dfrac{x}{y}} - 2\sqrt{\dfrac{y}{x}} + \sqrt{xy}$

---

## Historical Note / $\pi$

The number $\pi$ occurs naturally as the ratio of the circumference of a circle to its diameter. Since $\pi$ is irrational, it is not possible to get an exact value for it. Throughout history, however, mathematicians have tried to obtain better approximations for it.

The first known approximation (other than just using 3) was given in the Rhind mathematical papyrus as $(\frac{4}{3})^4$, or 3.1604 . . . . This was used until 240 B.C. when Archimedes calculated $\pi$ to be between $\frac{223}{71}$ and $\frac{22}{7}$, or 3.14, to two decimal places. Four hundred years later this approximation was improved slightly to $\frac{377}{120}$, or 3.1416.

In China, Tsu Ch'ung-chih gave a value for $\pi$ of $\frac{355}{113}$, or 3.1415929 . . . , which is correct to six decimal places. Indian mathematicians used $\frac{62,832}{20,000}$, although this was later refined to $\frac{754}{240}$.

Following the Middle Ages, European mathematicians once again tried to get better approximations for $\pi$. François Viète found $\pi$ to nine decimal places in 1579 and Adrianus Romanus calculated it to fifteen places fourteen years later. In 1706, the calculation had reached 100 decimal places and William Jones became the first person to use the symbol $\pi$ to represent the number. By 1737 $\pi$ was in general use.

In 1767 $\pi$ was shown to be an irrational number, although this did not stop people from calculating more decimal places. By the mid-nineteenth century $\pi$ had been calculated to over 400 places. In 1948 the last calculation by hand was done to 808 places.

Since 1949 computers have been used to calculate approximations for $\pi$. The first attempt in 1949 produced 2037 decimal places (after 70 hours). By 1967 the value had been calculated to over 500,000 places.

*Rational and Irrational Numbers*  **533**

# 11-10 Simple Radical Equations

**Objective**  To solve simple radical equations.

An equation that has a variable in the radicand is called a **radical equation.** Simple radical equations are solved by isolating the radical on one side of the equals sign and then squaring both sides of the equation.

**Example 1**  Solve $\sqrt{x} = 12$.

**Solution**

$$\sqrt{x} = 12$$
$$(\sqrt{x})^2 = 144 \quad \{\text{Square both sides.}$$
$$x = 144$$

$\therefore$ the solution is 144.  **Answer**

*Check:* $\sqrt{144} \overset{?}{=} 12$
$$12 = 12 \ \checkmark$$

**Example 2**  Solve $\sqrt{4x + 1} + 5 = 8$.

**Solution**

$$\sqrt{4x + 1} + 5 = 8$$
$$\sqrt{4x + 1} = 3$$
$$4x + 1 = 9$$
$$4x = 8$$
$$x = 2$$

$\therefore$ the solution is 2.  **Answer**

*Check:* $\sqrt{4(2) + 1} + 5 \overset{?}{=} 8$
$$\sqrt{8 + 1} + 5 \overset{?}{=} 8$$
$$\sqrt{9} + 5 \overset{?}{=} 8$$
$$8 = 8 \ \checkmark$$

When you square both sides of an equation, the new equation is not necessarily equivalent to the original equation. Therefore, you must *check every apparent root in the original equation* to see whether it is a root. By the multiplication property of equality, any root of the original equation is also a root of the squared equation. Thus, you are sure to find all the roots of the original equation among the roots of the squared equation.

**Example 3**  Solve $\sqrt{10x^2 - 96} - 2x = 0$.

**Solution**

$$\sqrt{10x^2 - 96} - 2x = 0$$
$$\sqrt{10x^2 - 96} = 2x \quad \{\text{Isolate the radical.}$$
$$10x^2 - 96 = 4x^2 \quad \{\text{Square both sides.}$$
$$6x^2 = 96$$
$$x^2 = 16$$
$$x = 4 \text{ or } x = -4$$

*Check:* $\sqrt{10(4)^2 - 96} - 2(4) \overset{?}{=} 0$
$$\sqrt{160 - 96} - 8 \overset{?}{=} 0$$
$$\sqrt{64} - 8 \overset{?}{=} 0$$
$$8 - 8 = 0 \ \checkmark$$

$\sqrt{10(-4)^2 - 96} - 2(-4) \overset{?}{=} 0$
$$\sqrt{160 - 96} + 8 \overset{?}{=} 0$$
$$8 + 8 \neq 0$$
$-4$ is not a solution.

$\therefore$ the solution is 4.  **Answer**

## Oral Exercises

**Solve.**

1. $\sqrt{x} = 5$
2. $\sqrt{y} = 6$
3. $\sqrt{d} = 11$
4. $\sqrt{y} = 20$
5. $\sqrt{4a} = 10$
6. $\sqrt{3m} = 9$

**State the first step in the solution of each equation.**

7. $\sqrt{3x} = 6$
8. $\sqrt{5a + 4} = 12$
9. $\sqrt{27z - 12} = 5z$
10. $\sqrt{z - 7} = 8$
11. $2\sqrt{3b} = 4$
12. $\sqrt{5x} - 3 = 12$

## Written Exercises

**Solve.**

**A**
1. $\sqrt{x} = 10$
2. $\sqrt{y} = 14$
3. $\sqrt{2m} = 8$
4. $\sqrt{3a} = 9$
5. $\sqrt{4m} = \frac{1}{3}$
6. $\sqrt{8x} = \frac{2}{5}$
7. $\sqrt{n} + 2 = 7$
8. $\sqrt{z} - 3 = 8$
9. $\frac{1}{3} + \sqrt{x} = 2$
10. $\sqrt{\frac{x}{2}} = 3$
11. $\sqrt{\frac{a}{5}} = 6$
12. $\sqrt{y - 3} = 2$
13. $\sqrt{m + 5} = 1$
14. $3\sqrt{2b} = 6$
15. $5\sqrt{3z} = 3$
16. $\sqrt{4x} + 2 = 6$
17. $\sqrt{3x} - 5 = 4$
18. $\sqrt{8a} + 3 = 4$
19. $\sqrt{2z + 3} + 1 = 4$
20. $\sqrt{5y - 2} + 3 = 9$
21. $\sqrt{6x - 1} - 4 = -1$
22. $\sqrt{\frac{4y}{3}} + 2 = 10$
23. $\sqrt{\frac{8b}{5}} - 3 = 4$
24. $\sqrt{\frac{7m}{6}} - 1 = 8$

**B**
25. $\sqrt{\frac{2x + 3}{5}} = 3$
26. $\sqrt{\frac{4n - 5}{7}} = 3$
27. $\sqrt{\frac{7k - 10}{9}} = 4$
28. $\sqrt{r} = 4\sqrt{5}$
29. $6\sqrt{t} = 18\sqrt{7}$
30. $6\sqrt{y} = 5\sqrt{10}$
31. $\sqrt{2a^2 - 5} = 11$
32. $2\sqrt{3c^2 + 2} = 10$
33. $4\sqrt{4y^2 + 5} = 36$
34. $\sqrt{x^2 + 4} = 2 - x$
35. $\sqrt{5b^2 - 36} = 2b$
36. $\sqrt{12m^2 - 45} = 3m$
37. $\sqrt{x^2 + 1} = 1 - x$
38. $\sqrt{3a^2 - 32} = a$
39. $\sqrt{7b^2 + 14} = 3b$

**C**
40. $\sqrt{a^2 + 8a} = 3$
41. $\sqrt{15x^2 - 12x} = 9x$
42. $\sqrt{x} + 2 = \sqrt{9x}$
43. $\sqrt{c^2 + 3c} = 2$
44. $\sqrt{10y^2 - 16y} = 4y$
45. $\sqrt{a} + 1 = \sqrt{4a}$

**Solve the following systems of equations.**

46. $2\sqrt{a} + 3\sqrt{b} = 13$
$4\sqrt{a} - 3\sqrt{b} = -1$

47. $5\sqrt{a} - 2\sqrt{b} = 4\sqrt{2}$
$2\sqrt{a} + 3\sqrt{b} = 13\sqrt{2}$

## Problems

**Solve.**

**A**

**1.** The square root of twice a number is 14. Find the number.

**2.** Twice the square root of a number is 22. Find the number.

**3.** One sixth of the square root of a number is 5. Find the number.

**4.** The square root of one sixth of a number is 5. Find the number.

**5.** When 4 times a number is increased by 5, the square root of the result is 11. Find the number.

**6.** When 6 is subtracted from the square root of twice a number, the result is 58. Find the number.

**B**

**7.** The radius of a circle is related to the area of a circle by the formula $r = \sqrt{\dfrac{A}{\pi}}$. Find the area of a circle whose radius is 15 cm. Express your answer in terms of $\pi$.

**8.** The radius of a cylinder is related to its volume and its height by the formula $r = \sqrt{\dfrac{V}{\pi h}}$. Find the volume of a cylinder whose radius is 12 cm and whose height is 25 cm. Express your answer in terms of $\pi$.

**9.** The velocity of a free-falling object can be found by using the formula $v = \sqrt{2gd}$, where $v$ is in m/s, $g = 9.8$ m/s², and $d$ is the distance in meters. Find the distance a ball falls if its velocity is 14 m/s.

**C**

**10.** The current $I$ that flows through an electrical appliance is determined by $I = \sqrt{\dfrac{P}{R}}$, where $P$ is the power required and $R$ is the resistance of the appliance. To use this formula, express the current in amperes (A), the power in watts (W), and the resistance in ohms ($\Omega$). If an electric hair dryer has a resistance of 60 $\Omega$ and draws 4.5 A of current, how much power does it use?

**11.** The geometric mean of two numbers is the positive square root of their product. Find two consecutive even integers whose geometric mean is $10\sqrt{26}$.

**12.** The period of a pendulum ($T$) is the amount of time (in seconds) it takes the pendulum to make a complete swing back and forth. The period is determined by the formula $T = 2\pi\sqrt{\dfrac{l}{9.8}}$ where $l$ is the length of the pendulum in meters. Find the length of a pendulum with a period of 6 seconds. Express your answer to the nearest tenth. (Use $\pi \approx 3.14$.)

# Self-Test 3

**Vocabulary**    simplest form of a radical                conjugate (p. 531)
                 (p. 527)                                  radical equation (p. 534)
                 rationalizing the denominator
                 (p. 527)

**Express in simplest form.**

**1.** $2\sqrt{3} \cdot 5\sqrt{3}$

**2.** $\sqrt{\dfrac{7}{9}} \cdot \sqrt{\dfrac{27}{21}}$                    Obj. 11-7, p. 527

**3.** $4\sqrt{5} + \sqrt{11} - 3\sqrt{11} + \sqrt{5}$    **4.** $5\sqrt{48} - 8\sqrt{27}$    Obj. 11-8, p. 529

**5.** $(3 - \sqrt{6})^2$    **6.** $(\sqrt{5} - \sqrt{2})(\sqrt{5} + \sqrt{2})$    Obj. 11-9, p. 531

**Rationalize the denominator.**

**7.** $\dfrac{4}{\sqrt{5} + 1}$

**8.** $\dfrac{\sqrt{3}}{\sqrt{3} - 2}$

**Solve.**

**9.** $\sqrt{y} + 3 = 5$    **10.** $\sqrt{5x - 2} + 3 = 6$    Obj. 11-10, p. 534

Check your answers with those at the back of the book.

---

# *Extra* / *Fractional Exponents*

In Chapter 4 you learned the Rule of Exponents for Multiplication, which states that for all positive integers $m$ and $n$, $a^m \cdot a^n = a^{m+n}$. Thus, you can simplify $2^3 \cdot 2^4$ as follows.

$$2^3 \cdot 2^4 = 2^{3+4} = 2^7$$

If the Rule of Exponents for Multiplication were to hold for all positive numbers, and not just for positive integers, what would be the value of $n$ in the equation $2^n \cdot 2^n = 2$?

Since    $2^n \cdot 2^n = 2^{n+n} = 2^{2n}$,

you have    $2^{2n} = 2$.

The bases are equal (and not $-1$, 0, or 1); therefore, the exponents must be equal. Thus, $2n = 1$, or $n = \frac{1}{2}$, and you have $2^{\frac{1}{2}} \cdot 2^{\frac{1}{2}} = 2$.
    Because $\sqrt{2} \cdot \sqrt{2} = 2$ and $(-\sqrt{2})(-\sqrt{2}) = 2$, it makes sense to define $2^{\frac{1}{2}}$ as either the positive or the negative square root of 2. Selecting the positive, or principal, square root, we define

$$2^{\frac{1}{2}} = \sqrt{2}.$$

---

*Rational and Irrational Numbers*    **537**

Radicals are not restricted to square roots. The symbol $\sqrt[n]{a}$ is used to indicate the principal $n$th root of $a$, where $n$ is a positive integer. Thus, you can have third (or cube) roots, fourth roots, fifth roots, and so on. As you have seen, the *root index, n,* is omitted when $n = 2$.

Just as the inverse of squaring a number is finding the square root of that number, the inverse of cubing a number is finding its cube root. For example, since $2^3 = 8$, $\sqrt[3]{8}$, read "the cube root of 8," is 2. Likewise, since $(-2)^3 = -8$, $\sqrt[3]{-8} = -2$.

Notice that it is possible to find the cube root of a negative number. In fact, if the root index is any odd positive integer, it is possible to find that root of a negative number. In general,

---

If $n$ is an odd positive integer, $\sqrt[n]{a^n} = a$.

If $n$ is an even positive integer, $\sqrt[n]{a^n} = |a|$.

---

**Example 1** Solve $5^n \cdot 5^n \cdot 5^n = 5$.

**Solution**
$$5^n \cdot 5^n \cdot 5^n = 5$$
$$5^{3n} = 5$$

Since the bases are equal the exponents are equal.

Thus, $\quad 3n = 1$

$$n = \frac{1}{3}$$

Is it always possible to find the $n$th root of $a$? Think of $a^n$. Since $a^n$ is always positive when $n$ is an even integer, $\sqrt[n]{a}$, and hence $a^{\frac{1}{n}}$, its *exponential* form, do not name a real number if $n$ is even and $a < 0$. For example, since $2^4 = (-2)^4 = 16$, $\sqrt[4]{-16}$, or $(-16)^{\frac{1}{4}}$, does not name a real number. Thus, we have the following definition.

---

For all integers $n > 1$,
$$a^{\frac{1}{n}} = \sqrt[n]{a},$$
unless $a < 0$ and $n$ is even.

---

**Example 2** Write each of the following radicals in exponential form.
   **a.** $\sqrt{3}$   **b.** $\sqrt[3]{6}$   **c.** $\sqrt[4]{2}$   **d.** $\sqrt[5]{-10}$

**Solution**   **a.** $\sqrt{3} = \sqrt[2]{3^1} = 3^{\frac{1}{2}}$   **b.** $\sqrt[3]{6} = \sqrt[3]{6^1} = 6^{\frac{1}{3}}$
   **c.** $\sqrt[4]{2} = \sqrt[4]{2^1} = 2^{\frac{1}{4}}$   **d.** $\sqrt[5]{-10} = \sqrt[5]{(-10)^1} = (-10)^{\frac{1}{5}}$

***Example 3*** Simplify.

$\qquad$ **a.** $36^{\frac{1}{2}}$  **b.** $27^{\frac{1}{3}}$  **c.** $(-32)^{\frac{1}{5}}$  **d.** $(-256)^{\frac{1}{4}}$

***Solution***  **a.** $36^{\frac{1}{2}} = \sqrt{36} = \sqrt{6^2} = 6$

$\qquad$ **b.** $27^{\frac{1}{3}} = \sqrt[3]{27} = \sqrt[3]{3^3} = 3$

$\qquad$ **c.** $(-32)^{\frac{1}{5}} = \sqrt[5]{-32} = \sqrt[5]{(-2)^5} = -2$

$\qquad$ **d.** $(-256)^{\frac{1}{4}} = \sqrt[4]{-256}$, which does not name a real number.

$\qquad$ You know that $\sqrt[3]{5} = 5^{\frac{1}{3}}$. But how would you write $(\sqrt[3]{5})^2$ in exponential form? If the Rule of Exponents for a Power of a Power is to be true for all positive exponents, then

$$(\sqrt[3]{5})^2 = (5^{\frac{1}{3}})^2 = 5^{2 \cdot \frac{1}{3}} = 5^{\frac{2}{3}}.$$

This suggests the following definition.

---

If $\sqrt[n]{a}$ is a real number and $m$ and $n$ are positive integers,
then $(\sqrt[n]{a})^m = a^{\frac{m}{n}}$.

---

***Example 4*** Write each of the following radicals in exponential form.

$\qquad$ **a.** $(\sqrt[3]{3})^2$  **b.** $(\sqrt{3})^3$  **c.** $(\sqrt[4]{2})^3$  **d.** $(\sqrt[5]{6})^4$

***Solution***  **a.** $(\sqrt[3]{3})^2 = (3^{\frac{1}{3}})^2 = 3^{\frac{2}{3}}$  **b.** $(\sqrt{3})^3 = (3^{\frac{1}{2}})^3 = 3^{\frac{3}{2}}$

$\qquad$ **c.** $(\sqrt[4]{2})^3 = (2^{\frac{1}{4}})^3 = 2^{\frac{3}{4}}$  **d.** $(\sqrt[5]{6})^4 = (6^{\frac{1}{5}})^4 = 6^{\frac{4}{5}}$

***Example 5*** Simplify.

$\qquad$ **a.** $9^{\frac{3}{2}}$  **b.** $81^{\frac{3}{4}}$  **c.** $(-8)^{\frac{2}{3}}$  **d.** $(-9)^{\frac{5}{2}}$

***Solution***  **a.** $9^{\frac{3}{2}} = (9^{\frac{1}{2}})^3 = (\sqrt[2]{9})^3 = (\sqrt{3^2})^3 = 3^3 = 27$

$\qquad$ **b.** $81^{\frac{3}{4}} = (81^{\frac{1}{4}})^3 = (\sqrt[4]{81})^3 = (\sqrt[4]{3^4})^3 = 3^3 = 27$

$\qquad$ **c.** $(-8)^{\frac{2}{3}} = [(-8)^{\frac{1}{3}}]^2 = (\sqrt[3]{-8})^2 = [\sqrt[3]{(-2)^3}]^2 = (-2)^2 = 4$

$\qquad$ **d.** $(-9)^{\frac{5}{2}} = [(-9)^{\frac{1}{2}}]^5 = (\sqrt{-9})^5$, which does not name a real number.

## Exercises

Write each of the following radicals in exponential form.

**1.** $\sqrt{5}$ $\qquad$ **2.** $\sqrt[5]{7}$ $\qquad$ **3.** $\sqrt[4]{3}$ $\qquad$ **4.** $\sqrt[3]{-10}$

**5.** $(\sqrt[3]{6})^2$ $\qquad$ **6.** $(\sqrt[4]{5})^3$ $\qquad$ **7.** $(\sqrt{2})^3$ $\qquad$ **8.** $(\sqrt[3]{3})^5$

Simplify. If the expression does not represent a real number, indicate this.

**9.** $49^{\frac{1}{2}}$ $\qquad$ **10.** $64^{\frac{1}{3}}$ $\qquad$ **11.** $(-27)^{\frac{1}{3}}$ $\qquad$ **12.** $(-81)^{\frac{1}{4}}$

**13.** $16^{\frac{3}{4}}$ $\qquad$ **14.** $9^{\frac{5}{2}}$ $\qquad$ **15.** $81^{\frac{1}{4}}$ $\qquad$ **16.** $(-9)^{\frac{3}{2}}$

**17.** $(25)^{\frac{3}{2}}$ $\qquad$ **18.** $(-64)^{\frac{2}{3}}$ $\qquad$ **19.** $27^{\frac{4}{3}}$ $\qquad$ **20.** $(-32)^{\frac{3}{5}}$

# Application / Boyle's Gas Law

Air and other gases have characteristics of temperature, pressure, and volume much the same as do liquids, such as water. Air temperature is measured in degrees, volume in cubic centimeters or liters, and pressure in millimeters.

Robert Boyle, a seventeenth-century English scientist, investigated many properties of air and gases. He conducted experiments to see how the pressure of a gas in an enclosed space is related to its volume. His discovery is used today in the modern internal combustion engine and in a simple basketball or bicycle pump.

Boyle observed that pressure on a confined gas reduces its volume. In fact, he found that with a constant temperature, the volume of a gas varies inversely with the pressure exerted on it. This statement, known as Boyle's Law, can be written in these two ways.

$$pV = k, \text{ where } k \text{ is a constant,}$$
$$V \text{ is the volume, and}$$
$$p \text{ is the pressure.}$$

or
$$pV = p'V', \text{ where } p' \text{ and } V' \text{ are the new}$$
pressure and the new volume,
respectively.

**Example**  A gas has a volume of 600 mL at a pressure of 760 mm. What is the volume of the gas at a pressure of 800 mm?

**Solution**
$$pV = p'V'$$
$$760 \times 600 = 800V'$$
$$\frac{760 \times 600}{800} = V'$$
$$570 = V'$$
$$\therefore \text{ the volume is 570 mL.}$$

## Exercises

1. A certain gas has a volume of 420 cm³ at a pressure of 720 mm. What will its volume be if the pressure is increased to 840 mm?

2. A gas kept at 760 mm of pressure occupies 2 L. What pressure must be exerted for the volume to decrease to 1.9 L?

3. A certain gas has a volume of 500 cm³ at a pressure of 750 mm. If the pressure is decreased to 625 mm, what is the resulting volume?

4. A gas occupies 2 m³ of space at 760 mm of pressure. It is compressed to 1 m³ of space. What is the new pressure?

5. An underinflated balloon contains 9 m³ of helium when the pressure is 760 mm. What is the volume of the balloon when it reaches an altitude where the pressure is 304 mm?

An architect must design offices, shopping malls, and other buildings to be safe and functional as well as attractive. Thus, architects must be able to solve engineering and technical problems in addition to being talented in architectural design.

Architecture involves a variety of skills. Architects are involved in all phases of the development of a structure. They draw detailed plans, specify building materials, and may assist in negotiating, hiring, and supervising contractors. The buildings they design must meet fire and building codes as well as other local standards.

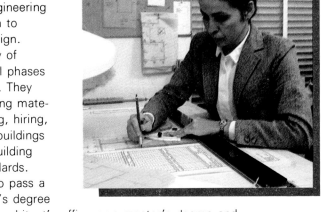

All states require architects to pass a licensing examination. A bachelor's degree and three years experience in an architect's office or a master's degree and two years experience usually qualify a person to take the licensing exam.

# Chapter Summary

1. A rational number can be expressed as a fraction in simplest form, $\frac{a}{b}$, where $a$ and $b$ are integers and $b > 0$. Rational numbers in fractional form can be expressed as either terminating or repeating decimals by dividing.

2. Irrational numbers are represented by nonterminating, nonrepeating decimals which may be rounded to a convenient number of places for use in computation. These numbers cannot be represented in fraction form.

3. Square roots may be rational or irrational. Irrational square roots may be approximated using a table of square roots or a calculator.

4. Some quadratic equations can be solved using the property of square roots of equal numbers (page 517).

5. Many problems involving right triangles can be solved using the Pythagorean theorem:

$$a^2 + b^2 = c^2$$

6. Radical expressions can be added, subtracted, multiplied, and divided. The product and quotient properties of square roots (pages 510, 511) are useful in simplifying expressions involving radicals. Divisions can often be simplified by rationalizing the denominator.

*Rational and Irrational Numbers* **541**

# Chapter Review

**Give the letter of the correct answer.**

11-1

1. Find the rational number halfway between $\frac{1}{2}$ and $\frac{7}{8}$.

   **a.** $\frac{3}{4}$ **b.** $\frac{11}{16}$ **c.** $\frac{2}{3}$ **d.** $\frac{5}{8}$

2. Compare $\frac{3}{4}$ and $\frac{9}{13}$.

   **a.** $\frac{3}{4} > \frac{9}{13}$ **b.** $\frac{9}{13} > \frac{3}{4}$ **c.** $\frac{3}{4} = \frac{9}{13}$

11-2

3. Express $\frac{5}{11}$ as a decimal.

   **a.** 0.45 **b.** $0.\overline{454}$ **c.** $0.\overline{45}$ **d.** $0.0\overline{45}$

4. Express $0.\overline{57}$ as a fraction in simplest form.

   **a.** $\frac{57}{100}$ **b.** $\frac{57}{99}$ **c.** $\frac{575}{1000}$ **d.** $\frac{19}{33}$

11-3

5. Find $\sqrt{5184}$.

   **a.** 720 **b.** 7.2 **c.** 72 **d.** 0.72

6. Find $\sqrt{\dfrac{256}{400}}$.

   **a.** $\frac{7}{10}$ **b.** $\frac{3}{4}$ **c.** $\frac{6}{5}$ **d.** $\frac{4}{5}$

11-4

7. Approximate $\sqrt{2700}$ to the nearest hundredth using the Table of Square Roots on page 650.

   **a.** 5.196 **b.** 51.96 **c.** 519.6 **d.** 51.9

8. Simplify $\sqrt{88}$.

   **a.** 8 **b.** $8\sqrt{11}$ **c.** $4\sqrt{22}$ **d.** $2\sqrt{22}$

11-5

9. Simplify $\sqrt{2.25a^4b^2c^6}$.

   **a.** $1.5a^2|bc^3|$ **b.** $1.5\sqrt{a^4b^2c^6}$ **c.** $1.5a^2bc^3$

10. Solve $5z^2 - 405 = 0$.

   **a.** $\{9\}$ **b.** $\{9, -9\}$ **c.** $\{3, -3\}$ **d.** $\{81, -81\}$

11-6

11. The shorter sides of a right triangle are 16 cm and 30 cm long. Find the length of the hypotenuse.

   **a.** 14 cm **b.** 46 cm **c.** 34 cm **d.** 1156 cm

12. Can a right triangle have sides 15 m, 36 m, and 39 m long?

   **a.** yes **b.** no

11-7

13. Simplify $\sqrt{15} \cdot \sqrt{50}$.

   **a.** $\sqrt{750}$ **b.** $5\sqrt{30}$ **c.** $6\sqrt{125}$ **d.** $5\sqrt{6}$

11-8

14. Simplify $\sqrt{16} + 3\sqrt{8} - 2\sqrt{2}$.

   **a.** $4 + 3\sqrt{8} - 2\sqrt{2}$ **b.** $4 + 5\sqrt{2}$ **c.** $4 + 4\sqrt{2}$ **d.** $8\sqrt{2}$

11-9

15. Multiply $(3 + \sqrt{7})(3 - \sqrt{7})$.

   **a.** $9 - \sqrt{7}$ **b.** $-40$ **c.** $9 - 2\sqrt{7}$ **d.** 2

**16.** Rationalize the denominator of $\dfrac{\sqrt{3}}{\sqrt{3} - 2}$.

    **a.** $\dfrac{\sqrt{3}}{5}$        **b.** $-3 - 2\sqrt{3}$    **c.** $\dfrac{3 + 2\sqrt{3}}{5}$     **d.** $3 + 2\sqrt{3}$

**17.** Solve $\sqrt{5x + 1} - 6 = 8$.                                          **11-10**

    **a.** 39               **b.** 3                **c.** 51           **d.** $\dfrac{13}{5}$

# Chapter Test

**1.** Find the rational number halfway between $\dfrac{5}{16}$ and $\dfrac{1}{32}$.          **11-1**

**2.** Arrange $\dfrac{77}{32}, \dfrac{56}{25}, \dfrac{64}{27}$, in order from least to greatest.

**3.** Express $\dfrac{7}{12}$ as a decimal.                                    **11-2**

**4.** Express $0.1\overline{6}$ as a fraction in simplest form.

**5.** Find the indicated square roots.                              **11-3**

    **a.** $\sqrt{\dfrac{169}{2304}}$      **b.** $\sqrt{0.0036}$

**6.** Use the Table of Square Roots on page 650 to approximate $\sqrt{4400}$ to     **11-4**
the nearest tenth.

**7.** Simplify:   **a.** $\sqrt{150}$     **b.** $4\sqrt{216}$

**8.** Simplify $\sqrt{121a^4b^{10}}$.                                  **11-5**

**9.** Solve $5a^2 - 80 = 0$.

**10.** In a right triangle, the hypotenuse is 19 m long, and one of the shorter    **11-6**
sides is 8 m long. Find the length of the other side to the nearest hundredth.

**11.** Is a triangle with sides 14 units, 48 units, and 50 units long a right triangle?

**Express in simplest form.**

**12.** $6\sqrt{243}$                          **13.** $\dfrac{6\sqrt{12}}{12\sqrt{6}}$                    **11-7**

**14.** $4\sqrt{2} + \sqrt{72}$                  **15.** $3\sqrt{32} - 5\sqrt{8}$             **11-8**

**16.** $(\sqrt{5} + 3)^2$                      **17.** $(\sqrt{7} - \sqrt{2})(\sqrt{7} + \sqrt{2})$      **11-9**

**18.** Rationalize the denominator of $\dfrac{6}{2\sqrt{5} - 3}$.

**19.** Solve $\sqrt{3x + 2} = 4$.                                      **11-10**

# Cumulative Review (Chapters 1–11)

**Simplify. Assume that no denominator is zero.**

**1.** $-27 \div 3 + 6 \times (-2)$    **2.** $(2ab^2)^2(3a^2 + 5ab + b^2)$    **3.** $(4a^3b + 9c^2)^2$

**4.** $(-12x + 7y)(x - 5y)$    **5.** $(3.2 \times 10^{-4})^2$    **6.** $(6x^2 + 10x + 9) \div (3x - 1)$

**7.** $\dfrac{7x^2 + 50x + 7}{x^2 + 6x + 9} \cdot \dfrac{2x^2 + 7x + 3}{2x^2 + 15x + 7}$    **8.** $\dfrac{3x^2 - 14x + 15}{x^2 + 10x + 25} \div \dfrac{3x^2 + 10x - 25}{x^2 - 25}$

**9.** $\dfrac{t-2}{t+4} + \dfrac{1}{t-2} + 3$    **10.** $\sqrt{4225}$    **11.** $\sqrt{112} - \sqrt{63}$    **12.** $2\sqrt{3}(5\sqrt{6} + 4\sqrt{2})$

**13.** $\dfrac{5\sqrt{75}}{\sqrt{90}}$    **14.** $\dfrac{4}{\sqrt{7} - 1}$    **15.** $\sqrt{\dfrac{2}{3}} + \sqrt{\dfrac{5}{6}}$

**Factor completely.**

**16.** $16x^4 - 72x^2y^2 + 81y^4$    **17.** $4c^2 - 4cd + d^2 - 9$    **18.** $22b^2 + 5b - 3$

**Graph the solution set. (In Ex. 19, use a number line.)**

**19.** $|2 - x| \le 4$    **20.** $4x + 3y = 3$    **21.** $x + 2y > 6$

**22.** Write an equation in standard form of the line that contains $(0, 4)$ and $(1, -1)$.

**23.** Find the least value of the function $f: x \rightarrow x^2 - 4x + 4$.

**24.** Express $0.\overline{5}$ and $0.1\overline{5}$ as fractions. Then find their sum.

**25.** Graph the solution set of the system: $\begin{aligned} x - y &< 3 \\ 2x + y &> -1 \end{aligned}$

**Solve each equation, inequality, or system. Assume that no denominator is zero. If there is no solution, state that fact.**

**26.** $2y - 3 = |-15|$    **27.** $y\%$ of $80 = 12$    **28.** $\dfrac{1}{3}y - 2 = \dfrac{1}{2}$

**29.** $4y^2 + 20y + 25 = 0$    **30.** $6t^2 + 7t = 3$    **31.** $\dfrac{1}{x} + \dfrac{2-x}{x+3} = \dfrac{1}{x+3}$

**32.** $\begin{aligned} x - 2y &= 8 \\ 3x + 2y &= 9 \end{aligned}$    **33.** $\begin{aligned} 2x - 5y &= -1 \\ 3x - 10y &= -1 \end{aligned}$    **34.** $\begin{aligned} 2x + 11y &= 3 \\ 5x + 28y &= 7 \end{aligned}$

**35.** $4 \le 2x - 3 \le 9$    **36.** $3|y - 1| > 12$    **37.** $7 - 3b < 9$

**38.** $2\sqrt{t} = 3\sqrt{2}$    **39.** $\sqrt{y - 1} = y - 3$    **40.** $\sqrt{z^2 + 7} = z - 1$

**41.** The hypotenuse of a right triangle is 18 cm long and another side is 9 cm long. Find the length of the third side to the nearest hundredth. (Use the Table of Square Roots on page 650.)

**42.** Two groups entering a museum each paid $63. One group included ten adults and nine children. The other included six adults and eighteen children. Find the admission price for children and for adults.

# Maintaining Skills

**Solve each system.**

***Example 1*** (Substitution Method)  $x - 2y = 1$
$$3x - 5y = 6$$

***Solution*** Solve one equation for one of the variables (in this case, $x$) and substitute in the other equation.

$$x - 2y = 1 \longrightarrow x = 2y + 1$$
$$3x - 5y = 6 \qquad 3(2y + 1) - 5y = 6$$
$$6y + 3 - 5y = 6$$
$$y + 3 = 6$$
$$y = 3$$

$x - 2(3) = 1; \; x - 6 = 1; \; x = 7$

The check is left to you. The solution is $(7, 3)$.

***Example 2*** (Multiplication with the Addition-or-Subtraction Method) $7x - 2y = 4$
$$3x + \; y = 11$$

***Solution***
$$\begin{array}{lll} 7x - 2y = 4 & & 7x - 2y = 4 \\ 3x + \; y = 11 & -\times 2 \longrightarrow & 6x + 2y = 22 \\ \hline & & 13x \qquad\;\; = 26; \; x = 2 \end{array}$$

$7(2) - 2y = 4; \; 14 - 2y = 4; \; -2y = -10; \; y = 5$

The check is left to you. The solution is $(2, 5)$.

**1.** $x + y = 1$
$\quad 2x + y = 0$

**2.** $x + y = 3$
$\quad 2x - y = 6$

**3.** $2x + y = 15$
$\quad x + 2y = 15$

**4.** $3x + 4y = -2$
$\quad 4x + 3y = -12$

**5.** $2x + 3y = 2$
$\quad 8x + 9y = 7$

**6.** $9x + 4y = 5$
$\quad y = 4x$

**7.** $4x + 5 = y$
$\quad 2x + y = 1$

**8.** $y - x = 20$
$\quad 2x + 3y = 10$

**9.** $3x - 4y = 9$
$\quad x + 2y = 13$

**10.** $5x - 6y = 2$
$\quad 4y - 5x = 12$

**11.** $x + 10y = 2$
$\quad \frac{1}{3}x + y = 3$

**12.** $\frac{4}{5}x - \frac{1}{2}y = 18$
$\quad \frac{1}{2}x - \frac{3}{4}y = 20$

**13.** $y = 7x$
$\quad 5x - 8y = 0$

**14.** $x - 2y = 5$
$\quad -2x + 3y = -5$

**15.** $2x + 3y = 11$
$\quad 3x + 14y = 7$

**16.** $5x + 6y = 4$
$\quad 3x + 6y = 3$

**17.** $4x + 3y = 8$
$\quad 5x + 4y = 13$

**18.** $5x - 6y = 1$
$\quad 2x - 3y = 7$

**19.** $6x - 5y = 0$
$\quad 5x - 3y = 7$

**20.** $2x - 7y = 9$
$\quad x + 8y = 16$

**21.** $3x - 5y = 7$
$\quad -2x + 7y = 10$

# 12 Quadratic Functions

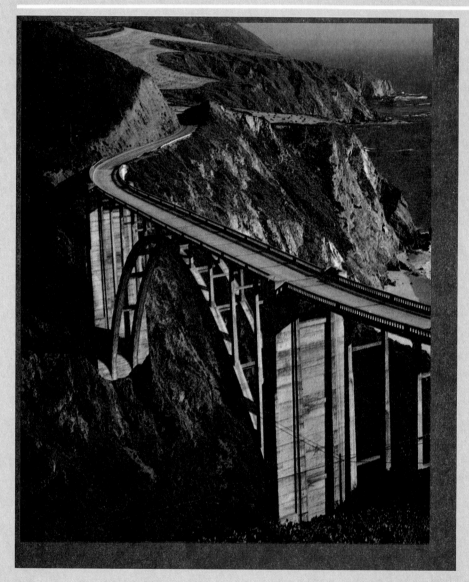

Parabolic curves, often used in bridge designs because of their strength and beauty, can be seen in this arch bridge on Coastal Highway 1 near Big Sur, California.

# Quadratic Equations

---

## 12-1 Quadratic Equations with Perfect Squares

**Objective**   To solve quadratic equations involving perfect squares.

You learned in Chapter 5 how to solve certain quadratic equations by factoring. In Chapter 11 you learned how to solve quadratic equations of the form $x^2 = k$. This section extends what you learned in Chapter 11 to any quadratic equation involving a perfect square. Later in this chapter you will learn more general methods that can be used to solve any quadratic equation or to determine that the equation has no real-number solutions.

The property of square roots of equal numbers enables you to analyze equations of the form $x^2 = k$ as follows:

---

If $k > 0$, then $x^2 = k$ has two real-number roots: $x = \pm\sqrt{k}$

If $k = 0$, then $x^2 = k$ has one real-number root: $x = 0$

If $k < 0$, then $x^2 = k$ has no real-number roots.

---

The property of square roots of equal numbers also suggests a basic strategy for solving quadratic equations such as the one in the following example.

**Example 1**   Solve $(x + 2)^2 = 49$.

**Solution**

$$(x + 2)^2 = 49$$
$$x + 2 = \pm 7$$
$$x = -2 \pm 7$$
$$x = 5 \text{ or } x = -9$$

Check: $(5 + 2)^2 \overset{?}{=} 49 \qquad (-9 + 2)^2 \overset{?}{=} 49$
$\qquad\quad (7)^2 \overset{?}{=} 49 \qquad\qquad (-7)^2 \overset{?}{=} 49$
$\qquad\quad 49 = 49 \text{ } \checkmark \qquad\qquad 49 = 49 \text{ } \checkmark$

$\therefore$ the solution set is $\{5, -9\}$.   **Answer**

An expression such as $(x + 2)^2$, $x^2$, or $(3x - 2)^2$ is called a **perfect square.** Whenever an equation can be expressed in the form

$$\text{perfect square} = k \quad (k \geq 0)$$

you can solve it by the method shown above. (You may find it helpful to reread Section 5-6 about squaring binomials.)

---

***Example 2*** Solve:  **a.** $3(x - 2)^2 = 42$    **b.** $y^2 + 8y + 16 = 36$

***Solution***    **a.** $3(x - 2)^2 = 42$
$$(x - 2)^2 = 14$$
$$x - 2 = \pm\sqrt{14}$$
$$x = 2 \pm \sqrt{14}$$

The check is left to you.

∴ the solution set is $\{2 + \sqrt{14},\ 2 - \sqrt{14}\}$.  ***Answer***

**b.** $y^2 + 8y + 16 = 36$
$$(y + 4)^2 = 36$$
$$y + 4 = \pm\sqrt{36}$$
$$y = -4 \pm 6$$

The check is left to you.

∴ the solution set is $\{2, -10\}$.  ***Answer***

The perfect squares occurring in Example 2 are $(x - 2)^2$ and $(y + 4)^2$. You should note that Example 2(b) could have been solved by factoring.

An equation that has a negative number as one side and a perfect square as the other side has no real-number solutions. The reason for this is that the square of any real number is always a nonnegative real number.

***Example 3*** Solve $3(2x - 6)^2 + 17 = 2$.

***Solution***    $3(2x - 6)^2 + 17 = 2$
$$3(2x - 6)^2 = -15$$
$$(2x - 6)^2 = -5$$

∴ there is no real-number solution.  ***Answer***

## Oral Exercises

**Express each trinomial as the square of a binomial.**

***Example***    $x^2 + 6x + 9 = (x + 3)^2$

**1.** $x^2 + 4x + 4$            **2.** $x^2 - 6x + 9$            **3.** $x^2 + 12x + 36$

**4.** $x^2 - 16x + 64$          **5.** $x^2 - 10x + 25$         **6.** $x^2 - 24x + 144$

**Solve.**

**7.** $3r^2 = 75$              **8.** $y^2 = \dfrac{1}{64}$             **9.** $5x^2 - 35 = 0$

# Written Exercises

**Solve. Express irrational solutions in simplest radical form. If the equation has no solution, write "no solution."**

**A**

1. $x^2 = 49$

2. $y^2 = \frac{36}{64}$

3. $t^2 = \frac{121}{144}$

4. $a^2 = -4$

5. $3x^2 = 108$

6. $5r^2 = 175$

7. $13x^2 = 52$

8. $x^2 - 32 = 0$

9. $x^2 + 32 = 0$

10. $m^2 - 48 = 0$

11. $6x^2 - 18 = 0$

12. $9m^2 - 63 = 0$

13. $4y^2 + 7 = 19$

14. $3r^2 - 5 = 7$

15. $2z^2 - 13 = -1$

16. $6y^2 - 2 = 16$

17. $2x^2 + 8 = 30$

18. $2t^2 + 8 = 1$

19. $(x + 3)^2 = 9$

20. $(r - 5)^2 = 8$

21. $(y + 2)^2 = 12$

22. $(t - 4)^2 = 24$

23. $(z - 3)^2 = 32$

24. $3(x - 1)^2 = 12$

25. $5(m - 8)^2 = 25$

26. $7(x + 2)^2 = 42$

27. $4(z + 3)^2 = 24$

28. $(3x + 2)^2 = 64$

29. $2(6r - 1)^2 = 32$

30. $6(5z - 3)^2 = 96$

**B**

31. $r^2 + 4r + 4 = 9$

32. $x^2 - 14x + 49 = 64$

33. $t^2 + 20t + 100 = 121$

34. $y^2 - 18y + 81 = 144$

35. $\frac{1}{3}x^2 - \frac{3}{16} = 0$

36. $\frac{1}{4}t^2 - \frac{9}{64} = 0$

37. $\frac{1}{4}r^2 - 4 = \frac{3}{4}$

38. $\frac{1}{6}x^2 - 4 = \frac{5}{6}$

39. $1.69y^2 + 5 = 5.64$

40. $0.49x^2 + 2 = 3.96$

41. $0.64z^2 - 0.91 = -0.55$

42. $5(t + 2)^2 = \frac{3}{5}$

43. $4(x - 3)^2 = \frac{1}{36}$

44. $\left(y - \frac{3}{7}\right)^2 = -\frac{8}{9}$

45. $\left(z - \frac{4}{9}\right)^2 = \frac{3}{16}$

**Solve each equation by factoring.**

46. $5y^3 - 45y = 0$

47. $7a^3 - 175a = 0$

48. $\frac{1}{3}t^3 - 12t = 0$

49. $4b^3 - \frac{1}{4}b = 0$

50. $6x^3 = 216x$

51. $8x^3 = 512x$

**Solve.**

**C**

52. $6(2x + 3)^2 = 24$

53. $5(6x - 1)^2 = 5$

54. $3(5x - 3)^2 + 2 = 8$

55. $4(7x + 5)^2 + 9 = 1$

56. $x^2 + 2x\sqrt{3} + 3 = 0$

57. $y^2 - 2y\sqrt{5} + 5 = 3$

58. How many real-number solutions are there to the equation $a(x - b)^2 = c$ if:

    **a.** $a > 0$ and $c > 0$?

    **b.** $a < 0$ and $c < 0$?

    **c.** $a < 0$ and $c > 0$?

    **d.** $a > 0$ and $c = 0$?

# 12-2 Completing the Square

**Objective**  To "complete the square" and to use the result to solve quadratic equations.

In Section 12-1 you learned that it is always possible to solve a quadratic equation that has the form:

$$\text{perfect square} = k \quad (k \geq 0)$$

If a quadratic equation does not have the form perfect square $= k$, it may be possible to transform it into one that does by a method called **completing the square.**

Study the perfect squares shown at the right. The main idea behind completing the square is shown.

Notice that in each case the coefficient of $x^2$ is 1, and that the constant term is the square of half the coefficient of $x$. This observation leads to the method described below. This method can be used to solve certain quadratic equations, as illustrated in Example 2.

$$(x + 5)^2 = x^2 \underbrace{+ 10x} + 25$$
$$\left(\tfrac{10}{2}\right)^2 = 25$$

$$(x - 3)^2 = x^2 \underbrace{- 6x} + 9$$
$$\left(-\tfrac{6}{2}\right)^2 = 9$$

$$(x + a)^2 = x^2 \underbrace{+ 2ax} + a^2$$
$$\left(\tfrac{2a}{2}\right)^2 = a^2$$

---

### Method of Completing the Square

For $x^2 + bx + \underline{\ ?\ }$ :

1. Find half the coefficient of $x$.

2. Square the result of Step 1.

3. Add the result of Step 2 to $x^2 + bx$.

---

**Example 1**  Complete the square.

    **a.** $x^2 + 20x + \underline{\ ?\ }$               **b.** $x^2 - 7x + \underline{\ ?\ }$

**Solution**    **a.** $x^2 \underbrace{+ 20x} + 100 = (x + 10)^2$     **b.** $x^2 \underbrace{- 7x} + \dfrac{49}{4} = \left(x - \dfrac{7}{2}\right)^2$

                  $\left(\tfrac{20}{2}\right)^2 = 100$                       $\left(-\tfrac{7}{2}\right)^2 = \dfrac{49}{4}$

**Example 2**  Solve $x^2 - 16x - 17 = 0$ by completing the square.

**Solution**

$$x^2 - 16x - 17 = 0$$
$$x^2 - 16x = 17$$

$$x^2 - 16x + \left(-\frac{16}{2}\right)^2 = 17 + \left(-\frac{16}{2}\right)^2 \quad \{\text{Complete the square.}$$

$$x^2 - 16x + 64 = 17 + 64$$
$$(x - 8)^2 = 81 \qquad \left\{\begin{array}{l}\text{Solve using the} \\ \text{method of Section 12-1.}\end{array}\right.$$
$$x - 8 = \pm\sqrt{81}$$
$$x = 8 \pm 9$$
$$x = 17 \text{ or } x = -1$$

The check is left to you.

$\therefore$ the solution set is $\{17, -1\}$.  **Answer**

**Example 3** Solve $5x^2 + 7x - 2 = 0$ by completing the square.

**Solution**  After adding 2 to both sides of the equation, divide both sides by 5 so that the coefficient of $x^2$ will be 1.

$$5x^2 + 7x - 2 = 0$$
$$5x^2 + 7x = 2$$
$$x^2 + \frac{7}{5}x = \frac{2}{5}$$
$$x^2 + \frac{7}{5}x + \left(\frac{7}{10}\right)^2 = \frac{2}{5} + \left(\frac{7}{10}\right)^2$$
$$x^2 + \frac{7}{5}x + \frac{49}{100} = \frac{2}{5} + \frac{49}{100}$$
$$\left(x + \frac{7}{10}\right)^2 = \frac{89}{100}$$
$$x + \frac{7}{10} = \pm\frac{\sqrt{89}}{10}$$
$$x = -\frac{7}{10} \pm \frac{\sqrt{89}}{10} = \frac{-7 \pm \sqrt{89}}{10}$$
$$x = \frac{-7 + \sqrt{89}}{10} \text{ or } x = \frac{-7 - \sqrt{89}}{10}$$

The check is left to you.

$\therefore$ the solution set is $\left\{\dfrac{-7 + \sqrt{89}}{10}, \dfrac{-7 - \sqrt{89}}{10}\right\}$.  **Answer**

You can use your calculator or a table of square roots to obtain decimal approximations to the irrational roots in Example 3. Using the Table of Square Roots on page 650,

$$\frac{-7 + \sqrt{89}}{10} \approx \frac{-7 + 9.43}{10} = \frac{2.43}{10} = 0.243 \approx 0.2$$

$$\frac{-7 - \sqrt{89}}{10} \approx \frac{-7 - 9.43}{10} = \frac{-16.43}{10} = -1.643 \approx -1.6$$

Thus, to the nearest tenth, the roots are 0.2 and $-1.6$.

## Oral Exercises

**Complete the square.**

1. $x^2 + 6x + \underline{\ ?\ } = (x + \underline{\ ?\ })^2$

2. $x^2 + 14x + \underline{\ ?\ } = (x + \underline{\ ?\ })^2$

3. $y^2 - 4y + \underline{\ ?\ } = (y - \underline{\ ?\ })^2$

4. $y^2 - 18y + \underline{\ ?\ } = (y - \underline{\ ?\ })^2$

5. $m^2 + 3m + \underline{\ ?\ } = (m + \underline{\ ?\ })^2$

6. $r^2 - 11r + \underline{\ ?\ } = (r - \underline{\ ?\ })^2$

7. $t^2 + 1.6t + \underline{\ ?\ } = (t + \underline{\ ?\ })^2$

8. $q^2 - \frac{1}{3}q + \underline{\ ?\ } = (q - \underline{\ ?\ })^2$

## Written Exercises

**Solve by completing the square. Give irrational roots in simplest radical form and then approximate them to the nearest tenth.**

**A**

1. $x^2 - 2x = 20$

2. $x^2 + 8x = 10$

3. $x^2 + 12x = -2$

4. $r^2 - 10r = -5$

5. $s^2 - 4s - 3 = 0$

6. $q^2 + 14q + 5 = 0$

7. $c^2 + 16c - 132 = 0$

8. $v^2 - 20v + 19 = 0$

9. $z^2 - 6z - 321 = 6$

10. $y^2 + 18y + 32 = 226$

11. $2b^2 + 12b = 18$

12. $5x^2 - 20x = 10$

13. $w^2 + w = 5$

14. $x^2 - 5x = 2$

15. $c^2 - 9c - 4 = 3$

16. $j^2 - 2j - 528 = 0$

17. $s^2 + 6s - 1147 = 0$

18. $3a^2 + 12a = 456$

**Solve the equations using two methods: (a) completing the square and (b) factoring.**

19. $x^2 - 14x + 45 = 0$

20. $y^2 + 18y + 56 = 0$

21. $a^2 + 28a - 60 = 0$

22. $3c^2 - 7c = 6$

23. $5k^2 - 4k = 1$

24. $4m^2 + 12m + 5 = 0$

**Solve. Write irrational roots in simplest radical form.**

**B**

25. $\frac{x^2}{2} - 3x = 8$

26. $\frac{2y^2}{3} - y - 3 = 0$

27. $m^2 - 2 = \frac{7m}{2}$

28. $a^2 + \frac{a}{3} = 3$

29. $\frac{2m^2}{3} - 2 = \frac{m}{2}$

30. $\frac{y^2}{2} - \frac{y}{4} = 3$

31. $x + 2 = \frac{3 + x}{6x}$

32. $y - 3 = \frac{4y - 4}{5y}$

33. $7t = \frac{20t - 2}{t + 1}$

34. $3m = \frac{m - 5}{m + 4}$

35. $3 + \frac{7r - 2}{r - 1} = -4r$

36. $2m - 5 = \frac{6}{m + 3}$

**Solve for $x$ in terms of $a$, $b$, and $c$. State the conditions on $a$, $b$, and $c$ for the equation to have real roots.**

**C**

37. $x^2 + bx + 1 = 0$

38. $x^2 + bx + c = 0$

39. $ax^2 + bx + c = 0$

# 12-3 The Quadratic Formula

**Objective:** To learn the quadratic formula and use it to solve equations.

Recall from Section 5–12 (page 223) that the general form of the quadratic equation is

$$ax^2 + bx + c = 0$$

where $a \neq 0$. You can solve this equation by the method of completing the square.

$$ax^2 + bx + c = 0$$

$$ax^2 + bx = -c$$

$$x^2 + \frac{b}{a}x = -\frac{c}{a}$$

$$x^2 + \frac{b}{a}x + \left(\frac{b}{2a}\right)^2 = -\frac{c}{a} + \left(\frac{b}{2a}\right)^2 \quad \{\text{Complete the square.}$$

$$\left(x + \frac{b}{2a}\right)^2 = -\frac{c}{a} + \frac{b^2}{4a^2}$$

$$\left(x + \frac{b}{2a}\right)^2 = \frac{b^2 - 4ac}{4a^2}$$

$$x + \frac{b}{2a} = \pm\sqrt{\frac{b^2 - 4ac}{4a^2}} \quad \{\text{If } b^2 - 4ac \geq 0$$

$$x = -\frac{b}{2a} \pm \sqrt{\frac{b^2 - 4ac}{4a^2}}$$

$$x = -\frac{b}{2a} \pm \frac{\sqrt{b^2 - 4ac}}{2a}$$

$$x = \frac{-b \pm \sqrt{b^2 - 4ac}}{2a}$$

The last equation in the solution above is called the **quadratic formula.** It gives the roots of $ax^2 + bx + c = 0$ in terms of the coefficients $a$, $b$, and $c$. In this solution, notice the assumptions that $a \neq 0$ and that $b^2 - 4ac \geq 0$.

---

## The Quadratic Formula

If $ax^2 + bx + c = 0$, $a \neq 0$, and $b^2 - 4ac \geq 0$,

then $$x = \frac{-b \pm \sqrt{b^2 - 4ac}}{2a}.$$

---

***Example***   Solve $3x^2 - 8x + 2 = 0$ using the quadratic formula.

***Solution***   $3x^2 - 8x + 2 = 0$

$$x = \frac{-b \pm \sqrt{b^2 - 4ac}}{2a} \quad \text{where } a = 3, b = -8, \text{ and } c = 2.$$

$$x = \frac{-(-8) \pm \sqrt{(-8)^2 - 4(3)(2)}}{2(3)} = \frac{8 \pm \sqrt{64 - 24}}{6}$$

$$= \frac{8 \pm \sqrt{40}}{6} = \frac{8 \pm 2\sqrt{10}}{6} = \frac{4 \pm \sqrt{10}}{3}$$

The check is left to you.

$\therefore$ the solution set is $\left\{ \dfrac{4 + \sqrt{10}}{3}, \dfrac{4 - \sqrt{10}}{3} \right\}$.   ***Answer***

Remember to express a quadratic equation in the form $ax^2 + bx + c = 0$ before using the quadratic formula. For example, to solve $3x^2 = 7x - 1$, first express the equation as $3x^2 - 7x + 1 = 0$ so that you can easily identify the values of $a$, $b$, and $c$.

## Oral Exercises

**State the values of $a$, $b$, and $c$ for each equation.**

**1.** $2x^2 + 7x + 3 = 0$     **2.** $3x^2 - 9x + 5 = 0$     **3.** $4x^2 + 8x - 3 = 0$

**4.** $6x^2 + 11x = 3$     **5.** $x^2 - 7x = 4$     **6.** $y^2 = 5y - 5$

**7.** $7m^2 = m + 3$     **8.** $9 - q^2 = 2q$     **9.** $5x^2 = 7x$

**10.** $z = 8z^2$     **11.** $4x^2 = 5$     **12.** $11t^2 = 0$

## Written Exercises

**Use the quadratic formula to solve each equation. Give irrational roots in simplest radical form; also approximate them to the nearest tenth.**

**A**   **1.** $x^2 + 3x + 1 = 0$     **2.** $x^2 + 5x + 3 = 0$     **3.** $x^2 + 4x - 6 = 0$

**4.** $2y^2 - 6y - 8 = 0$     **5.** $z^2 - 5z - 6 = 0$     **6.** $m^2 + 8m + 7 = 0$

**7.** $4t^2 + 5t + 1 = 0$     **8.** $2q^2 - 2q - 1 = 0$     **9.** $5a^2 - 6a + 2 = 0$

**10.** $4x^2 = 10x - 5$     **11.** $3b^2 + 4 = 7b$     **12.** $7r = 5 - 5r^2$

**Solve.**

**B**   **13.** $a^2 + 0.9a + 0.1 = 0$     **14.** $3x^2 - 1.8x + 0.03 = 0$     **15.** $2x^2 - 0.8x - 0.5 = 0$

**16.** $x^2 + \frac{3}{2}x + \frac{2}{3} = 0$     **17.** $\frac{1}{5}y^2 - \frac{5}{4}y = 1$     **18.** $2c^2 + \frac{1}{2}c + \frac{2}{3} = 0$

**19.** $\dfrac{x+4}{2x} = \dfrac{x-1}{x+1}$

**20.** $\dfrac{1}{3} - \dfrac{2}{2x+1} = \dfrac{3}{x}$

**21.** $\dfrac{1.5}{x-3} = 2x$

**22.** $\dfrac{x+3}{x-1} - \dfrac{7}{x+5} = 3$

**The roots of a quadratic equation $ax^2 + bx + c = 0$ are**

$$\dfrac{-b + \sqrt{b^2 - 4ac}}{2a} \quad \text{and} \quad \dfrac{-b - \sqrt{b^2 - 4ac}}{2a}.$$

**C**   **23.** Find the sum of the roots.

**24.** Find the product of the roots.

**25.** Write a quadratic equation whose roots are $3 \pm \sqrt{2}$. (*Hint:* Find the sum and the product of the roots. Then use the results of Exercises 23 and 24 to find values for $a$, $b$, and $c$.)

## Computer Key-In

### Exercises

1. Write a program that will solve quadratic equations by using the quadratic formula. Provide an output if the discriminant is negative.

Use your program to solve the following equations.

2. $2x^2 + 7x + 3 = 0$

3. $4x^2 - 7x + 3 = 0$

4. $3x^2 - 8x + 2 = 0$

5. $x^2 - 4x + 2 = 0$

6. $x^2 - 6x + 9 = 0$

7. $x^2 - 2x + 3 = 0$

*Note:* The program of Exercise 1 above can be used to do Exercises 1–12 on page 554.

## Extra / Imaginary Numbers

You know that there are no real-number solutions to the equation $x^2 = -9$. If you take another course in algebra, you will learn that equations like this have solutions that are *imaginary numbers*. Imaginary numbers involve the *imaginary unit*, $i$, defined to be the square root of $-1$.

$$i = \sqrt{-1} \qquad i^2 = -1$$

The definition of $i$ allows us to solve $x^2 = -9$ over the set of imaginary numbers. Thus:

$$x^2 = -9$$
$$x = \pm\sqrt{-9}$$
$$= \pm 3\sqrt{-1}$$
$$= \pm 3i$$

In general,

If $r > 0$: $\sqrt{-r} = i\sqrt{r}$

We write $i\sqrt{r}$ rather than $\sqrt{r}\,i$ to avoid confusion with $\sqrt{ri}$.

An interesting pattern occurs when we find $i^n$ for increasing powers of $n$:

$i^1 = \sqrt{-1}$       $i$     $i^5 = i^2 \cdot i^3 = (-1)(-i) = i$     $i$

$i^2 = -1$       $-1$     $i^6 = i^3 \cdot i^3 = (-i)(-i) = i^2 = -1$     $-1$

$i^3 = i \cdot i^2 = i(-1) = -i$       $-i$     $i^7 = i^3 \cdot i^4 = (-i)1 = -i$     $-i$

$i^4 = i^2 \cdot i^2 = (-1)(-1) = 1$       $1$     $i^8 = i^4 \cdot i^4 = 1(1) = 1$     $1$

Likewise, it can be shown that $i^9 = i$, $i^{10} = -1$, $i^{11} = -i$, $i^{12} = 1$, and so on.

### Exercises

Simplify to $i$, $-1$, $-i$, or 1.

**1.** $i^{13}$     **2.** $i^{22}$     **3.** $i^{15}$     **4.** $i^{24}$     **5.** $i^{17}$     **6.** $i^{19}$

**Example**    Simplify: **a.** $-\sqrt{-18}$   **b.** $\sqrt{20}\sqrt{-45}$   **c.** $\sqrt{\dfrac{-9}{16}}$

**Solution**    **a.** $-\sqrt{-18} = -\sqrt{-1 \cdot 2 \cdot 3^2} = -3i\sqrt{2}$

         **b.** $\sqrt{20}\sqrt{-45} = \sqrt{2^2 \cdot 5}\sqrt{-1 \cdot 3^2 \cdot 5} = 2\sqrt{5} \cdot 3i\sqrt{5} = 6i \cdot 5 = 30i$

         **c.** $\sqrt{\dfrac{-9}{16}} = \dfrac{\sqrt{-9}}{\sqrt{16}} = \dfrac{\sqrt{-1 \cdot 3^2}}{\sqrt{4^2}} = \dfrac{3i}{4}$

Simplify.

**7.** $\sqrt{-36}$     **8.** $-\sqrt{-75}$     **9.** $\sqrt{-80}$     **10.** $-\sqrt{-100}$

**11.** $\sqrt{8}\sqrt{-50}$     **12.** $\sqrt{-3}\sqrt{27}$     **13.** $\sqrt{12}\sqrt{-48}$     **14.** $(\sqrt{-4}\sqrt{9})^2$

**15.** $\sqrt{\dfrac{25}{-49}}$     **16.** $-\sqrt{\dfrac{-16}{81}}$     **17.** $-\sqrt{\dfrac{-36}{100}}$     **18.** $\dfrac{\sqrt{-150}}{-\sqrt{54}}$

Solve.

**19.** $x^2 = -121$     **20.** $x^2 + 28 = 0$     **21.** $x^2 = -98$     **22.** $x^2 + 240 = 0$

# 12-4 Graphs of Quadratic Equations: The Discriminant

**Objective**   To use the discriminant to determine the number of roots of the equation $ax^2 + bx + c = 0$ and the number of $x$-intercepts of the graph of the related equation $y = ax^2 + bx + c$.

In Section 9-6 (page 412), you learned that the graph of the function defined by the quadratic equation

$$y = x^2 + 2x - 3$$

is the parabola shown at the right. The $x$-coordinate of a point where the curve intersects the $x$-axis is called an ***x*-intercept** of the curve. This parabola has two $x$-intercepts, $-3$ and $1$, because $y = 0$ for these values of $x$. You can also see that the equation

$$x^2 + 2x - 3 = 0$$

has $-3$ and $1$ as roots.

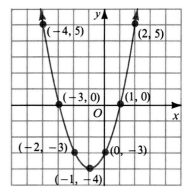

---

The roots of any quadratic equation of the form

$$ax^2 + bx + c = 0$$

are the $x$-intercepts of the graph of the related equation,

$$y = ax^2 + bx + c.$$

---

The algebraic fact that a quadratic equation can have two, one, or no real-number roots corresponds to the geometric fact that a parabola can have two, one, or no $x$-intercepts, as illustrated in the following examples.

### Example 1

*Equation:* $x^2 - 4x + 2 = 0$

*Related equation:* $y = x^2 - 4x + 2$

*Solution:*

$$x = \frac{-(-4) \pm \sqrt{(-4)^2 - 4(1)(2)}}{2(1)}$$

$$= \frac{4 \pm \sqrt{8}}{2}$$

$$= 2 \pm \sqrt{2}$$

$\therefore$ the solution set is $\{2 + \sqrt{2}, 2 - \sqrt{2}\}$.

*Graph:*

*Number of roots:* Two real-number roots

*Number of x-intercepts:* Two

## Example 2

*Equation:* $x^2 - 6x + 9 = 0$

*Solution:*

$$x = \frac{-(-6) \pm \sqrt{(-6)^2 - 4(1)(9)}}{2(1)}$$

$$= \frac{6 \pm \sqrt{0}}{2}$$

$$= 3$$

$\therefore$ the solution set is $\{3\}$.

*Number of roots:* One real-number root

*Related equation:* $y = x^2 - 6x + 9$

*Graph:*

*Number of x-intercepts:* One

## Example 3

*Equation:* $x^2 - 2x + 3 = 0$

*Solution:*

$$x = \frac{-(-2) \pm \sqrt{(-2)^2 - 4(1)(3)}}{2(1)}$$

$$= \frac{2 \pm \sqrt{-8}}{2}$$

There is no real-number root since $\sqrt{-8}$ does not exist in the set of real numbers.

*Number of roots:* No real-number roots

*Related equation:* $y = x^2 - 2x + 3$

*Graph:*

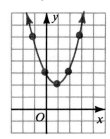

*Number of x-intercepts:* None

In each of Examples 1–3, the value of $b^2 - 4ac$ in the quadratic formula is shown in color. This value is the key to the number of real roots, as shown in the following chart.

| | Value of $b^2 - 4ac$ | Number of different real roots of $ax^2 + bx + c = 0$ | Number of x-intercepts of the graph of $y = ax^2 + bx + c$ |
|---|---|---|---|
| Case 1 | positive | 2 | 2 |
| Case 2 | zero | 1 (a double root) | 1 |
| Case 3 | negative | 0 | 0 |

Note that when $b^2 - 4ac$ is negative, no real-number root of the equation exists because square roots of negative numbers do not exist in the set of real numbers.

Because the value of $b^2 - 4ac$ discriminates, or distinguishes, the three cases, it is called the **discriminant** of the quadratic equation.

## Oral Exercises

**The value of the discriminant of an equation is given. Tell how many different real-number roots there are.**

**1.** 22        **2.** $-5$        **3.** 0        **4.** 1        **5.** 36

**Find the value of the discriminant.**

**6.** $x^2 - 3x + 4 = 0$      **7.** $-2x^2 + 7x - 3 = 0$      **8.** $4x^2 - 3x - 7 = 0$

## Written Exercises

**Write the value of the discriminant of each equation. Then use it to decide how many different real-number roots the equation has. (Do not solve.)**

**A**
   **1.** $x^2 - 4x + 3 = 0$      **2.** $x^2 - 5x + 7 = 0$      **3.** $x^2 + 12x + 36 = 0$

   **4.** $2y^2 + 5y - 4 = 0$      **5.** $9y^2 - 12y + 4 = 0$      **6.** $4t^2 - 3t + 5 = 0$

   **7.** $2y^2 + 12y + 18 = 0$      **8.** $2a^2 - a - 6 = 0$      **9.** $-3b^2 + 4b + 2 = 0$

   **10.** $4q^2 - 3q + 3 = 0$      **11.** $2c^2 - 1.4c + 0.1 = 0$      **12.** $\frac{1}{4}z^2 - 2z + 4 = 0$

**Without drawing the graph of the given equation, determine (a) how many points the parabola has in common with the x-axis, and (b) whether its vertex lies above, below, or on the x-axis.**

***Example***    $y = 4x - x^2 + 5$

       **a.** The $x$-intercepts of the graph are the roots of the equation

$$4x - x^2 + 5 = 0, \quad \text{or} \quad -x^2 + 4x + 5 = 0.$$

       Its discriminant is $(4)^2 - (4)(-1)(5) = 36$ and therefore it has two real-number roots. The parabola has two points in common with the $x$-axis.

       **b.** Since the coefficient of $x^2$ is negative, the parabola opens downward (see page 413). Its vertex must be above the $x$-axis (otherwise the parabola would not intersect the $x$-axis in two points).

**B**
   **13.** $y = x^2 - 5x + 5$      **14.** $y = 2x^2 + 4x - 3$      **15.** $y = 3 + 3x - x^2$

   **16.** $y = x^2 + 9 - 6x$      **17.** $y = 4x - 3 - 2x^2$      **18.** $y = 3x + 9 - 2x^2$

**C**
   **19.** Find $k$ so that the equation $9x^2 + 12x + k = 0$ has one real-number (double) root.

   **20.** Find $k$ so that the equation $x^2 - kx + 25 = 0$ has one real-number (double) root.

## Computer Exercises

1. Write a BASIC program that computes the value of the discriminant of a quadratic equation $AX^2 + BX + C = 0$, where the values of $A$, $B$, and $C$ are entered with INPUT statements. The program should then report the number of real roots of the equation.

2. Write a BASIC program that computes the sum and the product of the roots of a quadratic equation $AX^2 + BX + C = 0$, where the values of $A$, $B$, and $C$ are entered with INPUT statements.

## Computer Key-In

The program on page 491 can be modified to graph equations of the form

$$y = Ax^2 + Bx + C, \quad (A \neq 0).$$

First change lines 10 and 15:

```
10   PRINT "TO GRAPH THE PARABOLA"
15   PRINT "FOR Y = AX↑2 + BX + C:"
```

Copy lines from the program on page 433 into this program as shown:

```
20   Copy line 40
25   Copy line 50
30   IF A = 0 THEN 20
35   Copy line 70
40   Copy line 110
```

Add these lines:

```
45   LET M = X1 - 10
50   LET N = X1 + 10
```

Change line 80 to:

```
80   IF Y = A*X↑2 + B*X + C THEN 110
```

### Exercises

RUN the revised program for each of the following.

1. $y = x^2 + 2x - 8$
2. $y = x^2 - 4x + 2$
3. $y = x^2 - 6x + 9$
4. $y = x^2 - 2x + 3$
5. $y = x^2$
6. $y = 0.5x^2$
7. $y = 0.25x^2$
8. $y = 0.25x^2 - 8$

*Note:* The program above can be used to do Exercises 7–18 on page 416.

# Self-Test 1

**Vocabulary**   perfect square (p. 547)          *x*-intercept (p. 557)
completing the square (p. 550)   discriminant (p. 558)
quadratic formula (p. 553)

**Solve by using perfect squares.**

**1.** $6x^2 = 54$

**2.** $(x - 3)^2 = 7$     **Obj. 12-1, p. 547**

**Solve by completing the square.**

**3.** $a^2 - 12a + 35 = 0$

**4.** $x^2 - 6x - 16 = 0$     **Obj. 12-2, p. 550**

**Solve by the quadratic formula.**

**5.** $2x^2 - 3x - 2 = 0$

**6.** $t^2 - 3t - 6 = 0$     **Obj. 12-3, p. 553**

**Give the number of real roots.**

**7.** $2y^2 - 2y + 8 = 0$

**8.** $c^2 - c + 3 = 0$     **Obj. 12-4, p. 557**

Check your answers with those at the back of the book.

## *Career Note* / *Welder*

Welders are responsible for repairing and joining metal parts and products. Usually, a welder heats and fuses the metal pieces to be joined and may sometimes add a filler material to strengthen a joint. Welders must apply the correct amount of heat from the correct distance to accurately repair the break or strengthen the bond.

Some welders are employed in the construction of ships. Others construct bridges or weld pipes. Welders are highly skilled workers who must be knowledgeable about the melting properties of various metals.

Welders often have had some high school or vocational training in welding. Some companies prefer to train their own welders through apprenticeship programs. There is also an increasing demand for experienced welders with college training to work in researching and developing new applications.

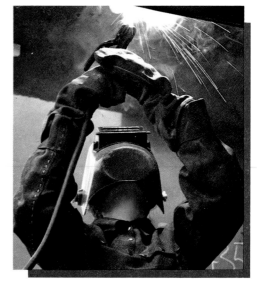

# Using Quadratic Equations

---

## 12-5 Methods of Solution

**Objective**  To choose the best method for solving a quadratic equation.

You have learned the following four methods for solving quadratic equations.

---

**Methods for Solving a Quadratic Equation**

1. Factoring
2. Using the property of square roots of equal numbers
3. Completing the square
4. Using the quadratic formula

---

Although the quadratic formula can be used to solve any quadratic equation in the form

$$ax^2 + bx + c = 0,$$

one of the other methods may be easier. Here are some guidelines that suggest when one of the other methods may be easier:

1. If the equation is in the form $ax^2 + bx = 0$ or if the factors are easily seen, use factoring;

2. If the equation is in the form $ax^2 + c = 0$, use the property of square roots of equal numbers;

3. If the equation is in the form $x^2 + bx + c = 0$ and $b$ is an even number, use the method of completing the square.

**Example**  Solve each quadratic equation using the most convenient method.

    **a.** $5x^2 - 80 = 0$                         **b.** $3x^2 - 4x - 1 = 0$

    **c.** $3t^2 - 36t = 0$                         **d.** $n^2 + 6n - 3 = 0$

**Solution**    **a.** $5x^2 - 80 = 0$            Use the property of square
                     $5x^2 = 80$             roots of equal numbers.
                       $x^2 = 16$
                       $x = \pm 4$

        $\therefore$ the solution set is $\{4, -4\}$.  ***Answer***

---

**b.** $3x^2 - 4x - 1 = 0$

Since no other method suggests itself, use the quadratic formula.

$$x = \frac{-(-4) \pm \sqrt{(-4)^2 - 4(3)(-1)}}{2(3)} = \frac{4 \pm \sqrt{28}}{6} = \frac{4 \pm 2\sqrt{7}}{6} = \frac{2 \pm \sqrt{7}}{3}$$

$\therefore$ the solution set is $\left\{ \dfrac{2 + \sqrt{7}}{3}, \dfrac{2 - \sqrt{7}}{3} \right\}$. **Answer**

**c.** $3t^2 - 36t = 0$        Factor.

$3t(t - 12) = 0$

$3t = 0$    or    $t - 12 = 0$

$\therefore$ the solution set is $\{0, 12\}$. **Answer**

**d.** $n^2 + 6n - 3 = 0$        Complete the square.

$n^2 + 6n = 3$

$n^2 + 6n + 9 = 12$

$(n + 3)^2 = 12$

$n + 3 = \pm\sqrt{12}$

$n = -3 \pm 2\sqrt{3}$

$\therefore$ the solution set is $\{-3 + 2\sqrt{3}, -3 - 2\sqrt{3}\}$. **Answer**

## Oral Exercises

**For each of the following quadratic equations, state which method you would use to solve the equation.**

**1.** $x^2 + 5x + 4 = 0$        **2.** $x^2 - 4x = 32$        **3.** $x^2 + 8x - 3 = 0$

**4.** $8x^2 + 11x = 0$        **5.** $11x^2 = 44$        **6.** $3x^2 - 5x = 4$

**7.** $x^2 + 7x + 2 = 0$        **8.** $2x^2 + 7x + 3 = 0$        **9.** $x^2 + 6x = 5$

**10.** $(x - 2)^2 = 7$        **11.** $5x^2 - 20x = 0$        **12.** $4x^2 - 2x - 3 = 0$

## Written Exercises

**A**    **1–12.** Solve the quadratic equations given in Oral Exercises 1–12. Write the answers in simplest radical form.

**Solve by the most efficient method. Write irrational answers in simplest radical form.**

**13.** $4x^2 + 7x = 2$        **14.** $\dfrac{(y + 3)^2}{2} = 10$        **15.** $5x^2 + 4x = 3$

Solve by the most efficient method. Write irrational answers in simplest radical form.

16. $x^2 - 8x = 11$

17. $\frac{2}{5}x^2 + \frac{2}{3}x = 1$

18. $\frac{1}{3x} = \frac{2x - 3}{2}$

19. $\frac{x - 2}{3x - 1} = \frac{2x + 1}{5x - 1}$

20. $0.75x^2 - 0.3x + 0.03 = 0$

21. $1.6x^2 - 0.6x = 0.4$

**B** 22. $5x(x - 3) + 4(x + 4) = 31 - 7x^2$

23. $4x(x + 2) + 6(x^2 - 1) = 14$

24. $(x + 3)^2 + 6(x + 3) = 16$

25. $8(x - 5)^2 + 3(x - 5) = 0$

26. $(3x + 2)(x - 1) - 13 = 2x(2 - x)$

27. $(4x - 3)^2 = (7x + 2)^2$

Solve. Be sure that you have found all real roots of each equation. Write irrational answers in simplest form. (*Hint:* Substitute $y$ for $x^2$.)

**C** 28. $12x^4 - 23x^2 + 10 = 0$

29. $4x^4 + 21x^2 - 18 = 0$

30. $2x^4 - 5x^2 = 0$

31. $8x^4 + 5x^2 + 4 = 0$

---

## Biographical Note / *Srinivasa Ramanujan*

Srinivasa Ramanujan (1887–1920) was a self-taught mathematician who made a number of contributions to modern mathematics. At age 16 he was awarded a scholarship to Government College in India for his proficiency in mathematics. However, he became so absorbed in his mathematical studies that he neglected to study English and lost his scholarship. He continued to study mathematics on his own, discovering over one hundred theorems.

Friends interested in his mathematical work convinced Ramanujan to write to G. H. Hardy, one of the leading specialists in number theory, at Cambridge University in England. Ramanujan enclosed about 120 of the theorems he had discovered. Convinced of his exceptional ability, Hardy brought Ra-

manujan to England, where he was admitted to Trinity College. Hardy was not always sure how to teach a student possessing such profound mathematical insight, but so lacking in formal training; nevertheless Ramanujan progressed rapidly. While in England, Ramanujan did a great deal of work in number theory. In 1918 he was elected a fellow of the Royal Society and of Trinity College.

# 12-6 Solving Problems Involving Quadratic Equations

**Objective**   To use quadratic equations to solve problems.

## Example

An architect wishes to design a rectangular building such that the area of the floor is 3 km². The length of the floor is to be 1 km longer than the width. To the nearest tenth of a kilometer what will be the length and the width of the floor?

## Solution

*Step 1*  The problem asks for the length and the width of the floor.

*Step 2*  Let $x$ = the width in kilometers.
Then $(x + 1)$ = the length.

*Step 3*  Use the formula for the area of a rectangle to write an equation.

$$x(x + 1) = 3$$

*Step 4*  Solve $x(x + 1) = 3$.

$$x^2 + x = 3$$
$$x^2 + x - 3 = 0$$

Use the quadratic formula.

$$x = \frac{-1 \pm \sqrt{(1)^2 - 4(1)(-3)}}{2(1)} = \frac{-1 \pm \sqrt{13}}{2}$$

From the Table of Square Roots on page 650:

$$\frac{-1 + \sqrt{13}}{2} \approx \frac{-1 + 3.61}{2} = \frac{2.61}{2} = 1.305 \approx 1.3$$
$$\frac{-1 - \sqrt{13}}{2} \approx \frac{-1 - 3.61}{2} = \frac{-4.61}{2} = -2.305 \approx -2.3$$

*Step 5*  Discard the negative root since a negative length has no meaning.
Check 1.3.

$$1.3(1.3 + 1) \overset{?}{=} 3$$
$$1.3(2.3) \overset{?}{=} 3$$
$$2.99 \approx 3 \; \checkmark$$

The numbers are approximately equal so the approximate solution is correct.
∴ the width of the floor is 1.3 km and the length is 2.3 km.  ***Answer***

## *Problems*

**Solve. Give irrational roots to the nearest tenth. Use the Table of Square Roots on page 650 or a calculator as necessary.**

**A**

1. The length of a rectangular park is 6 m longer than the width. If the area of the park is 135 m², find the length and the width.

2. The length of a rectangle is 3 times the width. The area of the rectangle is 75 cm². Find the length and the width.

3. The sum of a number and its square is 72. Find the number.

4. The difference of a number and its square is 182. Find the number.

5. The length of the base of a triangle is twice its altitude. If the area of the triangle is 100 cm², find the altitude. (*Hint:* Area of a triangle = $\frac{1}{2} \cdot$ base $\cdot$ altitude.)

6. The altitude of a triangle is 5 m less than its base. The area of the triangle is 80 m². Find the base.

7. If the sides of a square are increased by 2 cm, its area becomes 81 cm². Find the length of the sides of the original square.

8. Rudolph has a rectangular garden that measures 20 m by 16 m. Next year he wants to increase the area to 396 m² by increasing the width and length by the same amount. What will be the dimensions of the garden next year?

9. The perimeter of the large rectangular fish tank at the Seaside Aquarium is 172 m and its area is 1800 m². Find the length and the width of the fish tank.

**B**

10. Working alone, Marcia can paint a house in 3 hours less than Joe. Together Marcia and Joe can paint a house in 8 hours. How long does it take Joe to paint a house working alone?

11. Together Sara and Mary can mow the golf course in 15 hours. Alone it takes Mary 2 hours less than Sara. Find the time it takes each of them to mow the course alone.

12. A mathematics class planned a field trip to a computer center. The trip cost $240 to be paid for equally by each student. The day before the trip, 4 students decided not to go. This increased the cost by $2 per student. How many students went to the computer center?

13. The Calculator Club bought a $54 calculator for club use. If there had been 3 more students in the club, each would have had to donate 20 cents less. How many students were in the club?

14. Carla can ride her bike 2 mph faster than Karen. It takes Carla 48 minutes less to travel 50 miles than it does Karen. What is Carla's rate in miles per hour?

**C** 15. Pipe A can fill a tank in 2 hours, and pipe B can fill the tank in half the time it takes pipe C, a drain pipe, to empty the tank. When all 3 pipes are open, it takes 1.5 hours to fill the tank. How much time is required for pipe C to empty the tank?

## Computer Exercises

*For students with some programming experience*

Write a BASIC program that finds the largest or smallest value of $AX^2 + BX + C$. The values of $A$, $B$, and $C$ should be entered with INPUT statements.

## *Extra* / Quadratic Inequalities

The graph of the quadratic function $y = x^2 - 4x + 3$ can be used to illustrate the solutions of the following:

$$(1)\ x^2 - 4x + 3 = 0$$
$$(2)\ x^2 - 4x + 3 > 0$$
$$(3)\ x^2 - 4x + 3 < 0$$

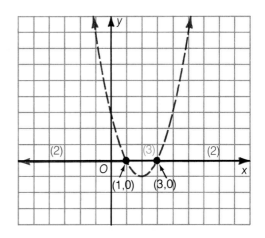

The solution set of the quadratic equation **(1)** is $\{1, 3\}$. These two values of $x$ are called the *zeros* of the quadratic function.

To solve the quadratic inequality (2) reason as follows:

a. If $(x, y)$ is on the graph, then
   $y = x^2 - 4x + 3$.

b. If $(x, y)$ is *above* the $x$-axis, then $y > 0$.

c. Therefore, if $(x, y)$ is on the graph *and* above the $x$-axis, then
   $y = x^2 - 4x + 3 > 0$.

d. ∴ the solution set for **(2)** is $\{x < 1\ \text{or}\ x > 3\}$ because these values of $x$ give points that are on the graph above the $x$-axis.

Similar reasoning shows that the solution set for **(3)** is $\{1 < x < 3\}$ because these values of $x$ give points on the graph *below* the $x$-axis.

***Example***    Solve for $x$.

     (1) $x^2 + 6x + 9 = 0$
     (2) $x^2 + 6x + 9 > 0$
     (3) $x^2 + 6x + 9 < 0$

***Solution***    Use the graph of $y = x^2 + 6x + 9$.

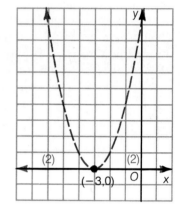

     (1) Factor the quadratic equation
        $x^2 + 6x + 9 = 0$.
        Since $(x + 3)(x + 3) = 0$,
        **$x = -3$.**
     (2) Since the graph lies above the
        $x$-axis for all $x$ except $-3$,
        $x^2 + 6x + 9 > 0$ for all **$x \neq -3$**.
     (3) There are **no values of $x$** for which
        $x^2 + 6x + 9 < 0$, since the graph
        does not go below the $x$-axis.

Graph each equation and mark the sections of the
$x$-axis which correspond to $y = 0$, $y > 0$, and $y < 0$.

**1.** $y = x^2 - 25$         **2.** $y = 2x + x^2$         **3.** $y = 9 - x^2$

**4.** $y = x^2 + x - 12$      **5.** $y = x^2 - 7x + 10$      **6.** $y = 3x^2 - 5x - 2$

Find the values of $x$ for which each expression represents a real number.

**7.** $\sqrt{x^2 - 5x}$         **8.** $\sqrt{x^2 + 6x + 8}$         **9.** $\sqrt{x^2 - 10x + 21}$

# Self-Test 2

**Solve the following quadratic equations using the most convenient
method.**

    **1.** $3(x + 2)^2 = 12$           **2.** $2x^2 + 6x + 3 = 0$     Obj. 12-5, p. 562

    **3.** $x^2 - 10x = 20$            **4.** $3x^2 + 9x = 0$

**Solve. Give irrational roots to the nearest tenth. Use the Table of
Square Roots on page 650 or a calculator as necessary.**

    **5.** The length of a rectangle is twice the width. The area of the     Obj. 12-6, p. 565
       rectangle is 200 cm². Find the length and width.

    **6.** A rectangular wading pool measures 50 m by 40 m. How wide
       must a concrete walk of uniform width around the pool be if
       the walk is to cover an area of 784 m²?

Check your answers with those at the back of the book.

# Chapter Summary

1. Any quadratic equation can be solved using the quadratic formula (see item 2 below). Some quadratic equations, however, may be more easily solved by factoring, applying the property of square roots of equal numbers, or by completing the square.

2. When $ax^2 + bx + c = 0$ and $a \neq 0$, the quadratic formula is expressed as follows:

$$x = \frac{-b \pm \sqrt{b^2 - 4ac}}{2a}$$

3. The graph of a quadratic equation of the form $y = ax^2 + bx + c$ is a parabola. The $x$-intercepts of the parabola correspond to the roots of the related quadratic equation $ax^2 + bx + c = 0$.

4. The discriminant, $b^2 - 4ac$, is used to determine the number of roots of a quadratic equation.

If $b^2 - 4ac > 0$, there are two real-number roots.

If $b^2 - 4ac = 0$, there is one (double) real-number root.

If $b^2 - 4ac < 0$, there are no real-number roots.

# Chapter Review

**Give the letter of the correct answer.**

**Solve.**

1. $2x^2 - 128 = 0$          12-1
   a. $\{64\}$      b. $\{64, -64\}$      c. $\{8\}$      d. $\{8, -8\}$

2. $(a + 3)^2 = 25$
   a. $\{22, 28\}$      b. $\{2, -8\}$      c. $\{2, -2\}$      d. $\{2, 8\}$

**Solve by completing the square.**

3. $x^2 + 4x - 77 = 0$          12-2
   a. $\{11, 7\}$      b. $\{-11, -7\}$      c. $\{11, -7\}$      d. $\{-11, 7\}$

4. $c^2 - 10c - 20 = 0$
   a. $\{-5 + 3\sqrt{5}, -5 - 3\sqrt{5}\}$      b. $\{3\sqrt{5} + 5, 3\sqrt{5} - 5\}$
   c. $\{5 + 3\sqrt{5}, 5 - 3\sqrt{5}\}$      d. $\{-3\sqrt{5} + 5, -3\sqrt{5} - 5\}$

**Solve by the quadratic formula.**

5. $5z^2 - 11z + 2 = 0$          12-3
   a. $\left\{-2, -\frac{1}{5}\right\}$      b. $\left\{2, \frac{1}{5}\right\}$      c. $\left\{2, -\frac{1}{5}\right\}$      d. $\left\{-2, \frac{1}{5}\right\}$

**Solve by the quadratic formula.**

**6.** $10y^2 - y - 3 = 0$

    **a.** $\left\{-\dfrac{3}{5}, -\dfrac{1}{2}\right\}$     **b.** $\left\{\dfrac{3}{5}, \dfrac{1}{2}\right\}$     **c.** $\left\{-\dfrac{3}{5}, \dfrac{1}{2}\right\}$     **d.** $\left\{\dfrac{3}{5}, -\dfrac{1}{2}\right\}$

**7.** Give the discriminant of $2x^2 - 3x - 2 = 0$.         12-4

    **a.** $-25$         **b.** $25$         **c.** $-5$         **d.** $5$

**8.** How many real roots does $x^2 - 5x + 2 = 0$ have?

    **a.** $0$         **b.** $1$         **c.** $2$         **d.** $3$

**9.** Give the best method for solving $2y^2 + 8y = 0$.         12-5

    **a.** Factoring         **b.** Property of square roots of
                                    equal numbers

    **c.** Completing the square     **d.** Quadratic formula

**Solve.**

**10.** The dimensions of a sheet of paper can be represented by consecutive odd    12-6
integers. If the area of the paper is 99 cm², find the dimensions.

    **a.** $l = 9$ cm     **b.** $l = 11$ cm     **c.** $l = 13$ cm     **d.** $l = 11$ cm
       $w = 7$ cm        $w = 9$ cm        $w = 11$ cm       $w = 13$ cm

# Chapter Test

**Solve.**

**1.** $25x^2 = 121$              **2.** $3(a - 5)^2 = 21$           12-1

**Solve by completing the square.**

**3.** $c^2 + 8c + 15 = 0$       **4.** $b^2 - 4b - 10 = 0$        12-2

**Solve by the quadratic formula.**

**5.** $2z^2 - 8z + 6 = 0$        **6.** $y^2 - 8y - 4 = 0$         12-3

**State the number of real roots.**

**7.** $2x^2 - 3x - 2 = 0$        **8.** $x^2 - 4x + 4 = 0$         12-4

**Solve by the easiest method.**

**9.** $9x^2 + 8x = 0$          **10.** $3x^2 - 10x - 4 = 0$      12-5

**Solve. Approximate irrational roots to the nearest tenth.**

**11.** A garden is currently 5 m wide and 8 m long. If the area of the garden    12-6
is to be doubled by increasing the width and the length by the same
number of meters, find the new dimensions of the garden.

# Cumulative Review (Chapters 1–12)

Evaluate if $a = -1$, $b = 1$, $c = 0$, $d = 3$, and $e = -\frac{5}{2}$.

**1.** $a(b + e)$

**2.** $(b \div d + e)^a$

**3.** $c \div e$

**4.** $(ab)^3 - (ab)^2$

**5.** $(de + ab)^c$

**6.** $e \div e^a$

**Simplify. Assume that no denominator is zero. Each variable represents a positive real number.**

**7.** $2 \cdot 58 - 7 \cdot 58 - (-58)$

**8.** $6^2 \div 3^2 + 4 \div 3$

**9.** $(6 - 13)(6 + 13)$

**10.** $4x - (0.4x + 1.2y)$

**11.** $15(3c - 4) + 5 - 9c$

**12.** $\left(-\frac{1}{8}x^5y^3z\right)(-16xy^2)$

**13.** $-\frac{4}{5}a^3b(-20ab^2 + 35b^3)$

**14.** $(5x^3y^2)^2(3x^4y^3)^3$

**15.** $\dfrac{-72wx^4y^5z}{-96x^3y^7z}$

**16.** $\dfrac{(3r^3s^4)^3}{(-9r^5s^6)^2}$

**17.** $(4u^2 - 2u + 1)(2u + 1)$

**18.** $a - 2(a - 9)$

**19.** $(9z - 5)(3z + 4)$

**20.** $(3a^3 - 2)^2$

**21.** $(8r^3t - 3v)(8r^3t + 3v)$

**22.** $(3.4 \times 10^{12})(0.3 \times 10^{-3})$

**23.** $\dfrac{12c^2 - 26cd + 12d^2}{12c^2 - 44cd + 24d^2}$

**24.** $(18x^2 - x - 4) \div (2x - 1)$

**25.** $(27x^3 + 64) \div (3x + 4)$

**26.** $\dfrac{b^2 + b - 12}{b + 2} \cdot \dfrac{b^2 - 4}{b^2 + 2b - 8}$

**27.** $\dfrac{3z^2 + 16z + 16}{z^2 + 6z + 9} \div \dfrac{z^2 + 3z - 4}{z + 3}$

**28.** $\dfrac{85k^8 + 51k^4 - 17k^2}{-17k^4}$

**29.** $\dfrac{a - 1}{3} - \dfrac{5 - 2a}{3}$

**30.** $\dfrac{n + 1}{2n - 3} + \dfrac{4}{n + 1} - 3$

**31.** $\dfrac{3}{m - 3} - \dfrac{1}{2m + 6}$

**32.** $-\sqrt{2.25x^6z^3}$

**33.** $3\sqrt{5}(\sqrt{80} - \sqrt{64})$

**34.** $(3\sqrt{2} - 1)^2$

**35.** $\sqrt{\dfrac{18a^7}{7}} \cdot \sqrt{\dfrac{112}{2a^5}}$

**36.** $\sqrt{108} - \sqrt{27} + \sqrt{6}$

**37.** $3\sqrt{80} + \dfrac{2\sqrt{35}}{\sqrt{7}}$

**38.** $(2\sqrt{5} + 5\sqrt{2})(8\sqrt{5} - 4\sqrt{2})$

**39.** $\dfrac{3\sqrt{5} - 4}{\sqrt{2} + 3}$

**Factor completely. If the polynomial cannot be factored, write "prime."**

**40.** $49r^2 + 56rs + 16s^2$

**41.** $4t^5 - 9t^3$

**42.** $30x^2 - 91x - 30$

**43.** $-16z^4 + 80z^3 - 64z^2$

**44.** $125a^4 + 45a^2$

**45.** $12a^2 - 5a - 12$

**46.** $2a^2 - ab + 6a - 3b$

**47.** $c^2 - 8c + 16$

**48.** $-10p^2 + 27p + 28$

**Solve each equation, inequality, or system. Assume that no denominator is zero. If there is no solution, state that fact.**

**49.** $\frac{1}{4}x - 3 = \frac{2}{3}$

**50.** $15 - 3(y + 1) = 14 - 5y$

**51.** $7w + 4 = |-56|$

**52.** $16 = 4.8x - 2.48$

**53.** $27\%$ of $t = 54$

**54.** $3|x| + 5 = 9$

**55.** $z^2 + 4z - 5 = 0$

**56.** $4t^2 - 20t + 25 = 0$

**57.** $12b^2 + 5b = 2$

**58.** $(3a - 2)(4a + 1) = 5$

**59.** $3x + 4y = 2$
$5x + 4y = -2$

**60.** $2x + y = 7$
$x - 2y = 11$

**61.** $\frac{x - 2}{8} - \frac{2x + 1}{12} = \frac{1}{3}$

**62.** $\frac{3x + 2}{x - 1} = \frac{3x + 4}{x + 1}$

**63.** $|t - 3| < 5$

**64.** $-4 \le 3t + 5 \le 13$

**65.** $0 \le 4 - 2t \le 7$

**66.** $\frac{7}{2}t + \frac{1}{3} \ge -\frac{5}{6}$

**67.** $2\sqrt{t + 1} = 6$

**68.** $\sqrt{x^2 + 3} = x - 3$

**69.** $\sqrt{3r + 1} = 2r - 6$

**70.** $\frac{1}{2}m^2 + 2m + 2 = 0$

**71.** $2t^2 + 5t + 1 = 0$

**72.** $3t^2 + 2t - 7 = 0$

**Graph the solution set. (In Exercise 73, use a number line.)**

**73.** $|x + 1| > 3$

**74.** $x + 2y = 5$

**75.** $3x - y < 4$

**76.** Write an equation in standard form of the line that contains $(1, 1)$ and $(6, -1)$.

**77.** Graph the function $f(x) = x^2 - 2x + 4$.

**78.** Write $0.4\overline{25}$ as a fraction in simplest form.

**79.** Graph the solution set of the system:
$$y > 2x - 3$$
$$2x - 2y < 1$$

**80.** Find the length, to the nearest hundredth of a meter, of the diagonal of a rectangle that is 12 m by 8 m. (Use the Table of Square Roots on page 650 or a calculator.)

**81.** A plumber and an assistant finished a job in 4 hours. The job would have taken the plumber 6 hours working alone. How long would the job have taken the assistant working alone?

**82.** If $a$ varies directly as $b$ and inversely as the square of $c$, and $a = 10$ when $b = 8$ and $c = 2$, find $a$ when $b = 20$ and $c = 5$.

**83.** During a canoe trip, Roberto paddled twice as many hours as Edward, and Jim paddled for one hour. If the three of them paddled less than a total of 10 hours, what is the number of hours that Roberto could have paddled?

**84.** During a 3000-mile flight, a plane encountered a strong tail wind that increased its speed by 100 mph. This increase in speed shortened the flying time by one hour. Find the speed of the plane relative to the ground.

# Mixed Review

## Skills and Problem Solving

1. Find the coordinates of the vertex and the equation of the axis of symmetry of the graph of $f(x) = x^2 - 6x + 14$.

2. The legs of a right triangle are 100 m and 50 m long. Find the length of the hypotenuse as a radical in simplest form.

3. How many liters of water must be added to 24 L of a 15% acid solution to make a solution that is 5% acid?

4. The sum of three consecutive odd integers is one third the square of the second. Find all such integers.

**Simplify. Assume that no denominator equals zero. Each variable represents a positive real number.**

5. $\dfrac{\sqrt{5} - 2}{\sqrt{6} + 1}$

6. $(7x - 3)(2x + 9)$

7. $\dfrac{3a^2b^4}{12c^4} \div \dfrac{9ab^3}{3c^4b}$

8. $9 \cdot 8 \div 4 + 36 \div 2 + 4$

9. $\dfrac{b}{b + 1} + \dfrac{5}{4b + 4}$

10. $(3^{-1} - 3^{-2})^{-2}$

11. $(6.2 \times 10^4)(3.1 \times 10^3)$

12. $\dfrac{2x + 12}{x^2 + 10x + 24}$

13. $4\sqrt{2}(2\sqrt{6} - 6\sqrt{3})$

14. $\dfrac{z^2}{z^2 - 1} - \dfrac{1}{z + 1}$

15. $-\dfrac{3}{4}mn^2(12m^2n - 8n^3)$

16. $\dfrac{3c^2 - 27}{15} \cdot \dfrac{5}{c^2 - 3c}$

17. $\dfrac{1}{4}\sqrt{8} - \dfrac{1}{2}\sqrt{12} + \dfrac{3}{4}\sqrt{27}$

18. $\dfrac{49a^2 - 14ab + b^2}{49a^2 - 7ab - 2b^2}$

19. $\sqrt{\dfrac{27c^5}{5}} \cdot \sqrt{\dfrac{170}{3c}}$

**Factor completely, if possible. If not, write "prime."**

20. $24y^3 - 3y^2$

21. $360$

22. $3x^2 - 27$

23. $35a^2 - 2ab - 6b^2$

24. $x^4 - 25x^2 + 144$

25. $4\pi r^2 - 2\pi rh$

26. $x^2 - 0.09$

27. $18t^3 + 39t^2 - 15t$

28. $1080$

29. Arrange in order from least to greatest: $4.0 \times 10^{-2}, \dfrac{43}{99}, 0.\overline{4}, -\dfrac{4}{9}, \dfrac{1}{2}, \dfrac{2}{5}$

30. Two trains leave a station at noon traveling in opposite directions. One train is traveling at 100 km/h, the other at 80 km/h. At what time will they be 270 km apart?

31. The Mas bought furniture at 25% off the regular price. Their total cost, including a 4% tax on the sale price, was $1170. What was the regular price, excluding tax?

**Graph each solution set.**

32. $3x - 2y \le 4$
    $2x + 3y \ge 7$

33. $3x - y = 1$

34. $x + 3y < 3$

35. $3y - 1 > 5 \quad \text{or} \quad 2 - 3y > -1$

36. $-9 \le -2x + 1 < 3$

**Solve each equation, inequality, or system.**

**37.** $7w + 1 = -|-125|$

**38.** $2a - 1 = 3a + 4$

**39.** $\dfrac{1}{2m} - \dfrac{1}{5m} = \dfrac{1}{10}$

**40.** $3x + 4y = 7$
$\quad\ 2x + 5y = 14$

**41.** $\dfrac{4}{3x + 2} + \dfrac{1}{x} = 1$

**42.** $\dfrac{5}{2}y + \dfrac{1}{3} > 7$

**43.** $\sqrt{1 - 5x} = 4$

**44.** $2c^2 + 5c + 3 = 0$

**45.** $x - 2y = 16$
$\quad\ x + y = 10$

**46.** $d^2 - 6d = 15$

**47.** $6 - n^2 = 0$

**48.** $\dfrac{1}{(x - 3)^2} + \dfrac{1}{x - 3} \geq 0$

**49.** $\sqrt{4a + 5} = 2a + 1$

**50.** $\dfrac{2a + 1}{a + 2} + \dfrac{a}{a + 1} = 2$

**51.** $\left|\dfrac{1}{2}x - 7\right| > 2$

**52.** Find an equation of the line through $(-4, 3)$ and $(2, 6)$.

**53.** The sum of twice one number and five times a second number is 5. The sum of three times the first number and twice the second number is $-9$. Find the numbers.

**54.** A painter can finish a job in 2 hours less than the assistant. Together they finish in 1 hour and 20 minutes. How long would the painter take working alone?

**55.** A street 6 m wide and 200 m long can be plowed in 20 min. How long will it take to plow a street 12 m wide and 300 m long?

**56.** Find 120% of 45.

**57.** Find $7\dfrac{1}{3}\%$ of 150.

**58.** If $c$ varies inversely as $d$, and $c = 3$ when $d = 1$, find $d$ when $c = 9$.

**59.** If $x$ varies directly as $y^2$ and inversely as $z$, and $x - 75$ when $y = 5$ and $z = 2$, find $x$ when $y = 4$ and $z = 3$.

**60.** Write $0.5\overline{27}$ as a fraction in lowest terms.

**61.** Find an equation in standard form of the line with slope 2 passing through the point $(-1, -1)$.

**62.** Find an equation in standard form of the line parallel to $x - y = 5$ passing through $(3, 3)$.

**63.** If $f(x) = x^2 + 6$, find $f(2)$ and $f(-4)$.

**64.** If $f(x) = 8x + 4x^2 - 7$, find $f\left(\dfrac{1}{2}\right)$ and $f(-5)$.

**65.** Sandra Chu invests a total of $2800, part at 9% and the rest at $9\dfrac{1}{2}\%$. If she receives $258.50 in annual interest, how much is invested at each rate?

**66.** If the sides of a square are increased by 2 cm, the area is increased by 100 cm². Find the area of the original square.

**67.** The average distance from the sun to Earth is $1.496 \times 10^8$ km. The average distance from the sun to Pluto is $5.090 \times 10^9$ km. What is the average distance from Earth's orbit to Pluto's orbit?

## Strategy for Success

Take your time and be sure to read each question and all the possible answers carefully. Although it is important to work quickly, you must be sure not to work so quickly that you lose accuracy. Remember that no partial credit is given.

**Decide which is the best of the choices given and write the corresponding letter on your answer sheet.**

**1.** Which number is $\frac{3}{5}$ of the way from $-\frac{4}{7}$ to $1\frac{1}{8}$?

(A) $\frac{31}{56}$  (B) $\frac{95}{56}$  (C) $\frac{93}{280}$  (D) $\frac{25}{56}$  (E) $\frac{57}{56}$

**2.** The length of a rectangle is five times the width. The area is 336.2 m². Find the width of the rectangle to the nearest tenth of a meter.

(A) 9.1 m  (B) 8.2 m  (C) 8.9 m  (D) 9.0 m  (E) 7.8 m

**3.** Two sides of a right triangle are 5 cm and 12 cm long. Find the length of the hypotenuse to the nearest tenth of a centimeter.

(A) 13.0 cm  (B) 10.9 cm  (C) 7.0 cm
(D) No such triangle is possible.
(E) Cannot be determined from the given information.

**4.** Evaluate $\frac{x(x+1)}{x+2}$ if $x = \sqrt{3}$.

(A) $3 - \sqrt{3}$  (B) $\sqrt{3} - 3$  (C) $-3 - \sqrt{3}$  (D) $\frac{1 + \sqrt{3}}{2}$

**5.** The sum of a positive integer and the square of the next consecutive integer is 131. Find the sum of the two integers.

(A) 19  (B) 20  (C) 21  (D) 22  (E) 23

**6.** The graph of an equation of the form $y = ax^2 + bx + c$ is shown at the right. Identify the true statement(s).

  I. $0 < a < 1$
  II. $b^2 > 4ac$
  III. $c > 0$
(A) I only  (B) II only  (C) III only
(D) I and II only  (E) I, II, and III

**7.** The equation $ax^2 + 3x + c = 0$ has two distinct roots. Which of the following is (are) possible?

  I. $a = 1, c = 2$    II. $a = -1, c = -2$    III. $a = -1, c = 2$
(A) I only  (B) II only  (C) III only
(D) I and II only  (E) I, II, and III

# Looking Ahead

## Geometry

---

### Points, Lines, and Angles

***Objective*** To represent points, lines, and angles and to measure angles.

You have illustrated relationships among numbers by representing them as points on a number line. Similarly, you have illustrated relationships among ordered pairs of numbers by representing them as points in a coordinate plane. The study of *points, lines,* and *planes* is the subject of the branch of mathematics called *geometry.*

*Geometric points* and *lines* are abstract ideas, not concrete objects. A point has no size; a line has no thickness. To illustrate these abstract ideas, however, you draw figures that do have size and thickness. To represent the idea of a geometric point, you draw a dot. To represent the idea of a geometric line, you draw a straight line.

A line determined by points $A$ and $B$ is denoted by $\overleftrightarrow{AB}$, or $\overleftrightarrow{BA}$. The arrowheads indicate that the line extends in both directions without ending.

line $AB$: $\overleftrightarrow{AB}$

The part of $\overleftrightarrow{AB}$ that consists of points $A$ and $B$ and all points of $\overleftrightarrow{AB}$ between $A$ and $B$ is called a **line segment,** or a **segment.** The segment is denoted by $\overline{AB}$, or $\overline{BA}$. The length of $\overline{AB}$ is denoted by $AB$.

segment $AB$: $\overline{AB}$

The part of $\overleftrightarrow{AB}$ that starts at point $A$ and extends without ending through point $B$ is a **ray,** denoted by $\overrightarrow{AB}$. $A$ is called the **endpoint** of $\overrightarrow{AB}$.

ray $AB$: $\overrightarrow{AB}$

side
vertex
side

An **angle** is a figure formed by two different rays that have the same endpoint. The rays are called the **sides** of the angle and the common endpoint is called the **vertex** of the angle. The angle shown above is formed by $\overrightarrow{AB}$ and $\overrightarrow{AC}$. It is denoted by $\angle A$, $\angle BAC$, or $\angle CAB$.

To find the **degree measure** of an angle, you use a protractor. Using the outer scale, you can see that the degree measure of $\angle NOL$ is 40. You may write this fact as $m \angle NOL = 40$, or $\angle NOL = 40°$. Also, $m \angle NOK = 90$ and $m \angle NOM = 130$.

Angles are classified according to their measures.

> An **acute angle** has measure between 0 and 90.
> A **right angle** has measure 90.
> An **obtuse angle** has measure between 90 and 180.
> A **straight angle** has measure 180.

You can find the degree measure of $\angle LOK$ in the diagram above by subtracting 40 from 90: $m \angle LOK = 50$. Do you see that $\angle LOM$ is a right angle? that $m \angle KOM = 40$? To state that $\angle NOL$ and $\angle KOM$ have equal measures, you write $m \angle NOL = m \angle KOM$.

## Oral Exercises

**Exercises 1–8 refer to the diagram below. Name each angle whose measure is given.**

**1.** $145°$    **2.** $55°$    **3.** $115°$    **4.** $90°$

**State the measure of each angle.**

**5.** $\angle DOF$    **6.** $\angle BOD$    **7.** $\angle COH$    **8.** $\angle EOH$

## Written Exercises

**In Exercises 1–4, name five different line segments in each diagram.**

**A**  **1.**

**2.**

**3.**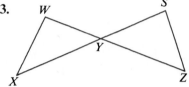

**4.**

Measure the given angle and classify it as acute, obtuse, or right.

**5.** $\angle AOB$

**6.** $\angle AOD$

**7.** $\angle AOC$

**8.** $\angle EOG$

**9.** $\angle BOE$

**10.** $\angle COH$

**11.** $\angle DOG$

**12.** $\angle EOH$

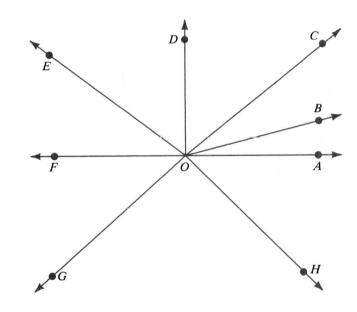

**Graph the solution set of each sentence on a number line. Identify the graph as a point, a line, a line segment, or a ray.**

**B**  **13.** $x = 5$

**14.** $x \geq -1$

**15.** $-3 \leq x \leq 2$

**16.** $x - 4 = 1$

**17.** $-6 \leq x - 2 \leq 0$

**18.** $x + 4 = 7 + x - 3$

**C**  **19.** $x - 2 \leq 6$  or  $x + 1 \leq 4$

**20.** $x - 4 \geq -7$  and  $x + 2 \leq 7$

**21.** $3x > 6$  or  $4x \leq 16$

**22.** $2x + 5 \leq 1$  and  $3x + 10 \geq 1$

# Pairs of Angles

**Objective**  To learn the names and properties of special pairs of angles.

Certain pairs of angles whose measures are related
are given special names.

The diagram at the right shows two lines inter-
secting at $O$ and forming $\angle AOB$, $\angle AOC$, $\angle COD$,
and $\angle DOB$. Two angles, such as $\angle AOB$ and
$\angle COD$, whose sides are rays in the same lines, but in
opposite directions are called **vertical angles.** $\angle AOC$
and $\angle BOD$ are also a pair of vertical angles.

Vertical angles have equal measures. You can use
a protractor to see that $m\angle AOB = m\angle COD$ and
$m\angle AOC = m\angle BOD$.

Two angles are **complementary angles** if the sum of their measures is
90. Each angle is called a **complement** of the other. The diagram at the left
below shows a pair of complementary angles.

$\angle G$ and $\angle F$ are complementary.       $\angle R$ and $\angle S$ are supplementary.
$\angle G$ is a complement of $\angle F$.            $\angle R$ is a supplement of $\angle S$.

Two angles are **supplementary angles** if the sum of their measures is
180. Each angle is called a **supplement** of the other. The diagram at the
right above shows a pair of supplementary angles.

**Example**    The measure of an angle is 32 less than the measure of its
supplement.

Find: **a.** the measure of the angle.
      **b.** the measure of its supplement.
      **c.** the measure of its complement.

**Solution**   Let $n =$ the measure in degrees of the angle.
Then $n + 32 =$ the measure of its supplement.

$$n + (n + 32) = 180$$
$$2n + 32 = 180$$
$$2n = 148$$
$$n = 74$$

**a.** The measure of the angle is 74.
**b.** The measure of its supplement is $(74 + 32)$, or 106.
**c.** The measure of its complement is $(90 - 74)$, or 16.

# Oral Exercises

**State the measure of the complement of an angle with the given measure.**

**1.** 12°     **2.** 68°     **3.** 45°     **4.** 84°     **5.** $x°$     **6.** $25y°$

**State the measure of the supplement of an angle with the given measure.**

**7.** 30°     **8.** 150°     **9.** 85°     **10.** 125°     **11.** $x°$     **12.** $12y°$

**Classify each statement as true or false.**

**13.** The measures of two supplementary angles are never equal.

**14.** If two angles have equal measures, then their complements have equal measures.

**15.** If an angle is obtuse, its supplement is obtuse.

**16.** If an angle is acute, its complement is acute.

**17.** A supplement of a right angle is also a right angle.

# Written Exercises

**In Exercises 1–4 use the diagram at the right. Assume that the measures of $\angle BCJ$ and $\angle EIJ$ are equal.**

**1.** List all the angles with measures equal to the measure of $\angle EIJ$.

**2.** List all the angles that are supplementary to $\angle EIJ$.

**3.** If $m\angle EIJ = 30$, then $m\angle JIF = \underline{\ ?\ }$.

**4.** If $m\angle BCK = 125$, then $m\angle ACK = \underline{\ ?\ }$.

**5.** The smaller of two supplementary angles has a measure that is 40 less than the larger. Find the measures of the two angles.

**6.** What are the measures of two supplementary angles, the larger of which measures 5 times the smaller?

**7.** Find the measure of an angle that measures 56 more than its complement.

**8.** Find the measure of an angle that measures one third of its supplement.

**B**     **9.** The sum of the measures of the complement and the supplement of an angle is 106. Find the measure of the angle.

**10.** The measure of the supplement of an angle exceeds six times the measure of the complement of the angle by 30. Find the measure of the angle.

**580**     *Looking Ahead*

# Triangles

***Objective*** To learn some properties of triangles.

A **triangle** is the figure formed by three segments joining three points not on the same line. Each segment is a **side** of the triangle. Each of the three points is a **vertex** of the triangle.

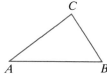

"Triangle *ABC*" can be written $\triangle ABC$.
Sides of $\triangle ABC$: $\overline{AB}$, $\overline{BC}$, $\overline{CA}$
Vertices of $\triangle ABC$: *A*, *B*, *C*
Angles of $\triangle ABC$: $\angle A$, $\angle B$, $\angle C$

    In any triangle, the sum of the measures of the angles is 180°. To check this statement for a particular triangle, measure each angle with a protractor and then find the sum of the measures. You can also show this by tearing off the corners of a paper triangle and fitting them together so that they form a straight angle, as shown below.

Here are some special triangles:

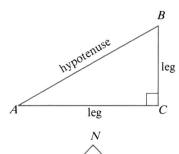

**Right triangle**
$m\angle C = 90$
$(AC)^2 + (BC)^2 = (AB)^2$
(Pythagorean theorem, p. 520, converse p. 521.)

The small square in the right triangle indicates the right angle.

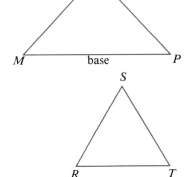

**Isosceles triangle**
$MN = NP$; $m\angle M = m\angle P$
**Base:** $\overline{MP}$
**Base angles:** $\angle M$ and $\angle P$

**Equilateral triangle**
$RS = ST = TR$
$m\angle R = m\angle S = m\angle T$
    $= 60$

## Oral Exercises

**Identify △$ABC$ as right, isosceles, or equilateral.**

1. $AB = 10$, $BC = 10$

2. $AB = BC = CA$

3. $m\angle B = 90$

4. $AB = 3$, $BC = 4$, $AC = 5$

5. $AC = BC$

6. $m\angle C = 23$, $m\angle A = 67$

7. $m\angle B = 60$, $m\angle C = 60$

8. $m\angle A = 40$, $m\angle B = 100$

## Written Exercises

**The measures of two angles of a triangle are given. Find the measure of the third angle.**

**A**

1. $37°$, $74°$

2. $111°$, $43°$

3. $84°$, $48°$

4. $90°$, $29°$

5. $23°$, $34°$

6. $63°$, $57°$

**In Exercises 7–12, use the converse of the Pythagorean theorem to determine whether the triangle is a right triangle.**

7. △$ABC$: $AB = 7$, $BC = 4$, $AC = 3$

8. △$DEF$: $EF = 8$, $FD = 10$, $DE = 6$

9. △$GHI$: $GH = 7$, $HI = 25$, $GI = 24$

10. △$JKL$: $JK = 15$, $KL = 17$, $JL = 8$

11. △$MNO$: $MN = 26$, $NO = 24$, $MO = 10$

12. △$PQR$: $PQ = 10$, $QR = 12$, $PR = 8$

13. If △$RST$ is a right triangle with $m\angle S = 90$, $RS = 6$, and $ST = 8$, find $RT$.

14. If △$STU$ is a right triangle with $m\angle S = 90$, $SU = 12$, and $ST = 5$, find $TU$.

15. If △$XYZ$ is a right triangle with $m\angle Y = 90$, $YZ = 12$, and $XZ = 15$, find $XY$.

16. If △$DEF$ is isosceles, $m\angle D = 40$, and $DE = DF$, find the measure of $\angle E$.

17. If △$MNO$ is isosceles, $m\angle N = 50$, and $MN = MO$, find the measure of $\angle M$.

18. If △$PQR$ is a right isosceles triangle, and $m\angle Q = 90$, find the measures of $\angle P$ and $\angle R$.

**In Exercises 19-24, $m\angle C = 90$ in △$ABC$. Find the length of the third side in simplest radical form given the lengths of the other two sides.**

**B**

19. $AC = 4$, $BC = 12$

20. $AC = 3$, $BC = 6$

21. $AC = 6$, $AB = 9$

22. $BC = 16$, $AB = 24$

**C**

23. $AC = BC = x$

24. $AC = y$, $AB = 2y$

# Problems

**Solve.**

**A**
1. In a right triangle, the measure of one acute angle is 5 times the measure of the other. Find the measure of each angle.

2. Find the measure of each angle of an isosceles triangle if the measure of the third angle is 10 times the measure of each base angle.

3. Find the measure of each angle of a triangle if the measure of the second angle is 4 times the measure of the first angle and the measure of the third angle is 7 times the measure of the first angle.

4. The measures of the angles of a triangle are in the ratio 4:5:6. Find the measure of each angle.

5. The measure of the second angle of a triangle is twice the measure of the first angle, and the measure of the third angle is 6 times the measure of the second angle. Find the measure of each angle.

6. The measure of the second angle of a triangle is 4 times the measure of the first angle and the measure of the third angle is 63 less than the measure of the second angle. Find the measure of each angle.

7. The measures of two angles of a triangle are equal. The measure of the third angle is $\frac{7}{8}$ of the sum of the measures of the first two angles. Find the measure of each angle.

8. How many degrees are there in each angle of a triangle if the measure of the second of the angles is twice that of the first, and the measure of the third is 5 more than 4 times that of the first?

**B**
9. The measure of the second angle of a triangle is 4 more than 3 times the measure of the first angle, and the measure of the third angle is 12 less than twice the measure of the second angle. Find the measure of each angle.

10. The sum of the measures of four angles is 360. The measure of the second angle is 3 more than twice the measure of the first angle, the measure of the third angle is 3 times the measure of the second angle, and the measure of the fourth angle is 9 more than the measure of the third angle. Find the measure of each angle.

**C**
11. The measure of the second angle of a triangle is 18 less than the measure of the complement of the first angle, and the measure of the third angle is 30 more than one half the measure of the supplement of the first angle. Find the measure of each angle.

12. Find the number of degrees in each angle of a triangle if the number of degrees in the first angle is 2 less than twice the number of degrees in the second angle, and the number of degrees in the third angle is 35 more than half the number of degrees in the first.

# Similar Triangles

***Objective*** To solve problems involving similar triangles.

An object viewed under a magnifying lens appears larger than it is, but its shape is not changed. Two figures that have the same shape are called *similar*.

    Two triangles are **similar triangles** when the measures of two angles of one triangle equal the measures of two angles of the other triangle. (Since the sum of the measures of the angles of a triangle is 180°, it follows that the remaining angles also have equal measures.) The triangles shown below are similar.

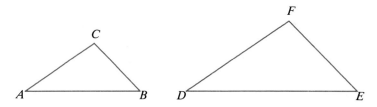

$$m\angle A = m\angle D,\ m\angle B = m\angle E,\ m\angle C = m\angle F$$

You indicate that triangles *ABC* and *DEF* are similar by writing

$$\triangle ABC \sim \triangle DEF.$$

Here angles with equal measures are listed in corresponding positions. They are called **corresponding angles.** The sides opposite corresponding angles are called **corresponding sides.** $\overline{AB}$ corresponds to $\overline{DE}$, and so on. *It is a geometric fact that the lengths of corresponding sides of similar triangles are proportional.* Thus,

$$\frac{AB}{DE} = \frac{BC}{EF} = \frac{CA}{FD}.$$

***Example 1*** In the diagram, $\triangle ABC \sim \triangle DEF.$
Find *AB* and *BC*.

***Solution*** Corresponding sides are
proportional:

$$\frac{AB}{45} = \frac{8}{24} \quad \text{and} \quad \frac{BC}{36} = \frac{8}{24}$$

Solving each proportion,
you have

$$AB = 15 \text{ and } BC = 12. \quad \textbf{\textit{Answer}}$$

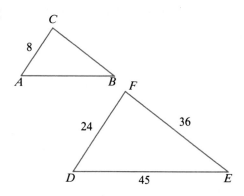

**Example 2** In the diagram, $\triangle ABC \sim \triangle EDC$. Find $BC$ and $DE$.

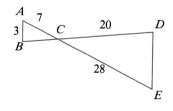

**Solution**   Corresponding sides are proportional:

$$\frac{BC}{20} = \frac{7}{28} \quad \text{and} \quad \frac{3}{DE} = \frac{7}{28}$$

Solving each proportion, you have

$BC = 5$ and $DE = 12$.   **Answer**

## Oral Exercises

**In the diagram for Exercises 1–3, $\triangle XYZ \sim \triangle XWV$.**

1. Name the corresponding angles.
2. Name the corresponding sides.
3. Name three equal ratios.

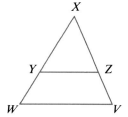

## Written Exercises

**A**   1. In $\triangle ABC$, $m \angle A = 60$ and $m \angle C = 80$. In $\triangle DEF$, $m \angle F = 60$ and $m \angle E = 80$. Write the corresponding angles and sides.

2. In $\triangle JKL$ and $\triangle MNP$, $m \angle J = m \angle P$ and $m \angle K = m \angle M$. Write three equal ratios.

**Classify each statement as true or false.**

3. All right triangles are similar.
4. All isosceles triangles are similar.
5. All equilateral triangles are similar.
6. All isosceles right triangles are similar.

**In Exercises 7–10, $\triangle ABC \sim \triangle DEF$. Find the lengths of the sides not given.**

7. $AB = 3$, $BC = 5$, $AC = 6$, $DE = 6$
8. $DE = 6$, $EF = 9$, $DF = 12$, $BC = 12$
9. $AB = 20$, $BC = 10$, $AC = 15$, $DE = 8$
10. $AB = 6$, $BC = AC = 8$, $EF = 12$

**In Exercises 11-14, $\triangle ABC \sim \triangle DEF$. Find the lengths of the sides not given.**

**B**  **11.** $AB = 6$, $BC = 8$, $DE = 9$, $DF = 15$

**12.** $AB = 12$, $BC = 18$, $DE = 8$, $DF = 16$

**13.** $BC = 14$, $AC = 35$, $EF = 6$, $DE = 12$

**14.** $AB = 16$, $BC = 14$, $DE = 28$, $DF = 49$

## Problems

**Solve.**

**A**  **1.** A triangle has sides with lengths of 8 cm, 12 cm, and 16 cm. If the shortest side of a similar triangle is 14 cm, find its longest side.

**2.** A vertical pole 3 m long casts a shadow 1 m long at the same time a building casts a shadow 12 m long. How tall is the building?

**3.** A bush 2 m tall casts a shadow 3 m long at the same time a tree casts a shadow 18 m long. Find the height of the tree.

**4.** An isosceles triangle has sides with lengths 12 cm, 12 cm, and 15 cm. The base of a similar triangle is 20 cm. Find the perimeter of the larger triangle.

**5.** To find the length of a swamp, two similar triangles were roped off. The measurements are shown on the diagram. How long is the swamp?

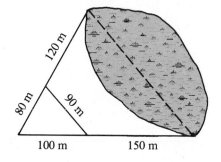

**B**  **6.** Given: $S$ is on $\overline{RU}$, $T$ is on $\overline{RV}$, $\triangle RST \sim \triangle RUV$. If $RS = 3x$, $SU = x$, $RT = 12$, and $ST = 15$, find $UV$.

**7.** Sara walks 4 m up a ramp and is 1 m above the ground. If she were to walk 8 m farther, how far above the ground would she be?

**8.** From a point on the ground 5 m from the base of a 6 m tree, it is possible to see the top of a 300 m building just over the top of the tree. How far is the point from the base of the building?

**C**  **9.** A boy whose eye level is 1.5 m above the ground wants to find the height of a tree $ED$. He places a plane mirror horizontally on the ground 15 m from the tree. If he stands at a point $B$ which is 2 m from the mirror $C$, he can see the reflection of the top of the tree. Find the height of the tree.

# Trigonometry

## Trigonometric Ratios

**Objective**   To find the sine, cosine, and tangent of an acute angle.

In the branch of mathematics called *trigonometry* you
learn more about the measurement of triangles.

Any acute angle, such as $\angle A$ in the diagram,
can be made an angle of a right triangle $ABC$. The
legs opposite and adjacent to this angle are labeled.
Ratios of the lengths of the sides of $\triangle ABC$ are called
**trigonometric ratios** of $\angle A$. These ratios have special
names and symbols.

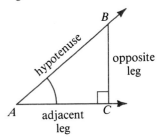

**sine** of $\angle A$ $= \dfrac{\text{length of leg opposite } \angle A}{\text{length of hypotenuse}} = \dfrac{BC}{AB}$
(symbol, sin $A$)

**cosine** of $\angle A$ $= \dfrac{\text{length of leg adjacent to } \angle A}{\text{length of hypotenuse}} = \dfrac{AC}{AB}$
(symbol, cos $A$)

**tangent** of $\angle A = \dfrac{\text{length of leg opposite } \angle A}{\text{length of leg adjacent to } \angle A} = \dfrac{BC}{AC}$
(symbol, tan $A$)

**Example 1**   Find the sine, cosine, and tangent of $\angle A$ and of $\angle B$.

**Solution**

$\sin A = \dfrac{5}{13}$     $\sin B = \dfrac{12}{13}$

$\cos A = \dfrac{12}{13}$     $\cos B = \dfrac{5}{13}$

$\tan A = \dfrac{5}{12}$     $\tan B = \dfrac{12}{5}$

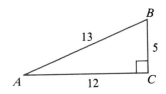

**Example 2**   Find the sine, cosine, and tangent of $\angle P$.

**Solution**     First use the Pythagorean theorem to find
$RQ$.

$$a^2 + 4^2 = 12^2$$
$$a^2 + 16 = 144$$
$$a^2 = 128$$
$$a = \sqrt{128} = 8\sqrt{2}$$

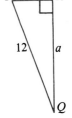

$\sin P = \dfrac{8\sqrt{2}}{12} = \dfrac{2\sqrt{2}}{3}$     $\cos P = \dfrac{4}{12} = \dfrac{1}{3}$     $\tan P = \dfrac{8\sqrt{2}}{4} = 2\sqrt{2}$

The values of the trigonometric ratios of an angle depend only on the measure of the angle and not on the particular right triangle that contains the angle. For example, in the two right triangles below, $\angle A$ and $\angle D$ have equal measures. It can be shown that the trigonometric ratios of $\angle A$ and $\angle D$ are also equal.

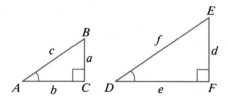

Since $m\angle A = m\angle D$ and $m\angle C = m\angle F = 90$, the triangles are similar and their corresponding sides are proportional:

$$\frac{a}{d} = \frac{c}{f}$$

Multiplying both ratios by $\frac{d}{c}$, you obtain the equivalent proportion

$$\frac{a}{c} = \frac{d}{f}, \text{ or } \sin A = \sin D.$$

You can show similarly that $\cos A = \cos D$ and $\tan A = \tan D$.

Because the values of $\sin A$, $\cos A$, and $\tan A$ depend only on the measure of $\angle A$ and not on the triangle containing $\angle A$, you can think of these trigonometric ratios as the values of three functions each having the set of acute angles as its domain. These functions are called **trigonometric functions**.

## Oral Exercises

**State the value of each trigonometric ratio for the triangle shown.**

1. $\sin A$
2. $\cos A$
3. $\tan A$
4. $\sin B$
5. $\cos B$
6. $\tan B$

7. $\sin X$
8. $\cos X$
9. $\tan X$
10. $\sin Y$
11. $\cos Y$
12. $\tan Y$

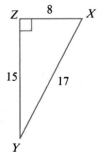

# Written Exercises

**For each right triangle shown, find sin A, cos A, tan A, sin B, cos B, and tan B. Write irrational answers in simplest radical form.**

**A**  **1.**

**2.**

**3.**

**4.**

**5.**

**6.**

**7.**

**8.**

**9.**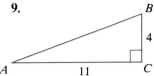

**In Exercises 10–13 △ABC is a right triangle with ∠C as the right angle. Show that the following statements are true.**

**B**  **10.** $\sin A = \cos B$

**11.** $\cos A = \sin B$

**12.** $(\sin A)^2 + (\cos A)^2 = 1$

**13.** $\tan A = \dfrac{\sin A}{\cos A}$

**C**  **14.** If $\cos Y = \dfrac{4}{5}$, find sin Y.

**15.** If $\sin Z = \dfrac{5}{8}$, find the sine of the complement of ∠Z.

**16.** If $\tan X = \dfrac{9}{40}$, find sin Z and cos X.

# Using Trigonometric Tables

**Objective**   To find values of trigonometric ratios for given angles, and measures of angles for given trigonometric ratios.

Values of the trigonometric ratios for degree measures of angles are needed to solve practical problems involving right triangles. A few values can be easily computed using the properties of special triangles and the Pythagorean theorem. For an isosceles right triangle:

$$\sin 45° = \frac{1}{\sqrt{2}} = \frac{\sqrt{2}}{2} \approx 0.707$$

$$\cos 45° = \frac{1}{\sqrt{2}} = \frac{\sqrt{2}}{2} \approx 0.707$$

$$\tan 45° = \frac{1}{1} = 1$$

Most values of trigonometric ratios have to be computed by advanced methods. Approximate values are listed in the table of trigonometric ratios at the back of the book. You can use the table to find $\sin A$, $\cos A$, and $\tan A$ for any angle with whole-number measure from 1° to 89°.

To find the values of $\sin 72°$, $\cos 72°$, and $\tan 72°$, locate 72° in the left-hand column of the portion of the table shown below and then read across the row to find:

$\sin 72° \approx 0.9511$

$\cos 72° \approx 0.3090$

$\tan 72° \approx 3.0777$

For convenience you may write $=$ instead of $\approx$ in equations such as these.

| Angle | Sine | Cosine | Tangent |
|-------|------|--------|---------|
| 1°    | .0175 | .9998 | .0175 |
| 70°   | .9397 | .3420 | 2.7475 |
| 71°   | .9455 | .3256 | 2.9042 |
| 72°   | .9511 | .3090 | 3.0777 |
| 73°   | .9563 | .2924 | 3.2709 |
| 74°   | .9613 | .2756 | 3.4874 |

The trigonometric table can also be used to approximate the measure of an angle if one of its trigonometric ratios is given. For example, the table indicates that an angle whose cosine is approximately 0.3420 has a measure of 70°.

Suppose that $\sin A = 0.9571$, a number not listed in the table. To find the approximate measure of $\angle A$, locate in the sine column the entries between which 0.9571 lies:

$$\sin 73° = 0.9563 \text{ and } \sin 74° = 0.9613.$$

$$73° < m\angle A < 74°$$

Since 0.9571 is closer to 0.9563 than it is to 0.9613, $m\angle A = 73°$, to the nearest degree.

For Exercises 1–12, use the portion of the table of trigonometric ratios shown on the previous page.

State the value of each trigonometric ratio.

**1.** sin 1°                    **2.** cos 71°                    **3.** tan 73°

**4.** cos 74°                   **5.** tan 71°                    **6.** sin 70°

Find the measure of $\angle A$ to the nearest degree.

**7.** cos $A = 0.9998$          **8.** sin $A = 0.9563$          **9.** tan $A = 2.9042$

**10.** tan $A = 3.4000$         **11.** sin $A = 0.9430$         **12.** cos $A = 0.2932$

## Written Exercises

Use the table at the back of the book to find sin $A$, cos $A$, and tan $A$ for the given measure of $\angle A$.

**A**   **1.** 10°                    **2.** 50°                    **3.** 85°

    **4.** 28°                    **5.** 45°                    **6.** 62°

    **7.** 18°                    **8.** 81°                    **9.** 34°

  **10.** 53°                   **11.** 7°                    **12.** 66°

Find the measure of $\angle A$ to the nearest degree.

**13.** sin $A = 0.9962$         **14.** cos $A = 0.8660$         **15.** tan $A = 2.0503$

**16.** cos $A = 0.4372$         **17.** sin $A = 0.6840$         **18.** tan $A = 6.5328$

**19.** tan $A = 0.4897$         **20.** cos $A = 0.9714$         **21.** sin $A = 0.9751$

**22.** tan $A = 1.3821$         **23.** sin $A = 0.7985$         **24.** cos $A = 0.6555$

**25.** tan $A = 4.0940$         **26.** cos $A = 0.0710$         **27.** sin $A = 0.6939$

## Challenge

Is the reasoning logical in each case?

**1.** The sum of the measures of the angles of a triangle is 180°. The sum of the measures of $\angle A$, $\angle R$, and $\angle Z$ is 180°. Therefore, $\angle A$, $\angle R$, and $\angle Z$ are the angles of a triangle.

**2.** A square is a rectangle with four sides of equal length. A rectangle has four right angles. Therefore, a square has four right angles.

# Numerical Trigonometry

**Objective**   To use trigonometric ratios to solve problems.

Trigonometric ratios can be used to solve practical problems involving right triangles. You can find values for these ratios from the table at the back of the book or from a scientific calculator.

**Example 1**   During a severe storm, a radio mast broke 39.6 m from the ground. The top of the mast now makes a 47° angle with the ground. How high was the radio mast?

**Solution**   Draw a triangle showing the known values. First find $x$, the length of the mast from the point where it broke to its top. Since $\triangle ABC$ is a right triangle,

$$\sin 47° = \frac{39.6}{x}, \quad \text{or} \quad x = \frac{39.6}{\sin 47°}.$$

From the table, $\sin 47° = 0.7314$.

Then $x = \frac{39.6}{0.7314} \approx 54.1$.

∴ to the nearest tenth of a meter, the radio mast was $54.1 + 39.6 = 93.7$ m tall.   **Answer**

   In surveying and navigation problems involving right triangles, the terms *angle of elevation* and *angle of depression* are used.
   In the diagram below, $\angle CBA$ is an angle of elevation, since the point $A$ is elevated with respect to an observer at $B$. $\angle DAB$ is an angle of depression, since the point $B$ is depressed with respect to an observer at $A$.

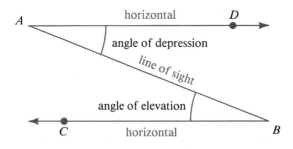

**Example 2**   At a point 86 m from the base of the Washington Monument, the angle of elevation to the top is 63°. To the nearest meter, what is the height of the Washington Monument?

**Solution**  Draw a triangle. You want to find $x$, the height of the Washington Monument.

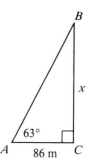

Since $\triangle ABC$ is a right triangle,

$$\tan 63° = \frac{x}{86}.$$

$x = 86(\tan 63°)$
From the table, $\tan 63° = 1.9626$.
Then $x = 86(1.9626) = 168.7836$.
∴ to the nearest meter, the Washington Monument is 169 m high.  **Answer**

## Oral Exercises

**State whether you would use the sine, the cosine, or the tangent ratio to find $x$ for each figure.**

1.

2.

3.

4.

5.

6.

## Written Exercises

**Use the table at the back of the book or a calculator as needed.**

**A** **1–6.** In Oral Exercises 1–6, find $x$ to the nearest whole number.

In right triangle $ABC$, with $m\angle C = 90$, find the other sides of the triangle to the nearest whole number from the following facts.

7. $m\angle A = 56$, $AB = 48$

8. $m\angle B = 21$, $AB = 72$

9. $m\angle B = 11$, $BC = 85$

10. $m\angle A = 65$, $AC = 28$

In right triangle $DEF$, $m\angle E = 90$. Find the measures of $\angle D$ and $\angle F$ to the nearest degree from the following facts.

**B**  11. $EF = 42$, $ED = 36$

12. $ED = 45$, $FD = 63$

13. $FE = 32$, $FD = 48$

14. $EF = 50$, $ED = 45$

In right triangle $XYZ$, $m\angle X = 90$. Find the measures of the other sides of the triangle to the nearest whole number from the following facts.

15. $m\angle Z = 41$, $XY = 65$

16. $m\angle Y = 64$, $XY = 70$

17. $m\angle Y = 27$, $ZX = 25$

18. $m\angle Z = 58$, $ZX = 90$

## Problems

Solve each problem, drawing a sketch for each. Express distances to the nearest unit. Use the table at the back of the book or a calculator as needed.

**A**  1. To the nearest meter, how far is it across the river?

2. To the nearest centimeter, how long is the cable that supports the pole?

3. To the nearest meter, how high is the cliff?

4. To the nearest meter, how far is the car from the tower?

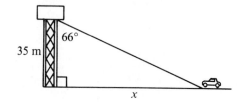

**5.** How deep will a submarine be if it travels 250 m at a 28° angle of depression?

**6.** The length of a water ski jump is 720 cm and the angle of elevation is 35°. Find the height of the ski jump.

**7.** A road rises 12 m vertically over a horizontal distance of 180 m. What is the angle of elevation?

**8.** If a plane flies 1° off course for 6000 km, how far away from the correct path will the plane be?

**B**  **9.** A train travels 600 m on a track with an 18° incline. How high above its starting point is the train?

**10.** From the top of a 20 m lighthouse, the angle of depression of the nearest point on the beach is 8°. Find the distance from the bottom of the lighthouse to the beach.

**11.** An airplane, at an altitude of 700 m, is directly over a water dam. The navigator finds the angle of depression of the airport to be 18°. How far is it from the dam to the airport?

**12.** A submarine travels through the water at a steady rate of 360 m/min on a diving path that forms a 4° angle of depression with the surface of the water. After 5 min, how far below the surface is the submarine?

**C**  **13.** The pilot of a hot air balloon at an altitude of 80 m sees landing sites in opposite directions. The angles of depression of the sites are 34° and 11°, respectively. How far apart are the sites?

**14.** A car is traveling on a level road toward a 2-km high mountain. The angle of elevation from the car to the top of the mountain changes from 6° to 15°. How far has the car traveled?

**15.** From the top of an office building, the angle of depression to the top of a motel is 23°. From the bottom of the office building, the angle of elevation to the top of the motel is 17°. The distance from the office building to the motel is 250 m. Find the height of the office building.

**16.** Two support cables to a TV antenna are anchored to the same spot on the ground 40 feet from the base of the tower. If one cable is fastened to the tower 40 feet above the ground and the other is fastened to the tower 60 feet above the ground, what is the measure of the angle between the cables?

# Probability

## Sample Spaces and Events

**Objective**  To list the sample space and events for a random experiment.

You have been solving mathematical problems that dealt with definite situations. You will now consider the branch of mathematics called **probability** that deals with the possibility, or likelihood, of an event occurring.

Suppose you toss a coin repeatedly in exactly the same manner. You know that on each toss it will land with either a head or a tail showing, but you cannot predict with certainty which it will be. An activity, such as tossing a coin, for which you cannot predict the outcome when you repeat the activity under essentially the same conditions is called a **random experiment.**

Although you do not know prior to each toss whether the result will be a head or a tail, you do know that only these two outcomes are possible. The set of all possible outcomes of a random experiment is called the **sample space** of the experiment. For the coin-tossing experiment, if the outcomes are denoted by $H$ and $T$, then the sample space is $\{H, T\}$.

Any possible subset of the sample space resulting from an experiment is called an **event.** When an event involves a single member of the sample space, it is called a **simple event.** In the coin-tossing experiment, there are two simple events: $\{H\}$ and $\{T\}$.

**Example 1**  For the experiment of turning the pointer on the spinner at the right, specify:
   **a.** the sample space for the experiment.
   **b.** the event that an odd number results.
   **c.** the event that a number less than 3 results.

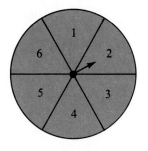

**Solution**  **a.** $\{1, 2, 3, 4, 5, 6\}$
   **b.** $\{1, 3, 5\}$
   **c.** $\{1, 2\}$

Suppose you now have two spinners, one blue and one green. A simple event in this experiment can be represented by the ordered pair $(b, g)$, where $b$ is the number from the blue spinner and $g$ is the number from the green spinner. The ordered pair $(3, 1)$ denotes the simple event "blue spinner shows 3 and green spinner shows 1."

**Example 2** For the two-spinner experiment, specify:

    **a.** the sample space for the experiment.

    **b.** the event that the sum of the numbers on the two spinners equals 3.

    **c.** the event that the sum of the numbers on the two spinners is greater than 5.

**Solution**    **a.** $\{(1, 1), (1, 2), (1, 3), (2, 1), (2, 2), (2, 3), (3, 1), (3, 2), (3, 3),$ $(4, 1), (4, 2), (4, 3)\}$

    **b.** $\{(1, 2), (2, 1)\}$

    **c.** $\{(3, 3), (4, 2), (4, 3)\}$

## Oral Exercises

**A penny and a nickel are tossed. The sample space is $\{(H, H), (H, T), (T, H), (T, T)\}$. Specify the following events.**

**1.** Two tails up

**2.** One head up and one tail up

**3.** Exactly one head up

**4.** At least one tail up

**Each letter of the word BASKET is written on a separate card. The cards are shuffled, and one card is drawn.**

**5.** Give the sample space for this experiment.

**6.** Give the event that the letter on the card is a vowel.

**7.** Give the event that the letter on the card is neither B nor T.

**Each letter of the word TRIANGLE is written on a separate card. The cards are shuffled, and one card is drawn.**

**8.** Give the sample space for this experiment.

**9.** Give the event that the letter on the card is a vowel.

**10.** Give the event that the letter on the card is neither R nor L.

## Written Exercises

**A** **1.** Each of the letters $A$, $B$, $C$, $D$, $E$, $F$, $G$, $H$, $I$, $J$, and $K$ is written on a card. The cards are shuffled and one card is drawn. For this experiment, specify:

    **a.** the sample space.

    **b.** the event that the letter is a vowel.

    **c.** the event that the letter is $C$, $F$, $G$, or $I$.

    **d.** the event that the letter is not $B$, $E$, $G$, $J$.

**2.** A bowl contains a yellow marble and a white marble. A second bowl contains a yellow, a green, a blue, and a red marble. One marble is taken from each bowl. For this experiment, specify:
   **a.** the sample space.
   **b.** the event that one marble is green.
   **c.** the event that at least one marble is yellow.
   **d.** the event that neither marble is yellow.

**3.** A hat contains cards numbered 2, 4, 8, and 15. A second hat contains cards numbered 1, 4, and 9. One card is drawn from each hat. For this experiment, specify:
   **a.** the sample space.
   **b.** the event that both numbers are the same.
   **c.** the event that both numbers are odd.
   **d.** the event that the sum of the numbers is greater than 12.
   **e.** the event that the sum of the numbers is less than 6.

**4.** A spinner is divided into four equal sections numbered 1, 2, 3, and 4. A second spinner is divided into four equal sections numbered 1, 5, 10, and 15. Each pointer is turned. For this experiment specify:
   **a.** the sample space.
   **b.** the event that both numbers are even.
   **c.** the event that neither number is odd.
   **d.** the event that the sum of the numbers is between 7 and 15.
   **e.** the event that the product of the numbers is greater than 30.

**B**  **5.** There are three on-off switches on a light panel.
   **a.** List the sample space.
   **b.** Write the event that at least two lights are on.
   **c.** Write the event that at least one light is off.
   **d.** Write the event that all three lights are off.

**6.** Li has a $10 bill and a $20 bill in his wallet. Cara has a $1 bill and a $20 bill in her wallet. Sid has a $5 bill in his wallet. A bill is randomly selected from each wallet. For this experiment, specify:
   **a.** the sample space.
   **b.** the event that the sum is even.
   **c.** the event that the sum is odd.
   **d.** the event that the sum is less than $30.

**For Exercises 7–11 refer again to the two-spinner experiment. The ordered pair $(b, g)$ denotes a simple event, as before.**

**7.** Specify the event that $b + g = 4$.

**8.** Specify the event that $b < g$.

**9.** Specify the event that $b + g$ is an even number.

**C**  **10.** Specify the event that $b > 2$ or $g \leq 2$.

**11.** Specify the event that $b$ is an even number or $g$ is an odd number.

# Probability

**Objective**  To find the probability that an event will occur.

Suppose you toss a single coin repeatedly. The sample space consists of two simple events, $\{H\}$ and $\{T\}$. Assuming that the coin is fair, the two simple events are **equally likely** to occur. That is, for large numbers of tosses, you would expect the number of heads, or the number of tails, appearing to be about one half the number of tosses.

The **probability** of an event is the ratio of the number of outcomes favoring the event to the total number of outcomes. Thus, in the case of a tossed coin, the probability of the simple event $\{H\}$ equals the probability of the simple event $\{T\}$. If the probability of $\{H\}$ is denoted by $P(H)$ and the probability of $\{T\}$ by $P(T)$, then,

$$P(H) = P(T) = \frac{1}{2}.$$

In general, for any probability $P$, $0 \leq P \leq 1$. If an event can never occur, it is assigned a probability of 0. If an event will always occur, the probability is 1.

Consider the spinner shown at the right. The sample space consists of five simple events, $\{Y, R, G, B, W\}$. If the spinner is fair, the five simple events are equally likely to occur.

Thus, $P(Y) = P(R) = P(G) = P(B) = P(W) = \frac{1}{5}$.

In general, if $\{a_1, a_2, a_3, \ldots, a_n\}$ is a sample space containing $n$ equally likely simple events, then:

$$P(a_1) = P(a_2) = P(a_3) = \cdots = P(a_n) = \frac{1}{n}$$

The sum of all probabilities assigned to all simple events in the sample space of a random experiment is 1. Thus,

$$P(a_1) + P(a_2) + P(a_3) + \cdots + P(a_n) = 1.$$

**Example**  A cube whose sides are numbered 1, 2, 3, 4, 5, and 6 is rolled. Find the probability of each event.

*Event A:* The number turned up is greater than 3.

*Event B:* The number turned up is greater than 2 and less than 5.

**Solution**  The sample space is $\{1, 2, 3, 4, 5, 6\}$. Since each simple event is equally likely to occur, the probability of each simple event is $\frac{1}{6}$.

Event $A = \{4, 5, 6\}$  　　　Event $B = \{3, 4\}$

$P(A) = \frac{3}{6} = \frac{1}{2}$  　　　$P(B) = \frac{2}{6} = \frac{1}{3}$

## Oral Exercises

**A letter is selected randomly from the word ALGEBRA. Name the probability of each event.**

**1.** It is a vowel.

**2.** It is a consonant.

**3.** It is a G.

**4.** It is an A.

**A cube whose sides are numbered 1, 2, 3, 4, 5, and 6 is tossed. Name the probability of each event.**

**5.** The number is even.

**6.** The number is 3 or 4.

**7.** The number is greater than 6.

**8.** The number is less than 7.

## Written Exercises

**A**  **1.** A jar contains 4 red marbles, 6 white marbles, and 2 blue marbles. A marble is drawn at random from the jar. Find the probability of each event.
  **a.** The marble is red.
  **b.** The marble is blue.
  **c.** The marble is either blue or red.
  **d.** The marble is green.
  **e.** The marble is either blue or white.

**2.** One card is drawn at random from a 52-card deck. Find the probability of each event.
  **a.** It is the 3 of diamonds.
  **b.** It is a black 10.
  **c.** It is a king.
  **d.** It is a heart.
  **e.** It is a 6 or 7.
  **f.** It is an 8, 9, or 10.

**3.** There are 25 students in a public speaking class. The order of speeches is determined by having students select a number from a box containing the numbers 1–25. Find the probability of each event.
  **a.** Being the first person to give a speech.
  **b.** Being one of the last 10 people to give a speech.
  **c.** Selecting a number between 10 and 16.
  **d.** Selecting a number divisible by 4.

**4.** The results of rolling two numbered cubes are shown in the table at the right. Copy and complete the table and then use it to find the probability of each event shown on the next page. $P(6)$ means "the probability of getting a sum of 6."

| 6 | (6, 1) | (6, 2) | ( ? ) | ( ? ) | ( ? ) | ( ? ) |
|---|--------|--------|-------|-------|-------|-------|
| 5 | (5, 1) | (5, 2) | ( ? ) | ( ? ) | ( ? ) | ( ? ) |
| 4 | (4, 1) | (4, 2) | ( ? ) | ( ? ) | ( ? ) | ( ? ) |
| 3 | (3, 1) | (3, 2) | ( ? ) | ( ? ) | ( ? ) | ( ? ) |
| 2 | (2, 1) | (2, 2) | (2, 3) | (2, 4) | ( ? ) | ( ? ) |
| 1 | (1, 1) | (1, 2) | (1, 3) | (1, 4) | (1, 5) | ( ? ) |
|   | 1 | 2 | 3 | 4 | 5 | 6 |

a. $P(6)$     b. $P(\text{not } 6)$
c. $P(4 \text{ or } 7)$   d. $P(11)$
e. $P(12)$    f. $P(2 \text{ or } 8)$
g. $P(5)$     h. $P(\text{not } 5)$
i. $P(\text{even number})$ j. $P(\text{odd number})$

5. A penny, a nickel, and a dime are tossed. Find the probability of each event.
   a. 3 heads
   b. exactly 2 tails
   c. at least 2 heads
   d. one or two heads

B 6. A penny, a nickel, a dime, and a quarter are tossed. Find the probability of each event.
   a. 4 tails
   b. exactly 2 heads
   c. at least 3 tails
   d. 2 or 3 heads
   e. no heads
   f. exactly 1 tail

7. A spinner is divided into three equal sections numbered 1, 2, and 3. A second spinner is divided into four equal sections numbered 2, 4, 6, and 7. Each pointer is turned. Find the probability of each event.
   a. $P(1, 4)$
   b. $P(2, \text{not } 2)$
   c. $P(3, 6)$
   d. $P(\text{even number, even number})$
   e. $P(\text{sum is } 7)$
   f. $P(\text{sum is less than } 8)$

C 8. A bag contains 1 red marble, 2 green marbles, and 3 white marbles. Two marbles are randomly selected. Find the probability of each event.
   a. 1 green and 1 white marble
   b. 2 white marbles
   c. 2 green marbles
   d. 2 marbles of the same color
   e. 1 red marble and a green or a white marble

## Calculator Key-In

Use a calculator and the formula $A = \sqrt{s(s - a)(s - b)(s - c)}$ (page 519) to find the approximate area of each triangle whose sides are given.

1. 7 cm, 11 cm, 14 cm
2. 13 mm, 18 mm, 27 mm
3. 12 m, 12 m, 16 m
4. 48 mm, 64 mm, 84 mm
5. 2.8 m, 3.9 m, 5.7 m
6. 15.8 cm, 16.9 cm, 23.4 cm
7. 9.2 cm, 11.8 cm, 17.1 cm
8. 37.1 m, 46.4 m, 69.7 m

# Statistics

## Frequency Distributions

***Objective***   To recognize and characterize frequency distributions.

The results of a test are of little value until they have been summarized and then analyzed. One way to summarize data is shown in the table at the right. The table shows the scores that were received on a test and how many students received each score. This table is called a **frequency distribution.**

| Score | Number of Students |
|---|---|
| 100 | 1 |
| 98 | 2 |
| 95 | 3 |
| 93 | 1 |
| 91 | 1 |
| 89 | 5 |
| 87 | 2 |
| 86 | 1 |
| 84 | 3 |
| 83 | 2 |
| 82 | 1 |
| 80 | 1 |
| 79 | 2 |
| 76 | 2 |
| 75 | 1 |
| 71 | 1 |
| 68 | 1 |
| 65 | 2 |
| 62 | 1 |

Another way to summarize data is shown in the graph below. This type of graph is called a **histogram.** In a histogram, data is grouped into convenient intervals. The intervals in this histogram of the test scores are 60–65, 65–70, and so on. A test score of 75 is considered to be in the interval 70–75, while a score of 80 is in the interval 75–80. In general, a "boundary" score is included in the interval to its left.

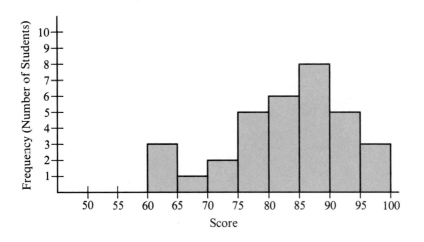

Frequency distributions are often analyzed by using numbers called *statistics.* One statistic used to indicate the center of a distribution is called the **mean.** The **mean** of a collection of data is the sum of the numbers divided by the number of numbers.

***Example 1***   The number of home runs that led the National League during five consecutive years was 40, 54, 47, 42, and 37. What is the mean (*M*) of the number of home runs?

**Solution**  $M = \dfrac{40 + 54 + 47 + 42 + 37}{5} = \dfrac{220}{5} = 44$  **Answer**

Other important numbers for analyzing a set of data are the *median,* the *mode,* and the *range.*

The **median** of a frequency distribution is the middle number when the data are arranged in order. If the number of data is even, the average of the two numbers closest to the middle is the median. Arranging the data from the test score table in increasing order gives a median of 84.

The **mode** is the most frequently occurring number in a frequency distribution. A set of data may have more than one, one, or no modes. From the table, the mode of the test scores is 89. The mode is most useful in analyzing nonnumerical data, such as color or taste preferences.

The **range** of a frequency distribution is the difference between the highest and the lowest values. For example, the range of the data in the table is $100 - 62$, or 38.

**Example 2**  Three numbered cubes are rolled 10 times. The sums of the numbers after each roll are, in ascending order, 6, 7, 9, 10, 10, 12, 13, 14, 15, and 17. Find the median, the mode, and the range of the data.

**Solution**  Since there is an even number of data, the median is the average of the middle two scores.

$$\frac{10 + 12}{2} = \frac{22}{2} = 11$$

Since 10 is the score that occurs most frequently, it is the mode.

The range is the difference between 17 and 6, or 11.

## Oral Exercises

1. The heights of three students are 60 in., 68 in., and 70 in. For the heights, find:

   **a.** the mean  **b.** the median  **c.** the range

2. In four days, Rachel earned $7, $5, $1, and $7. For her earnings, find:

   **a.** the mean  **b.** the mode  **c.** the median  **d.** the range

3. In five successive hockey games, the Fraser Flags scored 3, 2, 0, 1, and 4 goals, respectively. For this goal distribution, find:

   **a.** the mean  **b.** the median  **c.** the mode  **d.** the range

## Written Exercises

**For the data given in Exercises 1–6, find the mean, the median, the mode, and the range.**

A
1. 24, 53, 38, 39, 51
2. 8, 15, 42, 31, 15
3. 58, 62, 63, 70, 62, 73
4. 11, 9, 10, 9, 10, 9, 13
5. 25, 31, 22, 33, 33, 26, 25
6. 72, 78, 63, 49, 81, 50, 66
7. In six debate matches, Dana scored 28, 25, 28, 30, 24, and 29. Find the mean, the median, the mode, and the range of her scores.
8. Find the mean and the range for the average monthly temperatures given in degrees Celsius: $-1.5°$, $-2°$, $-1°$, $5°$, $24.5°$, $28°$, $33.5°$, $34°$, $28.5°$, $18.5°$, $6°$, $1.5°$.
9. In ten basketball games, Kim scored 9, 12, 11, 8, 11, 15, 15, 16, 15, and 19 points. To the nearest tenth of a point, find the mean, the median, the mode, and the range.
10. In a class of 25 students, the test scores were 78, 90, 95, 76, 65, 80, 90, 96, 100, 98, 84, 88, 81, 76, 100, 94, 90, 82, 74, 85, 90, 81, 79, 81, 88. First make a frequency table and then draw a histogram for the data.

B
11. Yon needs an average bowling score of 165 to bowl in a spring tournament. If he has scores of 150, 155, 177, and 161 in the first four games, what does he have to bowl in the fifth game to be eligible for the tournament?
12. If each score on an algebra test is increased by 10 points, how does this affect the:
    **a.** mean?        **b.** mode?        **c.** median?        **d.** range?
13. If each entry in a set of data is multiplied by four, how does this affect the:
    **a.** mean?        **b.** mode?        **c.** median?        **d.** range?
14. The mean of 6 numbers is 18. What is the sum of the numbers?

C
15. Find the mean of twelve numbers if the mean of the first five numbers is 20 and the mean of the last seven numbers is 32.
16. In an algebra class, Sherm has a score of 89 for each of the first eight weeks. For the ninth week, his score is 96. What does his score for the tenth week have to be in order for him to have a final mean score of 90?

# Summary

1. Geometry is the branch of mathematics that deals with the properties of sets of points such as lines, rays, angles, and triangles.

2. Two angles whose sides are rays in the same lines but in opposite directions are called vertical angles. Two angles are complementary if the sum of their measures is 90. Two angles are supplementary if the sum of their measures is 180.

3. The sum of the measures of the angles of a triangle is 180. Some special triangles are right triangles, isosceles triangles, and equilateral triangles.

4. Similar triangles have the same shape but not necessarily the same size. Their corresponding angles have the same measure and corresponding sides are proportional.

5. Trigonometry is the branch of mathematics involved with the measurement of triangles. Three trigonometric ratios are

   $$\sin A = \frac{a}{c}, \ \cos A = \frac{b}{c}, \text{ and } \tan A = \frac{a}{b}.$$

   Approximate values for these ratios are given in the table at the back of the book. Trigonometric ratios can be used to solve problems involving right triangles.

6. Probability is the branch of mathematics that is concerned with the possibility of an event occurring. For any event with probability $P$, $0 \le P \le 1$.

7. Statistics is involved with summarizing and analyzing data. This can be done by using histograms and frequency distributions.

# Review

**Give the letter of the correct answer.**

1. Which symbol denotes the line segment joining points $A$ and $B$?
     **a.** $AB$      **b.** $\overline{AB}$      **c.** $\overrightarrow{AB}$      **d.** $\overleftrightarrow{AB}$

2. Which angle is a right angle?
     **a.** $\angle A = 99°$    **b.** $\angle B = 89°$    **c.** $\angle C = 90°$    **d.** $\angle D = 100°$

3. Find the measure of the supplement of an angle with measure 49.
     **a.** 41      **b.** 141      **c.** 131      **d.** 51

4. Find the complement of an angle with measure $x$.
     **a.** $(90 - x)$    **b.** $(90 + x)$    **c.** $(180 - x)$    **d.** $(180 + x)$

**5.** Find the sum of the measures of the angles of a right triangle.

    **a.** 45°             **b.** 90°             **c.** 180°             **d.** 360°

**6.** If $\triangle ABC \sim \triangle DEF$, $\dfrac{AB}{DE} = \dfrac{8}{5}$, and $CA = 12$, find $FD$.

    **a.** 10             **b.** $\dfrac{96}{5}$            **c.** $\dfrac{2}{15}$           **d.** $\dfrac{15}{2}$

**7.** Use the diagram to find $\cos B$.

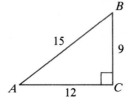

    **a.** $\dfrac{3}{4}$            **b.** $\dfrac{4}{5}$

    **c.** $\dfrac{3}{5}$            **d.** $\dfrac{4}{3}$

**8.** Use the table at the back of the book to find $\sin 54°$.

    **a.** 1.3764        **b.** 0.5878        **c.** 0.8090        **d.** 0.1584

**9.** The angle of elevation of the top of a tree from a point on the ground 800 cm from the base of the tree is 47°. Find the height of the treè.

    **a.** 600 cm        **b.** 858 cm        **c.** 585 cm        **d.** 546 cm

**10.** A cube with the letters $A$, $B$, $C$, $D$, $E$, and $F$ is rolled. Specify the event that the letter turned up is a vowel.

    **a.** $\{A, B, C, D, E, F\}$        **b.** $\{A, E, I, O, U\}$

    **c.** $\{A, E\}$              **d.** $\{B, C, D, F\}$

**11.** A spinner is divided into five equal sections, numbered 1, 2, 3, 4, and 5. The pointer is turned. Find the probability that the number the pointer stops on is even.

    **a.** 0             **b.** 1             **c.** $\dfrac{1}{5}$          **d.** $\dfrac{2}{5}$

**12.** Find the mean of 39, 43, 46, 52, 55.

    **a.** 47             **b.** 46             **c.** 16            **d.** 55

**13.** Find the range of 33, 43, 57, 61, 76.

    **a.** 54             **b.** 57             **c.** 43            **d.** 76

**14.** The histogram at the right shows the frequency distribution for the number of points scored in a game by a high-school basketball team for a season of 18 games. In how many games did the team score between 60 and 80 points?

Points per game

    **a.** 9             **b.** 6

    **c.** 11            **d.** 5

# Extra Practice: Skills

## Chapter 1

**Simplify each expression.**  (1-1, 1-2)

1. $5 + (4 \times 8)$
2. $(3 + 7) \times 2$
3. $(30 \times 3) + (5 \times 2)$
4. $(40 \div 4) - (9 - 5)$
5. $(30 + 3) \times (4 + 2)$
6. $(40 - 4) \div (9 - 5)$
7. $9 + 7 - 2 \times 8 \div 4$
8. $32 \div 8 + 3 \times 7 - 6$
9. $4 \times 6 - 16 \div 2 + 7$

**Evaluate each expression if $e = 2$, $f = 3$, $g = 4$, $u = 0$, $v = 5$, and $w = 1$.**  (1-1, 1-2)

10. $ev - f$
11. $5g + 4w$
12. $(uv) + (fg)$
13. $w(v - f) + g$
14. $(3g) \cdot (e + u)$
15. $(v - u)w + g$
16. $(e + f)(g + v)$
17. $e(u + v - w)$
18. $(4e - 2f)(v + w)$
19. $\dfrac{e + g}{v - f}$
20. $\dfrac{gv - 5e}{5 - 3u}$
21. $f(we + v) + \dfrac{g}{e}$

**Solve each equation if $x \in \{0, 1, 2, 3, 4, 5, 6\}$.**  (1-3)

22. $7 + x = 12$
23. $x - 4 = 2$
24. $8 - x = 3$
25. $x - x = 0$
26. $6x = 18$
27. $0 = 5x$
28. $8x = 32$
29. $x \cdot x = 36$
30. $x \cdot x = 1$
31. $\dfrac{1}{2}x = 2$
32. $\dfrac{1}{3}x = 2$
33. $x \cdot x = 5x$
34. $3x + 9 = 26$
35. $15 = 9x - 3$
36. $4x = x \cdot 4$
37. $x(9 - x) = 0$

**Represent the required numbers in terms of the given variables.**  (1-4)

38. What number is three more than twice the number $m$?
39. What number is four less than half the number $z$?
40. What number is two more than eight times the number $k$?
41. What number is the difference of five times a number $w$ and one?
42. What number is three times the sum of a number $h$ and six?

**Using the given variable, write an expression for the measure required to complete each statement.**  (1-4)

43. In $x$ weeks there are __?__ days.
44. In $y$ yards there are __?__ feet.
45. Barbara is $x$ years old. Four years ago she was __?__ years old.
46. Tony weighs $w$ lb. Ray is 7 lb heavier than Tony. Ray weighs __?__ lb.
47. Claudia is 5 years older than Carl. If Claudia is $n$ years old, then Carl is __?__ years old.

**Use the given facts to state an equation that represents the third statement.** (1-5)

**48.** The Lions scored 7 points less than the Bears. The Bears scored $x$ points. The Lions scored 73 points.

**49.** Henry is 4 years older than Celia. Celia is $m$ years old. The product of their ages is 140.

**50.** The length of a rectangle is 5 cm more than its width. Its width is $t$ cm. The area of the rectangle is 176 cm².

**Write an equation, using a variable you have chosen, that represents the given information.** (1-5)

**51.** A package of a dozen pencils costs $1.39. (Cost of one pencil)

**52.** The perimeter of a square is 52 m. (Length of a side)

**53.** All but 5 of the 34 invited guests came to the party. (Number of guests at the party)

**Use the five-step plan to solve each problem. Write out each step.** (1-6)

**54.** If half of a number is decreased by 12, the result is 30. Find the number.

**55.** A store has twice as many blue T-shirts as red T-shirts on a sale rack holding 48 red and blue T-shirts. How many red T-shirts are on the rack?

**56.** If 6 times a number is increased by 3, the result is 27. Find the number.

**Write a positive or negative number for each measurement.** (1-7)

**57.** 400 ft above sea level

**58.** A bank withdrawal of $50

**59.** Ten losses

**60.** Seven floors up

**61.** 2 points under par

**62.** 5 m underground

**Graph the given numbers on a number line.** (1-7)

**63.** $5, -2, \frac{1}{2}, 3, -4$

**64.** $-3, 0, 1, -2.5, 2$

**Simplify.** (1-8)

**65.** $-(7 - 4)$    **66.** $-(5 - 5)$    **67.** $[-(-8)] + 10$    **68.** $3 + [-(-6)]$

**69.** $2 + |-9|$    **70.** $|-8| + |5|$    **71.** $|-3| + |0|$    **72.** $|6| - |6|$

**73.** $|5| - |-5|$    **74.** $|-3.2| + |-0.8|$    **75.** $|-4.7| + |4.7|$    **76.** $|-2| - |0|$

**Replace each ___?___ with one of the symbols $<$ or $>$ to make a true statement.** (1-9)

**77.** $9 - 8 \underline{\ ?\ } -1$    **78.** $7 \underline{\ ?\ } 6 + 5$    **79.** $|0| \underline{\ ?\ } 1$

**80.** $-4.3 \underline{\ ?\ } -4.4$    **81.** $|-2| \underline{\ ?\ } -(-4)$    **82.** $|-6| \underline{\ ?\ } |-8|$

**83.** $-(7 + 3) \underline{\ ?\ } |-14|$    **84.** $-\frac{3}{7} \underline{\ ?\ } -\frac{2}{7}$    **85.** $-\frac{5}{8} \underline{\ ?\ } \frac{3}{8}$

# Chapter 2

(2-1)

**Simplify.**

1. $237 + 75 + 13 + 25$
2. $456 + 29 + 44 + 21$
3. $0.2 + 16.4 + 2.8 + 0.6$
4. $3.75 + 4.85 + 1.25 + 3.15$
5. $6\frac{3}{8} + 1\frac{2}{7} + 4\frac{5}{8} + 3\frac{5}{7}$
6. $25\frac{3}{4} + \frac{4}{5} + \frac{1}{4} + 2\frac{1}{5}$
7. $8 + 3m + 4$
8. $15 + 5f + 7$
9. $9 + 6w + 3$
10. $5(7u)$
11. $(8n)(11)$
12. $(4b)9$
13. $(3p)(4q)(5r)$
14. $(2x)(5k)(7l)$
15. $(10w)(3h)(2m)$

**Simplify. If necessary, draw a number line to help you.**

(2-2)

16. $(-4 + 8) + 9$
17. $(-7 + 10) + (-3)$
18. $[16 + (-21)] + 4$
19. $[-5 + (-13)] + 6$
20. $[0 + (-7)] + [-8 + (-22)]$
21. $[27 + (-7)] + [1 + (-1)]$
22. $-3 + (-4) + (-9)$
23. $(-5) + (-8) + (-6)$
24. $-7.2 + (-3.5) + 10.7$
25. $5.4 + (-3.1) + (-7.9)$

**Add.**

(2-3)

26. $9 + 8 + (-3) + 4$
27. $-6 + (-7) + 10 + 2$
28. $112 + (-32) + (-40) + (-25)$
29. $-265 + (-88) + 105 + 95$
30. $-[24 + (-8)] + [-(-4 + 6)]$
31. $[-9 + (-2)] + [-(-9 + 2)]$

**Replace each ___?___ with a number to make a true statement.**

(2-3)

32. $\underline{\phantom{?}} + (-8) = 2$
33. $-14 + \underline{\phantom{?}} = 5$
34. $3 + \underline{\phantom{?}} = -10$
35. $\underline{\phantom{?}} + (-5) = 4$
36. $0.7 + \underline{\phantom{?}} = -1$
37. $\underline{\phantom{?}} + 0.35 = -0.65$

**Simplify.**

(2-4, 2-5)

38. $48 - 218$
39. $53 - (-47)$
40. $-18 - (-5)$
41. $-27 - 56$
42. $133 - (62 - 59)$
43. $186 - (40 - 69)$
44. $(33 - 44) - (66 - 77)$
45. $(54 - 32) - (-8 + 13)$
46. $14 - (-8) - [6 - (-3)]$
47. $-18 - 7 - [-6 - (-11)]$
48. $6 + x - (6 - x) - x$
49. $y - (-4) - [y + (-4)] - 4$
50. $30\left(\frac{1}{6} + \frac{1}{3}\right)$
51. $\frac{1}{5}(24) + \frac{1}{5}(16)$
52. $\frac{1}{4}(16 + 12)$
53. $(0.25)(34) + (0.75)(34)$
54. $(37 \times 22) - (7 \times 22)$
55. $(16 \times 58) - (6 \times 58)$
56. $14m + 7m$
57. $15q + (-8)q$
58. $53n - 110n$
59. $79a - 37a$
60. $3u + 7u + 8$
61. $7(c + 3) + 6$

**Simplify.**

(2-5, 2-6)

**62.** $26 + 4(h + 3)$      **63.** $8(j - 4) + 17$      **64.** $23 + 6(t - 2)$

**65.** $5x + 9 + 3x + 11$      **66.** $(-5)m + 3 + 13m + 17$

**67.** $14u - 8 - 12u + 13$      **68.** $4h + 8k + (-2)h + 12k$

**69.** $9f + 3g - 7f + 7g$      **70.** $10x + 14y - 6x - 3y$

**71.** $(-27)(-5)$      **72.** $38(-2)$      **73.** $(-4)45$

**74.** $(-8)(-6)(30)$      **75.** $(-5)(-9)(-3)$      **76.** $(-13)(-14)(0)$

**77.** $5(-4)(-12)(-2)$      **78.** $-3(-2 - 9)$      **79.** $(-17 + 6)(-1)$

**80.** $(-6 \times 13) + (-6 \times 15)$      **81.** $[27 \times (-5)] - (27 \times 5)$

**82.** $-16 \times (-1) - [-16 \times (-11)]$      **83.** $7(-m + 6p)$

**84.** $-5(2u - h)$      **85.** $-4(6n - 9v)$

**86.** $-x + 7 + 6x - 5$      **87.** $4 - t - 8 - 7t$      **88.** $-l + 9 + 6l - 4$

**89.** $3(x + 4y) + (-4)(8x - y)$      **90.** $-4(2u + v) + 5(u - v)$

**91.** $-2(3c + d) - 3(5d - c)$      **92.** $7(e - f) - 3(2e - 3f)$

**Write an equation to represent the stated relationship.**

(2-7)

**93.** The sum of three consecutive integers is 75.

**94.** The sum of three consecutive odd integers is 87.

**95.** The sum of three consecutive even integers is 138.

**96.** The product of two consecutive integers is 156.

**97.** The greater of two consecutive odd integers is eight more than three times the lesser.

**98.** The smaller of two consecutive even integers is one less than half of the greater.

**Simplify each expression.**

(2-8, 2-9)

**99.** $-\frac{1}{11}(55)$      **100.** $-5000\left(\frac{1}{50}\right)$      **101.** $-\frac{1}{9}(-63)$

**102.** $112\left(-\frac{1}{7}\right)\left(-\frac{1}{2}\right)$      **103.** $-\frac{1}{5}(80)\frac{1}{4}$      **104.** $6uv\left(-\frac{1}{6}\right)$

**105.** $44xy\left(\frac{1}{4}\right)$      **106.** $\frac{1}{m}(3mn),\ m \neq 0$      **107.** $(8fg)\left(\frac{1}{f}\right),\ f \neq 0$

**108.** $\frac{1}{5}(-35a + 15)$      **109.** $(27h - 18)\frac{1}{3}$      **110.** $-\frac{1}{4}(-32e + 40f)$

**111.** $(42x - 63y)\left(-\frac{1}{7}\right)$      **112.** $\frac{1}{12}(-480 - 144m)$      **113.** $(-50p - 100q)\left(-\frac{1}{10}\right)$

**114.** $-392 \div 56$      **115.** $216 \div (-27)$      **116.** $55 \div \left(-\frac{1}{5}\right)$      **117.** $0 \div (-29)$

**118.** $\dfrac{-36}{-\frac{1}{6}}$      **119.** $\dfrac{8}{-\frac{1}{5}}$      **120.** $\dfrac{-12}{\frac{1}{4}}$      **121.** $\dfrac{0}{-\frac{1}{3}}$

**122.** $\dfrac{168m}{-12}$  **123.** $\dfrac{252a}{-8}$  **124.** $\dfrac{-756x}{7x}, x \neq 0$  **125.** $\dfrac{-253u}{-23u}, u \neq 0$

**126.** $-\dfrac{c}{17}(-17)$  **127.** $-9 \cdot \dfrac{x}{9}$  **128.** $\dfrac{8w}{7} \cdot 7$  **129.** $-\dfrac{5h}{3}(-3)$

## Chapter 3

**Solve.** $\hfill$ (3-1, 3-2, 3-3)

**1.** $a - 13 = 17$ $\qquad$ **2.** $c + 8 = 22$ $\qquad$ **3.** $s - 20 = -12$

**4.** $t + 14 = -33$ $\qquad$ **5.** $15 + h = 0$ $\qquad$ **6.** $0 = k - 13$

**7.** $f - 4 = |16|$ $\qquad$ **8.** $g + 7 = |-2|$ $\qquad$ **9.** $-x + 6 = 9$

**10.** $23 - y = 47$ $\qquad$ **11.** $-5 - m = 7$ $\qquad$ **12.** $13 = -q + 8$

**13.** $(e + 4) + 3 = 9$ $\qquad$ **14.** $6 = 10 + (n + 3)$ $\qquad$ **15.** $-5 + (1 + z) = 8$

**16.** $13u = 338$ $\qquad$ **17.** $-396 = 22a$ $\qquad$ **18.** $-12x = -444$ $\qquad$ **19.** $126 = -9w$

**20.** $\dfrac{1}{7}t = 13$ $\qquad$ **21.** $\dfrac{1}{8}h = -8$ $\qquad$ **22.** $11 = -\dfrac{1}{4}v$ $\qquad$ **23.** $-10 = -\dfrac{1}{5}m$

**24.** $-42 = \dfrac{n}{7}$ $\qquad$ **25.** $-\dfrac{c}{4} = 32$ $\qquad$ **26.** $-\dfrac{m}{27} = 0$ $\qquad$ **27.** $-\dfrac{m}{3} = -40$

**28.** $4x = -\dfrac{2}{7}$ $\qquad$ **29.** $-\dfrac{3}{2} = -9z$ $\qquad$ **30.** $\dfrac{1}{4}v = 2\dfrac{3}{4}$ $\qquad$ **31.** $3\dfrac{1}{2} = \dfrac{1}{2}u$

**32.** $5k + 8 = 43$ $\qquad$ **33.** $7h - 6 = 36$ $\qquad$ **34.** $-3 + 3m = -45$

**35.** $2z + 8z = 80$ $\qquad$ **36.** $9v - 5v = 44$ $\qquad$ **37.** $3l - 8l = 65$

**38.** $\dfrac{n}{5} + 9 = -11$ $\qquad$ **39.** $-\dfrac{x}{3} - 2 = 7$ $\qquad$ **40.** $\dfrac{5}{6}u + 15 = 0$

**41.** $x - 5 - 6x = -25$ $\qquad$ **42.** $0 = y - 14 - 3y$ $\qquad$ **43.** $e + 3e + 4e = 48$

**44.** $5(k + 3) = -10$ $\qquad$ **45.** $-\dfrac{4}{3}(n - 6) = 12$ $\qquad$ **46.** $2(v + 7) - 9 = 19$

**Use the five-step plan to solve each problem.** $\hfill$ (3-4)

**47.** The sum of 37 and three times a number is 67. Find the number.

**48.** Four times a number, decreased by 24, is $-20$. Find the number.

**49.** The perimeter of a rectangle is 108. If the length is 33, find the width.

**50.** An eighteen-year-old camp counselor is 6 years younger than three times the age of the girls in her cabin. How old are the campers?

**51.** The lengths, in meters, of the sides of a triangle are consecutive even integers. The perimeter is 18 m. How long are the sides?

**52.** Bruce's savings account contains $122 more than his younger brother's account. Together, they have $354. Find the amount in each account.

Solve each equation. If the equation is an identity or if it has no root, state that fact.

(3-5)

**53.** $10w = 8w + 14$  **54.** $x = 45 - 4x$  **55.** $48 - 6k = -12k$

**56.** $9m + 3 = 6m + 21$  **57.** $27 + u = 3 - 3u$  **58.** $4n + 1 = -1 + 4n$

**59.** $2(v - 8) = 6v$  **60.** $3l = 5(l - 6)$  **61.** $7t - 3 = 6(t + 2)$

**62.** $\frac{1}{3}(18 - 9c) = 6 - 3c$  **63.** $m - 5 = \frac{1}{2}(12 - 14m)$ ·  **64.** $\frac{4}{5}(25x - 15) = 50x + 38$

**65.** $5(3 + h) = 4(h + 2)$  **66.** $(6t - 3)2 = (4t + 7)3$  **67.** $7(n - 3) = 5(n - 3)$

Use the five-step plan to solve each problem.

(3-6, 3-7)

**68.** Jason is one fifth as old as his grandfather. In 4 years the sum of their ages will be 80. How old is each now?

**69.** The ages, in years, of three sisters are consecutive odd integers. Three years ago, the oldest sister was three times as old as the youngest. How old is each now?

**70.** Julius weighs twice as much as each of his twin brothers. If each of the twins gains 5 pounds and Julius gains twice that amount, the sum of the three brothers' weights will be 240 pounds. How much does each weigh now?

**71.** The width of a rectangle is 6 cm shorter than the length. A second rectangle, with a perimeter of 54 cm, is 3 cm wider and 2 cm shorter than the first. What are the dimensions of each rectangle?

**72.** Martha has some nickels and dimes worth $6.25. She has three times as many nickels as dimes. How many nickels does she have?

**73.** Elliot paid $1.50 a dozen for some flowers. He sold all but 5 dozen of them for $2 a dozen, making a profit of $18. How many dozen flowers did he buy?

**74.** Rachel spent $16.18 for some cans of dog food costing 79 cents each and some cans of cat food costing 69 cents each. She bought two more cans of cat food than of dog food. How many cans of each did she buy?

**75.** Victor earns $3 an hour working after school and $4 an hour working on Saturdays. Last week he earned $43, working a total of 13 hours. How many hours did he work on Saturday?

State a reason for each step in Exercises 76–78.

(3-8)

**76.** $6 + (15 + 4) = 6 + (4 + 15)$    _?_

          $= (6 + 4) + 15$    _?_

          $= 10 + 15 = 25$    _?_

**77.** $20 + (-4) = (16 + 4) + (-4)$    _?_

          $= 16 + [4 + (-4)]$    _?_

          $= 16 + 0$    _?_

          $= 16$    _?_

**78.** $-7 + 19 = 19 + (-7)$     ? 
$\phantom{-7 + 19 } = 12 + 7 + (-7)$     ? 
$\phantom{-7 + 19 } = 12 + 0$     ? 
$\phantom{-7 + 19 } = 12$     ?

# Chapter 4

**Simplify.**       (4-1)

**1.** $7^3$      **2.** $(-5)^4$      **3.** $-3 \cdot 2^4$      **4.** $(-2 \cdot 5)^3$

**5.** $7 + 5^2$      **6.** $(8 - 4)^3$      **7.** $6 - 2^5$      **8.** $(4 + 7)^2$

**9.** $5^3 \div (3^2 + 4^2)$      **10.** $(8^2 - 6^2) \div 7$      **11.** $4(9^2 - 4^3)$

**Evaluate if $a = -3$ and $b = 2$.**       (4-1)

**12.** $3a + b^2$      **13.** $(3a + b)^2$      **14.** $4a - b^3$      **15.** $(4a - b)^3$

**16.** $7 + ab^2$      **17.** $(7 + ab)^2$      **18.** $-\dfrac{3a}{b^2}$      **19.** $\left(-\dfrac{3a}{b}\right)^2$

**Add.**       (4-2)

**20.** $\begin{array}{l} 4x - 3 \\ 7x + 8 \end{array}$    **21.** $\begin{array}{l} 3b + 4 \\ -2b - 6 \end{array}$    **22.** $\begin{array}{l} 5m + 8 \\ 4m + 3 \end{array}$    **23.** $\begin{array}{l} -2t - 7 \\ 6t - 3 \end{array}$

**24.** $\begin{array}{l} 5k - 6l + 4 \\ -5k + 8l + 2 \end{array}$      **25.** $\begin{array}{l} 6x^2 - 2xy + 3y^2 \\ 4x^2 - \phantom{2}xy - \phantom{3}y^2 \end{array}$

**26.** $\begin{array}{l} 2m^2 - 3mn - 5n \\ -8m^2 \phantom{- 3mn} - \phantom{5}n \end{array}$      **27.** $\begin{array}{l} 5a^2 - 6ab \\ -2a^2 + 9ab - b^2 \end{array}$

**28–35.** In Exercises 20–27, subtract the lower polynomial from the upper one.

**Simplify.**       (4-3, 4-4)

**36.** $e^6 \cdot e^3 \cdot e$      **37.** $(4f^3)(2f^4)$      **38.** $(-3c^2d)(-4cd^2)$

**39.** $(-2gh^2)(5g^3h)$      **40.** $(3mn)(6m^2n)(2n^2)$      **41.** $(-5j^4k^2)(4jl^3)(-3kl^2)$

**42.** $\left(\dfrac{8}{3}x^5y\right)\left(\dfrac{9}{2}xy^6\right)$      **43.** $(-6a^3)\left(\dfrac{1}{6}a^3\right)$      **44.** $(3u^2v)(-7v^3)\left(\dfrac{4}{9}u^2\right)$

**45.** $3^w \cdot 3^{5-w} \cdot 3$      **46.** $4^2 \cdot 4^{a+1} \cdot 4^a$      **47.** $2^5 \cdot 2^{b+3} \cdot 2^{3-b}$

**48.** $(3p^5)(5p^2) + (7p^3)(2p^4)$      **49.** $(8d^3)(2d^7) - (3d^6)(4d^4)$

**50.** $(w^5)^2$      **51.** $(x^2)^5$      **52.** $y^2 \cdot y^5$      **53.** $z^n \cdot z^n$

**54.** $(a^n)^3$      **55.** $(b^3)^n$      **56.** $c^3 \cdot c^n$      **57.** $d^n \cdot d^n \cdot d^n$

**58.** $(5f)^2$      **59.** $(gh)^4$      **60.** $(6m^3)^2$      **61.** $(4mn^5)^3$

**62.** $(2u^3v)^5$      **63.** $(3a^5b^4)^2$      **64.** $(-7x^4)^2$      **65.** $-(8x^5)^3$

**66.** $(3k)^2(3k)^4$      **67.** $(-2l^3)^3 \cdot (5l^2)^2$      **68.** $-(4t^2)^2(3t)^3$      **69.** $(5x^2y)^3 \cdot 3xy^2$

**Multiply.**

(4-5, 4-6)

**70.** $7(x + 3)$    **71.** $5(y - 4)$    **72.** $-3(z - 2)$    **73.** $-8(1 + 4m)$

**74.** $3n(n + 5)$    **75.** $-4t(3 - 2t)$    **76.** $6k(2k - 7)$    **77.** $-5h(8h + 3)$

**78.** $9a(a^2 - 3a - 4)$    **79.** $-5b^2(3b^2 - 2b + 6)$

**80.** $\frac{1}{3}c(6c^2 - 3cd + 9d^2)$    **81.** $\frac{1}{2}uv^2(10u^2 - 4uv + 8v^2)$

**82.** $(m + 4)(m + 2)$    **83.** $(n - 3)(n + 5)$    **84.** $(a - 6)(a - 7)$

**85.** $(5x - 2)(x + 7)$    **86.** $(4y - 2)(3y - 1)$    **87.** $(6b + 4)(5b + 3)$

**88.** $(u + 3)(u^2 + 2u + 5)$    **89.** $(v - 1)(3v^2 + 4v + 7)$    **90.** $(3c - 5)(2c^2 - c + 8)$

**91.** $\begin{array}{r} 7x - 4y \\ 3x - 2y \\ \hline \end{array}$    **92.** $\begin{array}{r} 5a - 8b \\ 4a + b \\ \hline \end{array}$    **93.** $\begin{array}{r} e^2 + ef + f^2 \\ e + f \\ \hline \end{array}$    **94.** $\begin{array}{r} 3m^2 - 4mn + n^2 \\ 5m + n \\ \hline \end{array}$

**Solve for the given variable. State the restrictions, if any, for the formula obtained to be meaningful.**

(4-7)

**95.** $A = \frac{1}{2}ap;\ a$    **96.** $V = \frac{1}{3}Bh;\ h$    **97.** $A = \frac{1}{2}h(b_1 + b_2);\ b_1$

**98.** $y = mx + b;\ b$    **99.** $A = \pi r^2;\ r$    **100.** $S = (n - 2)180;\ n$

**101.** $F = \frac{9}{5}C + 32;\ C$    **102.** $P = \frac{A}{1 + rt};\ A$    **103.** $r = \frac{I}{Pt};\ t$

**Make a chart for each problem. Then solve.**

(4-8)

**104.** Two buses leave a depot at the same time, one traveling north and the other south. The speed of the northbound bus is 15 mph greater than the speed of the southbound bus. After 3 hours on the road, the buses are 255 miles apart. What are their speeds?

**105.** Exactly 10 min after Alex left his grandparents' house, his cousin Alison set out from there to overtake him. Alex drives at 36 mph. Alison drives at 40 mph. How long did it take Alison to overtake Alex?

**106.** A plane flew from the Sky City airport to the Plainsville airport at 800 km/h and then returned to Sky City at 900 km/h. The return trip took 30 min less than the flight to Plainsville. How far apart are the airports and how long did the trip to Plainsville take?

**107.** A poster is three times as long as it is wide. It is framed by a mat such that there is a 4 in. border around the poster. Find the dimensions of the poster if the area of the mat is 488 in².

**108.** A square piece of remnant material is on sale. A rectangular piece of the same material, whose length is 1 yd longer than a side of the square and whose width is $\frac{5}{9}$ yd shorter than a side of the square, is also on sale. If the square and the rectangle have the same area and you purchase both remnants, how much material will you get?

# Chapter 5

**List all the pairs of integral factors of each integer.** (5-1)

**1.** 42      **2.** 80      **3.** 91      **4.** 72      **5.** 52

**6–10.** Give the prime factorization of each integer in Exercises 1–5.

**Give the GCF of each group of numbers.** (5-1)

**11.** 126, 168      **12.** 144, 84      **13.** 65, 52      **14.** 90, 330

(5-2)

**Simplify each expression, assuming that no denominator equals zero.**

**15.** $\dfrac{12x^5}{4x}$      **16.** $\dfrac{25m^4n}{-15mn^6}$      **17.** $\dfrac{-7ab}{21ab^5}$      **18.** $\dfrac{-8(uv)^7}{-10(uv)^5}$

**19.** $\dfrac{(w^4)^2}{(w^5)^4}$      **20.** $\dfrac{(5k)^2}{5k^2}$      **21.** $\dfrac{(-3y)^3}{(y^3)^2}$      **22.** $\dfrac{(2c^5)(4c^3)}{(8c^2)^3}$

**Divide. Assume that no denominator equals zero.** (5-3)

**23.** $\dfrac{12e + 8}{4}$      **24.** $\dfrac{6x - 9y + 12}{3}$      **25.** $\dfrac{2x^3 + 6x^2 + x}{x}$

**26.** $\dfrac{18ab - 24a^2}{-6a}$      **27.** $\dfrac{15m - 25m^2 - 5m^3}{5m}$      **28.** $\dfrac{28h^5k^3 - 35hk^2}{7hk^2}$

**Factor each polynomial as the product of its greatest monomial factor and another polynomial.** (5-3)

**29.** $15w^2 - 10w + 5$      **30.** $9x^2 + 18x$      **31.** $7u^3 + 14u^2$

**32.** $12a^3 - 6a^2 + 18a$      **33.** $15c^2 + 3cd$      **34.** $8m^2n - 24mn^2$

**Write each product as a trinomial.** (5-4)

**35.** $(x + 5)(x + 3)$      **36.** $(b - 2)(b - 4)$      **37.** $(n - 3)(n + 7)$

**38.** $(e - 8)(e + 6)$      **39.** $(3 + m)(2 + m)$      **40.** $(3f + 2)(f + 5)$

**41.** $(4y - 3)(2y - 1)$      **42.** $(8z + 7)(z - 2)$      **43.** $(5n - 3)(4n - 2)$

**44.** $a(6a - 4)(5a - 3)$      **45.** $h(3h + 7)(4h + 9)$      **46.** $2x(9x - 1)(2x + 3)$

**Express each product as a binomial.** (5-5)

**47.** $(k - 5)(k + 5)$      **48.** $(3 - t)(3 + t)$      **49.** $(4d - 8)(4d + 8)$

**50.** $(w^2 - 6)(w^2 + 6)$      **51.** $(5m^2 + n)(5m^2 - n)$      **52.** $(ab + c^2)(ab - c^2)$

**Factor completely, using the table of squares.** (5-5)

**53.** $16e^2 - 9$      **54.** $36u^2 - 25$      **55.** $81 - f^2$      **56.** $144a^2 - 64b^2$

**57.** $49 - 100y^2$      **58.** $v^4 - w^4$      **59.** $s^6 - 4$      **60.** $16x^8 - 625$

**Express each square as a trinomial.** (5-6)

**61.** $(g + 7)^2$      **62.** $(k - 3)^2$      **63.** $(2x + 6)^2$      **64.** $(5y - 3)^2$

**65.** $(2m + 3n)^2$      **66.** $(7a - 5b)^2$      **67.** $(ef - 8)^2$      **68.** $(-4 + 9f)^2$

**Factor each trinomial as the square of a binomial.** (5-6)

**69.** $x^2 - 6x + 9$      **70.** $e^2 + 18e + 81$      **71.** $4 - 28h + 49h^2$

**72.** $64x^2 + 80xy + 25y^2$      **73.** $4m^2 - 36mn + 81n^2$      **74.** $16w^2 + 24wz + 9z^2$

**Factor completely, if possible. Check by multiplying the factors. If the polynomial is not factorable, write "prime."** (5-7, 5-8, 5-9)

**75.** $k^2 + 8k + 7$      **76.** $v^2 - 9v + 20$      **77.** $a^2 - 2a + 1$

**78.** $35 + 12u + u^2$      **79.** $b^2 - 16b + 48$      **80.** $w^2 + 18w + 80$

**81.** $x^2 + 13xy + 42y^2$      **82.** $m^2 - 10mn + 21n^2$      **83.** $e^2 - 15ef + 44f^2$

**84.** $c^2 + 3c - 18$      **85.** $x^2 - 2x - 35$      **86.** $k^2 + 8k - 32$

**87.** $h^2 - 7h - 18$      **88.** $b^2 + 7b - 30$      **89.** $t^2 - 4t - 45$

**90.** $a^2 - 2ab - 3b^2$      **91.** $u^2 + 3uv - 4v^2$      **92.** $m^2 - mn - 20n^2$

**93.** $2x^2 + 11x + 12$      **94.** $10e^2 - 12e + 3$      **95.** $10d^2 + d - 3$

**96.** $-10 - 26y - 12y^2$      **97.** $-7 - 39z - 18z^2$      **98.** $-10 + 24z - 8z^2$

**99.** $15x^2 + 13xy + 2y^2$      **100.** $8a^2 - 22ab + 12b^2$      **101.** $14m^2 - mn - 3n^2$

**Factor by grouping. Check by multiplying.** (5-10)

**102.** $8(m - 3) - 5m(3 - m)$      **103.** $6a(a + 2) + 4(a + 2)$

**104.** $u(u - 2v) - (2v - u)$      **105.** $b(b - 2)(b + 1) - 3 - 3b$

**106.** $a^2 + 2a + ab + 2b$      **107.** $7cw + 3c - 7w^2 - 3w$

**108.** $n^3 + n^2 - 6n - 6$      **109.** $64 - 64m^2 + m^4 - m^6$

**Factor completely. Check by multiplying.** (5-11)

**110.** $42x^3 + 68x^2 + 16x$      **111.** $60y^3 - 18y^2 - 6y$      **112.** $12x^5 - 20x^4 + 3x^3$

**113.** $16a^4 - 144a^2$      **114.** $4n^5 - 100n$      **115.** $28w^7 - 102w^5$

**116.** $36m^2 + 24mn + 4n^2$      **117.** $24cd - 12c^2 - 12d^2$      **118.** $-7x^3 + 14x^2y - 7xy^2$

**Solve and check.** (5-12)

**119.** $(a + 13)(a + 8) = 0$      **120.** $(f - 16)(f - 27) = 0$      **121.** $(2x - 4)(3x - 5) = 0$

**122.** $(6h - 5)(6h + 5) = 0$      **123.** $7w(4w + 3) = 0$      **124.** $m(2m + 7)(3m - 4) = 0$

**125.** $a^2 + 7a + 6 = 0$      **126.** $q^2 - 21q = -20$      **127.** $d^2 = 14d - 45$

**128.** $y^2 - 7y - 18 = 0$      **129.** $c^2 - 36 = -5c$      **130.** $h^2 = -3h + 54$

**131.** $6 - 23z - 4z^2 = 0$      **132.** $3m^2 + 1 = 4m$      **133.** $2t^2 = 10 + t$

**134.** $e^2 - 49 = 0$      **135.** $36g^2 = 16$      **136.** $w^3 - 9w = 0$

**137.** The sum of a number and its square is 56. Find the number.

**138.** Find two consecutive negative odd integers whose product is 143.

**139.** The length of a rectangle is 5 cm less than twice the width. If the area of the rectangle is 88 cm², find the dimensions of the rectangle.

**140.** Find two numbers that total 12 and whose squares total 74.

## Chapter 6

**Express in simplest form, noting any restrictions on the variable.**

**1.** $\dfrac{5m - 15}{m - 3}$

**2.** $\dfrac{2a + 1}{6a + 3}$

**3.** $\dfrac{7c - 7d}{7c + 7d}$

**4.** $\dfrac{6k - k^2}{36 - k^2}$

**5.** $\dfrac{3uv}{u^2v - v^2u}$

**6.** $\dfrac{8w^3}{8w^2 - 12w}$

**7.** $\dfrac{x^2 - 64}{x^2 - x - 56}$

**8.** $\dfrac{(e - 7)^2}{49 - e^2}$

**9.** $\dfrac{15m + 6n}{25m^2 - 4n^2}$

**10.** $\dfrac{a^2 + ab}{a^2 - ab}$

**11.** $\dfrac{(k - 3)(7k - 2)}{(2 - 7k)(k - 3)}$

**12.** $\dfrac{3x^2 + 17xy + 20y^2}{3x^2 - xy - 10y^2}$

**13.** $\dfrac{14 - 9t + t^2}{t^2 - 4}$

**14.** $\dfrac{u^2 - v^2}{u^2 + 2uv + v^2}$

**15.** $\dfrac{(5w - x)^5}{(x - 5w)^7}$

**16.** $\dfrac{(4s - 6)^2(3s - 2)}{(2 - 3s)(6 - 4s)}$

**Express each product as a fraction in simplest form.**

**17.** $\dfrac{5}{8} \cdot \dfrac{32}{25}$

**18.** $\dfrac{4}{3} \cdot \dfrac{3}{5} \cdot \dfrac{5}{7}$

**19.** $\left(\dfrac{-2}{5}\right)^2 \cdot \dfrac{15}{16}$

**20.** $\left(-\dfrac{3}{2}\right)^3 \cdot \dfrac{24}{9}$

**21.** $\dfrac{e}{f} \cdot \dfrac{f}{g} \cdot \dfrac{g}{h}$

**22.** $\dfrac{5}{w} \cdot \dfrac{w^2}{10}$

**23.** $\dfrac{8m}{3} \cdot \dfrac{9}{12m}$

**24.** $\dfrac{a^2}{3b} \cdot \dfrac{b^2}{4a}$

**25.** $\dfrac{14v}{12v^2} \cdot \dfrac{4uw^2}{7v^2}$

**26.** $\dfrac{a + 5}{a} \cdot \dfrac{a^2}{a^2 - 25}$

**27.** $\dfrac{4x - xy}{8x^2y} \cdot \dfrac{2}{16 - y^2}$

**28.** $\dfrac{m + n}{m - n} \cdot \dfrac{m^2 - n^2}{3m + 3n}$

**Simplify using the rules of exponents for the power of a product and the power of a quotient.**

**29.** $(5k^3)^2$

**30.** $\left(\dfrac{x}{7}\right)^2$

**31.** $\left(\dfrac{3x}{4}\right)^2$

**32.** $\left(\dfrac{2m}{3n^2}\right)^3$

**33.** $\left(-\dfrac{x^2}{5}\right)^3$

**34.** $\left(\dfrac{e}{f}\right)^3 \cdot \dfrac{e}{f}$

**35.** $\left(\dfrac{4c}{d}\right)^3 \cdot \dfrac{c^2}{8}$

**36.** $\left(\dfrac{7a}{b}\right)^2 \cdot \dfrac{3ab}{14}$

**Divide. Express the answers in simplest form.** (6-3)

**37.** $\dfrac{4}{9} \div \dfrac{16}{3}$

**38.** $\dfrac{a^2}{4} \div \dfrac{a}{12}$

**39.** $\dfrac{m}{3n} \div \dfrac{mn}{6}$

**40.** $\dfrac{8x^2}{5y} \div 4xy$

**41.** $\dfrac{e+f}{5} \div \dfrac{3e+3f}{15}$

**42.** $\dfrac{u^2-v^2}{u^2+v^2} \div (u+v)$

**43.** $\dfrac{5}{n^2-25} \div \dfrac{5n-15}{n+5}$

**44.** $\dfrac{4n-12}{4} \div \dfrac{5n-15}{8}$

**45.** $\dfrac{x^4-y^4}{2x^2+8x} \div \dfrac{x^2+y^2}{x^2-16}$

**46.** $\dfrac{4a^2-25}{6a^2} \div \dfrac{12a-30}{3a^4}$

**47.** $\dfrac{m^2+n^2}{8s-10t} \div \dfrac{7m+7n}{4t-6s}$

**Simplify.**

(6-3)

**48.** $\dfrac{1}{3} \div \dfrac{2}{6} \cdot \dfrac{5}{7}$

**49.** $\dfrac{x}{7} \div \dfrac{y^2}{x} \cdot \dfrac{7}{y}$

**50.** $\dfrac{e^2}{3} \cdot \dfrac{f^2}{e} \div \dfrac{e}{f}$

**51.** $\left(\dfrac{c}{3}\right)^2 \div \dfrac{c}{9} \cdot \dfrac{c}{3}$

**52.** $\left(\dfrac{w}{4}\right)^2 \div \left(\dfrac{w}{8} \cdot \dfrac{w}{2}\right)$

**53.** $\dfrac{a-b}{a+3b} \cdot \dfrac{3b+a}{b+a} \div \dfrac{b-a}{b+a}$

**Find the missing numerator.**

(6-4)

**54.** $\dfrac{5x}{11} = \dfrac{?}{33}$

**55.** $\dfrac{h-4}{7} = \dfrac{?}{14}$

**56.** $\dfrac{3k-5}{2} = \dfrac{?}{8}$

**57.** $\dfrac{6m-n}{7} = \dfrac{?}{35}$

**58.** $\dfrac{c}{d} = \dfrac{?}{c^3d}$

**59.** $\dfrac{4s}{5t} = \dfrac{?}{15st^2}$

**60.** $\dfrac{8}{7d+2} = \dfrac{?}{(7d+2)^2}$

**61.** $\dfrac{5}{e-1} = \dfrac{?}{e^2-1}$

**62.** $\dfrac{3}{h-2} = \dfrac{?}{2-h}$

**63.** $\dfrac{5}{z-3} = \dfrac{?}{z^2-3z}$

**64.** $\dfrac{w}{w+4} = \dfrac{?}{w^2+4w}$

**65.** $\dfrac{3}{a^2b} = \dfrac{?}{a^3b^2}$

**Express each group of fractions with their LCD.**

(6-4)

**66.** $\dfrac{2}{3}, \dfrac{4}{5}, \dfrac{3}{7}$

**67.** $\dfrac{x-2}{16}, \dfrac{x+3}{12}$

**68.** $\dfrac{3m-n}{10}, \dfrac{3m+n}{15}$

**69.** $\dfrac{1}{3cd}, \dfrac{4}{cd^2}$

**70.** $\dfrac{7}{e+f}, \dfrac{5}{e}, \dfrac{6}{f}$

**71.** $\dfrac{2w}{3x-9}, \dfrac{1}{x^2-9}$

**Simplify.**

(6-5)

**72.** $\dfrac{3}{a} + \dfrac{5}{a} - \dfrac{4}{a}$

**73.** $\dfrac{7}{2x} + \dfrac{6}{2x} - \dfrac{5}{2x}$

**74.** $\dfrac{u}{7} - \dfrac{3u+5}{7}$

**75.** $\dfrac{k+3}{5} - \dfrac{2k+7}{5}$

**76.** $\dfrac{c}{c-3} + \dfrac{1}{c-3} - \dfrac{8-c}{c-3}$

**77.** $\dfrac{4}{g-3} - \dfrac{3}{3-g}$

**78.** $\dfrac{3m}{m-n} + \dfrac{3n}{n-m}$

**79.** $\dfrac{5}{t^2} + \dfrac{3}{t}$

**80.** $\dfrac{4}{5x} - \dfrac{1}{15x^2}$

**81.** $\dfrac{1}{5wx} - \dfrac{3}{10w}$

**82.** $\dfrac{3k-2}{2k^3} + \dfrac{6}{k^2}$

**83.** $\dfrac{2}{3(x+2)} + \dfrac{x}{x+2}$

**84.** $\dfrac{5a-4}{6} + \dfrac{a-2}{9}$  **85.** $\dfrac{2h+4}{8} - \dfrac{h}{4} + \dfrac{3h-2}{10}$  **86.** $\dfrac{4(m-n)}{16} - \dfrac{3(m+n)}{12}$

**87.** $\dfrac{3}{x+2} - \dfrac{1}{x+3}$  **88.** $\dfrac{3z}{z^2-16} + \dfrac{z}{z-4}$  **89.** $\dfrac{u}{u-4} + \dfrac{3}{4-u}$

**Write each expression as a fraction in simplest form.** (6-6)

**90.** $7\dfrac{1}{3}$  **91.** $5 + \dfrac{1}{n}$  **92.** $4m - \dfrac{3}{m}$  **93.** $\dfrac{x}{y} + 3$

**94.** $6 - \dfrac{5}{k+3}$  **95.** $\dfrac{z}{z-2} + 7$  **96.** $\dfrac{x+3}{x} - 2$  **97.** $8h - \dfrac{h}{h+3}$

**98.** $3t + \dfrac{t}{2t+7}$  **99.** $5 - \dfrac{e+3}{e^2-1}$  **100.** $a + \dfrac{5a+3}{a+3}$  **101.** $2w - \dfrac{w+3}{w-3}$

**102.** $n - \dfrac{7}{n+2} - \dfrac{3n-1}{n+2}$  **103.** $\dfrac{v}{u+v} + \dfrac{u}{v-u} + 1$  **104.** $\dfrac{x}{x-4} + \dfrac{x}{x+4} - 3$

**Divide. Write your answer as a polynomial or mixed expression. Check.** (6-7)

**105.** $\dfrac{x^2+7x+10}{x+2}$  **106.** $\dfrac{z^2-2z-35}{z-7}$  **107.** $\dfrac{a^2-5a-3}{a+2}$  **108.** $\dfrac{n^2-16}{n+4}$

**109.** $\dfrac{7+k^2-4k}{k-5}$  **110.** $\dfrac{8y^2+6}{2y-1}$  **111.** $\dfrac{b^3-1}{b+1}$  **112.** $\dfrac{x^3+5}{x+3}$

**113.** $\dfrac{w^3+w^2+2w-4}{w-1}$  **114.** $\dfrac{u^3+2u^2-16}{u-2}$  **115.** $\dfrac{2t^2-13t+20}{2t-5}$

**116.** $\dfrac{2-9h+7h^2}{7h-2}$  **117.** $\dfrac{v^3+v^2+v+1}{v-2}$  **118.** $\dfrac{5n^2+6n^3+9}{3+2n}$

# Chapter 7

**State each ratio in simplest form.** (7-1)

**1.** 40 s : 2 min  **2.** 4 m : 250 cm  **3.** 3 kg : 45 g
**4.** $6y : 15y$  **5.** $36d^2 : 10d$  **6.** $(4a)^2 : 6a$
**7.** The ratio of old cars to new cars if there are 180 cars and 55 are new.
**8.** The ratio of wins to losses for a baseball team that played 84 games and won 48 of them.

**Solve each proportion.** (7-2)

**9.** $\dfrac{3}{5} = \dfrac{x}{15}$  **10.** $\dfrac{5}{7} = \dfrac{25}{a}$  **11.** $\dfrac{24}{7} = \dfrac{4}{c}$

**12.** $\dfrac{3x}{2} = \dfrac{2}{5}$  **13.** $\dfrac{15a}{64} = \dfrac{45}{32}$  **14.** $\dfrac{17d}{25} = \dfrac{51}{125}$

**15.** $\dfrac{x-4}{x} = \dfrac{7}{9}$  **16.** $\dfrac{3w}{10w+2} = \dfrac{2}{7}$  **17.** $\dfrac{8a-5}{5a-4} = \dfrac{13}{8}$

**Solve each equation.**

**18.** $\dfrac{a}{3} - \dfrac{a}{9} = 2$

**19.** $\dfrac{2x}{3} - \dfrac{x}{2} = 12$

**20.** $\dfrac{6}{7}b - \dfrac{1}{2}b = 5$

**21.** $\dfrac{2}{3}x - \dfrac{5}{9}x = -1$

**22.** $\dfrac{y + 2}{2} = \dfrac{2y}{3}$

**23.** $\dfrac{x + 1}{5} - \dfrac{3}{2} = \dfrac{3x - 6}{10}$

**24.** $\dfrac{12}{z} = \dfrac{4 + 4z}{z}$

**25.** $\dfrac{1}{x} + \dfrac{1}{3} = \dfrac{1}{2}$

**26.** $\dfrac{4}{5y} + \dfrac{y - 2}{y} = -\dfrac{1}{5}$

**27.** $\dfrac{c}{c + 3} = \dfrac{2}{5}$

**28.** $\dfrac{3m + 5}{6} - \dfrac{10}{m} = \dfrac{m}{2}$

**29.** $\dfrac{h}{2h + 4} - \dfrac{1}{h + 2} = 1$

**Evaluate.**

**30.** 80% of 700

**31.** 45% of 450

**32.** 3.25% of 48

**33.** 18 is 60% of what number?

**34.** 63 is 150% of what number?

**35.** What percent of 180 is 45?

**36.** What percent of 36 is 54?

**Solve.**

**37.** $1.2x = 48$

**38.** $0.6z = 180$

**39.** $0.08y = 64$

**40.** $0.4a - 0.7 = 2.9$

**41.** $0.3b + 0.03b = 99$

**42.** $0.05c = 6.6 - 0.06c$

**43.** How many kilograms of zinc are contained in 30 kg of an alloy containing 28% zinc?

**44.** Ed Jefferson bought a new suit that cost $140. If he also paid $6.30 in sales tax, find the sales tax rate.

**45.** A camera that originally cost $150 is on sale at 15% off the original price. Find the sale price.

**46.** How many kilograms of water must be added to 12 kg of a 30% salt solution to produce a 20% solution?

**47.** How many kilograms of water must be evaporated from 40 kg of a 10% salt solution to produce a 25% solution?

**48.** A coin-sorting machine can sort a certain number of coins in 15 minutes. A second machine can sort the same number of coins in 30 minutes. How long would it take both machines working together to do the job?

**49.** An air conditioner takes 20 minutes to cool a room. If a second air conditioner is used together with the first, it takes only 12 minutes to cool the room. How long would it take the second air conditioner alone to cool the room?

**Express each of the following numbers in scientific notation.**

**50.** 64,800,000

**51.** 147,000,000

**52.** 643 billion

**53.** 0.0000098

**54.** 0.000000006

**55.** 0.00000000001

**Evaluate.** (7-10)

**56.** $6^{-2}$      **57.** $5^{-3}$      **58.** $7^{-2}$      **59.** $9^{-3}$

**60.** $2^{-4} \cdot 2^{-3}$      **61.** $(6^{-2})^{-1}$      **62.** $\dfrac{3^{-4}}{3^{-3}}$      **63.** $\dfrac{8^{-2}}{8^{-4}}$

**Simplify. Give answers in terms of positive exponents.** (7-10)

**64.** $5z^{-2}$      **65.** $(9y)^{-3}$      **66.** $x^2y^{-5}$      **67.** $a^{-2}b^{-3}$

**68.** $uv^{-2}w^{-1}$      **69.** $d^{-4}e^2f^{-2}$      **70.** $(a^{-2}b^3)^2$      **71.** $(x^{-4}y^{-5}z^3)^{-3}$

# Chapter 8

**State whether each ordered pair of numbers is a solution of the given equation.** (8-1)

**1.** $x - 2y = 6$
     $(3, 0), (0, -3)$

**2.** $x + 3y = 9$
     $(3, 2), (-3, 4)$

**3.** $2x - y = 5$
     $(4, -1), (1, -7)$

**4.** $2x + 3y = 7$
     $(1, 2), (5, -1)$

**5.** $4x + 2y = 6$
     $\left(\dfrac{3}{2}, 0\right), (1, 1)$

**6.** $-3x + 4y = -7$
     $(1, -1), \left(2, \dfrac{1}{4}\right)$

**Solve each equation for $y$ in terms of $x$.** (8-1)

**7.** $x + 2y = 8$      **8.** $12x - 4y = 1$      **9.** $3x + 4y = 6$

**10.** $2x - 3y = 7$      **11.** $4x + 3y = 0$      **12.** $\dfrac{5}{x + y} = 8$

**Graph each equation.** (8-2)

**13.** $y = -7$      **14.** $x = 4$      **15.** $y = 3x + 2$

**16.** $y = 2x - 5$      **17.** $5x = 3y$      **18.** $8x - 2y = 0$

**19.** $3x + y = -6$      **20.** $4x + 3y = 12$      **21.** $2x + 3y = 7$

**Solve each system by the graphic method.** (8-3)

**22.** $x + y = 6$
     $x - y = 2$

**23.** $x + y = 9$
     $y = 2x$

**24.** $x + y = 0$
     $x + 2y = 2$

**25.** $y = 3 - x$
     $x + y = 5$

**26.** $y = \dfrac{2}{3}x + 1$
     $y = -\dfrac{2}{3}x + 5$

**27.** $y = \dfrac{1}{2}x + 1$
     $x + 2 = 2y$

**Solve by the substitution method.** (8-4)

**28.** $3x + y = 5$
     $y = 2x$

**29.** $m - 3n = -4$
     $2m + 6n = 5$

**30.** $2a + b = 4$
     $b = 1 - a$

**31.** $4c - 3d = 9$
     $2c - d = 5$

**32.** $x + 3y = 2$
     $2x + 3y = 7$

**33.** $3t - 2s = 5$
     $t + 2s = 15$

**Solve by using a system of two equations in two variables.** (8-5)

**34.** On a jury there are 3 fewer men than twice the number of women. If there were 2 more women on the jury, the numbers of men and women would be equal. How many men are on the jury?

**35.** Janet and Lynn live 8 miles apart in opposite directions from their office. If Lynn lives 1 mile less than twice as far from the office as Janet does, how far does each live from the office?

**Solve by the addition-or-subtraction method.** (8-6)

**36.** $r - s = -3$
$r + s = 9$

**37.** $c + 2n = -20$
$c - 2n = 30$

**38.** $x - 3y = 2$
$x + 4y = 16$

**39.** $6r + 5s = -8$
$2r - 5s = -16$

**40.** $12m + 3n = 51$
$7m - 3n = 44$

**41.** $8g + 7h = 26$
$8g - 10h = 60$

**Solve by using multiplication with the addition-or-subtraction method.** (8-7)

**42.** $v + w = 3$
$3v - 5w = 17$

**43.** $4a - 3b = -1$
$a - b = -1$

**44.** $3x - y = 3$
$x + 3y = 11$

**45.** $3x + 4y = -25$
$2x - 3y = 6$

**46.** $2w - 3z = -1$
$3w + 4z = 24$

**47.** $5a - 2b = 0$
$2a - 3b = -11$

**Solve by using a system of two equations in two variables.** (8-8, 8-9)

**48.** A plane can fly 1120 km in 80 min with the wind. Flying against the same wind, the plane travels the same distance in 84 min. Find the speed of the wind and the speed of the plane in still air.

**49.** The sum of the digits of a two-digit number is 7. With the digits reversed the number is 5 times the tens digit of the original number. Find the original number.

**50.** In five years Jenny will be two thirds as old as her aunt. Three years ago she was half as old as her aunt is now. How old are Jenny and her aunt now?

**51.** The numerator of a fraction is 1 less than the denominator. If 1 is subtracted from the numerator, and the denominator is unchanged, the resulting fraction has a value of $\frac{3}{4}$. Find the original fraction.

## Chapter 9

**In each exercise, the coordinates of two points of a line are given. Find the slope of the line.** (9-1)

**1.** $(1, 2), (4, 6)$

**2.** $(-7, 1), (-1, 2)$

**3.** $(-1, 6), (0, 0)$

**4.** $(-4, -3), (2, -3)$

**5.** $(2, 1), (8, -2)$

**6.** $(-7, -7), (6, -4)$

**Find the slope of each line whose equation is given.** (9-1)

**7.** $y = 7x - 3$      **8.** $y = \frac{1}{4}x + 2$      **9.** $3x - 2y = 8$

**10.** $y - 9 = 0$      **11.** $5x + 4y = 16$      **12.** $y = 1 - x$

**Determine whether the points in each exercise are collinear. If they are, find** (9-1)
**the slope of the line.**

**13.** $(2, 1), (0, -3), (4, 5), (-2, -7)$      **14.** $(0, 4), (9, -2), (-3, 6), (6, 0)$

**15.** $(-3, -2), (2, -4), (6, -5), (-5, 2)$      **16.** $(-5, 3), (0, 3), (5, 3), (-2, 3)$

**Through the given point, draw a line with the given slope.** (9-1)

**17.** $P(3, 1)$; slope 2      **18.** $P(-4, 5)$; slope 0      **19.** $P(0, -6)$; slope 5

**20.** $P(7, 0)$; slope $-3$      **21.** $P(-2, -3)$; slope $\frac{1}{4}$      **22.** $P(3, 4)$; slope $-\frac{2}{3}$

**Write an equation in standard form of the line that has the given slope and**
**$y$-intercept.** (9-2)

**23.** $m = 3, b = \frac{1}{2}$      **24.** $m = -4, b = \frac{3}{5}$      **25.** $m = \frac{1}{3}, b = 6$

**26.** $m = 0, b = -3.5$      **27.** $m = -\frac{3}{7}, b = \frac{3}{8}$      **28.** $m = -1.5, b = 2.7$

**Change each equation to the slope-intercept form. Then draw the graph,**
**using only the slope and $y$-intercept.** (9-2)

**29.** $x + y = -3$      **30.** $7x = 2y$      **31.** $4x - y = 3$
**32.** $2x + 2y = 6$      **33.** $-x + 5y = 10$      **34.** $3x - 4y - 5 = 0$

**Use the slope-intercept form of the equations to determine whether or not**
**each system has a solution.** (9-2)

**35.** $x - y = 2$      **36.** $3x - 2y = 6$      **37.** $x - 5y = -1$
    $y - x = -2$         $-2x - 3y = -12$         $5x + y = 3$

**Write an equation in standard form of the line that has the given slope and**
**passes through the given point.** (9-3)

**38.** $m = 3; (-3, -5)$      **39.** $m = -2; (3, -4)$      **40.** $m = \frac{3}{4}; (0, -2)$

**41.** $m = 0; \left(\frac{1}{2}, 3\right)$      **42.** $m = -\frac{1}{5}; (-5, 0)$      **43.** $m = \frac{7}{3}; (3, 7)$

**Write an equation in standard form of the line passing through the points.** (9-3)

**44.** $(2, 1), (6, 4)$      **45.** $(2, -1), (1, -7)$      **46.** $(0, 0), (6, -1)$
**47.** $(-3, 2), (-3, -4)$      **48.** $(-2, 8), (1, 2)$      **49.** $(6, -4), (-7, -7)$

**Given $f: x \rightarrow 5 - 3x$, find the following values of $f$.** $\qquad$ (9-4)

**50.** $f(4)$ $\qquad$ **51.** $f\left(-\dfrac{1}{3}\right)$ $\qquad$ **52.** $f(0)$ $\qquad$ **53.** $f(-5)$

**Given $G(n) = n^3 + 2n$, find the following values of $G$.** $\qquad$ (9-4)

**54.** $G(0)$ $\qquad$ **55.** $G(-2)$ $\qquad$ **56.** $G\left(\dfrac{1}{2}\right)$ $\qquad$ **57.** $G(3)$

**Find all the values of each function.** $\qquad$ (9-4)

**58.** $h(x) = 5 - 2x - x^2$, $D = \{1, 2, 3\}$ $\qquad$ **59.** $M(u) = \dfrac{6}{4u + 2}$, $D = \{-1, 0, 1\}$

**Find the range of each function.** $\qquad$ (9-4)

**60.** $r: z \rightarrow -3 - 4z$, $D = \{-2, -1, 0\}$ $\qquad$ **61.** $N: s \rightarrow \dfrac{10}{s - 3}$, $D = \{2, 4, 8\}$

**62.** $G: w \rightarrow (w - 1)(w + 1)$, $D = \{-2, 0, 2\}$ $\qquad$ **63.** $k: v \rightarrow v^2 - 4v + 2$, $D = \{3, 4, 5\}$

**State the domain and range of the function shown by each table.** $\qquad$ (9-5)

**64.**

| Longest Suspension Bridges | |
|---|---|
| Mackinac Straits | 3800 ft |
| Humber Estuary | 4626 ft |
| Golden Gate | 4200 ft |
| Ataturk | 3524 ft |
| Verrazano Narrows | 4260 ft |

**65.**

| Airports in U.S. | |
|---|---|
| 1930 | 1782 |
| 1940 | 2331 |
| 1950 | 6403 |
| 1960 | 6881 |
| 1970 | 11,261 |

**66.** Make a bar graph for the function shown in Exercise 64.

**67.** Make a broken-line graph for the function shown in Exercise 65.

**Find the coordinates of the vertex and the equation of the axis of symmetry of the graph of each equation. Use the vertex and at least six other points to graph the equation.** $\qquad$ (9-6)

**68.** $y = 4x^2$ $\qquad$ **69.** $y = -2x^2$ $\qquad$ **70.** $y = \dfrac{1}{5}x^2$

**71.** $y = -x^2 + 3x$ $\qquad$ **72.** $y = x^2 - 2x + 5$ $\qquad$ **73.** $y = 4 - \dfrac{1}{2}x^2$

**Find the least value of each function.** $\qquad$ (9-6)

**74.** $f: x \rightarrow x^2 + 7x$ $\qquad$ **75.** $g: x \rightarrow x^2 - 3x - 4$ $\qquad$ **76.** $h: x \rightarrow \dfrac{1}{2}x^2$

**Find the greatest value of each function.** $\qquad$ (9-6)

**77.** $f(x) = x - 3x^2$ $\qquad$ **78.** $g(x) = 2 - \dfrac{1}{3}x^2$ $\qquad$ **79.** $h(x) = -x^2 - x - 1$

**In Exercises 80 and 81, find the constant of variation.** (9-7)

**80.** $y$ varies directly as $x$, and $y = 12$ when $x = 60$.

**81.** $q$ is directly proportional to $p$, and $q = 144$ when $p = 24$.

**82.** If $n$ varies directly as $m$, and $n = 300$ when $m = 5$, find $n$ when $m = 15$.

**83.** If $b$ is directly proportional to $a$, and $b = 28.7$ when $a = 4.1$, find $b$ when $a = 13$.

**In each exercise find the missing value if $(x_1, y_1)$ and $(x_2, y_2)$ are ordered pairs of the same direct variation.** (9-7)

**84.** $x_1 = 35,\ y_1 = 7$

$x_2 = 105,\ y_2 = \underline{\ ?\ }$

**85.** $x_1 = 5.2,\ y_1 = 5$

$x_2 = \underline{\ ?\ },\ y_2 = 1$

**86.** $x_1 = \dfrac{3}{8},\ y_1 = \underline{\ ?\ }$

$x_2 = \dfrac{2}{5},\ y_2 = \dfrac{1}{10}$

**For the variation described, state (a) a formula and (b) a proportion. Use $k$ as the constant of variation.** (9-7, 9-8)

**87.** The circumference, $C$, of a circle is directly proportional to the diameter, $d$, of the circle.

**88.** The elongation, $e$, of a coil spring varies directly as the mass, $m$, suspended from it.

**89.** The length, $l$, of the shadow of a vertical object at a given time and location varies directly with the height, $h$, of the object.

**90.** The monthly rent, $r$, for each roommate in an apartment is inversely proportional to the number, $n$, of roommates.

**91.** The height, $h$, of a triangle of constant area varies inversely as the base length, $b$.

**92.** The number of tickets remaining to be sold, $n$, varies inversely as the number of tickets sold, $s$.

**Graph each equation if the domain and the range are both limited to the set of positive numbers.** (9-8)

**93.** $xy = 4$

**94.** $3xy = 1$

**95.** $x = \dfrac{10}{y}$

**96.** $\dfrac{x}{2} = \dfrac{4}{y}$

**Find the missing value if $(x_1, y_1)$ and $(x_2, y_2)$ are ordered pairs of the same inverse variation.** (9-8)

**97.** $x_1 = 5,\ \ y_1 = 8$

$x_2 = 4,\ \ y_2 = \underline{\ ?\ }$

**98.** $x_1 = 0.6,\ \ y_1 = 1.2$

$x_2 = \underline{\ ?\ },\ y_2 = 0.4$

**99.** $x_1 = \dfrac{1}{4},\ \ y_1 = \underline{\ ?\ }$

$x_2 = \dfrac{1}{6},\ \ y_2 = \dfrac{1}{2}$

**Translate each statement into a formula. Use $k$ as the constant of variation where needed.**

(9-9, 9-10)

**100.** The height, $h$, of a right circular cylinder of a given volume is inversely proportional to the square of the radius, $r$.

**101.** Wind pressure, $p$, on a flat surface varies directly as the square of the wind velocity, $v$.

**102.** The lateral area, $L$, of a cylinder varies jointly as the radius, $r$, of the base, and the height, $h$.

**103.** The volume, $V$, of a cone varies jointly as the height, $h$, and the square of the radius, $r$, of the base.

**104.** The rate of speed, $r$, of a moving body varies inversely as the time traveled, $t$, and directly as the distance traveled, $d$.

**105.** Centrifugal force, $F$, varies inversely as the radius, $r$, of the circular path, and directly as the square of the velocity, $v$, of a moving body.

# Chapter 10

**Classify each statement as true or false.**

(10-1)

**1.** $-8 > 7 > 6$

**2.** $-5 < -4 < 5$

**3.** $-1.5 < -1 < -0.05$

**4.** $-\frac{1}{2} < 0 < 1$

**5.** $7 > 0 > 2$

**6.** $-10 < -15 < -20$

**7.** $|-0.6| < 0.4$

**8.** $\left|-\frac{1}{3}\right| \geq 0$

**9.** $|5 - 3| < |3 - 5|$

**Solve each inequality if $x \in \{-4, -3, -2, -1, 0, 1, 2, 3, 4\}$.**

(10-1)

**10.** $5x \leq 15$

**11.** $-7x > 14$

**12.** $-4 - x \geq 0$

**13.** $x^2 < 10$

**Solve each inequality over the given domain and draw its graph.**

(10-1)

**14.** $32 < 8x$; {the positive numbers}

**15.** $-6 \leq k < 2$; {the negative integers}

**16.** $3 > t \geq -4$; {the integers}

**17.** $-2 < n < 2$; {the real numbers}

**Solve each inequality and draw its graph.**

(10-2)

**18.** $e - 8 > 12$

**19.** $13 > n + 9$

**20.** $4q < -20$

**21.** $-\frac{x}{7} < 14$

**22.** $\frac{m}{3} - 5 > -2$

**23.** $-3 > 7 + \frac{4}{5}k$

**24.** $5v + 3 > 18$

**25.** $48 - 6y < 0$

**26.** $7t < 6t + 8$

**27.** $8f - 5 > 4f + 11$

**28.** $-6(v - 3) \leq 42$

**29.** $5(m + 2) > 4(m - 1)$

**30.** $\frac{4}{9}h + 3 \leq \frac{1}{3}$

**31.** $2(w - 1) < \frac{3}{2}w$

**32.** $2z - \frac{1}{4}(3z + 8) > 0$

**In Exercises 33–37:** (10-3)
**a. Choose a variable to represent the number shown in color.**
**b. Use the variable to write an inequality based on the given information. (Do not solve.)**

33. Marquita sold 9 fewer magazine subscriptions than twice the number Juanita sold. Marquita sold at most 43 subscriptions.

34. Rick, who is not yet 16 years old, is 3 years older than Sam. (Sam's age)

35. Andrea lives 10 miles less than half as far as Roger lives from the beach. Andrea lives at least 25 miles from the beach.

36. The number of San Marcos High School students who ride the bus is one third the number who walk or ride their bikes. The total number of students is at least 1800.

37. Six years ago, Buford was less than half as old as he is now. (His present age)

**Solve each open sentence and graph each solution set that is not empty.** (10-4)

38. $-3 < n + 5 < 7$  
39. $-6 < -6 + w \le 2$  
40. $-4 \le 3a - 1 < 5$  
41. $-1 \le 8m + 7 \le 23$  
42. $u - 2 < -5$ or $u - 2 \ge 4$  
43. $k + 6 \le -3$ or $k + 6 > 2$  
44. $4t + 3 < -1$ or $4t + 3 > 7$  
45. $2x - 2 \le -8$ or $8 < 2x - 2$  
46. $-5e < 15$ and $6 + 3e < 0$  
47. $h - 4 \ge 2$ or $4 - h \ge 2$  

**Solve each open sentence and draw its graph.** (10-5, 10-6)

48. $|v - 6| = 3$  
49. $|8 - k| = 5$  
50. $|m| > 2\frac{1}{2}$  
51. $|x| \le 1.5$  
52. $|y + 5| > 2$  
53. $|3 + z| \le 4$  
54. $|7 - f| < 6$  
55. $|-4 - g| > 7$  
56. $|-a - 2| \ge 1$  
57. $4|s| + 2 \le 8$  
58. $5 - 3|z| < 14$  
59. $9 - |3 - b| > 2$  
60. $|8k| = 16$  
61. $\left|\dfrac{a}{2}\right| \ge 3$  
62. $\left|\dfrac{c}{4}\right| \le 1$  
63. $|5x - 3| = 17$  
64. $|7 + 6n| < 19$  
65. $|2w - 3| > 5$  
66. $\left|\dfrac{u}{3} + 4\right| = 1$  
67. $\left|\dfrac{v}{2} - 1\right| \le 3$  
68. $\left|\dfrac{u}{4} + 2\right| \ge 1$  
69. $|5 - (3 - 2x)| < 6$  
70. $7 + 3|2m + 1| = 13$  
71. $10 - 6|2 - k| \ge 22$  

**Graph each inequality.** (10-7)

72. $x < 3$  
73. $x \ge -4$  
74. $y > 0$  
75. $y \le -2$  
76. $y > x - 1$  
77. $y \le -x + 2$  
78. $y < 3 + 4x$  
79. $y \ge -5x - 1$

Transform each inequality into an equivalent inequality with $y$ as one side. Then graph the inequality. (10-7)

**80.** $x - y \geq 5$    **81.** $4x + y \leq -2$    **82.** $x - 3y > 6$

**83.** $6x - y < 2$    **84.** $y - 5x \geq 3$    **85.** $4y - 5x < 0$

**86.** $7x + 6y \geq x - 3$    **87.** $3y - 2 > 6x - 4$    **88.** $8y - 7 \leq 3(x + 2y)$

Graph each pair of inequalities and indicate the solution set of the system with crosshatching or shading. (10-8)

**89.** $y \leq 0$
$\quad\;\; x > 0$

**90.** $y \geq -3$
$\quad\;\; x \leq 2$

**91.** $y > 4x$
$\quad\;\; x < 3$

**92.** $x \geq -1$
$\quad\;\; y < 2x - 5$

**93.** $y < x + 3$
$\quad\;\; y > 3 - x$

**94.** $y \leq 5x - 4$
$\quad\;\; y \geq 2x + 1$

**95.** $x + y > 2$
$\quad\;\; x - y < 6$

**96.** $3x - 4y \leq 0$
$\quad\;\; x - 2y \geq -6$

# Chapter 11

Replace the __?__ with $<$, $=$, or $>$ to make a true statement. (11-1)

**1.** $\dfrac{17}{23}$ __?__ $\dfrac{15}{19}$    **2.** $-\dfrac{87}{29}$ __?__ $-\dfrac{39}{13}$    **3.** $\dfrac{197}{6}$ __?__ $33\dfrac{2}{7}$

Arrange each group of numbers from least to greatest. (11-1)

**4.** $-\dfrac{39}{8}$, $-4.7$, $-\dfrac{41}{9}$    **5.** $\dfrac{5}{7}$, $\dfrac{2}{3}$, $\dfrac{11}{15}$, $\dfrac{12}{17}$    **6.** $-\dfrac{4}{9}$, $-\dfrac{5}{8}$, $-\dfrac{6}{11}$, $-\dfrac{5}{7}$

Find the number halfway between the given numbers. (11-1)

**7.** $\dfrac{27}{41}$, $\dfrac{31}{37}$    **8.** $-\dfrac{17}{140}$, $-\dfrac{11}{32}$    **9.** $-5\dfrac{2}{7}$, $9\dfrac{1}{4}$

If $x \in \{0, 1, 2, 3\}$ state whether each fraction increases or decreases in value as $x$ takes on the values in increasing order. (11-1)

**10.** $\dfrac{5}{x + 1}$    **11.** $\dfrac{x - 3}{7}$    **12.** $\dfrac{8}{x + 2}$    **13.** $\dfrac{6 - x}{4}$    **14.** $\dfrac{10}{5 + 2x}$

Express each rational number as a terminating or repeating decimal. (11-2)

**15.** $\dfrac{4}{9}$    **16.** $-\dfrac{29}{24}$    **17.** $3\dfrac{11}{20}$    **18.** $-7\dfrac{5}{11}$    **19.** $\dfrac{41}{55}$

Express each rational number as a fraction in simplest form. (11-2)

**20.** $0.77$    **21.** $0.\overline{6}$    **22.** $-0.31\overline{8}$    **23.** $2.3\overline{7}$    **24.** $0.\overline{4135}$

**Find the difference of the given numbers. Then find the number halfway between them.** (11-2)

**25.** $\frac{5}{8}$ and 0.63

**26.** 0.66 and $0.\overline{6}$

**27.** $\frac{7}{11}$ and $0.6\overline{28}$

**Express both numbers as fractions and find their product.** (11-2)

**28.** $\frac{2}{5}$ and 0.85

**29.** $0.\overline{4}$ and $\frac{2}{3}$

**30.** $-2.2$ and $0.\overline{3}$

**Find the indicated square roots.** (11-3)

**31.** $\sqrt{441}$  **32.** $\sqrt{784}$  **33.** $\sqrt{2704}$  **34.** $\sqrt{5184}$  **35.** $\sqrt{10816}$

**36.** $\sqrt{0.04}$  **37.** $\sqrt{0.64}$  **38.** $\sqrt{1.96}$  **39.** $\sqrt{0.0144}$  **40.** $\sqrt{0.0036}$

**41.** $\sqrt{\dfrac{81}{225}}$  **42.** $\sqrt{\dfrac{1}{289}}$  **43.** $\sqrt{\dfrac{324}{1936}}$  **44.** $\sqrt{\dfrac{32}{50}}$  **45.** $\sqrt{\dfrac{320}{405}}$

**Simplify.** (11-4)

**46.** $\sqrt{63}$  **47.** $\sqrt{176}$  **48.** $2\sqrt{52}$  **49.** $4\sqrt{99}$  **50.** $5\sqrt{175}$

**51.** $10\sqrt{162}$  **52.** $\sqrt{192}$  **53.** $\sqrt{672}$  **54.** $\sqrt{224}$  **55.** $\sqrt{2646}$

**Approximate to the nearest tenth by using the square root table.** (11-4)

**56.** $\sqrt{720}$  **57.** $-\sqrt{800}$  **58.** $\sqrt{440}$  **59.** $\sqrt{8400}$  **60.** $-\sqrt{5400}$

**Simplify.** (11-5)

**61.** $\sqrt{169m^2}$  **62.** $\sqrt{48a^2}$  **63.** $\sqrt{125x^4}$  **64.** $\sqrt{54e^3}$  **65.** $-\sqrt{36t^6}$

**66.** $\sqrt{98u^2v^2}$  **67.** $-2\sqrt{72x^3y^2}$  **68.** $\sqrt{324r^4s^6}$  **69.** $-\sqrt{4.84w^4}$  **70.** $\sqrt{5.76c^6}$

**71.** $\sqrt{\dfrac{a^4b^6}{12c^2}}$  **72.** $\sqrt{\dfrac{48u^5v^2}{4uv^4}}$  **73.** $\sqrt{\dfrac{144k^8}{256}}$  **74.** $\sqrt{\dfrac{3600}{81m^{36}}}$  **75.** $\sqrt{\dfrac{225x^{40}}{16}}$

**76.** $\sqrt{x^2 + 8x + 16}$  **77.** $\sqrt{a^2 - 4a + 4}$  **78.** $\sqrt{81 + 18k + k^2}$

**Solve.** (11-5)

**79.** $g^2 = 49$

**80.** $h^2 - 64 = 0$

**81.** $25m^2 = 16$

**82.** $9x^2 - 4 = 0$

**83.** $6y^2 - 54 = 0$

**84.** $32t^2 - 27 = 0$

**Find both roots of each equation to the nearest tenth.** (11-5)

**85.** $a^2 = 132$

**86.** $b^2 - 208 = 0$

**87.** $11c^2 = 473$

**State whether or not the three numbers given could represent the lengths of the sides of a right triangle.** (11-6)

**88.** 21, 28, 35

**89.** 9, 9, 12

**90.** 45, 60, 75

**91.** 31, 41, 51

**92.** $6a, 8a, 10a, a > 0$

**93.** $5a, 7a, 9a, a > 0$

In Exercises 94–101, refer to the right triangle shown at the right. Find the missing length correct to the nearest hundredth.

(11-6)

94. $a = 3$, $b = 4$, $c = $ ?   95. $a = 5$, $b = 8$, $c = $ ?
96. $a = $ ? , $b = 9$, $c = 13$   97. $a = $ ? , $b = 10$, $c = 15$
98. $a = 8$, $b = $ ? , $c = 16$   99. $a = 20$, $b = $ ? , $c = 30$
100. $a = 12$, $b = \frac{3}{4}a$, $c = $ ?   101. $a = \frac{2}{3}b$, $b = 15$, $c = $ ?

**Express in simplest form.** (11-7)

102. $\sqrt{3} \cdot 4\sqrt{3}$   103. $2\sqrt{5} \cdot 3\sqrt{5}$   104. $\sqrt{7} \cdot \sqrt{6} \cdot \sqrt{2}$
105. $\sqrt{7} \cdot \sqrt{7} \cdot \sqrt{4}$   106. $5\sqrt{2} \cdot \sqrt{3}$   107. $8\sqrt{162}$
108. $\sqrt{\frac{5}{9}} \cdot \sqrt{\frac{9}{5}}$   109. $\sqrt{\frac{7}{5}} \cdot \sqrt{\frac{45}{14}}$   110. $\sqrt{5\frac{5}{6}} \cdot \sqrt{2\frac{4}{7}}$
111. $\frac{1}{4}\sqrt{\frac{16}{3}} \cdot \frac{1}{2}\sqrt{\frac{3}{2}}$   112. $\frac{12\sqrt{20}}{4\sqrt{3}}$   113. $\frac{11\sqrt{6}}{\sqrt{98}}$

**Simplify. Assume the radicands are nonnegative real numbers.** (11-7)

114. $(3\sqrt{y})(-5\sqrt{x^2y})$   115. $\sqrt{n}(\sqrt{n^3} + 3)$   116. $(7\sqrt{3})(-4\sqrt{6})(5\sqrt{22})$

**Simplify.** (11-8)

117. $9\sqrt{3} - 5\sqrt{3}$   118. $7\sqrt{2} + 6\sqrt{2}$   119. $3\sqrt{54} - 2\sqrt{6}$
120. $4\sqrt{28} + 6\sqrt{112}$   121. $-10\sqrt{18} - 5\sqrt{32}$   122. $\sqrt{242} - 3\sqrt{363}$
123. $\sqrt{8} - \sqrt{\frac{5}{6}}$   124. $\sqrt{\frac{2}{3}} - \sqrt{\frac{3}{2}}$   125. $5\sqrt{\frac{16}{7}} + \sqrt{\frac{9}{8}}$
126. $3\sqrt{63} + 2\sqrt{28} - \sqrt{35}$   127. $\sqrt{120} - \sqrt{270} + \sqrt{300}$
128. $2\sqrt{\frac{5}{3}} + 4\sqrt{\frac{3}{8}} - \frac{1}{2}\sqrt{68}$   129. $3\sqrt{5}(\sqrt{75} - 2\sqrt{12})$

**Express in simplest form.** (11-9)

130. $(5 - \sqrt{3})(5 + \sqrt{3})$   131. $(\sqrt{7} + 6)(\sqrt{7} - 6)$
132. $(\sqrt{6} - \sqrt{5})(\sqrt{6} + \sqrt{5})$   133. $(4 + \sqrt{2})^2$
134. $(5 - \sqrt{5})^2$   135. $(3\sqrt{2} - 4)^2$
136. $(\sqrt{11} + 3\sqrt{7})^2$   137. $2\sqrt{6}(5\sqrt{2} - 4\sqrt{3})$
138. $(4\sqrt{5} - 6)(2\sqrt{7} + 7)$   139. $(3\sqrt{14} + 2\sqrt{7})(5\sqrt{14} + 3\sqrt{7})$

**Rationalize the denominator of each fraction.** (11-9)

140. $\frac{5}{3 + \sqrt{7}}$   141. $\frac{2 + \sqrt{3}}{1 - \sqrt{5}}$

**Solve.** (11-10)

**142.** $\sqrt{m} = 7$

**143.** $\sqrt{6x} = \dfrac{3}{2}$

**144.** $\sqrt{a} - 5 = 4$

**145.** $\dfrac{1}{5} + \sqrt{y} = 1$

**146.** $\sqrt{\dfrac{x}{3}} = 6$

**147.** $\sqrt{n-2} = 9$

**148.** $4\sqrt{5t} = 8$

**149.** $\sqrt{3z} + 2 = 5$

**150.** $\sqrt{4k-5} + 1 = 8$

**151.** $\sqrt{\dfrac{5u}{2}} - 3 = -2$

**152.** $\sqrt{\dfrac{4c-3}{7}} = 3$

**153.** $8\sqrt{n} = 24\sqrt{5}$

# Chapter 12

**Solve. Express irrational solutions in simplest radical form. If the equation has no solution, write "no solution."** (12-1)

**1.** $m^2 = \dfrac{25}{49}$

**2.** $5a^2 = 60$

**3.** $w^2 + 52 = 0$

**4.** $x^2 - 108 = 0$

**5.** $7u^2 - 112 = 0$

**6.** $4c^2 + 7 = 23$

**7.** $3t^2 - 12 = -3$

**8.** $2n^2 + 9 = 4$

**9.** $(v + 5)^2 = 16$

**10.** $(z - 5)^2 = 6$

**11.** $3(k + 4)^2 = 81$

**12.** $4(f - 1)^2 = 60$

**13.** $2(h + 7)^2 = 42$

**14.** $(2x + 3)^2 = 100$

**15.** $7(3y - 1)^2 = 168$

**16.** $e^2 + 6e + 9 = 64$

**17.** $a^2 - 12a + 36 = 49$

**18.** $m^2 + 18m + 81 = 36$

**Solve by completing the square. Give irrational roots in simplest form and then approximate them to the nearest tenth.** (12-2)

**19.** $x^2 + 16x = -15$

**20.** $y^2 - 8y + 7 = 0$

**21.** $z^2 - 12z - 202 = 8$

**22.** $4a^2 + 10a = 12$

**23.** $b^2 - 3b = 5$

**24.** $3c^2 + 6c - 1233 = 0$

**Solve by (a) completing the square and (b) factoring.** (12-2)

**25.** $e^2 - 10e + 21 = 0$

**26.** $4f^2 - 18f = 10$

**27.** $6h^2 + 9h - 42 = 0$

**Solve. Write irrational roots in simplest radical form.** (12-2)

**28.** $\dfrac{m^2}{3} - 2m = 7$

**29.** $n^2 + \dfrac{n}{2} = 5$

**30.** $\dfrac{x^2}{2} - \dfrac{x}{4} = 2$

**Use the quadratic formula to solve each equation. Give irrational roots in simplest radical form; also approximate them to the nearest tenth.** (12-3)

**31.** $z^2 + 7z + 3 = 0$

**32.** $w^2 + 8w - 4 = 0$

**33.** $2u^2 - 10u - 6 = 0$

**34.** $5t^2 = -9t - 1$

**35.** $3k^2 + 2 = 5k$

**36.** $6m = 3 - 2m^2$

**37.** $x^2 + 0.3x - 0.2 = 0$

**38.** $n^2 + \dfrac{2}{3}n - \dfrac{1}{2} = 0$

**39.** $\dfrac{1}{2}y^2 - \dfrac{7}{2}y = 1$

Write the value of the discriminant of each equation. Then use it to decide how many different real-number roots the equation has. (Do not solve the equations.) (12-4)

**40.** $x^2 - 6x + 2 = 0$      **41.** $5n^2 + 3n + 7 = 0$      **42.** $-2t^2 + 4t - 2 = 0$

**43.** $3k^2 - 1.2k + 1.1 = 0$      **44.** $3s^2 + 6s + 3 = 0$      **45.** $\frac{1}{3}b^2 - b - 3 = 0$

Without drawing the graph of the given equation, determine (a) how many points the parabola has in common with the x-axis, and (b) whether its vertex lies above, below, or on the x-axis. (12-4)

**46.** $y = 3x^2 + 2x - 5$      **47.** $y = -6 + 3x - 2x^2$      **48.** $y = x^2 - 4x + 16$

Solve by the most efficient method. Write irrational answers in simplest radical form. (12-5)

**49.** $x^2 + 7x + 12 = 0$      **50.** $13x^2 = 52$      **51.** $5x^2 - 9x = 0$

**52.** $3x^2 - 11x = 2$      **53.** $x^2 + 8x + 3 = 0$      **54.** $(x - 3)^2 = 6$

**55.** $6x^2 + 4x = 1$      **56.** $\frac{(x + 4)^2}{3} = 8$      **57.** $\frac{3}{4}x^2 - \frac{2}{3}x = 1$

**58.** $\frac{1}{2x} = \frac{3x - 2}{3}$      **59.** $1.2x^2 - 0.4x = 0.2$      **60.** $\frac{2x - 1}{4x + 3} = \frac{x + 1}{3x - 2}$

**61.** $4x(x - 2) + 3(x + 8) = 27 + 5x^2$      **62.** $(x + 6)^2 + 2(x - 1) = 13$

Solve. Give irrational roots to the nearest tenth. Use the Table of Square Roots on page 650 or a calculator as necessary. (12-6)

**63.** The length of a rectangle is 6 times the width. The area of the rectangle is 84 cm². Find the length and width.

**64.** The difference of a number and its square is 56. Find the number.

**65.** The altitude of a triangle is 2 m less than the base. The area of the triangle is 84 m². Find the base.

**66.** Theresa is crocheting an afghan that is already 30 inches wide by 40 inches long. If she continues to crochet by increasing the width and the length by the same number of inches until the afghan's area is doubled, what will be the new dimensions?

# Extra Practice: Problem-Solving

## Chapter 1

**Use the five-step plan to solve each problem.**

(1-6)

1. A train is traveling at an average speed of 90 km/h. How far will it travel in 2.5 h?

2. If a number is decreased by 27, the result is 36. Find the number.

3. A football team finished its 12-game season with no ties. The team won twice as many games as it lost. How many games did the team win?

4. A store sold 102 record albums during a two-day sale. Twice as many albums were sold the second day as the first. How many albums were sold the first day?

5. If three times a number is increased by 11, the result is 68. Find the number.

6. A bank contains 57 nickels, dimes, and quarters. There are 8 more dimes than quarters and 5 more nickels than dimes. How much money is in the bank?

## Chapter 2

**Solve.**

(2-3)

1. A football team gained 23 yards on one play. However, the ball was brought back to the line of scrimmage and then the team was given a 15 yard penalty. How far was the ball from where it would have been had no penalty been assessed?

2. An elevator left the twenty-sixth floor of a building and went up eight floors, then down twelve, and back up four. Where was the elevator then?

3. At the beginning of the month the Cranes had $250 in their vacation fund. They were able to add $10 per week for four weeks. Then they had to take out $85 for emergency household repairs. How much was in the fund at the end of the month?

4. A neighborhood association collected $85 in dues, earned $280 at a garage sale, and got $124 in donations. The association needs $500 to build a playground. How much more must it collect?

5. An 8:00 A.M. flight from Boston to Minneapolis took three hours. The time in Minneapolis is one hour earlier than in Boston. What time was it in Minneapolis when the flight arrived?

**6.** A train is traveling at the rate of 100 km/h. A conductor is walking toward the back of the train at 5 km/h. What is the conductor's speed relative to the ground?

**Solve.**

1. Neon freezes at −248.61°C and boils at −246.09°C. Find the difference between the boiling point and the freezing point.  (2-4)

2. The highest point in California is Mount Whitney at 4418 m above sea level. The lowest is Death Valley at 86 m below sea level. Find the difference in altitude.

3. A candidate goes door to door along Main Street from a point 16 blocks west of campaign headquarters to a point 12 blocks east of headquarters. How many blocks has she gone?

4. Find the difference in degrees of longitude between Chicago at about 88°W and Rome at about 12°E.

5. Mount Everest at 8848 m above sea level is 9245 m higher than the Dead Sea. Find the altitude of the Dead Sea.

6. One winter day the temperature in Marshview reached a record high of 18.3°C. That was 22.7° higher than the average temperature for that day. Find the average temperature.

# Chapter 3

**Solve.**

1. A number increased by 13 is −5. Find the number.  (3-1)

2. A glass of milk costs 55¢. If a glass of milk and a sandwich cost $1.90, how much does the sandwich cost?

3. Fifteen less than a number is 43. Find the number.

4. A plane flew 145 km/h faster when it was flying with the wind than it would have flown in still air. If its speed with the wind was 970 km/h, find the speed of the plane in still air.

5. The Booster Club had $425 in its treasury. The members earned $642 selling refreshments. They donated $320 to the football team for bus rentals. How much money did they have left?

6. Seventy-six tickets were sold in advance for a museum field trip. Thirteen tickets were sold the day of the trip. Seven people had to return their tickets and did not go. How many people went altogether?

**Solve.**

1. The opposite of seven times a number is 238. Find the number.  (3-2)

2. One fourth of a number is 73. Find the number.

**3.** A 2.5 kg bag of apples costs 75¢. Find the cost per kilogram of the apples.

**4.** Frank works the same number of hours each week at a part-time job. In the first 8 weeks he worked 68 hours. How many hours did he work each week?

**5.** A rectangle is 24 cm long and has a perimeter of 72 cm. Find the width.

**6.** A restaurant cuts its large pizza into 8 slices and sells them for 75¢ each. If the pizzas were cut into 6 slices, how much would the restaurant have to charge for each slice to make the same amount?

**Solve.**

**1.** If you subtract 34 from the product of 15 and a number, you get 146. Find the number.                                        (3-4)

**2.** The perimeter of a rectangle is 152 m. The width is 35 cm. Find the length.

**3.** Carlene paid $131.44, including tax, for a desk. The tax was 31 cents less than $\frac{1}{16}$ the cost of the desk. Find the cost of the desk.

**4.** Twin Cinema I seats 150 more people than Twin Cinema II. If together they seat 1250 people, find the number of seats in Twin Cinema II.

**5.** A bank contains 36 nickels, dimes, and quarters. There are 4 more dimes than quarters and twice as many nickels as quarters. How many of each coin are in the bank?

**6.** The longest side of a triangle is 8 cm longer than the shortest side and 5 cm longer than the third side. If the perimeter of the triangle is 56 cm, find the lengths of the three sides.

**Solve.**

**1.** The larger of two consecutive integers is 10 more than twice the smaller. Find the integers.                                        (3-5)

**2.** Find a number whose product with 6 is the same as its sum with 45.

**3.** Five times a number, increased by 3, is the same as three times the number, increased by 27. Find the number.

**4.** The sum of two numbers is 20. Twice one number is 4 more than four times the other. Find the numbers.

**5.** The lengths of the sides of a triangle are consecutive odd integers. If the perimeter is 1 less than four times the shortest side, find the length of each side.

**6.** A sandwich costs 20¢ more than a salad plate. Six sandwiches cost as much as seven salad plates. Find the cost of each.

**Solve.**

1. Kevin is three times as old as Karen. In 6 years he will be twice as old as she. How old are both now?

(3-6)

2. Aaron, Betsy, and Charita work part-time at the public library. Betsy works 4 hours more each week than Aaron, and together they work half as many hours as Charita. How long does each person work if their total time is 45 hours?

3. In ten years Zachary will be half his father's age. If his father was 25 years old when he was born, how old is each now?

4. The length of a rectangle is 18 cm more than the width. A second rectangle is 6 cm shorter and 3 cm wider than the first and has a perimeter of 126 cm. Find the dimensions of each rectangle.

5. Becky's age is the sum of the ages of Ryan and Amy. Ryan is 2 years older than Amy, and Amy is one third as old as Becky. How old is each now?

6. A cup of skim milk has 10 more than half the calories of a cup of whole milk. A cup of whole milk has 40 more calories than a glass of apple juice. If the total number of calories in one cup of each is 370, find the number of calories in each.

**Solve.**

1. A collection of quarters and dimes is worth $6.75. The number of dimes is 4 less than three times the number of quarters. How many of each are there?

(3-7)

2. A total of 720 people attended a basketball game. Adult tickets cost $2.50 each and student tickets cost $1.50 each. If $1220 worth of tickets were sold, how many students and how many adults attended?

3. A worker earns $9 per hour for a regular workday and $13.50 per hour for additional hours. If the worker was paid $114.75 for an 11-hour workday, what is the length of a regular workday?

4. Carrots cost 75¢ per kilogram and potatoes cost 70¢ per kilogram. A shopper bought 9 kg of the vegetables for $6.60. How many kilograms of each did the shopper buy?

5. A collection of 102 nickels, dimes, and quarters is worth $13.60. There are 14 more nickels than dimes. How many quarters are there?

## Chapter 4

**Solve.**

1. Two trains leave a station at the same time, heading in opposite directions. One train is traveling at 80 km/h, the other at 90 km/h. How long will it take for the trains to be 425 km apart?

(4-8)

2. Grace leaves home at 8:00 A.M. Ten minutes later, Will notices Grace's lunch and begins bicycling after her. If Grace walks at 5 km/h and Will cycles at 15 km/h, how long will it take him to catch up with her?

3. A jet took one hour longer flying to Lincoln from Adams at 800 km/h than to return at 1200 km/h. Find the distance from Lincoln to Adams.

4. Gene spent 10 min riding his bicycle to a friend's house. He left his bike there and, with his friend, walked for 15 min to the gym. Gene rides his bicycle 10 km/h faster than he walks. If the entire trip covered a distance of 2.75 km, how far is it from his friend's house to the gym?

5. At noon, Sheila left a boat landing and paddled her canoe 20 km downstream and back. If she traveled 10 km/h downstream and 4 km/h upstream, what time did she arrive back at the landing?

**Solve.**

1. A rectangle is 4 m longer than it is wide. If the length and width are both increased by 5 m, the area is increased by 115 m². Find the original dimensions.  (4-9)

2. A rectangle is 3 cm longer and 2 cm narrower than a square with the same area. Find the dimensions of each.

3. A rectangular swimming pool is 4 m longer than it is wide. It is surrounded by a cement walk 1 m wide. The area of the walk is 32 m². Find the dimensions of the pool.

4. When the length of a square is increased by 6 and the width is decreased by 4, the area remains unchanged. Find the dimensions of the square.

5. A print is 10 cm longer than it is wide. It is mounted in a frame 1.5 cm wide. The area of the frame is 339 cm². Find the dimensions of the print.

**Solve.**

1. Find two consecutive integers whose sum is 104.  (4-10)

2. A plane averaged 1000 km/h on the first half of a round trip, but heavy winds slowed its speed on the return trip to 600 km/h. If the entire trip took 6 h, find the total distance.

3. Jill is 12 years older than Jack. In 8 years she will be three times his age. How old is Jack?

4. The side of a square is 2 cm longer than the side of a second square. If the area of the first square exceeds that of the second by 220 cm², find the side of each square.

5. Find three consecutive integers whose sum is four times the greatest integer.

# Chapter 5

**Solve.**

1. The sum of a number and its square is 132. Find the number. (5-13)

2. The sum of the squares of two consecutive positive odd integers is 202. Find the numbers.

3. A rectangle is 8 cm longer than it is wide. The area is 240 cm². Find the dimensions.

4. The sum of two numbers is 12 and the sum of their squares is 74. Find the numbers.

5. A rectangular flower garden is planted in a rectangular yard that is 16 m by 12 m. The garden occupies $\frac{1}{6}$ of the area of the yard and leaves a uniform strip of grass around the edges. Find the dimensions of the garden.

6. The edge of one cube is 4 cm longer than the edge of a second cube. The volumes of the cubes differ by 316 cm³. Find the length of the edge of each cube.

# Chapter 7

**Solve.**

1. Two numbers are in the ratio 2:3 and their sum is 125. Find the numbers. (7-1)

2. The measures of the angles of a triangle are in the ratio 2:3:5. Recall that the sum of the measures of the angles of a triangle is 180°. Find the measure of each angle.

3. Three numbers are in the ratio 2:3:5 and their sum is 200. Find the numbers.

4. The ratio of teachers to assistants to children at a day care center is 2:1:9. Of the 96 people at the center, how many are children?

5. A collection of quarters, dimes, and nickels is worth $22.80. If the ratio of quarters to dimes to nickels is 5:3:7, how many coins are there?

6. Two planes leave an airport at the same time heading in opposite directions. After 2 h, the planes are 376 km apart. If the ratio of their speeds is 22:25, find the speed of each plane.

**Solve.**

1. A 1.5 pound steak costs $5.25. Find the cost of a 2 pound steak. (7-2)

2. A poll showed that 400 voters out of 625 favor Question 1 in the town elections. If there are 7500 voters altogether, how many can be expected to vote in favor of the question?

3. Group-rate admissions to a museum cost $140.70 for a group of 42. How much would it have cost for a group of 50?

4. The tax on a restaurant meal that costs $24 is $1.44. Find the tax on a meal that costs $35.

5. The Sommers' scale is inaccurate. If it registers 120 lb for Karen, who actually weighs 116 lb, how much will it register for Neil, who actually weighs 174 lb?

6. On a wall map, 1 cm represents 25 km. Colorado is represented by a rectangle 25.8 cm long and 18.4 cm wide. Find the approximate area of Colorado in square kilometers.

**Solve.**

1. Juan is 2 years older than Sylvia. Four years ago Sylvia's age was five sixths of Juan's age. How old are both now?                                                    (7-3)

2. Three fifths of a number added to one fourth of the number is 51. Find the number.

3. Bart's age is one third of his mother's age. Seven years ago, his age was one fifth of hers. How old are both now?

4. A rectangle is 11 cm narrower than it is long. The length is two sevenths of the perimeter. Find the length and the width.

5. Two thirds of the coins in a collection of quarters and dimes are quarters. The collection is worth $12. How many dimes are there?

6. A bus, traveling at 90 km/h, takes 15.2 hours longer to get from Ardmore to Zephyr than a plane flying at 850 km/h. How far is it from Ardmore to Zephyr?

**Solve.**

1. The sum of a number and its reciprocal is $\frac{25}{12}$. Find the number.               (7-4)

2. The sum of a number and its reciprocal is $\frac{29}{10}$. Find the number.

3. The denominator of a fraction is 2 more than the numerator. If the numerator and denominator are increased by 2, the new fraction is $\frac{4}{15}$ greater than the original fraction. Find the original fraction.

4. The denominator of a fraction is 2 more than the numerator. The sum of the fraction and its reciprocal is $\frac{34}{15}$. Find the fraction.

5. If the speed limit is decreased by 10 km/h on a 100 km stretch of a highway, the trip will take a half hour longer than usual. What is the usual speed limit?

6. I can ride my bike 14 km/h faster than I can walk. It takes 17.5 min longer to walk 2.5 km than to ride. Find my walking speed.

**Solve.**

1. If there is a 6% tax on clothing, find the tax on a suit that costs $175.
   (7-5)

2. A real estate agent makes a 4% commission on all sales. How much does the agent make on a sale of $82,500?

3. A discount store sold a sweater for $32. If the discount was 20%, find the original price.

4. If the Ghannams' $84 monthly gas bill goes up 8%, what will be their new monthly payment?

5. An $840 personal computer is discounted 25%. What is the final cost?

6. How much greater is the income on $3600 invested at 12% than on $4200 invested at 8%?

**Solve.**

1. Last season, when a football team was doing poorly, weekly attendance averaged 42,000. This season attendance averages 56,700. What is the percent of increase?
   (7-6)

2. A single monthly issue of *Sports Spotlight* costs $2.25 at the newsstand. A yearly subscription costs $21.60. Find the percent of discount from the newsstand price.

3. Enrollment in the summer recreation program this year increased by 16% to 1711 people. How many people enrolled last year?

4. The Kerchners invested $7500 at 8% and $3500 at 5%. Find the total annual income from the two investments.

5. The Jokis invested a sum of money at 10%. They could have earned the same interest by investing $1600 less at 12%. How much did they invest?

6. The Sanjurjos invested three fourths of their money at 12% and the rest at 8%. If their annual income from the investment is $1320, how much have they invested?

*Chemistry*

**Solve.**

1. How many liters of water must be added to 20 L of a 75% acid solution to produce a solution that is 15% acid?
   (7-7)

2. How many liters of acid should be added to 4 L of a 10% acid solution to make a solution that is 80% acid?

3. A chemist mixes 16 L of a 40% acid solution and 24 L of a 16% acid solution. What is the percent of acid of the mixture?

4. How many kilograms of water must be evaporated from 84 kg of a 5% salt solution to produce a solution that is 35% salt?

## Grocery

**Solve.**

1. Students working at a refreshment stand mix cranberry juice at 50¢ per liter and apple juice at 35¢ per liter to make 120 L of a fruit drink worth 40¢ per liter. How many liters of each did they use?

2. A grocer mixes a premium blend worth $17 per kilogram with a blend worth $7 per kilogram to make 36 kg of a blend worth $11 per kilogram. How many kilograms of each type are included?

3. A butcher mixes 12 pounds of ground pork at $1.25 per pound with 24 pounds of ground beef at $2 per pound to sell as meat loaf mix. What should be the cost per pound of the mixture?

4. How many kilograms of cranberries at $2.10 per kilogram should a grocer mix with 10 kg of pineapple chunks at $1.20 per kilogram to make a relish worth $1.35 per kilogram?

## Investment and Wages

**Solve.**

1. A worker earns $1\frac{1}{2}$ times the regular wage for overtime. In one week the worker's total income was $625 for 35 hours of regular work plus 10 hours of overtime. What is the regular hourly wage?

2. The Esperanzas invested part of their $8000 at 12% and part at 8%. If their annual investment income is $825, how much is invested at each rate?

3. The Lees invested two thirds of their money at 12.5%, one fourth at 8%, and the rest at 6%. If their annual investment income is $1625, how much did they invest altogether?

4. An investor has $10,000 invested in two stocks. If one pays 15% and the other 16%, and the total annual income is $1520, how much is invested in each?

**Solve.**

1. Joe can do a job in 6 h and Charlie can do the same job in 5 h. What part of the job can they finish by working together for 2 h?  (7-8)

2. Charlotte can finish her paper route in 2 h. When Ralph helps, they finish in 45 min. How long would it take Ralph working alone?

3. A crew of 2 could put siding on a house in 30 h. Another crew of 3 could do the same job in 24 h. How long would it take all 5 people working together?

4. Flora can finish her chores in 4 h. One week after Flora worked alone for 1 h, she was joined by her younger sister Fiona and they finished the job in 2 h. How long would it have taken Fiona working alone?

**5.** One pipe can fill a tank in 50 min and a second pipe can fill it in 90 min. When the tank was empty, the first pipe was opened for 20 min, then shut. How long will it take the second pipe to finish the job?

**6.** One machine can produce an order of Wonder Widgets in 45 min. A second machine takes 60 min, and a third takes 90 min. How long would it take all three working together?

**Solve.**

(7-9)

**1.** The speed of light is about $3.00 \times 10^5$ km/s. The average distance from Earth to the moon is about $3.84 \times 10^5$ km. How long does it take light reflected from Earth to reach the moon?

**2.** At its farthest, the moon is about $4.07 \times 10^5$ km from Earth. At its closest, it is about $3.56 \times 10^5$ km from Earth. Find the difference between the two distances.

**3.** The average distance from the sun to Pluto is about $6.10 \times 10^9$ km. About how long does it take light from the sun to reach Pluto? (See Exercise 1 above.)

**4. a.** A parsec is about $3.3 \times 10^3$ light years. The star Deneb is about $5.0 \times 10^2$ parsecs from the sun. How many light years is that?
   **b.** A light year is about $9.5 \times 10^{12}$ km. Find the distance from Deneb to the sun in kilometers.

**5.** The approximate wavelength of visible light is $6.0 \times 10^3$ Angstrom units. An Angstrom unit is equal to $1.0 \times 10^{-8}$ cm. Find the wavelength of visible light in centimeters.

**Solve.**

(7-10)

**1.** The population of a certain area in $t$ years is expected to be $10(1.03)^t$ thousand people. Find the population (a) now (b) last year (c) next year.

**2.** A certain isotope has a half-life of 100 years. Starting with 100 g of the isotope, in $t$ years there will be $100(0.5)^{\frac{t}{100}}$ grams left. (a) How much will be left in 1000 years? (b) How much was there 1000 years ago?

**3.** A certain bacteria culture quadruples every 2 days. The number present $t$ days from now will be $1,000,000\,(4)^{\frac{t}{2}}$. How many bacteria were there 2 weeks ago?

**4.** A $10,000 investment earning 8%, compounded annually, will be worth $10,000(1.08)^t$ in $t$ years. What was the amount 4 years ago?

**5.** The growth rate of a certain city is such that its population $t$ years from now is given by the formula $12,000(1.06)^t$. What was the population 10 years ago?

**6.** In one country the cost of living has been increasing so that an item costing one dollar now will cost $(1.05)^t$ dollars $t$ years from now. How much did today's one-dollar item cost 5 years ago?

# Chapter 8

**Solve.**

(8-5)

1. A collection of 77 quarters and dimes is worth $12.50. How many quarters are there?

2. The sum of two numbers is 32. One number is 4 more than the other. Find the numbers.

3. The length of a rectangle is 3 less than twice the width. The perimeter is 54. Find the dimensions.

4. The sum of two numbers is 66. If the smaller number is subtracted from two thirds of the larger number, the result is one third the positive difference of the original numbers. Find the numbers.

5. If 1 is subtracted from the numerator of a fraction, the resulting fraction is $\frac{1}{3}$. If 2 is subtracted from the denominator, the resulting fraction is $\frac{1}{2}$. Find the original fraction.

6. If 2 is added to the numerator of a fraction, the resulting fraction is $\frac{2}{3}$. If 1 is subtracted from the denominator, the resulting fraction is $\frac{1}{2}$. Find the original fraction.

**Solve.**

(8-6)

1. The sum of two numbers is 36 and their difference is 6. Find the numbers.

2. The sum of two numbers is 73. When the smaller number is subtracted from twice the greater number, the result is 50. Find the numbers.

3. There are 158 members in the soccer program. There are 16 more boys than girls. How many boys are there?

4. If Cathy walks for 2 h and rides her bicycle for 1 h, she can travel 36 km. If she walks for 2 h and rides her bicycle for 2 h, she can travel 56 km. How fast can she walk? How fast can she ride her bicycle?

5. Craig has 38 quarters and dimes. If he had twice as many quarters, he would have $11. How many of each coin does he have?

6. Olivia's father is 30 years older than she. Seven years ago, the sum of their ages was equal to his age now. How old is each now?

**Solve.**

(8-7)

1. The sum of two numbers is 51 and their difference is 13. Find the numbers.

2. A collection of 27 nickels and dimes is worth $1.95. How many of each coin are there?

3. The side of a square house is 24 ft long, and the house is located on a lot which is 50 ft longer than it is wide. The perimeter of the lot is 20 ft more than 5 times the perimeter of the house. Find the length of the lot.

4. Museum passes cost $5 for adults and $2 for children. One day the museum sold 1820 passes for $6100. How many of each type were sold?

5. In a math contest, each team is asked 50 questions. The teams earn 15 points for each correct answer and lose 8 for each incorrect answer. One team finished with a score of 566. How many questions did this team answer correctly?

6. A grocer mixes two types of nuts, Brand A and Brand B. If the mix includes 4 kg of Brand A and 6 kg of Brand B, the mix will cost $6.20 per kilogram. If it includes 2 kg of Brand A and 8 kg of Brand B, it will cost $5.60 per kilogram. Find the cost per kilogram of each brand.

**Solve.**

1. A boat can travel 16 km/h against the current. The same boat can travel 30 km/h with the current. Find the rate of the boat in still water and the rate of the current.  (8-8)

2. A jet flies with the wind at 1100 km/h and against the wind at 750 km/h. Find the rate of the wind and the ground speed of the jet.

3. A swimmer can swim 4 km with the current in 24 min. The same distance would take 40 min against the current. Find the rate of the current and the speed of the swimmer.

4. A plane flies the first half of a 5600 km flight into the wind in 3.5 h. The return trip, with the same wind, takes 2.5 h. Find the speed of the wind and the ground speed of the plane.

5. A plane has a ground speed of 840 km/h. It can travel 3120 km with the wind in the same time it would take to travel 1920 km against the wind. Find the speed of the wind.

6. A rowboat can travel a distance of 66 km in 3 h with the current. The rowboat can travel 33 km in 3 h against the current. Find the rate of the current and the rate of the rowboat in still water.

# Chapter 9

**Solve.**

1. A beam bends 1.6 cm with a mass of 32 kg on it. If the amount of bending is directly proportional to the mass, find the amount of bending caused by a mass of 62 kg.  (9-7)

2. A baker uses 18 cups of flour to make 48 sandwich rolls. How many cups of flour are needed to make 104 sandwich rolls?

3. A grocer uses 22 kg of premium nuts in making 54 kg of a mixture. How much of the premium nuts is needed for 81 kg of the mixture?

4. On a scale drawing, a child 4 ft tall is represented by a figure 6 in. tall. How tall a figure should be used to represent an 11 ft elephant?

5. On a map, 1 cm represents 60 km. Find the actual area of a region represented on the map by a rectangle 7.5 cm by 8.4 cm.

6. A factory is to be built in the shape of a rectangular solid. The actual building will be 62 m long, 30 m wide, and 12 m high. A scale model is built with a scale of 1 cm to 5 m. Find the volume of the model.

**Solve.**

1. The time required to drive a given distance is inversely proportional to the speed. If it takes 7.5 hours to cover a distance at 84 km/h, how long will it take at 90 km/h?   **(9-8)**

2. A gear with 36 teeth revolves at 800 rpm and meshes with a gear with 24 teeth. Find the speed of the second gear if the speed varies inversely as the number of teeth.

3. How much would you have to invest at 8% to earn as much interest as $1250 invested at 12%?

4. A room is to be partitioned into a row of carrels. If each carrel is 1.8 m wide, there will be room for 16 carrels. How many carrels will fit if each is 1.92 m wide?

5. A mass of 18 g and a mass of 22 g are on the ends of a meter stick. Where should a fulcrum be placed to balance the meter stick?

6. A lever has a mass of 400 g on one end and a mass of 250 g on the other. The lever is balanced when the mass of 400 g is 0.75 m closer to the fulcrum than the other mass. How far from the fulcrum is the mass of 250 g?

**Solve.**

1. The stopping distance of a car varies directly as the square of its speed. If the stopping distance is 112 m at 64 km/h, find the stopping distance at 56 km/h.   **(9-9)**

2. The price of a diamond varies directly as the square of its mass. If a 1.4 carat diamond costs $1764, find the cost of a similar stone with a mass of 1.7 carats.

3. The height of a cone of given volume is inversely proportional to the square of the radius of the base. If a cone that is 4 units high has a base with radius 3 units, find the height of a cone of equal volume with a base of radius 6 units.

4. The time needed to fill a tank varies inversely as the square of the radius of the hose. If a hose of radius 3.5 cm takes 8 min to fill a tank, how long will it take using a hose of radius 2 cm?

**5.** The force between two magnets varies inversely as the square of the distance between them. Two magnets are initially 4 cm apart. They are moved 8 cm farther apart. What is the effect on the force?

**6.** The distance an object falls varies directly as the square of the time it falls. If an object falls 175.5 m in 6 s, how long would it take to fall 487.5 m?

**Solve.**

**1.** The cost of operating an appliance varies jointly as the number of watts, hours of operation, and the cost per kilowatt-hour. It costs 45¢ to operate a 3000-watt air conditioner for 2 h at 7.5¢ per kilowatt-hour. Find the cost of operating a 1200-watt dishwasher for 40 min.    (9-10)

**2.** The number of persons needed to do a job varies directly as the amount of work to be done and inversely as the time in which the job is to be done. If 8 factory workers can produce 520 items in 4 days, how many workers will be needed to produce 585 items in 3 days?

**3.** If 2 painters can cover 320 ft² in 3 h, how long will it take 3 painters to cover 840 ft²? (See Exercise 2 above.)

**4.** The mass of a metal disc varies directly as the thickness and the square of the radius. A disc 2 cm thick with radius 5 cm has a mass of 840 g. Find the mass of a disc of the same metal that has radius 3 cm and is 0.5 cm thick.

## Chapter 10

**Solve.**

**1.** The sum of two consecutive integers is less than 83. Find the pair of such integers with the greatest sum.    (10-3)

**2.** A collection of quarters and dimes is worth more than $20. There are twice as many quarters as dimes. At least how many dimes are there?

**3.** Four members of a bowling team had scores of 240, 180, 220, and 200. Find the lowest score a fifth person must get to maintain an average for the group of at least 220.

**4.** The sum of three consecutive even integers is less than 80. Find the greatest such integers.

**5.** When road repairs begin, the current speed limit will be cut by 40 km/h. It will then take at least 3.6 h to cover the same distance that can be covered in 2 h now. What is the speed limit now?

**6.** The length of a rectangle is 1 cm greater than twice the width. If each dimension were increased by 5 cm, the area would be at least 150 cm² greater. Find the least possible dimensions.

# Chapter 11

**Solve.**

1. A square has an area of 184 cm². Find the length of a side to the near-est tenth of a centimeter.

(11-5)

2. A square has the same area as a rectangle that is 25 m by 18 m. Find the length of a side of the square to the nearest tenth of a meter.

3. A square has the same area as a triangle that has a base of 8 cm and a height of 5 cm. Find the length of a side of the square to the nearest tenth of a centimeter.

4. A circle inside a square just touches its sides. The area of the circle is 226.08 m². Find the length of a side of the square to the nearest tenth of a meter. Use 3.14 for $\pi$.

5. A circular pool covers an area of 34.54 m². Find the radius of the pool to the nearest tenth of a meter. Use 3.14 for $\pi$.

6. A circular flower bed is surrounded by a walk that is 1 m wide. If the area of the whole region is 21.98 m², find the radius of the flower bed to the nearest tenth of a meter. Use 3.14 for $\pi$.

**Solve. Approximate each square root to the nearest hundredth.**

1. A state park in the shape of a rectangle has dimensions 50 m by 20 m. A road through the park follows the diagonal of the rectangle. Find the length of the road.

(11-6)

2. A rope from the top of a mast of a sailboat is attached to a point 2 m from the mast. If the rope is 6 m long, how tall is the mast?

3. The length of one side of a right triangle is one centimeter less than twice the length of the second side. The hypotenuse is one centimeter more than twice the length of the second side. Find the length of each side.

4. The bottom of a 7 m ramp is 5 m from the base of a loading platform. Find the height of the platform.

5. The length of the longer side of a right triangle is 3 cm more than the length of the shorter side. The length of the hypotenuse is 3 cm more than the length of the longer side. Find the length of each side.

**Solve.**

1. One fourth the square root of a number is 7. Find the number.

(11-10)

2. When 8 is subtracted from 3 times a number, the square root of the result is 10. Find the number.

3. Four times the square root of a number is 28. Find the number.

4. When 5 is subtracted from the square root of twice a number, the re-sult is 9. Find the number.

**5.** The geometric mean of two positive numbers is the positive square root of their product. Find two consecutive even integers whose geometric mean is $8\sqrt{15}$.

**6.** Find two consecutive positive odd integers whose geometric mean is $15\sqrt{3}$.

## Chapter 12

**Solve.**

1. The sum of a number and its square is 30. Find the number.    (12-6)

2. The foundation of a house is 13 m by 7 m. If the builder increases each dimension by the same amount, the area of the foundation will increase to 135 m². Find the new dimensions.

3. The perimeter of a rectangular yard is 138 m and the area is 540 m². Find the dimensions of the yard.

4. The sum of the squares of two consecutive even integers is 340. Find the integers.

5. One work crew can finish a job in 18 h less than a second crew. Working together, they can finish the job in 40 h. How long would each crew take working alone?

6. One number is 2 more than 3 times another. The sum of their squares is 212. Find the numbers.

## Table of Squares of Integers from 1 to 100

| Number | Square | Number | Square | Number | Square | Number | Square |
|--------|--------|--------|--------|--------|--------|--------|--------|
| 1 | 1 | 26 | 676 | 51 | 2601 | 76 | 5776 |
| 2 | 4 | 27 | 729 | 52 | 2704 | 77 | 5929 |
| 3 | 9 | 28 | 784 | 53 | 2809 | 78 | 6084 |
| 4 | 16 | 29 | 841 | 54 | 2916 | 79 | 6241 |
| 5 | 25 | 30 | 900 | 55 | 3025 | 80 | 6400 |
| 6 | 36 | 31 | 961 | 56 | 3136 | 81 | 6561 |
| 7 | 49 | 32 | 1024 | 57 | 3249 | 82 | 6724 |
| 8 | 64 | 33 | 1089 | 58 | 3364 | 83 | 6889 |
| 9 | 81 | 34 | 1156 | 59 | 3481 | 84 | 7056 |
| 10 | 100 | 35 | 1225 | 60 | 3600 | 85 | 7225 |
| 11 | 121 | 36 | 1296 | 61 | 3721 | 86 | 7396 |
| 12 | 144 | 37 | 1369 | 62 | 3844 | 87 | 7569 |
| 13 | 169 | 38 | 1444 | 63 | 3969 | 88 | 7744 |
| 14 | 196 | 39 | 1521 | 64 | 4096 | 89 | 7921 |
| 15 | 225 | 40 | 1600 | 65 | 4225 | 90 | 8100 |
| 16 | 256 | 41 | 1681 | 66 | 4356 | 91 | 8281 |
| 17 | 289 | 42 | 1764 | 67 | 4489 | 92 | 8464 |
| 18 | 324 | 43 | 1849 | 68 | 4624 | 93 | 8649 |
| 19 | 361 | 44 | 1936 | 69 | 4761 | 94 | 8836 |
| 20 | 400 | 45 | 2025 | 70 | 4900 | 95 | 9025 |
| 21 | 441 | 46 | 2116 | 71 | 5041 | 96 | 9216 |
| 22 | 484 | 47 | 2209 | 72 | 5184 | 97 | 9409 |
| 23 | 529 | 48 | 2304 | 73 | 5329 | 98 | 9604 |
| 24 | 576 | 49 | 2401 | 74 | 5476 | 99 | 9801 |
| 25 | 625 | 50 | 2500 | 75 | 5625 | 100 | 10,000 |

# Table of Square Roots of Integers from 1 to 100

Exact square roots are shown in red. For the others, rational approximations are given correct to three decimal places.

| Number | Positive Square Root | Number | Positive Square Root | Number | Positive Square Root | Number | Positive Square Root |
|--------|--------|--------|--------|--------|--------|--------|--------|
| N | $\sqrt{N}$ | N | $\sqrt{N}$ | N | $\sqrt{N}$ | N | $\sqrt{N}$ |
| 1 | 1 | 26 | 5.099 | 51 | 7.141 | 76 | 8.718 |
| 2 | 1.414 | 27 | 5.196 | 52 | 7.211 | 77 | 8.775 |
| 3 | 1.732 | 28 | 5.292 | 53 | 7.280 | 78 | 8.832 |
| 4 | 2 | 29 | 5.385 | 54 | 7.348 | 79 | 8.888 |
| 5 | 2.236 | 30 | 5.477 | 55 | 7.416 | 80 | 8.944 |
| 6 | 2.449 | 31 | 5.568 | 56 | 7.483 | 81 | 9 |
| 7 | 2.646 | 32 | 5.657 | 57 | 7.550 | 82 | 9.055 |
| 8 | 2.828 | 33 | 5.745 | 58 | 7.616 | 83 | 9.110 |
| 9 | 3 | 34 | 5.831 | 59 | 7.681 | 84 | 9.165 |
| 10 | 3.162 | 35 | 5.916 | 60 | 7.746 | 85 | 9.220 |
| 11 | 3.317 | 36 | 6 | 61 | 7.810 | 86 | 9.274 |
| 12 | 3.464 | 37 | 6.083 | 62 | 7.874 | 87 | 9.327 |
| 13 | 3.606 | 38 | 6.164 | 63 | 7.937 | 88 | 9.381 |
| 14 | 3.742 | 39 | 6.245 | 64 | 8 | 89 | 9.434 |
| 15 | 3.873 | 40 | 6.325 | 65 | 8.062 | 90 | 9.487 |
| 16 | 4 | 41 | 6.403 | 66 | 8.124 | 91 | 9.539 |
| 17 | 4.123 | 42 | 6.481 | 67 | 8.185 | 92 | 9.592 |
| 18 | 4.243 | 43 | 6.557 | 68 | 8.246 | 93 | 9.644 |
| 19 | 4.359 | 44 | 6.633 | 69 | 8.307 | 94 | 9.695 |
| 20 | 4.472 | 45 | 6.708 | 70 | 8.367 | 95 | 9.747 |
| 21 | 4.583 | 46 | 6.782 | 71 | 8.426 | 96 | 9.798 |
| 22 | 4.690 | 47 | 6.856 | 72 | 8.485 | 97 | 9.849 |
| 23 | 4.796 | 48 | 6.928 | 73 | 8.544 | 98 | 9.899 |
| 24 | 4.899 | 49 | 7 | 74 | 8.602 | 99 | 9.950 |
| 25 | 5 | 50 | 7.071 | 75 | 8.660 | 100 | 10 |

## Table of Trigonometric Ratios

| Angle | Sine | Cosine | Tangent | Angle | Sine | Cosine | Tangent |
|---|---|---|---|---|---|---|---|
| 1° | .0175 | .9998 | .0175 | 46° | .7193 | .6947 | 1.0355 |
| 2° | .0349 | .9994 | .0349 | 47° | .7314 | .6820 | 1.0724 |
| 3° | .0523 | .9986 | .0524 | 48° | .7431 | .6691 | 1.1106 |
| 4° | .0698 | .9976 | .0699 | 49° | .7547 | .6561 | 1.1504 |
| 5° | .0872 | .9962 | .0875 | 50° | .7660 | .6428 | 1.1918 |
| 6° | .1045 | .9945 | .1051 | 51° | .7771 | .6293 | 1.2349 |
| 7° | .1219 | .9925 | .1228 | 52° | .7880 | .6157 | 1.2799 |
| 8° | .1392 | .9903 | .1405 | 53° | .7986 | .6018 | 1.3270 |
| 9° | .1564 | .9877 | .1584 | 54° | .8090 | .5878 | 1.3764 |
| 10° | .1736 | .9848 | .1763 | 55° | .8192 | .5736 | 1.4281 |
| 11° | .1908 | .9816 | .1944 | 56° | .8290 | .5592 | 1.4826 |
| 12° | .2079 | .9781 | .2126 | 57° | .8387 | .5446 | 1.5399 |
| 13° | .2250 | .9744 | .2309 | 58° | .8480 | .5299 | 1.6003 |
| 14° | .2419 | .9703 | .2493 | 59° | .8572 | .5150 | 1.6643 |
| 15° | .2588 | .9659 | .2679 | 60° | .8660 | .5000 | 1.7321 |
| 16° | .2756 | .9613 | .2867 | 61° | .8746 | .4848 | 1.8040 |
| 17° | .2924 | .9563 | .3057 | 62° | .8829 | .4695 | 1.8807 |
| 18° | .3090 | .9511 | .3249 | 63° | .8910 | .4540 | 1.9626 |
| 19° | .3256 | .9455 | .3443 | 64° | .8988 | .4384 | 2.0503 |
| 20° | .3420 | .9397 | .3640 | 65° | .9063 | .4226 | 2.1445 |
| 21° | .3584 | .9336 | .3839 | 66° | .9135 | .4067 | 2.2460 |
| 22° | .3746 | .9272 | .4040 | 67° | .9205 | .3907 | 2.3559 |
| 23° | .3907 | .9205 | .4245 | 68° | .9272 | .3746 | 2.4751 |
| 24° | .4067 | .9135 | .4452 | 69° | .9336 | .3584 | 2.6051 |
| 25° | .4226 | .9063 | .4663 | 70° | .9397 | .3420 | 2.7475 |
| 26° | .4384 | .8988 | .4877 | 71° | .9455 | .3256 | 2.9042 |
| 27° | .4540 | .8910 | .5095 | 72° | .9511 | .3090 | 3.0777 |
| 28° | .4695 | .8829 | .5317 | 73° | .9563 | .2924 | 3.2709 |
| 29° | .4848 | .8746 | .5543 | 74° | .9613 | .2756 | 3.4874 |
| 30° | .5000 | .8660 | .5774 | 75° | .9659 | .2588 | 3.7321 |
| 31° | .5150 | .8572 | .6009 | 76° | .9703 | .2419 | 4.0108 |
| 32° | .5299 | .8480 | .6249 | 77° | .9744 | .2250 | 4.3315 |
| 33° | .5446 | .8387 | .6494 | 78° | .9781 | .2079 | 4.7046 |
| 34° | .5592 | .8290 | .6745 | 79° | .9816 | .1908 | 5.1446 |
| 35° | .5736 | .8192 | .7002 | 80° | .9848 | .1736 | 5.6713 |
| 36° | .5878 | .8090 | .7265 | 81° | .9877 | .1564 | 6.3138 |
| 37° | .6018 | .7986 | .7536 | 82° | .9903 | .1392 | 7.1154 |
| 38° | .6157 | .7880 | .7813 | 83° | .9925 | .1219 | 8.1443 |
| 39° | .6293 | .7771 | .8098 | 84° | .9945 | .1045 | 9.5144 |
| 40° | .6428 | .7660 | .8391 | 85° | .9962 | .0872 | 11.4301 |
| 41° | .6561 | .7547 | .8693 | 86° | .9976 | .0698 | 14.3007 |
| 42° | .6691 | .7431 | .9004 | 87° | .9986 | .0523 | 19.0811 |
| 43° | .6820 | .7314 | .9325 | 88° | .9994 | .0349 | 28.6363 |
| 44° | .6947 | .7193 | .9657 | 89° | .9998 | .0175 | 57.2900 |
| 45° | .7071 | .7071 | 1.0000 | | | | |

# Appendix: *Divide-and-Average Method*

**Objective**   To use the divide-and-average method.

If you do not have access to a calculator or a square-root table, you can still find an approximation to an irrational square root by using the divide-and-average method. This method is based upon the following.

If you divide a positive number by a positive number that is smaller than the positive square root of that number, the quotient will be larger than the square root.

**Example**   Approximate $\sqrt{51}$ to the nearest ten-thousandth.

**Solution**
1. Select the integer whose square is nearest 51 as your first approximation, $a$. Since $7^2 = 49$, let $a = 7$.

2. Divide 51 by $a$, carrying out the division to two more digits than are in the divisor:   $51 \div 7 \approx 7.28$

3. Find the average of $a$ and $\frac{51}{a}$:   $\frac{1}{2}(7 + 7.28) \approx 7.14$

4. Use the average as the new value for $a$. Continue repeating steps 2 and 3 as often as necessary.

   (Step 2)                    (Step 3)

   $51 \div 7.14 \approx 7.1428 \rightarrow \frac{1}{2}(7.14 + 7.1428) \approx 7.1414$

   $51 \div 7.1414 \approx 7.141456$

5. The approximation is accurate to at least as many digits as match in $a$ and $51 \div a$.

   $\therefore \ \sqrt{51} \approx 7.1414$.   ***Answer***

## *Written Exercises*

**Approximate each square root to the nearest hundredth.**

1. $\sqrt{29}$        2. $\sqrt{13}$        3. $-\sqrt{47}$        4. $-\sqrt{83}$        5. $\sqrt{350}$

6. $\sqrt{223}$        7. $-\sqrt{167}$        8. $-\sqrt{42.3}$        9. $\sqrt{23.8}$        10. $\sqrt{18.6}$

**Approximate each square root to the nearest ten thousandth.**

11. $\sqrt{15}$        12. $-\sqrt{23}$        13. $-\sqrt{39}$        14. $\sqrt{45}$        15. $-\sqrt{273}$

16. $\sqrt{190}$        17. $\sqrt{408}$        18. $\sqrt{11.9}$        19. $-\sqrt{40.7}$        20. $\sqrt{31.9}$

# Appendix: Summary of BASIC

BASIC is one of the so-called "higher-level" languages in which programs may be written for computers. It is translated by a *compiler* or *interpreter* inside the computer into a "machine language," which tells the computer what to do.

BASIC is essentially linear in character. Each *statement* is numbered in succession, often 10, 20, 30, . ... (page 9). The computer follows through the statements in numerical order and carries out the instruction in each statement as it comes to it. Some versions of BASIC require an

### END statement

for each program (page 9).

BASIC also includes several *commands,* which are not parts of programs and so do not have line numbers.

### The command RUN

This command tells the computer to RUN (or execute) the program (page 9).

### The command LIST

This command tells the computer to list the statements in numerical order. This is especially useful after changes have been made in a program and you want to see a clean copy of it (page 79).

A program must include both *input* and *output*. In the two-line program on page 9, the input and output are both in one statement, line 10. The input is the arithmetical expression and the output is its value, given by the PRINT statement. See later in this section for more information about PRINT statements.

The symbols for operations (pages 9 and 226) are:

+ for addition      * for multiplication
− for subtraction      / for division
( ) for grouping      ↑ or $^\wedge$ for raising to a power

The same order-of-operations rule is followed as in algebra. (See page 138.)

Other symbols used in BASIC are:

= for equals      < for less than
> for greater than      < > for not equal
< = for less than or equal      > = for greater than or equal

Very large and very small numbers are stated in E-notation, which is a version of scientific notation. (See page 322.)

BASIC handles variables much as you do in algebra. A variable may be denoted by a letter, a letter followed by a digit, or possibly other combinations of symbols as allowed by the various versions of BASIC. Values are given to variables, and operations are performed on them.

The *input* for a program often involves giving values to variables. There are several ways of doing this.

## (1) The INPUT statement

```
INPUT A
```

This statement will cause the computer to print a question mark and wait for the user to type in a value (page 17).

```
INPUT A, B
```

This statement will print only one question mark, but the computer will expect two values to be typed in, separated by a comma (page 107).

## (2) The LET statement

```
LET S = 0
```

This statement will give the value 0 to the variable *S* (page 58).

```
LET S = A + B
```

This statement will find the sum of the values of *A* and *B* and give this value to *S*.

```
LET S = S + N
```

This statement will take the value of *S*, add to it the value of *N*, and give *S* this new value (page 58).

Notice that the LET statement is not an equation. It should be read from right to left.

## (3) READ and DATA statements

A DATA statement contains a list of values that are to be given to one or more variables by a READ statement.

```
DATA 2, 5, 25, -10
READ N
```

This statement will read one value at a time from the DATA statement.

```
READ M, N
```

This statement will read two values in succession from the list of DATA (page 141).

The list of DATA may be broken up into several DATA statements. The DATA will be read as if there were one continuous list (page 141). DATA statements may be put anywhere in a program. They are usually put near the beginning or near the end for convenience.

If the list of DATA is to be read more than once, a

**RESTORE statement**

will be needed to direct the computer to start again at the beginning of the list (page 170).

*Output* is handled by

## PRINT statements.

`PRINT A`

This statement will print the value of *A*.

`PRINT "A"`

This statement will print the letter A. Any expression in quotation marks will be printed exactly as it appears—including spaces. (See page 17.)

`PRINT "A = ";A`

The *semicolon* will cause the value of *A* to be printed immediately following the expression in quotation marks. (See pages 17 and 58.)

`PRINT A, B`

The *comma* will cause the values of *A* and *B* to be printed spaced apart. (See page 117.)

`PRINT`

(a) This statement will cancel the effect of a semicolon or a comma at the end of the preceding line (page 186).
(b) By itself, the statement will print a blank line (page 17).

Sometimes it is helpful to separate blocks of a program with

## REM statements.

REM means *remark*. A REM statement may contain any comment that you wish to use to clarify the program (page 170). It will appear in the LISTing but have no effect on the program itself. A long comment may run over several lines (page 171), but each line must begin with REM. Any letters or symbols may follow the REM.

Sometimes in the construction of a program, it is necessary to change the line-by-line flow of the program. This is done by using

## Transfer statements.

`GOTO 00`

This is an *unconditional transfer* statement. It will transfer the execution to line 00. (See page 58.)

`IF (expression or relation) THEN 00`

This is a *conditional transfer* statement. If the expression or relation is true, (THEN) the execution will be transferred to line 00. Otherwise (ELSE), the execution will go ahead to the following line. (See pages 58 and 107.)

These transfers are often used together to form a *branched* program. (See page 107.)

An especially useful construction is a *loop;* that is, passing through the same block of steps several times. One form of a loop simply uses a

GOTO statement to return the execution to the beginning of the block of statements (page 58). Some provision must be made for ending such a loop. One way is to provide an ending number, such as the $-1$ on page 58. Sometimes such a loop requires the use of a *counter:*

```
LET C = 0
.   .   .   .   .   .
LET C = C + 1
```

This counter can be used to record the number of passes through the loop. (See page 79.)

When the number of passes through a loop is known ahead of time, a

**FOR-NEXT loop**

may be used. For a simple counter, use

```
FOR I = 1 to N
.  .  .  .  .  .  .
NEXT I
```

which will go through a block of statements $N$ times. (See page 117.)

If a sequence of values is to be given to a variable $X$, this form may be used:

```
FOR X = M TO N STEP S
.  .  .  .  .  .  .  .  .
NEXT X
```

This construction will give values to $X$ as follows (page 247):

$$M, M + S, M + 2 * S, \text{ and so on, up to } N.$$

IF $M < N$, then $S > 0$, but if $M < N$, then $S < 0$ (page 491). If $S = 1$, then the STEP portion may be omitted.

When one loop is contained within another loop, the loops are said to be *nested.* (See page 186.)

When a block of statements is to be used in several places in a program, it is often convenient to set off that block of statements as a *subroutine.* This is done by using

**GOSUB . . . RETURN statements.**

```
GOSUB 00
```

This statement will transfer the execution to line 00 (page 217). The block of statements forming the subroutine must end with:

```
RETURN
```

This statement will transfer the execution back to the line following GOSUB 00. (See page 217.)

BASIC has several special functions. Three of these are:

ABS(X)                                  SQR(X)

This function gives $|X|$. (See page 217.)    This function gives $\sqrt{X}$. (See page 526.)

`INT(X)`

This function gives the greatest integer less than or equal to *X* (page 186).

The following function is used in PRINT statements to adjust the spacing (page 171).

`PRINT TAB(OO);"A"`

This statement will skip over 00 spaces from the left margin before printing the letter A.

This TAB function can also be used to print out a table with computed spacing as shown in the multiplication table below. (Note also the uses of FOR-NEXT loops and REM statements.)

```
 5   REM---PRINTS COLUMN HEADINGS
 10  FOR I=0 TO 9
 20   PRINT TAB(I*3+3);I;
 30  NEXT I
 40  PRINT
 45  REM---PRINTS HORIZONTAL LINE
 50  FOR I=1 TO 34
 60   PRINT "-";
 70  NEXT I
 80  PRINT
 85  REM---PRINTS ROW HEADINGS
 86  REM---AND TABLE ENTRIES
 90  FOR I=0 TO 9
 100  PRINT I;"!";
 110  FOR J=0 TO 9
 120   PRINT TAB(J*3+3);I*J;
 130  NEXT J
 140  PRINT
 150  NEXT I
 160 END
 RUN
```

```
      0  1  2  3  4  5  6  7  8  9
------------------------------------
0!  0  0  0  0  0  0  0  0  0  0
1!  0  1  2  3  4  5  6  7  8  9
2!  0  2  4  6  8  10 12 14 16 18
3!  0  3  6  9  12 15 18 21 24 27
4!  0  4  8  12 16 20 24 28 32 36
5!  0  5  10 15 20 25 30 35 40 45
6!  0  6  12 18 24 30 36 42 48 54
7!  0  7  14 21 28 35 42 49 56 63
8!  0  8  16 24 32 40 48 56 64 72
9!  0  9  18 27 36 45 54 63 72 81
```

PRINT TAB statements may also be used in plotting graphs of functions. In doing this, the $x$-values are plotted vertically and the function values ($y$-values) are plotted horizontally. The following simple program will plot graphs on a 21 by 21 "grid" with the $x$-axis running vertically at TAB(13)—see lines 30, 140, and 200. The $y$-axis is suggested in lines 40 and 160. Lines 90 and 120 keep the graph within the chosen grid.

Copy and RUN this program. Then, by changing line 50, RUN it also for $y = x^2 - 9$, $y = x^3$, and $y = x^2 - 2x$.

```
10  PRINT "GRAPH OF A FUNCTION"
20  FOR X=-10 TO 10
30  IF X <> 0 THEN 50
40  PRINT "---";
50  LET Y=X
60  IF Y<0 THEN 120
70  IF Y=0 THEN 100
80  PRINT TAB(13);"!";
90  IF Y>10 THEN 150
100  PRINT TAB(Y+13);"*";
110  GOTO 150
120  IF Y<-10 THEN 140
130  PRINT TAB(Y+13);"*";
140  PRINT TAB(13);"!";
150  IF X <> 0 THEN 180
160  PRINT TAB(24);"---Y"
170  GOTO 190
180  PRINT
190  NEXT X
200  PRINT TAB(13);"X"
210  END
```

*Subscripted variables* are used to represent *lists,* or *arrays,* of values. For example,

$$A(1), A(2), A(3)$$

are often more convenient to use than $A$, $B$, $C$. (See page 171.)

If more than 10 (or in some cases 11) values are to be used, then a *dimension statement* is needed. For example,

DIM A(15)

will allow for values $A(1), A(2), \ldots , A(15)$ or, in some cases, $A(0), A(1), \ldots , A(15)$.

A *string* is a set of characters (including spaces) generally enclosed in quotation marks. A *string variable* is a variable having strings as values. Its name must end with $. 

As with numeric variables, values may be given to string variables by INPUT (page 107), LET, or READ . . . DATA statements.

Here is a portion of a program that shows how strings and string variables may be used in chatty kinds of programs.

```
10   REM---CHATTY PROGRAM
20   PRINT "WHAT IS YOUR NAME";
30   INPUT N$
40   PRINT "HELLO ";N$;"!"
50   PRINT "I AM GLAD TO MEET YOU."
60   PRINT "DO YOU ENJOY WORKING WITH ";
70   PRINT "ME (YES/NO)";
80   INPUT A$
90   IF A$="YES" THEN 120
100  PRINT "I AM VERY SORRY, ";N$;"."
110  GOTO 130
120  PRINT "I AM VERY GLAD, ";N$;"."
130  END
```

# Preparing for College Entrance Exams

If you plan to attend college, you will most likely be required to take college entrance examinations. Some of these exams attempt to measure the extent to which your verbal and mathematical reasoning skills have been developed. Others test your knowledge of specific subject areas. Usually, the best preparation for college entrance examinations is to follow a strong academic program in school, to study, and to read as extensively as possible.

The following test-taking strategies may prove useful:

- Familiarize yourself with the test you will be taking well in advance of the test date. Sample tests, with accompanying explanatory material, are available for many standardized tests. By working through this sample material, you become comfortable with the types of questions and directions that will appear on the test and you develop a feeling for the pace at which you must work in order to complete the test.

- Find out how the test is scored so that you know whether it is advantageous to guess.

- Skim sections of the test before starting to answer the questions, to get an overview of the questions. You may wish to answer the easiest questions first. In any case, do not waste time on questions you do not understand; go on to those that you do.

- Mark your answer sheet carefully, checking the numbering on the answer sheet about every five questions to avoid errors caused by misplaced answer markings.

- Write in the test booklet if it is helpful; for example, cross out incorrect alternatives and do mathematical calculations.

- Work carefully, but do not take time to double-check your answers unless you finish before the deadline and have extra time.

- Arrive at the test center early and come well prepared with any necessary supplies such as sharpened pencils and a watch.

College entrance examinations that test general reasoning abilities, such as the Scholastic Aptitude Test, usually include questions dealing with basic algebraic concepts and skills. The College Board Achievement Tests in mathematics (Level I and Level II) include many questions on algebra. The following first-year algebra topics often appear on these exams. For each of the topics listed on pages 661–663, a page reference to the place in your textbook where this topic is discussed has been provided. As you prepare for college entrance exams, you may wish to review the topics on these pages.

## Types of Numbers (pages 30–31, 72, 183)

| | |
|---|---|
| Positive integers | $\{1, 2, 3, 4, \ldots\}$ |
| Negative integers | $\{-1, -2, -3, -4, \ldots\}$ |
| Integers | $\{\ldots, -4, -3, -2, -1, 0, 1, 2, 3, 4, \ldots\}$ |
| Odd numbers | $\{1, 3, 5, 7, 9, \ldots\}$ |
| Even numbers | $\{0, 2, 4, 6, 8, \ldots\}$ |
| Consecutive integers | $\{n, n + 1, n + 2, \ldots\}$ ($n$ = an integer) |
| Consecutive even integers | $\{n, n + 2, n + 4, \ldots\}$ ($n$ = even integer) |
| Consecutive odd integers | $\{n, n + 2, n + 4, \ldots\}$ ($n$ = odd integer) |
| Prime numbers | $\{2, 3, 5, 7, 11, 13, \ldots\}$ |

## Properties and Axioms (pages 45–81)

Closure Axioms (p. 45)
Commutative Axioms (p. 45)
Associative Axioms (p. 46)
Reflexive Property (p. 47)
Symmetric Property (p. 47)
Transitive Property (p. 47)
Identity Axioms (pp. 50, 68)
Axiom of Opposites (p. 50)
Property of the Opposite of a Sum (p. 53)
Distributive Axiom (p. 64)
Multiplicative Property of Zero (p. 68)
Multiplicative Property of $-1$ (p. 68)
Property of Opposites in Products (p. 69)
Axiom of Reciprocals (p. 76)
Property of the Reciprocal of a Product (p. 77)

## Rules for Operations on Positive and Negative Numbers (pages 54, 69)

If $a > 0$, $b > 0$, then $a + b = |a| + |b|$.
If $a < 0$, $b < 0$, then $a + b = -(|a| + |b|)$.
If $a > 0$, $b < 0$, and $|a| > |b|$, then $a + b = |a| - |b|$.
If $a > 0$, $b < 0$, and $|a| < |b|$, then $a + b = -(|b| - |a|)$.
If $a > 0$, $b < 0$, then $ab < 0$.
If $a > 0$, $b > 0$, then $ab > 0$.

## Percents (pages 295–296, 300–301)

Converting decimals and fractions to percents
Percents greater than 100
Percents less than 1
Percent problems

## Solving Equations (pages 94, 99, 104, 223–224, 547, 553–554)

Transformation by substitution (p. 94)
Transformation by addition (p. 94)
Transformation by subtraction (p. 94)
Transformation by multiplication (p. 99)
Transformation by division (p. 99)
Factoring (pp. 223–224)
$x^2 = k$ (p. 547)
Quadratic formula (p. 553)
Discriminant (p. 558)

## Graphing (pages 30–37, 339–341, 412–415, 449–455, 468–469, 480–482, 484)

Points on a number line
Inequalities on a number line
Points and lines in a number plane
Inequalities in a number plane
Quadratic functions

## Factoring (pages 183–221)

Integers
$a^2 - b^2$
$ax^2 + bx$
$a^2 + 2ab + b^2$
$a^2 - 2ab + b^2$
$ax^2 + bx + c$

## Variation (pages 418–435)

Direct variation
Inverse variation
Direct variation involving powers
Inverse variation involving powers
Joint variation
Combined variation

## Simultaneous Equations (pages 346–351, 358–363)

The graphic method
The substitution method
The addition-or-subtraction method
Multiplication with the addition-or-subtraction method

## Algebraic Fractions (pages 239–268)

Simplification
Addition
Multiplication
Division

## Word Problems (pages 26, 72–73, 118–124, 146–147, 163–174, 194–195, 230–231, 278–286, 300–316, 378–380)

Age
Area
Consecutive integers
Cost and value
Digit
Fraction
Investment
Mixture
Percent
Proportion
Rate-of-work
Ratio
Uniform motion
Without solutions

# Glossary

**abscissa** (p. 339): The first coordinate in an ordered pair of numbers that is associated with a point in the coordinate plane. Also called the *x-coordinate*.

**absolute value** (p. 35): The positive number of any pair of opposite nonzero real numbers. The absolute value of a number $a$ is denoted by $|a|$. The absolute value of 0 is 0.

**acute angle** (p. 577): An angle having a measure between 0 and 90.

**addition axiom of order** (p. 454): For all real numbers $a$, $b$, and $c$:
1. If $a < b$, then $a + c < b + c$;
2. If $a > b$, then $a + c > b + c$.

**addition property of equality** (p. 93): If $a$, $b$, and $c$ are any real numbers and $a = b$, then $a + c = b + c$ and $c + a = c + b$.

**additive inverse** (p. 50): The additive inverse of the real number $a$ is the real number $-a$ such that $a + (-a) = 0$ and $(-a) + a = 0$. Also called *opposite of a*.

**addition-or-subtraction method** (p. 358): A method for solving a system of equations whereby the equations are added or subtracted to obtain a new equation with just one variable. Sometimes one or both equations must be multiplied by a number.

**angle** (p. 576): A figure formed by two different rays with the same endpoint. The rays are the *sides* of the angle and the common endpoint is called the *vertex*.

**angles of a triangle** (p. 581): *See under* triangle.

**area:** The area of a region is the number of unit squares it contains.

**arrow notation** (p. 404): A notation used in defining a function as $f : x \longrightarrow 7x + 1$.

**associative axioms** (p. 46): For all real numbers $a$, $b$, $c$:
Addition: $(a + b) + c = a + (b + c)$
Multiplication: $(ab)c = a(bc)$

**average** (p. 82): The average of $n$ numbers is the sum of the numbers divided by $n$.

**axes** (p. 340): *See under* coordinate axes.

**axioms** (p. 45): Statements that are assumed to be true. Also called *postulates*.

**axiom of comparison** (p. 453): For all real numbers $a$ and $b$, one and only one of the following statements is true: $a < b$, $a = b$, $b < a$.

**axiom of opposites** (p. 50): For every real number $a$, there is a unique real number $-a$ such that $a + (-a) = 0$ and $(-a) + a = 0$.

**axiom of reciprocals** (p. 76): For every nonzero real number $a$, there is a real number $\dfrac{1}{a}$ such that
$$a \cdot \frac{1}{a} = 1 \text{ and } \frac{1}{a} \cdot a = 1.$$

**axioms of closure** (p. 45): For all real numbers $a$ and $b$:
Addition: $a + b$ is a unique real number.
Multiplication: $ab$ is a unique real number.

**axis of symmetry (of a parabola)** (p. 413): If the graph of a parabola is folded so that its two halves coincide, the line on which the fold occurs is the axis of symmetry. For $y = ax^2 + bx + c$ $(a \neq 0)$, this axis is the line $x = -\dfrac{b}{2a}$.

**base (of a power)** (p. 137): One of the equal factors. In $b^n$, $b$ is the base.

**base angles of an isosceles triangle** (p. 581): *See under* isosceles triangle.

**base of an isosceles triangle** (p. 581): *See under* isosceles triangle.

**BASIC** (p. 9): A programming language.

**between** (p. 449): $b$ is between $a$ and $c$ if $a < b < c$ or $c > b > a$.

**binomial** (p. 143): A polynomial of two terms.

**boundary line** (p. 480): A line which separates the plane into two half-planes.

**circumference:** The perimeter of a circle.

**closed half-plane** (p. 480): The union of an open half-plane and its boundary.

**coefficient** (p. 143): In a monomial such as $-8x^2y$, the number $-8$ is called the coefficient, or numerical coefficient.

**combined variation** (p. 434): A function defined by an equation of the form $z = \dfrac{kx}{y}$, $k$ a nonzero constant.

**common factor** (p. 184): A factor of two or more integers.

**commutative axioms** (p. 45): For all real numbers $a$ and $b$:
Addition: $a + b = b + a$
Multiplication: $ab = ba$

**complementary angles** (p. 579): Two angles with 90 as the sum of their measures. Each is the *complement* of the other.

**completing the square** (p. 551): A method for transforming a quadratic equation into one with the form perfect square $= k$ ($k \geq 0$).

**complex fraction** (p. 267): A fraction whose numerator or denominator contains one or more fractions.

**conjugates** (p. 531): If $b$ and $d$ are both nonnegative, the binomials $a\sqrt{b} + c\sqrt{d}$ and $a\sqrt{b} - c\sqrt{d}$ are conjugates of one another.

**conjunction** (p. 468): A sentence formed by joining two open sentences by the word *and*.

**consecutive even integers** (p. 72): Obtained by counting by twos from any even integer.

**consecutive integers** (p. 72): Obtained by counting by ones from any given integer.

**consecutive odd integers** (p. 72): Obtained by counting by twos from any odd integer.

**constant monomial** (p. 143): A numerical term with no variable expression.

**constant of variation** (p. 418): In a direct variation expressed by $y = kx$, $k$ is the constant of variation. Also called *constant of proportionality*.

**converse** (p. 223): The converse of a statement is obtained by interchanging the "if" and "then" parts.

**coordinate** (p. 30): The number paired with a point on the number line.

**coordinate axes** (p. 340): The $x$- and $y$-axes in the number plane.

**coordinate plane** (p. 340): A plane in which a coordinate system has been set up.

**coordinate system** (pp. 339–340): A system of graphing ordered pairs of numbers in relation to two axes (horizontal and vertical) that intersect at right angles at their zero point (the origin).

**coordinates of a point** (p. 339): The abscissa and ordinate of the point, written as an ordered pair of numbers.

**corresponding angles** (p. 584): *See under* similar triangles.

**corresponding sides** (p. 584): *See under* similar triangles.

**cosine** (p. 587): The cosine of $\angle A$ of a right triangle $=$
$$\frac{\text{length of leg adjacent to } \angle A}{\text{length of hypotenuse}}.$$

**cubic equation** (p. 223): A polynomial equation of degree three.

**degree (measure of an angle)** (p. 577): $\frac{1}{180}$ of the rotation of a ray from one direction to its opposite.

**degree of a monomial** (p. 143): The number of times that a variable occurs as a factor in a monomial is the degree of the monomial in that variable. The sum of the degrees in each of the variables is the degree of the monomial. A nonzero constant has degree 0. 0 has no degree.

**degree of a polynomial** (p. 144): The greatest of the degrees of its terms after it has been simplified.

**denominator:** In the fraction $\frac{a}{b}$, $b$ is the denominator.

**density property** (p. 500): Between every pair of different rational numbers there is another rational number.

**difference** (p. 59): For any two real numbers $a$ and $b$, the difference $a - b$ is the number whose sum with $b$ is $a$.

**directly proportional** (p. 419): $y$ is directly proportional to $x$ if $(x_1, y_1)$ and $(x_2, y_2)$ are ordered pairs of a function, neither of which is $(0, 0)$, and this statement is true: $\frac{y_1}{x_1} = \frac{y_2}{x_2}$.

**direct variation** (p. 418): A function defined by an equation of the form $y = kx$, where $k$ is a nonzero constant.

**discriminant** (p. 558): The value of $b^2 - 4ac$ is called the discriminant of the quadratic equation $ax^2 + bx + c = 0$.

**disjoint sets** (p. 465): Sets with no members in common.

**disjunction** (p. 468): A sentence formed by joining two open sentences with the word *or*.

**distance formula** (p. 526): For any points $P_1(x_1, y_1)$ and $P_2(x_2, y_2)$:
$P_1P_2 = \sqrt{(x_2 - x_1)^2 + (y_2 - y_1)^2}.$

**distributive axiom of multiplication with respect to addition** (p. 64): For all real numbers $a$, $b$, and $c$:
$$a(b + c) = ab + ac$$
$$(b + c)a = ba + ca.$$

**divide-and-average method** (p. 652): A way to find closer and closer approximations to the square root of a number that is not a perfect square by continuing to average pairs of factors.

**divisible** (p. 191): One polynomial is said to be evenly divisible, or simply divisible, by another polynomial if the quotient is also a polynomial.

**domain of a function** (p. 404): One of the sets comprising a function, as the values of $x$ in $y = 7x + 1$.

**domain of a variable** (p. 10): The given set of numbers the variable may represent.

**double root** (p. 224): *See under* multiple root.

**empty set** (p. 112): The set with no members. Also called the *null set*.

**equal expressions** (p. 2): Expressions that name the same number.

**equation** (p. 10): An equation is formed by placing an equals sign between two numerical or variable expressions.

**equilateral triangle** (p. 581): A triangle with all sides of equal length.

**equivalent equations** (p. 94): Equations having the same solution set over a given domain.

**equivalent expressions** (p. 65): Expressions that represent the same number for all values of the variable that they contain.

**equivalent inequalities** (p. 454): Inequalities having the same solution set over a given domain.

**equivalent systems** (p. 351): Systems of equations having the same solution set.

**evaluating a variable expression** (p. 2): Replacing each variable in the expression by a given value and simplifying the result.

**even integers** (p. 72): The integers that are the products of 2 and any integer.

**event** (p. 596): Any possible subset of the sample space resulting from an experiment.

**expanded notation** (p. 319): Used to express a number as the sum of the digits associated with integral powers of 10.

**exponent** (p. 137): In a power, the number of times the base occurs as a factor.

**exponential form** (p. 138): The expression "$x^3$" is the exponential form of the third power of $x$.

**expressing in simplest form** (p. 239): Dividing the numerator and the denominator of a fraction by their greatest common factor.

**extremes** (p. 282): In the proportion $\frac{a}{b} = \frac{c}{d}$, $a$ and $d$ are the extremes.

**factor** (p. 46): When two or more numbers are multiplied, each of the numbers is a factor of the product.

**factored form** (p. 138): The expression "$x \cdot x \cdot x$" is the factored form of the third power of $x$, that is, $x^3$.

**factoring** (pp. 183, 191): Finding the factors of a number or an expression over a specified factor set.

**factor set** (p. 183): The name given to the set over which a number is factored.

**factored completely** (p. 221): Term used to describe a polynomial when it is expressed as the product of prime polynomials and a monomial.

**formula** (p. 13): An equation that states a rule about quantities such as measurements.

**fraction** (p. 239): An expression in the form $\frac{a}{b}$, $b \neq 0$.

**fractional equation** (p. 291): An equation that has a variable in the denominator of one or more terms.

**frequency distribution** (p. 602): A table summarizing data.

**function** (p. 404): A function consists of two sets, the *domain* and the *range,* and a *rule* that assigns to each member of the domain exactly one member of the range. Each member of the range must be assigned to at least one member of the domain.

**graph of an equation** (p. 340): Consists of all the points associated with the solutions of the equation.

**graph of a function** (p. 412): The graphs in the coordinate plane of all the ordered pairs that form the function.

**graph of a number** (p. 30): The point on the number line paired with a number.

**graph of an ordered pair of numbers** (p. 339): The point in the plane paired with an ordered pair of real numbers.

**graphic method** (p. 346): The method of solving a system of equations by using graphs.

**greatest common factor of integers** (p. 184): The greatest integer that is a factor of two or more integers.

**greatest common factor of two or more monomials** (p. 188): The common factor that has the greatest coefficient and the greatest degree in each variable.

**greatest monomial factor of a polynomial**
(p. 191): The greatest common monomial factor of its terms.

**grouping symbol** (p. 5): A device used to enclose an expression. Parentheses, brackets, and fraction bars are grouping symbols.

**half-plane** (p. 480): *See under* closed half-plane and open half-plane.

**histogram** (p. 602): A bar graph used to summarize a large set of data.

**horizontal axis** (p. 339): The horizontal number line in the number plane. Also called the *x-axis*.

**hyperbola** (p. 424): The graph of $xy = k$ for every nonzero value of $k$.

**hypotenuse** (p. 520): The side of a right triangle opposite the right angle.

**identity** (p. 113): An equation that is true for every value of the variable(s).

**identity axioms** (pp. 50, 68): For any real number $a$:
Addition: $a + 0 = 0 + a = a$
Multiplication: $a \cdot 1 = 1 \cdot a = a$.

**identity elements** (pp. 50, 68): 0 is the identity element for addition. 1 is the identity element for multiplication.

**imaginary numbers** (p. 555): Numbers involving the imaginary unit, $i$, which is defined to be $\sqrt{-1}$.

**inequality** (p. 450): A statement formed by placing an inequality symbol between two numerical or variable expressions.

**inequality symbols** (p. 37): Symbols used to show the order of pairs of real numbers. The symbol $\neq$ (p. 2) means "is not equal to."

**integers** (p. 30): The numbers in the set $\{\ldots, -3, -2, -1, 0, 1, 2, 3, \ldots\}$.

**intersection of sets** (p. 465): For any two sets $A$ and $B$, the set consisting of all members belonging to both $A$ and $B$ is the intersection of $A$ and $B$.

**inverse operations** (p. 103): Operations that "undo" each other; for example, addition and subtraction.

**inverse variation** (p. 424): A function defined by an equation of the form $xy = k$, where $k$ is a nonzero constant.

**inverse variation as the square** (p. 430): A function defined by an equation of the form $x^2y = k$, where $k$ is a nonzero constant.

**irrational numbers** (p. 515): Real numbers that cannot be expressed in the form $\frac{a}{b}$, where $a$ and $b$ are integers.

**irreducible polynomial** (p. 209): A polynomial that cannot be rewritten as a product of polynomials of lower degree.

**isosceles triangle** (p. 581): A triangle having two sides equal in length. The third side is called the *base* and the adjoining angles are the *base angles*.

**joint variation** (p. 434): A function defined by the equation $z = kxy$, where $k$ is a nonzero constant.

**least common denominator (LCD)** (p. 251): The least positive common multiple of the denominators of the given fractions.

**leg of a right triangle** (p. 581): One of the two sides that form the right angle.

**linear direct variation** (p. 418): *See under* direct variation.

**linear equation in one variable** (p. 223): A polynomial equation of degree one.

**linear equation in two variables** (p. 340): Any equation equivalent to one of the form $ax + by = c$, where $a$, $b$, and $c$ are real numbers with $a$ and $b$ not both zero.

**linear function** (p. 412): A function $f$ given by $f(x) = mx + b$.

**linear programming** (p. 487): A branch of mathematics concerned with maximizing or minimizing certain quantities.

**linear term** (p. 196): A term of degree one in the variable.

**line segment** (p. 576): A part of a line that consists of two points and all points between them.

**maximum point of a quadratic function** (p. 413): The point whose $y$-coordinate is the greatest value the function can have.

**mean** (p. 602): A statistic indicating the center of a distribution.

**means** (p. 282): In the proportion $\frac{a}{b} = \frac{c}{d}$, $b$ and $c$ are the means.

**mean proportional** (p. 285): When the means of a proportion are the same, the mean is called the mean proportional between the two extremes.

**median** (p. 603): The middle number of a frequency distribution when data are arranged in order.

**member of a set** (p. 10): Any object in the set.

**minimum point of a quadratic function** (p. 413): A point whose $y$-coordinate is the least value the function can have.

**mixed expression** (p. 260): A sum or difference of a polynomial and a fraction.

**mixed numeral** (p. 260): A numeral, like $3\frac{2}{5}$, that denotes the sum of an integer and a fraction.

**mode** (p. 603): The most frequently occurring number in a frequency distribution.

**monomial** (p. 143): An expression that is either a numeral, a variable, or a product of a numeral and one or more variables.

**multiple** (p. 75): The product of any real number and an integer is called a multiple of the real number.

**multiple root** (p. 224): A solution to an equation that occurs more than once.

**multiplication axiom of order** (p. 454): For all real numbers $a$, $b$, and $c$:
1. If $a < b$ and $c > 0$, then $ac < bc$; if $a > b$ and $c > 0$, then $ac > bc$.
2. If $a < b$ and $c < 0$, then $ac > bc$; if $a > b$ and $c < 0$, then $ac < bc$.

**multiplication property of equality** (p. 99): If $a = b$, then $ac = bc$ and $ca = cb$.

**multiplicative inverse** (p. 76): For a non-zero real number $b$, the real number $\frac{1}{b}$, for which $b \cdot \frac{1}{b} = 1$ and $\frac{1}{b} \cdot b = 1$. Also called *reciprocal*.

**multiplicative property of −1** (p. 68): For all real numbers $a$, $a(-1) = -a$ and $(-1)a = -a$.

**multiplicative property of zero** (p. 68): For all real numbers $a$, $a \cdot 0 = 0$ and $0 \cdot a = 0$.

**negative number** (p. 30): A number paired with a point on the negative side of a number line.

**nonterminating decimal** (p. 504): A decimal for which the division process is unending.

**numeral** (p. 1): An expression that names a particular number. Also called *numerical expression*.

**numerator:** In the fraction $\frac{a}{b}$, $a$ is the numerator.

**numerical coefficient** (p. 143): In a term, the factor that is not a variable; for example, 5 in $5xy$.

**obtuse angle** (p. 577): An angle with measure between 90 and 180.

**odd integer** (p. 72): An integer that is not even.

**open half-plane** (p. 480): One of the two regions into which a line separates the plane. The boundary line is not a member of either open half-plane.

**open sentences** (p. 10): Equations or inequalities containing variables.

**open sentence in two variables** (p. 335): An equation or inequality that contains two variables.

**opposite of a number** (p. 34): *See under* additive inverse.

**ordered pair** (p. 335): A pair of numbers, such as (1, 2), for which the order of the numbers is important.

**ordinate** (p. 339): The second coordinate in an ordered pair of numbers that is associated with a point in a coordinate plane. Also called *y-coordinate*.

**origin** (pp. 30, 339): The zero point on a number line. The zero point of the intersecting axes in a number plane.

**parabola** (p. 413): A graph of the equation $y = ax^2 + bx + c$ $(a \neq 0)$ where the domain is the set of real numbers.

**parallel lines** (p. 346): Lines in the same plane that do not intersect.

**percent** (p. 295): A notation for a ratio with the denominator 100. The word means "hundredths" or "divided by 100."

**perfect square** (p. 547): An expression such as $(x + 2)^2$, $x^2$, or $(3x - 2)^2$.

**perimeter**: The perimeter of a geometric figure is the distance around it.

**plotting a point** (p. 339): Locating the graph of an ordered pair of real numbers on the coordinate plane.

**polynomial** (p. 143): A sum of monomials.

**polynomial equation** (p. 223): An equation whose sides are both polynomials.

**positive number** (p. 30): A number paired with a point on the positive side of a number line.

**postulate** (p. 45): *See under* axiom.

**power** (p. 137): Exponential expressions such as $3^2$ and $3^4$ are powers of 3. The $n$th power of $b$ is defined as $b^n = \underbrace{b \cdot b \cdot b \cdot \ldots \cdot b.}_{n \text{ factors}}$

**prime factorization** (p. 183): The expression of a positive integer as a product of prime factors.

**prime factors** (p. 183): Factors that are prime numbers or prime polynomials.

**prime number** (p. 183): An integer greater than 1 that has no positive integral factor other than itself and 1.

**prime polynomial** (p. 209): An irreducible polynomial whose greatest monomial factor is 1.

**principal square root** (p. 510): The positive square root, denoted by $\sqrt{\phantom{x}}$.

**probability of an event** (p. 599): The ratio of the number of outcomes favoring an event to the total number of outcomes.

**proof** (p. 126): Logical reasoning using definitions, given facts, and axioms to show a theorem is true.

**property of completeness** (p. 515): Every decimal represents a real number, and every real number can be represented as a decimal.

**property of the opposite of a sum** (p. 53): $-(a + b) = (-a) + (-b)$.

**property of square roots of equal numbers** (p. 517): If $r$ and $s$ are any real numbers, then $r^2 = s^2$ if and only if $r = s$ or $r = -s$.

**proportion** (p. 282): An equation that states that two ratios are equal.

**protractor** (p. 577): An instrument used to find the degree measure of an angle.

**Pythagorean theorem** (p. 520): In any right triangle, the square of the length of the hypotenuse equals the sum of the squares of the lengths of the other two sides.

**quadrants** (p. 340): The four regions formed by the coordinate axes.

**quadratic direct variation** (p. 430): A function defined by an equation of the form $y = kx^2$, where $k$ is a non-zero constant.

**quadratic equation** (p. 223): A polynomial equation of degree two.

**quadratic formula** (p. 553): Given $ax^2 + bx + c = 0$, $a \neq 0$, $b^2 - 4ac \geq 0$, the formula is $x = \dfrac{-b \pm \sqrt{b^2 - 4ac}}{2a}$.

**quadratic function** (p. 413): A function $f$ given by $f(x) = ax^2 + bx + c \, (a \neq 0)$.

**quadratic polynomial** (p. 196): A trinomial, such as $8x^2 + 2x - 21$, whose term of greatest degree is quadratic.

**quadratic term** (p. 196): A term of degree two.

**quotient** (p. 80): The quotient $a \div b$, $b \neq 0$, is the number whose product with $b$ is $a$.

**radical** (p. 510): An expression of the form $\sqrt{a}$.

**radical equation** (p. 534): An equation that has a variable in the radicand.

**radical sign** (p. 510): The symbol $\sqrt{\phantom{x}}$.

**radicand** (p. 510): An expression beneath a radical sign.

**random experiment** (p. 596): An activity for which you cannot predict with certainty the outcome when the activity is repeated.

**range** (p. 603): The difference between the highest and lowest values in a frequency distribution.

**range of a function** (p. 404): One of the sets comprising a function, as the values of $y$ in $y = 7x - 1$.

**ratio** (p. 277): The ratio of one number to another (not zero) is the quotient of the first divided by the second.

**rational expression** (pp. 239, 499): A fraction; an expression for a rational number.

**rational number** (p. 499): A real number that can be written as the quotient of two integers.

**rationalizing a denominator** (p. 527): The process of expressing a fraction with an irrational denominator as an equal fraction with a rational denominator.

**ray** (p. 576): The part of a line that consists of a point $A$ and all points on the line on one side of $A$.

**real numbers** (p. 31): Any number that is either a positive number, a negative number, or zero.

**reciprocals** (p. 76): *See under* multiplicative inverse.

**reflexive property of equality** (p. 47): $a = a$.

**repeating decimal** (p. 504): A nonterminating decimal in which the same digit or block of digits repeats unendingly. Also called *periodic decimal*.

**relation** (p. 440): Any set of ordered pairs. Its *domain* is the set of first coordinates in its ordered pairs; its *range* is the set of second coordinates. Its *graph* comprises the graphs of all these ordered pairs.

**right angle** (p. 577): An angle with measure 90.

**right triangle** (p. 581): A triangle having one right angle.

**root of an open sentence** (p. 10): A solution of the sentence.

**rounding a decimal** (p. 506): Breaking off a decimal to achieve an approximation, by adding 1 to the value of the last digit kept if the first digit dropped is 5 or more, or, otherwise, by leaving unchanged the digits that are kept.

**sample space** (p. 596): The set of all possible outcomes of a random experiment.

**satisfy** (p. 10): Each member of the solution set of an open sentence satisfies that sentence.

**scientific notation** (p. 317): A number is written in this notation when it is expressed as a product of a number greater than or equal to 1, but less than 10, and an integral power of 10.

**set** (p. 10): Collection of objects.

**sides of an angle** (p. 576): *See under* angle.

**sides of an equation** (p. 10): The expressions joined by the symbol of equality.

**sides of an inequality** (p. 450): The expressions joined by an inequality symbol.

**sides of a triangle** (p. 581): *See under* triangle.

**similar terms** (p. 143): Terms that are exactly alike or that differ only in their numerical coefficients.

**similar triangles** (p. 584): $\triangle ABC$ and $\triangle DEF$ are similar triangles if $m\angle A = m\angle D$, $m\angle B = m\angle E$, and $m\angle C = m\angle F$. $\angle A$ and $\angle D$ are *corresponding angles* (as are $\angle B$ and $\angle E$, $\angle C$ and $\angle F$). The sides opposite corresponding angles are *corresponding sides*.

**simple interest** (p. 4): Simple interest $I$ on an investment of $P$ dollars at the interest rate $R$ for $T$ years is given by the formula $I = PRT$.

**simplest form of a fraction** (p. 239): The fraction $\frac{a}{b}$ is in simplest form when $a$ and $b$ have no common factor other than 1 and $-1$.

**simplest form of a polynomial** (p. 143): A polynomial is in simplest form if no two of its terms are similar.

**simplest form of a radical** (p. 527): The radical contains no integral radical with a square factor other than 1, no fractions under a radical sign, and no radicals in a denominator.

**simplifying a numerical expression** (p. 2): Replacing a numerical expression by the simplest form of its value.

**simplifying a variable expression** (p. 65): Replacing a variable expression by an equivalent expression having as few terms as possible.

**simultaneous equations** (p. 346): *See under* system of equations.

**sine** (p. 587): The sine of $\angle A$ of a right triangle $=$
$$\frac{\text{length of leg opposite } \angle A}{\text{length of hypotenuse}}.$$

**slope of a line** (p. 392): If $(x_1, y_1)$ and $(x_2, y_2)$ are two different points on a line, then slope $= \frac{y_2 - y_1}{x_2 - x_1}(x_1 \neq x_2)$. A horizontal line has slope 0; a vertical line has no slope.

**slope-intercept form** (p. 397): The equation of a line in the form $y = mx + b$ where the slope is $m$ and the $y$-intercept is $b$.

**solution** (p. 10): A value of a variable that converts an open sentence into a true statement.

**solution of an open sentence in two variables** (p. 335): An ordered pair of values for which the sentence becomes a true sentence.

**solution of a system of two equations in two variables** (p. 346): An ordered pair of numbers that satisfies both equations.

**solution set of an open sentence** (p. 10): The set that consists of the members of the domain of the variable for which the sentence is true is called the solution set of the sentence over that domain.

**solve** (p. 10): Find the solution set of an open sentence over a given domain.

**square root** (p. 510): The number $a$ is a square root of the number $b$ if $a^2 = b$.

**standard form of a linear equation** (p. 340): The form $ax + by = c$ where $a$, $b$, and $c$ are integers with $a$ and $b$ not both zero.

**standard form of polynomial equation** (p. 224): A polynomial equation where one side is 0 and the other side is a simplified polynomial arranged in descending powers of the variable.

**straight angle** (p. 577): An angle with measure 180.

**substitution method** (p. 350): A method for finding the solution of a pair of linear equations in two variables by: (1) solving one equation for one of the variables, (2) substituting the resulting expression in the other equation, (3) solving this derived equation, (4) finding the corresponding value of the other variable.

**substitution principle** (p. 2): Changing the numeral by which a number is named in an expression does not change the value of the expression.

**subtraction property of equality** (p. 93): If $a$, $b$, and $c$ are any real numbers and $a = b$, then $a - c = b - c$.

**supplementary angles** (p. 579): Two angles with 180 as the sum of their measures. Each is the *supplement* of the other.

**symmetric property of equality** (p. 47): If $a = b$, then $b = a$.

**system of equations** (p. 346): A set of equations in the same variables. Also called *simultaneous equations*.

**tangent** (p. 587): The tangent of $\angle A$ of a right triangle $=$
$$\frac{\text{length of leg opposite } \angle A}{\text{length of leg adjacent to } \angle A}.$$

**term** (p. 46): A mathematical expression using numerals or variables or both to indicate a product or a quotient.

**terminating decimals** (p. 504): A decimal in which the division process stops because a remainder of zero has been reached. Also called *finite* or *ending*.

**theorem** (p. 126): A statement that is shown to be true by using axioms, definitions, and other proved theorems in a logical development.

**transformation:** Each of the following always produces an equation equivalent to the original equation:

*by addition* (p. 94): Adding the same number to each side.

*by division* (p. 99): Dividing each side by the same nonzero number.

*by multiplication* (p. 99): Multiplying each side by the same nonzero number.

*by substitution* (p. 94): Replacing either side by an expression equivalent to it.

*by subtraction* (p. 94): Subtracting the same number from each side.

**transitive axiom of order** (p. 453): For all real numbers $a$, $b$, and $c$:
1. If $a < b$ and $b < c$, then $a < c$.
2. If $c > b$ and $b > a$, then $c > a$.

**transitive property of equality** (p. 47): If $a = b$ and $b = c$, then $a = c$.

**triangle** (p. 581): A figure formed by connecting three points not on a line by segments. In $\triangle ABC$: $\overline{AB}$, $\overline{BC}$, and $\overline{CA}$ are the *sides* of the triangle; $A$, $B$, and $C$ are the *vertices* of the triangle; and $\angle BAC$, $\angle ACB$, and $\angle CBA$ are the *angles* of the triangle.

**trigonometric functions** (p. 588): The functions having the set of acute angles as domain. $\sin A$, $\cos A$, $\tan A$.

**trigonometric ratios** (p. 587): Ratios of the lengths of the sides of a right triangle. *See* sine, cosine, and tangent.

**trinomial** (p. 143): A polynomial of three terms.

**trinomial square** (p. 204): A trinomial that is the square of a binomial.

**uniform motion** (p. 163): A term used to describe motion of an object when it moves without changing its speed or rate.

**union of sets** (p. 465): For any two sets $A$ and $B$, the set consisting of all members belonging to at least one of the sets $A$ and $B$ is the union of $A$ and $B$.

**unit distance** (p. 30): The distance between 0 and 1 on a number line.

**values of a function** (p. 405): Members of the range of the function.

**values of a variable** (p. 1): Numbers in the domain of the variable.

**variable** (p. 1): A symbol used to represent one or more numbers.

**variable expression** (p. 1): An expression that contains a variable. Also called an open expression.

**vertex of an angle** (p. 576): *See under* angle.

**vertex of a parabola** (p. 414): The minimum or maximum point of the graph of $y = ax^2 + bx + c$ $(a \neq 0)$.

**vertical angles** (p. 579): Two angles whose sides are rays in the same lines but in opposite directions.

**vertical axis** (p. 339): The vertical number line in the number plane. Also called the *y-axis*.

**vertices of a triangle** (p. 581): *See under* triangle.

**volume:** The volume of a solid is the number of unit cubes it contains.

**whole numbers** (p. 30): The set made up of the positive integers and zero; $\{0, 1, 2, 3, \ldots\}$.

**x-coordinate** (p. 339): *See under* abscissa.

**x-intercept** (p. 557): The $x$-coordinate of a point where a graph intersects the $x$-axis.

**y-coordinate** (p. 339): *See under* ordinate.

**y-intercept** (p. 396): The $y$-coordinate of a point where a graph intersects the $y$-axis.

**zero of a function** (p. 567): A zero of a function $f$ is a solution of the equation $f(x) = 0$.

**zero-product property** (p. 223): For all real numbers $a$ and $b$, $ab = 0$ if and only if $a = 0$ or $b = 0$.

# Index

Abscissa, 339
Absolute value, 35
  in open sentences, 472, 476
Acute angle, 577
Addition
  axioms for, *see under* Axioms
  of fractions, 255
  identity element for, 50
  on the number line, 49
  of polynomials, 144
  properties of, 84
  of radicals, 529
  rules for, 54
  of similar terms, 143
Addition-or-subtraction method, 358–359,
    362–363
Addition property of equality, 93
Additive inverse, 50
Algebra, 28
Angle(s), 576–577
  of depression, 592
  of elevation, 592
  of a triangle, 581
Applications
  Boyle's gas law, 540
  consumer credit, 129
  energy consumption, 242
  illumination, 439
  line of best fit, 411
  understanding product prices, 83
Area formulas and problems, 156, 194–195,
    231, 257, 279
Arrow notation, 404
Associative axiom(s), 46
Average, 82, 602–603
Axes, coordinate, 340
Axioms, 45
  addition, of order, 454
  additive, of zero, 50
  associative, 46
  of closure, 45
  commutative, 45
  of comparison, 453
  distributive, 64
  identity for addition, 50
  identity for multiplication, 68

multiplication, of order, 454
multiplicative, of one, 68
of opposites, 50
in proofs, 126
of reciprocals, 76
summary of, 85
transitive, of order, 453
*See also* Property
Axis
  horizontal, 339
  of symmetry, 413, 414
  vertical, 339

Bar graph, 408
Base of an isosceles triangle, 581
Base of a power, 137
BASIC, 9, 653–659
Between, 449
Binomials, 143
  containing square-root radicals, 531
  factoring products of, 199
  multiplying mentally, 196
  product of, 157, 196, 199
  squaring, 203
Biographical Notes
  de la Cierva, Juan, 281
  Einstein, Albert, 23
  Hypatia, 160
  Mitchell, Maria, 125
  Ramanujan, Srinivasa, 564
  Roebling, Emily Warren, 381
  Williams, Daniel Hale, 467
  Wu, Hsien, 220
Boundary line of a half-plane, 480

Calculator Key-In, 12, 79, 98, 190, 198, 311, 322,
    369, 487, 512, 601
Cancellation rule for fractions, 187
Career Notes
  accountant, 349
  architect, 541
  astronomer, 33
  electrical engineer, 150
  medical laboratory technician, 102
  nutritionist, 207
  welder, 561

Rationalizing the denominator, 527, 531
Ray, 576
Reading Algebra, xi
    independent study, 142
    inequalities, 458
    problem solving, 29
    problem-solving strategies, 370
    symbols, xiii
Real numbers, 31
    and the number line, 31
Reciprocal(s), 76
    of a product, 77
Reflexive property of equality, 47
Relation(s), 440
    graphs of, 440
Repeating decimal, 504
Review
    chapter, 41, 85, 132, 175, 233, 269, 329, 383,
        442, 492, 542, 569, 605
    cumulative, 88, 134, 178, 236, 272, 332, 386,
        446, 494, 544, 571
    mixed, 90, 180, 274, 388, 496, 573
    *See also* Extra Practice and Tests
Right angle, 577
Right triangle, 581
    Pythagorean theorem, 520
        converse of, 521
    trigonometric ratios associated with angles
        in, 587
Root(s)
    double, 224
    of open sentences, 10
    of quadratic equations, 223–224, 547
Rounding decimals, 506

Sample space, 596
Scientific notation, 317
Segment, 576
Self-Tests, *see* Tests
Set(s), 10
    disjoint, 465
    empty, 112
    factor, 183
    intersection of, 465
    member of, 10
    null, 112
    of rational numbers, 499
    of real numbers, 31
    solution, 10, 335, 346, 450
    union of, 465

Sides
    of an angle, 576
    of an equation, 10
    of an inequality, 450
    of a triangle, 581
Similar terms, 143
Similar triangles, 584–585
Simplest form
    of expressions having a square root radical,
        527
    of fractions, 239
    of polynomials, 143
Simple interest, 4, 301, 304
Simplifying
    expressions, 2, 65
    expressions having a square root radical,
        527
    fractions, 239
    polynomials, 143
    radical expressions, 527
    sums and differences of radicals, 529
Simultaneous equations, 346
    *See also* Systems of linear equations
Sine, 587
Slope of a line, 392
Slope-intercept form of a line, 397
Solution, 10, 335, 346, 450
    *See also* Root(s)
Solution set(s), 10, 335, 346, 450
    of a system of linear equations, 346
Solving equations, 10, 335
    by factoring, 223–224
    fractional, 291
    with fractional coefficients, 288
    having the variable in both sides, 112–113
    by inspection, 10
    plan for, 104
    quadratic, 223–224, 547–548, 550–551, 553–
        554
    radical, 534
    with similar terms, 103–104
    systems of linear, 346–347, 350–351, 358–
        359, 362–363
    by transformations, 93–95, 99–100, 103–104
Solving inequalities, 453–455
    quadratic, 567–568
    systems, 484
Solving problems, 24–26
Square(s)
    of binomials, 203

Trinomial square, 204
  completing, 550
  factoring, 203–204
True statement, 10

Uniform motion, 163
Union of sets, 465
Unique, 45, 184
Unit distance, 30

Value(s)
  of an expression, 2
  of a function, 405
  of a variable, 1
Variable, 1
  domain, 10
  value of, 1
Variation
  combined, 434
  constant of, 418, 424
  direct, 418, 425
  inverse, 424–425
  inverse as the square, 430
  joint, 434
  quadratic direct, 430
Venn diagrams, 465–466
Vertex (vertices)
  of angle, 576

of parabola, 414
  of triangle, 581
Vertical angles, 579
Vertical axis, 339
Volume, 150

Whole numbers, 30

$x$-axis, 339
$x$-coordinate, 339
$x$-intercept, 557

$y$-axis, 339
$y$-coordinate, 339
$y$-intercept, 396

Zero
  absolute value of, 35
  division by, 81
  identity element for addition, 50
  multiplication by, in transforming equations, 100
  multiplicative property of, 68
  square root of, 510
Zero of a function, 567
Zero-product property, 223

# Acknowledgments

Mechanical art: ANCO/Boston. Cover: Skolos, Wedell, & Raynor. Page xiv, Jeff Rotman; 18, Donald Dietz/Stock Boston; 22, NASA; 27, Henry Ford Museum, The Edison Institute; 28, The Bettmann Archives; 33, Lee Foster/Alpha; 44, H. Wendler/The Image Bank; 56, Focus on Sports Inc.; 57, Marc Solomon/The Image Bank; 62 top, B. Evans/Peter Arnold, Inc.; 62 bot., J. McNee/FPG; 64, Chris Brown/Stock Boston; 92 Pat Goudvis/Picture Group; 97, Focus on Sports Inc.; 102 top, Bill Gallery/Stock Boston; 102 bot., David York/MediChrome Div., The Stock Shop; 108, Tim Courlas; 121, Alvis Upitis/The Image Bank; 136, Richard L. Miller/The Picture Cube; 150, Tom Tracy/The Stock Shop; 161, Philip Jon Bailey/Stock Boston; 166, Tom Walker/Stock Boston; 167, Ellis Herwig/Stock Boston; 168, Alan C. Ross/Photo Researchers, Inc.; 169, Ulrike Welsch/Stock Boston; 173 bot., Tom Stack/Tom Stack & Assoc.; 182, Dick Pietrzyk/Alpha; 194, The Image Bank; 195, Gary Milburn/Tom Stack & Assoc.; 206, Brian Seed/Click/Chicago; 207, Michal Heron; 230, Jerry Wachter/Focus on Sports Inc.; 231, Colonial Homes Magazine; 238, Clyde H. Smith/Peter Arnold, Inc.; 257 top, J. Holland/Stock Boston; 257 bot., ALON/Leo deWys Inc.; 259, V. Phillips/Leo deWys Inc.; 261, Mike Mazzaschi/Stock Boston; 266, Don Carstens/Folio; 276, NASA; 278, Grant Heilman; 294, R. Valentine Atkinson/Focus on Sports Inc.; 299, Tcherevkoff Studio/The Image Bank; 313, Sepp Seitz/Woodfin Camp & Assoc.; 315, Lou Jones; 320, California Institue of Technology; 321, Eastman Kodak Co.; 328, Peter F. Palmisano; 334, Gary Milburn/Tom Stack & Assoc.; 338, Robert McKenzie/Tom Stack & Assoc.; 349, Michal Heron; 356, Ted Spiegel/Black Star; 361, Duane Bradford/Black Star; 367, Michael Melford/The Image Bank; 374, Dennis J. Cipnic/Photo Researchers, Inc.; 378, Grant Heilman; 390, Lou Jones; 391, Scott Dietrich/Click/Chicago; 400, Malcolm S. Kirk/Peter Arnold, Inc.; 413, Riley Caton/Alpha; 418, G. C. Gladstone/The Image Bank; 423, Sherman Hines/Masterfile; 429, Gregg Mancuso/Stock Boston; 430, Aileen Soslas/Tom Stack & Assoc.; 448, Phillip A. Harrington/Fran Heyl Assocs., Courtesy of I.B.M.; 461, Focus on Sports Inc.; 464, Mike Yamashita/The Stock Shop; 478, Hallinan/FPG; 488, Michael Philip Manheim/Photo Researchers, Inc.; 498, David Madison/Bruce Coleman Inc.; 502, Clyde H. Smith/Peter Arnold, Inc.; 519, D. P. Hershkowitz/Bruce Coleman Inc.; 536, Tim Courlas; 541, Michal Heron; 546, C. Seghers/Leo deWys Inc.; 561, John McGrail/Wheeler Pictures; 566, Katrina Thomas/Photo Researchers, Inc. Biography portraits: Gary Torrisi.

# Answers to Self-Tests

**Chapter 1, Self-Test 1, page 12**

**1.** 34 **2.** 8 **3.** 6 **4.** 1 **5.** 3 **6.** 3

**Chapter 1, Self-Test 2, page 28**

**1.** $9(n - 1)$ **2.** $60(t + 3)$ **3.** $\frac{1}{2}a = a - 7$
**4.** $c + (2c + 10) = 100$
**5.** 2.5 h

**Chapter 1, Self-Test 3, page 40**

**1.**
$$-3 \quad -2 \quad -1 \quad 0 \quad 1 \quad 2 \quad 3 \quad 4$$
**2.** 16 **3.** 5 **4.** Negative two is less than
one. **5.** $-5, -1, 0, 6$

**Chapter 2, Self-Test 1, page 63**

**1.** 9700 **2.** $20 + 3x$ **3.** 0 **4.** $-5$ **5.** $-6$
**6.** $-27$ **7.** $-9$ **8.** $-11$ **9.** 2

**Chapter 2, Self-Test 2, page 75**

**1.** $6y + 7$ **2.** $4x - 11$ **3.** $22 + 7z$
**4.** $18 + 5t$ **5.** $-270$ **6.** $a - 21$
**7.** $-18a + 30b$ **8.** $-70$ **9.** $n - 1; n + 1$
**10.** $x + (x + 2) = -44$

**Chapter 2, Self-Test 3, page 84**

**1.** $-6$ **2.** $\frac{1}{2x}$ **3.** $n$ **4.** $-6c + 8$ **5.** $-16$
**6.** $-6$ **7.** 2 **8.** $-9y$

**Chapter 3, Self-Test 1, page 106**

**1.** 42 **2.** 13 **3.** $-17$ **4.** $-90$ **5.** 375 containers of juice **6.** 7 **7.** 3

**Chapter 3, Self-Test 2, page 116**

**1.** 108 min **2.** 9 **3.** $-5$ **4.** Eagles, 14 hits;
Hawks, 17 hits

**Chapter 3, Self-Test 3, page 131**

**1.**

| | Now | 2 yr. ago | 3 yr. from now |
|---|---|---|---|
| Kay | $x - 5$ | $x - 7$ | $x - 2$ |
| Sid | $x$ | $x - 2$ | $x + 3$ |

**2.** Marcia, $6680; Dora, $3340 **3.** 96 dimes
**4.** (1) Assoc. axiom for add.; (2) Axiom of
opposites; (3) Identity axiom

**Chapter 4, Self-Test 1, page 147**

**1.** $a^3$ **2.** $(xy)^3$ **3.** 1 **4.** $-8$ **5. a.** $6x^2 - 12$
**b.** $4x^2 + 12x - 4$ **6. a.** $-8x^2y + 3$
**b.** $10x^2y - 6xy^2 + 11$ **7.** 19, 21, 23

**Chapter 4, Self-Test 2, page 160**

**1.** $-2x^7$ **2.** $18a^9$ **3.** $-2a^5$ **4.** $4^{2x}$
**5.** $-8x^{12}$ **6.** $-8x^{12}y^3$ **7.** $-16x^{12}y^4$
**8.** $16x^{12}$ **9.** $-32c + 4c^2$
**10.** $8x^3y^2 - 7x^2y^3 + \frac{1}{7}xy^4$ **11.** 13
**12.** $7a^2 - 62a + 48$
**13.** $-56t^3 + 114t^2 - 103t + 63$

**Chapter 4, Self-Test 3, page 174**

**1.** $V = \dfrac{kT}{P}$ **2.** 20 km/h **3.** 10 ft by 17 ft
**4.** no solution, contradictory facts

**Chapter 5, Self-Test 1, page 195**

**1.** $2^3 \cdot 3^2$ **2.** (1)(44), (2)(22), (4)(11),
$(-1)(-44), (-2)(-22), (-4)(-11)$ **3.** 4
**4.** $-\dfrac{3x}{y}$ **5.** $\dfrac{m^4}{4k}$ **6.** $12t^2$ **7.** $-5ab^4$
**8.** $7t^2 + 5t - 3$ **9.** $2xy^2(2x^3y - 4x + 3)$

**Chapter 5, Self-Test 2, page 207**

**1.** $6y^2 - 8y - 30$ **2.** $6x^3 - 28x^2 + 16x$
**3.** $x^2 - 49$ **4.** $81a^2 - 4b^2$
**5.** $(2x - 7)(2x + 7)$ **6.** $9(2x^2 - 3)(2x^2 + 3)$
**7.** $4y^2 + 20y + 25$ **8.** $9z^2 - 30zk + 25k^2$
**9.** $(3a + 2)^2$ **10.** $(4m - 3n)^2$

## Chapter 5, Self-Test 3, page 216

**1.** $(y + 5)(y + 3)$  **2.** $(x - 8)(x - 2)$
**3.** $(n - 7)(n + 4)$  **4.** $(v + 12t)(v - 3t)$
**5.** $(2x - 3)(3x - 5)$  **6.** $(3x - 2y)(x + 4y)$

## Chapter 5, Self-Test 4, page 232

**1.** $(a + b)(5 - 2c)$
**2.** $(n - 1 - 10t^2)(n - 1 + 10t^2)$
**3.** $2a(3a - 1)^2$  **4.** $-3(2x - y)(3x - 2y)$
**5.** $8, -4$  **6.** $-2$  **7.** $0, 11, -11$  **8.** $0, 6, -5$
**9.** 11 cm

## Chapter 6, Self-Test 1, page 250

**1.** $-3; a \neq 0, a \neq 2$  **2.** $\dfrac{2a - 3}{3a + 2}; a \neq -\dfrac{3}{2}$,

$a \neq -\dfrac{2}{3}$  **3.** $\dfrac{1}{12ab^2c}$  **4.** $\dfrac{x^2}{6}$  **5.** $-\dfrac{1}{2}$  **6.** $\dfrac{1}{3r^2}$

## Chapter 6, Self-Test 2, page 258

**1.** $15a^2b^2$  **2.** $-5a$  **3.** $\dfrac{3}{4(x - 2y)}, \dfrac{48}{4(x - 2y)}$
**4.** $\dfrac{2y(x + y)}{xy(x + y)}, \dfrac{3x(x + y)}{xy(x + y)}, \dfrac{5xy}{xy(x + y)}$  **5.** $\dfrac{4a + 1}{a}$
**6.** $\dfrac{4(7b - 6)}{21ab^2}$  **7.** 1  **8.** $\dfrac{9x - 1}{9(x - 1)}$

## Chapter 6, Self-Test 3, page 266

**1.** $\dfrac{9b + a}{b}$  **2.** $\dfrac{(2x - 1)(2x + 1)}{x}$  **3.** $\dfrac{a^2 + 1}{a + 1}$
**4.** $2x - 5$  **5.** $2b^2 - 3b + 7 + \dfrac{2}{b + 2}$

## Chapter 7, Self-Test 1, page 286

**1.** $3:5$  **2.** $40:1$  **3.** 63 questions  **4.** 54
**5.** $\frac{1}{16}$  **6.** 26

## Chapter 7, Self-Test 2, page 294

**1.** $-8$  **2.** 18  **3.** $-1$  **4.** $-6$  **5.** $-5$
**6.** no solution  **7.** 2, 3

## Chapter 7, Self-Test 3, page 305

**1.** $\frac{14}{25}$  **2.** $\frac{7}{8}$  **3.** $\frac{21}{20}$  **4.** 13.6  **5.** 6.25  **6.** 250%
**7.** 25%  **8.** $2160  **9.** $33\frac{1}{3}\%$

## Chapter 7, Self-Test 4, page 316

**1.** 24 kg  **2.** 0.2 kg  **3.** 18 days  **4.** $34\frac{2}{7}$ s

## Chapter 7, Self-Test 5, page 327

**1.** $1.5 \times 10^8$  **2.** $9 \times 10^{-9}$  **3.** 1  **4.** $\frac{1}{8}$
**5.** $-16$  **6.** $\dfrac{1}{x^5}$  **7.** $\dfrac{4}{a^2}$  **8.** $\dfrac{9}{a^8}$

## Chapter 8, Self-Test 1, page 345

**1.** yes; no  **2.** no; yes  **3.** $y = \dfrac{2x - 6}{3}$
**4.** $y = \dfrac{10 - 2x}{5}$

**5–7.**

**8.**

**9.**

**10.**
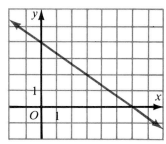

*Chapter 8, Self-Test 2, page 369*

**1.** (6,2)

**2.** (−1, −2)

**3.** (6, 4)  **4.** (0, 4)  **5.** 500 orchestra, 400 balcony  **6.** (6, 3)  **7.** (0, 4)  **8.** (−3, −2)  **9.** (3, 2)

*Chapter 8, Self-Test 3, page 382*

**1.** boat, 23 km/h; current 7 km/h  **2.** 96  **3.** Ella is 18; brother is 12  **4.** $\frac{4}{7}$

*Chapter 9, Self-Test 1, page 403*

**1.** $\frac{3}{2}$  **2.** 0  **3.** slope, $\frac{3}{7}$; y-intercept, −4  **4.** −3x + y = 5  **5.** x − y = 5

*Chapter 9, Self-Test 2, page 417*

**1.** 9  **2.** {2, 3, 6, 11, 18}  **3.** D = {boric acid, salt, sodium nitrate, sugar}; R = {4.8, 36, 88, 203.9}

Amount of Substance
Dissolved in 100 g Water at 20°C

**4.** (1, −1); x = 1  **5.** 1

*Chapter 9, Self-Test 3, page 438*

**1.** $259  **2.** 7 people  **3.** 196 km  **4.** 158.4 g

*Chapter 10, Self-Test 1, page 464*

**1.** −5 < −2 < −1  **2.** {−3, −2, −1, 0, 1, 2}
**3.** {the real numbers less than 8}

**4.** {the real numbers greater than or equal to −5}

**5.** at least 9 dimes

*Chapter 10, Self-Test 2, page 478*

**1.** {the real numbers greater than 3 or less than 2}

**2.** {−6, and the real numbers between −6 and 1}

**3.** {−2, 2, and the real numbers less than −2 or greater than 2}

**4.** {−2, and the real numbers between −2 and 1}

**5.** 8, 0

**6.** {1, 5, and the real numbers less than 1 or greater than 5}

**7.** 0, 2

**8.** {the real numbers between −3 and 1}

**9.** {$\frac{3}{2}$, 5, and the real numbers between $\frac{3}{2}$ and 5}

**10.** 7, −3

**11.** 3, −2

**12.** {the real numbers between −1 and 2}

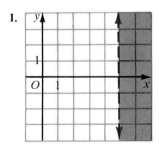

*Chapter 10, Self-Test 3, page 487*

**1.**

**2.** $y \le 3 - \frac{x}{2}$

**3.** $y < x - 5$, $y \ge -3x - 1$

*Chapter 11, Self-Test 1, page 513*

**1.** $\frac{71}{126}$ **2.** $\frac{31}{24}$ **3.** $\frac{223}{48}$ **4.** $\frac{3}{5}$ **5.** $-\frac{33}{20}$ **6.** $\frac{13}{12}$
**7.** 0.24 **8.** 1.375 **9.** $0.2\overline{3}$ **10.** $0.6857142$
**11.** $\frac{20}{99}$ **12.** 32 **13.** $\frac{8}{45}$ **14.** 1.6

*Chapter 11, Self-Test 2, page 524*

**1.** 9.84 **2.** 41.23 **3.** −0.94 **4.** $9|xy|$
**5.** $-12|a^3|b^4$ **6.** $0.5c^2$ **7.** {7, −7}
**8.** {8, −8} **9.** {$\frac{5}{6}$, $-\frac{5}{6}$} **10.** 22.02 **11.** no

*Chapter 11, Self-Test 3, page 537*

**1.** 30 **2.** 1 **3.** $5\sqrt{5} - 2\sqrt{11}$ **4.** $-4\sqrt{3}$
**5.** $15 - 6\sqrt{6}$ **6.** 3 **7.** $\sqrt{5} - 1$
**8.** $-3 - 2\sqrt{3}$ **9.** 4 **10.** $\frac{11}{5}$

*Chapter 12, Self-Test 1, page 561*

**1.** {3, −3} **2.** {$3 + \sqrt{7}$, $3 - \sqrt{7}$}
**3.** {5, 7} **4.** {8, −2} **5.** {2, $-\frac{1}{2}$}
**6.** $\left\{ \frac{3 + \sqrt{33}}{2}, \frac{3 - \sqrt{33}}{2} \right\}$ **7.** no real roots
**8.** no real roots

*Chapter 12, Self-Test 2, page 568*

**1.** {−4, 0} **2.** $\left\{ \frac{-3 + \sqrt{3}}{2}, \frac{-3 - \sqrt{3}}{2} \right\}$
**3.** {$5 + 3\sqrt{5}$, $5 - 3\sqrt{5}$} **4.** {0, −3}
**5.** 10 cm by 20 cm **6.** 4 m wide

# Answers to Selected Exercises

**CHAPTER 1   INTRODUCTION TO
ALGEBRA**

*Written Exercises, pages 3-4*   **1.** 8   **3.** 60
**5.** 6   **7.** 29   **9.** 170   **11.** 2   **13.** 2   **15.** 3
**17.** 10   **19.** 6   **21.** 55   **23.** 1   **25.** =   **27.** ≠
**29.** 300   **31.** 65   **33.** 59   **35.** $1250   **37.** 1
**39.** $\frac{1}{2}$   **41.** 0, 2

*Written Exercises, pages 7-8*   **1.** 8   **3.** 1
**5.** 69   **7.** 34   **9.** 25   **11.** $\frac{1}{2}$   **13.** 0   **15.** 8
**17.** 12   **19.** 61.6   **21.** 315   **23.** 16.28   **25.** ≠
**27.** =   **29.** ≠   **31.** =   **33.** =   **35.** ≠

*Computer Key-In, page 9*   **1.** 300   **3.** 1180
**5.** $(21 + 33)/6$; 9   **7.** $(24 + 10)*(24 - 10)$;
476

*Written Exercises, page 11*   **1.** {4}   **3.** {5}
**5.** {5}   **7.** {6}   **9.** {2}   **11.** {0}   **13.** {3}
**15.** {4}   **17.** {1}   **19.** {0, 1, 2, 3, 4, 5, 6, 7}
**21.** {4}   **23.** {2}   **25.** {8}   **27.** {7}
**29.** {0, 2}
**31.** {0, 6}   Answers may vary for Exs. 33
and 35   **33.** $x + 5 = 8$; $3z = 9$
**35.** $4k - 2 = 2(2k - 1)$; $2x + 1 = 2x + 1$

*Calculator Key-In, page 12*   **1.** 0   **3.** 0.1
**5.** 333,333

*Written Exercises, pages 15-17*   **1.** d   **3.** a
**5.** e   **7.** $2a + 2$   **9.** $\frac{1}{3}y - 6$   **11.** $30 - x$
**13.** $t - 6$   **15.** $12x$   **17.** $2w - 15$;
$2(2w - 15) + 2w$, or $6w - 30$   **19.** $a + 4$
**21.** $10s$; $10(s - 5)$   **23.** $y + 8y$, or $9y$ cents
**25.** $n - 5$   **27.** $r + 240$   **29.** $2(t - 6)$
**31.** $2s + (s - 6)$, or $3s - 6$
**33.** $c + 2(c - 29) + (c + 13)$, or $4c - 45$

*Written Exercises, pages 20-23*
**1.** $p + (p - 150) = 675$
**3.** $c + 5.5c = 105,000$   **5.** $2x - 1 = 47$
**7.** $t + (t + 3) = 29$   **9.** $74 = 2z + \frac{1}{2}$   **11.** $s$;
$4s = 68$   **13.** $a$; $a - 10 = 7$   **15.** $c$;
$285 - c = 14$   **17.** $p$; $\frac{1}{8}p = 0.95$   **19.** $h$;
$132h = 462$   **21.** $l$; $\frac{1}{100}l = 8.5$   **23.** $d$;
$d + 3.2 = 42.8$   **25.** $r$; $r + (2r + 3) = 24$
**27.** $s$; $s + s + (s + 9) = 54$   **29.** $a$;
$a + 10 = 3(a - 8)$   **31.** $m$; $m + 5 = 1 + 2m$
**33.** $s$; $(3s - 6) + s + (3s + 2) = 80$

*Problems, pages 26-27*   **1.** 8.6 units   **3.** 985.3
**5. a.** 24   **b.** 6   **7.** 9 men   **9.** 36 white eggs
**11.** 72 games   **13.** 105.5 m by 68.5 m
**15.** 110 wpm

*Reading Algebra, page 29*   **1.** $a = \frac{3}{2}x$
**3.** $0.8n + 100 = 660$   **5.** $\frac{2}{3}$ the total number
of cartons of milk and fruit juice served
**7.** yes; $c = 0.45(660)$   **9.** $x + \frac{1}{2}x + \frac{1}{3}x = 660$

*Written Exercises, pages 32-33*   **1.** 5, −5; 5
floors down   **3.** 190, −190; 190 m below sea
level   **5.** 18, −18; $18 loss   **7.** 15, −15; 15
km west   **9.** 85, −85; payments of $85
**11.** 1, −1; one second before liftoff   **13.** 50,
−50; a debit of $50   **15.** −1, 0, 1   **17.** −1,
2, 4   **19.** −5, −3, −1, 0   **21.** $-\frac{1}{2}, \frac{1}{2}$   **23.** S,
F   **25.** N, R   **27.** Q, A, U   **29.** M, P, T
**31.**   
-2  -1  0  1  2
**33.**   
-4  -3  -2  -1  0  1
**35.**   
-3  -2  -1  0
**37.**   
-2  -1  0  1  2
**39.** 7   **41.** −4   **43.** −1   **45.** 3

*Written Exercises, page 36*   **1.** −13   **3.** 0
**5.** 19   **7.** 8   **9.** 11   **11.** 14   **13.** $\frac{3}{2}$   **15.** 4
**17.** 1   **19.** 0   **21.** {0}   **23.** {$\frac{1}{2}$, $-\frac{1}{2}$}   **25.** no
solution; there is no real number whose abso-
lute value is negative.   **27.** {1, −1}   **29.** {5,
−5}   **31.** {5, −5}   **33.** {2, −2}   **35.** 1.8
**37.** 2.3   **39.** 6.3   **41.** 5.2   **43.** 1.7

*Written Exercises, pages 38-39*   **1.** $6 > -9$
**3.** $-8 > -20$   **5.** $6 < 6.5$   **7.** $-13 < 0$
**9.** $|-5| > 2$   **11.** $-(-2) > -(-1)$   **13.** <
**15.** <   **17.** >   **19.** >   **21.** <   **23.** <
**25.** <   **27.** <   **29.** −7, −5, 0, 8   **31.** −3,
−1, 2, 5   **33.** $-\frac{1}{2}, -\frac{1}{3}, -\frac{1}{4}, -\frac{1}{6}$   **35.** −1.5,
−0.7, 0.3, 1.4   **37.** −3.141, 3.14, 3.1416
**39.** $-4\frac{1}{2}, -4\frac{1}{3}, -4\frac{1}{6}$   **41.** $-(-1), -(-2)$,
$|-3|, |-6|$   **43.** Cal, Flo, Sal, Nell
**45.** false   **47.** true   **49.** false   **51.** true
**53.** true   **55.** false; negative numbers are less
than their opposites.

*Challenge, page 39* **1.** 21, 28, 36, 45, 55

*Chapter Review, page 41* **1.** d **3.** a **5.** c
**7.** b **9.** d **11.** a

*Maintaining Skills, page 43* **1.** 29.9476
**3.** 377.7 **5.** 1653.6 **7.** 16.522 **9.** 989.04
**11.** 45.79 **13.** $\frac{5}{8}, \frac{6}{8}$ **15.** $\frac{6}{21}, \frac{14}{21}$ **17.** $\frac{47}{45}$ **19.** $\frac{67}{72}$
**21.** $\frac{15}{52}$ **23.** $\frac{5}{6}$ **25.** $\frac{23}{21}$ **27.** $\frac{49}{64}$

## CHAPTER 2  WORKING WITH REAL NUMBERS

*Written Exercises, page 48* **1.** 550 **3.** 810
**5.** 5300 **7.** 13 **9.** 8 **11.** $10 + 2p$ **13.** $30x$
**15.** $96t$ **17.** $m + f + g + 11$ **19.** $110\ mkh$
**21.** $10,500\ cde$ **23.** no **25.** no;
$2 \div 4 = 4 \div 2$ is false **27. a.** 13 **b.** yes
**c.** no

*Written Exercises, pages 51-52* **1.** 10 **3.** 0
**5.** $-1$ **7.** $-8$ **9.** 28 **11.** $-36$ **13.** 20
**15.** $-38$ **17.** $-13$ **19.** $-11$ **21.** 0 **23.** 0
**25.** 6 **27.** $-15$ **29.** 9 **31.** $-38$ **33.** $-0.5$
**35.** 0

*Challenge, page 52* Fill 5 L container, pour it
in 8 L container; next fill the 5 L container
again, pour enough in 8 L container to fill it;
the remainder in 5 L container is 2 L.

*Written Exercises, pages 55-56* **1.** 19 **3.** 49
**5.** 107 **7.** 14 **9.** $-12$ **11.** $-26$ **13.** 24.8
**15.** $-35$ **17.** 0 **19.** $\frac{1}{2}$ **21.** $-\frac{9}{4}$ **23.** 2
**25.** $-4$ **27.** $-11$ **29.** 10 **31.** $-15$
**33.** $-1.6$

*Problems, pages 56-58* **1.** $818 **3.** 20th
floor **5.** $600 **7.** 12 fewer guests **9.** 3
blocks east, 9 blocks south **11.** 101 m below
sea level **13.** 12:30 P.M. **15.** $121.75

*Computer Key-In, page 58* **1.** 110 **3.** 17.62

*Written Exercises, pages 60-61* **1.** $-260$
**3.** 71 **5.** $-16$ **7.** $-7.2$ **9.** 184 **11.** 2.94
**13.** $-25$ **15.** $-25$ **17.** 121 **19.** 337 **21.** 0
**23.** $-9$ **25.** 1350 **27.** 12 **29.** 21 **31.** $-9$
**33.** 3 **35.** 116 **37.** $-84$ **39.** $y$ **41.** 17
**43.** $-19$ **45.** $-11$ **47.** $-5$ **49.** 0
**51.** $-14$ **53. a.** (1) definition of subtraction,
(2) commutative axiom of addition, (3) associative axiom of addition, (4) axiom of opposites, (5) identity axiom for addition

*Problems, pages 62-63* **1.** 4 h **3.** 85 years
old **5.** 3.8°C **7.** 91 blocks west **9.** $-88.3$°C

*Challenge, page 63* **1.** $4 = 1 + 3$; $9 = 3 + 6$;
$16 = 6 + 10$; $25 = 10 + 15$; $36 = 15 + 21$;
$49 = 21 + 28$; $64 = 28 + 36$; $81 = 36 + 45$;
$100 = 45 + 55$

*Written Exercises, pages 66-67* **1.** 27 **3.** 5
**5.** 830 **7.** $17a$ **9.** $25n$ **11.** $9t$ **13.** $-67q$
**15.** $9x + 12$ **17.** $9r + 34$ **19.** $7 + 6w$
**21.** $13a + 13$ **23.** $11x + 31$ **25.** $8p$ **27.** $4n$
**29.** $h - 10$ **31.** $4e + 20f$ **33.** $8x + 11y + 9$
**35.** $21a + 17b$ **37.** $11r + 12$
**39.** $34c + 14d + 50$
**41.** $7(c + d) + 2(3c + 2d)$; $13c + 11d$
**43.** $(-5 + 15y) + 8 + \frac{1}{2}(12y - 8)$; $21y - 1$
**45.** $69.95x + 69.95(x + 3)$; $(139.90x + 209.85)$
dollars **47.** $248x + 160$ **49.** $113n - 9p - 99$

*Written Exercises, pages 70-71* **1.** 84 **3.** 480
**5.** $-84$ **7.** 0 **9.** $-300$ **11.** 420 **13.** 18
**15.** $-80$ **17.** $-90$ **19.** $-8a + 40d$
**21.** $2r + 10s$ **23.** $4x + 4$ **25.** $6u - 11p$
**27.** $5.3t - 2s$ **29.** $-\frac{1}{3}m + 2n$
**31.** $-19x + 13y$ **33.** $3q - 9w$ **35.** $e + 3f$
**37.** $-22r - 31s$ **39.** $33 - 12g$
**41.** $-500p - 500$ **43.** (1) identity axiom of
multiplication, (2) distributive axiom, (3)
axiom of opposites, (4) multiplicative property
of 0

*Written Exercises, pages 74-75*
**1.** $x + (x + 1) = 87$
**3.** $x + (x + 1) + (x + 2) + (x + 3) = -106$
**5.** $x + (x + 2) + (x + 4) = 81$
**7.** $x(x + 2) = 168$ **9.** $x + 2 = 2x - 6$
**11.** $x + (x + 2) + (x + 4) + (x + 6) = 36$
**13.** $x + (x + 1) + (x + 2) + (x + 3) =$
$100 - 2[(x + 3) - 2x]$
**15.** $(x + 1) + (x + 2) = \frac{1}{2}x - 6$
**17.** $2[x + (x + 1)] - [(x + 2) + (x + 3)] = 15$
**19.** $\frac{1}{2}(x + 1) = (x + 2) - 80$
**21.** $(x - 5) + (x + 2) + (x + 9) = 195$

*Written Exercises, page 78* **1.** $-5$ **3.** $-10$
**5.** 1 **7.** $-3$ **9.** $-rs$ **11.** $5y$ **13.** $-8a + 10$
**15.** $9c - 2d$ **17.** $6m + 13k$ **19.** $-u + 6v$
**21.** $-4x - 17y$ **23.** $-27m$ **25.** $-r$ **27.** $t$
**29.** $-4$ **31.** $\pi$ **33.** 2

*Computer Key-In, page 79* **1.** 11 **3.** 3.524

*Calculator Key-In, page 79* **1.** 16 **3.** 0.00032
**5.** that number

*Written Exercises, pages 82–83* **1.** $-8$
**3.** $-99$ **5.** 343 **7.** $-80$ **9.** $-12a$
**11.** $-142$ **13.** $w$ **15.** $5c$ **17.** $-5\frac{1}{2}$ **19.** $-1$
**21.** $-3$ **23.** $-1$ **25.** $-3$ **27.** 0 **29.** 16
**31.** $\frac{a-b}{c} = (a-b) \cdot \frac{1}{c} = a \cdot \frac{1}{c} - b \cdot \frac{1}{c} = \frac{a}{c} - \frac{b}{c}$

*Chapter Review, pages 85–86* **1.** d **3.** c
**5.** b **7.** d **9.** b **11.** c **13.** d **15.** d **17.** a
**19.** d

*Cumulative Review, page 88* **1.** 2 **3.** 6
**5.** 57 **7.** 32 **9.** $-15$ **11.** $13x + 11y$
**13.** $-a - 11b$ **15.** 0 **17.** $-4$ **19.** $-3, -2,$
$-\frac{1}{2}, 0, 5, 7$
**21.**
**23.** $\{10, -10\}$ **25.** $\{-12\}$ **27.** $\{0\}$
**29.** $[(-2 + b) - 5] + 2(12b)$
**31.** $x + (x + 2) = 2(x + 2) - 2$

*Maintaining Skills, page 89* **1.** 11.32
**3.** 291.82 **5.** 2.5996 **7.** 0.757 **9.** 55
**11.** 662 **13.** 0.0025 **15.** 192 **17.** $\frac{2}{7}$ **19.** $\frac{3}{4}$
**21.** $\frac{9}{11}$ **23.** $\frac{1}{21}$ **25.** $\frac{1}{3}$ **27.** $\frac{1}{28}$ **29.** $\frac{1}{4}$ **31.** 1
**33.** $\frac{100}{49}$ **35.** $\frac{4}{5}$ **37.** $\frac{10}{21}$

*Mixed Review, page 90* **1.** $-15y$ **3.** $\frac{3}{2}$
**5.** 117
**7.**
**9.** $-\frac{1}{2}$ **11.** $-5$ **13.** $2x + 7 = (x - 3) + 5$
**15.** $|-x| - 8 = 4$; $-12$ **17.** $-155$ **19.** $-7,$
$-6, -\frac{1}{2}, 0, \frac{1}{5}, 0.3, \frac{1}{2}$

*Preparing for College Entrance Exams, page
91* **1.** D **3.** A **5.** E **7.** C


**CHAPTER 3   SOLVING EQUATIONS
AND PROBLEMS**

*Written Exercises, page 96* **1.** 26 **3.** 22
**5.** 168 **7.** 11 **9.** $-50$ **11.** $-24$ **13.** $-17$
**15.** $-10$ **17.** 29 **19.** $-4$ **21.** $-4$ **23.** 0
**25.** 2 **27.** $-6$ **29.** $-16$ **31.** $-4$ **33.** $-11$
**35.** 6 **37.** 109 **39.** $-2$ **41.** 7 **43.** 10, $-10$
**45.** 7, $-7$ **47.** 6, $-6$ **49.** 5, $-5$ **51.** 8, $-8$
**53.** 0 **55.** no solution

*Problems, pages 97–98* **1.** 49 **3.** $-23$ **5.** 44
points **7.** 15 members **9.** 94°C **11.** 64°
**13.** 454 employees **15.** $.35

*Calculator Key-In, page 98* **1.** 0.75
**3.** $-0.4375$ **5.** 0.025 **7.** $-0.24$ **9.** 0.96875
**11.–20.** Answers are the same.

*Written Exercises, page 101* **1.** 31 **3.** $-32$
**5.** $-256$ **7.** 169 **9.** 384 **11.** $-18$
**13.** $-24$ **15.** $-245$ **17.** $-297$ **19.** 0
**21.** 66 **23.** $-\frac{2}{7}$ **25.** 7 **27.** $-0.4$ **29.** 34
**31.** $-11$ **33.** 15, $-15$ **35.** 16, $-16$

*Problems, pages 101–102* **1.** $-47$ **3.** $-2736$
**5.** $24.50 **7.** 39 m **9.** 48 years old **11.** 44 h
**13.** 0.02 mps; 72 mph **15.** $78,750

*Written Exercises, page 105* **1.** 3 **3.** $-6$
**5.** 24 **7.** $-175$ **9.** $-2$ **11.** $-7$ **13.** $-4$
**15.** 0 **17.** $-105$ **19.** $-7$ **21.** $-1$
**23.** $-16$ **25.** 6 **27.** $-8$ **29.** $-12$ **31.** $-2$
**33.** $-4$ **35.** $-4$ **37.** 6 **39.** 2 **41.** $-34$
**43.** 4 **45.** 0 **47.** $-18$ **49.** 5 **51.** 7, $-7$

*Computer Exercises, page 106* **1. a.** 8 **b.** 2
**c.** $-10$ **d.** 33 **e.** 30 **f.** 18 **3. a.** 2, $-2$
**b.** no solution **c.** 0.5; $-0.5$ **d.** 30, $-30$
**e.** 18, $-18$ **f.** 18, $-18$

*Computer Key-In, page 107* **1.** 16 **3.** 5
**5.** 10

*Problems, pages 110–111* **1.** 76 **3.** 15 **5.** 87
**7.** 69 **9.** boat, $1250; motor, $250
**11.** 12 years **13.** 7 years old **15.** 26, 27, 28
**17.** $-31, -29, -27, -25$ **19.** 68 m, 70 m,
72 m **21.** 16, 19 **23.** 2 waterfalls
**25.** 529 cm² **27.** Carol, $24; Nina, $12; Lynn,
$18 **29.** Sally is 12; Tilly is 29; Angie is 19
**31.** A, 15,800 bottles; B, 7900 bottles;
C, 16,300 bottles **33.** 88, 89

*Written Exercises, pages 113–114* **1.** 8 **3.** 19
**5.** 12 **7.** $-13$ **9.** $-14$ **11.** $-13$ **13.** $-2$
**15.** no solution **17.** $-19$ **19.** $-16$ **21.** $-5$
**23.** identity **25.** 4 **27.** $-3$ **29.** identity
**31.** $-1$ **33.** identity **35.** $-1$ **37.** $-2$ **39.** 1

*Problems, pages 114–115* **1.** 48 **3.** 7 **5.** 23
**7.** 7, 8 **9.** $-14, -13$ **11.** 25 g **13.** 10 units
**15.** 6 years **17.** $56 **19.** 8, 12, 16, 20

**Computer Exercises, page 115** **1.** $-3$ **3.** no solution **5.** 3

**Computer Key-In, page 117** **1.** Line 110 adds the overtime pay to the regular wages. **3.** 7890, $375.38; 9870, $479.54; 7809, $438.07

**Problems, pages 120–121** **1.** Toby is 21. Sarah is 18. **3.** Bob is 22. Father is 46. **5.** 15 years **7.** first: length, 24 cm; width, 9 cm; second: length, 22 cm; width, 14 cm **9.** 125 lb **11.** Jack is 29. Jill is 16. **13.** Susan is 16. Ralph is 10. Neil is 5. **15.** Washington was 18. Jefferson was 7. **17.** juice, $1.25; soup, $1.75; fruit, $2.25 **19.** 65 calories **21.** Paul is 58. Matt is 10.

**Challenge, page 121** 90186 or 60189

**Problems, pages 123–124** **1.** 5 notebooks

|  | Number $\times$ Price $=$ Cost |  |  |
|---|---|---|---|
| Pencils | $x + 7$ | 20 | $20(x + 7)$ |
| Notebooks | $x$ | 120 | $120x$ |

**3.** 12 quarters, 24 dimes, 14 nickels

|  | Number $\times$ Value of coin $=$ Total value |  |  |
|---|---|---|---|
| Nickels | $50 - 3q$ | 5 | $5(50 - 3q)$ |
| Dimes | $2q$ | 10 | $20q$ |
| Quarters | $q$ | 25 | $25q$ |

**5.** 8 people **7.** apprentice, $15.50; plumber, $20 **9.** 7 quarters **11.** $5.50 **13.** The number of half-dollars is not a natural number. **15.** 68 pennies, 34 nickels, 30 dimes, 15 quarters **17.** 13 nickels, 9 dimes, 4 quarters

**Written Exercises, pages 128–129** **1. a.** (1) Associative axiom for multiplication (2) Axiom of reciprocals (3) Identity axiom for multiplication **b.** (4) Commutative axiom for multiplication (5) Commutative axiom for multiplication **3.** (2) Addition property of equality (3) Definition of subtraction (4) Associative axiom; Axiom of opposites **5.** (1) Definition of subtraction (2) Distributive axiom (3) Multiplicative property of $-1$

**Application, page 130** **1.** $2.40 **3.** $.68 **5.** total amount, $3420; interest, $420

**Chapter Review, page 132** **1.** a **3.** c **5.** a **7.** d **9.** a **11.** b

**Cumulative Review, page 134** **1.** 1 **3.** 4 **5.** 46 **7.** $-20$ **9.** $17\frac{1}{4}$ **11.** $2x - 2$ **13.** $-28$ **15.** $24y$ **17.** 8 **19.** $-2$ **21.** $-5$ **23.** $-4$ **25.** 1 **27.** no solution **29.** $-4$ **31.** 16 **33.** 18 **35.** 24 **37.** 11 **39.** $\frac{9}{5}$ **41.** 36 years old **43.** $7.80

**Maintaining Skills, page 135** **1.** $2\frac{1}{12}$ **3.** $5\frac{1}{5}$ **5.** $7\frac{7}{12}$ **7.** $9\frac{1}{4}$ **9.** $\frac{25}{6}$ **11.** $\frac{25}{9}$ **13.** $\frac{47}{13}$ **15.** $\frac{119}{12}$ **17.** $18\frac{1}{5}$ **19.** $-\frac{22}{21}$ **21.** 3 **23.** $3\frac{9}{40}$ **25.** $4\frac{3}{10}$ **27.** $21\frac{27}{35}$ **29.** $-2\frac{13}{22}$ **31.** $1\frac{11}{36}$ **33.** $-1\frac{13}{21}$ **35.** $26\frac{1}{12}$

## CHAPTER 4   POLYNOMIALS

**Written Exercises, page 140** **1.** $a^5$ **3.** $5y^3$ **5.** $-8x^2$ **7.** $-7x^2$ **9.** $x + y^2$ **11.** $(x + y)^2$ **13.** $\frac{1}{2}t^6$ **15.** $(\frac{1}{3}r)^2$ **17. a.** $-25$ **b.** 25 **19. a.** $-40$ **b.** $-1000$ **21. a.** 16 **b.** 1000 **23. a.** $-10$ **b.** 4 **25.** 18 **27.** 9 **29.** $-13$ **31. a.** 12 **b.** 36 **33. a.** 16 **b.** 1000 **35.** 0 **37.** 256 **39.** 0 **41.** 5

**Computer Exercises, pages 140–141** **1.** 1, 4, 27, 256, 3125 **3.** For $n > 1$, $n^n > n!$

**Computer Key-In, page 141** **1.** 1234, $425.50; 3412, $400; 4321, $516

**Reading Algebra, page 142** **1.** To add and subtract polynomials; to multiply monomials. **3.** A monomial is an expression that is either a numeral, a variable, or a product of a numeral and one or more variables. A sum of monomials is called a polynomial. **5.** $3x^2 + 5x - 4$ **7.** index, table of contents

**Written Exercises, pages 145–146**
**1.** $\underline{2a} - \underline{3b} + \underline{4a} + \underline{7b}$; $6a + 4b$
**3.** $\underline{7x^2} - \underline{3xy} + \underline{5xy} - \underline{4x^2}$; $3x^2 + 2xy$
**5.** $\underline{x^2y} + \underline{xy^2} - \underline{3x^2y} + \underline{xy}$; $-2x^2y + xy^2 + xy$ **7.** $8a + 5$ **9.** $3y + 5$ **11.** $7a^2 - 7a + 2$ **13.** $-2a^2 - 2ab - 8b$ **15.** $7x - 2y - 6z + 8$ **17.** $-2a - 9$ **19.** $6x - 11y - 1$ **21.** $-a^2 - 3a - 16$ **23.** $8a^2 - 2ab - 6b$ **25.** $12a - 9b - 1$ **27.** $8a^2 + 2a - 8$ **29.** $xy^2$ **31.** $2a - 7$ **33.** $x - 2y$ **35.** $4x^2 - 11$ **37.** $n^2 - 9m^2 + mn$ **39.** 1 **41.** 4 **43.** $\frac{4}{3}$ **45.** 8 **47.** $-3$ **49.** no solution

**Problems, pages 146-147** **1.** 25, 26 **3.** 58, 60, 62, 64 **5.** 22 **7.** 8, 9 **9.** 7, 9, 11 **11.** 17, 18, 19, 20 **13.** length, 25 m; width, 23 m

**Written Exercises, pages 149-150** **1.** $b^{10}$
**3.** $15a^8$ **5.** $6x^3y^3$ **7.** $24a^3b^4$ **9.** $-24c^5d^7$
**11.** $6a^5b^9$ **13.** $x^6$ **15.** $2y^5$ **17.** $4p^5r^3$
**19.** $b^{n+3}$ **21.** 32 **23.** $7ay^{a+7}$ **25.** $-128, 128$
**27.** $26a^4$ **29.** $-14x^9$ **31.** $-2x^3y^3$ **33.** $8x^5y^6$
**35.** $10ab, 6a^2b^2$ **37.** $18a, 10a^2$ **39.** $46x^2$
**41.** $6a^3$ **43.** $18a^3$

**Written Exercises, pages 152-153** **1. a.** $x^{12}$
**b.** $x^{12}$ **c.** $x^7$ **3. a.** $a^{2n}$ **b.** $a^{2n}$ **c.** $a^{2+n}$
**5. a.** 16 **b.** 64 **c.** 64 **7. a.** 18 **b.** 36
**c.** 36 **9.** $64n^2$ **11.** $32x^5$ **13.** $81n^8$
**15.** $\frac{1}{1000}x^{30}$ **17.** $16a^4b^8$ **19.** $8a^6b^{18}$
**21. a.** $9x^{10}$ **b.** $-9x^{10}$ **23. a.** $-27x^{15}$
**b.** $-27x^{15}$ **25.** $32a^5$ **27.** $10,000b^8$
**29.** $108x^7y^6$ **31.** $-\frac{1}{2}c^{15}d^8$ **33.** $72a^{5n}$
**35.** $2y^{2mn}$ **37.** $2x^4y^6$ **39.** $4c^5d^2$ **41. a.** $8x^3$,
$64x^3$ **b.** 8 times **43.** $2^{4x} \cdot 2^{4x} = 2^{8x}$

**Challenge, page 153** Dividing by $(r - s)$ is not defined because if $r = s$, then $r - s = 0$.

**Written Exercises, pages 155-156** **1.** $5a + 10$
**3.** $-8a + 24$ **5.** $4x^2 + 8x$ **7.** $-6b + 15b^2$
**9.** $5x^3 - 10x^2 - 15x$
**11.** $-16x^4 + 24x^3 - 32x^2$
**13.** $2a^3 - a^2b + 4ab^2$ **15.** $6b^3 - 15b^2 - 27b$
**17.** $-6n^4 + 8n^3 + 12n^2$ **19.** $11x^2 - 9x$
**21.** $2y^3$ **23.** $14x^3 - 14x^2$ **25.** $7x - 6$ **27.** 3
**29.** $-1$ **31.** $-\frac{5}{2}$ **33.** 7 **35.** 1 **37.** $\frac{2}{3}$ **39.** 64;
$80 - L$; $W + 50 - L$; $W + 60 - L$;
$W + G - L$ **41.** $2x^2 + 5x$
**43.** $2x^2 + 8x + 8$ **45.** $2x^{2n} - 3x^{n+1} + 4x^n$
**47.** $2b^{2n+2} + 3b^{n+3}$

**Challenge, page 156** $x = 12$

**Written Exercises, pages 158-159**
**1.** $a^2 + 8a + 15$ **3.** $c^2 - 3c - 10$
**5.** $2a^2 + 9a - 18$ **7.** $12t^2 + 7t - 10$
**9.** $x^3 + 5x^2 + 10x + 8$
**11.** $2a^3 + 5a^2 + 11a - 7$
**13.** $24x^3 - 23x^2 + 37x - 20$
**15.** $8 + 4t^2 - 3t^3$ **17.** $6n^2 + 3n - 45$
**19.** $16y^3 - 34y^2 + 11y + 6$
**21.** $6c^2 - 11cd - 7d^2$

**23.** $4x^3 - 4x^2y - xy^2 + y^3$ **25.** $ac, bc, ad, bd$;
$ac + bc + ad + bd = (a + b)(c + d)$;
$ac + bc + ad + bd = ac + bc + ad + bd$
**27.** $12 + 14n - 12n^2 + 16n^3$
**29.** $14 - 73y + 73y^2 - 20y^3$
**31.** $8c^3 - 55c^2d - 8cd^2 + 7d^3$
**33.** $24x^3 + 4x^2y - 16xy^2 + 4y^3$
**35.** $2y^4 - y^3z + 2y^2z^2 - 5yz^3 + 2z^4$ **37.** $\frac{1}{3}$
**39.** 5 **41.** $\frac{23}{5}$ **43.** $x^3 + 9x^2 + 27x + 27$
**45.** $2y^2 - xy - 5x^2$ **47. a.** (1) $x^3 + 1$ (2)
$x^4 - 1$ (3) $x^5 + 1$ **b.** (4) $x^6 - 1$ (5) $x^7 + 1$

**Computer Exercises, page 159**
**1.** $4 + 11x + 3x^2$; $2 - 3x + 7x^2$
**3.** $5x^3 + 9x^2 + 4x$; $4x + 9x^2 - 5x^3$

**Written Exercises, page 162** **1.** $r = \dfrac{C}{2\pi}$

**3.** $g = \dfrac{2s}{t^2}, t \neq 0$ **5.** $z = a$ **7.** $h = \dfrac{2A}{b + c}$,
$b + c \neq 0$ **9.** $F = \frac{9}{5}C + 32$ **11.** $t = \dfrac{A - P}{Pr}$,
$P \neq 0, r \neq 0$ **13.** $d = 4A - a - b - c$
**15.** $x = \dfrac{4}{a}, a \neq 0$ **17.** $w = -\dfrac{4}{a}, a \neq 0$
**19.** $l = \dfrac{2s}{n} - a, n \neq 0$ **21.** $n = \dfrac{360}{180 - a}$,
$a \neq 180$ **23.** $u = \dfrac{2b}{a}, a \neq 0$
**25.** $L = \dfrac{a + sr - s}{r}, r \neq 0$ **27.** $P = \dfrac{A}{1 + rt}$,
$r \neq -\dfrac{1}{t}$ **29.** $R = \dfrac{Cr}{C - Kr}, Kr \neq C$

**Problems, pages 166-167** **1.** 24 km/h **3.** 2:30
P.M. **5.** 4:30 P.M. **7.** 360 km **9.** 4 km
**11.** 400 m **13.** 215 km **15.** $\left(\dfrac{b}{s - r}\right)$ hours
**17.** 5:00 P.M.

**Problems, pages 169-170** **1.** length, 9 m;
width, 4 m **3.** Both are 400 cm$^2$
**5.** 3500 cm$^2$ **7.** length, 20 m; width, 15 m
**9.** 6 m **11. a.** $[8r + 2\pi r + \pi]$ m **b.** $6\pi$ m

**Computer Key-In, pages 170-171**

| **1.** ITEM | NO. SOLD | PRICE | COST |
|---|---|---|---|
| 2341 | 7 | 8.25 | 57.75 |
| 7204 | 4 | 10.95 | 43.80 |
| 3475 | 12 | 9.68 | 116.16 |
| 5068 | 15 | 11.49 | 172.35 |

**Problems, pages 172–174  1.** no solution; impossible to have the same number of dimes as quarters and have \$8  **3.** no solution; need to know either the amount of her gains or the amount of her losses  **5.** 90 km/h  **7.** no solution; six years ago Barbara had not been born according to the information in problem  **9.** no solution; there are no three consecutive integers whose sum is 36 more than the greatest consecutive integer  **11.** no solution; need to know the time traveled by automobile  **13.** 7 cm  **15.** no solution; the sum of their ages two years ago was greater than 10

**Chapter Review, pages 175–176  1.** d  **3.** b  **5.** d  **7.** d  **9.** d  **11.** b  **13.** a  **15.** b  **17.** b

**Cumulative Review, page 178  1.** $-72$  **3.** 0  **5.** $-14$  **7.** 45  **9.** $8z - 5$  **11.** $1600a^{5n}$  **13.** $-12x^4 + 8x^3 + 20x^2$  **15.** $15 - 2x - 8x^2$  **17.** 0  **19.** 0  **21.** no solution  **23.** $-12$  **25.** $-1$  **27.** $-3$  **29.** 11  **31.** 4  **33.** $-10$  **35.** $m = \dfrac{bn + c}{a}$  **37.** \$1.50  **39.** 15 cm × 13 cm

**Maintaining Skills, page 179  1.** 1045  **3.** $-44$  **5.** $-23$  **7.** $-85$  **9.** $\frac{5}{8}$  **11.** 19.15  **13.** 72  **15.** $-92$  **17.** $-21.275$  **19.** 3.282  **21.** $-28.96$  **23.** $-\frac{7}{15}$  **25.** $\frac{19}{17}$  **27.** 13  **29.** $-0.45$  **31.** $\frac{1}{2}$

**Mixed Review, page 180  1.** 4  **3.** no solution  **5.** $2x^2 + 2x - 12$  **7.** $3x - 1$  **9.** 1 year old  **11.** identity axiom for multiplication  **13.** associative axiom for multiplication  **15.** identity axiom for addition  **17.** 8  **19.** 18.75 km/h  **21.** $h = \dfrac{2A}{b_1 + b_2}$  **23.** 9, 11, 13, 15

**Preparing for College Entrance Exams, page 181  1.** B  **3.** B  **5.** A  **7.** C

## CHAPTER 5  FACTORING POLYNOMIALS

**Written Exercises, pages 184–185  1.** (1)(18), (2)(9), (3)(6), (−1)(−18), (−2)(−9), (−3)(−6)  **3.** (1)(37), (−1)(−37)  **5.** (1)(64), (2)(32), (4)(16), (8)(8), (−1)(−64), (−2)(−32), (−4)(−16), (−8)(−8)

**7.** (1)(101), (−1)(−101)  **9.** (1)(83), (−1)(−83)  **11.** (−1)(18), (−2)(9), (−3)(6), (1)(−18), (2)(−9), (3)(−6)  **13.** (−1)(37), (1)(−37)  **15.** (−1)(64), (−2)(32), (−4)(16), (−8)(8), (1)(−64), (2)(−32), (4)(−16)  **17.** (−1)(101), (1)(−101)  **19.** (−1)(83), (1)(−83)  **21.** $3^2 \cdot 11$  **23.** $2^3 \cdot 13$  **25.** $3^3 \cdot 7$  **27.** $2^2 \cdot 7 \cdot 17$  **29.** $2^3 \cdot 3 \cdot 17$  **31.** $2 \cdot 11^2$  **33.** $5 \cdot 7 \cdot 13$  **35.** $2^3 \cdot 3 \cdot 5^2$  **37.** 14  **39.** 36  **41.** 36  **43.** 175  **45.** 1  **47.** 13

**Challenge, page 185**  Browns' rate = 3 m/s; Coles' rate = 4 m/s; pond is 360 m wide

**Written Exercises, pages 189–190  1.** $3a^3$  **3.** $\dfrac{1}{3y^2}$  **5.** $\dfrac{3x^2y^2}{4}$  **7.** $\dfrac{2}{3b^4}$  **9.** $\dfrac{1}{x}$  **11.** $\dfrac{1}{3y}$  **13.** 8  **15.** $-\dfrac{8}{y^3}$  **17.** $\dfrac{4b^2}{a^5}$  **19.** $\dfrac{c^5}{13d^4}$  **21.** $3a^4$  **23.** $-2c^2d$  **25.** $-8x^4y^2$  **27.** $7b^3$  **29.** $a^4b^2$  **31.** $x^4y$  **33.** $2a^3b^2$  **35.** $8rs^2t^2$  **37.** $ab^2$  **39.** $x + y$  **41.** $\dfrac{8x^{n-1}}{7}$  **43.** $-x^{2n}y^n$  **45.** (1) Def. of division, (2) Prop. of the recip. of a product, (3) Comm. ax. for mult.; Assoc. ax. for mult., (4) Def. of division

**Calculator Key-In, page 190  1.** 3; $\frac{3}{13}$  **3.** 5; $\frac{5}{11}$  **5.** 26; $\frac{13}{18}$

**Written Exercises, pages 192–193  1.** $a + 2$  **3.** $6x - 3$  **5.** $x - 2y + 3$  **7.** $2y - 3x$  **9.** $2 - 3y - y^2$  **11.** $-4d^3 + 3cd + 2$  **13.** $6s^3t^2 - 5$  **15.** $3d^2k^2 - 5dk + 2d^2$  **17.** 780  **19.** 380  **21.** 8100  **23.** 850  **25.** 770  **27.** $3(3p - 2q + 1)$  **29.** $3a(5a - 3)$  **31.** $4a^2(a + 2)$  **33.** $5y(2y^2 - y + 3)$  **35.** $\frac{1}{2}h(b - a)$  **37.** $6a^2x(4a^2 - 3a + 2x)$  **39.** $8a(ab - 2b - 3)$  **41.** $-8r^8s^5(5s + 2r)$  **43.** $42w^2yz(3x^3 + 5wy^3z)$  **45.** $5x - 4$  **47.** $6x - 2$  **49.** $a + 5ab - a^2$

**Problems, pages 194–195  1.** $r^2(4 - \pi)$  **3.** $r^2(4 + \pi)$  **5.** $4r^2(4 - \pi)$  **7.** $2r^2(2\pi - 1)$  **9.** $r^2(4 + 3\pi)$

**Written Exercises, pages 197–198  1.** $x^2 + 9x + 14$  **3.** $a^2 - 9a + 20$  **5.** $c^2 + 10c + 21$  **7.** $a^2 - 14a + 45$  **9.** $2a^2 + 11a + 5$  **11.** $2a^2 + 3a - 27$  **13.** $x^2 - 2x - 63$  **15.** $b^2 + 5b - 24$  **17.** $6k^2 + 17k + 5$  **19.** $35a^3 - 74a^2 + 35a$  **21.** $12x^3 - 26x^2 - 10x$

**23.** $14k^3 - 27k^2 - 20k$
**25.** $6x^2 + 16xy + 8y^2$
**27.** $27a^2 - 51ab + 10b^2$  **29.** $2a^4 + a^2 - 21$
**31.** $x^6 + 4x^4 - 21x^2$
**33.** $3a^8 - 11a^4b^2 + 10b^4$  **35.** 26  **37.** 3
**39.** 1  **41.** $a = 9$, $b = 2$, $c = -6$
**43.** $x^{2n} - 16y^{2n}$

*Computer Exercises, page 198*
**1.** $x^2 + 8x + 15$  **3.** $8x^2 - 14x - 15$
**5.** $9x^2 - 4$

*Calculator Key-In, page 198*  **1.** 44  **3.** 11
**5.** 600  **7.** 728  **9.** 17.5

*Written Exercises, pages 200-201*  **1.** $a^2 - 9$
**3.** $9b^2 - 25$  **5.** $81a^2 - 49$  **7.** $64a^2 - 25b^2$
**9.** $9u^4 - v^2$  **11.** $r^2s^2 - t^4$  **13.** 391  **15.** 3596
**17.** 2499  **19.** 39,984  **21.** $(5y - 3)(5y + 3)$
**23.** $(12 - x)(12 + x)$
**25.** $(3a - bc)(3a + bc)$
**27.** $(x^3 - y^3)(x^3 + y^3)$
**29.** $(5t^3 - 12)(5t^3 + 12)$
**31.** $(15 - ab^2)(15 + ab^2)$
**33.** $(ab - c^2)(ab + c^2)(a^2b^2 + c^4)$
**35.** $(a - 1)(a + 1)(a^2 + 1)(a^4 + 1)(a^8 + 1)$
**37.** $3(2x + 3)$  **39.** $2(2a)$
**41.** $9(2x - 3y)(2x + 3y)$
**43.** $2xy(1 - 6x)(1 + 6x)$
**45.** $9t(3t^4 - 1)(3t^4 + 1)$
**47.** $2a(15a^2 - 2)(15a^2 + 2)$
**49.** $(x^n - y^n)(x^n + y^n)$
**51.** $(b^n - c^{2n})(b^n + c^{2n})$
**53.** $(a^{2n} - b^{3n})(a^{2n} + b^{3n})$
**55.** $y^3(y^n - 1)(y^n + 1)$

*Extra, page 202*  **1.** $x^3 + y^3$
**3.** $(w + 2)(w^2 - 2w + 4)$
**5.** $(n + 5)(n^2 - 5n + 25)$
**7. a.** $(z^2 - 1)(z^4 + z^2 + 1) =$
$(z - 1)(z + 1)(z^4 + z^2 + 1)$
**b.** $(z^3 - 1)(z^3 + 1) =$
$(z - 1)(z^2 + z + 1)(z + 1)(z^2 - z + 1)$
**c.** $z^4 + z^2 + 1 =$
$z^4 + z^2 + z^2 + 1 - z^2 =$
$(z^4 + 2z^2 + 1) - z^2 =$
$(z^2 + 1)^2 - z^2 =$
$(z^2 + 1 - z)(z^2 + 1 + z) =$
$(z^2 - z + 1)(z^2 + 1 + z)$

*Challenge, page 202*  **1.** 6 times

*Written Exercises, pages 205-206*
**1.** $x^2 + 4x + 4$  **3.** $a^2 - 8a + 16$
**5.** $4x^2 + 12x + 9$  **7.** $16k^2 - 40k + 25$
**9.** $16p^2 + 24pq + 9q^2$
**11.** $9x^2 + 42xy + 49y^2$
**13.** $a^2b^2 - 10ab + 25$  **15.** $4s^2t^2 - 28st + 49$
**17.** $9 - 30a + 25a^2$  **19.** $64x^4 - 16x^2 + 1$
**21.** $(n - 1)^2$  **23.** $(r - 2)^2$  **25.** $(9 - b)^2$
**27.** $(2x + 1)^2$  **29.** $(6 - 5a)^2$  **31.** $(8x - y)^2$
**33.** $(x^2 + 1)^2$  **35.** $(ab - 6)^2$  **37.** $(a^2 - 12)^2$
**39.** $(5x - 2)^2 = 25x^2 - 20x + 4$;
$(2 - 5x)^2 = 4 - 20x + 25x^2$
**b.** $(2 - 5x)^2 = (-1)(5x - 2)(-1)(5x - 2) =$
$(5x - 2)^2$  **41.** $(x^2 - 9)(x^2 - 9) = (x + 3)$
$(x - 3)(x + 3)(x - 3) = (x + 3)^2(x - 3)^2$
**43.** $3(z + 3)^2$  **45.** $2(3y - 1)^2$
**47.** $5(2x^2 + 3)^2$  **49.** $4k(2k^2 - 3)^2$
**51.** $(w + 3 - 2q)(w + 3 + 2q)$
**53.** $(5c - 2d - 1)(5c + 2d + 1)$  **55.** $-9$
**57.** $-1$  **59.** 7, 8, 9
**61.** $a^2 + 2ab + b^2 - (a^2 - 2ab + b^2) \overset{?}{=} 4ab$;
$a^2 + 2ab + b^2 - a^2 + 2ab - b^2 \overset{?}{=} 4ab$;
$4ab = 4ab$  **63. a.** 1225; 3025; 7225
**b.** $(10t + 5)^2 = 100t^2 + 100t + 25 =$
$[t(t + 1) \times 100] + 25$

*Written Exercises, pages 209-210*
**1.** $(x + 5)(x + 1)$  **3.** $(a - 3)(a - 1)$
**5.** $(r + 6)(r + 3)$  **7.** $(k - 4)(k - 7)$
**9.** $(z - 6)(z - 7)$  **11.** prime
**13.** $(y + 11)(y + 5)$  **15.** $(p - 9)(p - 8)$
**17.** $(10 - c)(2 - c)$  **19.** $(x - 7y)(x - 5y)$
**21.** $(s - 5t)(s - 6t)$  **23.** $(b + 8c)(b + 5c)$
**25.** $(s - 6t)(s - 7t)$  **27.** prime
**29.** $(d + 9e)(d + 3e)$  **31.** $(a - 8)(a - 15)$
**33.** $(9 - a)(12 - a)$  **35.** $(7n - x)(14n - x)$
**37.** 7, 11, $-7$, $-11$  **39.** 8, 16, $-8$, $-16$
**41.** 7, 8, 13, $-7$, $-8$, $-13$
**43.** $(x + 6)(x + 3)$
**45.** $(a + b - 4)(a + b - 2)$
**47.** $(a + 3)(a - 3)(a + 1)(a - 1)$
**49.** $(c + 3)(c - 3)(c^2 - 3)$
**51.** $(x^n - 19y^{2n})(x^n - 23y^{2n})$

*Computer Exercises, page 210*  **1.** yes  **3.** no
**5.** no

*Written Exercises, pages 212-213*
**1.** $(a + 5)(a - 1)$  **3.** $(y - 6)(y + 1)$
**5.** prime  **7.** prime  **9.** $(a + 7)(a - 5)$
**11.** $(z + 9)(z - 4)$  **13.** $(p - 7)(p + 3)$
**15.** prime  **17.** $(a - 6b)(a + 5b)$

**19.** $(p - 10q)(p + 5q)$
**21.** $(k - 15d)(k + 4d)$
**23.** $(x - 11y)(x + 2y)$
**25.** $(1 - 10ab)(1 + 2ab)$
**27.** $(1 - 8ab)(1 + 7ab)$ **29.** $(r - 24)(r + 6)$
**31.** $(40 + b)(20 - b)$ **33.** $(40 + x)(8 - x)$
**35.** $-27, 27, -3, 3, -12, 12$ Answers may vary for Exs. 37–41. **37.** $-18, -10$
**39.** $-140, -96$ **41.** $-26, -60$
**43.** $(x - 4)(x + 4)$
**45.** $(2x - y + 10)(2x - y - 6)$
**47.** $(x - 3)(x + 3)(x^2 + 1)$
**49.** $3(a^2 + 4)(a - 5)(a + 5)$

*Written Exercises, page 216*
**1.** $(2x + 3)(x + 1)$ **3.** $(5a + 1)(a + 1)$
**5.** $(7n - 1)(n - 1)$ **7.** $(5y - 1)(y - 3)$
**9.** prime **11.** $(2t + 3)(t - 2)$
**13.** $(8y - 9)(y + 1)$ **15.** $(k + 3)(7k - 2)$
**17.** prime **19.** $-(2y - 5)(y + 2)$
**21.** $(a + 2b)(a - b)$ **23.** $(9r + 2s)(r - 3s)$
**25.** $(5a - b)(5a + 3b)$
**27.** $(3x - 2y)(4x + 9y)$
**29.** $-(2x - 3)(6x + 7)$
**31.** $-(3c + 1)(16c - 15)$
**33.** $(3x + 1)(36x - 7)$
**35.** $(14y + 9)(3y + 1)$ **37.** $(2y + 5)(y + 5)$
**39.** $x^2(x - 4)(x + 4)$
**41.** $(5a - 5b + 2)(2a - 2b - 3)$

*Computer Key-In, page 217* **1.** $(1)(36)$, $(-1)(-36), (2)(18), (-2)(-18), (3)(12)$, $(-3)(-12), (4)(9), (-4)(-9), (6)(6)$, $(-6)(-6); (1)(-36), (-1)(36), (2)(-18)$, $(-2)(18), (3)(-12), (-3)(12), (4)(-9)$, $(-4)(9), (6)(-6), (-6)(6)$ **3.** $(1)(87)$, $(-1)(-87), (3)(29), (-3)(-29); (1)(-87)$, $(-1)(87), (3)(-29), (-3)(29)$

*Written Exercises, pages 219–220*
**1.** $(n - 3)(2t + 1)$ **3.** $(x + y)(3 - y)$
**5.** $(x^2 + 1)(2d - e + f)$ **7.** $(g + h)(z - 1)$
**9.** $(2 + x)(x - y + 2z)$
**11.** $(2m + n)(p - 4r)$ **13.** $(2w - 1)(z^2 - 6)$
**15.** $(2r + 5)(s - 6)$ **17.** $(p + q)(2 + a)$
**19.** $(q + r)(p + 2r)$ **21.** $(b + c)(a - 2)$
**23.** $(x^2 + 4)(2x + 1)$ **25.** $(4x - 3)(x - 2y)$
**27.** $(4y - 1)(y + 2a)$ **29.** $(2x + 7z)(2x - y)$
**31.** $(a - 2b - 3c)(a + 2b + 3c)$
**33.** $(6k - 2a + c)(6k + 2a - c)$
**35.** $(x - 4y - 3)(x - 4y + 3)$
**37.** $(x + 3 - y)(x + 3 + y)$

**39.** $(h - 6 - k)(h - 6 + k)$
**41.** $(5 - a - 2b)(5 + a + 2b)$
**43.** $(4y + 1 - 4z)(4y + 1 + 4z)$
**45.** $(a - 2b + 2)(a + 2b - 2)$
**47.** $(a - b - 5c)(a + b + 5c)$
**49.** $9(a - b - c)(a - b + c)$
**51.** $(a - b)(a - b - 3)$
**53.** $(2x^2 - 2x + 1)(2x^2 + 2x + 1)$
**55.** $(a - 2b^{2n})(a^{3n} - b)$

*Written Exercises, pages 222–223*
**1.** $5(a + b)^2$ **3.** $-7z(2z + 1)(z - 3)$
**5.** $8x(5x^2 + 7x - 2)$ **7.** $t^2(t - 3)(t + 1)$
**9.** $(x + 5)(y - 2)$ **11.** $36z(2z + q)(2z - q)$
**13.** $(x - y)(x + y)(x^2 + y^2)$
**15.** $2(x - 3)(x + 3)(x^2 + 9)$
**17.** $(a - 2b - 1)(a + 2b + 1)$
**19.** $(y - 2)(y + 2)(y - 1)(y + 1)$
**21.** $(b - 3)^2(b + 3)^2$ **23.** $5k(2k - 5)(k + 1)$
**25.** $2(x - 2y + 2)(x + 2y - 2)$
**27.** $4(a - 4)(a - 2)$ **29.** $(x - 1)(x - 2)(x + 2)$
**31.** $(m - k)(m + k + 1)$
**33.** $c(a - 2b - 3c)(a - 2b + 3c)$
**35.** $(x - a)(ax + a^2 - x)$
**37.** $(b - 3c)(a - 3b)(a + 3b)$
**39.** $2(1 - 2x - y)(1 + 2x + y)$
**41.** $(x + 1)^2(x - 2)$
**43.** $(x + 2y)(a - 3x + 6y)$
**45.** $2(p + 1)(p - 4)(p - 2)$
**47.** $(p - 2q - r + 2s)(p - 2q + r - 2s)$
**49.** $3(15x + y)(x - 4y)$
**51.** $-(b - c - a)(b - c + a)(b + c - a)$ $(b + c + a)$
**53.** $(a + 3b)^2(1 - a + 3b)(1 + a - 3b)$
**55.** $(x + y - x^2 + 2y^2)(x + y + x^2 - 2y^2)$
**57.** $(x - 1)(x - 2)(x + 2)$

*Written Exercises, page 225* **1.** $\{-17, -7\}$
**3.** $\{0, 35\}$ **5.** $\{-\frac{1}{2}, 3\}$ **7.** $\{0, 4, -\frac{7}{3}\}$ **9.** $\{0, \frac{8}{3}, -\frac{1}{3}\}$ **11.** $\{-9, 7\}$ **13.** $\{2, 3\}$ **15.** $\{5\}$
**17.** $\{1, 9\}$ **19.** $\{4, -4\}$ **21.** $\{2\}$ **23.** $\{0, 1, -1\}$ **25.** $\{6, -5\}$ **27.** $\{0, 5\}$ **29.** $\{\frac{5}{2}, -\frac{1}{2}\}$
**31.** $\{-8, 3\}$ **33.** $\{-\frac{1}{3}, \frac{1}{2}\}$ **35.** $\{3, -1\}$
**37.** $\{\frac{1}{4}, 7\}$ **39.** $\{-\frac{9}{2}, \frac{8}{3}\}$ **41.** $\{0, 7\}$ **43.** $\{-1, -2, 2\}$ **45.** $\{1, -1, 3, -3\}$ **47.** $\{0, 5, 9\}$
**49.** $\{-4, 3\}$ **51.** $\{2, -2\}$

*Computer Key-In, pages 226–227* **1.** A-loop: 80–160, 410, C-loop: 190–260; 400
**3.** $(x + 7)(x + 4)$ **5.** $(2x + 7)(2x + 3)$
**7.** $(2x + 1)(3x - 5)$ **9.** when the factors are in reverse order

**8** *Answers to Selected Exercises*

**Problems, pages 229-232** **1.** 8 or $-9$ **3.** $-6$
**5.** 10 or $-2$ **7.** 16 cm by 7 cm **9.** 13 cm by
8 cm **11.** 11 m by 11 m **13.** 15 or $-2$
**15.** 2 s, 3 s **17.** 30 s **19. a.** 3 s **b.** The
44.1 m height is reached only at 3 s. If it was
less than the maximum height, it would be
reached once going up and again coming
down. **21.** 6 **23.** 2 m **25.** 5 m **27.** 40 cm
by 60 cm

**Chapter Review, pages 233-234** **1.** c **3.** c
**5.** c **7.** d **9.** d **11.** b **13.** b **15.** d **17.** c
**19.** b **21.** b **23.** a

**Cumulative Review, page 236** **1.** $-12.7$
**3.** $-5t$ **5.** $5z - 7$ **7.** $216a^{12}b^6$
**9.** $3x^2y - x + \frac{8}{9}$ **11.** $25y^2 + 60y + 36$
**13.** $-4$ **15.** 1 **17.** $2p^2(3p - pr^2 + 4r^3st)$
**19.** $(2a + 3b)^2$ **21.** $(m - 6)(m - 3)$
**23.** $(3y - 1)(2y + 5)$ **25.** $(a + b)^2(a - b)$
**27.** $-6, 6$ **29.** 4 **31.** 10 **33.** $\{-3, 3\}$
**35.** $\{3\}$ **37.** $\{-\frac{1}{4}, \frac{3}{2}\}$ **39.** 60 km/h
**41.** 11 cm by 2 cm

**Maintaining Skills, page 237** **1.** 0.92 **3.** 2.5
**5.** 3.24 **7.** 1.7 **9.** 2.33 **11.** 0.68 **13.** $\frac{31}{50}$
**15.** $\frac{17}{20}$ **17.** $\frac{3}{10,000}$ **19.** 91% **21.** 80%
**23.** 3.2% **25.** 27.2 **27.** 0.08 **29.** 52 **31.** 70
**33.** 12 **35.** 450 **37.** 60 **39.** 20 **41.** 34

## CHAPTER 6 FRACTIONS

**Written Exercises, pages 240-241** **1.** 3, $a \neq 2$
**3.** $\frac{1}{3}$, $n \neq -\frac{1}{3}$ **5.** $\frac{2}{x + 1}$, $x \neq 1$, $x \neq -1$
**7.** $\frac{2}{x - y}$, $x \neq y$, $x \neq 0$, $y \neq 0$ **9.** $\frac{a + 4}{4 - a}$,
$a \neq 4$, $a \neq -4$ **11.** $\frac{1}{y - 5}$, $y \neq 5$, $y \neq -5$
**13.** $-\frac{1}{y - 2}$, $y \neq 2$ **15.** $\frac{1}{2x - y}$, $y \neq 2x$
**17.** $\frac{x + y}{x - y}$, $x \neq y$, $x \neq 0$ **19.** $\frac{x - 2}{x + 2}$, $x \neq -\frac{5}{2}$,
$x \neq -2$ **21.** $\frac{n - 3}{2n - 5}$, $n \neq -\frac{1}{2}$, $n \neq \frac{5}{2}$
**23.** $\frac{3x}{3x - 1}$, $x \neq \frac{1}{3}$, $x \neq 5$ **25.** $\frac{a - 5}{a + 2}$, $a \neq 2$,
$a \neq -2$ **27.** $\frac{x + y}{x + 3y}$, $x \neq -3y$, $x \neq y$
**29.** $x = c - d$, $c \neq -d$ **31.** $x = a + b$,
$a \neq b$

**33.** $x = 5k - 1$, $k \neq \frac{1}{5}$ **35.** $x = c - 2d$,
$c \neq d$ **37.** $x = a - 6$, $a \neq -6$ **39.** The correct answer is 22. The values $x = 4$ and $y = 6$
make the denominator of the original fraction
equal to 0, thus the fraction is not defined for
these values. **41. a.** 0 **b.** 4 **c.** undefined
**43.** $\frac{4x + 7y}{4x - 7y}$ **45.** $\frac{a}{2(3a - 5)}$ **47.** $1 + x$
**49.** $\frac{5 - x}{x + 5}$ **51.** $\frac{a - 3b}{a + 3b + 2}$ **53.** $\frac{a - 3b + 3}{3}$
**55.** 0 **57.** $-3$ **59.** $\frac{5}{2}$

**Application, page 243** **1.** 4¢ **3.** 387.5 kW · h;
$372

**Written Exercises, pages 246-247** **1.** $\frac{3}{2}$ **3.** $\frac{9}{5}$
**5.** $\frac{1}{3}$ **7.** $\frac{1}{6}$ **9.** $\frac{x}{2}$ **11.** $\frac{a}{d}$ **13.** $\frac{pq}{4}$ **15.** $\frac{2df}{27}$
**17.** $9a^{10}$ **19.** $\frac{a^2}{36}$ **21.** $\frac{125a^3}{27b^6}$ **23.** $\frac{x^8}{10,000}$
**25.** $\frac{a}{b}$ **27.** $\frac{24x}{5}$ **29.** $\frac{4x^2}{49}$ in.$^2$ **31.** $\frac{x^2}{6}$ **33.** $\frac{dy}{9}$
dollars **35.** $\frac{y}{y - 3}$ **37.** $-\frac{a + x}{3a}$
**39.** $\frac{(x - 2)(x - 4)}{x^2}$ **41.** $\frac{1}{2xy(3 + y)}$
**43.** $(2n - 1)^2$ **45.** $2x(2a - x)$ **47.** 1
**49.** $\frac{(2a + b)(d - 2c)}{(2c + d)(b - 2a)}$ **51.** 6 **53.** $\frac{3(a - b + c)}{(b - a + c)}$

**Computer Key-In, page 247** **1.** 1 is a factor of
every integer. **3.** 1, 3, 5, 7, 9, 11, 13, 15, 17,
19, 21, 23, 25

**Written Exercises, pages 249-250** **1.** $\frac{5}{6}$ **3.** $\frac{1}{2}$
**5.** $\frac{a^2}{3}$ **7.** $\frac{2n}{3}$ **9.** $\frac{2x}{3y}$ **11.** $\frac{25}{9x^2}$ **13.** 1 **15.** $\frac{2}{3}$
**17.** $\frac{c(a - b)}{abd}$ **19.** $-\frac{1}{(x + 1)^2}$ **21.** $\frac{a^2 + b^2}{a + b}$
**23.** $-\frac{3}{2(n + 3)(n - 1)}$ **25. a.** $\frac{15}{8}$ **b.** $\frac{10}{3}$ **c.** $\frac{r^2}{t^3}$
**27. a.** $\frac{n^2}{3}$ **b.** 3 **c.** 4 **29.** $\frac{1}{6a^5}$ **31.** $\frac{x(2x - 5)}{3(x - 4)}$
**33.** $a + b$ **35.** $-1$ **37.** $\frac{1}{4(3n - 5)}$ **39.** $\frac{5(s - 2)}{s - 4}$
**41.** $\frac{2(a + 3)}{a - 2}$

**Challenge, page 250** 16,807 hekats of grain

**Written Exercises, pages 253-254** **1.** 15
**3.** $6x$ **5.** $3(x - 3)$ **7.** $5(4 - a)$ **9.** $a^3$
**11.** $4mn^2$ **13.** $5(2n - 3)$ **15.** $-4$
**17.** $2(x - 1)$ **19.** $3y$ **21.** $6(x + 2)$

**23.** $2(x + 5)$  **25.** 18  **27.** 36  **29.** 12  **31.** 24
**33.** 100  **35.** $3(x - 2)$  **37.** $48x^2y^3$
**39.** $2(x - 1)(x + 1)$  **41.** $8a^2b^2$
**43.** $y(y - 3)(y + 3)$  **45.** $(a - 1)(a + 1)$
**47.** $12(y + 2)(y + 3)(y + 4)$

*Written Exercises, pages 256–258*  **1.** $\dfrac{1}{n}$  **3.** $\dfrac{1}{a}$

**5.** $\dfrac{x + 1}{3}$  **7.** $-x - 1$  **9.** $\dfrac{3 - 2n}{n - 2}$  **11.** $\dfrac{5}{2y - 7}$

**13.** $\dfrac{2x + 3}{x^2}$  **15.** $\dfrac{8x - 1}{6x^2}$  **17.** $\dfrac{12n - 1}{2n^3}$

**19.** $\dfrac{5x - 6}{6}$  **21.** $\dfrac{7y}{18}$  **23.** $\dfrac{8x + 9}{15}$  **25.** $\dfrac{n + 23}{24}$

**27.** $\dfrac{17a - 12b}{12}$  **29.** $\dfrac{7x + 1}{3}; \dfrac{x^2 - 1}{3}$

**31.** $\frac{9}{2}x + 2; \dfrac{7x(x + 1)}{12}$  **33.** $\dfrac{6(x - 1)}{(x - 3)(x + 3)}$

**35.** $\dfrac{3(x - 3)}{(x + 1)(x - 2)}$

**37.** $\dfrac{-y(y + 3)}{(y - 5)(y + 5)}$  **39.** $\dfrac{x^2 + y^2}{(x + y)(x - y)}$  **41.** 1

**43.** $\dfrac{z^2 + z - 1}{z(1 - z)(1 + z)}$  **45.** $\dfrac{a + b}{ab}$

**47.** $\dfrac{4}{(n - 5)(n + 5)}$  **49.** $\dfrac{3(3c + 2)}{(c + 1)(c + 2)^2}$

**51.** $\dfrac{2x - 1}{2x + 1}$  **53.** $\dfrac{-(2x^2 + 15x + 9)}{3(x - 3)(x + 3)}$  **55.** $\dfrac{-3}{cd}$

**57.** $\dfrac{-4}{(y + 1)^2(y - 1)^2}$

*Written Exercises, pages 261–262*  **1.** $\frac{21}{5}$

**3.** $\dfrac{6x + 1}{x}$  **5.** $\dfrac{3a^2 - 2}{a}$  **7.** $\dfrac{a + 2b}{b}$  **9.** $\dfrac{5x + 6}{x + 2}$

**11.** $\dfrac{-4x - 15}{x + 3}$  **13.** $\dfrac{6x^2 + 5x}{x + 1}$  **15.** $\dfrac{3n^2 - n - 5}{n^2 - 1}$

**17.** $\dfrac{n^2 + n - 2}{n + 1}$  **19.** $\dfrac{a^2 + 5a + 2}{a + 2}$  **21.** $x - 6$

**23.** $\dfrac{2x^2 - 1}{x(x + 1)}$  **25.** $\dfrac{4x}{x + 1}$  **27.** $\dfrac{-a + 15}{a - 3}$

**29.** $\dfrac{5x^2 + 5x - 6}{2x + 3}$  **31.** $\dfrac{a^4 - 2a^2 - 8}{a^2}$  **33.** $\dfrac{a + b}{a}$

**35.** $a - b$  **37.** $\dfrac{a}{a + 2}$  **39.** All three denominators used are common denominators and
yield an answer of $\dfrac{3x - 9}{x - 1}$.  **41.** $\dfrac{10y^2 + 18y - 400}{y}$
**43.** $-1$  **45.** $C = 4, D = 2$

*Computer Key-In, page 262*  **1.** 72  **3.** 195
**9.** The RUNs that have the smaller denominator first.

*Written Exercises, pages 265–266*  **1.** $x + 5$

**3.** $n + 6$  **5.** $y + 4 + \dfrac{2}{y + 2}$  **7.** $x - \dfrac{9}{x - 3}$

**9.** $n + 2 + \dfrac{18}{n - 5}$  **11.** $x - 2 + \dfrac{8}{x + 2}$

**13.** $x - 3 + \dfrac{2}{2x - 1}$  **15.** $2x - 1 + \dfrac{9}{2x + 1}$

**17.** $n^2 + 2n + 1$  **19.** $a^2 - 2a + 4$

**21.** $8x^2 + 6x + 4 - \dfrac{7}{3x - 2}$

**23.** $a^2 + 5ab - 7b^2$  **25.** $2x^3 - x^2 - 3x + 2$
**27.** $n^3 - 1$  **29.** $n^2 + 3n + 4$  **31.** $3n + 2$
**33.** $(3n + 2)(n - 1)(n - 2)$
**35.** $(2x + 1)(2x + 3)(x - 5)$  **37.** $-6$  **39.** 1
**41. a.** $x^{99} + x^{98} + \ldots + 1$
**b.** $x^{n-1} + x^{n-2} + \ldots + 1$
**43. a.** $x^{100} - x^{99} + x^{98} - x^{97} + \ldots + 1$
**b.** $x^{n-1} - x^{n-2} + x^{n-3} - \ldots + 1$

*Extra, pages 267–268*  **1.** $\frac{1}{5}$  **3.** $\dfrac{1}{v}$  **5.** 3

**7.** $\frac{1}{13}$  **9.** $\dfrac{6}{d}$  **11.** $\dfrac{r + 2s}{s - r}$  **13.** $\dfrac{z - 5}{z + 5}$  **15.** $\dfrac{k + 3}{k + 2}$

**17.** 1  **19.** $\dfrac{2z^2 - 2z}{2z^2 + z - 4}$  **21.** $x = \dfrac{z}{2 - z}$

**25.** $\dfrac{5n}{5 - n}$ articles  **27.** $\dfrac{w + 6}{3(w - 2)}$

**29.** $n^2 + 1$  **31.** $\dfrac{54e^2 - e - 29}{6(3e - 1)(3e + 1)}$  **33.** $\dfrac{1}{2s}$

**35.** $-\dfrac{1}{c - 3}$

*Chapter Review, pages 269–270*  **1.** c  **3.** a
**5.** b  **7.** d  **9.** a  **11.** d  **13.** c

*Cumulative Review, page 272*  **1.** 0.64
**3.** $-27a^6b^9c^{12}$  **5.** $20x^2 + 3x - 9$
**7.** $-17t - 3s$  **9.** $16t^4s^2 - 81$  **11.** 0
**13.** $a^2b(6a + 5ab - 3b)$  **15.** $2t(2t - 7)^2$
**17.** prime  **19.** $y(y + 8)(y - 4)$
**21.** $(2x - y + 1)(2x + y - 1)$  **23.** 36
**25.** $-6$  **27.** $\frac{4}{3}, -\frac{4}{3}$  **29.** 7, $-1$  **31.** $\dfrac{1}{a + 4}$

**33.** $\dfrac{a - b}{cd^2}$  **35.** $3b^2 - 2b + 1 - \dfrac{8}{2b - 3}$
**37.** twins, 16; mother, 40  **39.** 5 km

*Maintaining Skills, page 273*  **1.** 14 cm by
2 cm  **3.** 9 cm by 6 cm  **5.** 5 km

*Mixed Review, page 274*  **1.** 2 cm by 7 cm
**3.**

**5.** no solution  **7.** $-3$  **9.** home team; 2 points  **11.** $3a^2 + 8ab - 3b^2$  **13.** $-12$  **15.** $(2x + 1)(2x + 3)$  **17.** $10, -8$  **19.** 34  **21.** $-16$

*Preparing for College Entrance Exams, page 275*  **1.** E  **3.** D  **5.** D  **7.** B

## CHAPTER 7  APPLYING FRACTIONS

*Written Exercises, pages 279-280*  **1.** $1:6$  **3.** $1:100$  **5.** $14:1$  **7.** $22:1$  **9.** $2:1$  **11.** $4:3:1$  **13. a.** $14:19$  **b.** $8:15$  **15. a.** $24:19$  **b.** $4:3$  **17.** $5:8$  **19.** $2:1$  **21.** $3:1$  **23.** $1:2$  **25.** $(a + b):1$  **27.** $2:1$

*Problems, pages 280-281*  **1.** 18, 48  **3.** 360 girls  **5.** 200, 240, 280  **7.** 150 m³ cement, 300 m³ sand, 400 m³ gravel  **9.** 88 km/h, 66 km/h  **11.** 24 dimes, 16 nickels  **13.** 200 pencils  **15.** 900 full size cars

*Written Exercises, pages 284-285*  **1.** $\frac{15}{4}$  **3.** 3  **5.** $\frac{28}{15}$  **7.** $\frac{15}{4}$  **9.** $\frac{2}{3}$  **11.** $\frac{6}{7}$  **13.** 9  **15.** $\frac{3}{2}$  **17.** $\frac{4}{5}$  **19.** $-14$  **21.** 11  **23.** 18  **25.** 3  **27.** $-1$  **29.** 0  **31.** 9  **33.** 0  **35.** $\frac{7}{20}$  **37.** $\frac{c(c + d)}{d}$  **39.** $m = \frac{F}{r}, r = \frac{F}{m}$  **41.** $V = \frac{KT}{P}, T = \frac{PV}{K}$  **43.** 16

*Problems, pages 285-286*  **1.** $5.85  **3.** 20 L  **5.** $3\frac{3}{4}$ doz  **7.** 69 dentists  **9.** 5 acres  **11.** 262,995 km²

*Computer Exercises, page 286*  **1. a.** $0.\overline{6}$  **b.** 2.5  **c.** $0.\overline{45}$  **d.** $0.\overline{135}$

*Computer Key-In, page 287*  **1.** $\frac{3}{5}, \frac{6}{10}, \frac{9}{15}, \frac{12}{20}, \frac{15}{25}, \frac{18}{30}$, and so on.  **5.** For $A = 3, B = 5$ the areas are 15, 60, 135, 240, 375; for $A = 2, B = 6$, the areas are 12, 48, 108, 192, 300  **7.** For $A = 3, B = 5$ the ratio is $25:1$; for $A = 2, B = 6$, the ratio is $25:1$.

*Written Exercises, pages 289-290*  **1.** $\frac{6}{5}$  **3.** 4  **5.** $-1$  **7.** 8  **9.** 1  **11.** $\frac{12}{5}$  **13.** 11  **15.** $-\frac{2}{5}$  **17.** $\frac{1}{2}$  **19.** 0  **21.** 12  **23.** 5  **25.** 4  **27.** $-5$  **29.** 1  **31.** $\frac{1}{3}$  **33.** $-4$  **35.** $-\frac{7n}{13}$  **37.** $\frac{a + 3}{a}$

*Problems, pages 289-290*  **1.** 48  **3.** 15, 6  **5.** Jill is 15; Jack is 18  **7.** 15 cm by 6 cm  **9.** 8 km  **11.** 24 quarters, 8 dimes  **13.** 6 apples

*Written Exercises, pages 292-293*  **1.** 4  **3.** 9  **5.** 12  **7.** 2  **9.** 9  **11.** no solution  **13.** 0  **15.** no solution  **17.** all real numbers except $y = 2$  **19.** $y = 2$  **21.** $\{-\frac{1}{2}, 1\}$  **23.** all values except $n = -\frac{1}{2}$  **25.** 12  **27.** $\{0, 4\}$  **29.** no solution  **31.** $\frac{7}{13}$  **33.** 3  **35.** 1  **37.** 9  **39.** 8  **41.** $\{1, 4\}$  **43.** $\{4, -2\}$

*Problems, pages 293-294*  **1.** $\frac{2}{3}$ or $\frac{3}{2}$  **3.** $\frac{3}{2}$  **5.** 26, 14  **7.** $5\frac{1}{2}$ h  **9.** 24 people  **11.** 12 km/h

*Computer Exercises, page 294*  **1.** 60  **3.** 50

*Written Exercises, pages 297-298*  **1.** $\frac{1}{4}$  **3.** $\frac{1}{3}$  **5.** $\frac{3}{5}$  **7.** $\frac{1}{8}$  **9.** $\frac{1}{25}$  **11.** $\frac{5}{4}$  **13.** 96  **15.** 190  **17.** 0.06  **19.** 89  **21.** 483  **23.** 3000  **25.** 40  **27.** 180  **29.** 5.6  **31.** 80%  **33.** 2%  **35.** $33\frac{1}{3}$%  **37.** $3, $9  **39.** $24, $136  **41.** $11, $55  **43.** $120, $300  **45.** 20  **47.** 8  **49.** 20  **51.** 10  **53.** 86.25  **55.** 9.6  **57.** $x = -64,000$  **59.** $-56\frac{2}{3}$  **61.** $1230  **63.** 0.11  **65.** $2000

*Problems, page 299*  **1.** 60%  **3.** $85,000  **5.** $9500  **7.** $18.70  **9.** $39  **11.** $126  **13.** rural, 68 million people; urban, 153 million people  **15.** 360 calories

*Written Exercises, pages 302-303*  **1.** 10%  **3.** 5%  **5.** $12\frac{1}{2}$%  **7.** $3.64  **9.** $6.40  **11.** $50  **13.** 20%  **15.** 15%  **17.** $25.60  **19.** $7  **21.** $70

*Problems, pages 303-304*  **1.** $33\frac{1}{3}$%  **3.** 8%  **5.** 20%  **7.** $10,800  **9.** $42  **11.** $1600 at 6%, $4400 at 11%  **13.** $20,000  **15.** $1440

*Problems, pages 309-311*  **1.** 2 kg of cashews, 6 kg pecans  **3.** 50 g  **5.** $3.00  **7.** 13%  **9.** 25 g  **11.** 2 kg  **13.** 8 kg of apples, 12 kg of apricots  **15.** 65 km/h  **17.** 3.2 L acid, 4.8 L water  **19.** 8 kg  **21.** $5500 at 12%, $8500 at $5\frac{1}{2}$%  **23. a.** 25 km/h  **b.** 24 km/h  **25. a.** $2sx + rx$  **b.** $\frac{2s + r}{3}$  **27. a.** $0.05a + 0.10b$  **b.** $\frac{0.05a + 0.1b}{a + b}$

*Calculator Key-In, page 311*  **1.** 969.4  **3.** 637.5  **5.** 1625  **7.** $1816.83

*Challenge, page 311*  30 km

*Problems, pages 315–316*  **1.** $\frac{2}{5}$; $\frac{x}{5}$  **3.** $\frac{11}{20}$; $\frac{11x}{30}$
**5.** 1 h 12 min  **7.** 30 min  **9.** 36 min
**11.** 24 min  **13.** $13\frac{1}{3}$ min  **15.** 30 min
**17.** 12 h  **19.** 2 h  **21.** 2 h

*Written Exercises, pages 319–320*
**1.** 300,000,000 m/s
**3.** 2,000,000,000,000,000,000,000,000,000,000 kg
**5.** 0.00000136 cm
**7.** 0.00000000000000005 cm  **9. a.** $10^3$
**b.** $10^{-3}$  **11. a.** $10^6$  **b.** $10^{-6}$  **13.** $10^6$
**15. a.** $4.7 \times 10^3$
**b.** $4 \cdot 10^3 + 7 \cdot 10^2 + 0 \cdot 10^1 + 0 \cdot 10^0$
**17. a.** $9.081 \times 10^8$
**b.** $9 \cdot 10^8 + 0 \cdot 10^7 + 8 \cdot 10^6 + 1 \cdot 10^5 +$
$0 \cdot 10^4 + 0 \cdot 10^3 + 0 \cdot 10^2 + 0 \cdot 10^1 + 0 \cdot 10^0$
**19. a.** $2.1 \times 10^{-4}$
**b.** $0 \cdot 10^{-1} + 0 \cdot 10^{-2} + 0 \cdot 10^{-3} + 2 \cdot 10^{-4} +$
$1 \cdot 10^{-5}$  **21. a.** $1.02 \times 10^{-8}$
**b.** $0 \cdot 10^{-1} + 0 \cdot 10^{-2} + 0 \cdot 10^{-3} + 0 \cdot 10^{-4} +$
$0 \cdot 10^{-5} + 0 \cdot 10^{-6} + 0 \cdot 10^{-7} + 1 \cdot 10^{-8} +$
$0 \cdot 10^{-9} + 2 \cdot 10^{-10}$  **23. a.** $9.944 \times 10^{-1}$
**b.** $9 \times 10^{-1} + 9 \times 10^{-2} + 4 \times 10^{-3} + 4 \times 10^{-4}$
**25. a.** $1.7 \times 10^{10}$  **b.** $1 \cdot 10^{10} + 7 \cdot 10^9$
**27.** $2 \times 10^6$  **29.** $1.6 \times 10^9$  **31.** 1

*Problems, pages 320–321*
**1.** $9.4608 \times 10^{12}$ km  **3.** 4.3 years
**5.** $1.695 \times 10^{13}$ cm; yes; yes; yes; yes

*Written Exercises, pages 325–326*  **1.** $\frac{1}{5}$  **3.** $\frac{1}{25}$
**5.** $\frac{1}{81}$  **7.** $\frac{1}{729}$  **9.** $\frac{1}{16}$  **11.** $\frac{1}{32}$  **13.** 64  **15.** 81
**17.** 27  **19.** 64  **21.** $\frac{1}{81}$  **23.** 729  **25. a.** $\frac{4}{3}$
**b.** 8  **27. a.** 16  **b.** $\frac{16}{9}$  **29.** Division by zero is
not defined  **31.** $\frac{7}{x}$  **33.** $\frac{y^2}{x}$  **35.** $\frac{1}{a^6}$  **37.** $\frac{27}{x^6}$

**39.** $\frac{1}{x^2}$  **41.** $\frac{1}{a^6}$  **43.** $a^8$  **45.** $\frac{1}{c^7}$  **47.** $x^6$
**49.** $n^8$  **51.** 25  **53.** 0.0000128  **55.** 0.0000128
**57.** 625  **59.** 3  **61.** 2  **63.** $\frac{1}{\sqrt{x}}$; $\frac{1}{\sqrt[3]{x}}$

*Problems, page 327*  **1.** 0.7084252 kg;
0.5018663 kg  **3. a.** 15 million  **b.** 22 million
**c.** 10 million  **5. a.** $100(2.72)^4 \approx 5474$
**b.** $100(2.72)^{-4} \approx 2$
**c.** $100(2.72)^{12} = 16{,}399{,}358$
**d.** $100(2.72)^{-12} = 0$

*Calculator Key-In, page 328*  **1.** 0.6  **3.** 0.9
**5.** $68.\overline{3}$  **7.** $-5.75$

*Chapter Review, pages 329–330*  **1.** d  **3.** a
**5.** d  **7.** b  **9.** b  **11.** a  **13.** d  **15.** c

*Cumulative Review, page 332*  **1.** 12
**3.** $-16m^8n^7$  **5.** $25a^6b^2c^8$
**7.** $36t^2v^4 - 60tv^2 + 25$
**9.** $2x^3 - 11x^2y - 11xy^2 - 3y^3$
**11.** $\frac{1}{x^2z(3z + 1)}$  **13.** $5b + 3$  **15.** $x^{14}(x - 4)^2$
**17.** 12%  **19.** $(7z - 2)^2$
**21.** $(3b + 7)(2b + 3)$  **23.** $(12x - 1)(x + 4)$
**25.** 30  **27.** $-\frac{9}{2}$  **29.** $\{0, 1, 11\}$  **31.** 1
**33.** $7.4 \times 10^{-5}$  **35.** 14, 16  **37.** 12%
**39.** 56 min

*Maintaining Skills, page 333*
**1.** $9a^2 - 5a + 8$  **3.** $12 - 5x$  **5.** $12x - 20z$
**7.** $2x - 8y - 6$  **9.** $-\frac{13}{6}b$  **11.** $-6a^3b^4c$
**13.** $-m^5n^2p^3$  **15.** $16x^8y^{12}$  **17.** $r^{15}s^{11}t^7$
**19.** $64c^{12}d^{12}e^6 - 8c^{12}d^{12}r^6$
**21.** $3a^3b^2 - 3a^2b^3 + 3ab^4$
**23.** $c^2d^7 - 2c^3d^5 + c^5d^3$  **25.** $z^2 + 5z - 24$
**27.** $y^2 - 8y - 20$  **29.** $12z^2 - 9z - 3$
**31.** $81d^2 - 9$  **33.** $x^4 - 36$
**35.** $-2b^3 + 19b^2 - 37b + 14$

## CHAPTER 8  LINEAR EQUATIONS
## AND SYSTEMS

*Written Exercises, pages 337–338*  **1.** yes, yes
**3.** yes, yes  **5.** no, no  **7.** yes, no
**9.** $y = \frac{3x - 7}{2}$  **11.** $y = \frac{7x^2 - 4}{3}$
**13.** $y = \frac{4 - 3x}{3}$  **15.** $a = \frac{7 + 3b}{2}$
**17.** $q = \frac{4p}{3}$  **19.** $a = 8b$
**21.** $(1, 4), (3, 3), (5, 2), (7, 1), (9, 0)$
**23.** $(1, 11), (3, 6), (5, 1)$  **25.** $(0, 5), (3, 4),$
$(4, 3), (5, 0)$  **27.** $(1, 6), (2, 3), (3, 2), (6, 1)$
**29.** 13 45's, 1 LP; 9 45's, 2 LP's; 5 45's, 3
LP's; 1 45, 4 LP's  **31.** 4 pigs, 40 chickens
**33.** $(3, 9)$  **35.** $(19, 8)$  **37.** $y = \frac{2x}{x - 2}$

*Computer Exercises, page 338*  **1.** yes  **3.** yes
**5.** no

**Written Exercises, pages 343-344**
**1-11.**

**13.** parallelogram

**15.** rectangle

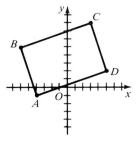

**17.** *E*  **19.** *Z, O*  **21.** *P, O, X, I*  **23.** *B*
**25.**

**27.**

**29.**

**31.**

**33.**

**35.**

**37.**

**39.**

**41.**

**43.**

**Computer Exercises, page 344**  **1. a.** yes
**b.** no  **c.** yes

**Challenge, page 345**  41

**Written Exercises, pages 348-349**
**1.**

**3.**

**5.**

**7.**

**9.**

**11.**

**13.**    **15.**

**17.** $(2, 4), (-2, 4)$   **19.** $(5, 5)$   **21.** $(-2, -4)$
**23.** $12$

*Written Exercises, pages 352–353*   **1.** $(5, 25)$
**3.** $(8, 2)$   **5.** $(1, 4)$   **7.** $(3, -1)$   **9.** $(\frac{1}{14}, \frac{5}{28})$
**11.** $(\frac{8}{11}, \frac{13}{11})$   **13.** $(1, -1)$   **15.** $(3, 5)$
**17.** $(5, -3)$   **19.** $(8, -2)$   **21.** $(12, 8)$
**23.** $(4, -3)$   **25.** $(3, -1)$   **27.** $(5, -26)$
**29.** infinite number; $(1, 10), (0, 8), (-4, 0)$
**31.** $A = 3, B = -1$   **33.** The equations have
no common solution, so their graphs are parallel lines.   **35.** $a = 5, b = 2$   **37.** yes
**39.** $a = 19, b = 31, c = 12$   **41.** $x = 5,$
$y = -1, z = 2$   **43.** $a = 1, b = 2, c = 3,$
$d = -4$

*Computer Exercises, page 353*   **1.** $(1, -1)$
**3.** no solution

*Problems, page 357*   **1.** 12 nickels   **3.** 18
quarters   **5.** Connie, $26.50; Dick, $9.50
**7.** Tracy, $32; Connie, $20   **9.** Pat, $52.50;
Mike, $35.50   **11.** 13 cm by 7 cm   **13.** $1000
**15.** 18, 20   **17.** $1.10   **19.** $5970   **21.** 8, 24
**23.** Carl, $9.60; Diane, $19.20; Ed, $17.20

*Written Exercises, pages 359–360*   **1.** $(5, 4)$
**3.** $(4, -3)$   **5.** $(10, -2)$   **7.** $(\frac{23}{4}, -\frac{1}{2})$
**9.** $(3, -2)$   **11.** $(-\frac{1}{3}, \frac{2}{3})$   **13.** $(\frac{1}{2}, \frac{1}{4})$   **15.** $(\frac{9}{2}, \frac{1}{4})$
**17.** $(5, -1)$   **19.** $(0, -1)$   **21.** $(1, -3)$

**23.** $(6, 4)$   **25.** $(24, \frac{5}{3})$   **27.** $a = 4, b = -3$
**29.** Both equations can be simplified to
$x - 4y = 0$.

*Problems, pages 360–361*   **1.** 8, 13   **3.** 424
girls   **5.** 14 bull's eye   **7.** walking, 8 km/h;
cycling, 30 km/h   **9.** Tom, $1.80; Maria,
$1.20   **11.** 15 3000-lb car, 3 5000-lb cars

*Challenge, page 361*   8 roosters, 11 hens, 81
chicks, or 12 roosters, 4 hens, 84 chicks

*Written Exercises, pages 364–365*   **1.** $(3, 2)$
**3.** $(1, 2)$   **5.** $(2, -2)$   **7.** $(1, -1)$   **9.** $(5, 4)$
**11.** $(-5, -3)$   **13.** $(2, 1)$   **15.** $(4, 1)$
**17.** $(-6, 0)$   **19.** $(4, 3)$   **21.** $(3, 4)$
**23.** $(20, 50)$   **25.** $(6, -9)$   **27.** yes
**29.** $(\frac{1}{2}, -1)$   **31.** $(\frac{2}{3}, \frac{5}{7})$   **33.** $\left(\frac{6}{5a}, -\frac{1}{5b}\right)$
**35.** $x = 1, y = 2, z = 4$   **37.** infinite number
of solutions in the form $(x, 8 - x, 6 - x)$

*Mixed Practice, pages 365–366*
**1.** $(1, 6)$   **3.** $(2, 1)$

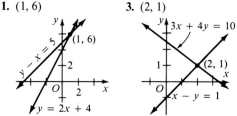

**5.** $(3, 1)$   **7.** $(1, -1)$   **9.** $(1, -1)$   **11.** $(7, 1)$
**13.** $(2, 0)$   **15.** $(14, 10)$   **17.** $(7, 4)$   **19.** $(5, 3)$
**21.** $(7, 3)$   **23.** $(4, 3)$   **25.** $(2, -1)$
**27.** $(-4, -6)$   **29.** $r = 90, s = 72, t = 18$
**31.** $(\frac{1}{4}, \frac{1}{5})$   **33.** $x = -\frac{46}{9}, y = -\frac{14}{9}, z = \frac{20}{3}$

*Problems, pages 366–368*   **1.** 16, 34   **3.** Al is
38; Jack is 25   **5.** 8000 cm²   **7.** 24 dimes, 76
quarters   **9.** 15 boys, 9 girls   **11.** 100 children   **13.** 480 g   **15.** grape, $1.20; orange,
$1.50   **17.** 280 kg cement, 210 kg sand, 140 kg
water   **19.** 120

**21.** stock A, $2000; stock B, $3000   **23.** 2 kg
**25.** $4500   **27.** 7 plums   **29.** 30 by 28

*Calculator Key-In, page 369*   **1.** $(2, 3)$

*Reading Algebra, page 370*  **1.** 85 dimes, 72 quarters  **3.** 800 km/h  **5.** 12 cm by 7 cm  **7.** 4 cm, 6 cm

*Problems, pages 373-374*
No current

**1.**

|  | Rate | × Time = | Distance |
|---|---|---|---|
| Downstream | 10 | 3 | 30 |
| Upstream | 10 | 3 | 30 |

Total time = 6 h
Average speed = 10 km/h

5 km/h current

| Rate | × Time = | Distance |
|---|---|---|
| 15 | 2 | 30 |
| 5 | 6 | 30 |

Total time = 8 h
Average speed = 7.5 km/h
**3.** $5.\overline{3}$ km  **5.** 17 km/h, 5 km/h  **7.** 500 km/h, 100 km/h  **9.** 770 km/h, 70 km/h  **11.** 15 km/h  **13.** 5 km/h

*Problems, pages 378-380*  **1.** 38  **3.** 79  **5.** 72  **7.** Alicia is 13.  **9.** Karen is 22.  **11.** Eiffel Tower was 95; Washington Monument was 100.  **13.** $\frac{5}{13}$  **15.** $\frac{5}{8}$  **17.** $\frac{12}{18}$  **19.** 360  **21.** 342  **23.** James is 18  **25.** $\frac{18}{81}$  **27.** $\frac{37}{73}$  **29.** $\frac{21}{12}, \frac{42}{24}, \frac{63}{36}, \frac{84}{48}$  **31.** father is 39; son is 16

*Challenge, page 380*  $a = 7, b = 6, c = 5$

*Chapter Review, pages 383-384*  **1.** c  **3.** b  **5.** c  **7.** d  **9.** c  **11.** b  **13.** d

*Cumulative Review, page 386*
**1.** $7p^2q + 4p - 21q^3$
**3.** $-3j^4k^4 + 24j^4k^3 - 27j^3k^4$
**5.** $42z^2 - 78z - 12$  **7.** $7t + 5$  **9.** $\frac{1}{5(x-3)}$
**11.** $7.2 \times 10^{11}$  **13.** $(8z + 9y)^2$  **15.** prime
**17.** $(2y + 1)(3y - 10)$  **19.** 16  **21.** 11  **23.** $\frac{6}{5}$
**25.** $\{\frac{1}{15}, -4\}$  **27.** $-160$  **29.** $(2, \frac{4}{3})$
**31.** (2, 1)  **33.** 660 km/h, 180 km/h  **35.** 7, 9 or $-1$, 1

*Maintaining Skills, page 387*
**1.** $5b^2c^3(5 + 3b^3c)$  **3.** $3u^4v(3u + 12v - 5v^2)$
**5.** $-8x^2y^3(3x^5y^2 - 4x^4 + y)$
**7.** $z(z - 11)(z + 11)$  **9.** $(7 - x^3)(7 + x^3)$
**11.** prime  **13.** $(4a - 5)^2$  **15.** $(5x + 3)^2$

**17.** $(b + 9)(b + 2)$  **19.** $(7d - c)(2d + c)$
**21.** $(x + 7)(x + 3)$  **23.** $(n - 2p)(n - 3p)$
**25.** $(t + 3)(r - 2s)$
**27.** $(s - 2t - 3)(s + 2t + 3)$
**29.** $(4a - 3b + 5)(4a + 3b - 5)$
**31.** $(3b + 5)(b - 1)$  **33.** $2(3m + 2)(m - 2)$
**35.** $z(5z + 1)(5z + 2)$  **37.** $(1 - 7y)(y + 3)$
**39.** $2(2b + 1)(3b - 5)$

*Mixed Review, page 388*
**1.** (1, 2)

**3.** 14  **5.** 4  **7.** 8  **9.** $(3x + 5)^2$  **11.** 3 km/h, 6 km/h
**13.** $(n)^2 + (n + 2)^2 = 8(n + n + 2) + 2$
**15.** $1.25 \times 10^6$  **17.** $(2, -2)$  **19.** $(\frac{1}{3}, \frac{1}{2})$

*Preparing for College Entrance Exams, page 389*  **1.** A  **3.** A  **5.** C

## CHAPTER 9  INTRODUCTION TO FUNCTIONS

*Written Exercises, pages 394-395*  **1.** $-\frac{1}{2}$
**3.** 1  **5.** $\frac{2}{11}$  **7.** 1  **9.** no slope  **11.** 0  **13.** 5
**15.** $-3$  **17.** 1  **19.** $-\frac{2}{3}$  **21.** $\frac{8}{3}$  **23.** 0
**25.** $-2$  **27.** not collinear
**29.**

**31.**            **33.**

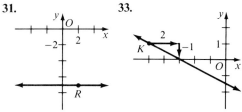

**35.** $AB$, 0; $BC$, $\frac{8}{9}$; $AC$, no slope   **37.** $\frac{1}{2}$, $y = 8$
**39.** $c = -16$   **41.** slope $AM = -\frac{5}{3}$; slope
$AC = -\frac{5}{3}$; thus $M$ lies on $AC$: slope $DB = \frac{3}{5}$;
slope $DM = \frac{3}{5}$; thus $M$ lies on $DB$

***Computer Exercises, page 395***   **1.** $(0, -1)$,
$(1, 1)$, $(2, 3)$, $(3, 5)$, $(4, 7)$   **3.** $(1, 5.5)$, $(2, 5)$,
$(3, 4.5)$, $(4, 4)$, $(5, 3.5)$, $(6, 3)$, $(7, 2.5)$, $(8, 2)$,
$(9, 1.5)$, $(10, 1)$

***Written Exercises, pages 399–400***
**1.** $-6x + 3y = 1$   **3.** $x - 5y = -20$
**5.** $30x - 5y = 3$   **7.** $14x - 6y = 1$
**9.** $y = -6$   **11.** $21x + 10y = -4$
**13.** $y = -x + 5$          **15.** $y = x - 4$

**17.** $y = \frac{1}{2}x - 3$        **19.** $y = -\frac{2}{3}x$

**21.** $y = \frac{4}{5}x + 3$        **23.** $y = \frac{2}{3}x - 2$

**25.** no solution   **27.** infinite number of solutions   **29.** no solution   **31.** $y = 3x - 4$

**33.** $-3$; 3   **35.** $-9$   **37.** 3   **39.** slope, $-\dfrac{A}{B}$;

$y$-intercept, $\dfrac{C}{B}$

***Written Exercises, page 402***   **1.** $-5$   **3.** $-7$
**5.** $-2x + y = 7$   **7.** $3x + y = 18$
**9.** $-3x + 2y = 6$   **11.** $4x + 5y = -34$
**13.** $x + 2y = 0$   **15.** $y = -4$
**17.** $-7x + 4y = -11$   **19.** $y = 1$
**21.** $2x + y = 10$   **23.** $-8x + 3y = -27$

**25.** $-5x + y = -1$   **27.** $3x + 4y = -6$
**29.** $3x - y = -6$   **31.** $-x + 2y = -6$
**33.** $-x + 3y = -7$   **35.** $x - 3y = -6$

***Computer Key-In, page 403***   **1. a.** slope =
$\dfrac{y_2 - y_1}{x_2 - x_1}$; when $x_2 = x_1$   **b.** $-2$, 0.75, no
slope, 0   **3. b.** $y = 1.5x - 3$; $x = 2$; $y = 3$

***Written Exercises, pages 406–407***   **1.** 7   **3.** 9
**5.** 15   **7.** 6   **9.** 0   **11.** 4   **13.** $-2$   **15.** $-\frac{14}{9}$
**17.** $-4$, 1, 6   **19.** 0, $-6$, $-24$   **21.** 5, 7, $6\frac{1}{2}$
**23.** $\{13, 5, -3\}$   **25.** $\{10, 5, -2\}$
**27.** $\{-\frac{1}{2}, -1, 1\}$   **29.** $\{3, -1\}$   **31.** $\{0, 2\}$
**33.** $\{0, 9, 64\}$   **35. a.** $-12$   **b.** 6   **37. a.** 0
**b.** 0, 1, $-1$   **39. a.** $-\frac{1}{2}$   **b.** $-1$   **41.** $-18$
**43.** 6   **45. a.** 2   **b.** 1   **c.** 2   **d.** 4   **47.** 0

***Computer Exercises, page 407***   **1.** $-13$, $-7$,
$-4$, 23   **3.** 0.0625, 0.5, 1, 2, 4, 16

***Challenge, page 407***   **1. a.** $\frac{2}{3}, \frac{3}{4}, \frac{4}{5}$   **b.** $\frac{100}{101}$

**c.** $\dfrac{n}{n + 1}$

***Written Exercises, pages 410–411***
**1.**

**3.**

**5.**

Cost of a Barrel of Crude Oil

**7.**

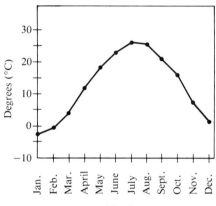

Average Monthly Temperature in Greenough

**9.** Answers may vary.

***Written Exercises, pages 416–417***

**1.**

**3.**

**5.**

**7.** $(0, 0)$, $x = 0$

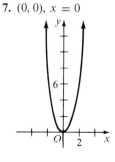

**9.** $(0, 0)$, $x = 0$

**11.** $(0, 0)$, $x = 0$

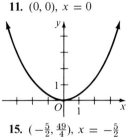

**15.** $(-\frac{5}{2}, \frac{49}{4})$, $x = -\frac{5}{2}$

**13.** $(1, -1)$, $x = 1$

**17.** $(0, 2)$, $x = 0$

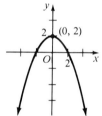

**19.** $-\frac{25}{4}$  **21.** $-\frac{49}{4}$
**23.** $-4$  **25.** $\frac{49}{4}$
**27.** 1  **29.** $\frac{1}{8}$

**31. a.**

**b.** graph moves up; graph moves down

**33. a.** $-4$  **b.** $-4, 1$  **35.** The zeros are where the graph of $f$ crosses the $x$-axis.

***Written Exercises, pages 421–422***  **1.** $\frac{1}{4}$  **3.** 7
**5.** 25  **7.** 1500  **9.** 600  **11.** 24  **13.** 1.2

**15.** $\frac{2}{3}$  **17. a.** $H = 49m$  **b.** $\frac{49}{1} = \frac{H_2}{m_2}$

**19. a.** $M = \frac{1}{6}E$  **b.** $\frac{M_1}{E_1} = \frac{14}{84}$

**21. a.** $R = 0.02059l$  **b.** $\frac{10.295}{500} = \frac{R_2}{l_2}$

***Problems, pages 422–423***  **1.** $243 \text{ m}^2$  **3.** 80 g
**5.** 40 g  **7.** 227 g  **9.** 5:162  **11.** 37 units
**13.** $1,125,000 \text{ m}^2$

**Challenge, page 423** 5 pennies, 1 nickel, 9 dimes

**Written Exercises, pages 426–427**
**1.**   **3.**

**5.** 81 **7.** 6.3 **9.** 18 **11. a.** $lw = 60$
**b.** $\frac{15}{w_2} = \frac{l_2}{4}$ **13. a.** $fl = 1.5$ **b.** $\frac{2.5}{l_2} = \frac{f_2}{0.6}$
**15. a.** $VP = 337,125$ **b.** $\frac{465}{P_2} = \frac{V_2}{725}$

**Problems, pages 427–429** **1.** 9 people
**3.** 80 cm **5.** 900 rpm **7.** 60 shares
**9.** 3.8 cm **11.** $2\frac{2}{3}$ yd **13.** The distance of the
12 g mass from the fulcrum is 70 cm. **15.** $\frac{1}{2}$
**17.** 0.4 m

**Computer Exercises, page 429** **1.** direct
**3.** neither

**Problems, pages 432–433** **1.** 3850 cm²
**3.** 63 m **5.** 562.5 lm/m² **7.** $\frac{1}{16}$ of the strength
at the first position **9.** $\sqrt{2}$ times **11.** 64:27

**Computer Key-In, page 433** **1.**
**3.**

**5.**

**Written Exercises, page 436** **1.** 16 **3.** 60
**5.** 2.5 **7.** $x$ is quadrupled; $x$ remains the
same **9.** $h$ is 12 times bigger.

**Problems, pages 436–437** **1.** 175 cm³ **3.** 10
ohms **5.** 10 students **7.** 558 kg **9.** 5.30
**11.** 18 joules **13. a.** 4 times **b.** halved
**c.** no change

**Application, page 439** **1.** 10 lx **3.** 3 m
**5.** 20 lx

**Extra, pages 440–441** **1.** $D = \{3, 2\}$,
$R = \{4, 3, 6, 0\}$, relation **3.** $D = \{2, 3, 4, 1\}$,
$R = \{-1, 0, 6, -3\}$, function
**5.** $D = \{-1, 1, 2, -2\}$, $R = \{1, 4\}$, function
**7.** $D = \{-1, 1, 2, 4\}$, $R = \{1, 2\}$, function
**9.** $D = \{-2, 2, 4\}$, $R = \{1, -1, 0, -3\}$ relation **11.** $D = \{-3, -2, -1, 0, 1, 2, 3\}$,
$R = \{1, 0, -1, -2\}$, function
**13.** not a function because of $(4, 4)$, $(4, -3)$

**15.** not a function because **17.** function
of $(-3, 0)$, $(-3, -2)$

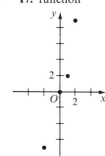

**19.** relation **21.** relation **23.** function

**Chapter Review, pages 442–443** **1.** c **3.** d
**5.** a **7.** c **9.** d **11.** b **13.** a **15.** d

**Cumulative Review, page 446** **1.** $6z + y$
**3.** $20m^4n + 6m^3n^2 + 10m^2n^3$
**5.** $25b^2 - 80bc + 64c^2$ **7.** $(4x + 7)(3x - 1)$
**9.** $3(z - 8)(z + 1)$ **11.** $\frac{(x + 3)(x - 1)}{2x - 1}$
**13.** $\frac{-3t^2 + 4t + 12}{(t - 2)(t + 2)}$ **15.** $x + y = 7$
**17.** $\{13, 7, 3, 1\}$ **19.**

$(-\frac{1}{2}, \frac{3}{4})$

**21.** 21 **23.** 54% **25.** $\{\frac{5}{6}, -\frac{5}{6}\}$ **27.** $\{0, -2\}$
**29.** $\{0, \frac{1}{3}\}$ **31.** $(\frac{3}{2}, \frac{7}{8})$ **33.** 102.4

*Maintaining Skills, page 447*   **1.** $\frac{a}{4}$   **3.** 8

**5.** $\frac{3(z-3)}{5z}$   **7.** $\frac{3t-1}{t-2}$   **9.** $5ab$   **11.** $\frac{2b+3}{b+1}$

**13.** $\frac{c+2}{c+1}$   **15.** $\frac{(r-6)(r+6)^2}{(r-3)(r+3)^2}$   **17.** $\frac{2x+3y}{x-y}$

**19.** $\frac{-2-w^2}{w-3}$   **21.** $\frac{v^2-v+8}{(v-1)(v+1)}$   **23.** $\frac{2b(2-b)}{2b-1}$

**25.** $\frac{d^2-2}{(2d+1)(d+1)}$   **27.** $\frac{6t}{t^2-4}$

**29.** $\frac{2x^2+13x-28}{(x-4)(x+3)}$

## CHAPTER 10   INEQUALITIES

*Written Exercises, pages 451–452*   **1.** $6 > -7$
**3.** $-12 \le -9$   **5.** $2 < 3 < 3.5$
**7.** $-20 < -15 < -10$   **9.** $2.8 > 2 > 0$
**11.** $|n| \ge n$   **13.** false   **15.** true   **17.** true
**19.** $\{-4, -3, -2, -1, 0, 1\}$
**21.** $\{-2, -1, 0, 1, 2, 3, 4\}$
**23.** $\{-4, -3, -2, -1, 0, 1, 2, 3, 4\}$
**25.** $\{-4, 4\}$
**27.**

**29.**

**31.**

**33.**

Answers may vary for Exercises 35 and 37.
**35. a.** $x = -2, y = -3$   **b.** $x = 3, y = 2$
**37. a.** $x = 3, y = 2$   **b.** $x = 3, y = -2$

*Computer Exercises, page 452*
**1.** $\{0, 1, 2, 3, 4, 5\}$   **3.** $\{4, 5\}$
**5.** $\{-3, -2, -1, 0, 1\}$

*Written Exercises, pages 456–457*   **1.** d   **3.** c
**5.** b   **7.** e   **9.** {the real numbers greater than
15}

**11.** {the real numbers less than $-8$}

**13.** {the real numbers less than $-324$}

**15.** $\{-1,$ and the real numbers less than $-1\}$

**17.** {the real numbers greater than $-4$}

**19.** {0, and the real numbers less than 0}

**21.** {the real numbers less than 6}

**23.** {the real numbers greater than $-15$}

**25.** {the real numbers less than 8}

**27.** {the real numbers less than 6}
**29.** {the real numbers greater than $-12$}
**31.** {4, and the real numbers less than 4}
**33.** {the real numbers less than 0}
**35.** $\{-7,$ and the real numbers less than $-7\}$
**37.** $\{\frac{2}{5},$ and the real numbers greater than $\frac{2}{5}\}$
**39.** $\{\frac{4}{3},$ and the real numbers greater than $\frac{4}{3}\}$

**41.** {the real numbers greater than $-8$}

**43.** {the real numbers greater than $-2$}

**45.** $\{-4,$ and the real numbers greater than $-4\}$

**47.** $\{-\frac{3}{2},$ and the real numbers less than $-\frac{3}{2}\}$

**49.** positive real numbers   **51.** zero   **53.** negative real numbers   **55.** none   **57.** true
**59.** true   **61.** false   **63.** true

*Reading Algebra, page 458*   **1. a.** greater than
**b.** open; right   **c.** {the real numbers
greater than 15}

**3. a.** greater than or equal to  **b.** closed; left  **c.** {4, and the real numbers less than 4}

$$-3\ -2\ -1\ \ 0\ \ 1\ \ 2\ \ 3\ \ 4\ \ 5\ \ 6\ \ 7$$

**5. a.** less than **b.** open; right
**c.** {the real numbers greater than $-15$}

$$-17\quad -15\quad -13\quad -11\quad -9\quad -7$$

**7. a.** greater than **b.** open; left
**c.** {the real numbers less than 6}

$$-1\ \ 0\ \ 1\ \ 2\ \ 3\ \ 4\ \ 5\ \ 6\ \ 7\ \ 8\ \ 9$$

**9. a.** less than **b.** open; right
**c.** {the real numbers greater than $-4$}

$$-6\ -5\ -4\ -3\ -2\ -1\ \ 0\ \ 1\ \ 2\ \ 3\ \ 4$$

**11. a.** greater than **b.** open; left
**c.** {the real numbers less than 7}

$$-1\ \ 0\ \ 1\ \ 2\ \ 3\ \ 4\ \ 5\ \ 6\ \ 7\ \ 8\ \ 9$$

***Written Exercises, pages 461–462***

**1.** $i + 2 < 21$  **3.** $a + \dfrac{a}{10} > 3000$

**5.** $\frac{1}{2}k + 15 \le 36$
**7.** $(m - 2) + m + (m + 2) \ge 51$
**9.** $5n + 10(2n) + 25(\frac{1}{2}n) \le 1140$
**11.** $3(r + 10) > 4r$  **13.** $2s + 1 \le 25 - s$
**15.** $n - 2 \ge \frac{1}{4}n + 15$
**17.** $5(n + 2) - (n + 1) \ge 9 + 2n$
**19.** $|a + b| \le |a| + |b|$

***Problems, pages 462–464***  **1.** 10 kg  **3.** 36, 37
**5.** 41, 43  **7.** Jane, at least 21; Terry, at most
29  **9.** 25 cm, 25 cm, 45 cm  **11.** 23 years old
**13.** 3 PM  **15.** at least 4 kg  **17.** 4, 5  **19.** 38
**21.** 10.92 km  **23.** $1999  **25.** 42, 43, 44

***Extra, pages 465–466***  **1.** {6, 9}
**3.** {0, 3, 4, 5, 6, 7, 8, 9}  **5.** {6}  **7.** {5, 6, 9}
**9.** {5, 6, 7, 8}  **11.** {$-4, -3, -2, -1, 0$};
{$-3, -2$}  **13.** {3, 4, 5, 6, 7, 8}; disjoint sets
**15.** {2, 3, 4, 6, 8, 10, 12}; {4, 6, 8}  **17.** {the
real numbers between $-1$ and 2}  **19.** {the
real numbers greater than $-3$}  **21.** {the real
numbers between $-3$ and 2}  **23.** {the real
numbers between $-1$ and 2}

**25.**

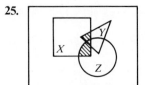

**27.** $X \cap (Y \cup Z) = (X \cap Y) \cup (X \cap Z)$
**29.**

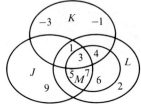

***Challenge, page 467***  Step 4: If you divide by
$3 - a$, which is negative (because $a > 3$), the
inequality must be reversed so that step 5 is
$a < 3 + a$.

***Written Exercises, pages 470–471***

**1.**

$$-7\ -6\ -5\ -4\ -3\ -2\ -1\ \ 0\ \ 1\ \ 2\ \ 3$$

**3.**

$$-2\ -1\ \ 0\ \ 1\ \ 2\ \ 3\ \ 4\ \ 5\ \ 6\ \ 7\ \ 8$$

**5.** {the real numbers between $-3$ and 2}

$$-5\ -4\ -3\ -2\ -1\ \ 0\ \ 1\ \ 2\ \ 3\ \ 4\ \ 5$$

**7.** {8, and the real numbers between 0 and 8}

$$-2\ -1\ \ 0\ \ 1\ \ 2\ \ 3\ \ 4\ \ 5\ \ 6\ \ 7\ \ 8$$

**9.** {$-2$, and the real numbers between $-2$
and 3}

$$-4\ -3\ -2\ -1\ \ 0\ \ 1\ \ 2\ \ 3\ \ 4\ \ 5\ \ 6$$

**11.** {$-2$, and the real numbers between $-2$
and 1}
$$-6\ -5\ -4\ -3\ -2\ -1\ \ 0\ \ 1\ \ 2\ \ 3\ \ 4$$

**13.** {4, and the real numbers less than $-2$ or
greater than 4}
$$-4\ -3\ -2\ -1\ \ 0\ \ 1\ \ 2\ \ 3\ \ 4\ \ 5\ \ 6$$

**15.** {$-2$, $\frac{2}{3}$, and the real numbers greater
than $\frac{2}{3}$ or less than $-2$}
$$-2\qquad -1\qquad 0\qquad \tfrac{2}{3}\ \ 1$$

**17.** {$-2$, 3, and the real numbers greater
than 3 or less than $-2$}

$$-4\ -3\ -2\ -1\ \ 0\ \ 1\ \ 2\ \ 3\ \ 4\ \ 5\ \ 6$$

**19.** {−3, 5, and the real numbers between −3 and 5}

**21.** 4, and the real numbers between −3 and 4}

**23.** −3, and the real numbers between −3 and 5}

**25.** ∅

**27.** {5, and the real numbers between −2 and 5}

**29.** {the real numbers greater than 15 or less than −1}

**31.** {the real numbers greater than 5 or less than −1}

**33.** {−$\frac{3}{2}$, 2, and the real numbers between −$\frac{3}{2}$ and 2}

**35.** {4, and the real numbers between 1 and 4}

**37.** {6, and the real numbers less than 6}

**39.** {0, 2, 4, 6}, {−2, 0, 2, 4}, {−4, −2, 0, 2}

**41. a.** $a = 20$, $b = 3$, $c = 40$, $d = 5$
**b.** $a = 4$, $b = -3$, $c = 0$, $d = -2$

***Written Exercises, page 475***  **1.** $|x| < 1$
**3.** $|x + 2| = 3$  **5.** $|x - 1| \geq 3$
**7.** {7, 9}

**9.** {1, −13}

**11.** {the real numbers between −2.5 and 2.5}

**13.** {the real numbers greater than −4 or less than −8}

**15.** {2, 10, and the real numbers between 2 and 10}

**17.** {−6, 2, and the real numbers greater than 2 or less than −6}

**19.** {−3, 3, and the real numbers greater than 3 or less than −3}

**21.** {the real numbers greater than 7 or less than −1}

**23.** {−4, 4, and the real numbers between −4 and 4}

**25.** {0, 4, and the real numbers greater than 4 or less than 0}

**27.** {−2, 2, and the real numbers between −2 and 2}

**29.** {$\frac{2}{3}$, 2}

**31.** {the real numbers greater than or equal to 3}

**33.** ∅

***Written Exercises, pages 477–478***
**1.** {5, −5}

**3.** {−3, 3, and the real numbers greater than 3 or less than −3}

**5.** $\{-3, 4\}$

**7.** $\{\frac{3}{2}, 3,$ and the real numbers between $\frac{3}{2}$ and 3$\}$

**9.** $\{-4, \frac{12}{5},$ and the real numbers between $-4$ and $\frac{12}{5}\}$

**11.** $\{15, -3,$ and the real numbers greater than 15 or less than $-3\}$

**13.** $\{$the real numbers between $-\frac{19}{3}$ and 7$\}$

**15.** $\{-1, \frac{1}{2}\}$

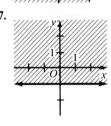

**17.** $\emptyset$

**19.** true   **21.** false, $a = -2$   **23.** true
**25.** $50°C$, $14°C$

*Written Exercises, pages 482–483*

**1.**

**3.**

**5.**

**7.**

**9.**

**11.**

**13.** $y < -x + 2$

**15.** $y \geq \frac{1}{2}x + \frac{7}{2}$

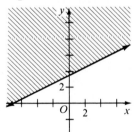

**17.** $y < 3x - 6$

**19.** $y \leq \frac{3}{2}x - 5$

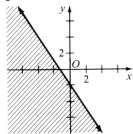

**21.** $y \leq -\frac{3}{2}x - 2$

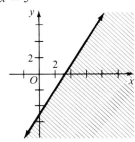

**23.** $y \leq -\frac{1}{3}x - \frac{7}{3}$

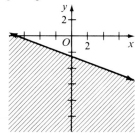

**25.** $y > -2$
**27.** $y \leq -\frac{2}{3}x + 2$
**29.** $y \geq \frac{5}{3}x + 5$  **31.** $y > \frac{1}{2}x - 2$
**33.** $y \leq -x + 4$

**35.**

**37.**

**39.**

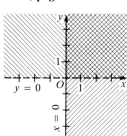

*Written Exercises, pages 485–487*
**1.**

**3.**

**5.**

**7.**

**9.**

**11.**

**13.**

**15.**

**17.**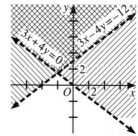

**19.** $y \geq -4$
$y < x - 4$

**21.** $y < -2x + 2$
$y < \frac{2}{3}x - \frac{10}{3}$

**23.** $x \geq 3$
$y \leq -x + 1$
$y \geq \frac{1}{7}x - \frac{25}{7}$

**25.**

**27.**

*Calculator Key-In, page 487* **1.** false **3.** false

*Extra, pages 487-490*
**1. a.**

**b.** $(\frac{4}{3}, -\frac{4}{3})$, $(2, -4)$, $(0, -2)$ **c.** maximum: $-4$; minimum: $-20$ **3. a.** $6c + 12s \le 2400$; $12c + 16s \le 3600$; $c \ge 0$; $s \ge 0$
**b.**

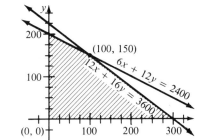

**c.** 100 acres of corn, 150 acres of soybeans; 0 acres of corn, 200 acres of soybeans

*Challenge, page 490* one sphere and one cube

*Chapter Review, pages 492-493* **1.** c **3.** c **5.** d **7.** b **9.** b **11.** b

*Cumulative Review, page 494* **1.** $-4b - 4$
**3.** $27x^{14}y^{12}$ **5.** $15c^3 - 23c^2d + 44cd^2 - 8d^3$
**7.** $\frac{x - 3}{3x + 2}$ **9.** $2.4 \times 10^6$ **11.** $y^2$
**13.** $6(5z^2 + 40z + 16)$
**15.** $(4z - y - 5)(4z + y + 5)$
**17.** $x - 2y = -7$
**19.** ![number line from -5 to 5 with open circles at -4 and 3]
$-5 -4 -3 -2 -1 \quad 0 \quad 1 \quad 2 \quad 3 \quad 4 \quad 5$
**21.** $\{7, -7\}$ **23.** 75 **25.** 0 **27.** $\{-1, -3\}$
**29.** $\{\frac{5}{3}, -1\}$ **31.** $-\frac{4}{3}$ **33.** $(1, 4)$ **35.** $(-1, 2)$
**37.** {the real numbers less than $-\frac{6}{5}$} **39.** $7\frac{1}{2}$ h

*Maintaining Skills, page 495* **1.** $\{-4, 10\}$
**3.** $-6$ **5.** $\{\frac{1}{5}, -1\}$ **7.** $\{-\frac{2}{5}, \frac{4}{3}\}$
**9.** $\{-\frac{9}{16}, 1\}$ **11.** 2 **13.** $-\frac{2}{5}$ **15.** no solution
**17.** 6 **19.** no solution **21.** no solution
**23.** 2

*Mixed Review, page 496*
**1.** $(4b - 5)(5b + 3)$ **3.** prime **5.** 10 **7.** 140
**9.** {the real numbers greater than 2 or less than $\frac{2}{3}$} **11.** $\{5, -3\}$ **13.** $-2$ **15.** 63 L
**17.** 12.05 km/h, 27.95 km/h **19.** 72
**21.** 15 m, 24 m, 33 m
**23.** ![number line from -2 to 8 with solid dot at 6]
$-2 -1 \quad 0 \quad 1 \quad 2 \quad 3 \quad 4 \quad 5 \quad 6 \quad 7 \quad 8$

*Preparing for College Entrance Exams, page 497* **1.** A **3.** D **5.** D

## CHAPTER 11 RATIONAL AND IRRATIONAL NUMBERS

*Written Exercises, pages 501-503* **1.** $>$
**3.** $<$ **5.** $<$ **7.** $>$ **9.** $<$ **11.** $-\frac{4}{9}, \frac{3}{8}, \frac{5}{6}$
**13.** $\frac{303}{56}$, 5.6, $\frac{107}{18}$ **15.** $-\frac{6}{7}, -\frac{3}{5}, -\frac{5}{9}, -\frac{3}{7}$
**17.** $\frac{61}{88}$ **19.** $-\frac{1497}{6720}$ **21.** $\frac{41}{21}$ **23.** increases
**25.** decreases **27.** $\frac{27}{28}$ **29.** $-\frac{31}{75}$ **31.** for example, $\frac{13}{24}$ **33.** $\frac{29a}{126}$ **35. a.** yes

**b.** $a + \frac{1}{2}(b - a) = \frac{a + b}{2}$ **37.** $w < z$

**37.** $z > w$

yes; no

**Written Exercises, pages 507–508** **1.** 0.375
**3.** $0.\overline{5}$ **5.** 1.24 **7.** $3.\overline{6}$ **9.** $-0.2\overline{7}$ **11.** $-2.35$
**13.** $0.8\overline{2}$ **15.** $-0.4\overline{8}$ **17.** $\frac{33}{50}$ **19.** $\frac{5}{9}$ **21.** $\frac{13}{40}$
**23.** $\frac{24}{5}$ **25.** $\frac{7}{99}$ **27.** $-\frac{37}{15}$ **29.** 0.753
**31.** $0.773\overline{8}$ **33.** $0.14\overline{53}$ **35.** $\frac{3}{8}$ **37.** $\frac{1}{3}$ **39.** $\frac{55}{486}$
**41. a.** $0.\overline{142857}, 0.\overline{714285}$
**b.** $0.\overline{714285} = 5(0.\overline{142857})$ **c.** $0.\overline{285714},$
$0.\overline{428571}, 0.\overline{857142}$ **43. a.** $0.0\overline{5}, 0.2\overline{5}, 0.7\overline{4}$
**b.** $1 = \frac{99}{99} = 0.\overline{99} = 0.\overline{9}$

**Computer Key-In, pages 508–509** **1.** $0.\overline{142857}$;
$0.\overline{285714}$; $0.\overline{428571}$; $0.\overline{571428}$; $0.\overline{714285}$;
$0.\overline{857142}$ **3.** $0.0\overline{714285}$; $0.2\overline{142857}$; $0.3\overline{571428}$;
$0.6\overline{428571}$; $0.7\overline{857142}$; $0.9\overline{285714}$

**Written Exercises, page 512** **1.** 5 **3.** 10
**5.** $-21$ **7.** $-14$ **9.** $\pm17$ **11.** 40 **13.** 42
**15.** 90 **17.** $\pm\frac{20}{9}$ **19.** $\frac{1}{16}$ **21.** $-\frac{27}{10}$ **23.** $\frac{32}{43}$
**25.** $\pm\frac{22}{23}$ **27.** $-0.7$ **29.** $\pm1.5$ **31.** 0.13
**33.** $-0.48$ **35.** 0.05 **37.** $-8$ **39.** $-8$
**41.** $-\frac{2}{5}$ **43.** $\pm\frac{5}{2}$ **45.** $\pm\frac{7}{8}$ **47.** $\frac{5}{12}$ **49.** $\frac{21}{100}$

**Calculator Key-In, page 512** **1.** 2.632148
**3.** 1.8707313 **5.** 1.3753959

**Challenge, page 513**
**1.**

**Written Exercises, page 516** **1.** 15 **3.** $2\sqrt{30}$
**5.** $30\sqrt{2}$ **7.** $27\sqrt{10}$ **9.** $60\sqrt{2}$ **11.** $50\sqrt{3}$
**13.** $8\sqrt{2}$ **15.** 85 **17.** $-69.3$ **19.** 95.9
**21.** 9.27 **23.** $-0.55$ **25.** $-0.28$ **27.** 346
**29.** 721

**Written Exercises, page 518** **1.** $12|a|$
**3.** $5b^2\sqrt{3}$ **5.** $4|ab|\sqrt{5}$ **7.** $9|z|$ **9.** $-3c^2$
**11.** $9|x|y\sqrt{7y}$ **13.** $2|r^3|s^2\sqrt{14}$ **15.** $3\left|\frac{m}{n}\right|$
**17.** $21|a^3|b^2$ **19.** $-1.8x^2$ **21.** $\frac{2|e|}{25}$ **23.** $\frac{13}{20s^6}$
**25.** $\frac{13|r^{25}|}{5}$ **27.** $|m-5|$ **29.** $\{4, -4\}$

**31.** $\{1, -1\}$ **33.** $\{\frac{5}{2}, -\frac{5}{2}\}$ **35.** $\{4, -4\}$
**37.** $\{\frac{5}{3}, -\frac{5}{3}\}$ **39.** $\{12.8, -12.8\}$
**41.** $\{14.3, -14.3\}$ **43.** $\{3.3, -3.3\}$
**45.** $\{4.4, -4.4\}$ **47.** $\{7.6, -7.6\}$
**49.** $\{8.6, -8.6\}$

**Problems, pages 518–519** **1.** 14.1 cm
**3.** 18 m **5.** $\frac{20}{3}$ mm **7.** $\sqrt{2}:1$ **9.** 18 s
**11.** 86.5 m²

**Written Exercises, page 523** **1.** 15 **3.** 8.06
**5.** 9.90 **7.** 8 **9.** 39.55 **11.** no **13.** yes
**15.** no **17.** no **19.** yes **21.** 9.49 **23.** 13.42
**25.** 23.43 **27.** $a = 18.96$, $b = 6.32$
**29.** $a = 28.85$, $b = 43.27$

**Problems, page 524** **1.** 25 cm **3.** 9 m **5.** 6,
8, 10 **7.** 51.96 cm **9.** 1.6 m

**Extra, pages 525–526** **1.** 8 **3.** 6.3 **5.** 6.4
**7.** 9.8 **9.** 11.2 **11.** 8.5 **13.** The lengths of
the sides are $\sqrt{17}$, $\sqrt{17}$, $3\sqrt{2}$. Since two sides
have equal length, the triangle is isosceles.

**Written Exercises, page 528** **1.** 6 **3.** $3\sqrt{10}$
**5.** $2\sqrt{35}$ **7.** 6 **9.** $72\sqrt{2}$ **11.** $\sqrt{2}$ **13.** $\frac{1}{4}\sqrt{10}$
**15.** $\frac{1}{3}\sqrt{2}$ **17.** $\frac{1}{10}\sqrt{3}$ **19.** $\frac{\sqrt{65}}{13}$ **21.** $4\sqrt{3}$
**23.** 56 **25.** $-10ab$ **27.** $4\sqrt{r} - r$
**29.** $-480\sqrt{2}$ **31.** $12x^2$ **33.** $112y$ **35.** $\frac{6x^2}{y}$
**37.** $4a - 6a\sqrt{6a}$ **39.** $24x^2 - 120x^3\sqrt{x}$
**41.** $135y^4\sqrt{5y}$ **43.** $50x^4y^2\sqrt{2} - 100x^2y^4$

**Written Exercises, page 530** **1.** $4\sqrt{2}$
**3.** $-16\sqrt{23}$ **5.** $27\sqrt{2}$ **7.** $-11\sqrt{7}$
**9.** $16\sqrt{2} - 9\sqrt{3}$ **11.** $-22\sqrt{2} - 14\sqrt{3}$
**13.** $12\sqrt{19} - 7\sqrt{11}$ **15.** $12\sqrt{7} - \sqrt{14}$
**17.** $-14\sqrt{2}$ **19.** $\frac{2}{3}\sqrt{6}$ **21.** $\frac{46\sqrt{2}}{5}$
**23.** $\frac{1}{15}\sqrt{30}$ **25.** $9\sqrt{5} - \frac{9}{5}\sqrt{10}$
**27.** $2\sqrt{14} - \frac{7}{2}\sqrt{2}$ **29.** $18 - 18\sqrt{2}$
**31.** $18x\sqrt{x} - 15x^2\sqrt{x}$ **33.** $\frac{5x}{12}$ **35.** $\frac{x\sqrt{a^2 + b^2}}{ab}$

**Written Exercises, pages 532–533** **1.** $-1$
**3.** 1 **5.** 12 **7.** $28 + 10\sqrt{3}$ **9.** $17 - 12\sqrt{2}$
**11.** $33 + 4\sqrt{65}$ **13.** $30\sqrt{2} - 40$
**15.** $-42\sqrt{2} + 70$ **17.** $9 + 2\sqrt{3}$
**19.** $54 - 21\sqrt{35}$ **21.** $208 + 25\sqrt{30}$
**23.** $-4 + 4\sqrt{2}$ **25.** $\frac{3 + \sqrt{3}}{6}$

**27.** $\dfrac{2 + \sqrt{5} + 2\sqrt{3} + \sqrt{15}}{-2}$  **29.** $\dfrac{21\sqrt{3} - 28}{11}$

**31.** $8 - 4\sqrt{7}$  **33.** $0$

**35.** $[x - (1 + \sqrt{3})][x - (1 - \sqrt{3})] = x^2 - 2x - 2$

**37.** $\left[x - \left(\dfrac{1}{3} + \dfrac{\sqrt{7}}{3}\right)\right]\left[x - \left(\dfrac{1}{3} - \dfrac{\sqrt{7}}{3}\right)\right] = 3x^2 - 2x - 2$

**39.** $x - y^2$  **41.** $15r^2s - rq\sqrt{s} - 6q^2$

***Written Exercises, page 535*** **1.** $100$ **3.** $32$
**5.** $\frac{1}{36}$ **7.** $25$ **9.** $\frac{25}{9}$ **11.** $180$ **13.** $-4$ **15.** $\frac{3}{25}$
**17.** $27$ **19.** $3$ **21.** $\frac{5}{3}$ **23.** $\frac{245}{8}$ **25.** $21$ **27.** $22$
**29.** $63$ **31.** $\pm 3\sqrt{7}$ **33.** $\{\sqrt{19}, -\sqrt{19}\}$
**35.** $6$ **37.** $0$ **39.** $\sqrt{7}$ **41.** $0$ **43.** $\{1, -4\}$
**45.** $1$ **47.** $(8, 18)$

***Problems, page 536*** **1.** $98$ **3.** $900$ **5.** $29$
**7.** $225\pi \text{ cm}^2$ **9.** $10 \text{ m}$ **11.** $50, 52$ or $-52, -50$

***Extra, pages 537-539*** **1.** $5^{\frac{1}{2}}$ **3.** $3^{\frac{1}{4}}$ **5.** $6^{\frac{2}{3}}$
**7.** $2^{\frac{3}{2}}$ **9.** $7$ **11.** $-3$ **13.** $8$ **15.** $3$ **17.** $125$
**19.** $81$

***Application, page 540*** **1.** $360 \text{ cm}^3$
**3.** $600 \text{ cm}^3$ **5.** $22.5 \text{ m}^3$ or $22,500,000 \text{ cm}^3$

***Chapter Review, pages 542-543*** **1.** b **3.** c
**5.** c **7.** b **9.** a **11.** c **13.** b **15.** d **17.** a

***Cumulative Review, page 544*** **1.** $-21$
**3.** $16a^6b^2 + 72a^3bc^2 + 81c^4$ **5.** $1.024 \times 10^{-7}$
**7.** $\dfrac{7x + 1}{x + 3}$ **9.** $\dfrac{4t^2 + 3t - 16}{(t + 4)(t - 2)}$ **11.** $\sqrt{7}$
**13.** $\frac{5}{6}\sqrt{30}$ **15.** $\dfrac{2\sqrt{6} + \sqrt{30}}{6}$
**17.** $(2c - d - 3)(2c - d + 3)$
**19.**

![number line from -3 to 7]

**21.**

**23.** $0$ **25.**

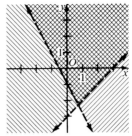

**27.** $15$ **29.** $-\frac{5}{2}$ **31.** $\{3, -1\}$ **33.** $(-1, -\frac{1}{5})$
**35.** $\{\frac{7}{2}, 6,$ and the real numbers between $\frac{7}{2}$ and $6\}$ **37.** $\{$the real numbers greater than $-\frac{2}{3}\}$ **39.** $5$ **41.** $15.59 \text{ cm}$

***Maintaining Skills, page 545*** **1.** $(-1, 2)$
**3.** $(5, 5)$ **5.** $(\frac{1}{2}, \frac{1}{3})$ **7.** $(-\frac{2}{3}, \frac{7}{3})$ **9.** $(7, 3)$
**11.** $(12, -1)$ **13.** $(0, 0)$ **15.** $(7, -1)$
**17.** $(-7, 12)$ **19.** $(5, 6)$ **21.** $(9, 4)$

# CHAPTER 12 QUADRATIC FUNCTIONS

***Written Exercises, page 549*** **1.** $\{7, -7\}$
**3.** $\{\frac{11}{12}, -\frac{11}{12}\}$ **5.** $\{6, -6\}$ **7.** $\{2, -2\}$ **9.** no solution **11.** $\{\sqrt{3}, -\sqrt{3}\}$ **13.** $\{\sqrt{3}, -\sqrt{3}\}$
**15.** $\{\sqrt{6}, -\sqrt{6}\}$ **17.** $\{\sqrt{11}, -\sqrt{11}\}$
**19.** $\{0, -6\}$ **21.** $\{-2 + 2\sqrt{3}, -2 - 2\sqrt{3}\}$
**23.** $\{3 + 4\sqrt{2}, 3 - 4\sqrt{2}\}$
**25.** $\{8 + \sqrt{5}, 8 - \sqrt{5}\}$
**27.** $\{-3 + \sqrt{6}, -3 - \sqrt{6}\}$ **29.** $\{\frac{5}{6}, -\frac{1}{2}\}$
**31.** $\{-5, 1\}$ **33.** $\{1, -21\}$ **35.** $\{\frac{3}{4}, -\frac{3}{4}\}$
**37.** $\{\sqrt{19}, -\sqrt{19}\}$ **39.** $\{\frac{8}{13}, -\frac{8}{13}\}$
**41.** $\{\frac{3}{4}, -\frac{3}{4}\}$ **43.** $\{\frac{37}{12}, \frac{35}{12}\}$
**45.** $\left\{\dfrac{16 + 9\sqrt{3}}{36}, \dfrac{16 - 9\sqrt{3}}{36}\right\}$ **47.** $\{0, 5, -5\}$
**49.** $\{0, \frac{1}{4}, -\frac{1}{4}\}$ **51.** $\{0, 8, -8\}$ **53.** $\{\frac{1}{3}, 0\}$
**55.** no solution **57.** $\{\sqrt{5} + \sqrt{3}, \sqrt{5} - \sqrt{3}\}$

***Written Exercises, page 552***
**1.** $\{1 + \sqrt{21}, 1 - \sqrt{21}\}, \{5.6, -3.6\}$
**3.** $\{-6 + \sqrt{34}, -6 - \sqrt{34}\}, \{-11.8, -0.2\}$
**5.** $\{2 + \sqrt{7}, 2 - \sqrt{7}\}, \{4.6, -0.6\}$
**7.** $\{-22, 6\}$ **9.** $\{3 + 4\sqrt{21}, 3 - 4\sqrt{21}\}, \{21.3, -15.3\}$ **11.** $\{-3 + 3\sqrt{2}, -3 - 3\sqrt{2}\}, \{-7.2, 1.2\}$ **13.** $\left\{\dfrac{-1 + \sqrt{21}}{2}, \dfrac{-1 - \sqrt{21}}{2}\right\}, \{1.8, -2.8\}$ **15.** $\left\{\dfrac{9 + \sqrt{109}}{2}, \dfrac{9 - \sqrt{109}}{2}\right\}, \{9.7, -0.7\}$ **17.** $\{31, -37\}$ **19.** $\{9, 5\}$
**21.** $\{-30, 2\}$ **23.** $\{1, -\frac{1}{5}\}$ **25.** $\{8, -2\}$

**27.** $\{-\frac{1}{2}, 4\}$   **29.** $\left\{\dfrac{3 + \sqrt{201}}{8}, \dfrac{3 - \sqrt{201}}{8}\right\}$

**31.** $\left\{\dfrac{-11 + \sqrt{193}}{12}, \dfrac{-11 - \sqrt{193}}{12}\right\}$

**33.** $\left\{\dfrac{13 + \sqrt{113}}{14}, \dfrac{13 - \sqrt{113}}{14}\right\}$

**35.** $\left\{\dfrac{-3 + \sqrt{29}}{4}, \dfrac{-3 - \sqrt{29}}{4}\right\}$

**37.** $\left\{\dfrac{-b \pm \sqrt{b^2 - 4}}{2}\right\}$, $b \geq 2$ or $b \leq -2$

**39.** $\left\{\dfrac{-b \pm \sqrt{b^2 - 4ac}}{2a}\right\}$, $b^2 - 4ac \geq 0$, $a \neq 0$

*Written Exercises, pages 554–555*
**1.** $\left\{\dfrac{-3 + \sqrt{5}}{2}, \dfrac{-3 - \sqrt{5}}{2}\right\}$, $\{-0.4, -2.6\}$

**3.** $\{-2 + \sqrt{10}, -2 - \sqrt{10}\}$, $\{1.2, -5.2\}$
**5.** $\{6, -1\}$   **7.** $\{-1, -\frac{1}{4}\}$   **9.** no solution

**11.** $\{\frac{4}{3}, 1\}$   **13.** $\left\{\dfrac{-9 + \sqrt{41}}{20}, \dfrac{-9 - \sqrt{41}}{20}\right\}$

**15.** $\left\{\dfrac{2 + \sqrt{29}}{10}, \dfrac{2 - \sqrt{29}}{10}\right\}$

**17.** $\left\{\dfrac{25 + 3\sqrt{105}}{8}, \dfrac{25 - 3\sqrt{105}}{8}\right\}$

**19.** $\left\{\dfrac{7 + \sqrt{65}}{2}, \dfrac{7 - \sqrt{65}}{2}\right\}$

**21.** $\left\{\dfrac{3 + 2\sqrt{3}}{2}, \dfrac{3 - 2\sqrt{3}}{2}\right\}$   **23.** $-\dfrac{b}{a}$
**25.** $x^2 - 6x + 7 = 0$

*Computer Key-In, page 555*   **3.** $\{0.75, 1\}$
**5.** $\{3.41, 0.59\}$   **7.** no solution

*Extra, pages 555–556*   **1.** $i$   **3.** $-i$   **5.** $i$
**7.** $6i$   **9.** $4i\sqrt{5}$   **11.** $20i$   **13.** $24i$   **15.** $\dfrac{5i}{7}$

**17.** $-\dfrac{3i}{5}$   **19.** $\{11i, -11i\}$
**21.** $\{7i\sqrt{2}, -7i\sqrt{2}\}$

*Written Exercises, page 559*   **1.** 4; two   **3.** 0;
one   **5.** 0; one   **7.** 0; one   **9.** 40; two
**11.** 1.16; two   **13.** two; below   **15.** two;
above   **17.** none; below   **19.** 4

*Written Exercises, pages 563–564*
**1.** $\{-1, -4\}$   **3.** $\{-4 + \sqrt{19}, -4 - \sqrt{19}\}$
**5.** $\{2, -2\}$   **7.** $\left\{\dfrac{-7 + \sqrt{41}}{2}, \dfrac{-7 - \sqrt{41}}{2}\right\}$
**9.** $\{-3 + \sqrt{14}, -3 - \sqrt{14}\}$   **11.** $\{0, 4\}$

**13.** $\{\frac{1}{4}, -2\}$   **15.** $\left\{\dfrac{-2 + \sqrt{19}}{5}, \dfrac{-2 - \sqrt{19}}{5}\right\}$

**17.** $\left\{\dfrac{-5 + \sqrt{115}}{6}, \dfrac{-5 - \sqrt{115}}{6}\right\}$
**19.** $\{-6 + \sqrt{39}, -6 - \sqrt{39}\}$

**21.** $\left\{\dfrac{3 + \sqrt{73}}{16}, \dfrac{3 - \sqrt{73}}{16}\right\}$

**23.** $\left\{\dfrac{-2 + 3\sqrt{6}}{5}, \dfrac{-2 - 3\sqrt{6}}{5}\right\}$   **25.** $\{5, \frac{37}{8}\}$

**27.** $\{\frac{1}{11}, -\frac{5}{3}\}$   **29.** $\left\{\dfrac{\sqrt{3}}{2}, -\dfrac{\sqrt{3}}{2}\right\}$
**31.** no solution

*Problems, pages 566–567*   **1.** 15 m by 9 m
**3.** 8 or $-9$   **5.** 10 cm   **7.** 7 cm   **9.** 50 m by
36 m   **11.** Sara, 31.0 h; Mary, 29.0 h   **13.** 27
students   **15.** 6 h

*Extra, pages 567–568*
**1.**

**3.**

**5.**

**7.** {all real numbers $\geq 5$ or $\leq 0$}
**9.** {all real numbers $\leq 3$ or $\geq 7$}

*Chapter Review, pages 569-570*  **1.** d  **3.** d
**5.** b  **7.** b  **9.** a

*Cumulative Review, pages 571-572*  **1.** $\frac{3}{2}$
**3.** 0  **5.** 1  **7.** $-232$  **9.** $-133$

**11.** $36c - 55$  **13.** $16a^4b^3 - 28a^3b^4$  **15.** $\frac{3wx}{4y^2}$

**17.** $8u^3 + 1$  **19.** $27z^2 + 21z - 20$

**21.** $64r^6t^2 - 9v^2$  **23.** $\frac{2c - 3d}{2(c - 3d)}$

**25.** $9x^2 - 12x + 16$  **27.** $\frac{3z + 4}{(z + 3)(z - 1)}$

**29.** $a - 2$  **31.** $\frac{5m + 21}{2(m - 3)(m + 3)}$

**33.** $60 - 24\sqrt{5}$  **35.** $12a$  **37.** $14\sqrt{5}$
**39.** $\frac{4\sqrt{2} + 9\sqrt{5} - 3\sqrt{10} - 12}{7}$

**41.** $t^3(2t - 3)(2t + 3)$
**43.** $-16z^2(z - 4)(z - 1)$  **45.** prime
**47.** $(c - 4)^2$  **49.** $\frac{44}{3}$  **51.** $\frac{52}{7}$  **53.** 200
**55.** $\{1, -5\}$  **57.** $\{\frac{1}{4}, -\frac{2}{3}\}$  **59.** $(-2, 2)$
**61.** $-16$  **63.** {the real numbers between $-2$
and 8}  **65.** $\{-\frac{3}{2}, 2,$ and the real numbers
between $-\frac{3}{2}$ and 2}  **67.** 8  **69.** 5

**71.** $\left\{\dfrac{-5 + \sqrt{17}}{4}, \dfrac{-5 - \sqrt{17}}{4}\right\}$

**73.** ![number line from -5 to 5 with open circles at -4 and 2]

**75.**

**77.**

**79.**

**81.** 12 h  **83.** less than 6 h

*Mixed Review, pages 573-574*  **1.** $(3, 5)$,
$x = 3$  **3.** 48 L  **5.** $\dfrac{\sqrt{30} - 2\sqrt{6} - \sqrt{5} + 2}{5}$

**7.** $\frac{ab^2}{12}$  **9.** $\frac{4b + 5}{4(b + 1)}$  **11.** $1.922 \times 10^8$
**13.** $16\sqrt{3} - 24\sqrt{6}$  **15.** $-9m^3n^3 + 6mn^5$
**17.** $\frac{2\sqrt{2} + 5\sqrt{3}}{4}$  **19.** $3c^2\sqrt{34}$  **21.** $2^3 \cdot 3^2 \cdot 5$
**23.** prime  **25.** $2\pi r(2r - h)$
**27.** $3t(3t - 1)(2t + 5)$  **29.** $-\frac{4}{9}, 4.0 \times 10^{-2}, \frac{2}{5},$
$\frac{43}{99}, 0.\overline{4}, \frac{1}{2}$  **31.** \$1500
**33.** ![graph of a line through origin]

**35.** ![number line from -1 to 9 with open circles at 1 and 2]
**37.** $-18$  **39.** 3  **41.** $\{-\frac{1}{3}, 2\}$  **43.** $-3$
**45.** $(12, -2)$  **47.** $\{\sqrt{6}, -\sqrt{6}\}$  **49.** $\{1\}$
**51.** {the real numbers less than 10 or greater
than 18}  **53.** $(-5, 3)$  **55.** 1 h or 60 min
**57.** 11  **59.** 32  **61.** $2x - y = -1$  **63.** 10;
22  **65.** \$1500 at 9%, \$1300 at $9\frac{1}{2}$%
**67.** $4.94 \times 10^9$ km

*Preparing for College Entrance Exams, page
575*  **1.** D  **3.** A  **5.** C  **7.** E

## LOOKING AHEAD

*Written Exercises, page 578*  **1.** Any five of
$\overline{LM}, \overline{MN}, \overline{NP}, \overline{LN}, \overline{LP}, \overline{MP}$  **3.** Any five of
$\overline{XY}, \overline{YW}, \overline{WX}, \overline{SY}, \overline{YZ}, \overline{SZ}, \overline{XS}, \overline{WZ}$

**5.** acute **7.** acute **9.** obtuse **11.** obtuse
**13.** point

**15.** line segment

**17.** line segment

**19.** ray

**21.** line

**Written Exercises, page 580** **1.** $\angle BCJ$, $\angle KCA$, $\angle FIH$ **3.** 150° **5.** 70°, 110° **7.** 73° **9.** 82°

**Written Exercises, page 582** **1.** 69° **3.** 48° **5.** 123° **7.** no **9.** yes **11.** yes **13.** 10 **15.** 9 **17.** 80 **19.** $4\sqrt{10}$ **21.** $3\sqrt{5}$ **23.** $x\sqrt{2}$

**Problems, page 583** **1.** 15, 75 **3.** 15, 60, 105 **5.** 12, 24, 144 **7.** 48, 48, 84 **9.** 18, 58, 104 **11.** 24, 48, 108

**Written Exercises, pages 585–586** **1.** $\angle A$, $\angle F$; $\angle B$, $\angle D$; $\angle C$, $\angle E$; $\overline{AB}$, $\overline{FD}$; $\overline{BC}$, $\overline{DE}$; $\overline{CA}$, $\overline{EF}$ **3.** false **5.** true **7.** $EF = 10$, $FD = 12$ **9.** $FE = 4$, $DF = 6$ **11.** $EF = 12$, $AC = 10$ **13.** $AB = 28$, $FD = 15$

**Problems, page 586** **1.** 28 cm **3.** 12 m **5.** 225 m **7.** 3 m **9.** 11.25 m

**Written Exercises, page 589** **1.** $\sin A = \frac{4}{5}$, $\cos A = \frac{3}{5}$, $\tan A = \frac{4}{3}$, $\sin B = \frac{3}{5}$, $\cos B = \frac{4}{5}$, $\tan B = \frac{3}{4}$ **3.** $\sin A = \frac{2\sqrt{29}}{29}$, $\cos A = \frac{5\sqrt{29}}{29}$, $\tan A = \frac{2}{5}$, $\sin B = \frac{5\sqrt{29}}{29}$, $\cos B = \frac{2\sqrt{29}}{29}$, $\tan B = \frac{5}{2}$ **5.** $\sin A = \frac{\sqrt{51}}{10}$, $\cos A = \frac{7}{10}$, $\tan A = \frac{\sqrt{51}}{7}$, $\sin B = \frac{7}{10}$, $\cos B = \frac{\sqrt{51}}{10}$, $\tan B = \frac{7\sqrt{51}}{51}$ **7.** $\sin A = \frac{\sqrt{2}}{2}$, $\cos A = \frac{\sqrt{2}}{2}$, $\tan A = 1$, $\sin B = \frac{\sqrt{2}}{2}$, $\cos B = \frac{\sqrt{2}}{2}$,

$\tan B = 1$ **9.** $\sin A = \frac{4\sqrt{137}}{137}$, $\cos A = \frac{11\sqrt{137}}{137}$, $\tan A = \frac{4}{11}$, $\sin B = \frac{11\sqrt{137}}{137}$, $\cos B = \frac{4\sqrt{137}}{137}$, $\tan B = \frac{11}{4}$ **11.** $\cos A = \frac{b}{c}$, $\sin B = \frac{b}{c}$

**13.** $\dfrac{\sin A}{\cos A} = \dfrac{\frac{a}{c}}{\frac{b}{c}} = \dfrac{a}{b} = \tan B$ **15.** $\dfrac{\sqrt{39}}{8}$

**Written Exercises, page 591** **1.** 0.1736, 0.9848, 0.1763 **3.** 0.9962, 0.0872, 11.4301 **5.** 0.7071, 0.7071, 1.0000 **7.** 0.3090, 0.9511, 0.3249 **9.** 0.5592, 0.8290, 0.6745 **11.** 0.1219, 0.9925, 0.1228 **13.** 85° **15.** 64° **17.** 43° **19.** 26° **21.** 77° **23.** 53° **25.** 76° **27.** 44°

**Challenge, page 591** **1.** no; $\angle A$, $\angle R$, $\angle Z$ are necessarily angles of a triangle.

**Written Exercises, pages 593–594** **1.** 20 **3.** 32 **5.** 59 **7.** $BC = 40$, $AC = 27$ **9.** $AC = 17$, $AB = 87$ **11.** $\angle D = 49°$, $\angle F = 41°$ **13.** $\angle D = 42°$, $\angle F = 48°$ **15.** $XZ = 75$, $YZ = 99$ **17.** $YZ = 55$, $YX = 49$

**Problems, pages 594–595** **1.** 18 m **3.** 226 m **5.** 117 m **7.** 4° **9.** 185 m **11.** 2154 m **13.** 530 m **15.** 182 m

**Written Exercises, pages 597–598**
**1. a.** $\{A, B, C, D, E, F, G, H, I, J, K\}$
**b.** $\{A, E, I\}$ **c.** $\{C, F, G, I\}$
**d.** $\{A, C, D, F, H, I, K\}$ **3. a.** $\{(2, 1), (2, 4),$ $(2, 9), (4, 1), (4, 4), (4, 9), (8, 1), (8, 4), (8, 9),$ $(15, 1), (15, 4), (15, 9)\}$ **b.** $\{(4, 4)\}$
**c.** $\{(15, 1), (15, 9)\}$ **d.** $\{(4, 9), (8, 9), (15, 1),$ $(15, 4), (15, 9)\}$ **e.** $\{(2, 1), (4, 1)\}$
**5. a.** $\{$(on, on, on), (on, on, off), (on, off, off), (on, off, on), (off, on, on), (off, on, off), (off, off, off), (off, off, on)$\}$ **b.** $\{$(on, on, on), (on, on, off), (on, off, on), (off, on, on)$\}$
**c.** $\{$(on, on, off), (on, off, off), (on, off, on), (off, on, on), (off, on, off), (off, off, off), (off, off, on)$\}$ **d.** $\{$(off, off, off)$\}$ **7.** $\{(1, 3),$ $(2, 2), (3, 1)\}$ **9.** $\{(1, 1), (1, 3), (2, 2), (3, 1),$ $(3, 3), (4, 2)\}$ **11.** $\{(1, 1), (1, 3), (2, 1), (2, 2),$ $(2, 3), (3, 1), (3, 3), (4, 1), (4, 2), (4, 3)\}$

*Written Exercises, pages 600-601* **1. a.** $\frac{1}{3}$
**b.** $\frac{1}{6}$ **c.** $\frac{1}{2}$ **d.** 0 **e.** $\frac{2}{3}$ **3. a.** $\frac{1}{25}$ **b.** $\frac{2}{5}$ **c.** $\frac{1}{5}$
**d.** $\frac{6}{25}$ **5. a.** $\frac{1}{8}$ **b.** $\frac{3}{8}$ **c.** $\frac{1}{2}$ **d.** $\frac{3}{4}$ **7. a.** $\frac{1}{12}$
**b.** $\frac{1}{4}$ **c.** $\frac{1}{12}$ **d.** $\frac{1}{4}$ **e.** $\frac{1}{6}$ **f.** $\frac{7}{12}$

*Calculator Key-In, page 601* **1.** 37.95 cm$^2$
**3.** 71.55 m$^2$ **5.** 4.92 m$^2$ **7.** 51.51 cm$^2$

*Written Exercises, page 604* **1.** 41, 39, none,
29 **3.** $64\frac{2}{3}$, $62\frac{1}{2}$, 62, 15 **5.** $27\frac{6}{7}$, 26, 25, and
33, 11 **7.** $27\frac{1}{3}$, 28, 28, 6 **9.** 13.1, 13.5, 15, 11
**11.** 182 **13. a.** 4 times greater **b.** 4 times
greater **c.** 4 times greater **d.** 4 times
greater **15.** 27

*Review, pages 605-606* **1.** b **3.** c **5.** c
**7.** c **9.** b **11.** d **13.** c

## EXTRA PRACTICE: Skills

*Chapter 1, pages 607-608* **1.** 37 **3.** 100
**5.** 198 **7.** 12 **9.** 23 **11.** 24 **13.** 6 **15.** 9
**17.** 8 **19.** 3 **21.** 23 **23.** {6}
**25.** {0, 1, 2, 3, 4, 5, 6} **27.** {0} **29.** {6}
**31.** {4} **33.** {0, 5} **35.** {2} **37.** {0}
**39.** $\frac{1}{2}z - 4$ **41.** $5w - 1$ **43.** $7x$ **45.** $x - 4$
**47.** $n - 5$ **49.** $m(m + 4) = 140$
**51.** $12p = 1.39$ **53.** $g + 5 = 34$
**55.** $2x + x = 48$; 32 blue T-shirts, 16 red
T-shirts **57.** 400 **59.** $-10$ **61.** $-2$
**63.**
**65.** $-3$ **67.** 18 **69.** 11 **71.** 3 **73.** 0
**75.** 9.4 **77.** $>$ **79.** $<$ **81.** $<$ **83.** $<$
**85.** $<$

*Chapter 2, pages 609-611* **1.** 350 **3.** 20
**5.** 16 **7.** $3m + 12$ **9.** $6w + 12$ **11.** $88n$
**13.** $60pqr$ **15.** $60hmw$ **17.** 0 **19.** $-12$
**21.** 20 **23.** $-19$ **25.** $-5.6$ **27.** $-1$
**29.** $-153$ **31.** $-4$ **33.** 19 **35.** 9 **37.** $-1$
**39.** 100 **41.** $-83$ **43.** 215 **45.** 17
**47.** $-30$ **49.** 4 **51.** 8 **53.** 34 **55.** 580
**57.** $7q$ **59.** $42a$ **61.** $7c + 27$ **63.** $8j - 15$
**65.** $8x + 20$ **67.** $2u + 5$ **69.** $2f + 10g$
**71.** 135 **73.** $-180$ **75.** $-135$ **77.** $-480$
**79.** 11 **81.** $-270$ **83.** $-7m + 42p$
**85.** $-24n + 36v$ **87.** $-4 - 8t$
**89.** $-29x + 16y$ **91.** $-3c - 17d$

Answers may vary for Exercises 93-97
**93.** $n + (n + 1) + (n + 2) = 75$
**95.** $n + (n + 2) + (n + 4) = 138$
**97.** $n + 2 = 3n + 8$ **99.** $-5$ **101.** 7
**103.** $-4$ **105.** $11xy$ **107.** $8g$ **109.** $9h - 6$
**111.** $-6x + 9y$ **113.** $5p + 10q$ **115.** $-8$
**117.** 0 **119.** $-40$ **121.** 0 **123.** $-31.5a$
**125.** 11 **127.** $-x$ **129.** $5h$

*Chapter 3, pages 611-613* **1.** 30 **3.** 8
**5.** $-15$ **7.** 20 **9.** $-3$ **11.** $-12$ **13.** 2
**15.** 12 **17.** $-18$ **19.** $-14$ **21.** $-64$
**23.** 50 **25.** $-128$ **27.** 120 **29.** $\frac{1}{6}$ **31.** 7
**33.** 6 **35.** 8 **37.** $-13$ **39.** $-27$ **41.** 4
**43.** 6 **45.** $-3$ **47.** 10 **49.** 21 **51.** 4 m, 6 m,
8 m **53.** 7 **55.** $-8$ **57.** $-6$ **59.** $-4$
**61.** 15 **63.** $\frac{11}{8}$ **65.** $-7$ **67.** 3 **69.** 5 years
old, 7 years old, 9 years old **71.** 16 cm by
10 cm, 14 cm by 13 cm **73.** 56 doz **75.** 4 h
**77.** substitution principle; associative axiom
of addition; axiom of opposites; identity
axiom for addition

*Chapter 4, pages 613-614* **1.** 343 **3.** $-48$
**5.** 32 **7.** $-26$ **9.** 5 **11.** 68 **13.** 49
**15.** $-2744$ **17.** 1 **19.** $\frac{81}{4}$ **21.** $b - 2$
**23.** $4t - 10$ **25.** $10x^2 - 3xy + 2y^2$
**27.** $3a^2 + 3ab - b^2$ **29.** $5b + 10$
**31.** $-8t - 4$ **33.** $2x^2 - xy + 4y^2$
**35.** $7a^2 - 15ab + b^2$ **37.** $8f^7$ **39.** $-10g^4h^3$
**41.** $60j^5k^3l^5$ **43.** $-a^6$ **45.** $3^6$ or 729 **47.** $2^{11}$
or 2048 **49.** $4d^{10}$ **51.** $x^{10}$ **53.** $z^{2n}$ **55.** $b^{3n}$
**57.** $d^{3n}$ **59.** $g^4h^4$ **61.** $64m^3n^{15}$ **63.** $9a^{10}b^8$
**65.** $-512x^{15}$ **67.** $-200l^{13}$ **69.** $375x^7y^5$
**71.** $5y - 20$ **73.** $-8 - 32m$
**75.** $-12t + 8t^2$ **77.** $-40h^2 - 15h$
**79.** $-15b^4 + 10b^3 - 30b^2$
**81.** $5u^3v^2 - 2u^2v^3 + 4uv^4$ **83.** $n^2 + 2n - 15$
**85.** $5x^2 + 33x - 14$ **87.** $30b^2 + 38b + 12$
**89.** $3v^3 + v^2 + 3v - 7$
**91.** $21x^2 - 26xy + 8y^2$
**93.** $e^3 + 2e^2f + 2ef^2 + f^3$ **95.** $a = \dfrac{2A}{p}$,
$p \neq 0$ **97.** $b_1 = \dfrac{2A - hb_2}{h}$, $h \neq 0$
**99.** $r = \sqrt{\dfrac{A}{\pi}}$, $A \geq 0$ **101.** $C = \frac{5}{9}(F - 32)$
**103.** $t = \dfrac{I}{Pr}$, $P \neq 0$, $r \neq 0$ **105.** $\frac{3}{2}$ h
**107.** 13.25 in. by 39.75 in.

**Chapter 5, pages 615–617**  **1.** (1)(42), (2)(21), (3)(14), (6)(7), $(-1)(-42)$, $(-2)(-21)$, $(-3)(-14)$, $(-6)(-7)$  **3.** (1)(91), (7)(13), $(-1)(-91)$, $(-7)(-13)$  **5.** (1)(52), (2)(26), (4)(13), $(-1)(-52)$, $(-2)(-26)$, $(-4)(-13)$  **7.** $2^4 \cdot 5$  **9.** $2^3 \cdot 3^2$  **11.** 42  **13.** 13  **15.** $3x^4$
**17.** $-\dfrac{1}{3b^4}$  **19.** $\dfrac{1}{w^{12}}$  **21.** $-\dfrac{27}{y^3}$  **23.** $3e + 2$
**25.** $2x^2 + 6x + 1$  **27.** $3 - 5m - m^2$
**29.** $5(3w^2 - 2w + 1)$  **31.** $7u^2(u + 2)$
**33.** $3c(5c + d)$  **35.** $x^2 + 8x + 15$
**37.** $n^2 + 4n - 21$  **39.** $6 + 5m + m^2$
**41.** $8y^2 - 10y + 3$  **43.** $20n^2 - 22n + 6$
**45.** $12h^3 + 55h^2 + 63h$  **47.** $k^2 - 25$
**49.** $16d^2 - 64$  **51.** $25m^4 - n^2$
**53.** $(4e - 3)(4e + 3)$  **55.** $(9 - f)(9 + f)$
**57.** $(7 - 10y)(7 + 10y)$  **59.** $(s^3 - 2)(s^3 + 2)$
**61.** $g^2 + 14g + 49$  **63.** $4x^2 + 24x + 36$
**65.** $4m^2 + 12mn + 9n^2$
**67.** $e^2f^2 - 16ef + 64$  **69.** $(x - 3)^2$
**71.** $(2 - 7h)^2$  **73.** $(2m - 9n)^2$
**75.** $(k + 7)(k + 1)$  **77.** $(a - 1)^2$
**79.** $(b - 12)(b - 4)$  **81.** $(x + 6y)(x + 7y)$
**83.** $(e - 4f)(e - 11f)$  **85.** $(x - 7)(x + 5)$
**87.** $(h - 9)(h + 2)$  **89.** $(t - 9)(t + 5)$
**91.** $(u + 4v)(u - v)$  **93.** $(2x + 3)(x + 4)$
**95.** $(5d + 3)(2d - 1)$  **97.** prime
**99.** $(5x + y)(3x + 2y)$
**101.** $(7m + 3n)(2m - n)$
**103.** $2(a + 2)(3a + 2)$  **105.** $(b + 1)^2(h - 3)$
**107.** $(7w + 3)(c - w)$
**109.** $(1 - m)(1 + m)(64 + m^4)$
**111.** $6y(5y + 1)(2y - 1)$
**113.** $16a^2(a - 3)(a + 3)$
**115.** $2w^5(14w^2 - 51)$  **117.** $-12(c \quad d)^2$
**119.** $\{-13, -8\}$  **121.** $\{2, \frac{5}{3}\}$  **123.** $\{0, -\frac{3}{4}\}$
**125.** $\{-6, -1\}$  **127.** $\{5, 9\}$  **129.** $\{4, -9\}$
**131.** $\{\frac{1}{4}, -6\}$  **133.** $\{\frac{5}{2}, -2\}$  **135.** $\{\frac{2}{3}, -\frac{2}{3}\}$
**137.** 7 or $-8$  **139.** 11 cm by 8 cm

**Chapter 6, pages 617–619**  **1.** $5;\ m \neq 3$
**3.** $\dfrac{c - d}{c + d};\ c \neq -d$  **5.** $\dfrac{3}{u - v};\ u \neq 0,\ v \neq 0,$
$u \neq v$  **7.** $\dfrac{x + 8}{x + 7};\ x \neq 8,\ x \neq -7$  **9.** $\dfrac{3}{5m - 2n};$
$m \neq \frac{2}{5}n,\ m \neq -\frac{2}{5}n$  **11.** $-1;\ k \neq 3,\ k \neq \frac{2}{7}$
**13.** $\dfrac{t - 7}{t + 2};\ t \neq 2,\ t \neq -2$  **15.** $-\dfrac{1}{(5w - x)^2};$
$w \neq \frac{x}{5}$  **17.** $\frac{4}{5}$  **19.** $\frac{3}{20}$  **21.** $\frac{e}{h}$  **23.** 2  **25.** $\dfrac{2uw^2}{3v^3}$

**27.** $\dfrac{1}{4xy(4 + y)}$  **29.** $25k^6$  **31.** $\dfrac{9x^2}{16}$  **33.** $-\dfrac{x^6}{125}$
**35.** $\dfrac{8c^5}{d^3}$  **37.** $\frac{1}{12}$  **39.** $\dfrac{2}{n^2}$  **41.** 1
**43.** $\dfrac{1}{(n - 3)(n - 5)}$  **45.** $\dfrac{(x - y)(x + y)(x - 4)}{2x}$
**47.** $\dfrac{(2t - 3s)(m^2 + n^2)}{7(4s - 5t)(m + n)}$  **49.** $\dfrac{x^2}{y^3}$  **51.** $\dfrac{c^2}{3}$
**53.** $-1$  **55.** $2h - 8$  **57.** $30m - 5n$
**59.** $12s^2t$  **61.** $5e + 5$  **63.** $5z$  **65.** $3ab$
**67.** $\dfrac{3x - 6}{48},\ \dfrac{4x + 12}{48}$  **69.** $\dfrac{d}{3cd^2},\ \dfrac{12}{3cd^2}$
**71.** $\dfrac{2wx + 6w}{3(x - 3)(x + 3)},\ \dfrac{3}{3(x - 3)(x + 3)}$  **73.** $\dfrac{4}{x}$
**75.** $\dfrac{-k - 4}{5}$  **77.** $\dfrac{7}{g - 3}$  **79.** $\dfrac{5 + 3t}{t^2}$  **81.** $\dfrac{2 - 3x}{10wx}$
**83.** $\dfrac{2 + 3x}{3(x + 2)}$  **85.** $\dfrac{3(h + 1)}{10}$  **87.** $\dfrac{2x + 1}{(x + 2)(x + 3)}$
**89.** $\dfrac{u - 3}{u - 4}$  **91.** $\dfrac{5n + 1}{n}$  **93.** $\dfrac{x + 3y}{y}$  **95.** $\dfrac{8z - 14}{z - 2}$
**97.** $\dfrac{8h^2 + 23h}{h + 3}$  **99.** $\dfrac{5e^2 - e - 8}{e^2 - 1}$
**101.** $\dfrac{2w^2 - 7w - 3}{w - 3}$  **103.** $\dfrac{2v^2}{(v + u)(v - u)}$
**105.** $x + 5$  **107.** $a - 7 + \dfrac{11}{a + 2}$
**109.** $k + 1 + \dfrac{12}{k - 5}$
**111.** $b^2 - b + 1 - \dfrac{2}{b + 1}$  **113.** $w^2 + 2w + 4$
**115.** $t - 4$  **117.** $v^2 + 3v + 7 + \dfrac{15}{v - 2}$

**Chapter 7, pages 619–621**  **1.** $1:3$  **3.** $200:3$
**5.** $18d:5$  **7.** $25:11$  **9.** 9  **11.** $\frac{7}{6}$  **13.** 6
**15.** 18  **17.** 12  **19.** 72  **21.** $-9$  **23.** $-7$
**25.** 6  **27.** 2  **29.** $-6$  **31.** 202.5  **33.** 30
**35.** 25%  **37.** 40  **39.** 800  **41.** 300
**43.** 8.4 kg  **45.** $127.50  **47.** 24 kg
**49.** 30 min  **51.** $1.47 \times 10^8$  **53.** $9.8 \times 10^{-6}$
**55.** $1.0 \times 10^{-11}$  **57.** $\frac{1}{125}$  **59.** $\frac{1}{729}$  **61.** 36
**63.** 64  **65.** $\dfrac{1}{729y^3}$  **67.** $\dfrac{1}{a^2b^3}$  **69.** $\dfrac{e^2}{d^4f^2}$
**71.** $\dfrac{x^{12}y^{15}}{z^9}$

**Chapter 8, pages 621–622**  **1.** no, yes  **3.** no, no  **5.** yes, yes  **7.** $y = \dfrac{8 - x}{2}$  **9.** $y = \dfrac{6 - 3x}{4}$
**11.** $y = -\frac{4}{3}x$

**13.**

**15.**

**21.**

**23.** $6x - 2y = -1$
**25.** $x - 3y = -18$
**27.** $24x + 56y = 21$

**17.**

**19.**

**29.** $y = -x - 3$

**31.** $y = 4x - 3$

**21.**

**23.** $(3, 6)$

**33.** $y = \frac{1}{5}x + 2$

**25.** no solution

**27.** infinite number of solutions

**35.** yes, infinite number of solutions  **37.** yes, one point  **39.** $2x + y = 2$  **41.** $y = 3$
**43.** $7x - 3y = 0$  **45.** $6x - y = 13$
**47.** $x = -3$  **49.** $3x - 13y = 70$  **51.** 6
**53.** 20  **55.** $-12$  **57.** 33  **59.** $\{-3, 3, 1\}$
**61.** $\{-10, 10, 2\}$  **63.** $\{-1, 2, 7\}$
**65.** $D = \{1930, 1940, 1950, 1960, 1970\}$,
$R = \{1782, 2331, 6403, 6881, 11,261\}$
**67.**                                **69.** $(0, 0)$, $x = 0$

**29.** $\left(-\frac{3}{4}, \frac{13}{12}\right)$  **31.** $(3, 1)$  **33.** $(5, 5)$  **35.** Janet, 3 mi; Lynn, 5 mi  **37.** $\left(5, -\frac{25}{2}\right)$  **39.** $(-3, 2)$
**41.** $(5, -2)$  **43.** $(2, 3)$  **45.** $(-3, -4)$
**47.** $(2, 5)$  **49.** 52  **51.** $\frac{7}{8}$

*Chapter 9, pages 622-626*  **1.** $\frac{4}{3}$  **3.** $-6$
**5.** $-\frac{1}{2}$  **7.** 7  **9.** $\frac{3}{2}$  **11.** $-\frac{5}{4}$  **13.** yes, 2
**15.** no
**17.**

**19.**

Airports in U.S.

**71.** $(\frac{3}{2}, \frac{9}{4})$, $x = \frac{3}{2}$  **73.** $(0, 4)$, $x = 0$

**75.** $-\frac{25}{4}$  **77.** $\frac{1}{12}$  **79.** $-\frac{3}{4}$  **81.** 6  **83.** 91
**85.** 1.04  **87. a.** $C = kd$  **b.** $\dfrac{C_1}{d_1} = \dfrac{C_2}{d_2}$
**89. a.** $l = kh$  **b.** $\dfrac{l_1}{h_1} = \dfrac{l_2}{h_2}$  **91. a.** $hb = k$
**b.** $h_1 b_1 = h_2 b_2$
**93.**                                      **95.**

**97.** 10  **99.** $\frac{1}{3}$  **101.** $p = kv^2$  **103.** $V = khr^2$
**105.** $F = \dfrac{kv^2}{r}$

*Chapter 10, pages 626–628*  **1.** false  **3.** true
**5.** false  **7.** false  **9.** true  **11.** $\{-4, -3\}$
**13.** $\{-3, -2, -1, 0, 1, 2, 3\}$
**15.** $\{-6, -5, -4, -3, -2, -1\}$

**17.** {the real numbers between $-2$ and 2}

**19.** {the real numbers less than 4}

**21.** {the real numbers greater than $-98$}

**23.** {the real numbers less than $-\frac{25}{2}$}

**25.** {the real numbers greater than 8}

**27.** {the real numbers greater than 4}

**29.** {the real numbers greater than $-14$}

**31.** {the real numbers less than 4}

**33. a.** $j$  **b.** $2j - 9 \le 43$  **35. a.** $r$
**b.** $\frac{1}{2}r - 10 \ge 25$  **37. a.** $p$  **b.** $p - 6 < \frac{1}{2}p$
**39.** {8, and the real numbers between 0 and 8}

**41.** $\{-1, 2,$ and the real numbers between $-1$ and $2\}$

**43.** $\{-9,$ and the real numbers greater than $-4$ or less than $-9\}$

**45.** $\{-3,$ and the real numbers greater than 5 or less than $-3\}$

**47.** {2, 6, and the real numbers greater than 6 or less than 2}

**49.** $\{3, 13\}$

**51.** $\{-1.5, 1.5,$ and the real numbers between $-1.5$ and $1.5\}$

**53.** $\{-7, 1,$ and the real numbers between $-7$ and $1\}$

**55.** {the real numbers greater than 3 or less than $-11$}

**57.** $\{-\frac{3}{2}, \frac{3}{2},$ and the real numbers between $-\frac{3}{2}$ and $\frac{3}{2}\}$

**59.** {the real numbers between $-4$ and $10$}

**61.** {$-6$, $6$, and the real numbers greater than $6$ or less than $-6$}

**63.** $\{4, -\frac{14}{5}\}$

**65.** {the real numbers greater than $4$ or less than $-1$}

**67.** {$-4$, $8$, and the real numbers between $-4$ and $8$}

**69.** {the real numbers between $-2$ and $4$}

**71.** $\emptyset$

**73.**

**75.**

**77.**

**79.**

**81.** $y \le -4x - 2$

**83.** $y > 6x - 2$

**85.** $y < \frac{5}{4}x$

**87.** $y > 2x - \frac{2}{3}$

**89.**

**91.**

**93.**

**95.**

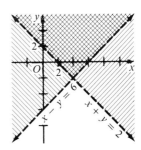

**1.** $<$ **3.** $<$
**5.** $\frac{2}{3}, \frac{12}{17}, \frac{5}{7}, \frac{11}{15}$ **7.** $\frac{1135}{1517}$ **9.** $\frac{111}{56}$ **11.** increases
**13.** decreases **15.** $0.\overline{4}$ **17.** $3.55$ **19.** $0.7\overline{45}$
**21.** $\frac{2}{3}$ **23.** $2\frac{37}{99}$ **25.** $0.6275$ **27.** $0.6\overline{32}$ **29.** $\frac{8}{27}$
**31.** $21$ **33.** $52$ **35.** $104$ **37.** $0.8$ **39.** $0.12$
**41.** $\frac{3}{5}$ **43.** $\frac{9}{22}$ **45.** $\frac{8}{9}$ **47.** $4\sqrt{11}$ **49.** $12\sqrt{11}$
**51.** $90\sqrt{2}$ **53.** $4\sqrt{42}$ **55.** $21\sqrt{6}$
**57.** $-28.3$ **59.** $91.7$ **61.** $13|m|$ **63.** $5x^2\sqrt{5}$
**65.** $-6|t^3|$ **67.** $-12|xy|\sqrt{2x}$ **69.** $-2.2w^2$
**71.** $\frac{a^2|b^3|\sqrt{3}}{6|c|}$ **73.** $\frac{3k^4}{4}$ **75.** $\frac{15x^{20}}{4}$ **77.** $|a-2|$
**79.** $\{7, -7\}$ **81.** $\{\frac{4}{5}, -\frac{4}{5}\}$ **83.** $\{3, -3\}$
**85.** $\{11.5, -11.5\}$ **87.** $\{6.6, -6.6\}$ **89.** no
**91.** no **93.** no **95.** $9.43$ **97.** $11.18$
**99.** $22.36$ **101.** $18.03$ **103.** $30$ **105.** $14$
**107.** $72\sqrt{2}$ **109.** $\frac{3}{2}\sqrt{2}$ **111.** $\frac{1}{4}\sqrt{2}$
**113.** $\frac{11}{7}\sqrt{3}$ **115.** $n^2 + 3\sqrt{n}$ **117.** $4\sqrt{3}$
**119.** $7\sqrt{6}$ **121.** $-50\sqrt{2}$ **123.** $\frac{12\sqrt{2} - \sqrt{30}}{6}$
**125.** $\frac{80\sqrt{7} + 21\sqrt{2}}{28}$ **127.** $10\sqrt{3} - \sqrt{30}$
**129.** $3\sqrt{15}$ **131.** $-29$ **133.** $18 + 8\sqrt{2}$
**135.** $34 - 24\sqrt{2}$ **137.** $20\sqrt{3} - 24\sqrt{2}$
**139.** $252 + 133\sqrt{2}$
**141.** $\frac{2 + \sqrt{3} + 2\sqrt{5} + \sqrt{15}}{-4}$ **143.** $\frac{3}{8}$ **145.** $\frac{16}{25}$
**147.** $83$ **149.** $3$ **151.** $\frac{2}{5}$ **153.** $45$

**1.** $\{\frac{5}{7}, -\frac{5}{7}\}$ **3.** no
solution **5.** $\{4, -4\}$ **7.** $\{\sqrt{3}, -\sqrt{3}\}$
**9.** $\{-1, -9\}$ **11.** $\{-4 + 3\sqrt{3}, -4 - 3\sqrt{3}\}$
**13.** $\{-7 + \sqrt{21}, -7 - \sqrt{21}\}$
**15.** $\left\{\frac{1 + 2\sqrt{6}}{3}, \frac{1 - 2\sqrt{6}}{3}\right\}$ **17.** $\{13, -1\}$
**19.** $\{-1, -15\}$ **21.** $\{6 + \sqrt{246}, 6 - \sqrt{246}\}$;
$\{21.7, -9.7\}$ **23.** $\left\{\frac{3 + \sqrt{29}}{3}, \frac{3 - \sqrt{29}}{2}\right\}$;
$\{4.2, -1.2\}$ **25.** $\{3, 7\}$ **27.** $\{-\frac{7}{2}, 2\}$
**29.** $\{-\frac{5}{2}, 2\}$ **31.** $\left\{\frac{-7 + \sqrt{37}}{2}, \frac{-7 - \sqrt{37}}{2}\right\}$;
$\{-0.5, -6.6\}$ **33.** $\left\{\frac{5 + \sqrt{37}}{2}, \frac{5 - \sqrt{37}}{2}\right\}$;
$\{5.6, -0.6\}$ **35.** $\{1, \frac{2}{3}\}$
**37.** $\left\{\frac{-3 + \sqrt{89}}{20}, \frac{-3 - \sqrt{89}}{20}\right\}$; $\{0.3, -0.6\}$
**39.** $\left\{\frac{7 + \sqrt{57}}{2}, \frac{7 - \sqrt{57}}{2}\right\}$; $\{7.3, -0.3\}$ **41.** no
real roots **43.** no real roots **45.** 2 roots
**47. a.** 0 points **b.** below **49.** $\{-3, -4\}$
**51.** $\{0, \frac{9}{5}\}$ **53.** $\{-4 + \sqrt{13}, -4 - \sqrt{13}\}$
**55.** $\left\{\frac{-2 + \sqrt{10}}{6}, \frac{-2 - \sqrt{10}}{6}\right\}$

**57.** $\left\{\frac{4 + 2\sqrt{31}}{9}, \frac{4 - 2\sqrt{31}}{9}\right\}$
**59.** $\left\{\frac{1 + \sqrt{7}}{6}, \frac{1 - \sqrt{7}}{6}\right\}$
**61.** $\left\{\frac{-5 + \sqrt{13}}{2}, \frac{-5 - \sqrt{13}}{2}\right\}$ **63.** 22.2 cm by
3.7 cm **65.** 14 m

## EXTRA PRACTICE: Problem-Solving

*Chapter 1, page 633* **(1-7)** **1.** 225 km **3.** 8 games **5.** 19

*Chapter 2, page 633* **(2-3)** **1.** 38 yd **3.** $205 **5.** 10 A.M. **(2-4)** **1.** 2.52° **3.** 28 blocks **5.** 397 m below sea level

*Chapter 3, page 634* **(3-1)** **1.** $-18$ **3.** 58 **5.** $747 **(3-2)** **1.** $-34$ **3.** 30¢/kg **5.** 12 cm **(3-4)** **1.** 12 **3.** $124 **5.** 16 nickels, 12 dimes, 8 quarters **(3-5)** **1.** $-9$, $-8$ **3.** 12 **5.** 7, 9, 11 **(3-6)** **1.** Kevin is 18; Karen is 6 **3.** Zachary is 15; father is 40 **5.** Ryan is 4; Amy is 2; Becky is 6 **(3-7)** **1.** 13 quarters, 35 dimes **3.** 7.5 h **5.** 36 quarters

*Chapter 4, page 636* **(4-8)** **1.** 2.5 h **3.** 2400 km **5.** 7 P.M. **(4-9)** **1.** 11 m by 7 m **3.** 9 m by 5 m **5.** 60 cm by 50 cm **(4-10)** **1.** no solution **3.** no solution **5.** $-5, -4, -3$

*Chapter 5, page 638* **(5-13)** **1.** $-12$ or 11 **3.** 20 cm by 12 cm **5.** 8 m by 4 m

*Chapter 7, page 638* **(7-1)** **1.** 50, 75 **3.** 40, 60, 100 **5.** 180 coins **(7-2)** **1.** $7 **3.** $167.50 **5.** 180 lb **(7-3)** **1.** Juan is 16; Sylvia is 14 **3.** Bart is 14; mother is 42 **5.** 20 dimes **(7-4)** **1.** $\frac{3}{4}$ or $\frac{4}{3}$ **3.** $\frac{1}{3}$ **5.** 50 km/h **(7-5)** **1.** $10.50 **3.** $40 **5.** $630 **(7-6)** **1.** 35% **3.** 1475 people **5.** $9600 **(7-7)** **Chemistry** **1.** 80 L **3.** 25.6% **Grocery** **1.** 40 L cranberry, 80 L apple **3.** $1.75/lb **Investment and Wages** **1.** $12.50/h **3.** $15,000 **(7-8)** **1.** $\frac{11}{15}$ **3.** 13 h 20 min **5.** 54 min **(7-9)** **1.** 1.28 s **3.** $2.03 \times 10^4$ s **5.** $6 \times 10^{-5}$ cm **(7-10)** **1. a.** 10,000 people **b.** 9709 people **c.** 10,300 people **3.** 61 bacteria **5.** 6701 people

***Chapter 8, page 643***   *(8-5)*   **1.** 32 quarters
**3.** 17 by 10   **5.** $\frac{5}{12}$   *(8-6)*   **1.** 15, 21   **3.** 87
boys   **5.** 20 dimes, 18 quarters   *(8-7)*   **1.** 19,
32   **3.** 150 ft   **5.** 42 questions   *(8-8)*
**1.** boat, 23 km/h; current, 7 km/h   **3.** current,
2 km/h; swimmer, 8 km/h   **5.** 200 km/h

***Chapter 9, page 644***   *(9-7)*   **1.** 3.1 cm
**3.** 33 kg   **5.** 226,800 km²   *(9-8)*   **1.** 7 h
**3.** $1875   **5.** 55 cm   *(9-9)*   **1.** 85.75 m   **3.** 1
unit   **5.** $\frac{1}{9}$ as great   *(9-10)*   **1.** 6¢   **3.** 5.25 h

***Chapter 10, page 646***   *(10-3)*   **1.** 40, 41
**3.** 260   **5.** 90 km/h

***Chapter 11, page 647***   *(11-5)*   **1.** 13.6 cm
**3.** 4.5 cm   **5.** 3.3 m   *(11-6)*   **1.** 53.85 m
**3.** 15 cm, 8 cm, 17 cm   **5.** 9 cm, 12 cm,
15 cm   *(11-10)*   **1.** 784   **3.** 49   **5.** 30, 32

***Chapter 12, page 648***   *(12-6)*   **1.** −6 or 5
**3.** 60 m by 9 m   **5.** 90 h, 72 h